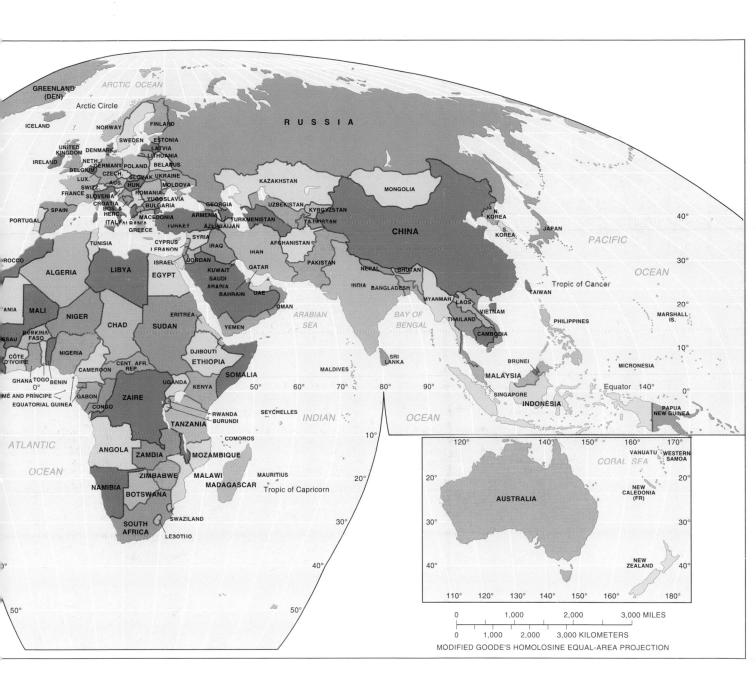

GREENLAND (DEN)

ARCTIC OCEAN

Arctic Circle

ICELAND

NORWAY

FINLAND

R U S S I A

SWEDEN   ESTONIA

UNITED KINGDOM   DENMARK   LATVIA
                          LITHUANIA

IRELAND   NETH.   POLAND   BELARUS
        GERMANY
        BELGIUM   CZECH.   SLOVAK   UKRAINE
        LUX.   HUN.   MOLDOVA
        SWITZ.   AUS.
FRANCE   SLOVENIA   ROMANIA
        CROATIA   YUGOSLAVIA
        BOS. &   BULGARIA
        HERC.
SPAIN   ITALY   MACEDONIA   GEORGIA
        ALBANIA   ARMENIA
PORTUGAL   GREECE   TURKEY   AZERBAIJAN

KAZAKHSTAN

MONGOLIA

UZBEKISTAN   KYRGYZSTAN
        TURKMENISTAN   TAJIKISTAN

N. KOREA

S. KOREA   JAPAN

CHINA   PACIFIC   40°

OCEAN   30°

ROCCO   TUNISIA   CYPRUS   SYRIA   IRAQ   IRAN   AFGHANISTAN
        LEBANON   PAKISTAN
ALGERIA   LIBYA   ISRAEL   JORDAN   NEPAL   BHUTAN   Tropic of Cancer
        EGYPT   KUWAIT   QATAR   TAIWAN
                SAUDI   BAHRAIN   INDIA   BANGLADESH   MYANMAR   LAOS   20°
ANIA   MALI   ARABIA   UAE   VIETNAM
        NIGER   CHAD   SUDAN   ERITREA   OMAN   ARABIAN   BAY OF   THAILAND   MARSHALL IS.
BURKINA   YEMEN   SEA   BENGAL   PHILIPPINES   10°
SSAU   FASO   CAMBODIA
CÔTE   NIGERIA   DJIBOUTI   SRI   BRUNEI   MICRONESIA
D'IVOIRE   CAMEROON   CENT. AFR.   ETHIOPIA   MALDIVES   LANKA   MALAYSIA
GHANA TOGO BENIN   REP.   SOMALIA   0°
0°   UGANDA   KENYA   50°   60°   70°   80°   90°   Equator   140°
MÉ AND PRÍNCIPE   GABON   ZAIRE   SINGAPORE   PAPUA
EQUATORIAL GUINEA   CONGO   RWANDA   INDONESIA   NEW GUINEA
        TANZANIA   BURUNDI   SEYCHELLES   INDIAN   OCEAN
                COMOROS
ATLANTIC   ANGOLA   ZAMBIA   MOZAMBIQUE   10°
OCEAN   ZIMBABWE   MALAWI   MAURITIUS
        NAMIBIA   BOTSWANA   MADAGASCAR   Tropic of Capricorn   20°
            SWAZILAND
        SOUTH   LESOTHO   30°
        AFRICA

Inset map:

120°   140°   150°   160°   170°
                VANUATU   WESTERN SAMOA
                CORAL SEA
20°   20°
                        NEW CALEDONIA (FR)
AUSTRALIA

30°   30°
                NEW ZEALAND
40°   110°   120°   130°   140°   150°   160°   180°   40°

0   1,000   2,000   3,000 MILES
0   1,000   2,000   3,000 KILOMETERS
MODIFIED GOODE'S HOMOLOSINE EQUAL-AREA PROJECTION

The WORLD ECONOMY

RESOURCES, LOCATION,

TRADE, AND

DEVELOPMENT

Second Edition

ANTHONY R. de SOUZA
National Geographic Society

AND

FREDERICK P. STUTZ
San Diego State University

Chapter 5 revised by
GERARD RUSHTON
The University of Iowa

Chapter 3 text revised by
JOHN WEEKS
San Diego State University

PRENTICE HALL
Englewood Cliffs, NJ 07632

Library of Congress Cataloging in Publication Data
de Souza, Anthony R.
        The world economy: resources, location, trade, and development/
    Anthony R. de Souza
          p.   cm.
        Rev. ed. of: A geography of world economy. 1990.
        Includes bibliographical references and index.
        ISBN 0-02-328722-5
        1. Economic geography.   2. Economic history - 1945 - I. Stutz,
    Frederick P.   II. de Souza, Anthony R.   Geography of world economy.
III. Title.
HC59.D398   1994
330.9-dc20   93-23408
                                 CIP

For Nadia, Jason, and Sam-A. R. de Souza

For Margaret, my loving mother-F. P. Stutz

Selected text and graphic images supplied courtesy of Environmental Systems Research Institute, Inc. Copyright © 1989,
1991, 1992 Environmental Systems Research Institute, Inc.

The portion of this book containing Environmental Systems Research Institute, Inc.'s copyrighted material may not be used, copied, reproduced,
or distributed in any form without the express written consent of Environmental Systems Research Institute, Inc.

Figures 1.13, 2.1, 2.9, 2.15, 3.5, 3.6, 3.8, 3.10, 3.12, 3.13, 7.7, 9.3, 9.12, 10.5, 10.6, 10.7, 10.10, 10.12, 10.16, 10.17, 10.19, 11.13, 11.15, 12.9, 12.10, 12.11, 13.1, 13.8,
13.15, are reproduced with permission from Rubenstein, J.M. 1994. *The Cultural Landscape: An Introduction to Human Geography*, 4th ed. New York: Prentice Hall.

Figures 5.5, 5.7, 6.5, 13.6, are reproduced with permission from Fisher, J.S. 1992. *Geography and Development: A World Regional Approach*.
New York: Prentice Hall.

Editor: Paul Corey
Production Supervisor: Kelly Ricci/Spectrum Publisher Services
Production Manager: Aliza Greenblatt
Text Designer: Hothouse Design
Cover Designer: Blake Logan
Cover Photograph: Martin Becka, Thailand, Damnoen Saduak, floating market, copyright © Tonystone Worldwide
Photo Researcher: Eve Kornblum
Line Illustrations: Academy Artworks
Maps: Maryland Cartographics
This book was set in 10/12 Meridien by Bi-Comp.

© 1994 by Prentice-Hall, Inc.
A Simon & Schuster Company
Englewood Cliffs, New Jersey 07632

ISBN 0-02-328722-5

Prentice-Hall International (UK) Limited, *London*
Prentice-Hall of Australia Pty. Limited, *Sydney*
Prentice-Hall Canada Inc., *Toronto*
Prentice-Hall Hispanoamericana, S.A., *Mexico*
Prentice-Hall of India Private Limited, *New Delhi*
Prentice-Hall of Japan, Inc., *Tokyo*
Simon & Schuster Asia Pte. Ltd., *Singapore*
Editora Prentice-Hall do Brasil, Ltda., *Rio de Janeiro*

PREFACE

The World Economy: Resources, Location, Trade, and Development adopts an international perspective to examine how people earn a living and how the goods and services they produce are geographically organized. It also emphasizes conflicting arguments and theories essential for understanding a world economy in rapid transition. Designed around the themes of distribution and economic growth, this textbook explores the nature of the dynamic, international environment and key international issues that arouse the concern and interest of geographers. Among the issues discussed are population growth, economic development in underdeveloped countries, pollution and resource depletion, food production and famine worldwide, patterns of land use, economic justice, international business, social and economic development, and multinational and international commerce.

Most important, we have made a concerted effort to globalize the economic geography curriculum. The trend toward globalizing the curriculum at the college level is major. Some educators have asked if it is the latest education fad or if it is the initial phase of a long-lasting, important shift in higher education. If education is meant to equip and enable students to live their lives fully and in a meaningful manner, then it seems obvious to us that the answer has to be the latter. *The World Economy* is in a position to take advantage of the student demand to globalize the curriculum. Increasing the global community's economic and political interdependence, which is tightly linked to the technology of the extraordinary global communications revolution, necessitates a global education for the twenty-first century. As David Grossman, former director of the Stanford University program on international, cross-cultural education, has pointed out that "students are becoming citizens within the context of this global era in human history and this calls for competencies which tradition-

ally have not been emphasized by schools." We attempt to emphasize these competencies in this book.

The Carnegie Report on Higher Education (1991) cogently sets forth the almost certain dangers that exist in the global future if such an emphasis is not adopted:

> The World has become a more crowded, more interconnected, more volatile and more unstable place. If education cannot help students see beyond themselves and better understand the interdependent nature of our world, then each new generation will remain ignorant, and its capacity to live competently and responsibly will be dangerously diminished. (p. 42)

It is easy to understand this point in light of the recent crises in Russia, the Middle East, and the Persian Gulf; in the economic unity being sought by the European Economic Community (EEC) and by Canada, the United States, and Mexico through the North American Free Trade Agreement (NAFTA); or by any number of political and economic crises that have occurred in the past few decades, which emphasize the crucial nature of a globally informed citizenry. That is why we argue that, among the myriad of other programmatic demands placed on universities across America, global education should have a high—perhaps the highest—priority.

The text progresses logically from one topic to another and is designed to be used in both geography and international business courses. We recommend that the chapters be read sequentially; however, because we wrote each chapter to stand on its own, the book can serve as a reference or as a refresher. Prepared as an introductory book on economic geography, international business, and international economies, the material can be read and understood without college-level prerequisites. Certain chapters can be omitted for short courses. For example, if the course is taught as a traditional economic geography course that emphasizes model development, Chapters 12, 13, and 14 may be omitted. If the book is used for courses in international business, world development, or world trade and economy, portions of Chapters 8, 9, and 10 may be omitted.

The World Economy offers specific pedagogical features, including new two-color and four-color world maps that illustrate, unlike any competing book, the spatial nature of the world economy. This new book contains more than 200 updated maps and graphs, many of which are modified from Goode's Homolosine Equal Area Projections. We enlarged the maps, increasing the size of Europe for intelligibility. It was our opinion that these maps were the best pedogogical tools available to teach students the spatial pattern of the world economy. The maps incorporate recent data from the *Statistical Abstracts of the United States,* the World Bank, the Population Reference Bureau, the Encyclopedia Britannica, and other sources, several of which were not published until August 1993. In addition, this book includes chapter objectives, end-of-chapter summaries, key terms, suggested readings, many photographs, and box essays, which illustrate principles of the world economy. A special effort has been made to offer modern examples of classical models and to provide summary charts, tables, and supply-demand curves that explain the dynamics of the world economy. Most of all, this book encourages students to think through problems, by providing the information and concepts necessary to help them evaluate issues without subscribing or submitting to a particular set of values.

World Space Economy, by de Souza and Foust in 1979, and *A Geography of World Economy*, by de Souza in 1990, concentrated heavily on the economic geography of the United States and on national effects of international processes. *The World Economy* takes a wider view, is 60% new, and enables students to appreciate what is going on, not only in the United States but also elsewhere in the world economy. This book has a special new emphasis on international business patterns and dynamics. An insular view of the world is untenable in the 1990s, as discussed. The world is too much "with us" everyday.

We are especially grateful to our colleagues who read the manuscript and offered useful comments. These colleagues are as follows: Dr. J. Harold Leaman, Villanova University; Edward J. Malecki, The University of Florida; Beth Mitchneck, The University of Arizona; Gordon Mulligan, Simon Fraser University; Bruce W. Pigozzi, Michigan State University; Dr. Debra Straussfogel, The Pennsylvania State University; and Paul Susman, Bucknell University. Jim Gerber and Art Kartman of the Economic Department at San Diego State University offered comments on Chapters 1 and 8, respectively. Gerry Rushton, formerly a member of the Department of Geography at San Diego State University and now at The University of Iowa, revised Chapter 5. John Weeks, at San Diego State University, revised Chapter 3 while Christa Stutz did the Instructor's Manual. We would like to especially thank James Rubenstein, author of *The Cultural Landscape: An Introduction to Human Geography,* for his help and inspiration.

We would like to thank Bennett Moe of Maryland Cartographics, Columbia, Maryland, for cooperating with us in mutually designing the maps; Academy ArtWorks for rendering the noncartographic art; Kelly Ricci and Kristin Miller for managing all aspects of manuscript production; Kathy Riley-King for copyediting; and the entire Macmillan staff, especially Felicia Nelson, assistant editor, and dashing Paul Corey, executive editor, who made possible the successful completion of this book. Naturally, however, all mistakes and omissions are ours.

Finally, we wish to thank our families—Nadia, Jason, and Sam de Souza, and Pamela, Christa, Tiffany, Derek, Janene, Michelle, and Weston Stutz—for their support and understanding during this busy time. We wish to especially thank Pamela Stutz for the hard work of typing the several drafts of this book. Speaking of hard work, Sam de Souza was Maryland All State in football in 1993; and Tiffany Stutz was California All-State in volleyball and basketball 1990, 1991, and 1992.

A. R. de Souza
F. P. Stutz

CONTENTS

◉ CHAPTER 10

Industrial Location: Firms 409

◉ CHAPTER 11

Industrial Location: World Regions 461

◈ C H A P T E R 14

Development and Underdevelopment 625

1

PROBLEMS AND SOLUTIONS IN AN UNSETTLED WORLD

OBJECTIVES

- To outline the development of the crises we now face in the world economy

- To introduce the major problems of environmental constraints and disparities in economic development

- To indicate why economic geographers are interested in development problems and how geography can help to resolve these problems

- To acquaint you with the field of geography and, in particular, with the major paradigms and concepts of economic geography

New York Stock Exchange. New York City is still the financial capital of the world, having supplanted London; however, Tokyo is fast-rising to the top.
(Source: New York Convention and Visitors Bureau.)

In his novel *Cataclysm*, World Bank's former vice president, William Clark, presents the following scenario. One day in 1987, debt-ridden Mexico proposes a global debt conference, but it is rejected by the Western industrial democracies. The rejection angers Third World countries and, as a group, they default on their debts. The Western powers retaliate by expelling the delinquent nations from the Bretton Woods Agreement. A North-South cold war develops. Cut off from the North's resources, aid, and markets, the underdeveloped South soon buckles under rampant food shortages and political chaos, but not before sending out their secret agents to infiltrate the North's major financial institutions. Once inside, the agents wreak havoc by feeding false data into the North's economic computers. Wall Street breaks down.

Clark's dramatic prediction has failed to materialize, but his novel warns that the "poverty bomb" is as capable of destroying the world as a nuclear bomb. To avert catastrophe, we must become aware of the world crisis and take it seriously. The world crisis may be conceived of as the long-term issue of human survival, in terms of population, food, energy, resources, and the environ-

ment. We have come to call these disparities in the distribution of wealth and in the quality of life the *problem of development*.

World development implies progress toward desirable goals. It is a concept full of hope and enthusiasm, even though the consequences of the jolting and dislocating process can be horrendous for people when long-standing traditions and relationships break down. The purpose of development is to improve the quality of people's lives—that is, to provide secure jobs, adequate nutrition and health services, clean water and air, cheap transportation, and education. Whether development takes place depends on the extent to which social and economic changes and a restructuring of geographic space help or hinder in meeting the basic needs of the majority of people.

Problems associated with the uncertainty and disorder of the development process occur at all scales, ranging from a Somalian villager's access to food and a modern clinic to the international scale of trade relations between rich and poor countries. Attempts to understand development problems at local, regional, and international levels must consider the principles of re-

IBM corporate headquarters, Armonk, New York. Whether measured in terms of value of sales, value of assets, or number of employees, IBM is one of the largest MNCs in the world. The domestic activities of multinationals are only a part of their worldwide activities. They are the epitome of direct investors abroad. In the first half of the 1990s, however, IBM has seen its market share for computer equipment drop sharply due to aggressive policies of Japanese companies, and such software systems as Apple™ and MicroSoft™. In 1993, MicroSoft had become the world's largest computer company in market value. IBM shares have taken a battering as the company has slashed its work force by 69,000 during the past 2 years in round after round of restructuring.
(Source: IBM.)

source use as well as the principles surrounding the exchange and movement of goods, people, and ideas. This text, written from a geographer's perspective, discusses these principles within the context of world crises.

Why is the world in crisis? What are some of the major problems that need immediate attention? Why are geographers interested in these problems? What concepts help geographers illuminate issues of resource-use inequalities and problems of poverty? How can the geographer's skills be used to help resolve these problems? This opening chapter sets out to answer these questions. Its objective is to prove to you that the world is in crisis, to focus your attention on some of the specific problem areas we deal with later in the text, and to help you understand the geographer's approach to the study of the world economy.

A WORLD IN CRISIS—A TIME OF OPPORTUNITY

◈

A crisis is a decisive turning point filled with uncertainty and disorder, the outcome of which may be life or death. A crisis may give rise to a new beginning if people are able to survive through a period of wrenching and rapid changes to the capitalist economic system.

Capitalism, the economic system based on profit and private property, is by nature crisis-prone. From its earliest days, it has been as ill as it has been intensely alive (Figure 1.1 and Table 1.1). Crises, as well as incredible productivity, technical advances, and global expansion, have been prominent features of capitalist development. Periods of boom characterized by increasing prices, production, technological innovation, and profits are always punctuated by crashes characterized by deflation, low growth rates, cost-reducing inventions, and declining profits. The events that will follow the present world economic crisis of the 1980s and 1990s in the ongoing accumulation process of the capitalist world are still unknown. Will this period of instability be followed by a resumption of the steady and sustained growth of the 1950s and 1960s?

The 1950s and 1960s were remarkably stable and predictable decades for the rich industrial countries. These years witnessed unparalleled prosperity and growth in the United States, the recovery of Europe from World War II, and the emergence of Japan as a tower of economic strength. In addition, developed countries commanded an increasingly disproportionate share of the benefits of the world economic system and multinational corporations (MNCs), or *transnationals*, controlled a growing share of world production and trade. Although most poor countries failed to benefit from the postwar boom, their problems were regarded as temporary aberrations to be corrected by the free-market system based on the U.S. dollar.

Vietnam and OPEC

After 1970, however, the economic system that had served developed countries so well began to falter. Nothing was certain anymore. A series of unfortunate events ended the postwar boom led by the United States. In 1971, the financial order collapsed with the devaluation of the U.S. dollar. But if there was a pivotal year, it was 1973. The year that began with the American withdrawal from Vietnam ended with the quadrupling of oil prices by the Organization of Petroleum Exporting Countries (OPEC). A year later, the economies of the Western countries slipped into a deep recession accompanied by high levels of unemployment and inflation. They recovered slightly from 1975 to 1978 before plunging into recession again in 1979 and 1980. The economies of the poor countries followed those of the Western countries. Even the socialist countries of Eastern Europe and the former USSR suffered from the general economic downturn. For a while the oil-exporting countries escaped the storm, but they, too, revealed their vulnerability when they were hit by declining oil prices in the mid-1980s.

In the United States, the recession of 1979/1980 was followed quickly by another more severe downturn in 1981/1982. Although the recovery that followed in 1983 was strong in the United States, many industrial nations languished in slow growth and high rates of unemployment well into the second half of the 1980s. The effects of stagnation throughout much of the industrial world were devastating for developing nations. Many middle-income and low-income countries depend on the economies of the high-income nations as a source of demand for their manufacturers and their primary products, such as minerals. Slow growth in the high-income nations nearly always results in a downturn in demand for products from developing nations and a worsening of the terms of trade for their products.

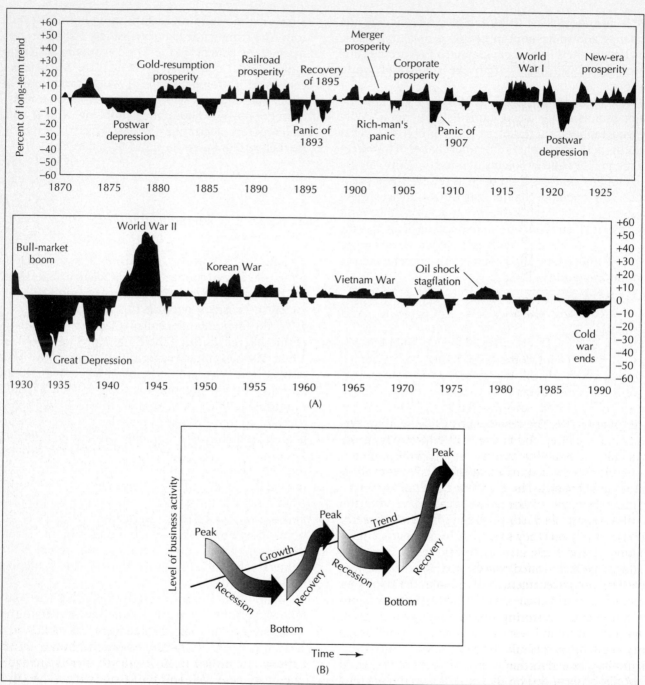

FIGURE 1.1

American business cycle fluctuations. The United States is the premier capitalist society in the world; however, over the long term, business trends have not been steady and even, but punctuated by periods of economic instability. Periods of expansion and rapid economic growth have usually been followed by a downtrend in economic activity, with declining levels of employment and output.

(Source: Adapted from McConnell and Brue, 1993, p. 130.)

◈

Table 1.1
United States Recessions 1950–1994

Period	Duration in Months	Depth (Percentage Decline in Real Output)
1953–1954	10	−3.0
1957–1958	8	−3.5
1960–1961	10	−1.0
1969–1970	11	−1.1
1973–1975	16	−4.3
1980	6	−3.4
1981–1982	16	−2.6
1990 ?	48*	−3.0*

*Through first quarter of 1994.
Source: Modified and expanded from NBER and Federal Reserve Bank of Boston.

◈

Table 1.2
Selected Heavily Indebted LDCs, 1990

Country	Total External Debt (Billions of Dollars)	External Debt as a Percentage of GNP
Brazil	111	35
Mexico	96	48
Argentina	65	123
India	63	27
Indonesia	53	56
Venezuela	33	75
Nigeria	33	114
Philippines	29	66
Thailand	23	32
Chile	18	72
Colombia	17	44

Source: The World Bank. 1991. World Development Report, 1991. New York: Oxford University Press, pp. 244–245, 250–251.

Falling prices for commodities sold by developing nations, particularly oil, led to the inability of many to make interest payments on the money they had borrowed from U.S. and European banks and governments during the 1970s. The result was the *Third World debt crisis*. In 1982, Mexico became the first country to acknowledge its inability to pay back its debt and was soon followed by a number of other Latin American and African nations. The debt crisis continued to drag on through much of the 1980s as one country after another experienced slow economic growth, falling prices for the goods they sold on the international market, and financial insolvency (Table 1.2).

Banks in the United States and Europe, together with national governments and international agencies such as the World Bank and the IMF, struggled to develop a plan for restoring economic growth in these countries and to find ways to deal with the immediate crisis of potential default. In most cases, partial debt relief was provided through a combination of measures, all of which depended on the willingness and ability of the debtor nations to undertake major restructuring of their economies and to impose severe austerity measures aimed at curbing expenditures. For example, tight monetary policies were imposed to curb inflation, protectionist barriers were dismantled or substantially reduced, and government expenditures for programs for the poor were significantly reduced. In many countries, the combination of these programs led to a falling standard of living for the majority of the nation.

Although growth remains elusive throughout much of Africa, many Latin American nations have begun to grow again. Growth has been particularly strong in the late 1980s and early 1990s in countries that began to orient their economies toward a more competitive world market. In many cases, however, even when overall economic growth returns, the real wages of the poorest members of society have remained far below their levels prior to the debt crisis of the 1980s.

Growth of East Asian Economy

Many of the changes that went on in the world economy during the 1980s were fueled by the remarkable growth of East Asia. Although there were exceptions (i.e., the Philippines), these nations remained largely free from the debt crisis. In Japan and the *Four Tigers* (South Korea, Taiwan, Hong Kong, and Singapore), a new wave of products began to sweep across the economies of North America and Europe. Other East Asian nations, such as Malaysia, Indonesia, and Thailand, began to follow the example set by the leaders, developing extremely competitive, export-oriented industrial sectors.

The nations of East Asia have not been content to

follow their natural comparative advantage in low wage, labor-intensive production, but have jumped right into value-added, sophisticated, high-tech production, which traditional economic theory says should have come much later in their development. They have been aided in part by developments in communication and information technology that allow MNCs to split up their production process and locate pieces of it around the globe (Figure 1.2). At the same time, however, they appear to have developed an alternative model of capitalism and international trade in which policymakers "govern" the market in ways that channel investment and consumption to strategic sectors, while still relying primarily on market forces and institutions to ensure that resources are allocated efficiently. These policies have posed a serious challenge to the economies of North America and Europe and will continue to generate friction and new developments well into the 1990s.

Collapse of Communism

A final historic change by the end of the 1980s was the collapse of the centrally planned economies of Central and Eastern Europe. The inability of central planning to meet the expectations of consumers and address serious environmental problems led to tremendous frustration and alienation for the citizens of these nations. In addition, the ever-widening disparities in the standards of living between citizens of nonmarket and developed market economies was visible proof of the failure of central planning. Given the political opening of "glasnost" in the former Soviet Union and the unwillingness of the Soviets to use military force to block change in its client states of Central Europe, the administrative bureaucracy of central planning lost its legitimacy and, consequently, its ability to organize and motivate their economies.

The transition from central planning to market or

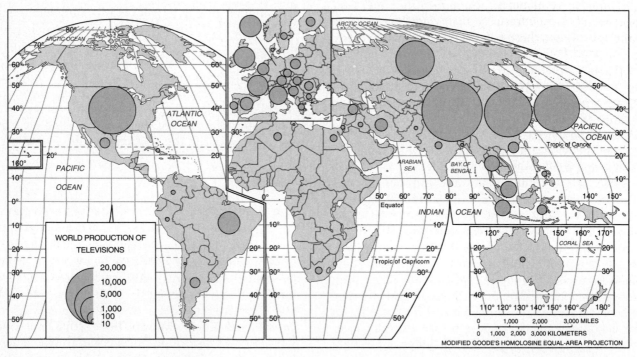

FIGURE 1.2
Manufacture of television receivers worldwide, 1990. In East Asian nations, there has been a great emergence in the production of consumer electronics within the last 10 years. In fact, Asia is the primary area of television manufacture, with more than two-thirds of the world's supply. The biggest single provider is China, which manufactures 22% of the world's total, followed by Japan and Korea, each having 14% of the world market share.
(Source: Data from United Nations, Industrial Statistics Yearbook, 1990, 1993b.)

quasi-market economies is filled with dangers and uncertainties. There are no handbooks or previous historical examples to draw lessons from and, as a result, many nations seem to be groping their way toward market economies in "fits and starts." The transition process is expected to take a decade or more in most of these nations, and the variation among nations will be substantial in the degree to which their economies become centered around market institutions.

In general, there are four major areas where reform must occur. Although the four areas are inseparable, the first task is usually the stabilization of the macro-economy through stopping both the movement toward hyperinflation and the continuous slump in production. Second, over the medium to longer term, markets must be created for goods and services as well as labor markets and financial markets. The third task is the privatization of some or all of the nation's shops, restaurants, hotels, factories, and other productive facilities. Finally, the states of Central and Eastern Europe must redefine their role in the economy. This extends from the creation of commercial codes for business, to the development of pension, health care, and education funding and systems, and the development of other social services and social and physical infrastructure. The last two chapters in the text discuss these issues in much greater depth.

The impact of these changes on the rest of the world will be substantial. Just as the industrialization of East Asia has posed an economic challenge to traditional economic powers, there is likely to be a new challenge coming from Central and Eastern Europe in the next decade or two. These nations have skilled labor forces, high rates of literacy, low wages, and a very bright future if they can overcome the problems of political instability. In addition, in the short term, the world economy will feel these changes in the form of increased competition for the capital resources necessary for rebuilding. Developing countries have already begun to discover that many potential lenders and providers of development assistance have shifted their attention to the enormous capital needs of Central and Eastern Europe.

Framework of the World Economy

The world in crisis is a subject that requires immediate and critical attention. Only by virtually boycotting front-page news is it possible to ignore the fact that we live in an age of crisis. We read of debt, unemploy-

ment, and limited food and energy resources. We read of demographic, ecological, environmental, industrial, and rural and urban problems. These problems are rooted in the structure and development of the world economic system, and their manifestations are aggravated by economic and political policies.

An understanding of the reasons for the new economic crisis begins by recognizing the domination of the world economy by developed countries and the existence of an international economic order established as a framework for an international economic system. The term *world economy* refers to the capitalist world economy, a multistate economic system that was created in the late fifteenth and early sixteenth centuries. As this system expanded, it took on the configuration of a core of dominant countries with a periphery of dominated countries. The dominant countries are in the industrial capitalist West, or the *First World* (Figure 1.3). The dominated countries, in the capitalist underdeveloped *Third World* in the South, are sometimes also called "developing" or, a bit more accurately, "less developed countries" (LDCs). Former Socialist countries of the East or countries of the formerly so-called *Second World*, have become increasingly linked to the capitalist world economy. Since 1953, East-West trade and East-South trade has increased. Beyond trade, the East-West/South international division of labor has been extended through long-term agreements for cooperative production, distribution, and finance. Perhaps the most symbolic expression of the accelerating connections between the Second World and the capitalist world economy is the branch office of Rockefeller's Chase Manhattan Bank at Number One, Karl Marx Square, Moscow, or the 100 Pizza Huts being built in the Ukraine.

The term *international economic system* refers to the system of geographically expanding and evolving capitalism and, in the world today, such underlying processes as the internationalization of capital. By internationalization of capital is meant the export of capitalist production, banking, and services through direct investment by firms that create subsidiaries abroad. MNCs are the principal actors of this export.

The term *international economic order* refers to institutions such as those extablished after World War II to reflect the style and interests of the United States. Among these institutions are the World Bank, the International Monetary Fund (IMF), and the General Agreement on Tariffs and Trade (GATT). As the hegemonic power, the United States created institutions that were required to establish a liberal international eco-

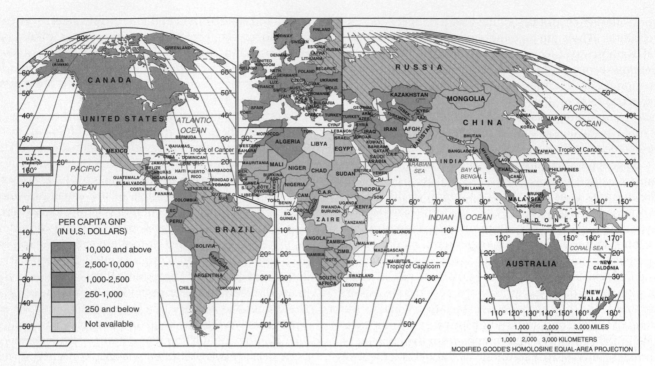

FIGURE 1.3

World variations and gross national product per person. Countries of the so-called First World, including North America, Western Europe, Japan, and Australia. These countries have gross national products per person at more than $10,000 per capita. Little data is presently available for the former Second World, including Eastern European socialist societies and the Soviet Union; however, now that the propaganda war is over, most Westerners realize that per capita incomes were falsely inflated. The remainder of the world consists of Latin America, Africa, and South and East Asia. Here, incomes are generally less than $2500 per capita. (See color insert page 1.1 top for more illustrative map.)

nomic order. Consequently, these institutions had a mandate to dismantle trade and currency restrictions of the interwar years and to facilitate capital mobility.

At any given time, the core of the world economy is dominated by one or more core states. In the postwar period preceding the 1970s, the United States was the principal power. The relative decline of U.S. power that became evident after 1973 was triggered by intense competition from rivalrous core states such as Japan and the Federal Republic of Germany. By the late 1970s, the world order created by the United States after World War II came to an end. And out of the old order, came the tentative birth of a new one.

The oil shock has been blamed for the worldwide crisis and the realignment of the world order, but capitalist competition was the cause of the trouble. A major reason for the breakdown of the postwar world was a decline in the rate of profit of many firms in the industrial West. Faced with intense global competition, firms had to "automate, emigrate, or evaporate" (Magirier, 1983, p. 61). Some firms did go out of business, but others responded to the challenge to automate and especially to "go international." They became more international due in large measure to the speed of travel and the technology of information handling.

New World Economic Order

Among the manifestations of the new world economic order are: (1) increased mobility of capital; (2) growing interpenetration of transnationals, banking, and industrial activities; and (3) the extension of the industrial frontier into an increasingly heterogeneous Third World. In recent years, we have seen the movement not only of labor-intensive industries (e.g., textiles and certain kinds of electronics) but also of capital-intensive industries (e.g., steel and automobiles), as well as some white-collar service industries (e.g., data processing) from high-cost areas of the First World to low-cost areas of the Third World (see Figure 1.2). We have seen increased mobility and rationalization of capital as evidenced by mergers, acquisitions, and the use of new technologies and labor processes. We have also seen the state become an increasingly important force in organizing world production, especially in underdeveloped countries where governments often keep wages low through repressive political policies. Governments also compete among themselves in providing attractive incentives for companies to come to their countries to produce goods and services for the world market.

The worldwide crisis has changed the daily life of people in most countries. Economic and social relations have become increasingly global. The globalization of product and financial markets has made people more dependent and vulnerable to events that occur in faraway places. What happens in places from Bangkok to Buenos Aires affects the salaries of municipal workers in Boston, the cost of a new home in Buffalo, or the solvency of pension funds in Bakersfield. The collapse of the Soviet Union in 1991 sent California unemployment rates skyrocketing in 1993 due to a lowered need for war planes and missiles.

The new global integration has brought with it all sorts of tensions and disruptions—closed factories, empty offices, home mortgage and farm foreclosures, millions of unemployed and hungry, explosions of violence, political repression, and fear. The result is a world of "international economic disorder" (Thrift, 1986, p. 12). A shift to economic planning and a reform of the world economy hold out hope for alleviating the crisis, but change can be slow in coming.

WORLD DEVELOPMENT PROBLEMS

◈

Two major elements of the current world economic crisis require immediate attention. One such element is the challenge to economic expansion posed by the environmental constraints of energy supplies, resources, and pollution (see Chapter 4). The other element is the enormous and explosive issue of disparities in the distribution of wealth between rich and poor countries, city and rural areas, wealthy and poor people, and men and women (see Chapter 13). Extreme disparities of wealth and income between developed and underdeveloped countries have led to Third World demands for a New International Economic Order (NIEO). This pro-

gram, which was initiated following the success of OPEC in raising oil prices, is an attempt to diminish existing disparities by distributing future economic growth more equitably.

Environmental Constraints

The world environment—the complex and interconnected links among the natural systems of air, water, and living things—is caught in a tightening vice. On the one hand, the environment is being squeezed by the massive overconsumption and waste of consumer culture and its ethos of "trying to keep up with the Joneses." On the other hand, the environment is being squeezed by the Third World's poor who destroy their resource base in order to stay alive. The constraints of diminishing energy supplies, resource limitations, and environmental degradation are three obstacles that threaten the possibility of future economic growth and life itself.

Energy is the key to the long-run sustainability of human life. The oil shock brought to the attention of many Americans the possibility of a world drained of energy. In 1973, OPEC raised oil prices and these prices continued to rise until 1981 (Figure 1.4). This action dealt a blow, but not a fatal blow, to the world economy. The so-called energy crisis stemmed more from the concerted action of OPEC to slow down production for political reasons than from an actual shortage of world oil reserves. In the 1980s, oil prices fell as demand for energy dropped. Unlike the 1970s, oil prices were shaped as much by world economic trends and the traditional oil-pricing system as by a cartel agreement. But the day will come when the pressure of demand will force oil prices to rise steadily, with no help from OPEC at all, unless substitutes for gasoline and heating oil are discovered. Without substitutes, proven oil reserves at current rates of extraction are projected to be exhausted in the next 30 to 40 years (Table 1.3).

There is already a significant poor-world energy problem. Oil is an unaffordable luxury for more than 50% of the world's population who cook and heat with fuelwood, charcoal, animal wastes, and crop residues. Even during the years of falling energy prices in the 1980s, Third World countries obtained more than 40% of their energy from noncommercial sources. In countries such as India, Haiti, Indonesia, Malaysia, Tanzania, and Brazil, fuelwood collection is a major cause of defor-

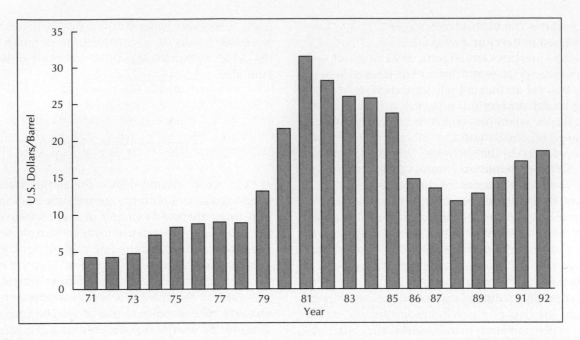

FIGURE 1.4

Average U.S. price per barrel of oil, 1971–1992. The price per barrel of oil peaked in 1981 with the Arab Oil Embargo. Since then, the price of a barrel of crude has dropped from $34 per barrel to a low of $12 per barrel in 1988. In the summer of 1993, a barrel of crude oil on the world market was approximately $20, effectively ruling out synthetic fuels, solar energy, and geothermal energy as sources of power because of the associated higher development and production costs. By 1994, a barrel had dropped to $15.

◈

Table 1.3

Petroleum Supply

	Reserves in Millions of bbl.	*Current Production in Millions of bbl. per Day*	*Possible Increases*
Iraq	100,000	3.0	
Kuwait	94,525	2.0	
Saudi Arabia	254,959	5.7	2.0
United Arab Emirates	98,105	2.1	0.5
Iran	92,860	3.0	
Venezuela	58,504	2.0	0.5
Former Soviet Union	58,400	11.1	
Mexico	56,365	2.5	0.1
U.S.	25,860	7.4	
China	24,000	2.8	
Libya	22,800	1.3	
North Sea	16,821	3.5	

estation—one of the most severe environmental problems in the underdeveloped world.

In addition to the eventual increase in oil prices and the intensifying poor-world fuel crisis, the availability of other natural resources will also affect economic growth. The demand for resources in the coming years will require vast investments in mineral extraction and food production. According to a study of global needs conducted for the United Nations by Wassily Leontief in 1977, the consumption of common minerals must rise fivefold and food production fourfold if a moderate rate of world economic growth is to continue. Above all, Leontief's study indicates that due to energy, mineral, and food constraints we will have about another 25 years of growth followed by an almost certain curtailment.

The fragility of the environment poses the most formidable obstacle to the economic process. Are there

Emissions from smokestacks, such as these in the Saar industrial region of West Germany, increase acidic deposition and contribute to the buildup of carbon dioxide in the atmosphere. Until recently, carbon dioxide released from fuel combustion and deforestation were considered the chief contributors to the greenhouse effect. In the 1980s it was discovered that other trace gases—methane, ozone, chlorofluorocarbons, nitrous oxide—contribute to greenhouse warming on a scale comparable to that of carbon dioxide. *(Source: United Nations.)*

limits to growth? Is the world overpopulated? Some of our present activities, in the absence of controls, may lead to a world that will be uninhabitable for future generations. Topsoil is being lost because of overcultivation, improper irrigation, plowed grassland, and deforestation. Water tables are falling. In the United States, parts of the Ogallala water basin under the Great Plains are at least half depleted. Forests are being torn down by lumber companies and by people trying to keep warm or cook their food. Water is being poisoned by domestic sewage, toxic chemicals, and industrial wastes. The waste products of industrial regions are also beginning to threaten the world's climate. Accumulated pollutants in the atmosphere—primarily carbon dioxide, methane, and chlorofluorocarbons—are said to be creating a *greenhouse effect* that will cause world temperatures to rise. The recent warming of the Pacific Ocean just 0.25°F has caused violent weather disruption in South America, with billions of dollars worth of damage. El Niño, as this ocean warming effect is called, has caused torrential rainfall in Mexico and southern California in 1993, resulting in flooding, mudslides, and massive loss of life.

Chlorofluorocarbons, which are used as aerosol propellants and coolants and in a variety of manufacturing processes, are blamed for damaging the earth's ozone layer. Ozone protects life from ultraviolet radiation given off from the sun. The U.S. Environmental Protection Agency (EPA) estimates that a 2.5% reduction in the ozone layer could cause 15,000 human cancers a year as well as extensive damage to plants and animal life. Yet another hazard to the environment is the fallout from nuclear bomb tests that took place in the 1950s and 1960s and from nuclear power reactor accidents such as those at Three Mile Island and Chernobyl.

These trends confirm the immediate need for monitoring, supervising, and controlling the economic process. Defenders of the market mechanism claim that some of these functions, particularly the allocation of scarce resources, can be performed by an efficient free-enterprise system. Critics of the market mechanism disagree; these few argue that it results in an inequitable allocation of scarce resources. Moreover, they claim that a free-enterprise economy is unable to monitor safety or to impose decisions about the rate of growth or its sharing within and among countries. Proponents of either position would agree, however, that the problems of the environment and its natural resources are now so great that planning the economic process is imperative, especially in view of the apparent linkage between environmental conditions and country income levels.

Environmental management must include policies regulating energy and other natural resources and policies curtailing activities that threaten the health and well-being of people. The shift to planning, which is already underway, is essential to ameliorate the problems caused by the economic system. It is also essential if the extraordinarily resilient and persisting system is to survive the worldwide crisis. These questions are further explored in Chapter 4.

Disparities in Wealth and Well-Being

There is poverty that afflicts the few in predominantly rich countries—hunger and malnutrition among families in Appalachia, bankrupt farmers on the Minnesota prairie, unemployed factory workers in Detroit, and single mothers on welfare in New York. This kind of poverty, that of poor individuals and families, is an issue of considerable importance. However, there is another kind of poverty that affects all but the few in poor countries; it is *mass poverty*. This is the most important world development problem of our time. You cannot doubt this assertion when you see the halt and maimed sidewalk people of Bombay, insistent begging children in the streets of Mexico City, or women and children carrying firewood on their backs in the countryside north of Nairobi. Mass poverty is intolerable and a crisis that we must grapple with and try to overcome.

Who are the world's poor? They are the 15 million children in Africa, Asia, and Latin America who die of hunger every year. They are the 1.2 billion people, or 24% of the world's population, who do not have access to safe drinking water. They are the 1.4 billion without sanitary waste disposal facilities. They are the 3 billion people—more than 50% of the world's population—who live in 43 countries in which the per capita income was less than $350 in 1990 (Figure 1.5). These people are caught in a *vicious cycle of poverty*.

The poor of the world are overwhelmingly the people of Third World countries that have failed to keep up with the economic levels of the West since the beginning of the modern colonial period in the sixteenth century (Figure 1.6). During the boom that followed World War II, the gross national product (GNP) (i.e., the total domestic and foreign output claimed by residents) of the developed countries rose from $1250 billion to $3070 billion. That increase was three and one-half times the GNP, $520 billion, of the underdeveloped

Who Are America's Homeless?

- 55% are single men
- 11% are single women
- 32% are families with children
- 22% are children

- 52% are African-American
- 33% are white
- 11% are Hispanic
- 3% are Native American
- 1% are Asian

- 28% are mentally ill
- 41% are substance abusers
- 9% have AIDS

- 17% are employed
- 18% are veterans

By 1993, 16% of all Americans were below the poverty line. Poverty afflicts the minority in predominantly affluent societies. Why are some people, such as this destitute woman in New York, excluded from the general well-being?
(Source: U.S. Department of Housing and Urban Development.)

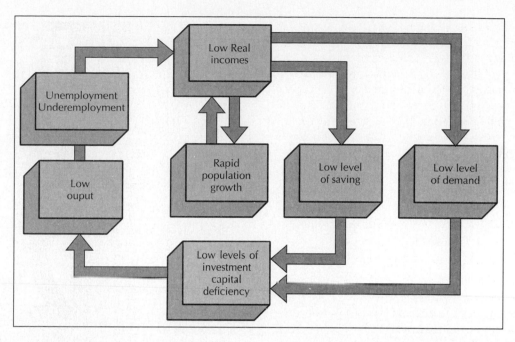

FIGURE 1.5

The cycle of poverty for Third World countries reinforces itself. Most Third World nations have low per capita income, which leads to a low level of saving and a low level of demand for consumer goods. This makes it very difficult for these nations to invest and save. Low levels of investment in physical and human capital result in low productivity for the country as a whole, which leads to underemployment and low per capita income. In addition, many of these countries are faced with rapid population growth, which contributes to low per capita incomes by increasing demand without increasing supply or output.

countries in 1972. Although per capita real income rose from $175 in 1952 to $300 in 1972, the per capita real income in developed countries rose from $2000 to $4000. Developed countries enjoyed 66% of the world's increase, whereas half of the world's population in underdeveloped countries (excluding China) made do with one-eighth of the world's income. By 1982, the national income of the United States (235 million people) was about equal to the total income of the Third World (more than 3000 million people). In that year, 43% of Third World countries had national incomes amounting to less than one-thousandth that of the United States. The national incomes of 89% of Third World countries were not equal to one-hundredth that of the United States.

The Third World is far from a homogeneous entity; that is, there are enormous differences among underdeveloped countries. *Physiological density* is one way in which the Third World varies. For some countries, a small amount of arable land and a large number of people can help create poverty (Figure 1.7). Mexico had a per capita GNP of $2290 in 1990; Bangladesh had $180 in 1989 (Table 1.4). There are also huge differences in wealth within countries and among people. In India in 1990, 14% of the population of the Punjab was below the official poverty line. By contrast, more than half the population (60%) in the state of Bihar in northeast India fell below the poverty line. Household income is also uneven. In Bangladesh, the richest 20% of the population gets six times as much as the poorest 20%; in Brazil, the richest get more than 30 times as much as the poorest (see Table 1.5). Land ownership is the ultimate indicator of economic inequality in the Third World. For example, in Bangladesh, 22% of the population owns 75% of the land; in Brazil, 1% owns 40%.

Despite the large differences between and within regions of these countries, there is a commonality that binds the Third World together. This commonality is an unfair economic system that fails to provide the poor with the basic human rights of adequate food, clothing, housing, and medical care. The misery of the Third World is now so intense that many countries must first benefit from a greater share of the world's wealth before they can even begin to better themselves, in absolute or relative terms. Except possibly for China and India, most Third World countries are presently too weak and

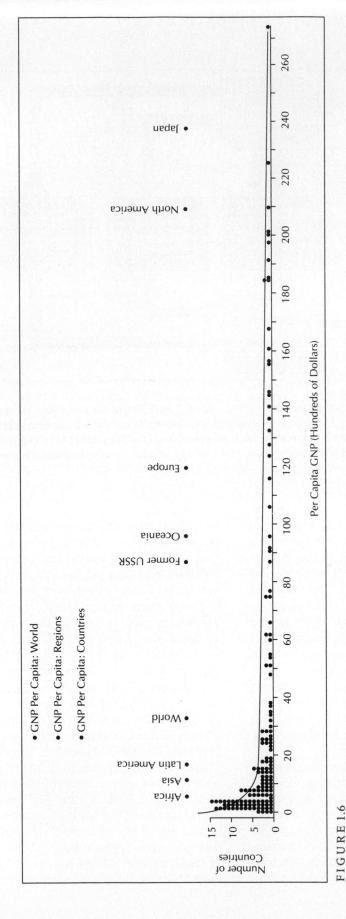

FIGURE 1.6

Per capita GNP and dollars for major cultural realms of the earth. Both North America and Japan are in a class by themselves, with slightly more than $20,000 per capita. Several European states match this level, including Switzerland, Germany, and Sweden. However, when individual currencies are converted to dollars and divided by the cost of living (or PPP, *Purchasing Power Parity*, as it is called by the World Bank), North America stands well above the others in per capita economic levels as the box in Chapter 13 shows.
(*Source: Adapted from Fisher, 1992, p. 15.*)

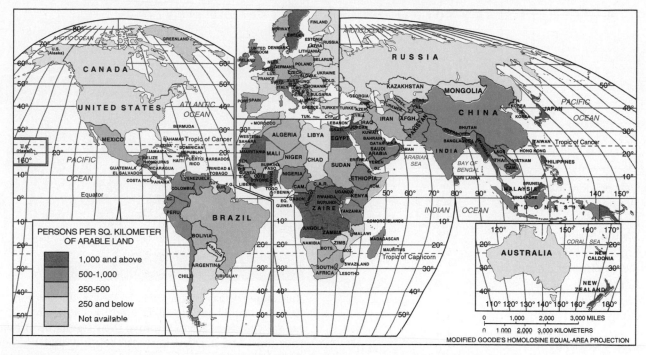

FIGURE 1.7

Persons per square kilometer of arable land. Physiological density is the number of people per unit area of land that can be used for agriculture suitably. The higher the physiological density, the greater the pressure people exert on the land and on food resources of a country. Geographers use physiological density rather than population density as a true measure of the population pressure on the land because it shows the potential availability of needed food resources. Pressure on the land can be better understood by converting square kilometers to square miles. To make the conversion, multiply the number of kilometers by three, as there are roughly 3 square kilometers per 1 square mile. (See Color Insert page 1.1 bottom for more illustrative map.)

Table 1.4

Selected Socioeconomic Indicators of Development

Country	(1) Per Capita GNP, 1989 (in Dollars)	(2) Life Expectancy at Birth, 1989 (Years)	(3) Infant Mortality per 1000 Live Births, 1989	(4) Adult Literacy Rate, 1985 (%)	(5) Daily Per Capita Calorie Supply, 1988	(6) Per Capita Energy Consumption, 1989*
Japan	23,810	79	4	99	2848	3484
United States	20,910	76	10	99	3666	7794
Brazil	2540	66	59	78	2709	897
Mauritania	500	46	123	17	2528	114
Haiti	360	55	94	5	1911	51
India	340	59	95	43	2104	226
Bangladesh	180	51	106	33	1925	51
Ethiopia	120	48	133	5	1658	20
Mozambique	80	49	137	28	1632	84

*Kilograms of oil equivalent.

Source: Statistical Abstract of the United States, 1991.

Table 1.5
Distribution of Household Income

	Poorest 20%	Wealthiest 20%
Developed Countries		
Netherlands (1977)	8.1	37.0
United Kingdom (1979)	7.3	39.2
United States (1972)	4.5	42.8
France (1975)	5.3	45.8
Underdeveloped Countries		
Bangladesh (1973–1974)	6.9	42.2
Hong Kong (1980)	5.4	47.0
Argentina (1970)	4.4	50.3
Venezuela (1970)	3.0	54.0
Malaysia (1973)	3.5	56.1
Kenya (1974)	2.6	60.4
Mexico (1977)	2.9	57.7
Brazil (1972)	2.0	66.6

Source: World Bank, 1985, pp. 228–229.

Rickshaw cyclists clog a street in Decca, Bangladesh, carrying people and goods around the city for pay. If the poorer countries are to improve their standards of living, they must find markets for both their raw materials and manufactured goods. An effort is presently underway between the richer industrialized nations of the north and the less developed countries of the south to establish new trading arrangements that are more fair to the developing nations. These discussions have been termed the North/South Dialogue.
(Source: UN photo 151 869/John Isaac.)

too enmeshed in the world's trading and financial system to withdraw and adopt relatively isolationist policies without considerable economic cost.

In response to glaring international disparities in income and wealth, political leaders of Third World countries have proposed a new world order with their NIEO program. The program was introduced at the Sixth Special Session of the General Assembly of the United Nations in 1974 and approved as a resolution on "Development and International Economic Cooperation" in the Seventh Session 1 year later. The group of underdeveloped countries (the Group of 77) that submitted their demands for an NIEO call for a redistribution of world income and wealth from the Northern Hemisphere to the Southern Hemisphere. They also want more control over the use of their own natural resources as well as over their interactions with developed countries.

NIEO is essentially trade-oriented. Underdeveloped countries want improved terms of trade and are seeking measures to ensure stable and equitable prices for their raw material exports. Moreover, they want improved access to developed markets, especially for processed commodities and manufactures. Underdeveloped countries also want a larger say in the transportation, marketing, and distribution of their products.

In addition to improved terms of trade, NIEO asks for more foreign aid and rescheduling of debts. It also asks for more control by underdeveloped countries of the international monetary system and of its institutions. NIEO wants an easier transfer of technology through new patent laws and commercial practice. It also calls for more regulation of transnational corporations in the interests of underdeveloped countries through the formulation, adoption, and implementation of an international code of conduct. NIEO also calls for a rapid increase in Third World food production, increased food aid from developed countries, seabed and ocean management, and the conservation of natural resources.

Although the NIEO proposals are a challenge to the existing liberal international order, the program cannot be considered revolutionary. For example, as far as improving world trade is concerned, NIEO only aims at terms of trade. There is little talk about changing the world division of labor. The NIEO program is really a charter for some kind of capitalism for everyone.

What are the prospects for the NIEO program? First, there is a gap between Third World rhetoric and reality; that is, when it comes to specific demands, Third World countries seldom present a unified front. For example, when something as meaningful as reducing the Third World's technological dependence on the MNCs is at stake, there is little common ground. In fact, many Third World countries are individually reducing or even eliminating the few restrictive provisions that they had imposed in the late 1960s and early 1970s. Malaysia, India, Zaire, Mexico, Argentina, and many other countries are all relaxing controls on foreign enterprises and are competing with each other to grant more concessions to the MNCs.

Second, there is little evidence to date that NIEO demands will be accepted by major developed countries in the near future. The tactic U.S. officials often use in North-South discussions about reconstructing the basis of international exchange is to "batten down the hatches and let the Southern hurricane of demands blow itself out." Indeed, the United States has often told the Third World that its demands are unnecessary when the world economy is in such fine shape, and that there are more pressing priorities when it is not doing so well.

With the debt crisis of the 1980s, the United States finally discovered it had a real stake in the prosperity of the Third World (see Table 1.2). The inability of some countries to make payments on their debt placed the financial structures of the United States and some European nations in jeopardy. Many U.S. banks, including some of the largest, would technically be insolvent if their loans to Third World nations were declared in default. This led to enormous pressure to resolve the immediate problems of the debt crisis, many of which were directly related to the poor economic performance of the economies of the debtor nations.

Unfortunately, for many of the debtors, the solution sometimes proved to be more painful than the problem itself. Under the guidance of the IMF and other international agencies, stringent limits were placed on the economic policies of debtors, with the result that a majority of citizens in these nations often found themselves worse off. The goals of *IMF conditionally*, as it came to be called, were to restore growth, reduce central government involvement in the economy, and expand the exports of goods and services, while reducing imports so that the debtor would have sufficient earnings of foreign revenue to make payment on the interest and principal of their debt.

There is little evidence that these policies helped to restore economic growth, but they did result in export surpluses that made debt servicing easier. As a consequence, the mid-1980s saw a remarkable reversal in the flow of financial resources—from the flow of the 1970s in which rich nations provided net financial transfers to poor nations to assist in the development effort, to a flow from poor to rich. (See tables in World Bank's *World Development Report*, 1992, p. 50.) In 1978, net financial transfers from rich to poor of long-term lending was 33.2 billion dollars. By 1988, the flow from poor to rich was 35.2 billion; the money went largely for interest payment and principal debt repayment. Needless to say, these transfers have become a serious obstacle to further economic development in poor countries where capital and financial resources are scarce and every dollar lost had repercussions through the economy.

Scarcity and Inequality

So far, our discussion of world development problems has considered the concepts of scarcity and inequality separately; but, in fact, these two concepts are intimately related. Economic growth, which proceeds faster in some places than others, creates the structure of the world economy with its pattern of inequalities.

Under the market mechanism people must be prepared to trade off growth and equality; that is, to accept inequality as a mechanism for stimulating growth. In developed countries, during the long postwar boom, most people were satisfied with this arrangement. As a result, there were few complaints about disparities in income and employment opportunities. In underdeveloped countries, the benefits of economic expansion never reached the masses. Underdeveloped countries of the world were dissatisfied with the relationship between growth and equality. As a result, they submitted demands in the form of the NIEO program to achieve a more equitable distribution of economic growth.

Glaring inequality between the rich and the poor and between developed and underdeveloped countries is not conducive to world peace and stability. Unfettered economic growth stimulates inequality, creates new wants, and leads to increased competition for resources. Moreover, the distributional problems that growth creates have been responsible in greater measure for heated debates on limits to growth than has the fear of running out of scarce resources.

THE GEOGRAPHIC PERSPECTIVE

◈

World development problems are of immense interest to geographers. Many development problems have geographic solutions or, more accurately, partial solutions. They certainly raise the important geographic questions of location and accessibility, relationships between settlements and land use, changing transport and communication linkages, efficient flows of commodities, and the spread of ideas and innovations. They also raise questions about center-periphery relations at a hierarchy of scales ranging from a farmer's access to a market to connections between First and Third Worlds.

Before exploring the geographic character of the world in crisis, however, you should be acquainted with the geographer's perspective. What exactly is geography? What are the concerns of economic geography, and how has this part of the discipline changed over the years? What are the fundamental concepts of the geographer's enterprise? What useful knowledge and advice do geographers provide to help resolve development problems? Answers to these questions will give you a framework for understanding how geographers go about the task of analyzing and interpreting problems of the world economy.

The Field of Geography

Geography is concerned with place. Geographers describe the changing pattern of places, explain how these patterns evolved, and attempt to unravel their meaning. Geography's continuing quest is to understand the physical and cultural features of places and their natural settings on the face of the earth. Geography uses a distinctive language—the *language of maps*. A map reveals human excitement, wonder, and concern for spatial relations. The oldest recorded map was carved about 15,000 years ago on a piece of mammoth bone at an ice age camp on the bank of the River Dnieper in southwestern Russia. Since then, geographers have systematically recorded what is where on the face of the earth. Modern geographers also use the map as a research tool to ask and answer questions about spatial relations.

The spatial dimension is central to geography. It is also central to the internationally interdependent character of our lives. Events in one place have a direct and immediate impact on events in other places. An increase in the price of OPEC oil swells the coffers of countries such as Kuwait and Saudi Arabia, but impoverishes other countries such as Tanzania and Bangladesh that feel the pinch much more than the United States or Japan. To keep their trucks moving, poor countries must pay for oil in hard currencies that leave less money for fertilizers, schools, hospitals, and new development projects.

In order to describe, sample, measure, and explain physical and human elements on the earth, geographers refer to knowledge and insights derived from other disciplines. Thus, geography can be viewed as a synthesizing discipline. And some scholars—such as Russell Peterson, President Emeritus of the National Audubon Society, and James Michener, famous novelist—argue that geography is in a unique position to demonstrate the relatedness of all knowledge.

So broad is the field of geography that no one scholar can hope to have expertise in more than a few areas of the discipline. For that reason, geographers specialize in one or two topics or regions. There are physical, urban, rural, social, political, and economic geographers. The study of each topic may embrace the whole world or may be confined to one or more areas. Some geographers use all the topical specialties in exploring a particular region. In the case of this text, the scope is the world, and, therefore, economic geography is emphasized.

Trends in Economic Geography

Economic geography is concerned with the spatial organization and distribution of economic activity, the use of the world's resources, and the distribution and expansion of the world economy. In its infancy, economic geography was called commercial geography, which developed during the era of European exploration and discovery from the fifteenth century through the nineteenth century. There was much excitement and adventure then. Commercial geographers were on sea voyages, and their reports brought masses of factual information about other lands to merchants and government officials.

Probably the best known commercial geography was written by British scholar G. G. Chisholm in 1899. In his view, the purpose of commercial geography was to stimulate intellectual interest in geographic facts relating to trade; hence, virtually all of his book was an inventory of commodity and trade statistics. Such a treatment was not highly regarded by those who wanted to see an analytical rather than a descriptive approach to economic geography.

The term "economic geography" was coined in the United States in 1888. Twelve years later, Ellen Stemple authored a book with that title, and by the end of World War I, economic geography was a respected part of the discipline. In fact, in 1925, a new journal, *Economic Geography*, began publication.

As a distinct field of study, economic geography was affected by three major themes of geography: (1) human-environmental relations, (2) areal differentiation, and (3) spatial organization. Although all three thematic approaches have always been present, a human-environmental emphasis flourished largely by itself until the 1930s; areal differentiation was most influential from the late 1930s to the late 1950s; and spatial organization has since emerged as the dominant approach. To better understand the fundamental concepts of geography we examine later in the text, it is useful to first take a brief look at these three approaches.

Human-Environmental Relations

The economists hoped that economic geographers would apply the principles of classical economic theory in a geographic context. However, events turned out otherwise. The geographers sought to explain variations in economic development in terms of *environmental determinism,* or *environmentalism* for short. For example, Ellsworth Huntington in 1924 argued that certain areas of the globe stimulated human efficiency more than others. The industrial countries, in Huntington's view, had the most "stimulating climates," whereas most Third World countries had "difficult climates" (see Figure 1.7).

The environmental dictum was ideologically acceptable during the years of twentieth-century colonial expansion. It helped to justify the view that economic "backwardness" in Africa, Asia, and Latin America was caused by "unfavorable" climates that induced low levels of productivity among indigenous peoples. Disease,

climate, and the "colored races" were also seen as major obstacles to white settlement in the tropics. Many of the American Geographical Society's Special Publications from the 1920s to the early 1950s were devoted to environmental questions about human physiology and European residence in the tropics (Jefferson, 1921; Pelzer, 1945; Price, 1939).

Few, if any, geographers who study human-environmental relations now claim that the physical environment is the sole determinant of people's economic behavior. Geographers now place emphasis on human adaptation and adjustment to potentialities in the environment. They attempt to discover how particular groups of people, especially in a local area, organize their thoughts about the environment and how to come to grips with it (Porter, 1965).

Areal Differentiation

Economic geographers were badly "burnt" in their encounter with environmentalism and its underlying preoccupation with race. The main reaction to the period of excessive environmental determinism was to adopt the view that all geographic phenomena were unique and that theory building was of little value. Hence, for a period between the late 1930s and the late 1950s, the primary focus of concern was *areal differentiation*—differences rather than similarities—among places.

The *unique approach* resulted in detailed descriptions of production, exchange, and consumption. At the teaching level, textbooks were organized by regions or topics, and they contained voluminous factual data. In some respects, these texts resembled nineteenth-century commercial geographies. At the research level, scholarly papers and monographs became increasingly specialized.

The areal differentiation concept, which led to some of the great regional writing on which much of the present academic status of geography was built, led geographers to overlook the need for comparative studies. Areal differentiation dominated geography at the expense of *areal integration.* In the 1950s and 1960s, geographers such as Peter Haggett from Bristol, UK, and others, such as Brian Berry, Bill Garrison, Richard Morrill, Waldo Tobler, John Nystan, and Art Getis, from the University of Washington, scorned the unique approach. They argued that economic geography needed to become a theoretical subject, which it did.

Spatial Organization

This theme in geography came to the fore in the decade of the 1960s. It has done a great deal to help geographers think in new ways about geographic distributions and spatial relations. *Spatial organization* is concerned with how space is organized by individuals and societies to suit their own designs. It provides a framework for analyzing and interpreting location decisions (e.g., market versus raw material location, accessibility versus transportation costs) and spatial structures (e.g., land-use patterns, industrial location, settlement). The popularity of the organization-of-space theme was influenced by governments who were subsidizing geographic research, especially for planning and policy-oriented studies. It was also influenced by the "quantitative revolution," with its emphasis on quantification and experimentation with a wide range of statistical techniques. A more important emphasis, however, was on the formulation of hypotheses, data collection and the search for theory. This empirical approach aimed at building theory was called *logical positivism*. Economic geographers found some of the theories they were looking for in the social and biological sciences, including location and general systems theory.

Location theory attempts to explain and predict geographic decisions that result from aggregates of individual decision making. The main aim of location theorists is to integrate the spatial dimension into classical economic theory. The origins of location theory stem from the work of Johann Heinrich von Thünen on agricultural location in the 1820s and subsequent contributions to industrial and settlement theory by Alfred Weber and Walter Christaller. They developed normative (i.e., theory-building) models relating to business and industry in a world of pure competition that assumed entrepreneurs are completely rational and attempt to maximize profits with perfect knowledge of the cost characteristics of all locations. This image of an entrepreneur became known as "economic person"; that is, an omniscient, rational individual who is driven by a single goal—to maximize profits.

Location theorists often use *general systems theory* as a framework for explaining the interrelatedness of places and activities. In particular, a spatial system is a set of interdependent and interactive parts—land uses, business firms, trade flows, and regions. In more abstract terms, a spatial system consists of movements (e.g., people, goods) that result in channels along which the movements occur, called networks (e.g., roads), which are structured around nodes (e.g., towns, villages) that

are organized as a hierarchy, with the interstitial zones viewed as surfaces (Haggett, 1965, p. 18).

In the 1970s and 1980s there were at least three departures from location theory. First, *behavioral geographers* criticized location theory for its emphasis on abstract patterns of land use and maximization of profits. They questioned the relevance of location theory for understanding location decisions and spatial structures in the real world. They also noted that economists were replacing the image of *economic person* with the *satisficer*. According to the satisficer concept, people rarely achieve, or even wish to achieve, maximum profits. They seek a variety of goals and often trade off some income to realize other goals. The satisficer idea led to a shift in economic geography from economic person to how people perceive risks and opportunities and how their perceptions affect decision making. The notion that we live in a world that is a probabilistic mixture of choice, calculation, and chance is evident in studies of resource management (Saarinen, 1969).

Second, *phenomenological geographers* rejected the perception of the "economic person" and the notion that we live in an "objective world." Life takes on meaning only through individual experiences and needs; for example, resources have no existence apart from human wants. The phenomenological approach in geography is based on a relationship between the observer and the observed. The scholar looks at a problem from the subject's viewpoint, or "lived world." Phenomenology took a step back from the progress of location theory of the 1960s by rejecting most theory. Since experience in the field was individualistic, there was no need for models or theory.

An illustration of the phenomenological approach is work on "mental maps." A mental map compares personal views with the collective image. The map in Figure 1.8, for example, is a preference surface of where Pennsylvania State University students would most like to live if they had no financial worries or concern about finding a job after graduation. It uses a simple scaling with the most preferred state at one hundred, and the least preferred at zero.

Third, *Marxist geographers* charged that traditional theories of spatial organization obscure more than they reveal. In their view, location theories are narrowly conceived and blind to historical facts—designed primarily to serve the goals of those who wield power in the economic system. These geographers believe that a Marxist view can provide a more precise set of ideas about the world economy by recognizing and drawing attention to the power relations of societies. They see

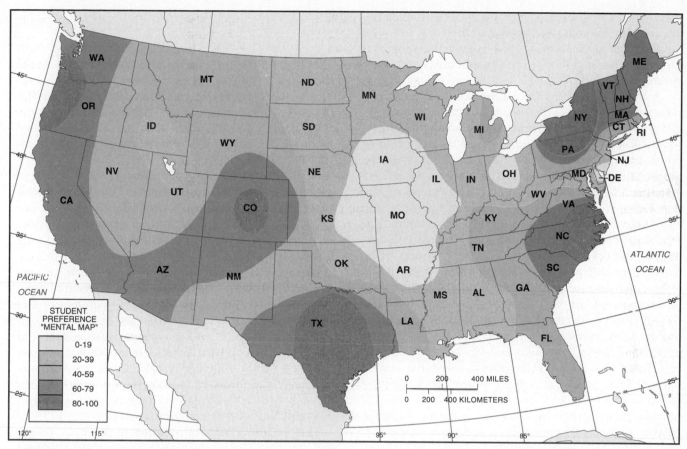

FIGURE 1.8
The preference surface or mental map of students at Pennsylvania State University in 1982. Mental maps such as this one have been created for almost every state and for rural regions as well. Every map has similar properties. Local regions are ranked quite high as shown by the darker shades in this map. In addition, Colorado and the Rockies, as well as the West Coast and Florida, are always ranked high. Most evaluators in this case, students at universities across the country, prefer amenity rich areas.
(Source: Gould, 1983, p. 161.)

the relations of places in the context of the world's political economy. They recognize a contemporary reality—the disadvantageous situation of most people with respect to the control and use of resources—and expose the structure that preserves and intensifies that situation. Marxist geographers acknowledge and analyze prevailing value systems, a topic largely ignored by most economic geographers.

Radical Humanists of the 1990s

More recently, *radical feminists* and *radical gay rights activists* have used some of the same Marxist arguments

to argue that men, especially nongay men, have structured the social and economic environments of the political economy to favor themselves over women and gays.

Most Marxist thinkers and counterculture radicals, who gained numbers during the days of the Vietnam war, have softened their stance a bit in their challenge of capitalism and the market economies of the world. This is primarily due to the utter collapse of the Soviet Union by the year 1990 in the achievement of its economic and social goals. A number of radicals have been influenced by phenomenology, as previously discussed, and reject notions of objectivity or the existence of theory in economic geography, because to them, all experience is personal. These *deconstructionists*, descendants of postmodern and new-age mentalities, have become *humanistic.* They seek to view the world through the eyes of the exploited population that they seek to study. Some of the research on the homeless population, the inner city unemployed, or undocumented temporary workers are examples.

A major thrust has been made by counterculture radicals who now call themselves *radical humanists,* arguing that labor, the environment, and the means of production have for centuries been dominated by the white, male power establishment. This power structure has been, and continues to be, they argue, exploitive, greedy, and dehabilitating to women, members of minority groups, foreign cultures (especially those of the Third World), and also to the environment. Radical humanists propose that this new understanding of "politically correct" research thinking and writing, with its undergirding plot of exploitation and domination, replace neoclassical location theory and analysis as the principle paradigm of future economic geography.

The majority of research in economic geography today remains location theory and analysis. It aims to understand "what" products and services are produced and "how" they are produced (that is, with what combination of resources), as well as "where" they are produced and "why there?" The radical humanist's principle aim is to expose the fallacy of currently accepted answers to these three questions and, most important, to answer the "for whom" question in a politically correct manner.

Economic geography has been characterized by major changes in thinking. These shifts reflect a need to deal with new realities of the world. However, to attempt to reduce the mosaic of views of the economic geographer's task to one or two general views would be misleading. Nonetheless, many geographers would agree that the theme of spatial organization is particularly valuable in helping us to understand world development problems. This theme receives more attention than others in this text.

Some Fundamental Concepts of Space and Location

When geographers study development issues, they ask questions about the world's space, as we have shaped, structured, and organized it. They answer these questions with the aid of concepts. The major concepts used in this book are grouped under three headings: (1) properties of space, (2) spatial process and structure, and (3) spatial interaction.

Properties of Space

Geographers examine space at multiple levels. There is a hierarchy of spatial perspectives from personal space to international space. Personal space is the familiar "close-at-hand" world of the individual. International space is the entire world—those vast areas controlled more by governments and institutions than by individuals.

Geographers also consider various dimensions of space. They sometimes consider three-dimensional space (a volume) or one-dimensional space (a line between two points), but most of the time they consider two-dimensional patterns that can be represented on a plane. Maps are examples of two-dimensional space.

Geographers divide space into *abstract space* and *concrete space.* Abstract space is a conceptualization of one-, two-, or three-dimensional space independent of any point of reference on the earth's surface. It is homogeneous in all respects and movement is equally easy in all directions. On a plane, abstract space is called an *isotropic surface;* it allows geographers to develop normative models of idealized landscapes. Concrete space is the actual surface of the earth, with all the variety and differentiation of the real world.

Only a few terms are required to describe, define, and measure space. Imagine a sheet of blank paper representing a two-dimensional abstract space. This featureless plane devoid of pattern is of no interest to geographers, but once some phenomena are mapped onto the paper, a pattern begins to emerge. *Point, line,* and *area* are the most elementary terms that can be used to describe this pattern. Points may represent cities or manufacturing plants; lines may represent transport arteries or boundaries between areas; and areas may represent agricultural or manufacturing regions.

The spatial elements of *point, line,* and *area* may be used to define the basic geographic concepts of *distance, direction,* and *connectivity.* If two points are placed on our blank piece of paper, point A can be described in terms of its distance from point B and vice versa (Figure 1.9a). If point A is chosen as an arbitrary starting place, all other points can be defined in terms of their distance and direction from point A. A line can be defined as a series of points or a given distance from a point in a specific direction (Figure 1.9b). A series of defined lines describes a bounded area (Figure 1.9c). The concept of connectivity refers to how well points are linked to others (Figure 1.10). Point A is connected to many other points by lines, whereas B is connected to only a few points. The points may represent cities and the lines

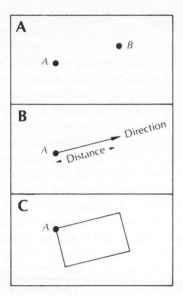

FIGURE 1.9
Point, line, and area defined by distance and direction.
Points usually represent places on a map as cities or intersections or the sighting of some plant or species.
Lines usually represent flows of goods or services, telephone or information contact, or transportation routes.
Areas can be political units such as cities, counties,
states, service areas of companies, or resource production areas from any country in the world.

scheduled air-passenger flights. Point A has a higher
degree of connectivity than point B.

Other measures of space are extensions of the concepts of distance, direction, and connectivity. An area
may be defined by a series of distances and directions.
Once defined, these terms can be used to describe and
measure the area's size and shape. The size and shape

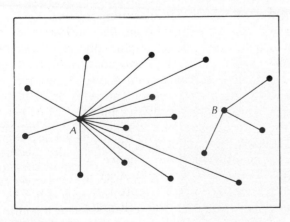

FIGURE 1.10
Connectivity—the overall level of interconnection in a
network.

of an area has economic implications. A farm that is
too large or too small may not be conducive to efficient
operation. A large country is more likely than a small
one to have the resources needed for economic development, but then again largeness may inhibit effective
control and organization. Other things being equal,
compact countries have an advantage over countries
with less efficient shapes. For example, the long, narrow
shape of Chile creates problems for communication and
national unity.

Agglomeration and accessibility are extensions of the
concept of distance. Consider two clusters of points (Figure 1.11). Points in cluster A are closer together than
points in cluster B. Cluster A represents greater agglomeration or reduced aggregate distance. For example, a
shopping center reduces the distance consumers must
travel to purchase goods by clustering many stores at
one point. A city itself is a clustering strategy reducing
aggregate distance among residential, business, and recreational functions.

Accessibility is the concept of being close to things
(Figure 1.12). Point X has a high degree of accessibility
and point Y has a low degree of accessibility. Accessibility is, therefore, another measure of aggregate nearness.
Agglomeration refers to aggregate nearness of points in
a cluster, whereas accessibility refers to the nearness of
a given point to other points.

Basic geographic concepts and their extensions are
absolute concepts when applied to an abstract space
such as an isotropic surface. Absolute measures of space
also apply to concrete spaces. A kilometer on the earth's
surface is the same as any other kilometer. Yet, the use
of relative measures of distance, direction, and connectivity often provide a more meaningful view of concrete
space than the use of absolute measures.

For example, *relative location* is measured by the cost,
in both money and time, required to overcome it. These
costs are referred to as the *friction of distance*. The handi-

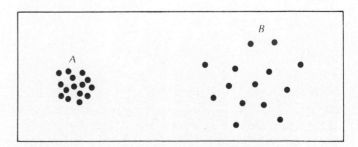

FIGURE 1.11
Agglomeration—reducing aggregate distance among economic functions or points through clustering.

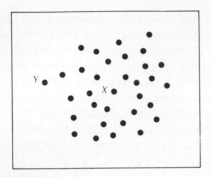

FIGURE 1.12
Accessibility. Point X has a higher accessibility than point Y because it is closer to all other points taken as a group. It has relative nearness.

cap of distance has declined historically because of transport improvements, but it may increase in the future with a rise in the cost of oil. In general, the retarding effect of distance is less in developed countries with their modern and well-managed transport systems than it is in underdeveloped countries. At the same time, geographic space is much more "sticky" in traffic-clogged New York or Washington, DC than it is in rural Wyoming.

Concrete qualities of space are referenced to specific points or areas on the earth's surface. Any location requires a fixed reference point. Geographers deal with two kinds of location: absolute and relative. *Absolute location* (site) is position in relation to a conventional grid system, such as latitude and longitude or street addresses. *Relative location* (situation) is position with respect to other locations. It is a measure of connectivity and accessibility, and it usually changes over time. The concept of relative location is of greater interest to economic geographers than absolute location.

To illustrate the importance of relative location, consider the position of New York City. The absolute location of New York (40° 45' north latitude and 74° 00' west longitude) tells us nothing about the city if we are interested in understanding why it became one of the world's great cities and ports. In 1820, there were four main ports on the northeastern seaboard competing for trade between the United States and Europe: Boston (pop. 61,000), Baltimore (pop. 63,000), Philadelphia (pop. 64,000), and New York (pop. 131,000). But New York's slight edge over its rivals became unassailable after 1825. Why? Geographers find the answer in the relative location of New York. The Appalachian Highlands represented a cost and time barrier (high friction

By 1993, New York City's population was 15.8 million, and it remains the largest city in the United States. Because the city's geographic situation is strategic, the city serves as a gateway between rich hinterlands and as a port to the rest of the world.
(*Source: New York Convention and Visitors Bureau.*)

and distance) between the resources of the American interior and the return flow of manufactured goods from Europe. New York is at the mouth of the Hudson River, which is almost at sea level all the way to Albany where it is joined by the Mohawk River that cuts through the Appalachians (Figure 1.13). In 1825, the Erie Canal was completed linking the Hudson-Mohawk corridor with Lake Erie. An advantageous location relative to a primary traffic artery provided a major impetus for New York's explosive growth during the nineteenth century. By 1840, New York with a population of 349,000 was nearly three and one-half times the size of its closest rival, Baltimore.

The concept of relative location is vital to our understanding of the integration of the world economy. *Spatial integration*—the linking of points of production (absolute location)—was mandatory for the development of the economic system. It involved, through the construction of transport networks, the transformation of absolute space into relative space. Growth of the world economic system, proceeding at different rates in various regions, determines the relativity of geographic space.

Spatial Process and Spatial Structure

A *spatial process* is a movement or location strategy. Geographers are interested in movements, such as the flow of raw materials to processing plants, the distribution of finished products from manufacturing plants, and the trade in commodities. Also of interest are location strategies, such as the decision of Chagga farmers on the slopes of Mount Kilimanjaro to grow coffee, the choice of the most accessible place for a new school serving children in villages of a rural area in India, and the decision of Japanese companies to locate assembly

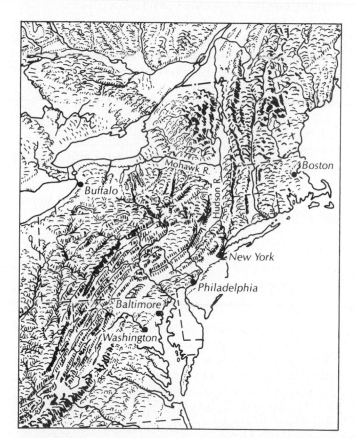

FIGURE 1.13
The Hudson-Mohawk corridor and the relative location, or situation, of New York. New York has a good harbor, was centrally located among the other 12 colonies, and was connected to the interior of America by water routes. These three locational and accessibility factors meant that it became the primate city of America rather than Philadelphia, Boston, or Washington.

Vancouver is at the terminus of Canada's transcontinental transport routes, including TransCanadian Highway and both Transcontinental Railway Lines. It is also at the mouth of two river canyons, the Fraser and the Thompson. It has grown, due to its site and situation, to become Canada's second-ranking port city. It is the first-ranking city in western Canada, as well as an attractive place to live because of the temperate climate created by its proximity to the marine influences of the Pacific Ocean. It acts as a super port for the exportation of coal and ores to Japan at Robert's Bank, 22 miles to the south; this advantage has added to its urban influence. *(Source: Porterfield/Chickering, Photo Researchers, Inc.)*

plants near the U.S. market in cities along the U.S.-Mexican border.

Spatial structure is the internal organization of a distribution—the location of the elements of distribution with respect to each other. Spatial structures limit, channel, or control spatial processes. Since they are the result of huge amounts of cumulative investment over years and centuries, large alterations to the spatial structures of towns, regions, or countries are difficult to make.

Spatial structure and spatial process are circularly causal. Structure is a determinant of process, and process is a determinant of structure. For example, the existing distribution of regional shopping centers in a city will influence the success of any new regional shopping center in the area.

Spatial Interaction

Flows of goods, people, and information are collectively known as *spatial interaction*. The amount of spatial interaction tends to decline with distance (Figure 1.14). This rule, called the *distance-decay effect*, holds for all sorts of things and all sorts of geographic scales. Information people have about places declines with distance and, at larger geographic scales, air-passenger traffic is subject to the same effect.

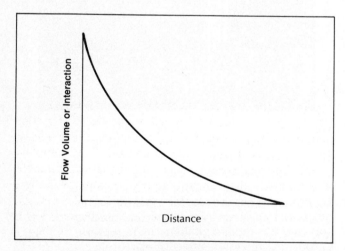

FIGURE 1.14
The distance-decay effect. The greater the distance traveled, the fewer the number of trips that will occur. This rule of transportation is true not only for air travel, but also for pipeline movements, telephone traffic, and automobile traffic. Is it true for your own pedestrian travel as well?

The amount of interaction between places is also a function of their size. Big places generate more information, people, and goods than small places. New York and Chicago have more interaction than New Orleans and Cincinnati, even though both pairs of cities are about the same distance apart.

To explain the bases for spatial interaction, geographers make use of the concepts of *complementarity, intervening opportunity,* and *transferability.* Movement occurs between two places when there is a supply of goods or services in one place and a demand for them in another place. The oil fields of Saudi Arabia and Kuwait have complementary relations to the industrialized countries of North America, Europe, and Japan. Movement between places is modified or even eliminated because of the existence of intervening opportunities. Fewer goods and services move between Boston and Philadelphia because New York lies between them. Chicago attracts fewer immigrants from the Dakotas because of the intervening opportunities offered by Minneapolis-St. Paul. "In a sense, intervening opportunities are spatial sponges soaking up potential interaction between complementary places" (Abler, Adams, and Gould, 1971, p. 194). The third condition for spatial interaction is transferability—the friction of distance. All movement increases costs, and costs increase with distance. If the costs of traversing a distance are too great, movement will not take place despite complementarity and the absence of intervening opportunities. Chapter 6 is devoted to spatial interaction in economic geography.

Geographic Research in Aid of Development

A basic function of geographic research is to influence planning or organized action and the development of policy. An equally important function is to influence scholars, teachers, and students in the field and in the other social and environmental sciences.

The sort of knowledge and advice geographers provide their important constituencies fits under three headings: (1) human-environment, (2) spatial organization, and (3) the inventorying and monitoring of research. In the human-environment area, geographers provide information about the best match between the environment and the product realized from the environment. They provide information about how the biophysical environment, ecosystem management, and systems of livelihood are linked. In the area of spatial organization, geographers provide information about the kinds of spatial structures that favor processes of development and the procedures that can bring these structures into being. Inventorying research involves the collection and analysis of information, especially for planning the use of human and natural resources. Monitoring research provides information about change—whether certain changes are harmful to people, the resource base, or both, and whether the goals of development are being achieved.

Economic Geographers

Economic geographers—university researchers (e.g., Michigan State University, San Diego State University); local, state, and federal government (e.g., Aid for International Development Department, the State Department); or private industry (e.g., Exxon, IBM, or McDonalds's)—work to solve local, national, and international problems in a variety of settings. Some geographers have produced research in aid of international development in the Third World. The work of Iowa professor Gerard Rushton, in developing a series of health care centers in India; the work of New York professor Jeffery

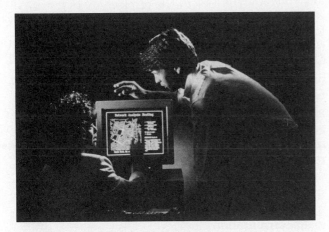

Economic geographers study human-environmental problems, inventory and monitor resources, and provide expertise to better manage large corporations. Key questions include, "What should be produced?", "How should it be produced?", "Where should it be produced?", and "For whom should it be produced?"
(Source: Environmental Systems Research Institute, Redlands, CA.)

Osleeb, in tracking the spread of disease in Africa; the work of Tennessee professor Bruce Ralston, in improving transportation efficiency in Africa; and the work of California professor Janet Franklin, in checking desertification in Africa are but a few of the hundreds of examples that exist as an example of academic-based research. Many geography departments have multimillion dollar annual research budgets in aid of development supplied by both private foundations as well as local, state, and federal governments.

For each score of economic geographers, working at the international level, and usually funded by the U.S. government or international governments, there are hundreds working at the national and state level with funding from both the federal and state governments, as well as from the private sector. Researchers at the city and regional level surpass the national level by a factor of 10. Here, local governments and businesses provide the support and needed research agendas.

Geographers do not always solve development problems directly, but their skills and ways of thinking can help to resolve the world crisis. Our major responsibility as teachers and students is to try to understand the world in crisis and to explore the causes of that reality. The world, developed and underdeveloped, poses challenges of immense importance and complexity. In this exciting and dangerous age of uncertainty, we can help to meet these challenges.

SUMMARY AND PLAN

◈

To justify the assertion that the world is in the midst of economic crisis, we provide evidence of two challenges to the present world order—first, the challenge of constraints of energy supplies, resource availabilities, and pollution dangers; second, and equally formidable, the problem of the distribution of wealth. Will these problems exceed the capabilities of the capitalist system? Will capitalism, which has demonstrated a remarkable capacity for adaptability over the centuries, be able to push through this age of crisis?

The unsettled state of the world arouses the concern and the interest of the geographer. World development problems raise geographic questions, and the actual development involves varying degrees of change across geographic space. In this chapter, we present the geographer's perspective. We provide a definition of the field and introduce the main concepts and paradigms geographers use to interpret and explain world development problems at a variety of scales, ranging from small areas and regions to big "chunks" of the world.

This text describes how geographers study and analyze the world economy and how they attempt to resolve world development problems. The variety of perspectives that geographers use to approach principle economic, location, and allocation problems are addressed. In Chapter 2, alternative world views, as derived from four basic political economies, are the focus of discussion. It is important to appreciate various perspectives and be aware of how different attitudes and views can influence approaches to foster development. Conflicting arguments and theories are interwoven in the remaining chapters.

These chapters, which progress in logical sequence, are organized around the themes of distribution and economic growth. Chapters 3 and 4 deal with population and resources, the prime variables in economic geography. To understand the effects people and resources exert on the world economy, we need to learn about the principles of location. Chapters 5 to 11 supply the foundation stones required to understand these principles: decision making, transportation, agricultural land use, urban land use, cities as service centers, and industrial location from the standpoint of firms and world regions.

The two chapters on industrial location provide a link between the development of businesses and the development of places—a link vital to the issues discussed in the remaining chapters. Chapters 12 and 13 deal with the expanding world of international business—its operations, environments, and patterns. The final chapter examines the geography of development and underdevelopment and illustrates how economic growth and resource use can combine to create a world of uneven and unequal development.

◈

KEY TERMS

absolute location
absolute space
accessibility
agglomeration
areal differentiation
areal integration
complementarity
concrete space
connectivity
development
direction
distance
distance-decay effect
economic person
environmental determinism
Four Tigers
friction of distance
general systems theory
greenhouse effect
human-environmental relations
international economic order
international economic system
internationalization of capital

intervening opportunity
isotropic surface
location theory
logical positivism
Marxist geographers
phenomenological approach
physiologic density
point, line, area
purchasing power parity
radical humanist
relative location
satisficer
spatial integration
spatial interaction
spatial organization
spatial process
spatial structure
Third World debt crisis
transferability
transnationals (or MNCs)
vicious cycle of poverty
world economy

◈

SUGGESTED READINGS

Bhagwati, J. N., ed. 1977. *The New International Economic Order: The North-South Debate.* Cambridge, MA: MIT Press.

Bodman, A. R. 1991. Weavers of influence: The structure of contemporary geographic research. *Transactions of British Geographers,* New Series, 16:21–37.

Frank, A. G. 1980. *Crisis in the World Economy.* London: Heinemann.

———. 1981. *Crisis in the Third World.* London: Heinemann.

Gaile, G. L., and Willmott, C. J., eds. 1989. *Geography in America.* New York: Merrill/Macmillan.

Gould, P. 1985. *The Geographer at Work.* London: Routledge and Kegan Paul.

International Institute for Environment and Development and World Resources Institute. 1988. *World Resources 1988–89.* New York: Basic Books.

Janelle, D. G., ed. 1992. *Geographical Snapshots of North America.* New York: Guilford.

Johnston, R. J. 1979. *Geography and Geographers: Anglo-American Human Geography Since 1945.* London: Edward Arnold.

Johnston, R. J., and Taylor, P. G., eds. 1986. *A World in Crisis? Geographical Perspectives.* New York: Blackwell.

Laszlo, E.; Baker, R., Jr.; Eisenburg, E.; and Raman, V. 1978. *The Objectives of the New International Economic Order.* New York: Pergamon.

Lozoya, J.; Estevez, J.; and Green, R. 1979. *Alternative Views of the New International Economic Order.* New York: Pergamon.

Martin, G. J., and James, P. E. 1991. *All Possible Worlds: A History of Geographical Sales.* New York: John Wiley & Sons.

Porter, M. E. 1990. *The Competitive Advantage of Nations.* New York: The Free Press.

Rubenstein, J. M. 1994. *An Introduction to Human Geography,* 4th ed. New York: Macmillan.

Sheppard, E. 1990. Modeling the capitalist space economy: Bringing society and space back. *Economic Geography,* 66:201–228.

2

ECONOMIC GEOGRAPHIES, POLITICAL ECONOMIES, AND WORLD VIEWS

◈

OBJECTIVES

- To understand the four principal political economies of the world

- To state the four questions important to understanding the world economy

- To explain why it is useful to analyze and understand alternative world views

- To emphasize that, due to culture, economy, and politics, there is no one world view that is considered to be indisputable reality

- To compare and contrast conservative, liberal, and radical mind-sets in economic geography

◈

The United Nations' General Assembly: An international forum for discussion of diverse issues.
(Source: UN photo 172.801/Yutaka Nagata.)

Almost every day we hear of development problems: overpopulation in the Sahel of Africa, hunger and malnutrition in Bangladesh, balance-of-payments difficulties in Central America, massive unemployment in northern England, and the farm credit crisis in the United States. Yet, there is little agreement on what causes these human tragedies or how they might be prevented.

The classic fable of five blind men touching an elephant serves as an analogy for this dilemma. Each feels a different part of the elephant and thinks he knows what it is. The man who grabs the tail thinks he's holding a rope; the one who grabs the leg believes it's a tree trunk; the one who touches the elephant's side says it's a wall; the one who feels the ear is certain it's a big leaf; and the one who holds the trunk exclaims that it's a snake.

To illustrate the dilemma more concretely, consider a hypothetical discussion on the world food problem. One American who is pessimistic about the world's resources declared, "Soaring numbers of people are overrunning our food supplies. It seems to me that the lifeboat ethic is not such a bad solution to the situation. Countries like Bangladesh are basket cases. If we continue to give them handouts, it will only serve to maintain high population growth rates. Compassion is a luxury we can no longer afford. We have to learn to let the starving die for the survival of the human race." A United Nations adviser stated, "I think that high population growth rates and consequent population pressure, land fragmentation, poor soils, and unreliable rainfall keep people from feeding themselves. The best way to stabilize overpopulation and food scarcity problems is to provide the poor with contraceptives." A World Bank official added, "People are hungry because of inefficient food production. If we want to solve the world food supply situation, we have to transform traditional agricultural methods. The only way to do this is for rich industrial countries to supply progressive farmers with imported technology, new types of seeds, artificial fertilizers, pesticides, irrigation, and machinery." A Marxist from Niger commented, "The cause of hunger is not the tropical environment, not too many people, not scarcity of available land, not lack of technology, and not overconsumption by greedy Americans. The real problem is the unequal distribution of global wealth, which is the end result of capitalist countries gaining control of the global economy. The only guarantee of long-term food security is for us Third World people to take control of our own food resources."

Different perspectives on the causes of world hunger lead to a variety of solutions that have different effects on people. If human suffering and misery are to be alleviated, we must appreciate alternative world views and understand how different ideologies influence efforts to resolve crisis situations. Here, an important question naturally arises: Does one perspective provide more meaningful insights into world development problems than another? To answer this question, we must be aware that scholars use different theoretical and analytical frameworks to argue their cases. Such awareness can only be achieved if we embrace a level

These villagers are planting rice in Bangladesh. This nation, with some of the world's most fertile land, is also home to some of the world's hungriest people. Is there a world view that sheds more light on this paradox than others?
(Source: World Bank.)

of learning that permits us to think critically about the world.

LEARNING IN AN IDEOLOGICAL WORLD

This chapter describes four different political economies of the world, as well as the main questions of economic geography. The chapter then turns to levels of learning and explains why most of us find it difficult to alter the way we think and learn. It demonstrates that a world view is part of a particular theoretical perspective. We also introduce three general perspectives: conservative, liberal, and radical. A comparison of these competing mind-sets will help you appreciate their crucial assumptions and the policies that stem from them.

Levels of Learning

People acquire knowledge on at least four recognizable levels. *First-level learning* involves simple perception of fact. For example, if we are hungry, we are conscious of that fact. In *second-level learning,* at least two facts are interrelated. During a drought we harvest less food per unit area and, therefore, we recognize the increased likelihood of hunger. When we attain a higher level of consciousness within an existing system, we are learning on the *third level.* Several options are possible: (1) if there is recurring drought, we can improve food yields either by planting drought-resistant crops or by irrigating traditional crops; or (2) if we choose not to change our traditional agricultural practices, there will be less food. Our understanding of the world comes mainly from this level of learning. At the third level, learning is laced with a strong dose of ethnocentrism.

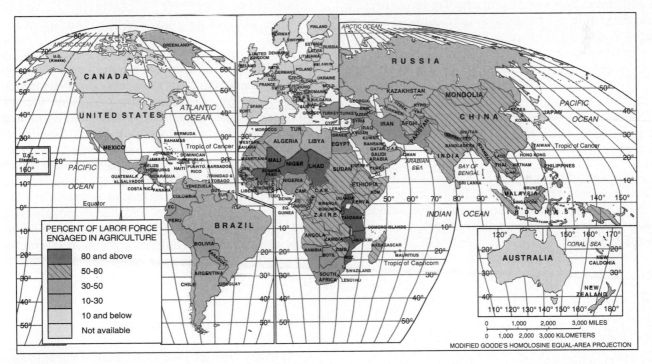

FIGURE 2.1

The percentage of labor force engaged in agriculture, 1990. Note that more economically advanced nations have a lower portion of labor in agriculture. The United States, Canada, Europe, and Australia are examples. The most important priority for people in the world is to secure enough food to survive and prosper. Developing countries in Latin America, Africa, and Asia have a greater dependency on food production for survival as a percentage of not only GDP, but also as a percentage of total workers engaged in agriculture. Sixty percent of all workers in the world are engaged in agricultural pursuits; less than 4% of the workers in Europe and Anglo-America are engaged in agriculture. Most of these people earn their living working in offices, stores, and factories. (See color insert page 1.2, top, for more illustrative map.)

It traps us into thinking that our way of seeing the world is the only way to see the world. Consequently, we tend to rely on strategies that optimize existing institutions rather than consider a wide range of alternative strategies.

When *fourth-level learning* is achieved, we can perceive the nature of existing systems, reexamine them, and perhaps improve or change them to create new options. If we stay with the overpopulation/food scarcity issue, we can consider solutions beyond improved food yields when we evaluate the entire agricultural system. For example, we could consider expropriating prime agricultural lands that are now used to produce export crops such as coffee and cotton. This land could be given back to local farmers who could then produce food for their own needs instead of depending on purchased food and food from the industrialized countries (Figure 2.1). In fourth-level learning, the goal is to move beyond present perceptions of reality. This point can be illustrated by a simple problem. Try to connect the following nine points with four continuous straight lines:

```
•   •   •

•   •   •

•   •   •
```

If you stay within the area delimited by the points, you will not find the solution. But if you move outside the self-imposed square, the following solution quickly comes to mind:

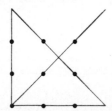

Similarly, if we are to understand different approaches to world problems, we must be willing to broaden the basis of our inquiry to include alternative ideologies outside the traditional norms that limit how we perceive problems and solutions.

Ideological Inertia

Most of us find it difficult to change the way we think and learn. Our perspectives on the world tend to persist. This ideological inertia is not surprising in that we are shaped by the culture, language, and habits of the particular setting in which we were born and raised (see Figure 2.2 and Table 2.1). The problem develops when our personal view of the world prevents us from seeing it another way. A drawing by Henri de Toulouse-Lautrec, which is a perceptual illusion, illustrates this point (Figure 2.3). Those of us who see an old woman in the picture have difficulty seeing a young woman, and vice versa. To learn to see is to impose order on stimuli. The manner in which we impose order is determined by our expectations and, therefore, is value-laden.

Distortions and Abstractions of Reality

In an ideological world, value-free positions are impossible to maintain, even in science. Scholars use different paradigms or frameworks that guide the way questions are asked about observed reality. To a large extent, these frameworks govern the particular facts gathered and the manner in which they are analyzed; thus, they stipulate the form of the answers, if not the answers themselves. They lead us to see what we want to see, to explain what we want to explain.

Concepts, classifications, and "facts" are distortions and abstractions of reality that are laden with theory. They are predicated on different cultural and theoretical perspectives. The following examples clarify this argument.

THE WORLD IN STATISTICS

Similarly, any attempt to summarize the world statistically presupposes some model as a basis for selecting "facts" to represent "reality." What classification or grouping of countries do we choose? We could choose the World Bank country groupings shown in Table 2.2.

In this classification, countries are grouped primarily according to whether they are "developing" or "developed." After this initial breakdown, they are grouped into six categories: low-income economies, middle-

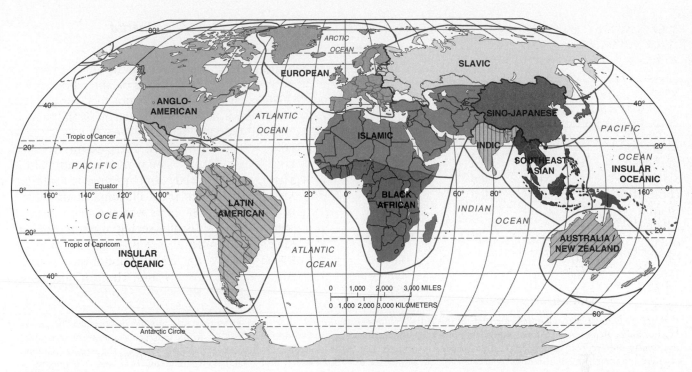

FIGURE 2.2
Cultural realms of the world. Ten spatially continuous cultural realms can be identified on a world map. Each culture realm has a set of common features that distinguished it from other cultural realms. Culture is the sum of all learned patterns of behavior, institutions, values, and belief systems of the population. There is greater internal homogeneality within each cultural realm than there is between cultural realms. The 10 regions identified on the map here have economic, political, religious, linguistic, and ethnic similarities.

income oil importers, middle-income oil exporters, high-income or capital-surplus oil exporters, industrial market economies, and East European nonmarket economies. The emphasis of the classification is on relative income (GNP per capita), the need for energy (oil), the type of technology used (industrialization), potential access to high technology (capital surplus), and the type of institutional structure (centrally planned or market economy). Using this mix of criteria, the world's land area, population, and GNP per capita may be divided into groups.

This classification is neither objective nor value-free. Why are some countries called "developed" and others "developing"? Why are they sometimes also called "less developed" or "underdeveloped" in other classifications? Classifications are abstractions of reality and are not as innocuous as they appear at first glance. They originate from particular theories or underlying ideologies.

The World Bank classification is based on a Western conception of development. It stresses that a free market is the most effective path to economic growth and the improvement of human well-being. By contrast, another conception of development is used by Third World *dependency theorists*. By dependence is meant a conditioning situation in which the economies of one group of countries are underdeveloped by the development of others. Dependency theorists argue that developing countries suffer not from less development but from underdevelopment.

THE FOUR WORLDS

The division of the world into First World, Second World, Third World, and even Fourth World is also laden with theory. For Westerners, the First World includes the countries of Western Europe, North America, Australia, New Zealand, and Japan. Some would even include the Republic of South Africa and Israel. The Second World was represented by the Soviet Union and Eastern Europe; whether this designation will remain

◈

Table 2.1
Economic and Cultural Indexes by Cultural Realm*

	GDP	Power-Distance	Individualism	Uncertainty Avoidance	Sex-Role Differences	Religion
Anglo-Am	Hi	Hi	Hi	Lo	Hi	Protestant
European	Hi	Med	Med	Lo	Lo	Protest/Catholic
Slavic	Lo/Med	Med	Med	Med	Med	Orthodox/Catholic
Latin Am	Lo/Med	Med	Hi	Med	Hi	Roman Catholic
Islamic	Lo	Med	Med	Hi	Hi	Islam
Africa	Lo	Lo	Lo	Med	Lo	Mixed
Indic	Lo	Lo	Lo	Med	Hi	Hindu
China	Lo	Lo	Lo	Hi	Lo	Buddhist
Japanese	Hi	Med	Lo	Hi	Hi	Shinto/Buddhist
SE Asia	Lo	Lo	Lo	Hi	Hi	Buddhist

*Culture traits have been identified for each of the culture realms in Figure 2.2. GDP is the gross domestic product per person. The power-distance index measures the extent of inequality toleration among individuals in a culture. It defines the degree to which less powerful individuals in a society are accepted as equals to other members of society. The individualism index measures the degree to which the culture maintains an interest in their immediate family versus a feeling of collectivism, in which a society protects the interest of members at large. The uncertainty avoidance index measures the degree to which a culture can tolerate unstructured or unpredictable events in the socioeconomic milieu by adopting strict codes of behavior or belief systems. Sex-role differences observe the relationships between men and women and the roles that they play. Highly masculine cultures expect men to be separate, assertive, and in leadership capabilities. Whereas in societies with low sexual differentiation, men and women share similar roles; there is less occupational segregation by gender. Many other cultural traits could be added to this list. The chart demonstrates that there are basic cultural, social, and economic differences between and among culture realms of the earth. The realms identified here are for large territories of the world. Many differences exist at the regional level as well. In this table, China and Japan are separated because of their large GDP and sex-role differences. The last column on religion is self-explanatory.
Source: Data in Cols. 2 through 5 from Hofstede, 1980.

FIGURE 2.3
A picture of . . . ?

seems doubtful. The Third World consists of the remaining countries in Latin America, Africa, the Middle East, and Asia. The Fourth World is really a subset of the Third World. There are the scarcest countries on earth with less than $150 per capita per year. These are the so-called "basket cases." Through the eyes of the "free world," the Second, Third, and Fourth Worlds are associated with negative and undesirable traits (i.e., lack of freedom, poverty) in contrast to the positive and desirable characteristics of First World countries (Figure 2.4). The strong geographic regionalism of countries, north to south, is striking.

Because there is no one indisputable reality, it is desirable to be aware of different economies, systems and world views. For this reason, we have attempted to select and organize the material for this text from a broad base of inquiry. The focus is on a comparative approach in which different perspectives are explained and contrasted. Looking at the world through different ideological lenses better enables us to meet the challenge of world development problems. The way in which a

◉

Table 2.2
GNP Per Capita, Population and Growth Rates

	GNP Per Capita		Population	
	Dollars, 1989	*Annual Growth Rate, 1965–1989 (%)*	*Millions, 1989*	*Annual Growth Rate, 1980–1989 (%)*
Industrially advanced countries: IACs (19 nations)	18,330	2.4	830	0.7
Less developed countries: LDCs (97 nations)				
Middle-income LDCs (56 nations)	2040	3.3	1105	2.1
Low-income LDCs (41 nations)	330	2.9	2948	2.0

Source: Data from World Bank. 1991. World Development Report, 1991. New York: Oxford University Press.

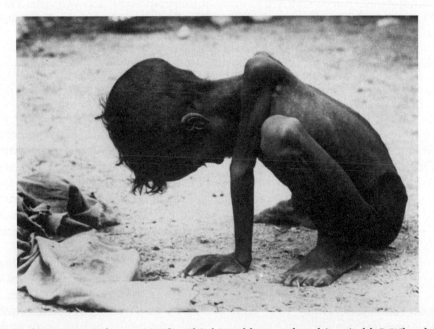

Hunger strikes hardest in the young. Is hunger in the Third World natural and inevitable? What human action can help end the hunger of millions of people? These are difficult questions to answer. This Ethiopian child has been the victim of not only economic underdevelopment, but also of civil war and lack of rainfall. Operation Restore Hope, carried out by U.N. Forces in Somalia, found solutions to the hunger problem to be extremely elusive and costly. *(Source: WHO/UNICEF/W. Campbell.)*

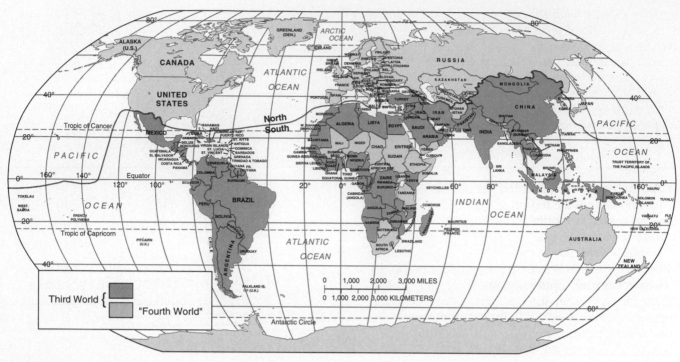

FIGURE 2.4

The Third and "Fourth" Worlds. The Third World consists of Latin America, Africa, and South and East Asia. These are the areas of the world that are the least developed. The Fourth World consists of the least developed of the Third World nations with the lowest per capita incomes, usually below $350. The countries included are grouped in the Sahel area of Africa, South Africa, and in scattered locations throughout South and East Asia. The strong north/south division of developed versus undeveloped nations is striking. The First World, or the most developed countries, includes Anglo-America and Europe. Former communist and socialist countries of Eastern Europe and the Soviet Union appear as more developed than the Third World and were formerly called Second World countries. While this designation is no longer appropriate as many of these former Soviet countries look toward the European community for economic ties and membership, their per capita GNPs are closer to Third World nations. We now understand that per capita incomes for the former Soviet Union and Eastern European nations were for a long time overstated for propaganda purposes.

society answers the four questions of economic geography depends on its ideology.

THE FOUR QUESTIONS OF THE WORLD ECONOMY

◙

The basic problem of economic geography deals with *scarcity* in space and the methods to overcome it so that a fair distribution of resources can occur. The problem of scarcity does not strike people in the United States or Canada in quite the same way as it does those people in the Third World. We are used to seeing grocery stores'

goods, but it is quite the opposite situation in much of the rest of the world. Scarcity in space has always been a problem for mankind from the earliest days, and much of the remainder of this text aims at describing the processes whereby scarcity has originated and how the world can overcome it.

The *four basic questions of economic geography* and the world economy arise for each country and each economic system in an effort to overcome their society's scarce resources. The answers to the questions will vary by the type of political economy—capitalist, command economy, traditional economy, or some hybrid form.

Question 1: With human and capital resources available, exactly *what* should be produced and at what level or scale of production?

Question 2: Now given what should be produced and production levels, exactly *how*, or with what combination of techniques, labor and capital inputs and other resources, should the output be produced?

Question 3: Once it is agreed upon what will be produced and how it will be produced, the next question is, *where* should the output be produced? A related question is once spatially dispersed economic activity exists, why is it here?

Question 4: After producing the output at geographic locations from the resources available, exactly which groups should receive what share of the goods and services? That is, *who* will receive the goods?

The field of economics centers on question No. 1; international business centers on question No. 2; political economy centers on question No. 4. By far, the core of economic geographic studies through the decades has centered on question No. 3. A shift in the field is starting, which emphasizes the need to answer Nos. 2 and 4. Also note that these four questions have been stated in the "normative," or the third level of inquiry. That is, they ask what is the best answer to these questions. As is the case with all sciences, most of our study is at the first and second level of inquiry; that is, we try to first describe, then explain, economic phenomena in this text. Only then can we hope to answer the normative questions.

The Factors of Production

We have all heard of the *factors of production*. However, what does this phrase really mean given the four previously listed questions, which are basic to all the economic geographies of the world's countries? The factors of production usually include land, labor, capital, and entrepreneurial skills (management). *Land* can be divided up into not only the units of physical geographic space that exists across the earth, but also into the amount of *raw materials* extracted from the earth. *Labor* is the human, physical input from individuals required in the production process. *Capital* is the machines, tools and infrastructure, storage, transportation, and distribution facilities used by labor to produce the goods from the spatially dispersed raw materials. (Here, capital or *real capital* is an economic resource. *Money capital* is not

Baku, the oil capital of the former USSR. At the end of 1991, the communist system and the USSR collapsed. The Commonwealth of Independent States (CIS) was formed, and Mikhail Gorbachev was removed from power. Further, state-assisted industry and subsidized economy has completely imbalanced the Russian continent, requiring them to receive financial aid from their former capitalist enemies. The advantages of Baku's geographical position as a meeting place of the trade routes from Russia, Persia, Central Asia, and the Caucasus, make the oil fields on the Caspian Sea an important economic factor. The city of Baku is the capital of the Republic of Azerbaijan, with a population of 2 million people.
(Source: Photo by Sebastiao Salgado/Magnum Photos.)

a resource and is not included in capital.) *Entrepreneurial skill*, or management, is the coordinating effort used to combine land, resources, labor, and capital to produce goods and services.

The interdependencies of economic geography are that the factors of production, land, resources, labor, capital, and entrepreneurial skill can be substituted for one another in the final production process to attain variations of the four questions. For example, the production of goods and services is still a possibility in nations that have almost no land or no resources by substituting capital and labor with the addition of increased transportation costs. These are the factors that account for the prodigious east Asian and Japanese economies of the 1990s.

Generally speaking, the lack of two or more factors of production can relegate a country to great levels of depravation. The amount of interchange between the factors of production determine how the output will be produced. *Compensation* is made in the form of *rent*, which is paid for the use of someone else's land; *wages*, which are paid for the use of labor; *interest*, which is paid for the use of capital; and *profits*, which are the reward paid for entrepreneurial ability.

The factors of production are employed differently within each political economy. No two countries employ the same mix of the factors of production to produce the same products. Different areal sizes, amounts of technology and capital, entrepreneurial skills, and quantities of labor, as well as differing political, cultural, and historic factors, means that each country must answer *what is produced? how is it produced? where is it produced?* and to *whom will it be given?* in different ways. Each country will dictate the amount of individual freedom, the amount of social support, and the process of distribution in answering these basic questions, based on their political, cultural, and economic philosophies. These political economic systems are discussed next.

POLITICAL ECONOMIES

◈

World societies use four basically different governmental and economic systems to coordinate their economic geography. Historically, the United States and Europe have differed with much of the rest of the world in their economic geography based primarily on two factors: (1) the method by which economic geography and the market mechanism is coordinated and controlled, and (2) the groups that control and own the resources and means of production in a society. Briefly, we discuss the political economic systems of the world: *pure capitalism;* the *command economy* of Marxism; *mixed political economy,* including fascism and socialism; and the *traditional economy* of developing nations. Following this, we describe the competing mind-sets in economic geography, with regard to the conservative, liberal, and radical, or Marxist viewpoints, to address the problems and prospects created by the study of economic geography.

Capitalistic Economies

Pure, or laissez-faire, capitalism is the economic geographic system that is characterized by the private ownership of the economic means of production and minimum governmental intervention. In such a system, sometimes called *market economy,* a series of competitive markets and prices are used to coordinate economic geographic activity and final production levels. Freedom of enterprise and choice is the distinguishing factor in this type of economy. In pure capitalism, each individual, or firm, seeks to maximize his or her own self-interest.

Now, we must answer our four basic questions: What will be produced? How will it be produced? Where will it be produced? For whom will it be produced? Only profitable products will be produced based on market demand and price. Price will be maintained by the utility and value of the good, based on consumers maximizing self-interests. How and where the goods are produced is based on labor and technology efficiency and the lowering of production costs through wise selection of locations. The most efficient producers, based on capital inputs, transportation, and the division of labor, as reflected in low prices and quality of goods through competition, are the survivors. Their production processes and locations will dictate how and where goods will be produced in a market economy.

Pure capitalism features two groups of decision makers—private households and businesses. The mechanisms that operate to bring households and businesses together are the *resource market* and the *product market,* or the *circular flowing market system* (Figure 2.5). Households provide labor, land, capital, and management to the resource market and receive wages from it; they also consume from the product market and receive goods and services from it. Businesses, in contrast, receive resources (i.e., land, labor, capital, and management) from the resource market, and provide costs (i.e., money income, wages, rents, interest, and profit) to it. Businesses are also active in the product market by providing goods and services to it (that households consume) and receiving revenue from it in the form of sales.

Through the use of wages as income, households demonstrate their *demand* for goods and services provided by businesses. In like manner, businesses use their resources and capital to provide a *supply* of those goods and services in the same market. Product prices are thus determined by the interactions of demand and supply decisions. Looking at the top half of Figure 2.5, the resource market households are sellers in the resource

FIGURE 2.5
Circular flow in the capitalist economy. The circular flow in the capitalist economy involves a resource market where households supply resources to businesses, and where businesses provide money income to households. It also consists of the product market where businesses manufacture and produce goods and services for households, while households provide money revenue from their wages and income to consume such goods and services. In the resource market, shown in the upper half of the diagram, households are on the supply side and businesses are on the demand side. The bottom half of the diagram shows the product market; households are on the demand side and businesses are on the supply side.
(Source: Adapted and modified from McConnell and Brue, 1993, p. 59.)

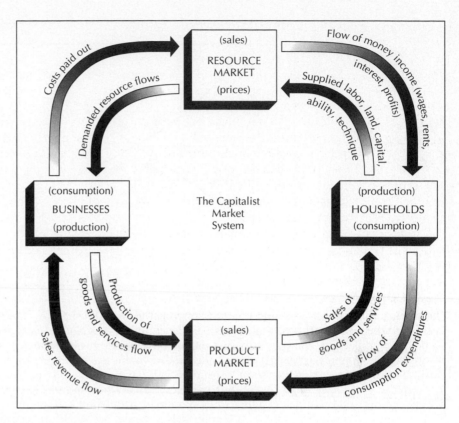

market (inner circle) and businesses are buyers (outer circle). Looking now at the bottom half, households are now the buyers of the product market (inner circle) and businesses are the sellers (outer circle). Resources, goods, and services circulate counterclockwise in the inner circle, while money flows clockwise in the outer circle.

Capitalism is based on laws of supply and demand. These laws lead to market equilibriums, assuming that there are many buyers and sellers, that the market alone determines the prices of products and the output produced, and that each buyer and seller in the market acts in his or her own self-interest as a rational being.

The *law of demand* states that prices and the quantity of the good or service, purchased by the buyers, are inversely related. Another way to say this is that the higher the price, the lower the total quantity that will be demanded by the consumer in the marketplace. Conversely, the lower the price, the greater the total quantity that will be demanded. A *demand curve* shows the schedule of total goods that all consumers are willing to buy at each price (Figure 2.6).

The *law of supply* conversely states that the level of prices and the quantity of goods supplied are directly

related. As prices increase, sellers offer more goods to be purchased because they can make a greater profit. The *supply curve* then is the schedule that relates the total amount of a good or service that all sellers, together, are willing to sell at each possible price. To the seller, it is the price multiplied times the total good or service sold, that equals earnings. From earnings, production costs must be subtracted to yield net income or profit. The amount of money remaining after costs are subtracted from total income is the principal factor that gives suppliers a willingness to produce more or less of a commodity or service.

Unlike the command economic system, if the gap between costs and earnings is small or it is negative, the producer may change production to something that yields a higher return in the marketplace over the long run. However, if the difference between earnings and costs is large or the producer becomes more efficient, he or she will most likely put more resources into the production of his or her good or service in order to obtain greater total sales. The point at which supply and demand curves meet is called the *equilibrium price*—the price and quantity where supply is equal to demand at a particular price. The equilibrium price does not leave

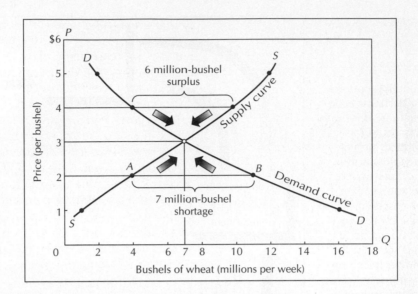

FIGURE 2.6
The market equilibrium price and quantity for wheat in the United States, 1993. On August 15, 1993, the price per bushel of wheat in the United States was $3. The equilibrium quantity was 7 million bushels of wheat per week. At $2 per bushel, farmers will only supply 4 million bushels per week (point A). However, because of the low price a whopping 11 million bushels per week is demanded (point B). Therefore, there is a shortage of 7 million bushels per week. The shortage means that some consumers will pay more than $2 per bushel, and they will bid higher in the marketplace. Gradually, their higher bids will bring more wheat farmers into the market so that both price and quantity are bid up to $3 per bushel and 7 million bushels. A different scenario in which farmers offer wheat at $4 per bushel brings a demand of only 4 million bushels of wheat per week. But, farmers are willing to provide 10 million bushels per week at the $4 price. The 6 million bushel surplus at $4 per bushel will not occur because the price is unrealistically high. Prices will fall, thus increasing the demand by consumers and reducing the supply by farmers back to the equilibrium price.

suppliers with unsold goods or consumers with unfilled demand.

The Command Economy

Almost the exact opposite on the political economy compass from pure capitalism is that of the command economy, sometimes known as Marxism or Communism. It is a form of totalitarianism, in which the means of production and all property and resources are owned and controlled by a central government that serves as the economic planning agency. All prices, quotas, levels of production, plant location and size, and any other major decision regarding the use of the means of production and resources, as well as the distribution of output and price levels, are set by the central bureaus of the command economy.

Production units, plants, and firms are owned by the government, and production quotas and output targets are established externally, not on the basis of market factors, demand, and supply but according to central directives. Consumer goods frequently are produced secondarily to capital goods in such economies, or an emphasis is placed on heavy industry, military might, and collectivized farming on huge state-run farms.

How are the four critical questions of economic geography answered in the command economy? The answers to the "how," "what," "where," and "for whom" questions posed alone are determined purely on the basis of state leaders' choice, not on market factors. In the last chapter, we present, in economic terms, the reasons why the Soviet economy failed and the challenges Russia and other former Soviet republics face in the future.

While it is difficult to find pure capitalism or a pure command economy anywhere in the world today, the United States' economic geography comes close to capitalism, followed by the economies of Canada, and many of the economies of Western Europe and Japan, as well as some Latin American and Asian countries. The command economy of the former Soviet Union and that of present-day Peoples Republic of China were certainly

The Russian Parliament, Moscow, the former USSR. Boris Yeltsin is at the Balcony of the Parliament, celebrating his rise to power. Demonstrators celebrate at the barricade after the news of the coup's defeat; the coup had attempted to return the USSR to hard-line communist rule. By 1994, the Russian people, for the first time, had elected a parliament and approved a new constitution.
(Source: Photo by Stig Stasig/2maj/Impact Visuals.)

the largest experiments of this nature in the history of the world. Other countries have tried to imitate the policies of the former Soviet Union and China, including North Vietnam, North Korea, Cuba, Nicaragua, and a number of African countries.

With the fall of the Soviet Union in 1991 and the breakup of its soviet socialists republics, the command economy, as a political economic form of geography, has certainly received a damaging blow. Most political economists now agree that the command economy form is a failure.

Mixed Economic Systems

Most economic and political economies of the world are positioned somewhere between the extremes of pure capitalism and the pure command economy. The U.S. economy, for example, leans toward pure capitalism, but has important modifications that help to stabilize the economy. The government is an active agent in redistributing wealth, providing basic services, and producing certain goods that would not be otherwise available because of their money-losing nature. The U.S. Post Office and the Army are examples.

The American form of government-supported capitalism has spawned large economic enterprises in huge MNCs. While China and the former Soviet Union approximated the command economy, important market mechanisms were retained to help determine prices and levels of production. Private ownership of land and resources has been allowed by Deng Xiaoping Ding in China for 20 years, and vestiges of private ownership had been creeping into Soviet society at approximately the time of its collapse in 1991. Russia, the former Soviet Republics, China, and most of Eastern Europe are now moving their economies toward a more market-oriented capitalistic system, and the difficulties of such a shift are addressed in Chapter 14.

Private ownership and the market system, which are typical of U.S. economic geography, do not always fit together. This is the case with central planning by military dictatorships in Latin America. Private ownership of property and the means of reduction are allowed, but at the same time, the economy is highly controlled. Nazi Germany was also typical of this approach.

In former Yugoslavia, now involved in late stages of a civil war, market socialism was the rule of the day. Public ownership of land and resources were regulated by market mechanism, which relied on free markets and supply and demand to regulate economic geography.

To some extent, the Canadian, British, French, and Scandinavian socialist economies also resemble hybrid, or mixed, systems. Sweden is a good example, where although 95% of land and resources are under private ownership, the government has set economic standards and prices and strongly affected the redistribution of income by taxing individuals who make more than $50,000 at the 80% level. A health network such as Sweden's, from "cradle to the grave," is highly desired by other nations. The United States has been unwilling to pay for such a system.

In addition, the Japanese economic system is an example of a hybrid system, which involves private ownership. It also receives a great deal of government support and regulation, which produces a growth economy in which government favors those businesses that are the most profitable and successful.

The Traditional Economy

Most of the world population falls into another political economy known as the *traditional economy*. Here, price, exchange, distribution, and income are regulated by many years of convention, culture, and custom. In India, Southeast Asia, Middle America, and most of Africa and South America, economic and social caste and heredity define economic roles of individuals and upward mobility, or lack thereof. There is a strong fatalism among members of society; that is, it is widespread thinking that economic conditions are locked and will not improve, and that one's individual position in society cannot change. Religious and cultural values frequently dictate the societal norms as well as economic aspirations, and the status quo is self-perpetuated.

Most of the traditional economies are poor by western standards, by the standards of the command economies, or by the mixed economic systems of Asia. In traditional economies, the "what," "how," "where,"

Egyptian farmer tilling the soil at the oasis of El Faiyum. This field is being prepared for the growing of cotton, to meet a worldwide demand for cotton clothing. In the future, the poorer countries of the world will have to rely on agriculture to raise their standards of living and to supply the capital they need to create industries. Agricultural production, therefore, must be increased. Many developing countries have placed their limited capital into the manufacturing sector, thus providing less than enough food for their hungry people. This capital is needed to purchase equipment, fertilizers, and new and better seeds, and to develop vast irrigation schemes and land reforms. Some developing countries, such as Egypt, have grown a disproportionate amount of nonfood crops for the export revenue it generates.
(Source: United Nations/Photo by B.P. Wolff.)

and "for whom" questions are answered with the observance of culture, habit, and custom, tempered by a strong dose of pragmatism.

In future chapters, we discuss economic development of less developed countries, traditional economies, and the difficulty they face in making a choice as to which economic model to use. These countries need a model that will result in the greatest welfare to their populations, in simultaneous growth, and in compatibility of their societal and cultural norms.

WHAT SHOULD BE PRODUCED?

◎

The first question that a society faces is the "what" question, what should be produced? We address this question briefly here, as well as in future chapters (e.g., Chapter 7 and 10). Each economy faces scarcity and limited amounts of resources; each society is faced with trade-offs. If more of one good is produced, less of another good will be available, given a fixed set of resources. A factory can produce cruise missiles or airplanes, but not both at the same time. One axiom of economic geography is that, for an economy operating at nearly full production, more of product A can be produced only at the expense of, or by producing less of, product B. *Opportunity cost* is the amount of product B we must give up to produce a unit of product A. Within the limits of their resources, needs, and time frame, societies must trade off resources and decide "what" shall be produced, over and over again.

Each of us is faced with similar trade-offs and opportunity costs. The question of whether to save for graduate school or buy a new car may be a difficult choice. We may choose to live near our downtown office on expensive land, but have a short commute, saving time. Or, we may choose to live in a distant suburb on a cheaper piece of land (per unit area), consume more of it than the downtown condo would require, but have a farther (and more costly from an opportunity cost perspective) commute.

Production Possibilities Curve

In order to demonstrate the opportunity costs societies face, consider an economy that produces only two commodities—PCs and pizzas. Figure 2.7 and Table 2.3

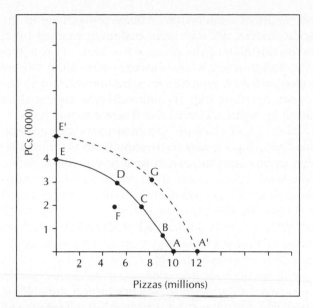

FIGURE 2.7
The production possibilities curve of PCs and pizzas. The curve ABCDE describes a schedule of trade-offs for a two-commodity society. The society can choose to produce only PCs at the cost of producing no pizzas (point E), or it can choose to produce only pizzas and no PCs at point A. Points B, C, and D along the curve suggest trade-offs between the commodities. As a society chooses to produce a large amount of one or the other commodity, the opportunity cost goes up and a smaller amount of the remaining commodity can be produced. Point G outside the curve suggests a level of production that has not yet been attained by the available resources and the technology of the society, but toward which it is moving. Point F under the curve suggests a possible condition of unemployment or underutilization of resources for the society.

give information on the opportunity costs of producing PCs and pizzas.

The trade-off between PCs, shown in thousands, and pizzas, shown in millions, can be seen. At point A, 11 million pizzas can be produced, but all the resources

◈

Table 2.3
Production Possibilities of PCs and Pizzas

Product	A	B	C	D	E
PCs ('000)	0	1	2	3	4
Pizzas (mil)	10	9	7	5	0

have been put to this effort and none are left for PCs. At point B, the number of pizzas has been reduced to 9 million, which allows 1000 PCs to be produced with available levels of technology and resources. Finally, at point E, 4000 PCs can be produced, but no resources are left for pizzas. While no society is a mere two commodity economy, the example shows various opportunity costs, or trade-offs, of goods and resources within the society that can be compromised to produce more of one commodity than another. To gain more of a good, in this case pizzas, we must pay more because the resources used to make pizzas and PCs are not perfectly interchangeable. To produce more PCs, we must change equipment and technology and retrain individuals.

Figure 2.7 shows us that amongst any pair of goods and services, resources are not perfectly interchangeable. Consequently, to increase the output of one commodity, there must be a reduction in the output of one or more other commodities. Societies, therefore, must choose what products and services will be produced because there will be a reduction in the number of other products and services.

ANSWERING THE "HOW" QUESTION

The dotted line in the production possibilities curve (see Figure 2.7) represents economic growth. The only way we can move from the solid line to the dotted line is to increase the amount of resources, acquire more labor, or increase the level of employed technology, meaning more efficient machinery or technical skills of the work force, to develop new ways of using the resources to a maximum.

Moving from curve E-A to E'-A' answers the question of "how" production takes place. The goal of all societies is to move from present production levels, through a growth process, to higher production levels in the future. The problem is selecting a strategy that produces the most benefits for the society as a whole. This involves techniques to measure increased benefits from higher production and answering the question "for whom," so that a society can measure the benefit of distributing goods to social groups. These factors, used to determine "how" production takes place and "who" receives the goods, depend on the type of political economy—capitalism, command economy, mixed systems, or a traditional system, as previously described.

FUTURE VERSUS PRESENT ECONOMIC GROWTH

⬚

One of the basic choices that economic managers must make is a production mix that favors either capital goods, which are devoted to future production, versus consumer goods, which satisfy a present want and need in society. (Capital goods are goods that are used to produce other goods, while consumer goods are goods that are used by individuals for their own needs and wants, in the short-run.) After World War II, the Soviet Union and the United States made different choices along the production possibilities curve. The Soviet Union decided to put an emphasis on capital goods for long-term economic growth and emphasized truck factories, large electric plants, mechanized agricultural farms, and a heavy military arsenal. In the United States, the emphasis was on producing consumer goods for a victorious country, which had put up with the shortages and inconveniences of war. Automobiles, television sets, single-family homes, and a variety of clothing and shoes, flooded the markets in America. In the Soviet Union, resources were shifted away from consumer goods toward capital goods, whereas in the United States, a larger population of resources were shifted away from capital goods and toward consumer goods.

During the next 45-year period, the people of the Soviet Union suffered inconvenience and shortage, as the command economy rebuilt its production base. By 1989, the people of the Soviet Union, informed of their lack of consumer goods, as compared to western countries by Radio Free Europe and ubiquitous television transmission, finally grew tired of constantly being exploited and of suffering from low standards of living. At the same time, the population of the United States enjoyed a high consumption level and a standard of living that was unparalleled by any society in the world. At the same time, the United States did not avoid producing capital goods and a strong economic base. Both the Soviet Union's and the United States' decisions were appropriate for the resource levels available and for the desires of the political economy of each.

The pleasure of buying a new car now and skipping graduate school may be sacrificing future economies. Third and fourth world nations today have had to make the same choices, often with disappointing results. Many times, the population has pressured the government to fulfill demands for consumer goods at the expense of capital goods needed to develop a society in the twentieth century that will be competitive in the world market. All too often, the result has been that the productivity of the country has been in areas that did not allow it much future growth, leaving the country underdeveloped, with dim prospects for the future. The country opted for export, nonfood cash crops, such as cotton or sugar, and used the revenue to buy guns.

Now, observe Figure 2.8. On the left-hand side, country X has chosen a disproportionate commodity mix, emphasizing consumer goods over capital goods. Note point A for country X. In this hypothetical example, country X's growth during the next 50-year period is shown, by the outward curves and arrows, to be moderate at best. Compare the production possibilities curve of country X to country Y on the right side. Country Y chose to answer the "how" question of production by emphasizing capital goods over consumer goods. Note point A on country Y's production possibilities curve. Fifty years later, the overall growth of both capital goods and consumer goods are substantially more than that of country X. Country Y's emphasis on production for present consumption has sacrificed its production for its future generations, because of its slower growth rate. Country Y has sacrificed, in the short-run, consumer goods and private consumption, so that its long-run growth is faster. Another way of stating the differences is that country X has sacrificed the opportunity costs of more growth in the future to satisfy a present demand for consumer goods.

Japan Versus the United States

In our example, the former Soviet Union was a typical country Y, while the United States was an example of country X. However, because of the great burden on the population and the sacrifice of forgoing consumer goods for the desired extra growth in the overall economy, the former Soviet Union was unable to achieve either economic superiority or satisfaction of the masses. In the end, the old Soviet system collapsed because of political repression, the robbing of the individual work ethic, and the great sacrifice of its population to sustain a substantial capital goods and infrastructure production.

Now consider Japan, which during the last 50 years made decisions described in Figure 2.8 by country Y. It emphasized present austerity of consumer goods in support of capital goods, which we know all too well,

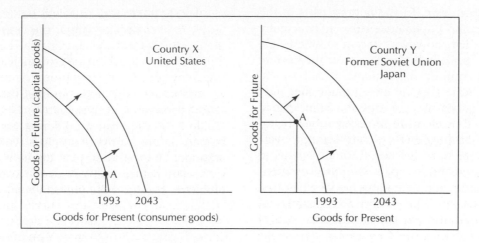

FIGURE 2.8
Two countries with opposite production trade-offs. A country's present choice of substitution between "goods for the future" and "goods for the present" on its production possibilities curve will help determine the economy's future growth and the production possibilities curve's new location. Country X has chosen a greater proportion of consumer goods, or goods for the present, at the expense of capital goods, or goods for the future, shown on the left. Country Y has chosen a greater proportion of capital goods, or goods for the future, as opposed to a modest proportion of consumer goods, or goods for the present, as shown on the right side. Country X's production choice results in a growth curve, which is moderate and upward to the right. Country Y's selection of an aggressive future-oriented economy results in a greater rightward shift to the production possibilities curve, suggesting greater overall economic growth.

were used to produce mass quantities of automobiles and electronics such as the world had never seen. Japan grew at a much faster rate than the United States, over the same period of time, and still leads the United States in a number of major commodities. Japan has been investing 25% to 30% of its domestic output in capital goods, machinery, equipment, and robotics. This figure compares to only 10% for the United States. General

Motors was more interested in immediate profits and the paying of dividends to their stockholders, rather than on the tenacious improvement of their production processes. During the period from 1960 to 1993, Japan's domestic output has expanded at approximately 6% per annum, while the United States' has expanded at a 3% clip. Japan's production possibilities curve shifted outward at twice the rate of the United States'. (See country Y versus country X in Figure 2.8.) In 1980, the per capita GNP of Japan was $16,700. The per capita GNP of the United States for 1980 was approximately the same. By 1993, however, Japan's GNP per capita had grown to $26,400, while the United States' had only grown to $22,990, but Japan's prices were also up.

Somalia and the Sahel of Africa

In western society, from Western Europe to the United States and Canada and westward to Japan, rightward shifts of the production possibilities curve have always been the rule. The economy has, in the long-run, always grown in western society, either at a

G-7 economic summit in Tokyo in July 1993.
(Source: Reuters/Bettmann/Photo by Andy Clark.)

low rate or at a high rate. In the poorest parts of the world, the production possibilities curve may actually be shifting to the left, however. Recent famine in the Sahel of Africa, especially in the east, near the horn of Africa, including countries of Ethiopia, Chad, Sudan, and Somalia, indicate that neither present consumer goods or capital goods may be growing from year to year (see Figure 2.4). Because of drought, ecological destruction, encroaching deserts (desertification), over-grazing, and, as we have learned through Operation Restore Hope in Somalia, rampant warlords comman-deering food supplies and defending feudal territories, production has dwindled in almost all categories of goods. For example, the per capita GNPs in each of these countries mentioned has decreased by an average of 10% from 1980 to 1993.

The importance of *production possibility analysis* is obvious for developing countries, as well as for highly developed countries. First, any product that is produced has an opportunity cost and will lower the output of other products in the society that could have been pro-duced. Politicians have called this a "zero sum game." The sum of all commodities produced can neither ex-pand nor contract in the short-run. One must "rob from Peter to pay Paul," so to speak. Second, if a country uses resources inefficiently, a lower level of societal gain will accrue, and levels of unemployment, underemploy-ment, and underutilization will develop. In Somalia, starvation is the result. Third, the only way that the production possibilities curve can move upward to the right, which means a growth economy, is for a country to improve its technological base, expand its resources, or improve its labor productivity. The United States has recently passed the North American Free Trade Agreement (NAFTA) to do primarily the latter; improve its labor productivity by exporting labor-intensive man-ufacturing to Mexico. Finally, the last lesson to be learned from production possibility curve analysis is that whatever goods are produced in the short-run will likely have a major impact on the society in the future, especially on its ability to grow and meet a greater range of its society's needs.

Now, we turn to the world views of economic geog-raphers, which are an outgrowth of the political econo-mies previously discussed, in an attempt to explain why it is important to understand conservative, liberal, and radical mind-sets. It seems clear that there is no one indisputable reality. To a great extent, the "what," "how," and "for whom" question can be understood for a society, only with an understanding of their politi-cal and economic mind-sets.

COMPETING MIND-SETS IN THE WORLD ECONOMY

◾

Analytically, this text compares three general theo-retical perspectives: conservative, liberal, and radical (Table 2.4). They rest on different assumptions about human nature, normative values, culture, and social authority. They also employ different concepts to de-scribe the nature and causes of world development problems, based on the political economies.

The Conservative Perspective

The *conservative view* of the world economy is inher-ited from the ideas of Adam Smith (1723–1790), David Ricardo (1772–1823), and their latter-day followers. Conservatives assume that people need positive and negative material incentives to be productive. They are convinced that a capitalistic free-enterprise economy based on competition and maximizing profits allows egoistic and calculating individuals to achieve max-imum personal worth and well-being. Individual decision-making units (i.e., individuals, households, firms) act freely and rationally to produce a harmonious and moving equilibrium by means of market forces. Consequently, the process of social and economic change is a gradual cumulative and unidirectional evo-lution. Faith in the efficiency and optimality of private market mechanisms, especially those of supply and de-mand, allows conservatives to postulate a limited role for governments. They are likely to point to mainte-nance of social order as the single most important func-tion of the state to ensure that capitalism can operate freely. *Conservatives* hold that government involvement in the economy usually causes more problems than it solves. They argue that many national and international problems trace to government interference and that the solutions to these problems lie in fewer government regulations and programs. Finally, conservatives believe that social change occurs gradually through the free actions of individuals in the marketplace.

The conservative approach to development prob-lems rests on two points. First, more participation by poor countries in the world economy, not less as some socialists argue, will ensure faster and greater economic growth. The main theory conservatives used to assert

◈

Table 2.4
Alternative Explanations of Reality Under Capitalism

Alternative Paradigms	Human Nature	Work Incentives	Analysis Based on	Human Goals	Nature of Market Exchange Economy	Nature of Societal Problems	Role of State	Social Change
Conservative Focus on individuals: persons or companies	Humans are naturally unproductive and individualistic	Essentially material: (1) positive—raise in income, (2) negative—unemployment	Classical and neoclassical economics: competition and individuals maximizing profits	Maximum personal liberty and material well-being	Harmonious state of equilibrium created by supply and demand forces	(1) Individuals: lack of motivation, unrealistic demands, culture of poverty, racial inferiority, (2) Government interference in the economy	Ideally, only police power to maintain law and order so that the market can work freely	Gradual change results from individual interactions in the market place
Liberal Focus on individuals and groups in society	Humans are naturally unproductive, but of goodwill	Essentially material: (1) positive raise in income, (2) negative—unemployment	Keynesian economics: competition and individuals maximizing profits with government assistance	Individual equality and social justice (equal opportunity)	State of equilibrium, achievable with government involvement in the economy	(1) Monopolistic tendencies in major economic sectors, (2) Insufficient and inappropriate government programs	Police power and offsetting inadequacies in the economy whenever basic human needs and social justice are not achieved	Rapid change through government actions
Radical Focus on classes in society	Humans are naturally productive and cooperative	None really necessary; socially valuable rewards	Marxist economics: labor theory of value, theory of surplus value, theory of class struggle and revolution	Social equality: from each according to one's ability, to each according to one's need	Contradictions and crises of production and consumption; exploitation of workers; irrational allocation of natural and human resources	Private ownership of resources; production for profit rather than for human use; alienation; class conflict; unequal regional development	Police and economic power is used to maintain and enhance capitalism	Revolutionary change through mass movements to transform society's structure and values

Source: Vogeler and de Souza, 1980, pp. 8–9.

that poor countries will benefit from more interaction in the world economy is Ricardo's theory of *comparative advantage*. Ricardo wrote:

It is quite important to the happiness of mankind that our enjoyments should be increased by a better division of labor, by each country producing those commodities for which by its situation, its climate and its other material or its artificial advantages, it is adapted, and by their exchanging them for the commodities of other countries. . . . Under a system of perfectly free commerce, each country naturally devotes its capital and labor to such employments as are most beneficial to each. This pursuit of individual advantage is admirably connected with the universal good of the whole. (cited in Harrington, 1977, p. 36)

Ricardo illustrated his trade theory by means of a two-country labor-cost model. The theory holds that it is in the best interest of poor countries to exchange more labor for less. According to conservatives, this unequal division of labor works to the advantage of all, allowing each country to make the best use of its natural resources, stock of skills, and infrastructures. Moreover, any deviation from free trade sacrifices efficiency and reduces world output and income. An example of a contemporary Ricardian is Henry Kissinger, former U.S. secretary of state. In 1975, at the Seventh Special Session of the United Nations General Assembly, he stated, "Comparative advantage and specialization, the exchange of technology and the movement of capital, the spur to productivity that competition provides—these are central elements of efficiency and progress. For developing nations, trade is perhaps the most important engine of development" (cited in Harrington, 1977, p. 37).

Second, difficulties of economic growth in poor countries can be traced to internal obstacles in local environments and indigenous cultures. The tropical environment, in particular, is viewed as a major obstacle to progress. Soils are poor and fragile; rainfall is unreliable; and numerous endemic, debilitating diseases reinforce low levels of productivity. Above all, conservatives hold that the traits of individuals, rather than international market forces, prevent the advancement of people in poor countries. They account for the lack of development on the basis of cultures; traditional religious beliefs, values, and habits of life; insufficient incentives and entrepreneurship; and unstable political systems.

The Liberal Perspective

The *liberal view* of the world did not attract much attention until the depression of the 1930s and John Maynard Keynes' (1883–1946) analysis of the causes of unemployment. In "the general theory of employment, interest, and money," Keynes (1936) discredited the conservative belief that the capitalist economic system is self-righting. He did not think that a modern capitalist economy would sustain a high enough level of investment to maintain full employment. While advocating government control of the level of economic activity in the national interest (state capitalism), he advised that the economy in general be left free to respond to the decisions of welfare-maximizing consumers and profit-maximizing producers.

Keynes presented an alternative to socialism. His theory, which permitted government to borrow and spend the proceeds to cure an economic depression, did not amend the conservative paradigm to any great degree. It was designed less to alter market-exchange economies than to preserve and revitalize them.

Like Keynes, liberals of the present day do not launch a thorough-going critique of either the conservative theory of human nature or the capitalist system. Indeed, *liberals* share with conservatives the view that people are naturally unproductive, and they share a faith in the capitalist system. Unlike conservatives, however, they place great emphasis on the goals of individual equality and social justice. To achieve these goals, they believe that government legislation and programs are necessary. Although liberals criticize inequality of opportunity based on wealth, position, and power, they understand that certain inequalities are based on inherited characteristics such as family structure or ethnic culture (e.g., culture of poverty). The state redistributes wealth by taxing the rich to assist the poor and, therefore, societal changes can occur more rapidly than under the conservative laissez-faire model. They attribute problems at national and international levels to monopolistic tendencies in major economic sectors and insufficient and/or inappropriate government programs. In their view, the state must intervene on behalf of everyone whenever market mechanisms fail to satisfy consumer preferences or provide basic human needs (e.g., housing, health care, food, and adequate income). John Kenneth Galbraith's (1967, 1969) analyses of the industrial state and the affluent society reflect this perspective.

Liberals share with conservatives many of the same assumptions about barriers and bottlenecks to development in poor countries. They believe that traditional values and social institutions are the prime obstacles to development, and they are convinced that the town is the gateway for innovations. As centers of innovation, large towns can transmit modern values and social institutions to smaller centers and rural areas. Although liberals also employ the "blaming-of-victim" approach (Ryan, 1972) to explain the causes of world problems, they, unlike conservatives, are willing to provide governmental assistance to the world's needy. Consequently, liberal governments provide unilateral and multilateral foreign aid (e.g., U.S. Agency for International Development, World Bank); food aid (e.g., U.S. Food for Peace Program); volunteers (e.g., Peace Corps); and military and technical assistance.

The Radical Perspective

Conservative and liberal perspectives are sometimes collectively known as traditional or orthodox approaches. According to *radicals*, their analyses do not go to the roots of problems. Radicals argue that, in capitalist societies, the dynamics of socioeconomic organization (mode of production, in Marxist terms) produce certain kinds of class and institutional structures that result in a particular set of social problems. In their view, such problems cannot be solved without changing the form of socioeconomic organization at national and international levels.

Contrary to conservatives and liberals, radicals assume that people are naturally productive and cooperative and, therefore, that material rewards are not really necessary. They also assume that people are not inherently passive; rather, that passive, unproductive, or uncooperative behavior is in response to demands the economic system makes on them. Radicals reject the liberal's belief that people can enjoy equality of opportunity in a class society when the majority produces the wealth and when power is in the hands of the few. In such a society, the pursuit of profit by the dominant class shapes all aspects of life, including the quality of personal relations. Under capitalism, they argue, human needs are subordinated to the needs of the marketplace. Only commodities (goods and services) that have exchange value are produced, while other "use values" remain unmet. For example, the United States sells most of its food surplus to countries that can afford to buy it (exchange value) rather than distributing food to countries on the basis of need (use value).

Radicals claim that in a market economy the state predominately serves the interests of the ruling class, not the workers whose labor produces more wealth than is returned to them in the form of wages. Karl Marx (1818–1883) called this extra wealth "surplus value," or the product of exploitation.

Exploitation of workers can be intensified and surplus value increased when employers stretch the working day. If the work week were stabilized, employers could expand surplus value by substituting capital for labor. Marx argued that the process of introducing even more labor-saving equipment is inimical to workers. Displaced laborers form a reserve army of the unemployed, which keeps wages at minimal levels. Employed workers know that others are readily available to take their jobs if productivity falls.

The essence of the radical argument is that the engine that drives economic growth is capital accumulation for its own sake. The argument holds that economic growth is always unbalanced, since competitive production fails to achieve equilibrium. Short-run cyclical crises (i.e., unemployment and declining rates of profit) are cor-rected by increasing rates of accumulation through concentration (i.e., the trend toward larger, more efficient firms in each industry) and by geographic extension (i.e., imperialism). Periodic crises become more frequent over time. During each crisis, big capitalists devour little capitalists; individual capitalism becomes corporate capitalism. Capitalists seek larger outputs and bigger profits, and they deploy bigger machines that replace more and more laborers. Thus, the misery and alienation of workers intensifies in an increasing class struggle that charts the course of socioeconomic development.

From this sketch of Marxist theory, it is plain that radicals argue that inequality of wealth among classes originates in the capitalist system. Exploitation of one class by another is based on the private ownership of the means of production. From the radical perspective, irreconcilable conflict between classes is the key to understanding the need for revolutionary change through mass movements.

Uneven development pertains not only to the unequal distribution of wealth among classes, but also to the geographic dimension of development—underdevelopment and dependence. Radicals argue that Third World countries were underdeveloped first by the development and expansion of Europe; later, neo-European countries (the United States, Canada, Australia); and most recently, Japan. The capitalist world economy causes underdevelopment by generating and reinforcing an *infrastructure of dependency* that includes institutions, social classes, and processes, such as urbanization, industrialization, and modernization. Dependency is, therefore, not an external matter. Foreign exploitation is possible only when it finds support among local elites who profit from it. To break out of dependency and to achieve development, radicals argue that underdeveloped countries must go beyond capitalism to a collectively owned and collectively governed economic system. To achieve the goals of socialism, political leaders have followed different paths—Fidel Castro took a military approach in Cuba whereas Julius Nyerere favored an evolutionary approach in Tanzania.

SUMMARY

When geographers or other experts examine problems of the world economy, they bring to the task a set of values that shapes the results of the inquiry. In this chapter, we illustrate how five experts with different ideologies offered five different explanations for the causes of world hunger. It is, therefore, important that we become aware of different theoretical frameworks experts use to argue their cases. Such awareness can only be achieved if we are willing to acknowledge that our own way of seeing the world is not the only way of seeing the world.

A presentation is laden with theory and presupposes some framework as a basis for selecting and organizing material. It involves abstraction and distortion as epitomized in our examples of presenting the world in map form, summarizing the world statistically, and dividing the world into First, Second, Third, and Fourth Worlds. We argue that our understanding of the world is enhanced when alternative theoretical perspectives are considered in a comparative framework.

Next, we offer four economic geography questions, which are explored in more detail throughout the remainder of the text. The answers to the questions of "what," "how," "where," and "for whom" are understandable, given one's context or from a reference based on four political economies.

Production possibilities analysis demonstrated the interrelationships and trade-offs to the questions of "what" should be produced and "how" it should be produced.

The last section of the chapter looks at conservative, liberal, and radical perspectives. These perspectives are an integral part of the chapters that follow. Each viewpoint lumps many different theories and models together. The categorization of theories and models into three groups is an abstraction, but is most useful for providing alternative explanations of world development problems. The labels "conservative," "liberal," and "radical" are less important than the ideas behind them.

◧

KEY TERMS

capital
circular flowing market system
command economy
comparative advantage
compensation
conservative view
demand
dependency theorists
entrepreneurial skill
factors of production
four questions of economic geography
four worlds
GDP
GNP
ideology
infrastructure of dependency
interest
labor
land
law of demand
law of supply

liberal view
Mercator projection
mixed economic systems
money capital
opportunity cost
Peters projection
product market
production possibilities analysis
profits
pure capitalism
radical view
raw materials
real capital
rent
resource market
scarcity
theoretical perspective
traditional market
value-free
wages

SUGGESTED READINGS

Benton, T. 1977. *Philosophical Foundations of the Three Sociologies*. London: Routledge and Kegan Paul.

Berry, B.; Conkling, E.; and Ray, E. 1993. *The Global Economy*. Englewood Cliffs, NJ: Prentice Hall.

Berry, B. J. L. 1989. Comparative geography of the global economy: Cultures, corporations, and the nation state. *Economic Geography*, 65(1):1–18.

Bodman, A. R. 1991. Weavers of influence: The structure of contemporary geographic research. *Transactions of British Geographers*, New Series 16:21–37.

Cole, K.; Cameron, J.; and Edwards, C. 1983. *Why Economists Disagree: The Political Economy of Economics*. London: Longman.

Economic Report of the President, 1991. Washington, DC: Library of Congress.

Gaile, G. L., and Willmott, C. J., eds. 1989. *Geography in America*. New York: Merrill/Macmillan.

Galbraith, J. K. 1977. *The Age of Uncertainty*. Boston: Houghton Mifflin.

Gordon, D. 1971. *Problems in Political Economy*. Lexington, MA: D.C. Heath.

Heyne, P. 1991. *The Economic Way of Thinking*. New York: Macmillan.

Janelle, D. G., ed. 1992. *Geographical Snapshots of North America*. New York: Guilford.

Martin, G. J., and James, P. E. 1991. *All Possible Worlds: A History of Geographical Sales*. New York: John Wiley & Sons.

Rubenstein, J. M. 1994. *An Introduction to Human Geography*, 4th ed. New York: Macmillan.

Sayer, A., and Walker, R. 1993. *The New Social Economy: Reworking the Division of Labor*. Cambridge, MA: Blackwell.

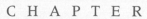
POPULATION AND THE WORLD ECONOMY

❖

OBJECTIVES

- To describe and account for the world distribution of human populations
- To examine the economic causes and consequences of population change
- To describe the major demographic and economic characteristics of a population
- To describe and explain economic migrations, past and present
- To consider how population growth affects development
- To apply demographic insights to regional economic change

❖

Crowds of people gather at the Syracuse University Carrier Dome sports complex. *(Source: Michael J. Okoniewski/The Image Works.)*

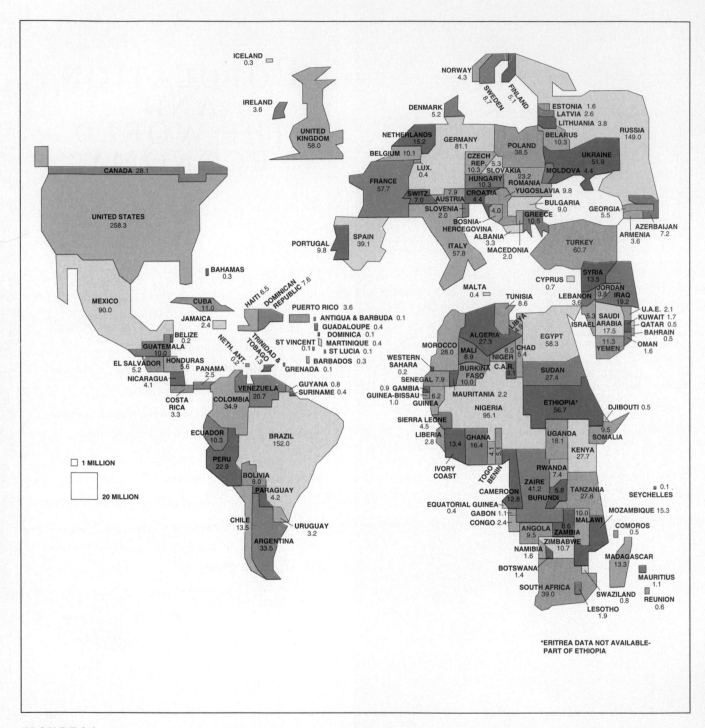

FIGURE 3.1
Cartogram of 1993 world population. This map shows the area of each country in proportion to its population. Geographic space has been transformed into population space. Asia dominates the map, especially China, with its 1.2 billion people, and India, with its almost 900 million people. Europe is much larger than on a normal map, where countries are sized in proportion to their geographic space. Both South America and Africa show up much smaller than their normal size, because their populations are relatively small.
(Source: de Blij and Muller, 1993.)

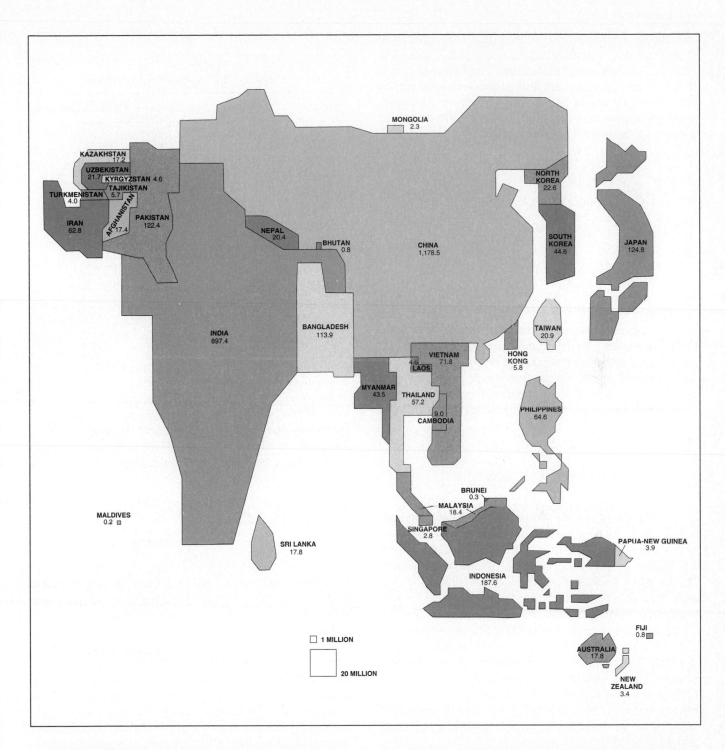

Human beings are the most important element in the world economy. People are not only the key productive factor, but their welfare is also the primary objective of economic endeavor. People are the producers as well as the consumers of goods and services. As world population continues to grow by leaps and bounds, we face the critical question of whether there is an imbalance between producers and consumers. Does population growth prevent the sustainability of development? Does it lead to poverty, unemployment, and political instability?

To help answer these questions, this chapter examines the determinants and consequences of population change for developed and underdeveloped countries. It analyzes population distributions, characteristics, and trends. It also reviews competing theories on the causes and consequences of population growth. It concludes with an application of demographic methods to the process of regional economic change.

POPULATION DISTRIBUTION

◙

In 1994, there were more than 5 billion people in the world; these people were very unevenly distributed. Such contrasts in population distribution are studied on different scales of observation. *Population distribution* refers to the arrangement, spread, and density of people. On a macroscale, we examine broad geographic areas, such as continents, countries, and regions. On a microscale, we look at small areas, such as population variations within cities. In this discussion, the emphasis is on population distributions across large geographic areas.

Population Size

A comparison of the world's population by continents shows that Asia's population is the largest, as it has been for several centuries. In 1992, Asia contained 3.2 billion people or 59% of the world's population. Europe (511 million) and Russia (149 million), along with the other republics of the Soviet Union (135 million), were home to about 16%, Africa (654 million) to 12%, Latin America (453 million) to 8%, North America (283 million) to 5%, and Oceania (28 million) to less than 1%. The populations of the underdeveloped continents—Africa, Asia (excluding Japan and Russia), and Latin America—accounted for three out of every four humans alive in 1992. Of the 4.2 billion in the underdeveloped world, 73% lived in Asia, 16% lived in Africa, and 11% lived in Latin America.

Given such large variations among continents, it is not surprising that national population figures show even more variability (Figure 3.1). Ten out of the world's nearly 200 countries account for two-thirds of the world's people (Table 3.1). Five countries—China, India, the United States, Indonesia, and Brazil—contain

◙

Table 3.1

The Ten Most Populous Countries

Country	Population in 1992 (in Millions)
China	1166
India	883
United States	256
Indonesia	185
Brazil	151
Russia	149
Japan	124
Pakistan	122
Bangladesh	111
Nigeria	90

Source: Population Reference Bureau. 1992. World Population Data Sheet.

half of the world's population. Approximately 21% of all people lived in China, 16% in India, 5% in the United States, and 3% each in Indonesia and Brazil. Six of the top 10 countries in population size—China, India, Indonesia, Japan, Bangladesh, and Pakistan—are in Asia. Only 3 of the 10 most populous nations are considered to be developed (the United States, Russia, and Japan).

Population Density

Because countries vary so greatly in size, national population totals tell us nothing about crowding. Consequently, population is often related to land area. This ratio is called population density—the average number of people per unit area, usually per square mile or kilometer. Several countries with the largest populations have relatively low population densities (Table 3.2). For example, the United States is the fourth most populous country, but in 1992 it had a population density of only 71 people per square mile. If the entire world population were placed inside the United States, its population density would be roughly equivalent to that of England. The United States is one of the more sparsely populated areas of the world (Figure 3.2).

Many of the world's most crowded countries are small city-states or islands, such as Hong Kong (14,315 people per square mile) and Singapore (12,347 people

◈

T a b l e 3.2

The Ten Most Densely Populated Countries
(based on countries with at least 5000 square miles
of territory)

Country	Population (Millions)	Area (Sq Miles)	Population Density
Bangladesh	111.4	55,600	2004
Taiwan	20.8	12,460	1672
South Korea	44.3	38,020	1165
Netherlands	15.2	14,410	1055
Japan	124.4	143,750	865
Belgium	10.1	11,750	855
Rwanda	7.7	10,170	759
Sri Lanka	17.6	25,330	696
India	882.6	1,269,340	695
Israel	5.2	8020	653

Source: Population Reference Bureau. 1992. World Population Data Sheet.

per square mile). Excluding countries with a very small area (such as Hong Kong or Singapore), Bangladesh is the world's most crowded nation (see Table 3.2). In Bangladesh, more than 100 million people are crowded into an area the size of Iowa. Three of the top 10 densely populated countries—the Netherlands, Japan, and Belgium—are developed, whereas another three—South Korea, Taiwan, and Israel—are newly industrializing countries (NICs). The remainder are clearly less developed nations, reminding us that the relationship between density and development is a complex one.

Contrary to popular opinion, not all crowded countries are poor. But what explains the fact that many people in the Netherlands or Singapore live well on so little land? What part of the explanation lies in their industrious people and their ability to adapt to change? What part of the explanation lies in their history of trade or their relative locations? Singapore is on one of the great ocean crossroads of the world. But being on a crossroads has worked no similar miracle for Panama. In 1992, Singapore had a per capita income ($12,310) that was nearly seven times that of Panama ($1830).

Population density is a potentially valuable abstraction, but it conceals much variation. Egypt had a reasonably low figure of 144 people per square mile in 1992, but 96% of the population lives on irrigated, cultivated land along the Nile Valley where densities are extremely

high. Similarly, in the United States there are densely populated and sparsely populated areas. Large areas to the west of the Mississippi are essentially devoid of people, whereas the Northeast is densely settled. The island of Manhattan, for example, has a density that is virtually the same as Hong Kong.

Most people are concentrated in but few parts of the world (see Figure 3.2). Four major areas of dense settlement are East Asia, South Asia, Europe, and the eastern United States and Canada. In addition, there are minor clusters in Southeast Asia, Africa, Latin America, and along the U.S. Pacific coast.

FACTORS INFLUENCING POPULATION DISTRIBUTION

◈

Is there a reason for the massing of people in some areas? One possible explanation is physical environment. People tend to concentrate along edges of continents, at low elevations, and in humid midlatitude and subtropical climates. Lands deficient in moisture, such as the Sahara Desert, are sparsely settled. Few people live in very cold regions, such as northern Canada, arctic Russia, and northern Scandinavia. Equatorial heat and moisture, as in the Congo and Amazon basins, appear to deter settlement. In addition, many mountainous areas—whether because of climate, thin stony soils, or steep slopes—are inhospitable habitats. There are, however, many anomalies relative to population distribution and physical environment correlations. For example, more people inhabit highland than lowland environments in many Latin American and East African locales due to opressive heat at lower elevations. For example, Mexico City is at an elevation of 7000 feet.

Caution must be exercised in ascribing population distribution to natural elements alone. Furthermore, to hold that natural elements control population distribution is deterministic. Certainly climatic extremes, such as insufficient rainfall, present difficulties for human habitation and cultivation. However, given the forces of technology, the deficiencies of nature increasingly can be overcome. Air-conditioning, heating, water storage, and irrigation are examples of the extensive measures that technology offers to residents of otherwise harsh environments.

If physical environments alone cannot explain

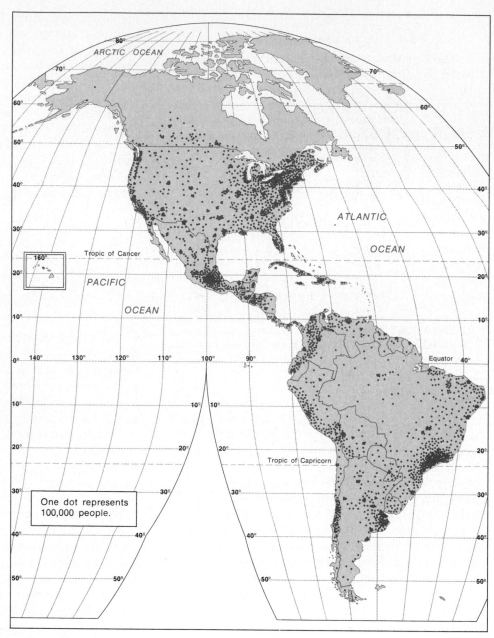

One dot represents 100,000 people.

PERCENT OF WORLD
POPULATION
BY REGION

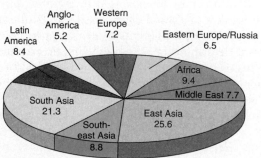

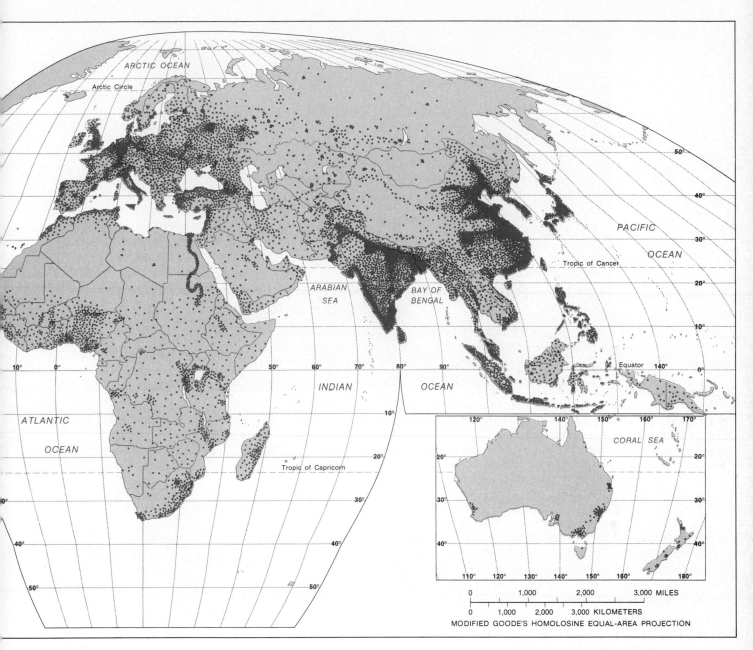

FIGURE 3.2
Population dot map of the world. This map shows population clusters within each country. Population density is shown on this map as a concentration of dots, with one dot representing 10,000 people. Population density is defined as the number of phenomena occurring within a real unit. Population density worldwide is normally expressed as the number of people per square mile. Population density in East Asia, notably China and Japan, as well as South Asia, including Bangladesh, India, and Pakistan, is extremely high. Population density in Northern Asia, Africa, and South and North America is quite low, comparatively speaking. Three major and two minor areas of world population concentration occur. These are: (1) East Asia; (2) South Asia; (3) Europe; and (4) Northeastern United States, Southeastern Canada; and (5) Southeast Asia, especially the country of Indonesia and the Island of Java.

Mexico City is a spectacular example of a primate city. But most of its residents dwell a world apart from the glitter of the high-rise corridor. By 1994, Mexico had a population of 92 million, and Mexico City arguably comprised one-quarter of that amount. It is difficult to calculate the true size of Mexico City because of the myriad of squatter settlements on the outskirts of town without water, sewer, or streets. For the first time, Mexico City is showing signs of leveling off and even declining in population due to the urban pollution and squalor it has generated. *(Source: Mexican Government Tourism Office.)*

population distribution, what other factors are involved? Human distributions are molded by the organization and development of economic systems. They are influenced by cultural traits, which also affect demographic components of fertility, mortality, and migration. Such social disasters as war may alter population distribution on any scale. Social and political decisions, such as tax policies or zoning and planning ordinances, are eventually reflected on the population map. None of these factors, however, can be considered without reference to historical circumstance. Present population distribution is explicable only in terms of the past. For example, the nineteenth-century industrial revolution made British coal sites major centers of population concentration and economic growth. Populous areas in Britain associated with coal include the Birmingham-Coventry district, Bradford-Leeds, Stoke-on-Trent, Manchester, South Wales, and Glasgow in Scotland. The influence of coal upon population distribution in Britain is still strong, yet its significance is waning as other sources of energy free industry and people from the coalfields.

Urbanization

The city is the most impressive and forceful expression of humankind's struggle with nature. It is a built environment—a giant resource system—that has little regard for the physical environment. As a center of commodity production and final consumption, it exerts a major influence on population distribution. Population concentrations reach their most extreme form in cities.

Modern urban growth is the result of agricultural, industrial, and transport revolutions of the late eighteenth and nineteenth centuries in Europe. The agricultural revolution allowed farmers to produce a surplus of food needed for growing nonagricultural populations. The industrial revolution spurred the mass movement of surplus population away from the countryside and into the emerging factories in cities. And the transport revolution permitted the cheap and fast distribution of the goods required by an expanding urban population. These three developments also increased the size of the trade areas that acted as markets for the goods and services of the growing towns.

The outcome of these revolutions was an increase in the size of urban areas and in the level of urbanization. *Urban growth* is the increase in the size of city populations. Cities grow through natural increase—the excess of births over deaths—and through in-migration. *Urbanization* refers to the process through which the proportion of population living in cities increases. An urban area may be defined on the basis of numbers of residents. In the United States, any place with at least 2500 residents is classified as urban. There are no universal standards, however. Countries have developed their own criteria for differentiating urban from rural places.

Urban growth and urbanization occur simultaneously in most countries, but their rates vary. Indian cities are growing by about 3.6% annually, but the percentage of total population in urban places is increasing slowly, from 20% in 1970 to 26% in 1992. Brazil, with a similar urban growth rate, is experiencing a much faster rate of urbanization. The percentage of total population living in urban areas increased from 46% in 1970 to 74% in 1992.

World urbanization has increased dramatically since 1800. In 1800, some 50 million people—about 5% of the total population—lived in urban areas. By 1992, more than 2 billion people, about 43% of the total population, lived in cities.

Levels of urbanization vary widely among regions and countries of the world (Table 3.3 and Figure 3.3). In 1992, developed countries were 73% urbanized, whereas underdeveloped countries were only 31% urbanized. Latin America has become a predominately urban continent since the end of World War II, but Asia and Africa are still overwhelmingly rural.

The degree of urbanization in a country usually corresponds to its level of economic development. In general, developed countries have the highest urbanization and income levels (see Figures 3.3 and 3.4), but the relationship between town-dwelling population and the level of income per person does not imply that urbanization equals development. (Compare Figures 3.3 and 3.4 with Figure 1.3.) Third World urbanization is not being

◼

Table 3.3

Proportion of Urban Area Population

Region	1950	1970	1985	1990	2000
World	29	37	41	43	47
Developed countries	54	67	72	73	74
Underdeveloped countries	17	25	31	34	39
Africa	16	23	30	33	39
Latin America	41	57	69	72	77
East Asia	17	27	29	30	37
South Asia	16	21	28	30	37
North America	64	74	74	74	75
Former Soviet Union	39	57	66	68	71
Europe	56	67	72	73	75
Oceania	61	71	71	71	71

Source: International Institute for Environment, Development, and World Resources, 1987, p. 27.

accompanied by a rapid increase in prosperity. High urban growth rates are diluting capital resources and reducing living standards. They are generating congestion, deteriorating services, slums, and employment problems.

To understand the role of rapid population growth in urban problems, it is necessary to distinguish between the increasing proportion of urban to total population (urbanization) and the absolute growth of urban population (urban growth). Urbanization increased during the economic expansion of developed countries from 17% in 1875 to 26% in 1900. It also increased at about the same rate in the Third World between 1950 and 1975; the rise was from 17% to 27%. This comparison suggests that economic development rather than population growth is the main determinant of urban growth. But Third World urban population increased at an annual rate of 4.1% between 1950 and 1975, far faster than the rate of 2.8% a year in developed countries between 1875 and 1900. Urban growth rates reflect national growth rates. In the Third World, urban growth is paralleled by high rates in rural areas. Natural increase accounts for 60% of the urban population growth. Rural-to-urban migration accounts for the remaining growth.

The most striking feature of Third World urbanization is the growth of huge primate cities—cities that dominate the urban landscape of a nation. In less devel-

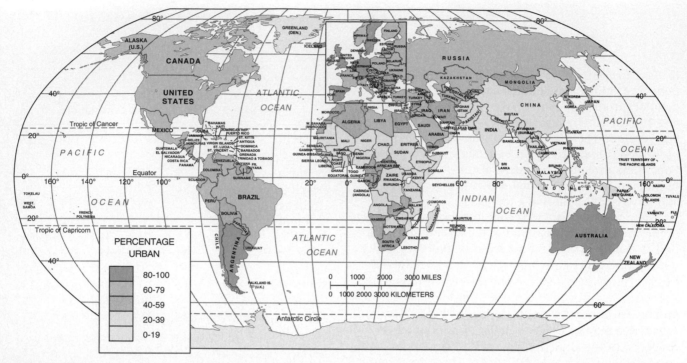

FIGURE 3.3

World urbanization. The level of urbanization varies worldwide and is dependent on a number of factors, including economic development. If the level of economic development is low, a large portion of the population is engaged in hunting/gathering and agriculture. These activities are not conducted in cities. As a society becomes more developed, a greater proportion of the population is engaged in manufacturing and the service industries, which are normally concentrated in cities. The most urbanized countries of the world include Northwestern Europe, North America, Australia, and New Zealand. Least urbanized countries of the world are located in East Asia, South Asia, and Africa.

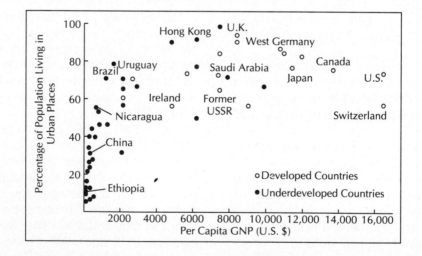

FIGURE 3.4

Relationship between per capita GNP and urbanization. The percentage of population living in urban places generally increases with per capita GNP. Ethiopia and other low-income countries of the world have a low percentage of population living in urban places. Japan, Germany, Canada, and the United States are examples of countries with relatively high GNP per capita and a high proportion of population living in urban places—close to 80%. Some countries such as the United Kingdom and Hong Kong have high percentages of their populations living in urban places, but moderate per capita GNPs. This is due to a space availability problem. Why do countries in Latin America have a higher percentage of population living in urban places than their per capita GNP would suggest?

(Source: Data from Population Reference Bureau, 1987.)

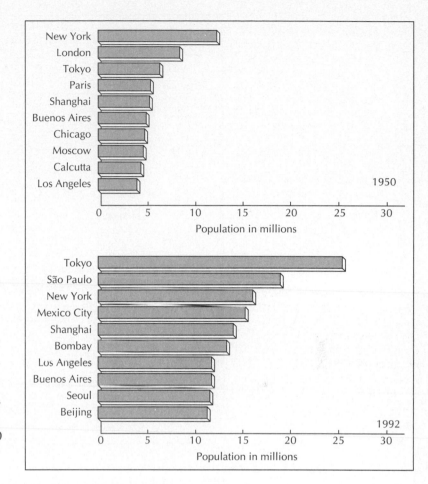

FIGURE 3.5
The 10 most populous world cities in 1950 and 1992. In 1950, only one city, New York City, exceeded 10 million people, but by 1992, at least 10 cities exceeded 10 million. Tokyo had become the world's largest city with more than 25 million people. In 1950, 7 of the top 10 world cities were found outside the Third World, but by 1992, 7 of the top 10 cities were Third World cities.
(Source: Weeks, 1994, p. 357.)

oped nations, such a city is typically the political capital as well as the center of industry, finance, and commerce. In 1950, only three cities in underdeveloped countries ranked in the top 10 in the world (Figure 3.5). By 1990, the number had grown to 7, and it is projected that in the year 2000 all but 2 of the top 10 cities will be in the Third World. Compared with developed countries, the projected rates of big city growth are very rapid indeed (Table 3.4). A large part of the population of many Third World countries is concentrated in a major center of growth called a *primate city*. At least one in five people in Argentina, Iraq, Peru, Chile, Egypt, South Korea, Mexico, and Venezuela lived in a primate city. At the present time, cities such as Lima, Bangkok, Baghdad, and Buenos Aires account for more than 40% of the total urban population of their respective countries (Figure 3.6).

POPULATION GROWTH OVER TIME AND SPACE

◈

To this point we have set the world stage in demographic terms, but we now need to put population growth into the context of changes over time and variability across space. The chief force affecting world population distribution was once migration. This was true until European transoceanic movements were disrupted during the economic depression of the 1930s. Today, the main cause is natural increase—the excess of births over deaths. Human population is increasing, and threatens to go on increasing. Each year an additional 93 million people inhabit the earth. The major impetus

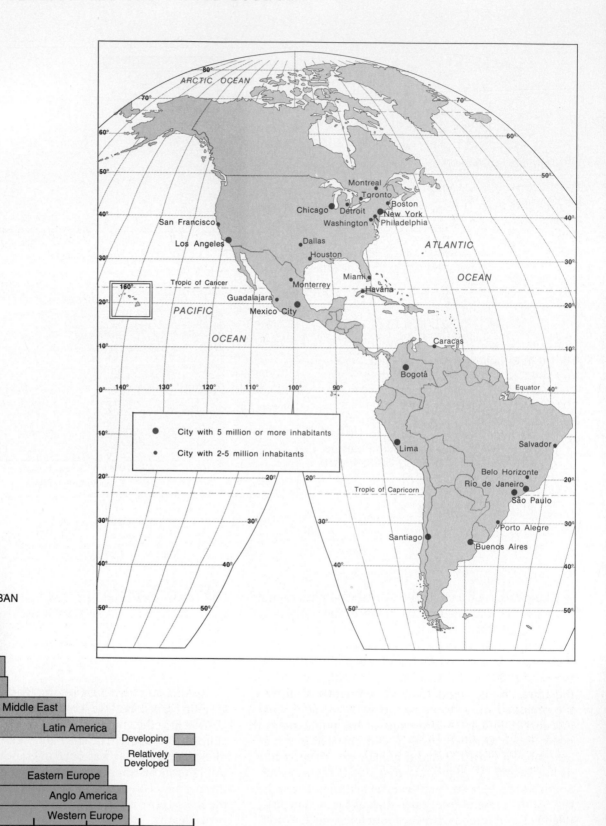

PERCENT URBAN

Sub-Saharan Africa
South Asia
Southeast Asia
East Asia
Middle East
Latin America

Developing

Relatively Developed

Eastern Europe
Anglo America
Western Europe

0   20   40   60   80   100

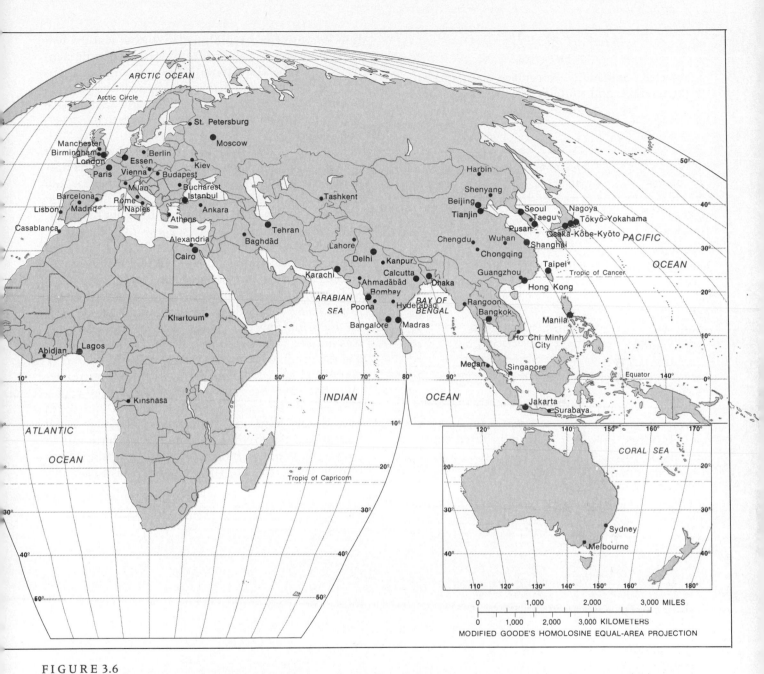

FIGURE 3.6

Major cities of the world. Cities with populations of more than 2 million are shown on this map. While urbanization of a country usually increases with per capita income, more than 10 million cities are located in the developing world, especially in East and South Asia. Europe has more than its proportional share of large cities, while Africa has a noticeable lack of large cities. The growth of large cities in developing countries suggests the overall rapid growth of populations and the migration from rural areas to the city as more jobs are offered in the manufacturing sector and fewer labors are required in the agricultural sector.

◎

T a b l e   3.4

Projected Populations, Percentage of Total Urban Populations, and Number of Cities Larger than 4 Million People

	2000		
Region	Population (Millions)	Percentage of Urban	Number of Cities
World	681	21.7	79
Developed countries	167	16.5	20
Underdeveloped countries	514	24.2	59
Africa	74	20.4	12
East Asia	154	23.0	14
South Asia	199	25.8	23
Latin America	123	28.6	12

Source: U.N. Food and Agricultural Organization. 1985. The State of Food and Agriculture, 1984.

to world population growth comes from underdeveloped countries, in which more than three-fourths of humankind dwell. With more than 4 billion people already and another billion expected by the year 2000,

how will the Third World manage? How will the vast population increase affect efforts to improve living standards? Will the Third World become a permanent underclass in the world economy? Or will the reaction to an imbalance between population and resources be waves of immigration and other spillovers to the developed countries?

The *demographic transition* describes the pattern of population change experienced historically by the now developed countries of Europe, North America, and Asia, and it is the most pervasive theory with regard to what we can expect in the future from other countries. In its basic format, the theory suggests that all societies were characterized by high birth and high death rates until roughly the time of the industrial revolution. Beginning in Europe and then spreading to North America, the death rate began to decline as an accompaniment to the rising standards of living that went along with the industrial revolution. The drop in the death rate was not at first matched by a decline in the birth rate and the result, of course, was an increase in the rate of population growth (Figure 3.7). This is the phenomenon that gave rise to the term "population explosion"—it is the *transition* from high birth and death rates to low birth and death rates. This latter phase results from the eventual response of the birth rate to downward pressure. Industrialization, which first lowered the death rate, ultimately produces the motivations

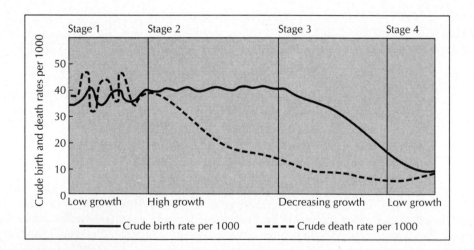

FIGURE 3.7

The demographic transition. Four stages of demographic change are experienced by countries as they develop from primitive to modern. Stage 1: Both high crude birth rates and crude death rates occur in the early stages of civilization. The resulting crude natural increase is quite low. Stage 2: Declining crude death rate, but a continually high crude birth rate, results in an increasing population growth rate. Stage 3: Crude death rates remain low, while crude birth rates start to decline rapidly, resulting in a rapid but declining growth rate. Stage 4: Both crude death rates and birth rates are low, resulting in a low natural increase.

for families to limit family size and over time, the birth rate drops enough to once again reach parity with the death rate and then population growth slows or stops.

The current rapid growth rate of the world population is a recent phenomenon. It took from the emergence of humankind until 1850 for the world population to reach the billion mark. The second billion was added in 80 years (1850–1930), the third billion was added in 30 years (1931–1960), the fourth in 16 years (1960–1976), and the fifth in only 11 years (1977–1987). Although the overall rate of population growth is slowing down, a sixth billion will be added before the year 2000 (Figure 3.8).

The immediate cause for the surge in the growth of the world population is the difference between the crude birth rate and the crude death rate. The crude *birth rate* is the number of babies born per 1000 people per year, and the crude *death rate* is the number of deaths per 1000 per year. For example, the U.S. birth rate in 1992 was 16 and the death rate was 9. During that year, the growth rate was 16 minus 9, or 7 per 1000, which is a percentage *rate of natural increase* of 0.7.

Like all living things (and some that are inanimate, such as your savings account), human populations have the capacity to grow exponentially (1,2,4,8) rather than arithmetically (1,2,3,4), which is why population can increase so rapidly. Thus, the historical pattern of population growth shown in Figure 3.8 does indeed look like an explosion. We can express this intuitively by talking about the *doubling time*—the number of years that it takes a population to double in size, given a particular rate of growth. For example, at an annual increase of 0.7% per year, the doubling time for the U.S. population is 100 years. As growth rates increase, doubling times decrease sharply. At 1.7%, the rate of world increase in 1992, the doubling time is 41 years. The rate of growth in Mexico is 2.3% and the doubling time is 30 years. In general, the doubling time for a

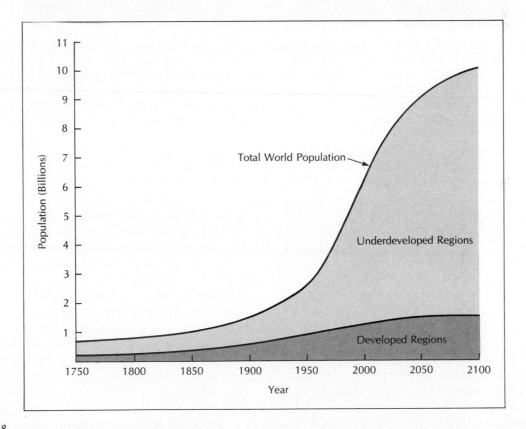

FIGURE 3.8
A major upturn in the logistic growth curve occurred around 1950 with important improvements in agriculture and an increasing food supply. In addition, medical science breakthroughs, such as polio and chickenpox vaccines, and improvements in nutrition substantially reduced death rates. Population growth rates are expected to slow by 2050 as the above improvements in science and nutrition permeate the Third World.

The trains are crowded in Bangladesh. Here, in one of the world's most fertile lands, the combination of high population density and the concentration of land into fewer and fewer hands contributes to continuing poverty and hunger. By 1994, India had a population of 900 million and a birth rate of 31 per 1000 population per year. Due to its 2.1% natural increase, its doubling time is 34 years. However, India's infant mortality rate is still rather high, at 91 deaths per 1000 births, while that of North America by comparison is only 8. In 1993, India's per capita GNP was $330 (in U.S. dollars). By 1994, Bangladesh had a population of 120 million people and a natural increase of 2.4%, giving it a doubling time of only 29 years. In 1993, its per capita GNP was $220 (in U.S. dollars). *(Source: World Bank.)*

population can be determined by using the *rule of seventy*, which means that you divide 70 by the average annual rate of rate. Thus, for Mexico, 70 divided by the growth rate of 2.3 equals a doubling time of 30 years. Therefore, 70 divided by 3 equals 23 years.

Most of the world's population growth is occurring in the underdeveloped world (Figure 3.9). Of all the continents, Africa has the fastest rate of growth. In 1992, the population of Africa was growing by 3% per year. For Kenya, with a fertility rate of nearly seven births per woman, the rate was 3.7%. At that rate of increase, Kenya's 1992 population of 26 million will double in just 19 years.

Rapidly declining death rates and continued high birth rates are the cause of this explosion. Death rates have been falling to fewer than 10 deaths per 1000 people each year in Asia and Latin America, and to about 14 per 1000 in Africa. Birth rates are changing less spectacularly (Figure 3.10). They are highest in

Africa (43 births per 1000 people annually), Latin America (28 per 1000), and Asia (30 per 1000). These latter figures compare with birth rates of 12 per 1000 in Europe and 16 per 1000 in North America.

After accelerating for two centuries, the overall rate of world population growth is slowing down. In 1992, population was growing at 1.7% a year, down from a peak of 2% in the late 1960s. The rate of growth is expected to continue to decline to about 1.5% in 2000 and 1% in 2020. However, the absolute size of population will continue to increase because the size of the base population to which the growth rate applies is so large (Figure 3.11).

The United Nations projects world population at 6.1 billion in 2000 and 8.5 billion in 2025. Almost all of this increase will occur in the developing countries. The largest absolute increase is projected for Asia, reflecting its huge population base. Future population growth will further accentuate the uneven distribution of the

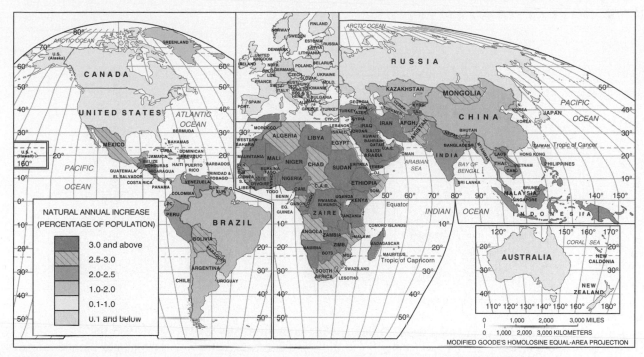

FIGURE 3.9

Natural annual increase in world population, 1993. The natural annual increase is the rate of growth of a population for a particular year. The fastest growing areas of the world include Africa, Central America, and Southwest Asia. Here, growth rates exceed 2.5%, with a number of countries in Central America and Africa actually exceeding 3% per year. Three percent growth per year does not seem like a high growth rate, however, it indicates total population doubling time for a country of only 23 years. With a 2% growth rate, a country would double in 35 years. For a 1% growth rate, a country may double in 70 years. Natural increase in Europe as a whole is only .2%, and several countries have declining rates of growth. (See Color Insert page 1.2, bottom, for more illustrative map.)

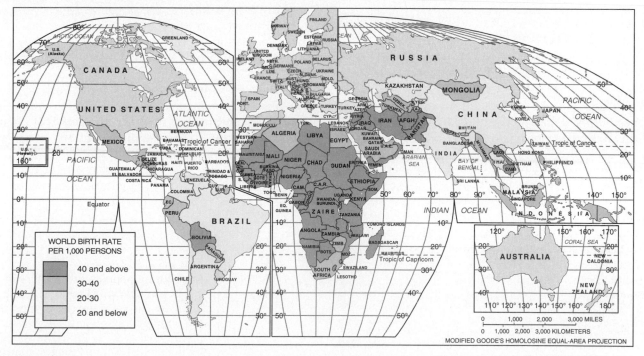

FIGURE 3.10

World birth rate, 1993. The world birth rate is the number of children born each year per 1000 people that live in a country. The world birth rate closely mirrors the natural annual increase. *Crude* birth or death rates means that we are counting a country's population as a whole and not studying separate rates of birth for women of different age groups, or by income or racial character. Again, Central America, Africa, and Southwest Asia lead the world in the rate of crude birth. (See Color Insert page 1.3, top, for more illustrative map.)

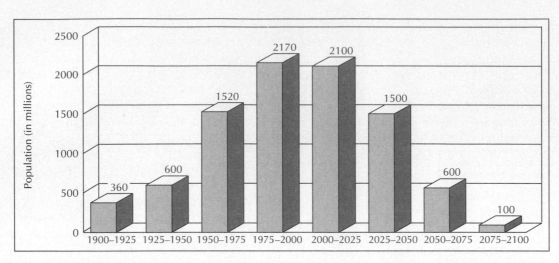

FIGURE 3.11
Net additions to the world's population betwen 1900 and the year 2100. The world's population has increased expo-
nentially in the 20th century. The period from 1975 to the year 2000 will show the largest quarter decade of increase,
with more than 2 billion people being added to the world's population, followed by the period from 2000 to 2025.
From there, the world's population should slow down in rate of increase.
(Source: Weeks, 1994, p. 35.)

world's population. In 1992, 77% of the world's population lived in the underdeveloped world, but by the year
2025, the proportion will increase to 84% (Figure 3.12).

POPULATION PROCESSES

◈

We discussed the fact that the rate of natural increase
for a country is measured as the difference between the
birth rate and the death rate. Births and deaths represent

two of the three population processes; the third is migration. Every population displays some combination of
these three processes as the determinant of its pattern
of growth. In general, we can express the relationship
among them using the *demographic equation:*

Population at Time 2 = Population at Time 1
+ Births − Deaths + In-migration − Outmigration

Thus, in order to understand the current demographic situation in any country or region of the world,
we must understand all three of these basic demographic processes. The population of any geographic

	Area		
	More Developed Nations	Less Developed Nations	World
Projection to year 2025 (in millions)	1354	7150	8504
Population in 1990 (in millions)	1207	4085	5292
Increase (1990–2025) (in millions)	147	3065	3212
Percent of increase attributable to each area	5%	95%	100%

Source: United Nations, 1991, World Population Prospects 1990 (New York: United Nations), Table 12.
Note: Projections made by the United Nations suggest that the world's population will exceed 8 billion
by the year 2025. Ninety-five percent of that growth will probably occur in the less developed nations.

FIGURE 3.12
Most future population growth will occur in less developed nations. These nations are currently the site of most of
the population growth in the world, approximated at 95%. Projections made
by the United Nations suggest that the
world's population will exceed 8 billion
persons by the year 2025.
(Source: Weeks, 1994, p. 35.)

area changes through the interaction of three demographic variables: births, deaths, and migrations. The difference between births and deaths produces natural increase (or decrease) of a population. Net migration is the difference between immigrants and emigrants. Natural increase usually accounts for the greatest population growth, especially in the short run. However, in the long run, migration contributes far more than the number of people moving into an area because the children of immigrants add to the population base.

Fertility and Mortality

Earlier in the chapter we mentioned the demographic transition as a theory that describes the fertility and mortality changes that have occurred in the developed societies and that may provide some guidance for future demographic trends in the less developed world. Thus far, only North America, Europe, and East Asia have moved completely through the demographic transition. Elsewhere in the world, largely in the Southern Hemisphere, death rates have dropped dramatically, especially since the end of World War II, but birth rates remain well above death rates, resulting in the high rate of population growth we have been describing.

It is important to remember that death rates do not drop evenly as an economy develops over time. *Infant mortality rates* (deaths to babies under age 1) tend to drop earliest and quickest. It was not uncommon in premodern societies to find an infant mortality rate in excess of 200 infant deaths per 1000 live births—20% or more of all babies died before reaching their first birthday. Nowhere in the world today are rates that severe, but the highest rates (averaging 100 infant deaths per 1000 live births) are found in sub-Saharan Africa (Figure 3.13).

Because the drop in the death rate disproportionately affects the very young, it acts exactly like an increase in the birth rate—more babies survive to grow to adulthood. Life spans likewise increase (Figure 3.14). One of the reasons why the very young are more affected is that as the death rate drops it does so initially because communicable diseases are brought under con-

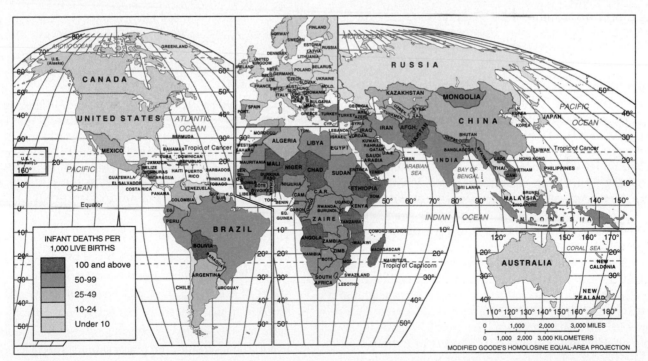

FIGURE 3.13

Infant deaths per 1000 live births, 1993. Infant mortality rates are the number of deaths of infants under 1 year of age per 1000 live births for a country. World infant mortality rates average approximately 75 per 1000 for 1993. The United States, for example, averaged 8 deaths per 1000 live births, but several European nations had lower infant mortality rates. As with natural income increase and world birth rates, infant deaths per 1000 live births are related to development. Infant deaths per 1000 live births are highest in Africa and Southwest Asia, more than 100 in many cases. (See Color Insert page 1.3 bottom, for more illustrative map.)

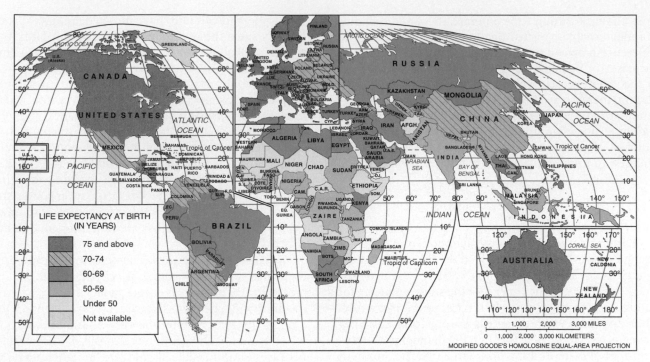

FIGURE 3.14
Life expectancy at birth. Babies born in 1993 are expected to live an average of 64 years. Life expectancy, however, ranges from the high 70s in Northwestern European nations and in North America and Australia to the low 30s in some African nations. (See color insert page 1.4, top.)

trol, and the very young are particularly susceptible to such diseases. The control of communicable disease has the serendipitous economic side effect of reducing the overall illness level in society, thus promoting increased labor productivity. Workers miss fewer days of work, are healthier when they do work, and are able to work productively for more years than when death rates are high. Eventually, as death rates drop, the timing of death shifts increasingly to the older ages, to the years beyond retirement when the economic impact on the labor force is minimal.

Although death rates have declined throughout the world, it is still true that mortality is lowest in the Northern Hemisphere (especially in northwest Europe and in Japan) and highest in the Southern Hemisphere (especially in sub-Saharan Africa). A virtually identical pattern prevails in the world with respect to fertility.

Fertility levels fell first in Western Europe, followed quickly by North America, and more recently by Japan, and then the remainder of Europe. In all of those areas of the world, reproductive levels are near, or even in some countries below, the level of generational replacement. Elsewhere in the world, however, birth rates remain at much higher levels, although in China and Southeast Asia the birth rates are dropping very quickly.

There has been a modest decline in South Asia, the Middle East, and much of Latin America, but few signs of a decline have yet been seen in most of sub-Saharan Africa. The seeming intransigence of birth rates in Africa has baffled many analysts, but Australian demographers (Caldwell and Caldwell, 1990; Caldwell, Orubuloye, and Caldwell, 1992) have argued that the explanation lies in the very different way in which African society tends to be organized:

> The core of African society is its emphasis on ancestry and descent. In religious terms, this is usually reflected by a belief in the intervention of ancestral spirits in the affairs of the living. In social terms, the emphasis is reflected in the strength of ties based on the family of descent—the lineage. A person's true spiritual home, and in some societies the physical home for a lifetime, is the lineage, rather than the conjugal family. (Caldwell and Caldwell, 1990, p. 119)

The consequence of the African family structure is that children continue to be economic assets to the family (the lineage) even though the resulting high rate of population growth is very difficult for each nation to cope with.

In Mali, women often have to travel several miles from their villages to gather firewood. Their heavy workloads are one of the factors that contribute to high fertility. The children are needed to help with house chores and farmwork. As of January 1994, Mali had a population of 10 million and a natural increase of 3%, giving it a doubling time of 23 years. As is the case in most African countries south of the Sahara, the infant mortality rate of 111 per 1000 live births is relatively high. Their per capita GNP in 1993 was $300 (in U.S. dollars).
(Source: F. Mattioli for WFP/FAO.)

Overall, then, almost all the world's nations are experiencing more births than deaths each year, with the biggest gap being found in the less developed nations and the narrowest difference existing in the more developed nations. In addition to these patterns of natural increase, many areas of the world are also impacted by migration.

Migration

Migration is a purposeful movement involving a change of permanent residence. It is a complex phenomenon that raises a lot of questions. Why do people move? What factors influence the intensity of a migratory flow? What are the effects of migration? And what are the main patterns of migration?

CAUSES OF MIGRATION

Most people move for economic reasons. They move to take better-paying jobs or search for jobs in new areas. They also move to escape poverty or low living standards. Some people move because of cultural pressures or adverse political conditions. Others move to fulfill personal dreams. Whatever the motive, migrants seek generally to better themselves. The causes of migration are sometimes divided into "push-and-pull" factors. Push factors might be widespread unemployment, population pressure, shortage of land, famine, or war. Hunger in Sweden in the 1860s is a good example of a push factor. In the half century between 1861 and 1910, more than 1 million Swedes moved to the United States. In the late 1970s and early 1980s, the various communist purges in Vietnam, Kampuchea, and Laos "pushed" out approximately 1 million refugees who resettled in the United States, Canada, Australia, China, Hong Kong, and several countries in Western Europe. Pull factors may be free agricultural land, the "bright lights" of a Third World primate city, or a booming economy. The rich oil-exporting countries in the Middle East act as a pull factor for millions of immigrants seeking employment. In Kuwait, nearly 80% of the work force was composed of foreigners at the time of Iraqi invasion in 1991.

Migrations can be voluntary or involuntary. Most movements are voluntary, such as the westward migration of pioneer farmers in the United States and Canada. Involuntary movements may be forced or impelled. In forced migration, people have no choice; their transfer is compulsory. Examples include the African slave trade and the deportation or "transportation" of British convicts to the United States in the eighteenth century. In impelled migration, people choose to move under duress. In the nineteenth century, many Jewish victims of the Russian pogroms elected to move to the United States and the United Kingdom without the immediate lash of fear.

THE ECONOMICS OF MIGRATION

Many reasons exist for migration, including religious discrimination, cultural differences, and political factors. This section examines migration of a voluntary nature, due to economic purposes. This category of migration comprises the largest single category of human migrations throughout history. Consider two regions as shown in Figure 3.15. One region, Region A on the right, is a highly industrialized country (i.e., the United States or Germany). The region on the left, Region B, is a less developed region (i.e., Mexico, Morocco, or Greece). A labor market exists in each, and the developed region is shown on the right side as a downward sloping demand curve. The quantity of labor is measured on the horizontal axis and the price of labor is measured on the vertical axis. As the price increases on the vertical axis, the demand for labor decreases, and as the price decreases, the demand for labor in the developed country increases. The supply curve S1 in the developed country, increases upward to the right, suggesting that a greater supply of labor is available at

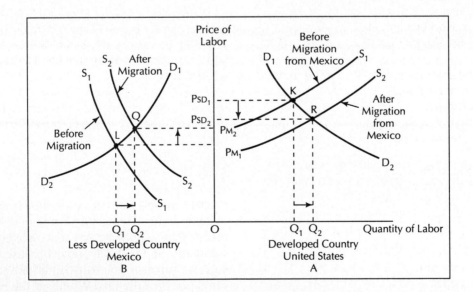

FIGURE 3.15
Migration and wage differentials. The quantity of labor is measured on the horizontal axis, and the price of labor is measured on the vertical axis. As the price increases on the vertical axis, the demand for labor decreases in both the developed country and the less developed country. The supply curves of both developed and undeveloped countries slope upward, suggesting a greater supply of labor is available at higher prices. Because the equilibrium price of labor is higher in the developed country than it is in the undeveloped country, labor migrations occur from less developed to developed, or from B to A, to take advantage of higher wages. The greater the wage differential, both the greater the flow and the longer the distance of flow. The wage rate differential between San Diego and Tijuana, for example, is 8 to 1 for comparable occupations.
(Source: Adapted from Stutz, 1992c).

Filipino migrant workers battle hot times in
Kuwait. Filipinos working on the road
construction project are bused back to their
camp. They put in an 8-hour shift and often
several hours overtime with no break. Head
coverings protect from the heat. Kuwaities and
Bangladeshics have been attracted to Kuwait by
clean-up contracts and large construction
projects, many resulting from the war. The pay
is poor and working conditions harsh. Of
Kuwait's resident population of 2 million, more
than half are noncitizens lured by oil wealth,
despite the misery of working conditions.
(Source: Stuart Franklin/Magnum Photos.)

higher prices. As the price for labor increases, individuals who would not care to work at lower wages, now come into the marketplace. They substitute work at higher prices for staying home and taking care of children, going to school, or being in retirement or semi-retirement.

In order to facilitate the analysis for the less developed country, such information is shown on the left side of Figure 3.15. Instead of measuring the quantity of labor from zero to the right for the less developed country, we now measure it from zero to the left. Price remains on the vertical axis. The supply curve in the less developed country slopes upward to the left and the demand curve slopes downward to the left. In this manner, we get a back to back set of supply and demand curves for a less developed country and developed country.

Observe the equilibrium position of the supply and demand for labor in the developed country before migration occurs. This occurs at point K. Also note the equilibrium position for the supply and demand of labor in the less developed country. This equilibrium position occurs at L. In classical *labor migration theory*, there is

an assumption that information about job availability and labor wages differentials is available and known by workers. Labor in the less developed country finds out about jobs available in the developed country at higher wage rates. Now because the equilibrium price in Region A is quite a bit higher than that in Region B, labor migrates from Region B to Region A to take advantage of higher wages. The greater the differential, the greater the flow and the longer distance the flow can operate. In Region A, extra labor is now coming into the region, which is used to working for lower wages. Because the extra labor is supplied over and above the indigenous supply and the labor is used to working at lower wages, the supply curve moves downward toward the right. The new equilibrium is R. In addition, since the labor pool has left Region B, the supply of labor is reduced. The supply curve moves upward and to the right in Region B, thus raising the equilibrium price to Q. The new equilibrium price in Region A, at R, is at a lower level than it was prior to labor migration. Thus, migration will continue as long as there is a difference between the wages of Region A and Region B, which exceed a cost associated with migration. In the case of flows from Mexico to the United States, most categories of employment are paid two to five times the rate in Mexico. Consequently, the flows both on a daily basis (Figure 3.16), and on a longer-term basis (Figure 3.17) continue to occur at high levels (Figure 3.18).

In classical migration theory, transportation costs and other costs associated with moving an individual or family are included, such as selling a property and purchasing one in the new region. The costs of labor in the different regions will not be exactly equalized. But classical trade and migration theory tell us that the long-run price of labor in the two regions should come into close harmony with one another. Relocation and similar migration costs should be split up over the period of work remaining in the life of the mover.

However, when we observe real world labor movements and price differentials, we find that wage rates do not seem to be converging between regions. Major discrepancies occur in the wages paid in various regions of the United States and Europe, as well as in South America and India. If classical theory held, the problems of the world would not exist with regard to variations based on labor rates. There would be simply less difference per capita in incomes. One major reason that major labor differential rates exist is because of the imperfections in the migration system knowledge. Many workers in the less developed countries do not know that jobs they may be qualified for in more highly developed

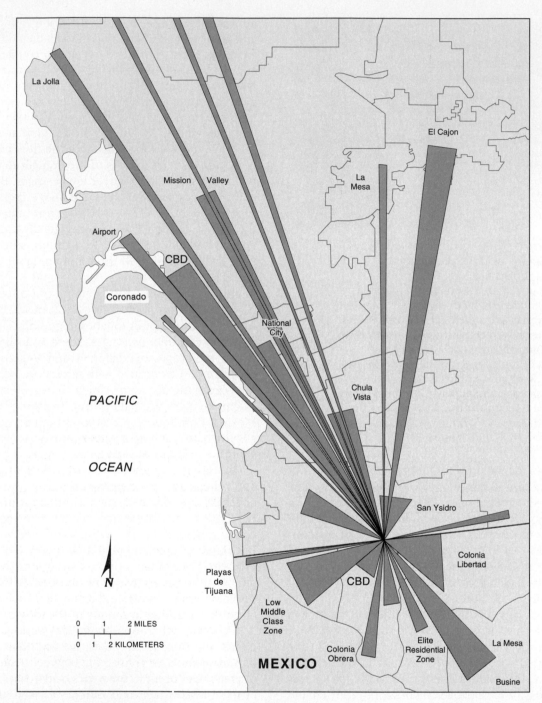

FIGURE 3.16
Labor flow from Mexico. Daily labor migrations occur from Tijuana, Mexico to San Diego, California. The labor flow is caused by wage differentials. Pay for the same type of job in San Diego is eight times higher than it is in Tijuana, Mexico. Laborers in Tijuana must obtain a green card or work permit to work in the United States. Most laborers leave their home early to get in line at the border crossing gate. Eighty percent of the laborers that live in Tijuana and work in San Diego return home to Mexico daily. Sweat shop manufacturing, auto repair, landscaping and agriculture work, and service job categories associated with restaurants and hotels comprise the chief labor categories.
(Source: Stutz, 1992d, p. 92.)

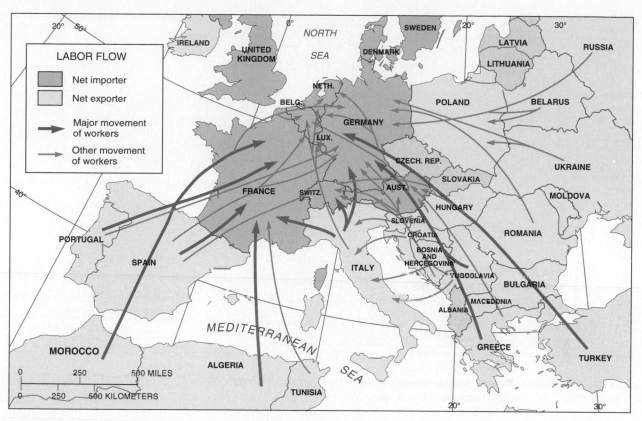

FIGURE 3.17
Guest worker labor flows in Europe. Guest worker labor flows occur principally from North African and Southern European nations, where wages are low, to Northwestern European nations, where the population is aging and labor rates are much higher. Here, labor flow is for much longer durations than a single day, as in the case of Tijuana to San Diego. Labor flow is influenced by several factors, including distance, similarity of culture and language, and cooperative agreements between exporting and importing countries regarding rules of migration and labor occupation.

countries even exist. Even a worker in Appalachia who is skilled may not know of the jobs available for him in New York City at a much higher wage rate. In addition, there are social costs involved in making the move. As an individual contemplates changing locations and even countries, he is beset by a series of social factors, including lack of friends and knowledge and the feeling of uneasiness in his new setting. Consequently, the largest number of international labor migrants are young males who do not have families to relocate.

Cultural differences also exist. The cultural shock of a developed nation, especially when one does not have the resources to live adequately or does not speak the native language, presents social problems. Institutional barriers also exist, such as the status of immigration or the length of time allowed in the host country. For example, disdain for the manner of dress, language, and religious practice as well as racial discrimination in

employment and on the street, present barriers to the relocating worker. Blacks, Puerto Ricans, Mexican Americans, and women have encountered such resistance in the past in America in their search for improved working conditions and wages. Consequently, we cannot expect that economic forces will lead to a total smoothing of wage inequities throughout a country or throughout the world. At best, only a small portion of the population in a low wage region is sensitive to and has the ability to gain access to and higher pay from the developed nation. Therefore, there will continue to be a discrepancy in per capita earnings between less developed countries and developed countries and between depressed regions and economically healthy regions within countries.

Finally, the more urbanized the region is at the destination, compared to that of the origin, the more attractive it is for potential migrants.

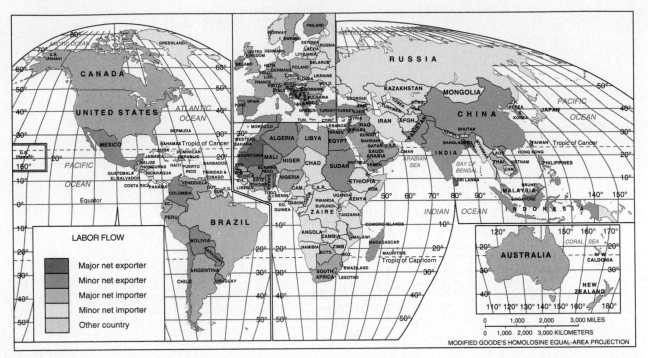

FIGURE 3.18

Guest worker labor flow export and import countries. The availability of work and wage rates account for major labor flows throughout the world, from countries lacking in jobs and high rates to countries with jobs available at relatively higher wage rates. Major labor flows occur from Mexico and the Caribbean to the United States and Canada; from South American countries to Argentina, Venezuela, and Peru; from North Africa and Southern European nations to Northwestern Europe; from Africa and Asia to Saudi Arabia; and from Indonesia to Malaysia, Singapore, and Australia. Migrants vary by age. Young adults are the most likely to be migrants because of their desire for an improved life and energy in overcoming travel and hardships. Young adults also have fewer ties to their hometowns.

BARRIERS TO MIGRATION

The intensity of a migration flow is reduced by would-be migrant characteristics, political restrictions, and distance. In the late nineteenth century, British sociologist E. G. Ravenstein (1885, 1889) studied migration in England and concluded that most people move short distances and that the frequency of moves declines with distance. All movement costs except long-distance moves are more expensive than short-distance ones. Subsequent studies have modified some of Ravenstein's generalizations on the migration process. The concept of intervening opportunity, for example, holds that people's perception of a far-away place's comparative advantage is changed when there are closer opportunities. In steamship days, many British emigrants chose South Africa rather than crossing another ocean to Australia.

Almost all countries regulate the flow of immigration. The United States limits immigration to approximately 600,000 persons annually. In addition, an estimated 5,000,000 persons enter the United States illegally and live in a half-world of constant threat. Billions of dollars are spent annually to police the borders of the United States, and much of this money is used to try to keep Mexicans out.

CHARACTERISTICS OF MIGRANTS

Some countries have higher rates of migration than do others—both into and within the country. In general, the countries that have long histories of migration, such as the United States, Canada, and Australia, have higher migration rates in the modern world than do other countries, such as China, where migration is far less common. When people do move, they are far more likely to be young adults than they are any other group. In some parts of the world women are more prone to

In 1993, the American border patrol arrested more than 30 million persons passing illegally from Mexico into the United States. Each day, along the 2000 mile (3750 km) frontier, Mexicans attempted to pass through the 3-meter high grilled fence, separating the two countries, to enter their neighboring country to the north. Most people are captured, returned to Mexico, and freed the same day; however, the majority of these Mexicans will try again and eventually be successful. This clandestine immigration makes important problems for the United States. This photo shows a portion of the fence separating Tijuana, Mexico, on the left, from San Diego, on the right. Children born to undocumented women in the United States immediately become legal citizens. Many women make the perilous journey and stay with friends until the delivery date. With the recent passage of NAFTA, will the flow of undocumented people from Mexico to the United States increase or decrease in the short run and the long run? Why do you think so?
(Source: J.P. Laffont/Sygma.)

migration than men, and in other parts of the world, men are more likely to be migrants, although the increasing ease of transportation and communication may be breaking down these gender differences. Regardless of gender, it is the young who move, as can be seen in Figure 3.19, which displays migration data for the United States.

CONSEQUENCES OF MIGRATION

Migration has demographic, social, and economic effects, due especially to the fact that migrants tend to be young adults and often the more ambitious and better educated members of a society. Obviously, the movement of people from Region A to Region B causes the population of A to decrease and B to increase. Because of migratory selection, the effects are more complicated. If the migrants are young adults, their departure increases the average age, raises the death rate, and low-

ers the birth rate in Region A. For the region of in-migration, B, the opposite is true. Thus, A's loss and B's gain is accentuated in the short run. If migrants to Region B are retirees, their effect is to increase the average age, raise the death rate, and lower the birth rate in the region of reception. Arizona, for example, has attracted a large number of retirees resulting in a higher-than-average death rate.

Conflict is a fairly frequent social consequence of migration. It often follows the mass movement of people from poor countries to rich. There were tensions in Boston after the Irish arrived. And the same tensions have come with recent migrants—Cubans to Miami and Puerto Ricans to New York. Social unrest and instability also follow the movement of refugees from poor countries to other poor countries. Generally, poor migrants have more difficulty adjusting to a new environment than the relatively well-educated and socially aware. But migrants, on frequent occasion, do suffer from guilt. Many migrants to the United States feel they should go

FIGURE 3.19
During 1990, as during the previous decades of American history, young adults were the most likely group to migrate. *(Source: Weeks, 1994, p. 199.)*

back to their home country to share in its tasks and problems.

The economic effects of migration are varied. With few exceptions, migrants contribute enormously to the economic well-being of places to which they come. For example, guestworkers were indispensable to the economy of West Germany prior to reunification. Without

them, assembly lines would have closed down, and patients in hospitals and nursing homes would have been unwashed and unfed. Without Mexican migrants, fruits and vegetables in Texas and California would go unharvested and service in restaurants and hotels would be nearly nonexistent.

In the short run, the massive influx of people to a

The Yugoslavian Civil War. Bosnian soldiers run across a gap between buildings at the front line, exposed to enemy fire as they retreat from a failed assault. Soldiers fire and run, and enemy bullets hit the ground at their feet. Brcko, a Muslim city on the River Saba in northern Bosnia, was ethnically cleansed by Serbian forces. In the fall of 1993, citizens of Brcko and surrounding villages formed an impromptu defense force that halted Serbian advances. Such ethnic cleansing has caused thousands of Muslims to migrate to avoid being killed by the Serbs.
(Source: James Nachtwey/Magnum Photos.)

region can cause problems. The U.S. Sunbelt states have benefited from new business and industry but are hard-pressed to provide the physical infrastructure and services required by economic growth. In Mexico, migrants to Mexico City reduce the standard of living in their competition for scarce food, clothing, and shelter. Despite massive relief aid, growing numbers of refugees in the Third World impoverish the economies of host countries.

Emigration can relieve problems of poverty. If the Irish and Italians had remained at home in the nineteenth century, they would have added to the population pressure. External migration relaxed the problem of poverty and may have averted revolution in Jamaica and Puerto Rico in the 1950s and 1960s. However, emigration can also be costly. Some of the most skilled and educated members of the population of Third World countries migrate to developed countries. Each year, the income transferred through the "brain drain" to the United States amounts to billions of dollars, although billions of dollars are also sent back home in the form of remittances to family members who stayed behind.

PATTERNS OF MIGRATION

To examine patterns of migration, it is helpful to consider migration as either external (international) or internal (within a country). It is also convenient to subdivide external migration into intercontinental and intracontinental, and internal migration into interregional, rural-urban, and intermetropolitan. International migrations, so important in the past, are now far exceeded by internal population movements, especially to and from cities.

The great transoceanic exodus of Europeans and the Atlantic slave trade are spectacular examples of intercontinental migration. In the five centuries before the economic depression of the 1930s, these population movements contributed strongly to a redistribution of the world's population. It has been estimated that between 9 and 10 million slaves, mostly from Africa, were hauled by Europeans into the sparsely inhabited Americas. The importance of the "triangular trade" of Europe, Africa, and the Americas can hardly be exaggerated, especially for British economic development. Africans were purchased with British manufactured goods. They were transported to plantations where they undertook production of sugar, cotton, indigo, molasses, and other tropical products. The processing of these products created new British industries. Plantation owners and slaves provided a new market for British manufacturers whose profits helped further to finance Britain's industrial revolution.

The Atlantic slave trade was dwarfed by the voluntary intercontinental migration of Europeans. Mass emigration began slowly in the 1820s and peaked on the eve of World War I, when the annual flow reached 1.5 million. At first, migrants came from densely populated northwestern Europe. Later they came from poor and oppressed parts of southern and eastern Europe. Between 1840 and 1930, at least 50 million Europeans emigrated. Their main destination was North America, but the wave of migration spilled over into Australia and New Zealand, Latin America, Asia, and southern Africa. These new lands were important for Europe's economic development. They offered outlets for population pressure and provided new sources of foodstuffs and raw materials, markets for manufactured goods, and openings for capital investment (Figure 3.20).

Since World War II, the pattern of intercontinental migration has changed. Instead of heavy migratory flow from Europe to the New World, the tide of migrants is overwhelmingly from underdeveloped to developed countries. Migration into industrial Europe and continued migration to North America is spurred partly by widening technological and economic inequality and by rapid rates of population increase in the underdeveloped world.

The era of heavy intercontinental migration is over. Mass external migrations still occur, but at the intracontinental scale. In Europe, forced and impelled movements of people in the aftermath of World War II have been succeeded by a system of migrant labor. The most prosperous industrial countries of Europe attract workers from the agrarian periphery. France and Germany are the main receiving countries of European labor migration. France attracts workers especially from Spain, Italy, and North Africa (see Figure 3.17). And West Germany draws workers from Italy, Greece, and Turkey. Migrant workers from southern Europe usually have low skills and perform jobs unacceptable to indigenous workers. Similarly, thousands of Mexicans, many of whom are illegal aliens, find their way to the United States each year to work (see Figure 3.16).

The system of extraterritorial migrant labor also exists in the underdeveloped world, most notably in Africa, where laborers move great distances to work in mines and on plantations. In West Africa, the direction of labor migration is from the interior to coastal cities and export agricultural areas. In East Africa, agricultural estates attract extraterritorial labor. In Southern Africa,

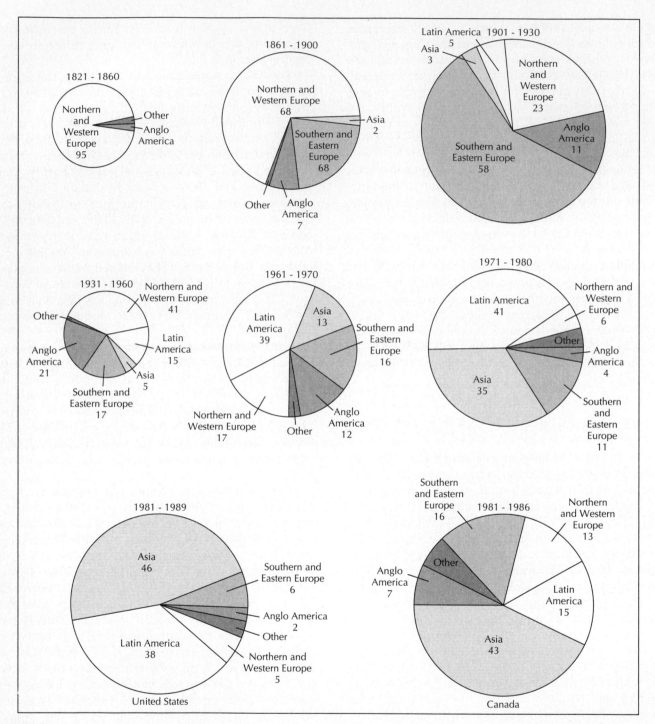

FIGURE 3.20

United States immigration history from 1821 to 1989. The circles represent immigration to the United States for various time periods and are proportionate in size to the total number of immigrants per period. Until 1900, Northern and Western Europe were the principal sources of immigration to the United States. From 1900 to 1930, Southern and Eastern Europe comprised the greater proportion of immigrants to the United States. Europe continued to supply America with the greatest proportion of immigrants until the 1960s. From 1961 to 1980, Latin America replaced Europe as the most important source of immigration. Asia became the largest source of immigration to the United States in the 1980s.

migrants focus on the mining-urban-industrial zone that extends from southern Zaire in the north, through Zambia's Copper Belt and Zimbabwe's Great Dyke, to South Africa's Witwatersrand in the south.

In the modern era, the refugee problem has swung from Europe to the Third World, and then back to the Balkan states of Eastern Europe. Refugee generating and receiving countries are concentrated in Africa (6 million people), Southeast Asia (4 million), and Latin America (2 million). The causes of refugee movement include wars or ideology (i.e., Vietnam, World War II, Afghanistan) (Figure 3.21); racial and ethnic persecution (i.e., South Africa, Bosnia-Herzegovina); economic insufficiency increased by political intervention (i.e., Ethiopia, Chad) (Figure 3.22); and natural and human-caused disasters (i.e., Belize hurricane of 1961, Bhopal chemical accident of 1984).

Colonizing migration and population drift are two types of interregional migration. Examples of colonizing migration include the nineteenth-century spontaneous trek westward in the United States and the planned eastward movement in the USSR beginning in 1925.

Refugees in Somalia. The United Nations' high commission for refugees has estimated that there are 2 million refugees in some 40 special camps and more than half a million others outside camps in Somalia. Sixty percent of the refugees are children. By 1994, Somalia had a population of 10 million, with a natural increase of 3.1%. It is one of the poorest and most ravaged countries in the world. Recent drought, famine, and disruption by warlords have prevented UN relief supplies from reaching refugee camps such as this one.
(*Source: UN Photo 146 497/Peter Magubane.*)

General drifts of population occur in almost every country, and they accentuate the unevenness of population distribution. Since World War I, there has been a drift of black Americans from the rural South to the cities of the nation's industrial heartland. Since the 1950s in the continental United States, there has been net out-migration from the center of the country to both coasts and a shift of population from the Frost- and Rust-Belt states to the Sunbelt (Figures 3.23 and 3.24).

The most important type of internal migration is rural-urban migration, which is usually for economic motives. The relocation of farm workers to industrial urban centers was prevalent in developed countries during the nineteenth century. Since World War II, migration to large urban centers has been a striking phenomenon in nearly all underdeveloped countries. Burgeoning capital cities, in particular, have functioned as magnets attracting migrants in search of "the good life" and employment.

In highly urbanized countries, intermetropolitan migration is increasingly important. Although many migrants to cities come from rural areas and small towns, they form a decreasing proportion. Job mobility is a major determinant of intercity migration. So, too, is ease of transportation, especially air transportation. For intermetropolitan migrants from New York, the two most popular destinations are Miami and Los Angeles.

POPULATION STRUCTURE

◈

Except for total size, the most important demographic feature of a population is its age-sex structure. The age-sex structure determines the needs of a population; therefore, it has significant policy implications. A fast-growing population implies a high proportion of young people under the working age. A small proportion of workers results in a smaller output per capita, all else being equal. A youthful population also puts a burden on the education system. And when this cohort enters the working ages, a rapid increase in jobs is needed to accommodate them. By contrast, countries with a large proportion of older people must develop retirement systems and medical facilities to serve them. Therefore, as a population ages, its needs change from schools to jobs to medical care.

The age structure of a country is often examined through the use of population pyramids. They are built

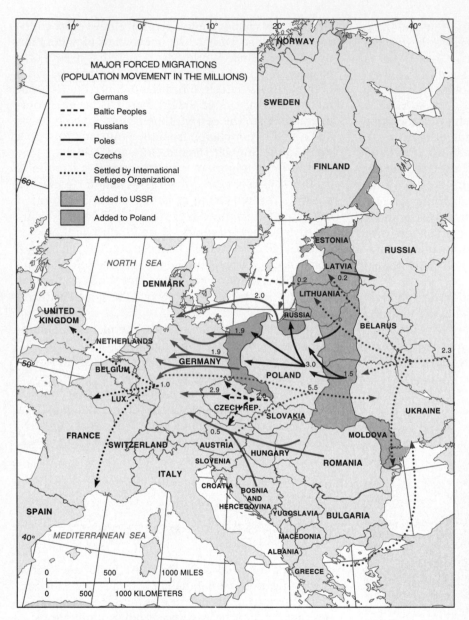

FIGURE 3.21
Major forced migrations in Europe.
The redrafting of country boundaries
after World War II created an immense set of forced migrations. The
largest movements included Germans
who had to resettle in Germany and
vacate the territory given to Poland,
and Polish who had to resettle in Poland, vacating that area of Poland
given to the U.S.S.R.

up in 5-year age groups; the base representing the youn-
gest group, the apex the oldest. Population pyramids
are compared by expressing male and female age groups
as percentages of total population. The shape of a pyramid reflects long-term trends in fertility and mortality
and short-term effects of "baby booms," migrations,
wars, and epidemics. It also reflects the potential for
future population growth or decline.

Three representative types of pyramid may be distinguished. One is the squat, triangular profile (Fig. 3.25a).
It has a broad base, concave sides, and a narrow tip. It is
characteristic of underdeveloped countries having high

(even if declining) birth rates, such as exemplified by
Chile or by Mexico in 1990. In fact, the number of
Mexicans working or looking for work will have more
than doubled between 1980 and 2000, from 20 million
to 42 million. What does Mexico's population future
portend? Will the Mexican economy be able to support
such an increase, or will the potential for out-migration
be enhanced?

In contrast, the pyramid for the United States in
1990 describes a slowly growing population. Its shape is
the result of a history of declining fertility and mortality
rates, augmented by substantial immigration. With

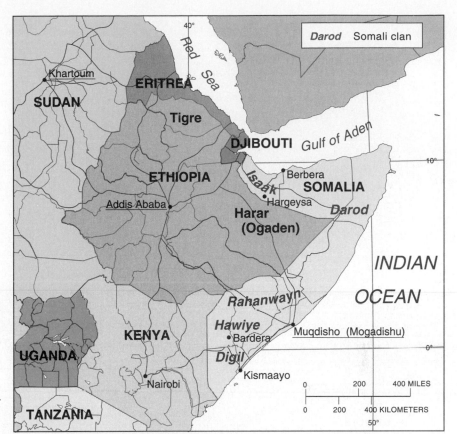

FIGURE 3.22

Forced migrations in the Horn of Africa. Civil war, famine, and drought have caused major migrations in the Horn of Africa. Native Somalians living in Ethiopia have been forced to migrate back to Somalia, while an almost equal number of Ethiopians have been pushed out of Somalia. Eritrea has sent more than half a million people fleeing for their lives to Sudan because of the civil war with Ethiopia. Southern Sudanese have immigrated on a large scale because of civil war and drought.

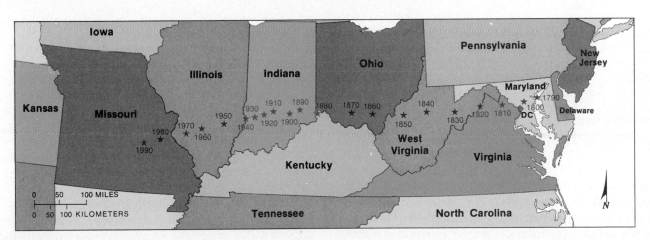

FIGURE 3.23

The population center of the United States. Since the first U.S. census in 1790, the center of population of the United States has moved steadily west and, at a somewhat slower pace, south. The giant leap was made in 1960 when both Hawaii and Alaska were added to the United States as the 49th and 50th states. Until this point, the population center of the United States paralleled Interstate 70. For the first time in history, the population center of the United States moved west of the Mississippi River in 1980. In 1990, the center of population was at Rolla, Missouri, 100 miles southwest of St. Louis. The new pattern seems to have shifted in a more southerly direction, with a large population attraction to the southwestern United States, especially southern California. The new population center seems to be drifting southwest, paralleling Interstate 44.

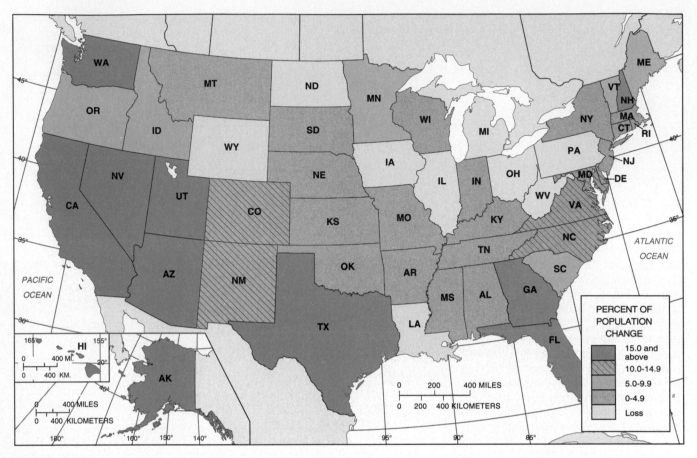

FIGURE 3.24
Percent of population change in the United States 1980 to 1990. The most rapidly growing states between 1980 and 1990 were located in the West and the South. States of the Northeast, South, Midwest, and Great Plains grew at a much lower rate, or even lost population in some cases. Texas, California, and Florida accounted for almost 50% of the population growth during this period, and each registered at approximately a 25% growth rate. A few less populated states, such as Arizona and Nevada, actually had population growth rates at much higher levels. (See color insert page 1.4 bottom.)

lower fertility fewer people have entered the base of the pyramid; with lower mortality a greater percentage of the "births" have survived until old age. As a result, the U.S. population has been aging, meaning that the proportion of older persons has been growing. The pyramid's flattened chest reflects the "baby dearth" of the depression years when total births dropped to about 2.5 million from an average of close to 3 million a year. At the time, the fertility rate dropped close to 2.1, which is the level that leads to a stable population if maintained indefinitely. The bulge at the waist of the pyramid is a consequence of the *baby boom* that followed World War II. In the mid-1950s, the fertility rate increased to 3.8 and the number of births each year exceeded 4 million. After 1964 there was another "baby bust." By 1976, the fertility rate had fallen to 1.7, a level below replacement.

Members of the baby-boom generation, however, were having children in the 1980s. Thus, even though the birth rate is lower than ever before, the U.S. population continues to grow from natural increase as well as from immigration.

A few developed countries have very low rates of population growth—in some cases *zero population growth* (ZPG) or *negative population growth* (NPG). They have low birth rates, low death rates and, in some cases, net out-migration. France and Denmark are examples (Figure 3.25b). Because of very low fertility for a long time, the country is experiencing very slow population growth and, although there is a steady stream of foreigners (especially Algerians) being let into the country, France works hard to limit immigration. Population decline is an economic concern to many European

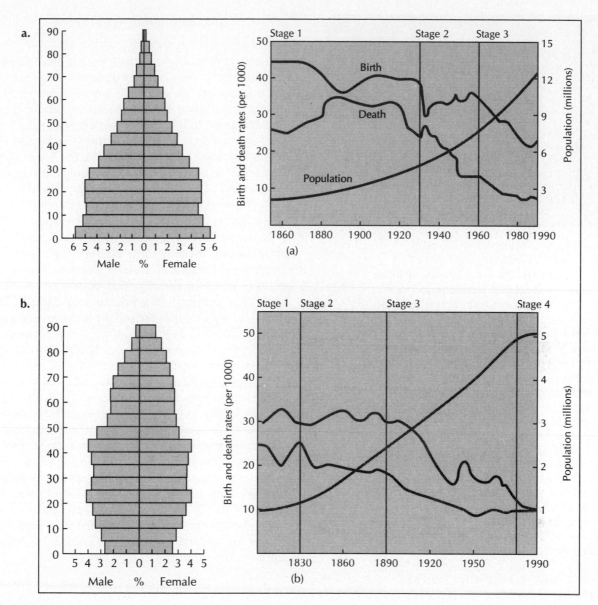

FIGURE 3.25

(a) The population pyramid (left) and the demographic transition (right) for Chile are shown. The vertical axis measures age, and the horizontal axis measures population by gender. Chile entered stage 2 of the demographic transition in 1930 when death rates abruptly declined. It entered stage 3 in approximately 1960 when birth rates began to decline. It has yet to enter stage 4, and the population continues to rise dramatically. Because of its status as a developing country, it has a relatively broad-based pyramid. Population members younger than 15 and older than 65 are dependent populations. (See Color Insert 1 for more illustrative map.)

(b) The population pyramid and demographic transition for Denmark are shown. The shape of the so-called pyramid is quite different than that of Chile. Because of lower birth rates, the population pyramid is more in the shape of a spark plug. Denmark, who entered this stage in 1830 and stage 3 in 1890, entered stage 2 of the population pyramid 100 years earlier than Chile. In the 1970s, Denmark entered stage 4, and its current population growth is zero. (See color insert page 1.5.)

Chinese children in Shanghai welcoming visitors from America. By January 1994, China's population reached 1.2 billion, or more than one-fifth of the world population. Considering its Third World status and its huge size, it has a remarkably low 1.2% average natural increase. One child per family is the norm, and it is enforced by the government with a series of economic sanctions. While the per capita income is only $370 (in U.S. dollars) per person, it represents one of the largest markets in the world. The United States and other developed countries are presently trying to open the Chinese market and, therefore, have given China a most favored nation trading status in spite of its poor human rights record. (*Source: Paolo Koch/Rapho/Photo Researchers, Inc.*)

countries. Who will fill the future labor force? Is the solution the immigration of guestworkers from Third World countries?

DEMOGRAPHIC CHARACTERISTICS

◈

Demographic characteristics are those qualities of humans that we often label as *human capital*, including educational attainment, labor force participation, occupation, and income. However, these characteristics, which are often called *achieved characteristics*, are often confounded by the existence of *ascribed characteristics*, with which we are born and which may affect our ability to achieve our desired level of living. These ascribed characteristics include race and ethnicity (often mixed up with religion) and gender. These interrelationships are shown in Figure 3.26.

Educational Attainment

There is probably no characteristic more important to demographic trends than education level. Education has a profound set of effects on all types of human behavior, including fertility, mortality, and migration. Education also influences almost every aspect of a person's life chances. Virtually without exception in the world, the more educated a person, the fewer children the person is likely to have, the longer the person is likely to live, and the more likely the person is to migrate. Educational attainment has increased significantly over time in the United States (Figure 3.27).

In the developed countries, nearly all adults are literate (although there is some controversy about this in the United States) and, indeed, the majority of adults are high school graduates. But, in less developed nations, large numbers of adults are not literate. World Bank data indicate that 50% of the Algerian adult population is illiterate, as is 62% of the adult population in Haiti, 70% in Pakistan, and nearly all adults (88%) in Somalia. "Less developed" and "uneducated" go together, hand-in-hand.

On the more positive side, there is also a clear relationship in the United States between education and income. To be sure, knowledge of the relationship is what spurs many students to stay in college. Table 3.5 shows the relationship as of 1991 in the United States. You can see that males with a postgraduate degree who were working full-time, year-round were earning an average of $49,093 in 1991, nearly $30,000 a year more than the men who had not graduated from high school. Income for women is lower, but you can see that the pattern is the same.

Labor Force Participation

The population of a country is conventionally divided into two parts: the economically active and the economically inactive. Economically active people are the productively employed and temporarily unemployed. They compose what is known as the income-earning labor force. Men are still dominant in the paid labor force but the proportion of men to women is changing slowly. In 1950, women accounted for 31% of the world's income-earning labor force; in 1985, the figure was 35%. But the absolute number of women engaged in wage and employment increased consider-

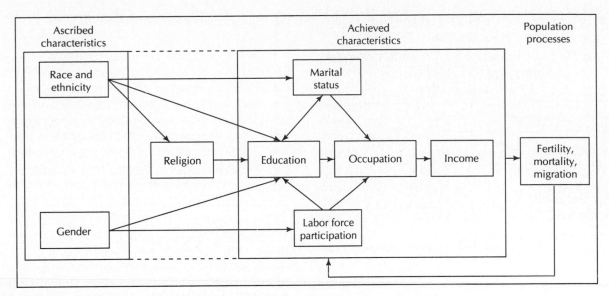

FIGURE 3.26
Population characteristics affect population processes and are also affected by them.
(Source: Weeks, 1994, p. 262.)

ably. Between 1975 and 1985 more than 100 million women joined the labor force, and in 1985 an estimated 676 million women were gainfully employed.

Official labor-force statistics are deceiving, however. They exclude adults and children in the informal sector, whose work may involve begging, shoe shining, selling handicrafts, prostitution, drug dealing, or petty theft. They also ignore the invisible, unpaid work of men, women, and children. Women workers are especially invisible to official enumerators, in particular, in the case of women who do agricultural work. In 1970, Egypt's census revealed that only 3.6% of women did agricultural work, but local surveys discovered that up to 40% of women were actually involved in planting, tilling, and harvesting. In Africa, women generally do the lion's share of such work. Women's agricultural work is underestimated in the developed world as well.

Women are also engaged in other forms of unpaid work—cooking food, feeding infants, washing and mending clothes, and collecting water and firewood. A woman in a Pakistani village spends approximately 60 hours per week on domestic work. And in the developed world, women who are "just housewives" work an average of 56 hours per week.

FIGURE 3.27
Educational attainment in the United States between 1940 and 1990. Educational attainment has increased substantially in the United States between 1940 and 1990. In 1940, 24% of the population achieved high school graduation, while only 3% of the population graduated from college. By 1990, however, 80% of the population had achieved a high school degree, while more than 20% of the population had graduated from college.
(Source: Weeks, 1994, p. 264.)

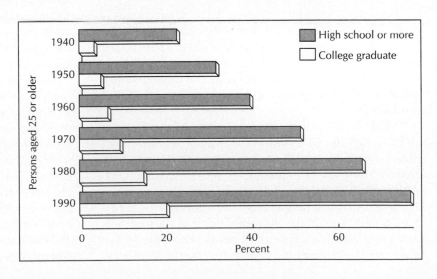

◈

Table 3.5
Annual Median Income for Year-Round, Full-Time Workers Age 25 and Older: United States, 1991

Educational Attainment	Males	Females
Less than High School	19,654	13,816
High School Graduate	26,515	18,323
Some College	31,566	22,227
College Graduate	39,115	28,042
Postgraduate	49,093	33,771

Source: U.S. Bureau of the Census. 1992. Educational Attainment in the United States: March 1991. Current Population Reports, Series P-20, No. 462, Table 8.

The wage-earning labor force engages in thousands of different kinds of activities that may be classified into four sectors, as follows:

- *Primary activities,* including agriculture, mining, quarrying, forestry, hunting, and fishing
- *Secondary activities,* including manufacturing and construction
- *Tertiary activities,* including all services, commerce, transportation, storage, and trade (Figure 3.28)
- *Quaternary activities,* including the collection, processing, and dissemination of information.

Economic development alters labor-force composition. As the U.S. economy grew, the proportion of the labor force in secondary and tertiary activities increased at the expense of primary activities, particularly agriculture (Figure 3.29). Compared with the United States, the share of the labor force in agriculture in the contemporary Third World is high.

The ratio of industrial to agricultural workers provides a measure of a nation's economic advancement and power. As expected, underdeveloped countries have a low ratio of industrial to agricultural workers. Although manufacturing industries are moving to the Third World, most people have been barely touched by the iron embrace of the industrial age that is more than 200 years old. The majority of people continue to live their lives by rhythm of the seasons, not of machines.

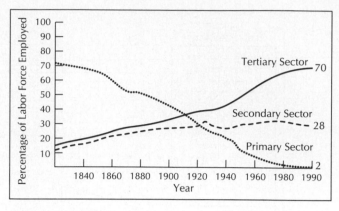

FIGURE 3.28
The changing composition of the U.S. labor force. Between 1820 and 1990, the primary economic sector of the economy fell from more than 70% of the labor force to less than 2%, while the secondary sector increased from 11% to 32% in 1980. Since 1980, the secondary sector has fallen to 28%. The tertiary sector has risen from 15% in 1820 to more than 70% today. Interestingly, in 1916, each of the three sectors of the economy accounted for approximately 33% of the labor force. By 1995, the tertiary and quaternary sectors had exceeded 75%. The secondary sector had fallen to 23%.

UNEMPLOYMENT

Unemployment means able and willing workers with no jobs. In the United States, the jobless rate was 3.4% in 1971, 9% during the recession of 1974/1975, and 6.7% in 1991. Levels of unemployment are much higher for women, blacks, and the young than for adult males. Unemployment of young people (24 years of age and under) was 16% in 1991. Unemployment figures, however, underestimate the problem. People who have failed to find work and stop trying are excluded from the statistics. Moreover, the figures fail to account for adults, especially women, who want formal employment but who never obtain it because of domestic responsibilities or the lack of acceptable occupations.

In underdeveloped countries, official unemployment is a phenomenon of an urban sector composed of a minority of the population. Although unemployment rates are officially around 10%, an estimated 25% of those living in Third World cities survive outside the mainstream economy, and a further 750 million are unemployed or underemployed in the rural sector. People who work less than a specified number of hours are not underemployed. Underemployment is the gap between the amount of labor required for a decent living and the actual payment given for work; thus, underemployment is an index of poverty.

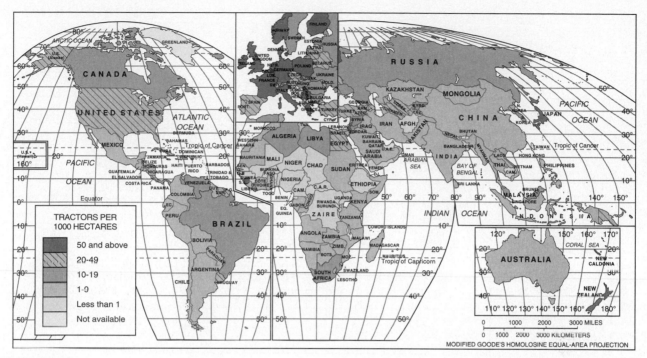

FIGURE 3.29
Farm workers in developed countries have more tractors than their counterparts in less developed countries. One such farmer can produce enough food to feed 50 to 100 others allowing these people to work in the secondary and tertiary sectors of the economy. A fourth sector is sometimes identified, the quaternary sector, which is comprised of those occupations dealing with the information economy. Which developing countries are well supplied with tractors? (See color insert for more illustrative map.)

Income

Per capita income is the most familiar index to measure a population's relative development, its economic well-being and its capacity to consume. The distribution of total GNP among selected countries is striking. The wealth produced by the United States and Canada alone is nearly five times greater than the combined GNPs of Africa and Latin America, which have about three and one-half times the population of North America. In 1992, North America had a per capita income of $21,580. The corresponding figures for Africa and Latin America were $630 and $2170, respectively.

However well income per capita may seem to reflect international disparities, this measure should be viewed with caution. First, it fails to indicate ways in which incomes are distributed through the strata of societies. In most underdeveloped countries, wealth is concentrated in a small elite. Even within developed countries, major inequities in the internal distribution of income exist. A second problem stems from the fact that countries measure income per capita in a variety of ways. Finally, the per capita income indicator fails to take into account economic activities outside national monetized accounting systems in underdeveloped countries. Street vending, for example, which plays an important role in the lives of many people in the Third World, is not officially accounted for. For these reasons, per capita income has only limited utility, and often serves only to publicize the problem of poverty.

To delve more deeply into the problems of poverty, social scientists have constructed multidimensional measures of human well-being. An example is the Population Crisis Committee's (1987) Human Suffering Index constructed from 10 variables: income per capita, average annual inflation rate, average annual growth of labor force, average annual growth of urban population, infant mortality rate, daily per capita calorie supply, percentage of population with access to clean drinking

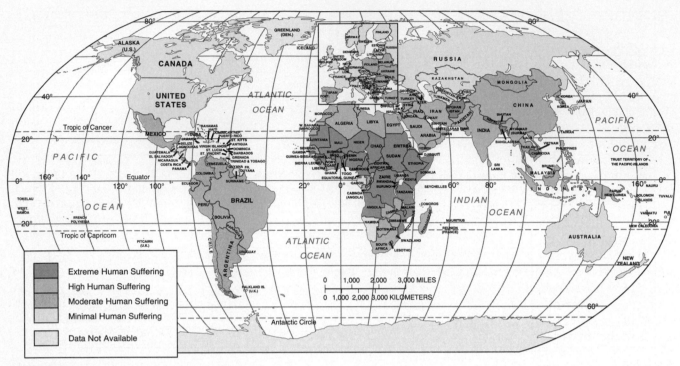

FIGURE 3.30

The human suffering index. The human suffering index measures income per capita, average annual inflation rate, average annual growth of labor force, average annual growth of urban population, infant mortality rate, daily per capita calorie supply, percentage of population with access to clean drinking water, energy consumption per capita, adult literacy rate, and personal freedoms. On this basis, human suffering shows up to be the most severe in the developing world, especially in Africa and portions of South Asia.
(Source: Based on Population Crisis Committee data, 1987.)

water, energy consumption per capita, adult literacy rate, and personal freedom/governance. Each of 130 countries was assigned a score of zero (high) to 10 (low) for each variable, and these scores were added together to form an index. Countries ranged from Mozambique (most human suffering) to Switzerland (least human suffering) (Figure 3.30). The *Human Suffering Index* is a useful descriptive measure of the differences in living conditions among countries.

ECONOMIC GROWTH AND ECONOMIC DEVELOPMENT

◈

Economic growth refers to an increase in the total amount of wealth in a nation (or whatever your unit of analysis might be) without regard to the total number of people, whereas economic development relates that

amount of wealth to the number of people. For example, in 1990 in the United States, the total national income was $5.3 trillion (Population Reference Bureau, 1991). For the 250 million Americans in 1990, that averaged out to $21,100 per person per year in income. In Switzerland in the same year, national income was "only" $206 billion, but since there are far fewer Swiss (a little less than 7 million), average (per capita) income was higher in Switzerland ($30,270) than in the United States.

In contrast to those two wealthy nations is a country like India, whose total estimated income in 1990 of $301 billion was higher than Switzerland's, but the far larger number of people in India (more than 860 million) reduced the per person income to just $350 per year. Thus, the "average" American (if there is such a person) has 60 times the income of the "average" Indian. National income in India, even in constant dollars (controlling for inflation), was 44% higher in 1985 than it was in 1975, but the population also was growing

ECONOMIC GROWTH AND ECONOMIC DEVELOPMENT 95

very quickly and, as a result, per capita income increased only 18% in that 10-year span (United Nations, 1988).

So far we have discussed economic development in terms of average income, but those averages frequently hide inequalities and disparities in the distribution of income. It may happen that the per capita increase in productivity profits only a few people rather than the entire population, and, in fact, some economists argue that a concentration of income is the only way that enough money can be saved for further investment and further economic growth. Kuznets (1965), for example, has suggested that income inequality characterizes the early phases of economic development when capital formation is so crucial; only later is it possible to spread the income around. A loose analogy might be made to a family that wants to "develop economically" by purchasing a home. Assuming that a substantial amount of cash must be saved for the down payment and closing costs, the members of the family may well have to do without things they would like to consume, because all the extra money is being accumulated for the house purchase. Only when the house has been bought can the sacrifice cease and the family income be more spread around among its members. The analogy is not perfect, but it illustrates a point well-known to early industrial entrepreneurs—a delay of gratification is required if income is going to be reinvested for further growth.

Economic growth often involves the introduction of machines that work more efficiently and cheaply than humans, which can lead to the paradoxical situation in which per capita income in a nation may rise (that is, economic growth occurs) but the actual standard of living of almost the entire population may fall (that is, a general lack of economic development). Bauer (1972) has discussed this difference between growth and development and has noted that the opposite paradox could also occur. For example, per capita income could go down, but the level of living could rise as a result of income redistribution. Of course, in this latter example, real economic development occurs only if the improved standards of living can be maintained.

In sum, economic development in its broadest sense means a sustained increase in the socioeconomic welfare of a population. There is a major problem, though, in the measurement of economic development, since for the most part the data we have refer only to levels of income, not to distribution of income. Thus, we have to use those data to make inferences about the nature of the changes occurring within a society. As a matter of fact, if we could accurately measure economic development as we have defined it, the entire debate

about its relationship to population growth might be resolved.

The Debate—Statistical Bases

There is an almost indisputable statistical association between economic development and population growth; that is, when one changes, the other also tends to change. As you probably already know, two things can be related to each other without one causing the other. Furthermore, the patterns of cause and effect can conceivably change over time. Does population growth promote economic development? Are population growth and economic development only coincidentally associated with each other? Or is population growth a hindrance to economic development? That is the debate.

The problem is that the data presently available lend themselves to a variety of interpretations. In Figure 3.31, we have compared 1990 per capita GNP (a common measure of income) with rates of population growth in 143 countries. You can see that in general, countries in which average income levels are low tend to be clustered around the high end of population growth rates. Thus, we have partitioned the graph into four parts. The solid horizontal line represents the average per person income ($3760) in the world, while the dashed vertical line represents the average rate of population growth in the world (1.7% per year). Therefore, Jordan is a nation that is below the world average in terms of income, but well above with respect to population growth. Joining Jordan in that quadrant are most of the non–oil-producing nations of Africa, Asia, and Latin America.

At the other extreme are the wealthier countries with low rates of population growth, exemplified by Switzerland but also including the United States, Canada, Japan, and the countries of western and northern Europe. The countries that do not fit the expected pattern include the oil-producing Middle Eastern nations such as the United Arab Emirates, where fertility rates are only now beginning to decline, following the fairly recent rise in oil-based wealth. Also off the track are those countries that have not been able to translate low rates of population growth into higher standards of living. Virtually all of these countries, such as Hungary, are either just emerging from decades of state socialism or are still centrally planned economies (including the People's Republic of China).

Clearly, a low rate of population growth is no assurance of a high income, and vice versa. Further, such

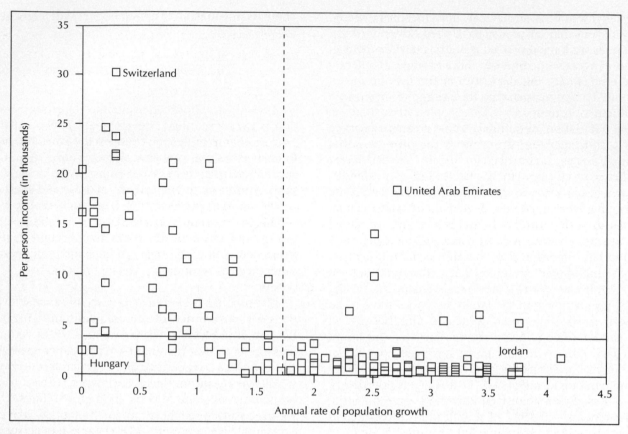

FIGURE 3.31
Per person income and annual rate of population growth. In 1990, as in previous years, there was a high rate of population growth associated with low levels of income.
(Source: Weeks, 1994, p. 384.)

data, taken from just one point in time, cannot be used to establish a cause-and-effect relationship. Numerous studies have attempted to relate change *over time* in the rate of population growth to the change *over time* in income levels. The results have generally been inconclusive. They have attributed this ambiguity to the inadequate research base that currently exists, but at the same time they have concluded that rapid population growth may be somewhat detrimental to economic development, at least in the poorer nations. Critics have argued that the National Research Council report ignored or misinterpreted information that could have led them convincingly to conclude that population growth is bad for economic development (Daly, 1986; Potter, 1986). Others have viewed the inconclusiveness as evidence that no relationship exists between population growth and economic development (Simon, 1986). Thus, the relationship can be interpreted in several different ways, depending on your ideological predilections.

The Debate—Ideological Bases

The debate, then, over population growth and economic development historically has been three-cornered. In the first corner, arguing that population growth stimulates development, you will typically find nationalists—people seeking freedom for their country from economic and political exploitation by more powerful nations. A frequent corollary of nationalism is the idea that more people will bring more productivity and greater power. Another form of nationalism is that which appeared as the official United States position at the 1984 International Population Conference in Mexico City—in any free-market system, population growth stimulates demand and, thus, helps the economy.

In the second corner, you will find Marxists (and others, as well) arguing that social and economic injustice result simultaneously from the lack (or slowness) of economic development and the (erroneous) belief that there is a population problem. The Marxist position maintains that no cause-and-effect relationship exists between population growth and economic development; that is, poverty, hunger, and other social welfare problems associated with lack of economic development are a result of unjust social and economic institutions, not population growth.

Finally, in the third corner you find those who have historically antagonized the Marxists, namely the *neo-Malthusians*. They are, of course, latter-day advocates of the thesis that population growth, unless checked, will wipe out economic gain. The difference between Malthus and the neoMalthusians is that Malthus was opposed to birth control, whereas neoMalthusians are strong advocates of birth control as a preventive check to population growth. Let us examine these three positions in more detail.

IS POPULATION GROWTH A STIMULUS TO ECONOMIC DEVELOPMENT?

Probably the best-known exponent of the idea that population growth is the trigger of economic development is a British agricultural economist, Colin Clark. Clark (1967) insists that, in the long run, a growing population is more likely than either a nongrowing or a declining population to lead to economic development. He points to the history of Europe, in which the industrial revolution and the increase in agricultural production were accompanied almost universally by population growth. Clark's argument is based on the thesis that population growth is the motivating force that brings about the clearing of uncultivated land, the draining of swamps, and the development of new crops, fertilizers, and irrigation techniques, all of which are linked to "revolutions" in agriculture (Clark, 1967). The kernel of Clark's argument, which is advanced also by Boserup (1965, 1981), has often been repeated around the world (especially by the Catholic Church) and is well-stated in the following:

[Population growth] is the only force powerful enough to make such communities change their methods, and in the long run transforms them into much more advanced and productive societies. The world has immense physical resources for agriculture and mineral production still unused. In industrial communities, the beneficial economic effects of large and expanding markets are abundantly clear. The principal problems cre-

ated by population growth are not those of poverty, but of exceptionally rapid increase of wealth in certain favoured regions of growing population, their attraction of further population by migration, and the unmanageable spread of their cities. (Clark, 1967, Preface)

This same line of reasoning is part of a strategy of development forwarded by Hirschman, who has argued that: (1) an increase in population size will lower a population's standard of living unless people reorganize their lives to increase production; (2) it is "a fundamental psychological postulate" that people will resist a lowering in their standard of living; and (3) "the activity undertaken by the community in resisting a decline in its standard of living causes an increase in its ability to control its environment and to organize itself for development. As a result, the community will now be able to exploit the opportunities for economic growth that existed previously but were left unutilized" (Hirschman, 1958, p. 177).

The thesis that population growth is beneficial to economic development does, however, have some foundation. In both Europe and the United States, there is a reasonable amount of evidence to suggest that development may well have been stimulated by population increase. Indeed, some historians regard preindustrial declines in death rates in Europe, associated partly with the disappearance of the plague (perhaps also with the introduction of the potato) as the spark that set off the industrial revolution. The reasoning goes that the lowered death rates created a rise in the rate of population growth, which then created a demand for more resources [see Clark (1967) for a review]. An analogous example of population growth influencing development is the case of the American railroad, which opened up the frontier and hastened resource development in the United States. Fishlow (1965) has demonstrated that the railroad, which actually helped to accelerate the economic development of the western states, was following people westward.

Although history may show that population growth was good for development in the now highly industrialized nations, statistics also reveal very important differences between the European-American experience and that of modern, less developed nations. The less developed countries today are not, in general, retracing the steps of the currently developed nations. For example, less developed nations are building from a base of much lower levels of living than those that prevailed in either Europe or the United States in the early phases of eco-

Third World female children are less likely to receive a good education than female children in more developed countries. It is much more difficult for these children to achieve a prominent economic or political position in their society, compared to opportunities available to women in the developed economies. This scene shows an elementary school for girls in Manila, Philippines. The school, operated by the Immaculate Conception Sisters, was built by the parents of the children and the nuns of the nearby convent. *(Source: United Nations.)*

nomic development (Boserup, 1981; Kuznets, 1965). Furthermore, although the rate of economic growth in many underdeveloped countries has recently been higher than at comparable periods in the history of the developed nations, population growth is also significantly higher. They have much higher rates of population growth than European or American countries *ever* had, with the possible exception of the colonial period of American history. In fact, the rates of population growth in the underdeveloped world seem to be virtually unparalleled in human history.

It appears that population growth may have helped to stimulate economic growth in the developed countries "by forcing men out of their natural torpor and inducing innovation and technical change, or by speeding up the replacement of the labour force with better educated labor" (Ohlin, 1976, p. 9). The less developed nations of today, however, do not seem to require any kind of internal stimulation to be innovative. They can see in the world around them the fruits of economic development, and quite naturally they want to share in as many of those goodies as possible—a situation often referred to as "the revolution of rising expectations."

People in less developed nations today know more about economic development and, by studying the history of the highly industrialized nations, they can see how it was once achievable. If it was ever true that the existence of more people meant a greater chance of producing the genius that will solve the world's problems, it is a difficult argument to sustain today. As Nathan Keyfitz has pointed out, "the England that produced Shakespeare and shortly after that Newton held in all 5 million people, and probably not more than one million of these could read or write. . . . The thought that with more people there will be more talent for politics, for administration, for enterprise, for technological advance, is best dismissed. . . . For the most part, innovation comes from those who are comfortably located and have plenty of resources at their disposal" (quoted in United Nations Fund for Population Activities, 1986, p. 16). In any event, it seems unlikely that a spark such as population growth is necessary any longer, although there really is little solid evidence one way or another.

Controversy is always fed by contradictory evidence and, in 1981, Julian Simon, an economist at the University of Maryland, popularized his thesis that a growing human population is the "ultimate resource" in the search for economic improvement. Eschewing the Malthusian idea that resources are finite, Simon (1989) suggests that resources are limited only by our ability to invent them and that, in essence, such inventiveness increases in proportion to the number of brains trying to solve problems. Coal replaced wood as a source of energy only to be replaced by oil, which may ultimately be replaced by solar energy, if we can figure out how to do it properly. From Simon's vantage point, innovation goes hand in hand with population growth, although he is quick to point out that *moderate*, rather than fast (or very slow), population growth is most conducive to an improvement in human welfare.

Simon, however, makes a crucial assumption: to be beneficial, population growth must occur in an environment in which people are free to be expressive and creative. For him, that means a free-market or capitalist system. Marxists, of course, balk at such a suggestion.

IS POPULATION GROWTH UNRELATED TO ECONOMIC DEVELOPMENT?

The usual Marxist view is that population problems will disappear when other problems are solved, and that economic development can occur readily in a socialist society. Marx (and Engels) believed that each country at each historical period has its own law of population and that economic development is related to the political-economic structure of society, not at all to population growth. Indeed, Marx seemed to be arguing that whether population grew as a nation advanced economically was due to the nature of social organization. In an exploitive capitalist society, the government would encourage population increase to keep wages low, whereas in a socialist state there would be no such encouragement. Socialists argue that every member of society is born with the means to provide his or her own subsistence; thus, economic development should proportionately benefit every person. The only reason it might not is if society is organized to exploit the workers by letting capitalists take large profits, thereby depriving laborers of the full share of their earnings.

Leaders of less developed nations have argued that the world economic system operates the same way. The developed nations of the Western hemisphere "are charged with buying raw materials cheap from developing countries and selling manufactured goods dear, thus putting developing countries permanently in the role of debtors and dependents" (Walsh, 1974, p. 1144). They have suggested further that if the economic power of the developed nations could be reduced and theirs enhanced, the boost to development in their nations would dissipate problems such as hunger and poverty that are currently believed to be the result of too many people. At such time the population problem will disappear because, they argue, it is not really a problem after all. The socialist view, then, is that when all other social problems (primarily economic in origin) are taken care of, people will deal easily with any population problem if, indeed, one occurs. This was obviously the attitude of Friedrich Engels, who wrote in a letter in 1881, "If at some stage communist society finds itself obligated to regulate the production of human beings . . . , it will be precisely this and this society alone, which can carry this out without difficulty" (quoted in Hansen, 1970, p. 47).

Supporters of this position have some evidence to which they can appeal. In Russia, in the 1920s after the Communist revolution, Lenin repealed anti-abortion laws and abolished the restrictions on divorce in order to free women. The result was a fairly rapid decline in the birth rate (although it turned out to be too rapid for the government's taste and, in the 1930s, abortions were again made illegal). The Cuban response to a Marxist government was exactly the opposite. Shortly after the Cuban revolution in 1959, the crude birth rate soared from 27 births per 1000 population in 1958 to 37 per 1000 in 1962. A Cuban demographer, Juan Perez de la Riva, has explained that after the revolution, rural unemployment disappeared, new opportunities arose in towns, and an exuberant optimism led to a lowering of the marriage age and an abandonment of family planning (Stycos, 1971)—an ironically "Malthusian" response to a Marxist reorganization of society. Since then the birth rate has reestablished its prerevolutionary decline, facilitated by the easing of restrictions on abortion and the increasing availability of contraceptives (Hollerbach, 1980). The underlying causes of the more recent decline in fertility are similarly nonMarxist in nature: (1) increasing modernization, especially of the rural population; and (2) an economy that deteriorated after the initial flush of revolutionary success (Diaz-Briquets and Perez, 1981).

In sum, the evidence from Marxist countries such as Russia, Cuba and, indeed, China suggests that a revolution may alter the demographic picture of a nation, but the relationship to economic development is somewhat cloudy. Indeed, the previously Marxist, centrally planned economies of eastern Europe and Russia are those in which low rates of population growth have not been translated into commensurately high levels of living. On the contrary, there is widespread speculation that low birth rates in these countries have been a response to the economic limits placed on the family, especially scarce housing and limited consumer goods.

The idea that population growth and economic development may be only tenuously related to one another is also reflected in recent empirical work that seems to support a nonMarxist, but still "neutral," view of the relationship between population growth and per capita income. Using data for developing societies for the period of 1965 to 1984, Bloom and Freeman (1986) have concluded that despite rapid population growth, the labor markets in most developing countries were able to absorb the large population increase at the same time that per worker incomes were rising and productivity was increasing. In other words, a society's initial response to rapid population growth is to work harder to support its new members. But can that be sustained?

S. Preston (1986) has argued that it could be sustained in those areas that have sufficient natural resources and, more important, that are making increasingly efficient use of the major societal resource—human capital. This means not simply more people (as Simon seems to infer) but a better-educated and better-managed labor force, combined with improved methods of communication and transportation (the economic infrastructure). Small, oil-rich nations have been able to increase their per person wealth quickly through the sale of a highly valued resource, and they have done so without much concern over their high rates of population growth. At the same time, there are other areas of the world in which problems are so deeply rooted and resources are so scarce that every additional human being will likely aggravate the economic condition of the society. In Bangladesh, it appears that real agricultural wages in the 1970s were actually below the level of the 1830s, and much of this decline occurred after population growth accelerated in the 1950s (Preston, 1986). For such a country, it is fairly easy to make the case that population growth is probably detrimental to economic development.

IS POPULATION GROWTH DETRIMENTAL TO ECONOMIC DEVELOPMENT?

In the industrialized world it is popular to support the neoMalthusian position that economic development is hindered by rapid population growth. In its basic form, it is a simple proposition. Regardless of the reason for an economy starting to grow, that growth will not be translated into development unless the population is growing slower than the economy. An analogy can be made to business. A storekeeper will make a profit only if expenses (the overhead) add up to less than gross sales. For an economy, the addition of people involves expenses (a demographic overhead) in terms of feeding, clothing, sheltering, and providing education and other goods and services, and if the demographic overhead equals or exceeds the GNP, then no improvement (that is, no profit) will have occurred in the overall standard of living.

Let us illustrate the point further with a few numbers and a graph; see Figure 3.32. Between 1970 and 1980, the total national income of Mexico increased by a phenomenal 90% even after adjusting for inflation (United Nations, 1983). Yet during this time the population was increasing in size by more than one third, and as a result the rise in per person income was about 28%. Thus, population growth consumed 69% of the total improvement in national income. During that same period in the United States, national income rose by 27%, but only 11% of that rise was eroded by population increase. So, U.S. per capita income rose by 24%, nearly as much as in Mexico, but the economy had to grow only one-third as fast to accomplish the feat. Be aware, of course,

that income per person is only an average and, obviously, not everybody shared in that rise in wealth, either in the United States or in Mexico. This was particularly true in Mexico, where the economic rise could not be sustained. Indeed, it was based heavily on borrowing against future oil sales, but the price of oil fell and the Mexican economy stumbled badly in 1982. Of course, the population continued to increase, so per capita income in Mexico in 1988 was lower than it had been in 1980.

The situation seems simple enough. If populations were growing more slowly, then economic development could take place more easily; therefore, the neoMalthusians conclude that population growth is detrimental to economic development. Demeny (1981) has gone so far as to suggest that material progress in less developed nations ''is so hindered by current demographic patterns and prospective demographic developments that in the foreseeable future a further widening of the . . . income gap [between developed and less developed nations] is highly probable'' (p. 308). This position is so prevalent in Western society that we will discuss it in more detail, looking at the relationship from both sides.

Economic Development as a Source of Population Change

So far we have been looking at only one side of the relationship between population growth and economic development, that is, the consequences of economic change when population changes. If we are to fully understand the position that population growth is a hindrance to economic development, we need to look at the other side of the coin as well. Most available data suggest it was economic development that spurred the decline in mortality and eventually helped motivate the decline in fertility in the industrialized countries. In other words, economic development was a stimulus first to a rise in the rate of population growth and then to a slowing in its growth rate. It is this relationship that underlies the theory of the demographic transition and that is pointed to by Marxists in rebuttal of the neoMalthusian argument.

These relationships were clearly outlined by Coale and Hoover (1958) in a study that is unprecedented in its impact on theory and research on population growth and economic development. They note that economic

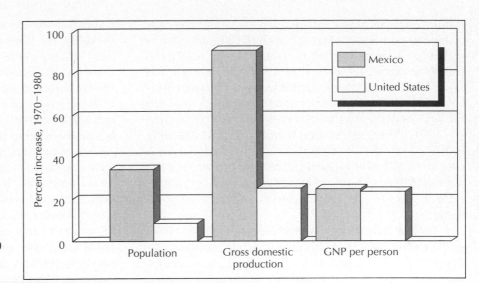

FIGURE 3.32
Population, gross domestic production, and gross national product per person for Mexico and the United States between 1970 and 1980. The rapid population growth caused the Mexican economy to work harder than the American economy for the same per person GNP between 1970 and 1980.
(Source: Weeks, 1994, p. 390.)

development led to a mortality decline in the developed countries and that it was also the economic development of those countries that has led to mortality declines in the rest of the world. This is true whether you accept our earlier suggestion that population growth may have initially stimulated the economic growth that led to the industrial revolution. The important point here is that the demographic transition theory suggests that the same economic development that lowered death rates will have within it the motivation for couples to lower birth rates. Yet, since the death rates in the less developed nations dropped as a result of someone else's economic development, why should we expect a rise in motivation to limit fertility without similar intervention? More important, why should we care whether fertility declines? What difference will it make to the future well-being of a population to continue with high birth and low death rates? The neoMalthusians, of course, answer that it may make a big difference.

Impact of Population Growth Rates on Economic Development

Population growth can make a difference in how many resources are consumed in the world, how much we have to pay for resources such as food and gasoline, and how much elbow room we have in the world. Population growth anywhere in the world may well threaten the quality of our own existence, as well as inhibit the improvement of life in those countries strug-

gling to develop economically under the burden of daily-increasing numbers of people. Actually, at least three different aspects of population change affect the course of economic development—rates of growth, population size, and age structure.

The starting point of economic development is the investment of capital. *Capital* represents a stock of goods used for the production of other goods rather than for immediate enjoyment. While capital may be money spent on heavy machinery or on an assembly line, it can better be thought of as anything we invest today to yield income tomorrow (Spengler, 1974). This means not only equipment and construction, but also investments in human capital, such as education, health, and, in general, the accumulation and application of knowledge. For an economy to grow, the level of capital investment must grow. Clearly, the higher the rate of population growth, the higher the rate of investment must be; this is what Leibenstein (1957) called the *population hurdle*. If a population is growing so fast that it overreaches the rate of investment, then it will be stuck in a vicious Malthusian cycle of poverty; that is, the economic growth will have been enough to feed more mouths but not enough to escape from poverty.

The problem is complicated by the fact that in today's rapidly growing populations poverty is already rampant, potentially impeding the ability of a nation to save enough money for the investment required to push its economy into rapid growth (Mason, 1988). Furthermore, most of the less developed nations in the world today have histories of being colonized and dependent on other countries for their economic and political fortunes. Often this has meant that "not only were economic problems neglected but the native leadership was trained in political conflict rather than economic statesmanship" (Kuznets, 1965, p. 182). Heavy reliance is therefore placed on *foreign capital,* money earned and saved by slower growing, richer nations. In those countries, of course, the initial capital investment required for development was much less in relative terms than it is today. There are several reasons for this, including the fact that the developed nations started out with considerably lower rates of population growth and did not have to jump into a well-advanced world economic system that requires high levels of technology to compete.

The less developed nations face a different set of world circumstances in trying to improve economically than did the developed nations. Many of these circumstances are probably (although not necessarily) hurdles. One example is energy—where will it come from? Vast amounts of energy, of course, are required for agriculture, manufacturing, transportation, and daily living. Water, wood, and coal were early resources that were cheaply converted to energy, but the world has become increasingly dependent on oil and, as you know, the price of oil has increased dramatically since the early 1970s. Countries that are hardest hit are, of course, the less developed nations that have few energy resources themselves. Only if oil-producing nations invest their profits in those countries that are hardest hit can the less developed nations hope to keep their economies growing. Marxists, on one hand, would argue that such an issue has no relevance to population growth, since a Communist world would distribute resources justly among those who need them. NeoMalthusians, on the other hand, would point out that regardless of the economic order prevailing in a nation or in the world, a rapidly growing population will make it harder for an economy to find its way than would a slow-growing population.

Impact of Population Size on Economic Development

As a population grows larger, the ability to garner resources for development may grow progressively smaller. This is true for individual nations just as it is true for the entire world. Although we can conjure up images of standing room only at the point at which all economic activity most certainly would have to stop, in reality, the limit is far less than that. But how much less? This is a question that is still puzzling yet has been the object of a good deal of scrutiny, as researchers have tried to define an optimum population size for the earth or for a particular country. In trying to determine an optimum size, we ask how large a population can be before the level of living begins to decline.

It is widely recognized that there are economies of scale associated with size; that is, too few people may retard economic development as surely as too many people might. The world is much better off economically with 5 billion people than it was with 1 billion. General Motors can produce a car far more cheaply than you could build one, precisely because they sell so many cars that they can afford the expensive assembly plants that reduce production costs per car. Although larger is sometimes more economical, a population may grow too large to be efficient or so large that, at a given level of living, it will exhaust resources. When it reaches that point, it is said to have exceeded its carrying capacity, or the size of population that could theoretically be maintained indefinitely at a given level of living.

The carrying capacity will vary according to which level of living you might choose for the world's population. The lower that level, the greater the number of people that can be indefinitely sustained. However, if the desired level of living is too high, you may well exceed the carrying capacity and start draining resources at a rate that will lead to their exhaustion. Once you have done that, you lower the long-run carrying capacity. For example, if you and everyone else in the world were content to live at the level of the typical South Asian peasant, then the number of humans that the world could carry would be considerably larger than if everyone were trying to live like the General Motors board of directors. Indeed, it is highly doubtful that the world has enough resources for 5 billion people to ever approach the successful business executive's level of living.

The most elaborate and well-known empirical investigation of an optimum population size for the world is the Club of Rome study, *Limits to Growth* (Meadows, 1974; Meadows, Meadows, Randers, and Behrens, 1972). Their study addressed the question of what size of population will enable the earth to maximize the socioeconomic well-being of its citizens.

After building a computer model simulating various paths of population growth and capital investment in resource development, this team of social scientists came to the conclusion that the world's population is so large and is consuming resources at such a prodigious rate that, by the year 2100, resources will be exhausted, the world economy will collapse, and the world's population size will plummet. After introducing their most optimistic assumption into the model, the Meadows' team described the potential result in the following way:

Resources are fully exploited, and 75 percent of those used are recycled. Pollution generation is reduced to one-fourth of its 1970 value. Land yields are doubled, and effective methods of birth control are made available to the world population. The result is a temporary achievement of a constant population with a world average income per capita that reaches nearly the present U.S. level. Finally, though, industrial growth is halted, and the death rate rises as resources are depleted, pollution accumulates, and food production declines. (Meadows et al., 1972, p. 147)

This was the gloomiest forecast of the impact of population size on economic development since the publication of Ehrlich's *Population Bomb* (1968), in which worldwide famine and war were seen as almost inevitable results of continued increases in the world's population. It was another variation on the Malthusian theme that the growth of population tends to outstrip resources. Taken at face value, it could be viewed as so discouraging that there would be no point in worrying any longer; the population that we have at hand is already too large and has too much momentum for continued growth to permit further sustained improvements in the human condition. Of course, as the authors of *Limits to Growth* freely acknowledge, their models do not replicate the complexities of the real world, or are they attempting to predict the future. Nonetheless, the study demonstrates the possibility that for the world as a whole, the optimum population is probably no larger than the present level.

The implications of this position are rather striking. Meadows et al. (1972) discuss the need for "dynamic equilibrium" in which population and capital remain constant, while other "desirable and satisfying activities of man—education, art, music, religion, basic scientific research, athletics, and social institutions . . ." also flourish (p. 180). In 1977, President Carter directed that a study be conducted "of the probable changes in the world's population, natural resources, and environment through the end of the century" (Council on Environmental Quality, 1980). The result was the "Global 2000" report, released in 1980, and containing equally dreary conclusions:

If present trends continue, the world in 2000 will be more crowded, more polluted, less stable ecologically, and more vulnerable to disruption than the world we live in now. . . . Barring revolutionary advances in technology, life for most people on earth will be more precarious in 2000 than it is now. . . . At present and projected growth rates, the world's population would reach 10 billion by 2030 and would approach 30 billion by the end of the twenty-first century. These levels correspond closely to estimates by the U.S. National Academy of Sciences of the maximum carrying capacity of the entire earth. (Council on Environmental Quality, 1980, pp. 1–3)

There is little comfort here for countries not yet fully developed, since for them, the implication is that they should cease growing demographically and hope for a redistribution of income from the wealthier nations.

Before you take those gloomy forebodings too seriously, let us look at a comment on the idea of a population decline in the wake of economic collapse. Van de Walle (1975) has noted that the *Limits to Growth* model assumes historical reversibility, which insinuates that mortality rates could rise in the future just as they declined in the past. Van de Walle feels that is an unwarranted assumption, since our knowledge of nutrition would not be lost, nor would we lose our ability to reorganize life around different standards of living that could maintain health despite a reduced supply of food. Let us be reminded of Simon's argument that specific resources, such as oil, may be finite, but in broad, generic terms, energy as a resource may be infinite. We just need to be clever enough to unlock the mysteries of the universe.

The Malthusian specter of sheer numbers of people exhausting available resources is rather overwhelming and, as a result, it disguises other, more subtle negative consequences that population growth has for economic development. These consequences are far more certain to be problems than are worldwide famine, war, or economic collapse. The consequences to which we refer are those associated with the age structure of rapidly growing populations.

Impact of Age Structure on Economic Development

A rapidly growing population has a young age structure. This means that a relatively high proportion of the population is found in the young ages. Two important economic consequences of this youthfulness are that the age structure affects the level of dependency, and it puts severe strains on the economy to generate savings for the investment needed for industry and for the jobs sought by an ever-increasing number of new entrants into the labor force.

DEPENDENCY

A major theme of the Coale and Hoover (1958) study of economic development (which we mentioned earlier in the chapter) is that a high rate of population growth leads to a situation in which the ratio of workers (people of working age) to dependents (people either too young or too old to work) is much lower than if a population is growing slowly. This means that in a rapidly growing society each worker will have to produce more goods (that is, work harder) just to maintain the same level of living for each person as in a more slow-growing society. This may seem like an obvious point. The father of six children will have to earn more money than the father of three just to keep his family living at the same level as the smaller family. But it goes deeper than that. A nation depends at least partially on savings from within its population to generate investment capital with which to expand the economy, regardless of the kind of political system that exists. With a very young age structure, money gets siphoned into taking care of more people (buying more food, and so on) rather than into savings per se (Kelley, 1973). As Mason (1988) has pointed out, a very old age structure may also be conducive to low levels of saving, since in the retirement ages people may be taking money out rather than putting it in.

ENTRY INTO THE LABOR FORCE

In a growing population, the number of prospective entrants into the labor force is also growing every year, as each group of young people matures to an economically active age. If economic development is to occur, the number of new jobs must at least keep pace with the number of people looking for them. The expansion of jobs is, of course, related to economic growth, which in turn relies on investment and may be harder to generate with a young age structure:

In countries like Pakistan and Mexico, for example, the work force will grow at about 3% per year (from 1985 and 2000). In contrast growth rates in the United States, Canada and Spain will be closer to 1% per year, Japan's work force will grow just 0.5%, and Germany's work force (including the Eastern sector) will actually decline (Johnston, 1991).

When the rate of labor force growth is slow, the new job entrants can simply step into the places vacated by people dying or retiring. As the rate of population growth increases and the age pyramid flattens out at the bottom, the ratio of new seekers to those leaving the labor force goes up rapidly. Bradshaw and Frisbie (1983) calculated that in Mexico, from 1990 and 2000, the economy will have to create 330 new jobs for every 100 people leaving through death or retirement just to maintain current levels of employment. In the United States, only 159 new jobs per 100 people leaving the labor force are projected to be needed during the same time period. Can the Mexican economy work that much harder than the United States economy? Maybe. If not, the pressure on Mexicans to migrate to the United States will, of course, continue.

Can the Three Positions Be Reconciled?

The fact that all three positions in the debate over population growth and economic development tend to be strongly held suggests that there are compelling elements of theoretical and empirical validity to each position. Blanchet (1991) has suggested that the reason for this may be that the relationship between the two factors cannot be described by a simple, straight line. In the early stages of economic development, population growth may simultaneously stimulate and be spurred by economic development. Sustaining that economic momentum in the short run may have little to do with population growth. It is more dependent on things like political stability, organizational efficiency, and other cultural and economic factors. However, to reach high levels of income in the long run may require that the rate of population growth slow substantially. Thus, the relationship between population growth and economic development changes in rough accordance with the stage of the demographic transition through which a country is passing.

The relationship is further complicated by the increasing globalization of the world economy. Most analyses of population growth and economic development deal with countries as separate and distinct entities. While that may have characterized the past few centuries, it seems less relevant today. We are in the midst of a massive intermingling of national economies and work forces [see, for example, Johnston (1991)]. As a consequence of high levels of economic interdependence among countries and high levels of labor migration throughout the world, it is now harder than ever to understand how population growth and economic development may be related to one another at any given moment and place.

Policy Implications of the Debate

We have tried to summarize the main aspects of each of the three major positions in the world debate over population growth and economic development. Ultimately, of course, each of these positions must be reconciled with the fact that population growth cannot continue for very long, regardless of its short-run impact on economic development. In the long run, the rate of population growth must go to zero, because the planet simply cannot tolerate growth indefinitely. Furthermore, virtually no one would dispute that as the growth rate of the world's population subsides, it is vastly preferable that it do so because the birth rate has declined, not because the death rate has increased. Thus, ultimately, fertility must decrease if the human condition is to be maximized. None of the three positions discussed is inconsistent with a long-run decline in fertility, but each has different approaches to dealing with birth rates in the short run.

If you believe that population growth is good for societal development, then you are probably a pronatalist and argue that birth control will have to wait until your country increases its population. If you are a Marxist, you will most likely suggest that the only reasonable use of birth control is to free women from the domination of men. If you are a neoMalthusian, you will no doubt argue that family planning is a necessary precursor to economic development, and that a few dollars spent on family planning may be worth a hundred dollars in industrial investment. In other words, you will believe that it is less costly and more economically advantageous to spend money preventing births than to spend it trying to raise and find jobs for more people (Demeny, 1971; Enke, 1960).

THE APPLICATION OF DEMOGRAPHIC INSIGHTS TO REGIONAL ECONOMIC AND ENVIRONMENTAL CHANGE

◉

Our analysis throughout the chapter has been focused either on countries (where development occurs) or on individuals (who are the producers and consumers of the goods and services involved in economic development). We conclude the chapter with an overview of applying demographic insights to: (1) the *firm*—the organization in which people produce the goods and services required for a society to improve its overall level of well-being, and (2) the *city*—the organization that plans and governs a society so it can function smoothly and efficiently.

Demographic Insights for the Firm

Businesses can be likened in many ways to the human beings who staff them—they are born, they grow and mature, they die, and, in between birth and death, some of them migrate. Each of these demographic processes is of crucial importance in economic geography because the number, size, and distribution of firms in an area helps to determine the economic well-being of the region. The study of these processes has been variously labeled as "organizational ecology" [see, for example, Hannan and Freeman (1989)] or, more recently, firmography (meaning the demography of the firm).

The organizational ecology approach has focused especially on the birth and survival of firms, relating both processes to the density of similar organizations. New, innovative types of businesses, created (by definition) in an area in which very few such firms exist, have a fairly high mortality rate. However, as the number of similar firms increases, the survivability of all increases because they come to be viewed as more legitimate members of the community and the demand for their goods and/or services goes up. In a sense, then, there is safety in numbers—an advantage to agglomeration that is well known to regional scientists. However, density may increase beyond a critical point that is conceptually similar to the carrying capacity. This will vary from one type of business to another, but when that point is reached, the competition for resources (such as customers) will discourage the birth of new companies and will speed up the demise of some existing companies (Hannan and Carroll, 1992). Just as some humans survive the plague while others die, some businesses survive the competitive process, especially those that are well-embedded in the community network (Baum and Oliver, 1992).

The regional pattern of births, deaths, and migration is of special interest to geographers since it brings into play the issue of land use patterns and transportation linkages. A recently constructed data base in the Netherlands has allowed Dutch geographers to track the birth, death, and movement of firms in that country with interesting results. Data reveal that the migration of firms is fairly limited and exhibits distinct distance-decay. Firms that move are likely to go only a short distance, especially out of the central city into the suburbs, but rarely do they make interregional moves. Furthermore, firms that are growing (the "healthier" firms) tend to be located closest to the major urban or suburban centers as well as near the major transportation arteries. Chapters 10 and 11 discuss the location and behavior of firms. These are not surprising findings, but they help to support the planning processes of urban policymakers. We now turn to that planning process.

Demographics Used in the Planning Process of Cities

Without proper planning, modern cities would wander aimlessly and be unable to ensure a high quality of life for their residents. This last section describes demographics used in the planning process by urban policymakers. The example is taken from San Diego, California, but represents similar efforts in 100 other cities throughout the world.

The population of the San Diego region increased by more than half a million people between 1980 and 1990, making it one of the fastest growing metropolitan areas in the United States. In 1984, the San Diego region reached 2 million residents. During 1987, the region experienced a growth rate of 3.6%, bringing the total population to 2,328,328 residents by the end of the year and to 2.5 million by 1990. San Diego County is currently the fifteenth largest metropolitan area in the nation in terms of population and the fifth largest legal city. It is the fourth largest county in the nation (behind Los Angeles, California; Cook, Illinois; and Harris, Texas). Overall, the county also experienced the third largest numeric increase in population between 1980 and 1988, behind Los Angeles, California and Maricopa County in Arizona. It is evident that such rapid development creates many problems in the provision of physical and social infrastructure at acceptable cost, in preserving the quality of the environment, in safeguarding the safety of the populace, and in many other areas.

The San Diego Association of Governments (SANDAG) is a quasi-government agency consisting of the County of San Diego in the southwestern corner of California, as well as 18 cities located therein. It has a board of directors of elected officials from each local jurisdiction and has three main functions:

- To promote regional planning among local governments
- To maintain a regional information system of demographic and economic data for businesses in the region
- To provide technical planning assistance to the 19 member government agencies

A key input to these functions is SANDAG's long-range forecast of population, housing, and economic activities for the entire San Diego region and for the smaller geographic areas within it. Locally, this product is known as the Regional Growth Forecast (RGF). The RGF has a wide variety of uses and applications and is based on a large computer geographic information system (GIS). It helps determine the need for transportation systems and the size and location of public facilities such as fire stations, schools, hospitals, and sewage and water treatment plants. The RGF is also used to assess water and energy demands for county agencies and geographic areas and can help predict the future quality of the region's air based on developmental aspects of land uses and population growth. Local governments that do not have a large planning and GIS capacity make use of the RGF and other products of local technical assistance from SANDAG as they evaluate housing needs for their constituencies and update their general

FIGURE 3.33
The San Diego Association of Governments produces a Regional Growth Forecast based on population, housing, employment, and income data from the U.S. Census and from locally generated surveys. Economic policy functions and historical data series, as well as land-use policy assumptions, are also used to produce the Regional Growth Forecast. The Regional Growth Forecast has a wide variety of uses and applications and is based on a large geographic information system (GIS). It helps determine the need for transportation systems and the size and location of public facilities, such as fire stations, schools, hospitals, and sewage and water treatment plants.
(Source: Parrott and Stutz, 1992, p. 248.)

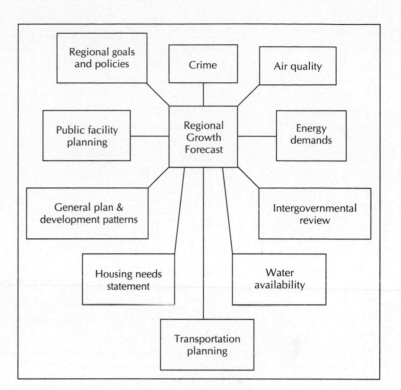

and community plans. Uses of the RGF are summarized in Figure 3.33.

There are two phases to the RGF process, and four major models are used to obtain the projected population and land-use values. The first phase uses the Demographic and Economic Forecasting Model (DEFM), which produces a forecast for the San Diego region as a whole. The second phase employs three allocation models to disaggregate the RGF tabulations to each of the geographic sub-areas in the county. Figure 3.34 presents the overall relationships between the various models, data bases, and GIS for the RGF system.

The first of the allocation models is the Basic Employment Allocation Model (BEM). It provides the future distribution of basic employment in the region, primarily on the basis of the policies of the local jurisdictions on industrial development and on the present split between industrial and service employment. This distribution then becomes the input to the Projective Land Use Model (PLUM). PLUM allocates other activities such as population, housing units, persons per household, and local service (or nonbasic employment) to sub-areas based on the location of the basic employment, the availability of usable land, physical accessibility to major activity centers, residential locations in the region, and land-use policies of the local jurisdictions.

This allocation is made for Zones for Urban Modeling (ZUM), which are collections of census tracts and traffic analysis zones within a local jurisdiction. The last regional model involved is the Sophisticated Allocation Process (SOAP). It allocates population and housing and employment activities to the smallest geographic level or the Master Geographical Reference Area (MGRA).

The files generated by the SOAP program allow forecast data to be retrieved in one of several ways, depending on the needs of each city within the county. SANDAG has developed report programs to display data either for a single variable or as a complete profile. Table 3.6 is an example report: it gives subregional forecast model outputs. This information can be retrieved and printed out for standard geographic areas such as traffic analysis zones (TAZ), census tracts or entire cities or for any user-defined geographic area. Results for the last of these are accomplished by a program which aggregates MGRA-level data to approximate to the nonstandard shape of the user-defined polygons. Forecast data can also be retrieved for any radial distance, driving distance or driving time from a given point (such as particular land parcel, street intersection, or major activity center such as a shopping center, stadium, or employment node). An example of output from the projection pro-

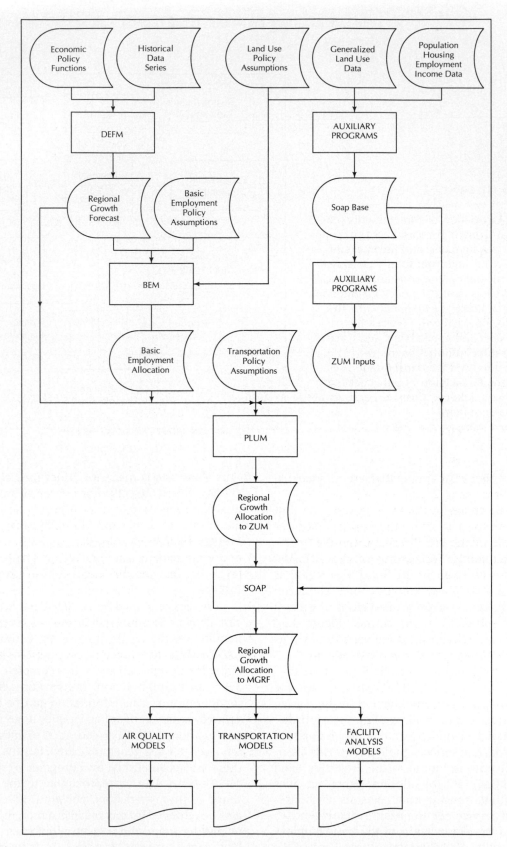

FIGURE 3.34

The San Diego Association of Governments Urban Development Modeling System Flowchart. The previous Regional Growth Forecast generated numbers and projection figures. This model uses the Regional Growth Forecast, economic policy functions, historical data series, land-use policy assumptions, and generalized land use data to project popula-

◈

Table 3.6
SANDAG Sub-Regional Forecast Model Outputs

Population	**Occupied housing units**
Total population	Total occupied units
Household	Single family
Group quarters	Multiple family
Civilian	Mobile homes
Military	Persons per household
Employment	**Land use**
Total employment	Total acres
Civilian	Developed
Basic	Single family
Agriculture (SIC 1–9)	Multiple family
Mining (SIC 10–14)	Mobile homes
Manufacturing (SIC 20–39)	Basic
Transportation (SIC 40, 42, 44–47)	Local serving
Wholesale (SIC 50, 51)	1986 Freeway
State and federal government (SIC 90, 91, 92)	Vacant developable
Hotel (SIC 70)	Low density single family
Basic military*	Single family
Local serving	Multiple family
Retail trade (SIC 52–59)	Mixed use
Retail services (SIC 72, 74–88)	Local serving
Business services (SIC 73, 89)	Industrial
Construction (SIC 15–17)	Unusable
Finance, insurance and real estate (SIC 60–67)	Redevelopment/infill acres
Local government (SIC 93, 94)	Single family to multiple family
Local serving transportation (SIC 41, 48–49)	Single family to mixed use
Uniformed military†	Single family to local serving
	Multiple family to mixed use
	Multiple family to local serving
	Single family intensification
	Multiple family intensification

* All military persons at their place of work, excluding persons living on-base in barracks or on-board ships. Civilian persons working on military bases are included in the State and federal government category.
† Basic military + military group quarters.
SIC: Standard Industrial Classification
Source: Parrott and Stutz. 1992. p. 251.

tion levels, basic employment allocation, and local employment allocation, which is economic activity for the local area, to produce land allocations for 10-, 20-, and 30-year planning horizons. Three outputs of such a model include not only land use in the future, but also air quality, models, transportation, infrastructure needs, and future public facility sightings.
(Source: Parrott and Stutz, 1992, p. 248.)

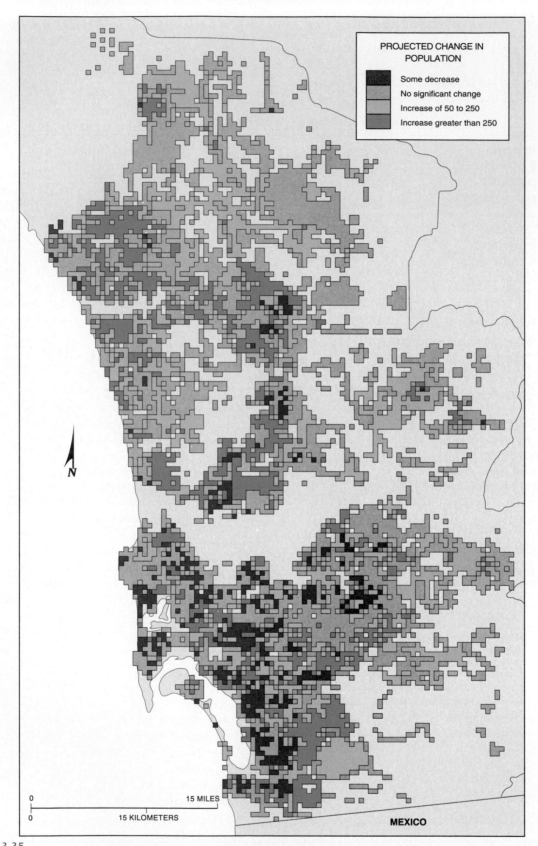

FIGURE 3.35
One of the outputs of the Urban Development Model, shown in Figure 3.34, is the projected change in San Diego County's population by one-quarter square mile grid scale. This map shows the change in population between 1986, the base year, and the year 2010. Downtown San Diego is located 25 kilometers north of the Mexican border and next to San Diego Bay. The greatest increase in population is projected to occur in the southern regions of San Diego, near the Mexican border, and in areas well to the north of downtown. These locations represent the greatest amount of available developable space. Unshaded areas to the east of San Diego represent mountainous terrain, while the large open area 45 kilometers north of the Mexican border represents a naval air station and environmentally sensitive wildlife habitats. *(Source: Parrott and Stutz, 1992, p. 252.)*

grams is Figure 3.35, which shows total change in population by grid cell between the base year 1986 and the year 2010.

SUMMARY

◈

Because people are the most important element in the world economy, it is essential to learn about population distribution, qualities, and dynamics. After considering the variable distribution of populations and their demographic, cultural, and economic characteristics, we examined the processes of population change. The components of population change are migration and natural increase. The principal force affecting world population distribution used to be migration, now it is natural increase.

Although the population growth rate is falling, the world's population is projected to increase for decades to come due to the large momentum built into the vast and youthful population of the Third World. As a result, there is considerable interest in the question of whether and how population growth affects economic growth. We compared and contrasted a number of viewpoints, including conservative and progressive. Some were optimistic; others, pessimistic. Most population experts believe that overpopulation deters growth, depletes natural resources, and destroys the environment. Hence, efforts must be made to slow population growth. Organized fertility-reduction programs, however, must be combined with development strategies that give poor people more control over the processes of social change that affect their lives. The organizational ecology of the firm examines its birth, migration, and survival. Finally, population projections have valuable roles to play in the planning and survival of cities.

◈

KEY TERMS

achieved characteristics
ascribed characteristics
baby boom
baby bust
birth rate
capital
carrying capacity
death rate
demographic equation
demographic transition
doubling time
fertility rate
geographic information system (GIS)
human capital
human suffering index
infant mortality rate
labor force
labor migration theory
law of diminishing returns
limits to growth
migration
natural increase

negative population growth
neoMalthusianism
optimum population size
organizational ecology
physiological density
population bomb
population composition
population distribution
population hurdle
population pyramid
primary activities
primate city
"push-and-pull" factors
rate of natural increase
regional growth forecast (RGF)
rule of seventy
secondary activities
tertiary activities
unemployment
urban growth
urbanization
zero population growth

◈

SUGGESTED READINGS

Baum, J., and Oliver, C. 1992. Institutional embeddedness and the dynamics of organizational populations. *American Sociological Review*, 57:540–559.

Birdsall, N. 1980. *Population Growth and Poverty in the Developing World*. Population Bulletin, Vol. 35, No. 5. Washington, DC: Population Reference Bureau.

Caldwell, J., and Caldwell, P. 1990. High fertility in sub-Saharan Africa. *Scientific American*, May:118–125.

Caldwell, J.; Orubuloye, I. O.; and Caldwell, P. 1992. Fertility decline in Africa: A new type of transition. *Population and Development Review*, 18(2):211–242.

Hannan, M., and Carroll, G. 1992. *Dynamics of Organizational Populations*. New York: Oxford University Press.

Hannan, M., and Freeman, J. 1989. *Organizational Ecology*. Cambridge, MA: Harvard University Press.

Jones, H. R. 1981. *Population Geography*. New York: Harper and Row.

Knox, P. L. 1994. *Urbanization: An Introduction to Urban Geography*. Englewood Cliffs, NJ: Prentice Hall.

Mamdani, M. 1973. *The Myth of Population Control*. New York: Monthly Review Press.

Merrick, T. W. 1986. *World Population in Transition*. Population Bulletin, Vol. 41, No. 1. Washington, DC: Population Reference Bureau.

National Research Council. 1986. *Population Growth: Consequences and Policy Implications*. Washington, DC: National Academy Press.

Newman, J. L., and Matzke, G. E. 1984. *Population: Patterns, Dynamics, and Prospects*. Englewood Cliffs, NJ: Prentice Hall.

Ogden, P. 1984. *Migration and Geographical Change*. Cambridge, England: Cambridge University Press.

Parrott, R., and Stutz, F. P. 1992. Urban GIS applications. In Maguire, Goodchild, and Rhind (eds.), *GIS: Principles and Applications*. London, England: Longman.

Rubenstein, J. M. 1994. *An Introduction to Human Geography*, 4th ed. New York: Macmillan.

Sauvey, A. 1961. *Fertility and Survival: Population from Malthus to Mao Tse Tung*. New York: Chatto.

Simon, J. L. 1986. *Theory of Population and Economic Growth*. Oxford, England: Basil Blackwell.

Stutz, F. P. 1992a. Urban and regional planning. In T. Hartshorn (ed.), *Interpreting the City: An Urban Geography*. New York: John Wiley & Sons.

Stutz, F. P. 1992b. Maquiladoras branch plants: Transportation—labor cost substitution along the U.S./Mexican border. In *Snapshots of North America*. Washington, DC: 27th Congress of the International Geographical Union Official Book.

Stutz, F. P. 1992c. San Diego: The next high amenity Pacific Rim world city. In Blakeley and Stimson (eds.), *The New City of the Pacific Rim*. Berkeley: University of California, Institute of Urban and Regional Development.

Stutz, F. P. 1992d. Labor shed of Tijuana in relation to the U.S. mexican border. In T. Hartshorn (ed.), *Interpreting the City: An Urban Geography*. New York: John Wiley & Sons.

Stutz, F. P.; Parrott, R.; and Kavanaugh, P. 1992. Charting urban space-time population shifts using trip generation models. *Urban Geography*, 13(5):468–475.

Thomas, I. 1980. *Population Growth*. London: Macmillan Education.

Weeks, J. 1994. *Population: An Introduction to Concepts and Issues, Updated Fifth Edition*. Belmont, CA: Wadsworth.

RESOURCES AND ENVIRONMENT

⬧

OBJECTIVES

- To describe the nature, distribution, and limits of the world's resources

- To examine the nature and extent of world food problems and to make you aware of the difficulties of solving them

- To describe the distribution of strategic minerals and the time spans for their depletion

- To consider the causes and consequences of the "energy crisis" and to examine present and alternative energy options

- To examine the nature and causes of environmental degradation

- To compare and contrast "growth-oriented" and "balance-oriented" life-styles

⬧

Mining coal—the world's most abundant fossil fuel.
(Source: International Labour Office.)

Our prosperity depends on the availability of natural resources and the quality of the environment. Yet economic activities in developed countries, and increasingly in underdeveloped countries, are depleting resources and degrading the environment. How did we get into this situation? What can be done to effectively manage resources and protect the environment?

According to Marxists, the world got into trouble under the capitalist law of accumulation. They argue that mindless exploitation of nature pushes society to the limits of its resource base. Although technological change may roll back resource limitations, capitalist accumulation soon reaches these new limits. But is capitalist resource use bound to be wasteful, polluting, and socially irresponsible? And is the situation any better in socialist economies? In the former Soviet Union, there is widespread evidence of oil spills, extinction of fishing grounds, high levels of air pollution, and considerable loss of topsoil. There is also evidence that the battle is being lost to conserve water, soil, and forest resources

in socialist Mozambique, Vietnam, and north Korea. Marxists counter this evidence by saying that, ideally, socialism has the capacity to make resource use less wasteful and more socially acceptable.

Those who do not endorse a Marxist view may be divided into two broad groups: resource optimists and pessimists. The *resource optimists* believe that economic growth in a capitalist society can continue indefinitely; they see "no substantial limits . . . either in raw materials or in energy that the price structure, product substitution, anticipated gains in technology and pollution control cannot be expected to solve" (Notestein, 1970, p. 20). In contrast, *pessimists* assert that there are limits to growth imposed by the finiteness of the earth—by the fact that air, water, minerals, space, and usable energy sources can be exhausted or overloaded. They believe these limits are near and, as evidence, point to existing food, mineral, and energy shortages and to areas now beset by deforestation and erosion. To pessimists, a world with a projected population of 10 billion in the year 2100 is unthinkable. Population and economic growth ought to stop.

Some scholars think that academic debate on resources and the environment is counterproductive, evading practical issues that demand our immediate attention. Geographer Thomas Vale (1985) argued that resource and environmental problems do not yield to ideological theories and solutions. For example, the purpose of Marxists in Central America is to create more egalitarian societies, but the achievement of that goal will not save the rain forests. Continued population growth will require, for food production, the rain forests to be "freed" from destruction by the removal of foreign interests. Improvements in the diets of people in Central America will also hasten the need for cleared forestland. Saving the forest environment is only possible if population growth ceases.

Vale recommends that we keep our purposes in mind and try to understand how to achieve our ends. If our purpose is to create a habitable world for generations to follow, how can we redirect present and future output to serve that end? One solution is to transform our present "growth-oriented" life-style, which is based on a goal of ever-increasing growth, to a "balance-oriented" life-style designed for harmony and endurance. A *balance-oriented life-style* would include an equitable and modest use of resources, a production system compatible with the environment, and small-scale technology. The aim of a balance-oriented world economy is maximum human well-being with a minimum of material consumption. Growth occurs, but only

The earth is our only suitable habitat.
(*Source: NASA/U.S. Geological Survey EROS Data Center, Sioux Falls, South Dakota.*)

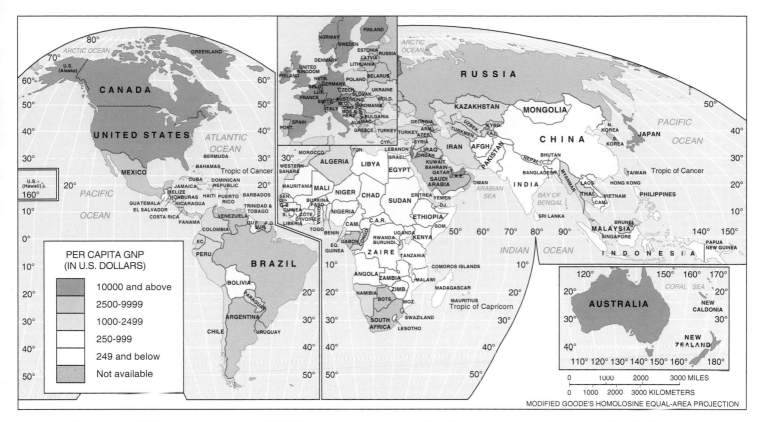

ABOVE: The annual GNP per capita exceeds $15,000 in most relatively developed countries, compared to less than $1000 in most developing countries. Several petroleum-rich countries in southwestern Asia have relatively high GNPs per capita, although by other measures they may rank among the developing countries. The difference in annual GNP per capita between relatively developed and developing countries has grown since the early 1980s.

BELOW: Physiological density refers to the number of people per unit area of agricultural land. The higher the physiological density, the greater the pressure people exert on the land and food resources of a country. Geographers use physiological density rather than population density as a true measure of the population pressure on the land because it shows the potential availability of needed food resources.

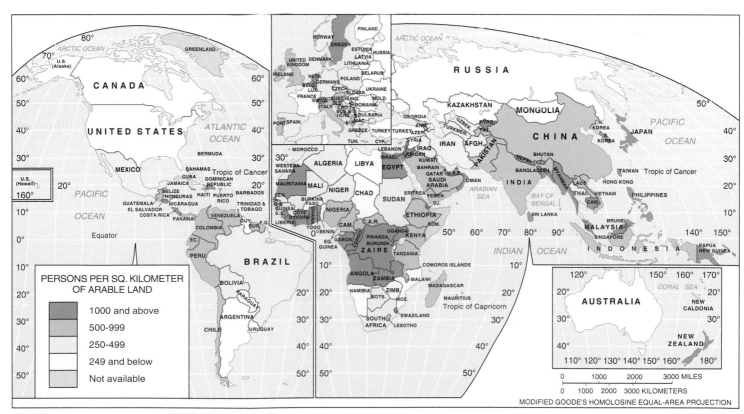

1.1

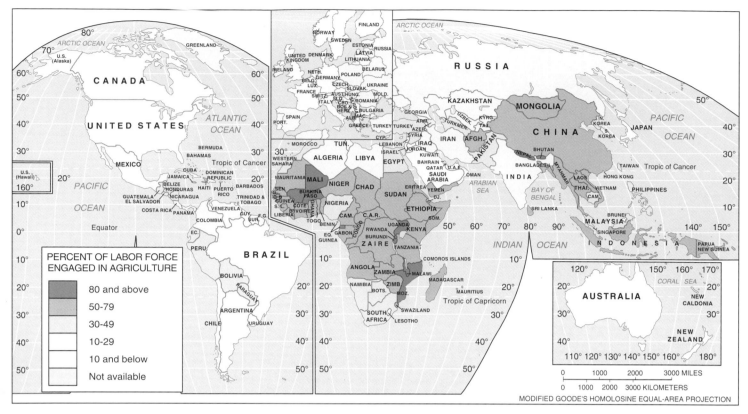

ABOVE: Note that the more economically advanced nations have a lower portion of the labor force engaged in agriculture. The United States, Canada, Europe, and Australia are examples. The most important priority for people throughout the world is to secure enough food to survive and prosper. Sixty percent of all workers in the world are engaged in agricultural pursuits; less than 4% of the workers in Europe and Anglo-America are engaged in agriculture. Most of these people earn their living working in offices, stores, and factories.

BELOW: The natural annual increase is the rate of growth of a population for a particular year. The fastest growing areas of the world include Africa, Central America, and Southwest Asia. In these countries, growth rates exceed 2.5%, with a number of countries in Central America and Africa actually exceeding 3% per year. Three percent growth per year does not seem like a high growth rate; however, it indicates a total population doubling time for a country to be only 23 years. The natural increase in Europe is only 0.2 percent.

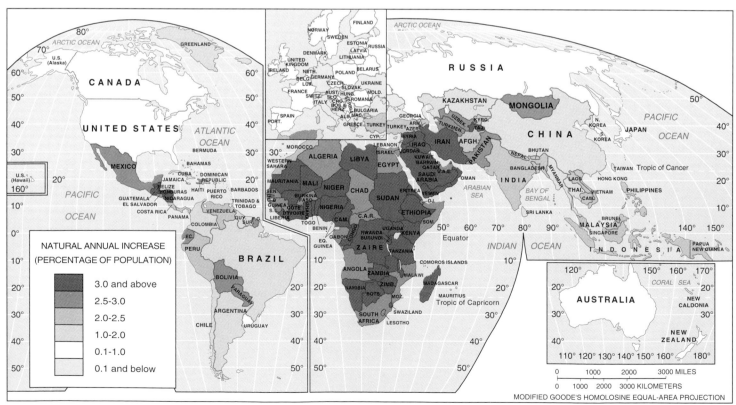

1.2

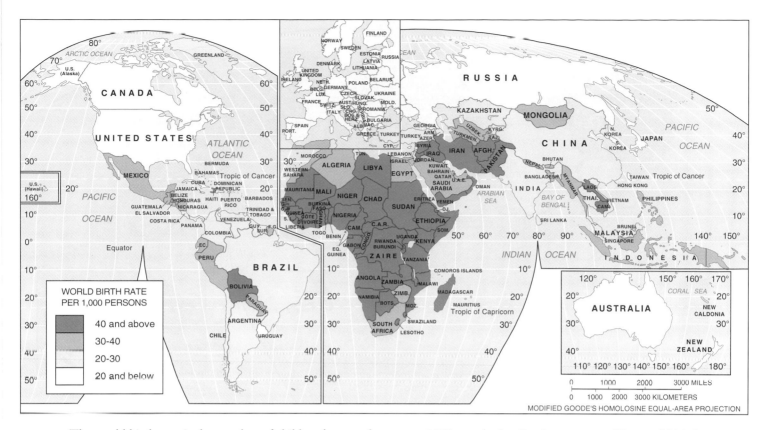

ABOVE: The world birth rate is the number of children born each year per 1000 people that live in a country. The world birth rate closely mirrors the natural annual increase. Crude birth rate measures a country's population as a whole and does not study separate rates of birth for women of different age groups, or by income or racial character. Again, Central America, Africa, and Southwest Asia lead the world in crude birth rate.

BELOW: Infant mortality rates are the number of deaths of infants under the age of 1 year per 1000 live births for a country. World infant mortality rates averaged approximately 75 per 1000 for 1993. The United States, for example, averaged 8 deaths per 1000 live births, but several nations had lower infant mortality rates. As with natural annual increase and world birth rates, infant deaths per 1000 live births are related to development.

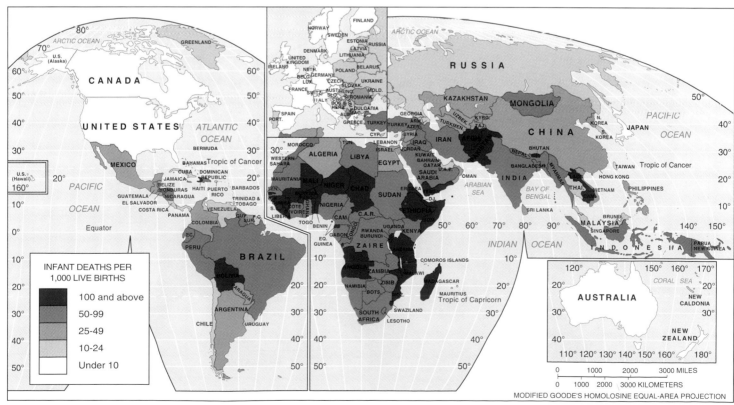

1.3

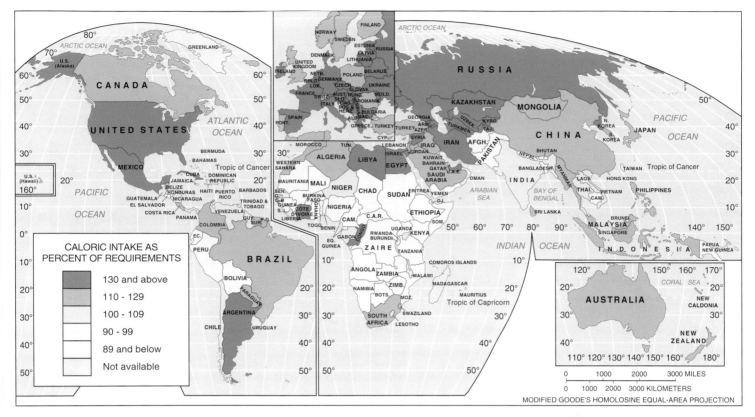

ABOVE: Highly developed regions of the world receive, on the average, 130% of the daily caloric requirements (2400 calories per day) as set by the U.S. Food and Agricultural Organization (FAO). Some countries in South America and south Asia, and many countries in Africa, receive less than 90% of the daily caloric requirements needed to sustain body and life. Averages must be adjusted according to age, gender, and body size of the person and by regions of the world. Averages also hide destitute subpopulations.

BELOW: The greatest number of proven petroleum reserves exists in countries of the Middle East surrounding the Persian Gulf, in particular the Arabian Peninsula. This area includes more than 50% of all proven world reserves. Mexico and Venezuela also show a disproportionately large share of proven reserves.

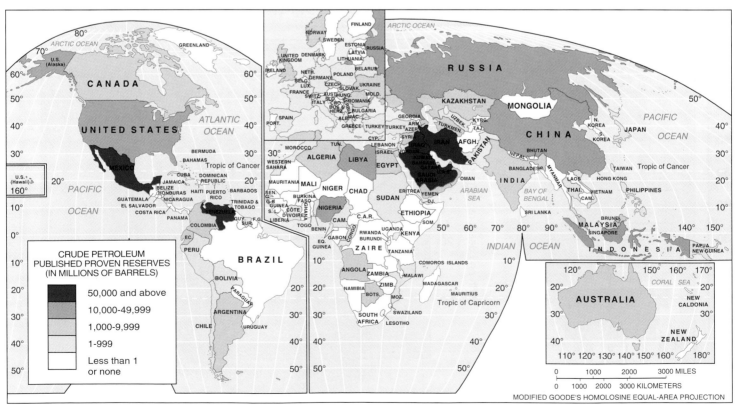

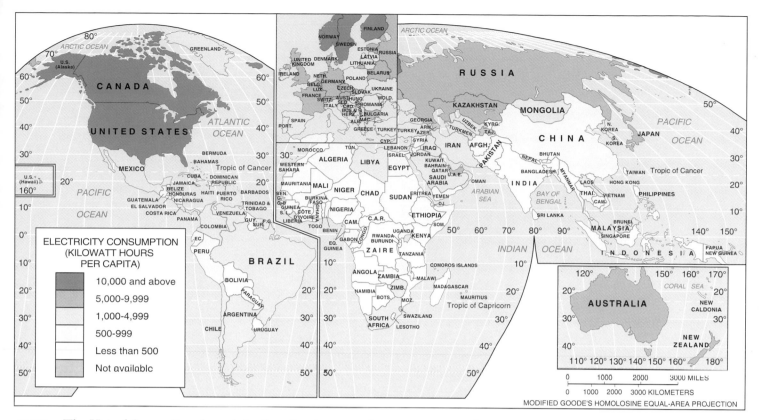

ELECTRICITY CONSUMPTION (KILOWATT HOURS PER CAPITA)

- 10,000 and above
- 5,000-9,999
- 1,000-4,999
- 500-999
- Less than 500
- Not available

MODIFIED GOODE'S HOMOLOSINE EQUAL-AREA PROJECTION

ABOVE: The United States, Canada, and the Scandinavian countries consume more electricity per capita than any other countries. When the electricity usage of the United States, Canada, Europe, and Russia are combined, 75% of electricity usage in the world is accounted for, but these same countries account for only 20% of the world's population. By comparing this map to the map of crude petroleum reserves, deficit areas of the world, such as Europe and Japan, can be seen.

BELOW: The United States, followed by the former Soviet Union and China, produce more coal than any other countries. Australia, India, and South Africa also produce substantial amounts of coal. Since coal is bulky and more costly to transport than liquid oil, less coal is shipped internationally to supply world energy demands. Alternative energy sources, such as wind power, geothermal, and solar-based approaches offer hope, however, until radical breakthroughs in energy technology occur, coal will remain America's greatest energy source.

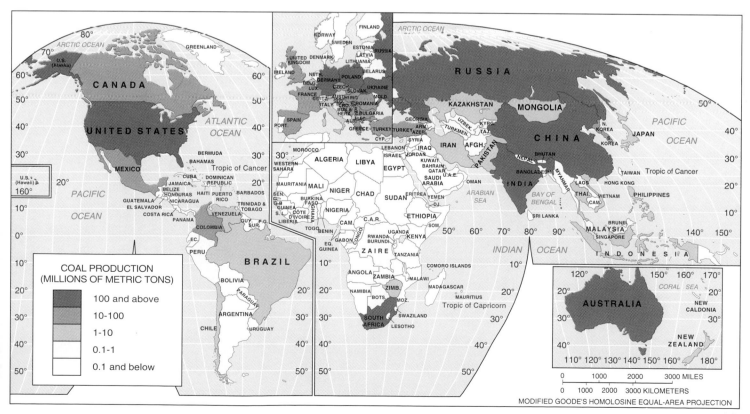

COAL PRODUCTION (MILLIONS OF METRIC TONS)

- 100 and above
- 10-100
- 1-10
- 0.1-1
- 0.1 and below

MODIFIED GOODE'S HOMOLOSINE EQUAL-AREA PROJECTION

1.7

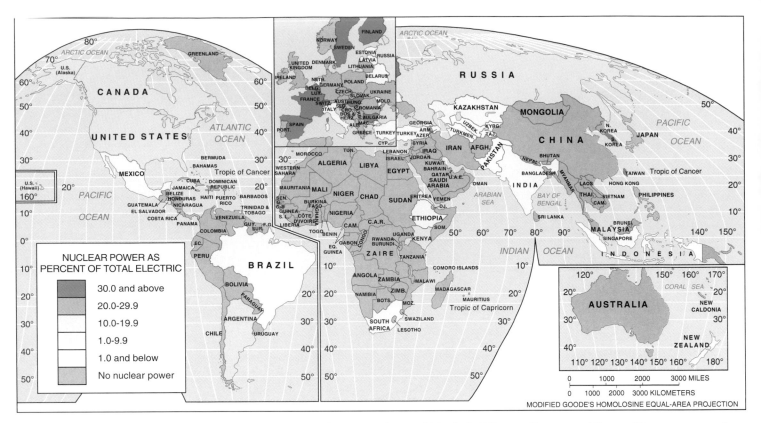

NUCLEAR POWER AS
PERCENT OF TOTAL ELECTRIC

30.0 and above
20.0-29.9
10.0-19.9
1.0-9.9
1.0 and below
No nuclear power

MODIFIED GOODE'S HOMOLOSINE EQUAL-AREA PROJECTION

ABOVE: The most important areas of nuclear energy production in the world include Western Europe and Japan. These are areas that have a relatively small amount of fossil fuels to satisfy local demand for energy. In Europe, for example, France, Germany, and the Scandinavian countries of Sweden and Finland produce more than 50% of their electrical energy from nuclear sources. Nuclear power is much less prevalent in the developing nations of the world because of extremely high-scale economies, or start-up costs, and the need for expensive uranium fuels. Public sentiment seems to be against future use of nuclear power. Besides the possibility of melt-down, the problems of nuclear waste are immense.

BELOW: Areas of dominant influence (ADIs) are based on radio, television, and newspaper advertising. ADI for cities approximates the breaking point between cities based on the law of retail gravitation model as applied to adjacent pairs of cities.

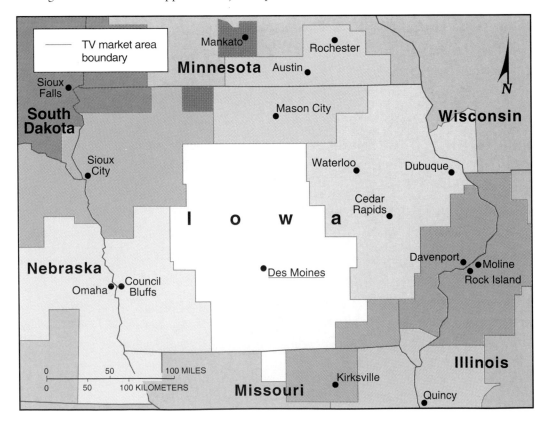

1.8

growth that truly benefits people. However, what societies, rich or poor, are willing to dismantle their existing systems of production to accept a life-style that seeks satisfaction more in quality and equality than in quantity and inequality? Are people who are programmed for maximum consumption by a value system constantly reinforced through advertising willing to change their ways of thinking and behaving?

This chapter, which discusses growth-oriented versus balance-oriented philosophies of resource use, deals with the complex components of the population-resources issue. Have population and economic growth rates been outstripping supplies of food, minerals, and energy? What is likely to happen to the rate of demand of food, minerals, and energy? What is likely to happen to the rate of demand for resources in the future? Could a stable population of 10 billion be sustained indefinitely at a reasonable standard of living utilizing currently known technology? These are the salient questions with which this chapter is concerned.

RESOURCES AND POPULATION

◈

Popular perception appreciates the need to reduce population growth, but overlooks the need to limit economic growth that massively exploits resources. A maximum-growth economy assumes a world that can tolerate rampant waste, unlimited pollution, and indestructible ecosystems.

The developed world has suffered from a view of limitless resources; yet, its affluent way of life is threatened in a world economy under great stress. The industrial West is liquidating the resources on which it was built. Underdeveloped countries are aggravating the situation. Their growing populations put increasing pressures on resources and the environment, and their governments aspire to affluence through Western-style urban industrialization. But the production technology and patterns of consumption in the developed countries depend on the intensive use of energy resources. Poor countries do not have the means for running the high-energy systems that are manifest in Western countries.

Even by conservative estimates, a middle-class "basket of goods" requires six times as much in resources as a basket of essential or basic goods. The expansion of GNP through the production of middle-class baskets means that only a small minority of people in poor countries would enjoy the benefits of economic growth. There are resource constraints that prevent the large-scale production of middle-class goods for swelling numbers of people in underdeveloped countries.

However, measures of material well-being (e.g., per capita incomes, calories consumed, shelter and clothing, life expectancy) show that people in many countries are better off today than their parents or grandparents. Consider per capita income growth rates between 1960 and 1990. Virtually every country recorded some improvement in per capita income. The lowest growth rates occurred among the poorest Third World countries. The highest growth rates occurred not in First World countries, but among the wealthiest Third World countries. The largest increases in per capita income occurred in Brazil and in newly industrializing countries on the western margins of the Pacific.

There are problems with this optimistic assessment. These improvements are averages; they say nothing about the distribution of material well-being. In addition, the gap between rich and poor countries widened during the period. In 1960, per capita income in Pakistan was $104, whereas that in the United States was $5484. By 1992, even though Pakistan's per capita income had grown almost as rapidly as that of the United States in the interim, the levels were $400 and $23,560—a gap between the two countries more than $15000 greater than in 1960. The growing gap in per capita income between developed and underdeveloped countries is due in part to the more rapid population growth in underdeveloped countries, which reduces the benefits of economic growth.

Another difficulty is that the world may be achieving improvements in material well-being at the expense of future generations. This would be the case if economic growth were using up the world's resource base or environmental carrying capacity faster than new discoveries and technology could expand them.

Carrying Capacity and Overpopulation

Population growth and increasing use of resources in traditional ways cannot continue indefinitely. If present trends of population growth and resource depletion continue, the world could eventually be brought into a stationary state known as carrying capacity. *Carrying capacity* refers to the population that can be supported by available resources. A population decline occurs when population outstrips resources available for sustaining life. Decline may result from overpopulation relative to the food supply or to the rate of consumption of energy and resources.

The immediacy of the population-resources problem is much debated. Pessimists believe that the world will enter a stationary state. They point to the food crisis and famine in parts of Ethiopia and adjacent countries in 1984 as a result of overpopulation. In contrast, optimists believe in the saving grace of modern technology. Technological advances have increased agricultural yields; they have enabled us to produce more electric power. In the last 200 years, the world's carrying capacity has been raised, and future technical innovations hold the promise of raising carrying capacity still further. Modern technologies use fewer resources, allow fewer wastes per unit of product than old ones, and will even solve pollution problems.

Economist Ernest Schumacher (1973) sounds a note of caution. In his view, a completely technical solution to the population-resources problem may never be realized. Technologies may be unable to cope with the critical matter of supplying growing populations with raw materials for existence in light of the second law of thermodynamics. This law holds that the amount of energy in the universe is fixed, but the amount of work that can be derived from that energy is irreversibly diminished. For example, once gasoline is burned in the engine of an automobile, its value as a source of useful energy is gone forever.

The answer to the population-resources problem also depends on the standard of living deemed acceptable. To give people an essential basket of goods instead of a middle-class basket of goods would roll back resource limitations. The establishment of a basic goods economy depends on our capacity to develop alternatives to the high-energy, material-intensive production technologies characteristic of the industrial West. Already, there are outlines of a new theory of productive resources based on the conservation of energy, materials, and capital that is suited to the needs of a basic goods economy. Some of the main ideas are: (1) the adoption of a sun-based organic agriculture to replace energy-intensive chemical agriculture; (2) the conservation of energy through the harvesting of renewable sources of energy; (3) the use of appropriate or small-scale technology, labor-intensive methods of production, and local raw materials; and (4) the decentralization of production in order to increase local self-reliance and minimize the transport of materials. These productive forces would minimize the disruption of ecosystems

Water for Chad. Water is an important ingredient to sustain human life. Fifty percent of the world's people do not have adequate, clean water. Villagers in Chad are delighted as the water pours out of a new water system they have worked together to construct. The system is part of an anti-desertification project funded by the United Nations Development Program and the U.S. government. Acute water shortage in many parts of the world requires solutions that will be costly, technically difficult, and politically sensitive. Water scarcity contributes to the impoverishment of many countries in east and west Africa, threatening their ability to increase food production fast enough to keep pace with modern population growth.
(Source: Ruth Massey/UNDP.)

and engage the unemployed in useful, productive work. Current trends indicate that economies engaging people in useful labor that produces essential goods for human consumption face neither unemployment nor overpopulation. The availability of secure supplies of basic goods will also provide the best motivation for reducing family size. Most elites in Third World countries appear unwilling, however, to place top priority on the production and distribution of goods to satisfy basic human needs.

Optimum Population and the Quality of Life

The best possible world would be one with an optimum population that permits progressive improvements in human well-being; however, what is optimum for one country may not be for another. Furthermore, governments of rich industrial countries set the terms for what is optimal or suboptimal in relation to resources. And yet it is only through the operation of the world economy that wealthy countries can appropriate the resources necessary to support the large numbers of people who enjoy middle-class life-styles.

In simple terms, human well-being is a function of the relationship between population and the ability to make efficient use of resources. If we assume fixed resources and population growth in a country, then average well-being diminishes as resources are consumed. In reality, the situation is much more complex. Other factors are involved—some make the situation better, others make it worse. For example, improved extraction techniques, recycling, and finding substitutes for resources decrease the rate of resource depletion, but increasing the per capita rate of consumption and misuse of technology can accelerate resource depletion and increase pollution.

TYPES OF RESOURCES AND THEIR LIMITS

All economic development comes about through human labor and skills. In order to produce goods and services, we need to obtain natural resources. What are natural resources and what are their limits?

Resources and Reserves

Resources have meaning only in terms of technical and cultural appraisals of nature and must be defined with reference to a particular level of development. *Resources*, designated by the entire box in Figure 4.1, include all the materials of the environment that may some day be used under specified technological and socioeconomic conditions. Because these conditions are always subject to change, we can expect our determina-

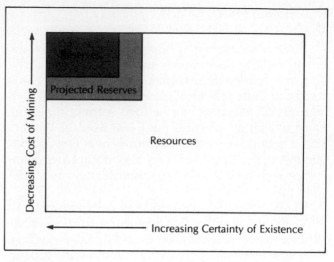

FIGURE 4.1

Classification of resources. Resources include all materials of the environment that may some day be used under future technological and socioeconomic conditions. Reserves are resources that are known and available, with current technologies and at current prices. Projected reserves are reserves based on expected future price trends and technologies available.

tions of what is useful to also change. For example, oil bubbling to the surface in ancient Persia was a nuisance, but it is a vital source of energy and export earnings to modern Iranians. Although it is hard to imagine, iron ore may eventually cease to be useful when replaced by some other material.

At the other end of the extreme are reserves, designated by the upper left-hand box in Figure 4.1. *Reserves* are quantities of resources that are known and available for economic exploitation with current technologies and at current prices. A financial analogy clarifies the distinction between reserves and resources. Reserves are liquid assets, like money in a checking account, and resources are frozen assets or future income that cannot be used for this month's car payments.

When current reserves begin to be depleted, the search for additional reserves is intensified. Estimates of reserves are also affected by changes in prices and technology. If prices increase or costs of mining decrease, it becomes feasible to mine lower grade ores; consequently, the quantities available for current exploitation must be reassessed. *Projected reserves* represent estimates of the quantities likely to be added to reserves because of the discoveries and changes in prices and technologies projected to occur within a specified period, for example, 50 years.

Renewable and Nonrenewable Resources

Natural resources may be classified in various ways, but the primary distinction is made between nonrenewable and renewable resources. *Nonrenewable resources* consist of finite masses of material, such as fossil fuels and metals, which cannot be used without depletion. They are, for all practical purposes, fixed in amount. This is because they form very slowly over time. Consequently, their rate of use is very important. Large populations with high per capita consumption of goods deplete these resources fastest.

Many nonrenewable resources are completely altered or destroyed by use; petroleum is an example. Other resources, such as iron, are available for recycling. Recycling possibilities expand the limits on the sustainable use of a nonrenewable resource. At present, these limits are very low in relation to current mineral extraction.

Renewable resources are those resources capable of yielding output indefinitely without impairing their productivity. They include soil, vegetation, air, and water. Renewal is not automatic, however; resources can be depleted and permanently reduced by misuse. Productive fishing grounds can be destroyed by exploitation. Fertile top soil, destroyed by erosion, can be difficult to restore and impossible to replace. The future of agricultural land is guaranteed only when production does not exceed its maximum sustainable yield. The term maximum sustainable yield means maximum production consistent with maintaining future productivity of a renewable resource.

The misuse of resources is often described in terms of the *tragedy of the commons* (Hardin, 1968). This metaphor refers to the way public resources are ruined by the isolated actions of individuals. We appear to be unwilling to use a minimum share of a resource. People who fish, when there is no rule of capture law, are likely to try to catch as many fish as they can, reasoning that if they don't, others will. Similarly, dumping waste and pollutants on public waters and land or into the air is the cheapest way to dispose of worthless products. There is an apparent unwillingness to dispose of these materials by more expensive means unless mandated by law.

Limits of Natural Resources

The limitations natural resources place on growth can be illustrated with two simple models: one, for a renewable resource; the other for a nonrenewable resource.

Renewable Resource

Let us assume that: (1) a renewable resource, such as soil, produces a single consumer good, food; (2) maximum sustainable yield per hectare is fixed; and (3) cultivated land and food production grow exponentially. Eventually, no more arable land can be freed for cultivation without destroying all of the surrounding forest environment, so that the economy reaches point C (Figure. 4.2). The best strategy would be to stop growth at C and maintain maximum sustainable yield thereafter, but this is difficult to accomplish in practice. The physical limits are often reached quickly. For example, when production increases at an annual rate of 4% per annum, the doubling time is only about 18 years. Arable land soon becomes a scarce factor of production. Furthermore, farmers at C, accustomed to increasingly high outputs, will take whatever steps they feel necessary to maintain the improvement. Thus, they clear additional forest land and overcrop existing arable land, ruining the precious soil. To avoid this outcome, a better strategy would be to slow growth at say, B, and follow path ABD or, more cautiously, path ABE.

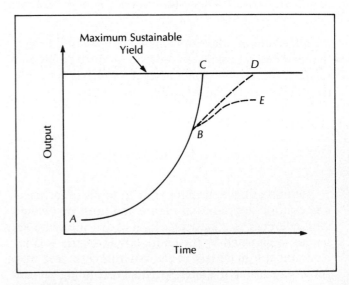

FIGURE 4.2
Limits to growth of a renewable resource.
(Source: Based on Lecomber, 1975, p. 38.)

FIGURE 4.3
Limits to growth of a nonrenewable resource. Nonrenewable resources include minerals, such as iron, copper, and bauxite and fossil fuels, such as oil, natural gas, and coal. They become depleted with use and are not replenished by nature, as is the case with renewable resources. Nonrenewable resources will eventually be exhausted because of the earth's finite supply. The goal is to slow the rate of use of nonrenewable resources so that substitutes can be developed. Reducing population growth rates, reducing use rates, and increasing efficiency of extraction are temporary measures, which prolong nonrenewable resource life.

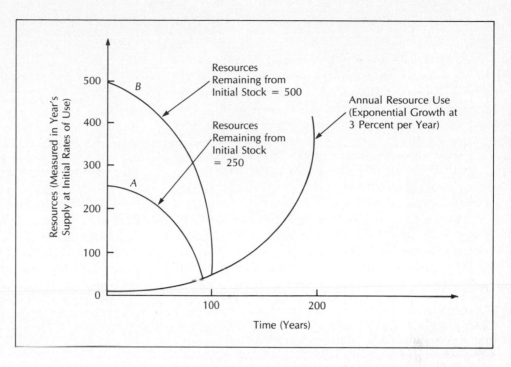

Nonrenewable Resource

Let us assume that our nonrenewable resource is coal and that population and resource productivity are fixed. Coal supplies are soon exhausted (Figure 4.3). At 3% annual growth in mining activity, the depletion time for a 250 years' supply of coal is 80 years (curve A). Even if coal supplies are doubled, the depletion time is postponed only 25 years (curve B).

These two models demonstrate that resources, both renewable and nonrenewable, are exhaustible. However, the models project resource depletion on the assumption that resource productivity is fixed. We know, however, that resource productivity can be expanded by technical progress or by substitution of other resources.

FOOD RESOURCES

◈

People need access to enough food at all times for an active and healthy life. Food security is also important because good nutrition is an investment in the productivity of a country's population. Although there are enough food resources to provide for all, there is no food security for hundreds of millions of people. Somewhere between 340 and 730 million people (excluding China whose government refuses to release much demographic information) suffer from chronic malnutrition (lack of protein, vitamins, and essential nutrients), and an even larger number suffer from undernutrition (lack of calories). These people are concentrated in the underdeveloped world (Figure 4.4), but they are increasingly apparent in the developed world.

Nutritional Quality of Life

The gulf between the well-fed and the hungry is vast. Average daily calorie consumption is 3300 in developed countries and 2100 in underdeveloped countries. The largest number of calories available is in Ireland and the lowest number available is in Ghana (Table 4.1). A similar pattern emerges in considering "calorie requirement satisfaction." This measure is defined as the calories needed per day to sustain a person at normal levels of activity and health. People in Ghana eat only 68% of what they need compared to Ireland's 162%. But these are average figures. There are people on the breadline in Ireland, and there are those who have enough to eat in Ghana. Averages mask extremes of *undernourishment* and overconsumption.

Even with a high calorie satisfaction, people may

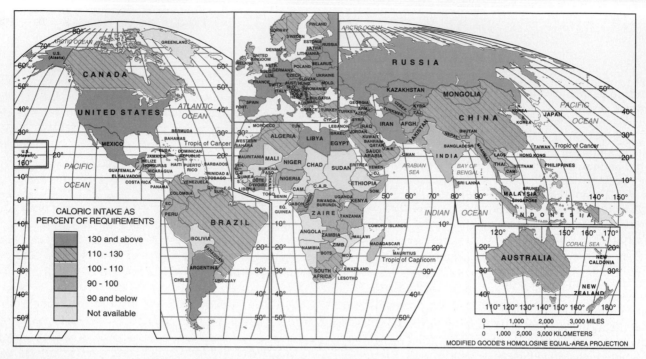

FIGURE 4.4

Caloric intake as a percentage of adult daily requirements. Highly developed regions of the world receive, on the average, 130% of the daily caloric requirements (2400 calories per day) set by the United Nations Food and Agricultural Organization (FAO). Some countries in South America, South Asia, and many countries in Africa, receive less than 90% of the daily caloric requirements needed to sustain body and life. Averages must be adjusted according to age, gender, and body size of the person and by regions of the world. Although it appears from this map that the great majority of world populations are in relatively good shape with regard to calories per capita (food supply), remember that averages, which are used in this case, tend to overshadow destitute groups in each country that receive less than their fair share. Again, the situation is most severe in the Sahel or center belt of Africa. (See Color Insert page 1.6, top, for more illustrative map.)

◉

Table 4.1

Calorie Intake and Calorie Requirement Satisfaction

	Highest Calorie Intake			*Lowest Calorie Intake*	
Country	*Calorie Intake per Person per Day*	*Percentage of Requirements*	*Country*	*Calorie Intake per Person per Day*	*Percentage of Requirements*
Ireland	4054	162	Ghana	1573	68
Denmark	4023	150	Chad	1620	68
East Germany	3787	145	Mali	1731	74
Belgium	3743	142	Kampuchea	1792	81
Bulgaria	3711	148	Uganda	1807	78
Yugoslavia	3642	143	Mozambique	1844	79
United States	3616	137	Burkina Faso	1879	79
Czechoslovakia	3613	146	Haiti	1903	84
UA Emirates	3591	N.A.	Bangladesh	1922	83
Libya	3581	152	Guinea	1987	86

Source: World Bank, 1985.

not have an adequate intake of protein, fat, vitamins, and other essential nutrients. The most important measure in assessing nutritional standards is the daily per capita availability of calories, protein, fat, calcium, and other nutrients. In Latin America, the best-fed populations live in Argentina and Uruguay; the worst-fed live in Haiti and Bolivia.

Data for assessing the nutritional quality of life based on national averages conceal wide regional differences in the quality and content of the diet. People of the Pampas in Argentina have a better diet than those who live in southern Patagonia. In Brazil, people in the northeast have a far less nutritious diet than those who live in the states of São Paulo and Rio de Janeiro.

The sharpest nutritional differences, however, are not from country to country or from one region to another within countries. They are between the rich and the poor. The wretched of the earth carry the major burden of hunger.

Causes of the Food Problem

Hunger in the Third World is often attributed to the low productivity of the tropical soils, the frequency of droughts, and the impact of storms such as hurricanes. Although the environment does have a bearing on the food problem, it has limited significance compared to the role of socioeconomic conditions. Hunger is overwhelmingly a problem attributable to human endeavor.

POPULATION AND URBANIZATION

Population growth is one cause of the food problem. However, presently, at the global level, there is no food shortage. In fact, food production is increasing faster than population growth. Even by the end of the twentieth century, there should be enough food to feed the projected 6 billion people if productivity continues to increase at current rates. Beyond the year 2000, the situation is more uncertain. Much will depend on dietary standards, but also on the possibilities for unfavorable climatic change and loss of agricultural capacity through such factors as soil erosion. Breakthroughs in food production technology may be able to compensate for these types of adverse conditions, should they occur.

The promising global food situation is not reflected at the scale of continents and countries. Between 1960 and 1980, food production increased at similar rates in developed and underdeveloped countries. Yet the increase was cancelled in the underdeveloped world where rapid population growth reduced food production per capita. Since that time, the ability of the Third World to feed itself has declined.

The food and hunger problem is most severe in sub-Saharan Africa. Food production is not keeping pace with population growth. During the 1970s, the annual gain in food production fell to about 1.3%, less than one-half the population growth rate of 2.7%. And between 1981 and 1983, per capita food production plunged 14%.

Sub-Saharan Africa went from near food self-sufficiency in 1970 to heavy food dependence by the mid-1980s. In 1984, imports provided 20% of the region's cereal requirement. Despite food imports, a high proportion of the population is chronically malnourished. Declining per capita food production combined with chronic malnutrition means that when drought strikes, as it did in the early 1970s and again in the 1980s, the result can be severe physical and mental damage—even starvation. In the mid-1980s Chad, Ethiopia, Mali, Mauritania, Mozambique, and Niger confronted famine. Food supplies were also inadequate in Angola, Botswana, Burkina Faso, Burundi, Kenya, Lesotho, Rwanda, Senegal, Somalia, Sudan, Tanzania, Zambia, and Zimbabwe.

The pace of Third World urbanization has also contributed to the food problem. In recent decades, millions and millions of people who previously lived in rural areas and produced some food have relocated in the urban areas where they must buy food. As a result of urbanization, there is a higher demand for food in the face of a lower supply. This problem has contributed to rising food costs, inflation, and indebtedness.

MALDISTRIBUTION

The problem of food distribution has three components. First, there is the problem of moving food from one area or region to another. Although transport systems in underdeveloped countries lack the speed and efficiency of those in developed countries, they are not serious impediments to the movement of commodities under normal circumstances. Food can reach stores in the most isolated regions just as easily as batteries and matches. The problem arises either when massive quantities of emergency food aid must be transported quickly or when the distribution of food is disrupted by political and military conflict. For example, food shortages in southern Africa, which trace to the 1981 to 1983 drought, have been exacerbated by the military activities of the guerrillas of the Mozambican National Resistance movement. The guerrillas destroyed key transport systems, preventing supplies of seeds and fertilizers from reaching local farmers and making it impossible for food-surplus countries such as Zimbabwe and Malawi to ship food to deficit regions.

Second, serious disruptions in food supply in the Third World are traceable to problems of marketing and storage. Food is sometimes hoarded by merchants until prices rise and then sold for a larger profit. Also, much

Third World farmers, such as these in Indonesia, depend on high rice yields. Rice is the staple food for more than one-half the world's population. While rice and other grains supply energy and some protein, people must supplement grains with fruits, nuts, vegetables, dairy products, fish, and meat in order to remain healthy. (*Source: World Bank.*)

food in the tropics is lost due to poor storage facilities. In the 1970s, up to 30% of Tanzania's harvested crops were destroyed in storage by vermin. Improvements in storage facilities would provide people, especially in the villages, with security against disasters, including a breakdown of communications.

A third aspect of the distribution problem is the inequitable allocation of food. Only a few regions have large grain surpluses. They are Australia, western Europe, and North America. The grain belt of North America is the global breadbasket. With about 6% of the world's population—and approaching zero population growth—Canada and the United States account for 25% of all grain output. But food grain is not always given when it is most needed. Food aid shipments and fluctuating grain prices are intimately related. Thus, U.S. food aid was low around 1973, a time of major famine in the Sahel region of Africa, because cereal prices were at a peak. To remedy the grain gluts of previous years, the U.S. government paid farmers $3 billion to take 50 million hectares out of production. The induced grain shortage was made even greater by sales of wheat to the former Soviet Union. Food, unavailable to feed the hungry of Africa, was used to feed cattle to increase the supply of meat in the former Soviet Union.

Cooperation between the "haves" and "have nots" is possible, however, and has been demonstrated. During the Ethiopian famine of 1986, a privately organized group of socially conscious Westerners rallied support to provide relief to the starving of the Sahel. In this instance, grain surpluses were successfully converted to life-saving relief supplies. In the 1990s, Somalia was aided.

CIVIL UNREST

Constant regional rebellion and civil unrest have plagued many places in Africa. Ethiopia, Sudan, and Somalia have been bothered by decades of civil strife. The people in Northern Somalia call their territory Somaliland. They declared their independence from the rest of Somalia in 1971. Since no one recognized their independence movements, they began to fight amongst themselves. Meanwhile, warlords ravage the south of Somalia.

Eritrea wants independence from Ethiopia. The Addis Ababa government has chosen to starve out this northern territory until it succumbs to national policies. In southern Sudan, some of the rebel factions want a complete break with the north. The Sudan government has again tried to starve the seccession of the southern regions of Sudan.

Memorable examples of depriving food to secessionist areas were when the Ibadan government in Nigeria starved the Biafrans or when the Addis Ababa government in Ethiopia starved the Eritreans into submission with 6 million people dying in the process. Such conflicts divert resources from civilian use and complicate the stability of the governments, creating famine and prohibiting developmental aid from the United States and other Western nations (see box, The Anatomy of Starvation, on pages 126–128.)

ENVIRONMENTAL DECLINE

As the population pressure increases on a given land area, the need for food pushes limits of agricultural use to the limits and marginal lands, that are subject now to desertification and deforestation, are brought into production. The cutting of trees allows a desert to advance, as the wind break is now absent. Trees do provide for fuel and shelter, but their roots also hold in the viable top soil, which takes 100 years to develop 1 inch. Desert winds allow fragile top soils to be blown away and ruined for agricultural use.

Cattle dung is a principal source of cooking fuel in the absence of wood, but this distracts once again from the soil fertility because of the lack of organic matter being added to the soil, as is done throughout most of Asia.

Overuse of land deforestation has lowered the capacity of the land to absorb moisture. This diminishes agricultural productivity and increases the chance of drought. In some places, midlatitude agricultural techniques have been imported from the United States and Canada. For example, grain growing areas of Tanzania and Kenya. While herders and scavenger tribes, such as the Masai, have been displaced, a large tillage has been realized in the short run. However, since the land consists of volcanic soil, is not organic (as in the United States and Canada), and is subject to heavy periods of torrential rain, as opposed to a more seasonal moderation in precipitation, these lands are now subject to high levels of erosion.

In addition, there are few facilities for crop storage. Grain that is produced must be consumed quickly. One-third of Africa's tonnage of food and grains is lost to rats, mice, and other vermin. Consequently, it is difficult to accumulate a surplus in years of harvest to make due for lean years of drought that tend to arrive in groups of two or three.

GOVERNMENT POLICY AND DEBT

Government policy has, to a large extent, emphasized investment in military equipment at the expense of increasing agricultural production. The World Bank estimates that African nations spend four times as much on military hardware and acquisition than they do on agriculture. For example, Somalia and Ethiopia spend more than 40% of their GNP on weapons of warfare.

In addition, some African governments have provided food at an artificially low price so that most members of a society could afford sufficient amounts. However, this has robbed the incentive for the farmer because the farmer cannot make a fair living from such low commodity prices. At the same time, African governments have accepted large levels of foreign aid and food aid to offset immediate hunger problems, but have not placed an emphasis on the solution to their food problems. Food stuffs only provide temporary relief, and in the long run, the population is as bad as before.

The International Monetary Fund estimates that between 1975 and 1990, the average debt of African nations is well into the billions, and the aggregate debt is more than 200 billion as of 1993. Simply put, African nations have no surplus capital to invest in their infrastructure or food production systems, but must conversely install austerity to reduce, not increase, levels of government services, and food and basic measures to contain endemic diseases, such as sleeping sickness, malaria, river blindness and, more recently, the high infestation of HIV virus found in central Africa.

Millions of African children die every year because their governments cannot provide them with 10¢ worth of basic vaccines to combat the ever-present endemic diseases that plague Africa.

POVERTY

The inequitable allocation of food is related to poverty, the major cause of the hunger problem. Food goes to markets that can afford it, not to where it is needed most. Where food is produced is immaterial as long as costs are minimized and a profitable sale can be made. As one U.S. rancher commented on the costs of production, ''Here's what it boils down to—$95 per cow per year in Montana, $25 in Costa Rica'' (Lappé and Collins, 1976, p. 203). Thus, in the midst of hunger, beef is exported for profit. If Americans are prepared to pay more for meat than many Costa Ricans, then it is not surprising that the market fails to include the poor.

THE ANATOMY OF STARVATION

"Restore Hope," the U.S. mission to Somalia, was actually a challenge to the cessation of starvation that still plagues the nation. More than 5000 people have died of starvation within the last 2 years (as of 1993), and starvation threatens 40% of the remaining 6 million. Following, we look at the anatomy of starvation and what must be done to counterbalance it so that the body can recuperate.

SELF-CANNIBALIZATION

1. When the body does not receive adequate food and nutrition, the body provides a substance called glycogen, a starchy substance that it stores in the liver and feeds on.

2. The first thing the body loses is strength. Soon afterwards the pulse, heartbeat, and blood pressure start to take a precipitous drop.

3. The body begins to feed off of itself, using muscle and fat. Large amounts of water are lost. As water, which comprises 50% of the body, is depleted, the body begins to shrink.

4. The body's loss of water causes a total imbalance in all fluids and causes the distended, swollen stomachs, which are seen in starving persons. This is caused by edema, a fluid that is collecting in the cells.

5. A human body can withstand only a loss of 25% of its average weight and still survive. Beyond that, death comes within 30 to 50 days. The body's organs tend to shrink and waste away, losing their function. Intestines wither, making it impossible for the body to use food properly. The heart shrinks from an average of 14 ounces in an adult, to half that size.

6. The endemic diseases of Africa compound the problem. Intestinal disease from unsanitary disease cause diarrhea, preventing the body from absorbing valuable nutrients and moisture, which are passed out. The immune system starts to give up and other diseases, such as malaria, river blindness, and sleeping sickness, make inroads.

7. Self-cannibalization leads to disorientation as people start to lose hope. Mothers may even steal food from their children as they panic and become disoriented.

BABIES AND YOUNG CHILDREN

1. Babies born to starving mothers have a much lower likelihood of survival and are usually drastically underweight. The baby's survival is frequently based on the availability of breast milk, but a starving mother cannot produce it. Babies that do survive may have birth defects, partial loss of mental capacitating powers, and emotional problems.

2. The human body is an incredible machine, and although a baby from a starving mother may have its growth stunted, with proper care after delivery, from helping agencies, these skeletal children are often restored to complete health and permanent brain damage is avoided.

3. For older children, months of starvation can be overcome, but it is not uncommon for older children that were deprived of food in their early years, to have brain damage and chronic disease.

This African mother can do little to save her child's life. He is suffering the complications of undernutrition and malnutrition. World per capita food production figures from 1970 to 1993 are disappointing. Asia has managed to increase production fast enough to stay well ahead of population growth, but Latin America and the near East, including Southwest Asia, the Middle East, and North Africa, have barely managed to stay even with the population. The worst report is from Africa, where population growth is outstripping food production year by year. Per capita food production in Africa has been falling steadily for the last 25 years. Worse declines have come in Angola, Botswana, Gabon, Mozambique, Ruwanda, Somalia, Ethiopia, and Sudan. Many factors contribute to these fluctuations, including drought, changing world prices, and civil and ethnic unrest. Hundreds of thousands of tribal members have been killed and even more made homeless in 1994 alone in the countries of Ruwanda and South Africa.
(Source: UNICEF/WHO photo by B. Campbell.)

◈

RESTORING HOPE AND HEALTH

For the United States, to restore hope and health in Somalia will require more than the sharing of abundant government rations with multitudes of starving people in the refugee camps. It is a long, slow process for the body to recuperate and rehabilitate itself.

1. In the refugee camps, the worst cases are children and adults whose body functions and intestines have withered. They cannot digest food and use it for body nourishment without disrupting the balance that exists in their bodies. They must be fed intravenously, just as a hospital patient who cannot chew or swallow.

2. An IV supplying carbohydrates is immediately used in the bloodstream by different parts of the body. The brain is the first organ to be resuscitated.

3. The next step is to provide the patients with a tiny amount of liquid orally. This is a solution of water, sugar, and salt.

4. After several days, the next step is to feed the patients a liquid soup that is highly nutritious, comprised of ground maize, sunflower oil, sugar, vegetable oil, and bean flour. The solution in Somalia is called "Unamix," a formula developed by the United Nations to save starving populations. Weeks later, milk and solid foods will be administered.

AGRICULTURE

Closely associated with poverty as a cause of hunger in the Third World is the structure of agriculture, including land ownership. Land is frequently concentrated in a few hands. In Bangladesh, less than 10% of rural households own more than one-half of the country's cultivable land. Sixty percent of Bangladesh's rural families own less than 2%. In fact, many of them own no land at all. They are landless laborers who depend on wages for their livelihoods. But without land, there is often no food.

Most food for domestic consumption is produced by small farmers who often have yields equal to, or higher than, those of large farmers. Large landowners underutilize land, labor, and water. Small farmers till the soil with their hands and know their work determines what they will eat. The incentive for large landowners is not as great, and the incentive for their wage laborers is often minimal.

Third World agriculture has expanded in recent decades. The expansion is in the export sector, not in the domestic food-producing sector, and it is often the result of deliberate policy. Governments and private elites have opted for modernization through the promotion of export-oriented agriculture. The assumption is that capital-intensive agriculture based on modern technology, management, and know-how spurs development. The result is the growth of an agricultural economy based on profitable export products and the neglect of those aspects of farming that have to do with producing food for local populations.

Increasing Food Production

Hunger is a problem that affects only the poor—those who lack the opportunity to participate in the economy in a way that allows them to support themselves. Yet hunger is usually considered a problem of inadequate food production. According to this view, growing more food will end hunger. Food supplies can be increased by: (1) expanding the amount of land under cultivation, and (2) increasing yields per unit of land.

EXPANDING THE CULTIVATED AREA

The world's potential available land for cultivation is estimated to be twice the present cultivated area. Vast reserves are theoretically available in Africa, South America, and Australia, and smaller reserves in North America and in the former Soviet Union (Figure 4.5). But estimates of unused cultivable land are misleading. Unused cultivable land is unevenly distributed and rarely exists where the need for it is greatest. Land suitable for cultivation at a reasonable cost and with present technology is easier to find in temperate areas than in the tropics, where fragile soils and aridity are limiting factors.

The uneven distribution of cultivable land is most evident in sub-Saharan Africa. Although the region has plenty of land to feed the current population and many more people, there exist large areas that are insufficiently fertile to feed the people living on them. Fourteen

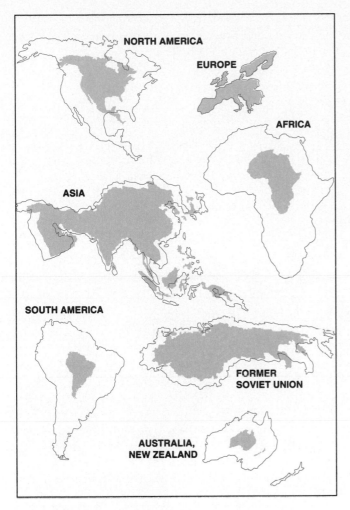

FIGURE 4.5
Continents sized in proportion to the area of their potentially arable land. The silhouette map within each outline shows how much of that potentially arable land is cultivated.

countries had 1990 populations that were too large in relation to their cultivable land to achieve and maintain food self-sufficiency, assuming subsistence farming methods. These countries account for one-third of sub-Saharan Africa's land area and about one-half of its population. Twenty-one countries will be unable to support their populations by the year 2000 if technology remains unchanged. Seven of these countries—Burundi, Kenya, Lesotho, Mauritania, Niger, Rwanda, and Somalia—will be unable to achieve food self-sufficiency by the year 2000 with the continuing rapid growth of their populations, even if farming methods were to advance to the "intermediate levels" now existing on commercial farms in Asia and Latin America, where

fertilizers and pesticides, improved seed varieties, and simple conservation techniques are being used. Eleven countries have plenty of underused land and could support populations at least five times their 1975 size, even at subsistence farming levels.

About half of the world's potentially arable land lies within the tropics, especially in the rain forests of the Congo and Amazon basins. Growing crops on cleared forestland has not proved very successful, however. Once the trees are chopped down, the thin soils are vulnerable to rain and soon lose their nutrients. Farmers have only a few seasons to reap light yields before the soil is gone. They are left with rock, clay, or hardpan (acidic subsoil that is difficult to work).

Most of the remaining land reserves exist in areas of excessive dryness. This land must be irrigated if it is to become productive, but irrigation schemes are expensive to construct and administer. Moreover, irrigated agriculture is possible only in a small proportion of the world's dry lands. It is restricted to areas near rivers, such as the Nile, that flow through deserts and to areas where abundant ground water is available.

The expansion of agriculture into rain forest and desert environments contributes to deforestation and desertification. Since World War II, about one-half of the world's rain forests in Africa, Asia, and Latin America have disappeared. If destruction continues at the current pace, one-half of what is left will have gone by the end of the twentieth century. *Desertification*—the growth of human-made deserts—threatens about one-third of the world's land surface and the livelihood of nearly a billion people. Many of the world's major rangelands are at risk (Figure 4.6). The main factor responsible for desertification is overgrazing, but deforestation (particularly the cutting of fuelwood), overcultivation of marginal soils, and salinization caused by poorly managed irrigation systems are also important influences. Deforestation and desertification are destroying the land resources on which the development of many Third World countries depend.

RAISING THE PRODUCTIVITY OF EXISTING CROPLAND

The quickest way to increase food supply is to raise the productivity of land under cultivation. Remarkable increases in agricultural yields have been achieved in developed countries through the widespread adoption of new technologies. Corn yields in the United States are a good illustration. Yields expanded rapidly with

DESERTIFICATION
OF THE WORLD

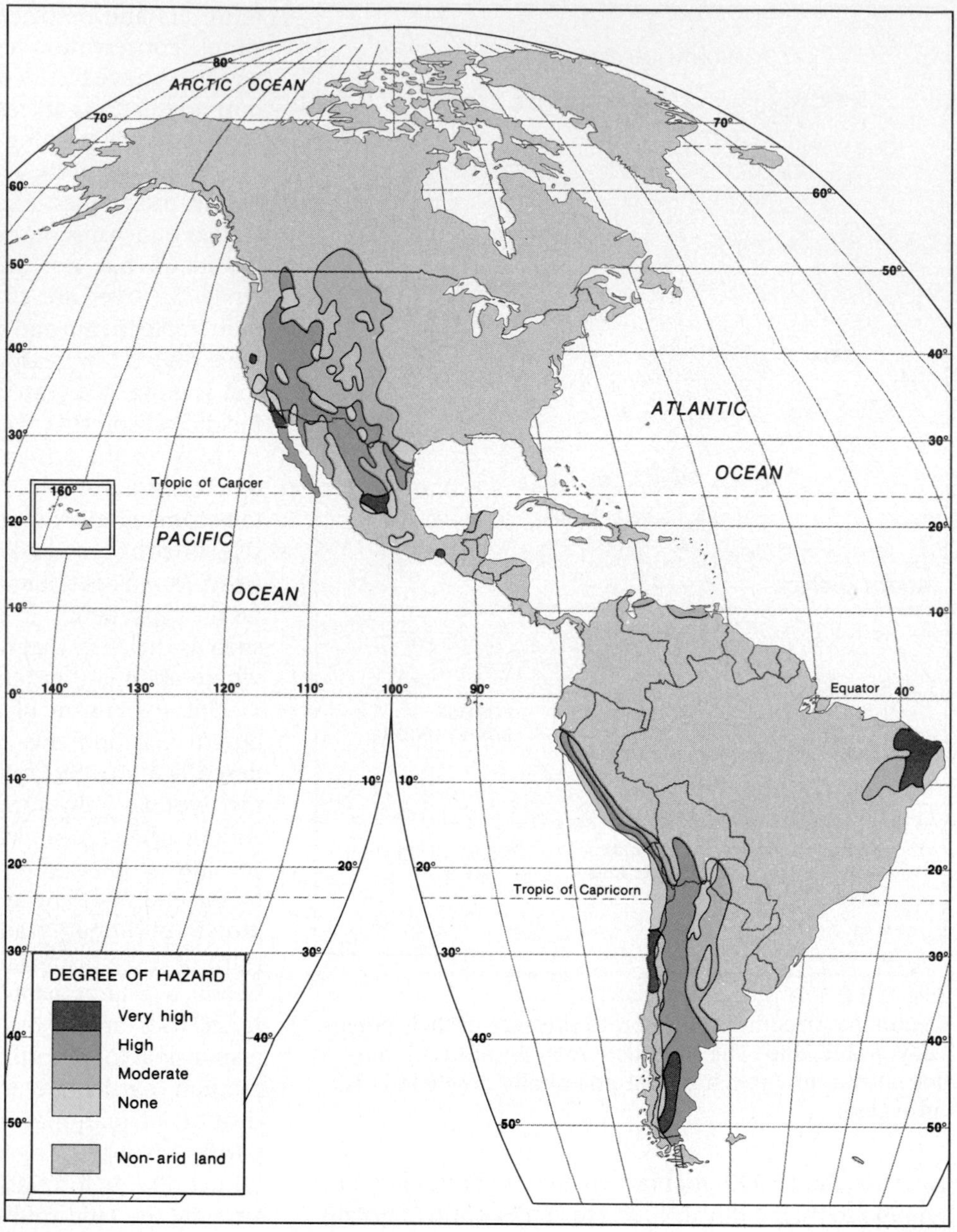
ARCTIC OCEAN
PACIFIC
OCEAN
ATLANTIC
OCEAN
Tropic of Cancer
Equator
Tropic of Capricorn
DEGREE OF HAZARD
Very high
High
Moderate
None
Non-arid land

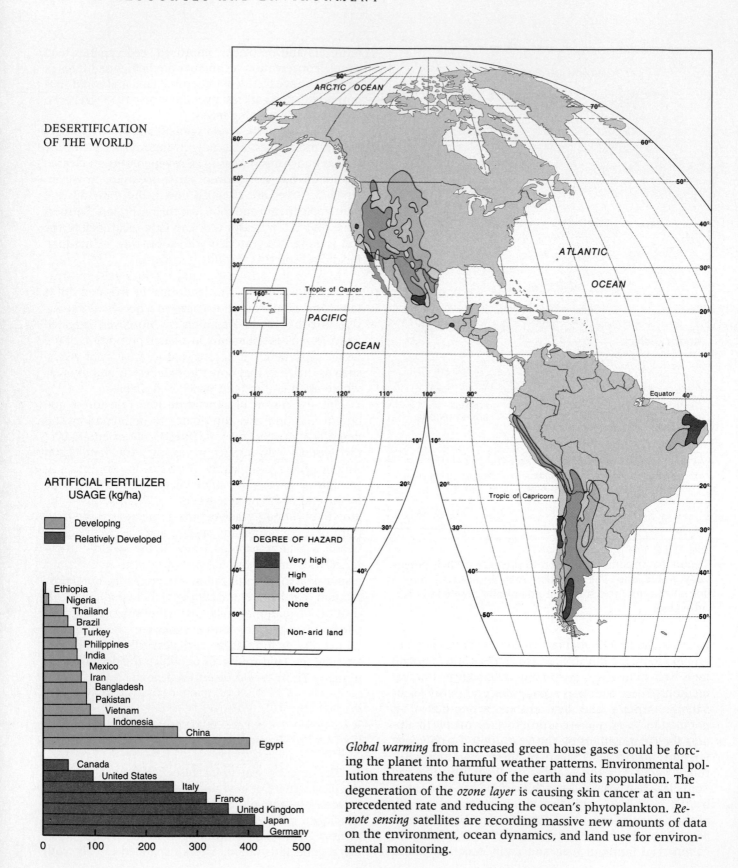

ARTIFICIAL FERTILIZER
USAGE (kg/ha)

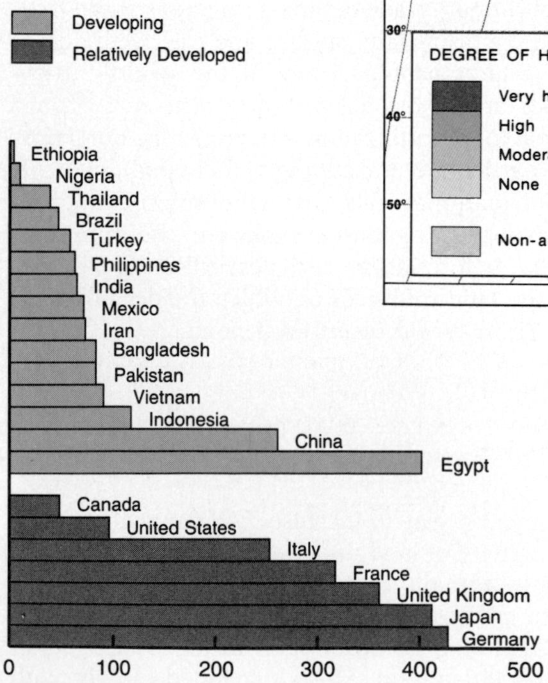
Developing
Relatively Developed
Ethiopia
Nigeria
Thailand
Brazil
Turkey
Philippines
India
Mexico
Iran
Bangladesh
Pakistan
Vietnam
Indonesia
China
Egypt
Canada
United States
Italy
France
United Kingdom
Japan
Germany
0
100
200
300
400
500

Global warming from increased green house gases could be forcing the planet into harmful weather patterns. Environmental pollution threatens the future of the earth and its population. The degeneration of the *ozone layer* is causing skin cancer at an unprecedented rate and reducing the ocean's phytoplankton. *Remote sensing* satellites are recording massive new amounts of data on the environment, ocean dynamics, and land use for environmental monitoring.

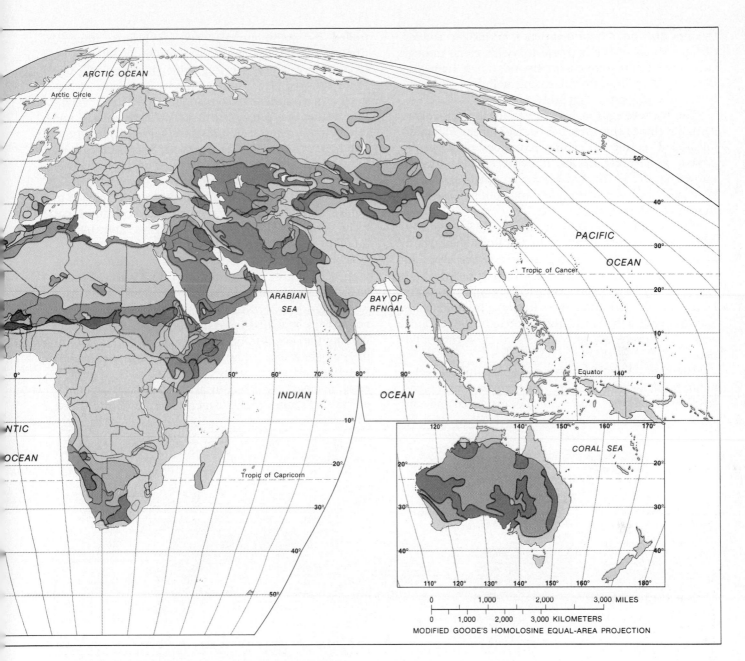

FIGURE 4.6   WORLD DESERTIFICATION
The main problem is overuse by farmers and herdsmen. Approximately 9% of the earth's surface has lost its topsoil due to overuse of lands by humans, creating desertification. An additional 25% of the earth's surface is now threatened. Topsoil is being lost at a rate of approximately 30 billion metric tons a year. Approximately 20 million acres of agricultural land are wasted every year to desertification by agricultural overuse. Plants have a fibrous root system, which holds the soil in place. When plants are uprooted by overplowing, or by animals that eat not only the portion of the grass but also the roots, the plants that stabilized shifting soil are removed. When the rains come, water erosion can wash away the remaining topsoil. Sand particles, which are heavier than the humus, remain behind and start to form dunes.

the introduction of hybrid varieties, herbicides, and fertilizers. Much of the increase in yields came through successive improvements in hybrids. Just how long these yields will go on increasing will depend on the future development of hybrids.

The Western approach for increasing land productivity in developed countries has been proposed for underdeveloped countries. This technology-package approach to farming in the underdeveloped world is known as the *Green Revolution*, in which new high-yielding varieties of wheat, rice, and corn are developed through modern plant genetics.

The Green Revolution began in 1943 when four American scientists, financed by the Rockefeller Foundation, introduced new wheat and maize seeds on mainly large farms in the Sonora District of Mexico. It was not very long before crop yields began to increase. Following this triumph, the Rockefeller Foundation teamed up with the Ford Foundation to introduce "miracle" rice to selected parts of Asia, such as the Philippines.

The Green Revolution is a major scientific achievement, but it is not a panacea. It depends on new seeds, fertilizers, pesticides, and herbicides produced and controlled by multinationals such as Fisons, Imperial Chemical Industries, and Standard Oil. It depends on large-scale, one-crop farming, which is ecologically unstable because of its susceptibility to pestilence. It depends on controlled water supplies, which have increased the incidence of malaria, schistosomiasis, and other human diseases. It is restricted primarily to wheat, rice, and corn hybrids that are strictly low-grade protein foods. It is confined mainly to a group of 18 heavily populated countries that extend across the subtropical part of the world from Korea in the east to Mexico in the west (Figure 4.7). It is also benefiting countries that include 18% of the world's land surface and that are home to 56% of the world's population.

Politically, the Green Revolution promises more than it can deliver. Its sociopolitical application has been largely unsatisfactory. Even in areas where the Green Revolution has been technologically successful, it has not always benefited large numbers of hungry people without the means to buy the newly produced food. In the Punjab, India, it has benefited mainly the farmers who were already wealthy enough to adopt a complex integrated package of technical inputs and management practices. Farmers make bigger profits from the Green

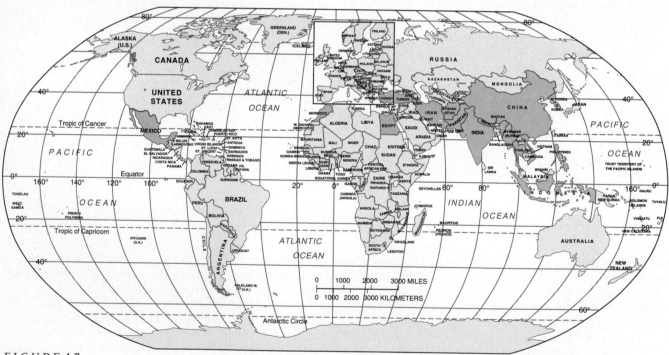

FIGURE 4.7
The chief benefiting countries of the Green Revolution. Countries indicated in blue represent these countries. The Green Revolution was the result of plant scientists genetically developing high yielding varieties of staple food crops such as rice in East Asia, wheat in the Middle East, and corn in Middle America. By crossing "super strains" that produced high yields with more genetically diverse plants, both high yield and pest resistance were introduced.

Revolution when they purchase additional land and mechanize their operations. Some effects of labor-displacing machinery and the purchase of additional land by rich farmers include agricultural unemployment, increased landlessness, rural-to-urban migration, and increased malnutrition for the unemployed who are unable to purchase the food produced by the technology of the Green Revolution.

Where does the food produced by the new technology go? In Pakistan, much hybrid maize is processed into corn sweetener for soft drinks purchased by urban middle- and upper-income groups. In Colombia, large quantities of rice go to feedlots and breweries. In Mexico, more basic grains are consumed by animals than by 20 million peasants. In Central America, export fruits and vegetables that have been turned back from the United States are fed to livestock or dumped instead of being given to local people too poor to buy food (Lappé and Collins, 1976, p. 2).

The Green Revolution is not winning its battle against hunger because it focuses on food production. The world food problem is not so much one of food production, but of food demand in the economic sense. Unfortunately, the Green Revolution does nothing to increase the ability of the poor to buy food.

We have portrayed the Green Revolution as a poisoned gift. It has helped to create a world of more and larger commercial farms alongside fewer and smaller peasant plots. However, given a different structure of landholdings and the use of appropriately intermediate technology, the Green Revolution could help underdeveloped countries on the road toward agricultural self-sufficiency and the elimination of hunger. Intermediate technology is a term that means low-cost, small-scale technologies "intermediate" between primitive stick-farming methods and complex agroindustrial technical packages.

Creating New Food Supplies and Sources

Expanding cultivated areas and raising the productivity of existing cropland are two methods of increasing food production. A third is the identification of new food sources. There are three ways to identify new food sources: (1) cultivate the oceans, or aquaculture; (2) develop high-protein cereal crops; and (3) increase the acceptability and palatability of inefficiently used present foods.

AQUACULTURE

Fishing and the cultivation of fish and shellfish from the oceans is not a new idea. The world seems well supplied with fisheries because oceans cover three-fourths of the globe. However, historically, world fishery totals have provided a very small amount of the world food supply.

Between 1950 and 1987, consumption of fish from the oceans did increase at a more rapid rate than the growth of population worldwide and even exceeded beef as a source of animal protein in some countries. However, since 1987, world fish catch has actually leveled off and declined (Figure 4.8) in some portions of the world. Oar fishing has been particularly noticeable in the North Atlantic and Pacific Oceans. In the Pacific, Russian, Japanese, Canadian, and American fishermen fished roughly the same areas and created a shortage, whereas in the North Atlantic, European, Canadian, and American fishermen overfished the once abundant commercial marine fisheries.

In the South Pacific, Peru and Ecuador extended their 3-mile nautical territory to 200 miles. These coun-

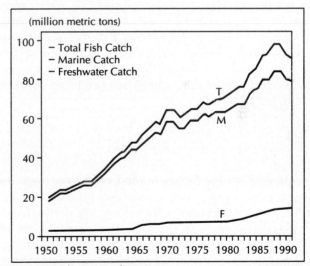

Note: 1990 figure is preliminary.

FIGURE 4.8
The global fish catch has been increasing over the last 20 years. Fish, crustaceans, and mollusks reached 100 million metric tons in 1989 and then decreased to 85 million tons in 1990, according to figures from the Food and Agricultural Organization (FAO) of the United Nations. Reduced quotas for some North Atlantic fish species, due to conservation techniques, were partially responsible for the 1990 decline.
(Source: World Resources Institute, 1993, p. 179.)

tries then arrested Californian and Mexican tuna fishing boats and impounded the catch and the vessel for territorial violations. Iceland, at the same time, extended its territorial jurisdiction to 50 miles to protect endangered continental shell-fishing beds. While these three countries have been criticized, they have economies based heavily on fishing and have seen this portion of their economy level off, and even decline, in past years. For example, between 1970 and 1975, 75% of Peru's principal fish, the anchovy, was lost to overfishing. The Peru experience suggests that the ocean is not a limitless fish resource, as did the quest for blue whales, a century earlier, which depleted the world supply.

Aquaculture, or fish farming, has been practiced in some countries, such as Japan. It accounts for 5% of the world's fish caught yearly. In China, interior lakes are seeded and harvested, producing 45% of China's fish catch. Both the former Soviet Union countries and India have major fish-farming industries.

The fish and sea products provide most of the protein in the Japanese diet. Not only do fish supply much needed food stuffs without adding to the demand for additional agricultural land, but it also fulfills a tenet of the Buddhist religion. In Japan, aquaculture includes the farming of seaweed, fish, and shellfish. Here, inlets from the sea, which are screened and fenced off with underwater wire, provide pens for fish seeding in growth. In the United States, trout are raised in fish hatcheries and then seeded into mountainous streams in the west; in the east, catfish are produced in some quantities on farms.

HIGH-PROTEIN CEREALS

Another source of future food production rests in higher protein cereal crops. Scientists from around the world are experimenting with various high-yield, high-protein cereal crops in the hope that development of hybrid seeds will be able to help the protein deficiency of populations in developing countries who do not have available meats from which to gain their protein needs, such as populations in First World nations.

Fortification of present rice, wheat, barley, and other cereals with minerals, vitamins, and protein-carrying amino acids is an approach that also deserves attention. This approach is based on the fortified food production in developed nations and stands a greater chance of cultural acceptance because individual food habits do not necessarily need to be altered. But developing countries rely on unprocessed, unfortified foods for 95% of their food intake. Large-scale fortification and processing, to feed hunger areas of Asia and Southeast Asia, would require major technological innovation and scale economies to produce enough food to have an impact on impoverished societies.

MORE EFFICIENT USE OF FOODS

In portions of Latin America and Asia, and in much of central Africa and Southeast Asia, people's choice of foods to satisfy their consumer preferences, as well as religious taboos and cultural values, are becoming limited. The selection of foods, based on social customs and unrelated to harsh economic realities (i.e., environmental and nutritional factors), needs to be supplemented with information concerning more efficient use of foods presently available. Thus, an effort needs to be made to increase the palatability of present foods that are in sufficient supplies in these less developed areas.

Fish meal is a good example. Presently, one-third of the world's fish intake is turned into fodder for animals and fertilizer. Fish meal is rich in Omega 3 fatty acids and amino acids necessary for biological development. However, in many places, the fish meal is not used because it does not meet with approval regarding taste and texture.

Another underused food resource throughout the world is the somewhat less than totally palatable soybean. Most of the soybeans in the world today wind up being processed into animal feed or fertilizer, or into industrial production of nondigestable materials. In addition, the world demand for tofu sprouts and other recognizable foods, derivative of the soybean, do not have a world appeal as of yet. However, the soybean is an incredibly rich legume in both protein and amino acids. In some places in the world, hot dogs, hamburgers, and cooking oils are produced at least partially from soybeans and are acceptable. New food products need to be created from the soybean in developing countries because of its high-protein efficiency. This will greatly supplement dwindling supplies of more palatable foods.

In some countries, soft drinks are made from soybeans, and in America, a popular milk substitute for children with galactosemia is soy powder, stocked in every grocery store in America. The babies do not seem to mind, plus they get much less arterior plaque buildup than the babies who drink cow's milk.

The Kenyan rangelands on which these herders' cattle graze are in jeopardy. With growing grazing pressures, more than 60% of the world's rangelands and at least 80% of African, Asian, and Middle Eastern rangelands are now moderately to severely desertified. About sixty-five million hectares of once productive land in Africa have become desert during the last 50 years.
(Source: World Bank.)

EXPAND EXPORTS FROM FOOD SURPLUS COUNTRIES

Very few countries of the world are net food exporters. The largest food exporter is the United States, with smaller supplies provided in most years by Canada, Argentina, and Australia. An alternative to increasing food supplies in developing nations is for the richer countries of the world, such as the United States, Canada, Argentina, and Australia, to increase their food production and exports to the countries that have chronic shortfalls. The three most important crops to such countries are wheat, corn, and rice.

Because of high population densities and the fact that most cultivatable land is in use, Europe for many years was the only net exporting continent in the world. However, even though other areas have potentially arable land that is not being used, Asia, South America, Africa, and the former Soviet Union have become net importers of food. Asia became a net importer of wheat by 1955, as well as Africa and eastern Europe by 1960. Latin America became a net importer of food in the 1970s. For these developing areas of the world, the principal causes of net food import were rapidly growing populations; that is, populations that grew faster than the food supply.

The United States of America is now by far the leading exporter of food in the world. The United States accounts for three-fourths of all corn and soybean exports, one-half of the wheat exports, and one-quarter

Alternatives for Solving

The World Food Problem

Many proposals have been advanced for dealing with world hunger and malnutrition. The two alternatives that follow are based on sharply contrasting views of what lies at the heart of the problem.

TRIAGE

William and Paul Paddock's book, *Time of Famines* (1976), argues for triage as an inevitable and acceptable solution to the world food problem. Triage, a variant of "lifeboat ethics," is the notion popularized by Garrett Hardin in 1974.

> "Triage" is a term used in military medicine. It is defined as the assigning of priority of treatment to the wounded brought to a battlefield hospital in a time of mass casualties and limited medical facilities. The wounded are divided on the basis of three classifications: (1) Those so seriously wounded they cannot survive regardless of the treatment given them; call these the "can't-be-saved." (2) Those who can survive without treatment regardless of the pain they may be suffering; call these the "walking wounded." (3) Those who can be saved by immediate medical care. (Paddock and Paddock, 1976, p. 206).

Applying this system to the food problem, Paddock and Paddock (1976) argued that limited stocks of American foods should not be made available to nations that form the "can't-be-saved" group. Food aid also should not go to the "walking wounded" nations because they have the necessary agricultural resources or foreign exchange to obtain the food they require. Only nations that can be saved should be recipients of American food. According to the authors, compassion is a luxury no longer affordable in this era of scarcity. We must learn to let people die for the survival of the human race.

TRANSFORMING THE WORLD ECONOMIC SYSTEM

In *Food First* (1977), Lappé and Collins explain that the cause of hunger is not too many people, not scarcity of arable land, not lack of technology, and not overconsumption by the wealthy. For Lappé and Collins, no country, not even a Bangladesh, is a "basket case." Every country has the capacity to feed itself. The real food problem is the inequality generated by the world's political economy. Social justice must become a priority.

> There is no other road to food security—for others or for us. Americans are made to believe that if justice becomes a priority, production will be sacrificed. We have found the opposite to be true. It is the land monopolizers, both the traditional bounded elites and corporate agribusiness, that have proved themselves to be the most inefficient, unreliable, and destructive users of food resources. The only guarantee of long-term productivity and food security is for people to take control of food resources here and in other countries. (Lappé and Collins, 1977, pp. 8–9).

of rice exports worldwide. Canada, France, and Australia have joined the United States as a major wheat exporter, but Thailand has recently replaced the United States as the leading rice exporter, and such poor Asian countries as Pakistan, Vietnam, and India have also joined the rice exportation trade. Russia is by far the leading grain importer and also imports large supplies of rice, corn, and wheat. Asian countries and Southeast Asian countries primarily import rice, while China, Japan, and the former Soviet Union import corn and grain.

A SOLUTION TO THE WORLD FOOD SUPPLY SITUATION

What is to be done about the world food problem? As we have emphasized, there is a widely shared belief that people are hungry because of insufficient food production. Thus, we are often treated to the "new release" approach to hunger. We learn of breakthroughs—protein from petroleum, harvests of kelp, extracts from alfalfa—to expand food supply. We are told that strains on the food-producing capacity of the world would be lessened if the affluent one-third of humankind did not consume two-thirds of the world's total food supply. We are even reminded that the food crisis would be lessened if Americans consumed one less hamburger per week.

But the fact is that food production is increasing faster than population, and still there are more hungry people than ever before (Figure 4.9). Why should this be so? It could be that the production focus is correct, but soaring numbers of people simply overrun even these dramatic production gains. Or it could be that the diagnosis is incorrect—scarcity is not the cause of hunger and production increases, no matter how great, can never solve the problem.

The simple facts of world grain production make it clear that the overpopulation/scarcity diagnosis is actually incorrect. Present world grain production could more than adequately feed every person on earth. Even during the "scarcity" years, 1972 to 1973, there was 9% more grain per person than in "ample" 1960. Inadequate production is clearly not the problem.

Ironically, the focus on increased production has actually compounded the problem of hunger by transforming agricultural progress into a narrow technical pursuit instead of the sweeping social task of releasing vast, untapped human resources (see box on page 136). We need to look to the policies of governments in underdeveloped countries to understand why people are hun-

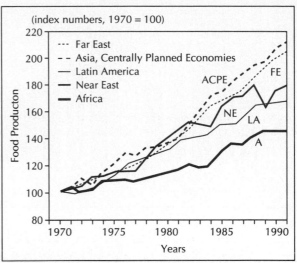

Notes:
a. Far East = Bangladesh, Bhutan, Brunei Darussalam, East India, Indonesia, Republic of Korea, Lao People's Dem Macao, Malaysia, Maldives, Myanmar, Nepal, Pakistan Singapore, Sri Lanka, Thailand.
b. Asia, Centrally Planned Economies = Cambodia People's Republic of Korea, Mongolia, Vietnam.
c. Near East = *Africa:* Egypt, Libya, Sudan. *Asia:* Afghanistan, Cyprus, Gaza Strip (Palestine), Islamic Republic of Iran, Lebanon, Oman, Qatar, Kingdom of Saudi Arabia, Syria Turkey, United Arab Emirates, Yemen Arab Republic

FIGURE 4.9
The index of food production in developing regions shows that most regions of the world have increased dramatically in the last 20 years. Asia and the centrally planned economies have almost doubled their food production since 1970, whereas the Far East has increased by approximately 90%. Latin America and the Near East have increased by 60% and Africa 40%. Per capita food supplies are falling in Africa, however.
(Source: World Resources Institute, 1992, p. 96.)

gry even when there is enough food produced to adequately feed everyone. These policies influence the access to knowledge and the availability of credit to small farmers, the profitability of growing enough to sell a surplus, and the efficiency of marketing and distributing food on a broad scale.

The fact is that small, carefully farmed plots are more productive per unit area than large estates because they use fewer costly inputs (Figure 4.10). Yet, despite considerable evidence from around the world, Third World government production programs ignore small farmers. They rationalize that working with bigger production units is a faster road to increased productivity. Often, many small farms is the answer.

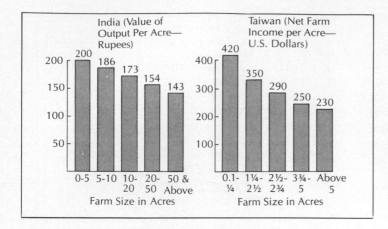

FIGURE 4.10
Small farm efficiency in India and Taiwan. Small, carefully formed plots are more productive per unit area than large estates throughout the world because they use fewer costly inputs. Each unit of land is more intensively worked and there is a higher density of laborers per acre.

NONRENEWABLE MINERAL RESOURCES

▣

Although we can increase world food output, we cannot increase the supply of minerals. A mineral deposit, once used, is gone forever. The term *mineral* refers to a naturally occurring inorganic substance in the earth's crust. Thus, silicon is a mineral whereas petroleum is not, since the latter is of organic origin. Although minerals abound in nature, many of them are insufficiently concentrated to be economically recoverable. Moreover, the richest deposits are unevenly distributed and are being depleted.

Except for iron, nonmetallic elements are consumed at much greater rates than elements used for their metallic properties. Industrial societies do not worry about the supply of most nonmetallic minerals, which are plentiful and often widespread. There is no foreseeable world shortage of nitrogen, phosphorus, potash, or sulfur for chemical fertilizer or of sand, gravel, clay, or dimension stone for building purposes. Those commodities the industrial and industrializing societies do worry about are the metals—the raw materials of economic power.

On a per capita basis, Americans use more minerals than any other people. They consume almost one-third of the world's minerals to supply less than 5% of the world's population. If the entire world population were to use metals at the same rate as the United States did in 1990, world production of iron would have to increase 75 times, that of copper 100 times, and that of tin 250 times.

Depletion Curves and Depletion Rate Estimates

Depletion means the time it takes to consume a proportion of a resource—typically 80%. It is not meaningful to speak about completely running out of a resource. Ultimately, it is uneconomic to exploit marginal deposits because of either low quality or inaccessibility.

To project the lifetime of a nonrenewable resource, we construct depletion curves (Figure 4.11). Curve A assumes the prevalent practice of mining, using, and discarding a resource. Curve B assumes improved mining techniques and recycling. Curve C assumes not only improved mining techniques and recycling, but also reduced demand. Obviously, a substitute resource would negate curves A, B, and C. In many cases projections based on depletion curves have been revised in light of more advanced resource location methods.

Location and Projected Reserves of Key Minerals

Only five countries—Australia, Canada, South Africa, the United States, and the former Soviet Union—are significant producers of at least six strategic minerals vital to defense and modern technology (Figure 4.12). A larger number of mainly Third World countries are major producers of between one and six minerals required by modern industry. Of the major mineral-producing countries only a few—notably the United States and the former Soviet Union—are also major processors and consumers. The other major processing and consuming centers—Japan and western

FIGURE 4.11
Depletion occurs for nonrenewable resources. Curve A assumes the practice of mining, then using, and quickly discarding a resource. Curve B shows more efficient mining technology, plus the additional efficiency of recycling practices. Curve C assumes improved mining, recycling, and a lower level of use per person. The depletion time for a resource is the time it will take for 80% of the proven reserves of that resource to be used up.

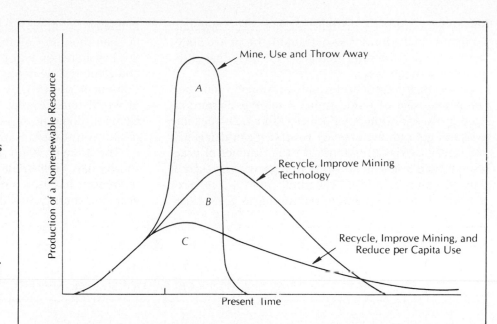

FIGURE 4.12
Major producers of strategic minerals.
(Source: Based on data from U.S. Bureau of Mines, 1986.)

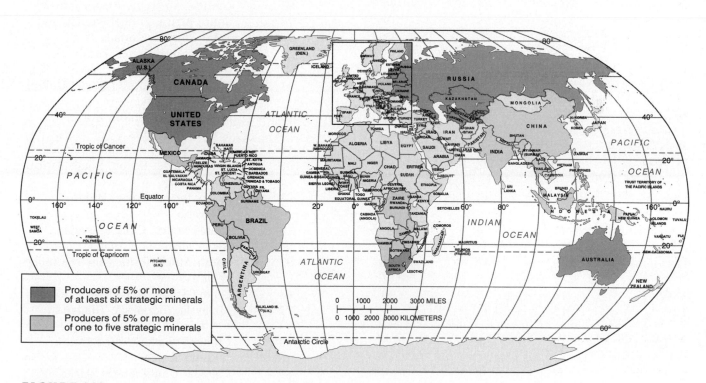

European countries—are deficient in strategic minerals. Compared to the former Soviet Union, the United States lacks several important metallic ores, including chromium and manganese.

How good is the world supply of strategic minerals? Our knowledge of world mineral reserves is summarized by the U.S. Bureau of Mines (Table 4.2). The table indicates the number of years 16 strategic minerals will last under two assumptions: (1) the number of years reserves will last with consumption growing at current rates (Column 2), and (2) the number of years reserves will last with consumption continuing to grow exponentially (Column 3). Data in Column 3 are more realistic than those in Column 2; they indicate that most of the key minerals will be exhausted within 100 years and some will be depleted within a couple of decades. Column 4 shows U.S. consumption as a percentage of world total. Except for molybdenum, an alloying element, domestic production is insufficient to cover production (Column 5).

The United States is running short of domestic sources of strategic minerals (Table 4.3). Its dependency on imports has grown rapidly since 1950; prior to that year, the country was dependent on imports for only

◈

Table 4.2

Projected Reserves of Selected Strategic Minerals

Resource	Static Index (Years)*	Exponential Index (Years)†	U.S. Consumption as a Percentage World Total	Percentage of U.S. Consumption Imported	Sources of Major Resources
Aluminum	100	31	42	97	Guinea, Australia, Brazil, Jamaica
Chromium	420	95	19	73	South Africa, Zimbabwe, Finland
Cobalt	110	60	32	95	Zaire, Zambia, Canada
Copper	36	21	33	27	Chile, United States, Zambia, Canada, USSR
Gold	11	9	26	31	South Africa, former Soviet Union, United States
Iron	240	93	28	22	former Soviet Union, Brazil, Australia, India
Lead	26	21	25	16	United States, Australia, Canada
Manganese	97	46	14	100	former Soviet Union, South Africa, Australia
Mercury	13	13	24	57	Spain, former Soviet Union, Algeria
Molybdenum	79	34	40	0	United States, Chile, Canada
Nickel	150	53	38	68	New Caledonia, Canada, Cuba
Platinum	130	47	31	92	South Africa, former Soviet Union, Zimbabwe
Silver	16	13	26	64	United States, Canada, Mexico
Tin	17	15	24	72	Malaysia, Indonesia, Thailand, China
Tungsten	40	28	22	68	China, Canada, United States, South Korea
Zinc	23	18	26	69	Canada, United States, Australia

* Static Index refers to the number of years reserves will last to 80% depletion with consumption growing at current rates.
† Exponential Index refers to the number of years reserves will last to 80% depletion with consumption growing at 2.5% per annum.
Source: U.S. Bureau of Mines, 1986, pp. 5–6.

◉

Table 4.3

U.S. Import Reliance for Key Minerals

Mineral	Percent Imported	Source
Arsenic	100%	Sweden, Canada, Mexico
Columbium	100%	Brazil, Canada, Thailand, Nigeria
Graphite	100%	Mexico, China, Brazil, Madagascar
Manganese	100%	Republic of South Africa, France, Gabon, Brazil
Mica (sheet)	100%	India, Belgium, Japan, France
Strontium (celestite)	100%	Mexico, Spain, China
Yttrium	100%	Australia
Gem Stones	99%	Bel-Lux, Israel, India, Republic of South Africa
Bauxite & Alumina	97%	Australia, Guinea, Jamaica, Suriname
Tantalum	92%	Thailand, Brazil, Australia, Canada
Diamond (industrial)	89%	Republic of South Africa, UK, Ireland, Bel-Lux
Fluorspar	88%	Mexico, Republic of South Africa, Spain, Italy, China
PT-Group Metals	88%	Republic of South Africa, UK, former Soviet Union
Cobalt	86%	Zaire, Zambia, Canada, Norway
Tungsten	80%	China, Canada, Bolivia, Portugal
Chromium	75%	Republic of South Africa, Zimbabwe, Turkey, Yugoslavia
Nickel	74%	Canada, Australia, Norway, Botswana
Tin	73%	Brazil, Thailand, Indonesia, Bolivia
Potash	72%	Canada, Israel, German Dem. Rep., former Soviet Union
Zinc	69%	Canada, Mexico, Peru, Australia
Cadmium	66%	Canada, Australia, Mexico, Fed. Rep. of Germany
Barite	63%	China, Morocco, India
Silver	57%	China, Mexico, UK, Peru
Asbestos	51%	Canada, Republic of South Africa
Gypsum	37%	Canada, Mexico, Spain
Silicon	33%	Brazil, Canada, Norway, Venezuela
Iron Ore	28%	Canada, Brazil, Venezuela, Liberia
Copper	25%	Canada, Chile, Peru, Zaire, Zambia, Mexico
Aluminum	24%	Canada, Japan, Venezuela, Brazil
Cement	20%	Canada, Mexico, Spain
Iron & Steel	19%	EEC, Japan, Canada, Republic of Korea
Lead	15%	Canada, Mexico, Peru, Australia, Honduras
Salt	12%	Canada, Mexico, Bahamas, Chile, Spain
Beryllium	11%	Brazil, China, Switzerland, Republic of South Africa
Titanium	8%	Japan, former Soviet Union
Nitrogen	7%	Canada, former Soviet Union, Trin. & Tob., Mexico
Sulfur	6%	Canada, Mexico

four designated strategic minerals. If measured in terms of the percentage imported, U.S. dependency increased from an average of 54% in 1960 to 78% in 1990.

The United States is not only dependent on imports for more than 50% of the minerals it consumes, but also depends heavily on certain countries for particular minerals. The United States imports most minerals from "friendly" countries such as Canada, Brazil, and South Africa. In 1985, the United States imported 33% of its manganese, 45% of its platinum, and 56% of its chromium from South Africa. Dependency on South

Africa for these three critical substances helps to explain U.S. foreign policy toward that nation.

Minerals projected as future needs by the United States are unevenly distributed around the world. Many are concentrated in the former Soviet Union and Canada and in the underdeveloped countries of Africa, Asia, and Latin America. Whether these critical substances will be available for U.S. consumption may depend less on economic scarcity and more on international tensions and foreign policy objectives.

Is the U.S. technological society gravely threatened by the degree to which domestic supplies must be supplemented by importing them from other countries? The need for a country to import a particular material does not mean that the material is unavailable at home. We have merely scratched the solid crust of the earth for the materials we need. Given an economical source of ultraterrestrial energy (solar radiation) and even more ingenious methods of extraction. who can say how much of our mineral needs could eventually be obtained domestically? The environmental cost of "moving mountains" to win these commodities would be another matter, however.

MINING ACTIVITIES IN THE UNITED STATES

The total estimated value of nonfuel mineral resources produced in 1993 was approximately $35 billion (dollar value per capita was the highest in Wyoming and Nevada). Approximately half of that value was localized production of cement, which is listed by the U.S. Bureau of Mines as a mineral. It also included sand, gravel, stone, clay, and lime. These relatively low valued minerals are extracted in large quantities, with California producing approximately 10% of the total, followed by Texas with approximately 7.5%. Arizona and Utah are large copper producers, and Florida produces large amounts of phosphate rock.

Iron ore is still the leading mineral resource in Michigan and Minnesota, the latter famous for its Masabi Range, which fuels most of the steel in the Great Lakes States. Gold is an important mineral mined in Nevada, California, South Dakota, and Montana, while copper is mined in New Mexico, Arizona, and Michigan. Texas, Washington, and Utah mine large amounts of magnesium, and Colorado seems to have a lock on the iron additive, molybdenum, although smaller proportions are mined in New Mexico, Arizona, and Idaho.

The United States receives its largest supply of domestic silver from Idaho, Nevada, Montana, and Arizona. The annual nonfuel mineral production in dollars per square mile is the highest in Florida, Michigan, Maryland, and New Jersey, where it exceeds $25,000 per square mile per year. If one calculates the value of annual nonfuel mineral production on a per capita basis, then the low-population Rocky Mountain states of Wyoming and Nevada lead the list, with Montana, Idaho, Utah, Arizona, and New Mexico in a second position. These states average more than $1000 per capita per year in the value of nonfuel mineral productions.

Noncoal mining, excluding uranium tailings and overburden, produces 15,000 pounds of solid waste per person per year. It is by far the largest producer of solid waste in America. Copper, iron ore, and phosphate mining create much of the waste, most of it in the form of soil and rock removed to gain access to ores, called *mine tailings*. These tailings are deposited in piles or filled into lakes and ponds.

In 1990, there were 2000 surface impoundments at 500 separate sites where metals had been mined. In addition, there were another 2500 surface impoundments at 1200 nonmetallic mine sites. These impoundments pose considerable contamination risks to streams and ground water supplies because liquid wastes are stored and treated in unlined natural surface sites. Dissolved mining wastes can contain toxic minerals, including molybdenum, copper, arsenic, selenium, and sulfuric acid.

MINERAL LEASING ON FEDERAL LANDS IN AMERICA

In the United States, the U.S. government has encouraged exploitation of the nation's mineral resources on government-owned lands. Copper, silver, gold, magnesium, uranium, and other "hard rock" minerals are now being mined under 54,000 patents. A patent is required to exploit minerals on U.S. government properties. Mining phosphate, potassium, sodium, lead, sulfur, and zinc is allowed through lease programs by the U.S. government. The large majority of leased lands for nonfuel mineral production in the United States are in the states of New Mexico and Utah, where potassium is mined; in Wyoming and Nevada, where sodium is mined; and in Missouri, where lead and zinc are mined. Almost all of the production in Idaho and Montana is for phosphate. Three-fourths of California's mining is for the extraction of sodium.

Importation of Key Minerals to the United States

The United States is well-endowed with key minerals that should last well beyond the year 2050, among them being boron, magnesium, molybdenum, phosphorous, potash, titanium, and silicon. *Reserve deficiency minerals* are defined as those minerals for which reserves in the United States are not sufficient to meet anticipated near-term industrial needs. Some of the examples include gold, silver, mercury, tungsten, and zinc. The United States contains essentially no reserves for cobalt, chromium, aluminum, tin, manganese, platinum, and asbestos (see Table 4.3).

It is true that some of these minerals are present in the United States in some quantities, but they are not extractable at market rates or they are too environmentally damaging or politically unacceptable to mine at a market rate. Table 4.3 also shows strategic mineral dependencies, which are primarily for national defense purposes. Critical minerals, such as copper, nickel, and vanadium, are deemed to be vital to America's strategic interest and can be supplied from the United States, itself, or Canada, while cobalt manganese, ferro manganese, chromium, and platinum must be attained from other nations that are not always so friendly to the United States.

The United States also stockpiles minerals for emergency purposes, according to the Strategic and Critical Mineral Stockpiling Act of 1979. Minerals in this category that are heavily stockpiled in the United States include asbestos, crystal, diamonds, manganese, mercury, quartz crystal, silver, talc, tin, and tungsten. Now that the Cold War is over and the strategic nuclear threat has declined, stockpiling goals have been relaxed somewhat.

Ocean Mineral Resources and Recycling

Affluent countries are unlikely to be easily defeated by a looming mineral shortage. They will devote more attention to programs for discovering new deposits, developing substitutes, and improving mining technology. Certainly, these countries will emphasize recycling and reusing minerals, and they may be forced to extract more resources from the sea. Are the oceans and recycling the answer to our mineral problems?

MINERALS FROM THE SEA

Vast mineral resources exist in sea water and on the ocean floor. With existing technology, however, only a

Miners sort rocks containing tin, which will be crushed and melted. This scene is from part of the largest mine in Bolivia, the "Twentieth Century" plant in the region of Oruro. The United States, Japan, Russia, and countries of the EEC consume the majority of the world's metals. Only six developing nations—Algeria, Brazil, China, India, the Republic of Korea, and Mexico—make it into the top 10 consumers of selective metals. Five countries—the United States, South Africa, Russia, China, and Australia—hold more than half of the world's reserves of the 15 most important world metals. *(Source: Sebastia Salgado, Jr./ Magnum Photos.)*

few minerals (i.e., magnesium, table salt) are abundant enough to be extracted from sea water profitably. The deep ocean floor is unlikely to solve mineral shortages. The only known minerals on ocean floors are manganese oxide nodules that contain about 24% magnesium, 14% iron, and small amounts of copper, nickel, and cobalt. Although manganese mining is feasible, political considerations are postponing actual mining operations. Developed countries are fighting among themselves over who should be allowed to exploit seabed wealth. Leaders of underdeveloped countries are opposed to exploitation of these resources by developed countries. They maintain that deep ocean resources belong to all people and should be divided equally.

RECYCLING RESOURCES

Every year in the United States, huge quantities of household and industrial waste are disposed of at sanitary landfills and open dumps. These materials are sometimes called "urban ores" because they can be recovered and used again. For years, the United States has been recycling scarce and highly valuable metals such as iron, lead, copper, antimony, silver, gold, and platinum, but large amounts of scrap metals are still being wasted. Although we could recover a much greater proportion of scrap with improved technology and economic incentives, recycling will not solve our environmental problems. Reclaiming and recycling depends on one resource that for the most part cannot be recycled—energy.

Environmental Impact of Mineral Extraction

Mineral extraction has a varied impact on the environment, depending on mining procedures, local hydrological conditions, and the size of the operation. Environmental impact also depends on the stage of development of the mineral—exploration activities usually have less of an impact than mining and processing mineral resources.

Minimizing the environmental impact of mineral extraction is in everyone's best interest, but the task is difficult because demand for minerals continues to grow and ever-poorer grades of ore are mined. For example, in 1900 the average grade of copper ore mined was 4% copper. By 1973, ores containing as little as 0.53% copper were mined. Each year more and more rock

has to be excavated, crushed, and processed to extract copper. In fact, the immense copper mining pits in Montana, Utah, and Arizona are no longer in use because foreign sources, mostly in underdeveloped countries, are less expensive.

Open-pit mines and quarries amount to a small fraction of the total area of a country. In general, their impact on the environment is local, but as long as the future remains technological and materialistic, the demand for minerals is going to increase. Lower and lower quality minerals will have to be used and, even with good engineering, environmental degradation will extend far beyond excavation and surface plant areas.

ENERGY

◆

Commercial energy, which accounts for more than 80% of all human energy use, is the lifeblood of modern economies. Indeed, it is the biggest single item in international trade. Oil alone accounts for about one-quarter of the volume of world trade.

Until the energy shocks of the 1970s, commercial energy demands were widely thought to be related to population growth and rising affluence. Suddenly, higher prices in the international oil market brought energy demands in the industrial countries to a virtual standstill. The increase in oil prices even surprised energy analysts. It signalled a change in the control of the oil market from the international oil companies headquartered in the United States to the capitals of the producing countries.

There have been many attempts to account for the transition of power within the international oil market. Was it the international oil companies' scramble for higher profits? Was it a result of the U.S. government's effort to preserve American leadership in the international oil market? Or was it greed on the part of the sheiks? Whatever the answer, Americans came face-to-face with the "energy crisis," especially during the winter of 1976/1977. A combination of below normal temperatures and a shortage of fuel was devastating. Thousands of factories were cut back to "plant protection" levels and had to shut down, and more than 3 million workers were laid off. Americans appreciated that this was not "just another crisis." They learned first hand that when energy fails, everything fails in an urban-industrial economy.

During the 1980s energy demand forecasts were consistently excessive, resulting in excess capacity in energy industries. Oil prices fell from a high of more than $30 in 1981 to $15 in 1987, shaking predictions made in 1980 that costs would soar to more than $40 per barrel. OPEC, once considered an invincible cartel, lost oil sales between 1980 and 1987. Its share of world oil output dropped from 57% in 1975 to 30% in 1985 as non-OPEC countries expanded production. Many Third World countries, strapped by heavy energy debts, were relieved to see prices falling. Oil-exporting underdeveloped countries, such as Mexico, Venezuela, and Nigeria, which came to depend on oil revenues for an important source of income, were hurt the worst.

Although prices rose to $25 per barrel during the Persian Gulf War of 1991, due to reduced production, prices fell to $15 per barrel again by 1994, due to world recession and reduced demand. True, there appears to be no world oil crisis now, but what of the next 20 to 40 years? Will there be ways to keep oil expensive around the year 2015? (See Figure 4.21.)

Energy Production and Consumption

Most commercial energy produced is from nonrenewable resources; and most renewable energy sources, particularly wood and charcoal, are used directly by producers, mainly poor rural people in underdeveloped countries. Although there is increasing interest in renewable energy development because of the growing scarcity of easily accessible fossil fuels, commercial energy is the core of energy use at the present time. Only a handful of countries produce several times more commercial energy than they consume (Figure 4.13). The top 10 energy surplus countries, ranked by size of surplus, are Saudi Arabia, Mexico, Iran, Venezuela, Indonesia, Algeria, Kuwait, Iraq, Lybia, Qatar, Nigeria, and the United Arab Emirates. Nearly one-half of all African countries are energy paupers. And several of the world's leading industrial powers—notably Japan, many western European countries, and the United States—consume more energy than they produce.

The United States leads the world in total energy

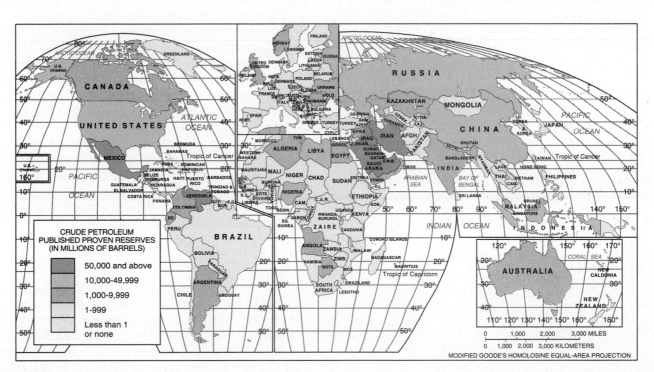

FIGURE 4.13
Crude petroleum reserves. The greatest number of proven petroleum reserves exist in countries of the Middle East surrounding the Persian Gulf, in particular the Arabian Peninsula. This area includes more than 50% of all proven world reserves. Mexico and Venezuela also show a disproportionately large share of proven reserves. (See Color Insert page 1.6, bottom, for more illustrative map.)

consumption, but Canada and Norway are the highest per capita users. With only 5% of the world's population, the United States consumes about one-quarter of the world's energy. By contrast, underdeveloped countries also consume about one-quarter of the world's energy but they contain 77% of the population. Thus, there exists a striking relation between energy consumption and income per capita (Figure 4.14). Maps of the consumption of electric power and of major oil and coal flows also reinforce the image of the developed world as the all-consuming energy sink (Figures 4.15 and 4.16). Most of the poorer underdeveloped countries receive a meager energy ration, well below levels consistent even with moderate levels of economic development. They do not have the money to buy a better energy ration. Commercial energy consumption in industrialized countries has been at consistently high levels with oil providing 40% of the total energy used, followed by coal and natural gas each providing approximately 30%. A sharp decline in oil consumption occurred after the first OPEC price hike in 1978 (Figure 4.17). In developing countries, commercial energy consumption has been at low but increasing levels. Coal is most important in non-oil exporting countries. Gas is a much less important source of energy (Figure 4.18).

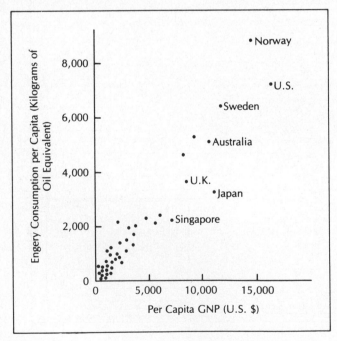

FIGURE 4.14
Relationship between per capita GNP, 1985, and commercial energy consumption, 1985.
(Source: World Bank, 1987.)

OIL DEPENDENCY

Because Americans were seriously affected by the 1973 Arab oil embargo and imported oil as a proportion of total demand increased from 11% in the late 1960s to 50% in the mid-1970s, political leaders called for a national policy of oil self-sufficiency to end U.S. dependency on uncertain suppliers of petroleum. President Richard Nixon implemented such a policy in 1973 and, 4 years later, President Jimmy Carter reaffirmed the policy and its purposes. In 1985, President Ronald Reagan also endorsed this policy, but called for minimum government intervention and greater reliance on market forces to supply current and future energy requirements. The Reagan administration proposed the development of energy sources on most federal land and off-shore sites, filled a 500-million gallon strategic oil reserve, and encouraged the development of nuclear power. At the same time, air and water pollution regulations were relaxed, tax credits for home energy conservation expenditures were ended, a bill to compel firms to build energy-efficient appliances was vetoed, and fuel-economy standards for new cars were delayed, then later passed.

These conflicting policies did not help to end U.S. dependency on imported oil. They did, however, downgrade federal efforts to encourage American households and companies to conserve fossil fuels. High-priced oil from OPEC temporarily reduced U.S. consumption of oil (by 39% between 1973 and 1986), but in the mid-1980s dependence on cheap imported oil began to rise again in response to lower prices.

Although the United States is dependent on imported oil, most of it does not come from the Middle East. The United States imports 37% of the oil it consumes, but only 4% of that oil comes from the Persian Gulf (Table 4.4). Japan, Italy, and France are much more dependent on Persian Gulf oil.

PRODUCTION OF FOSSIL FUELS

The Arab oil embargo stimulated fossil fuel production in the United States and throughout the world. In the United States, coal production increased in the mid- and late-1970s in response to the increase in the price and decrease in the supply of OPEC oil. In the 1980s, the apparent decline of the OPEC cartel and the entry of important new producers—notably Mexico, Britain, and Norway—led to a drop in oil prices. The willingness of new producers and others, such as Saudi Arabia, to

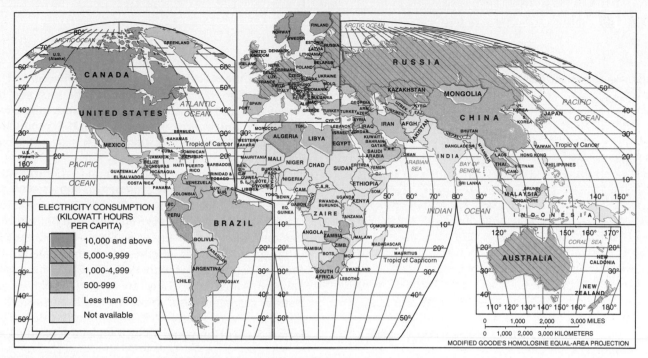

FIGURE 4.15

World per capita electricity consumption. The United States, Canada, and the Scandinavian countries consume more electricity per capita than any other countries. When the electricity usage of the United States, Canada, Europe and Russia is combined, 75% of electricity usage in the world is accounted for, but only 20% of the people. By comparing this map to the map of crude petroleum proven reserves, the deficit areas of the world such as Europe and Japan, which have high energy needs but low fossil fuel resources, can be seen. In addition, there are areas in the world with high fossil fuel resources but low energy needs, such as the Middle Eastern countries, Mexico, Venezuela, Indonesia, Argentina, Algeria, Nigeria, and China. (See Color Insert page 1.7, top, for more illustrative map.)

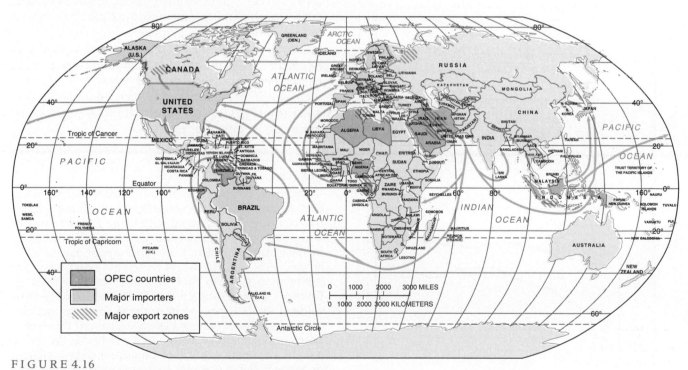

FIGURE 4.16

Major world oil flows traded on the international market.
(Source: Based on data from United Nations, 1990.)

A. All Industrialized Countries

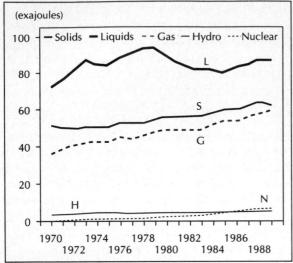

B. OECD Industrialized Countries

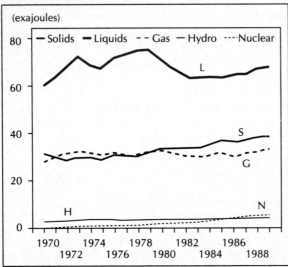

C. Central Europe and the Former Soviet Union

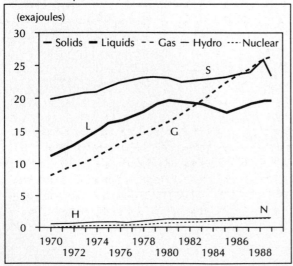

put oil on the world market forced a reduction in U.S. oil production. If it had not been for the long war between Iran and Iraq, the drop in oil prices might well have had more drastic consequences on U.S. production and on the economies of the oil-rich states of Texas, Oklahoma, and Louisiana.

The embargo made Americans and other industrial societies aware of their dependency on imported oil and on the world distribution of fossil fuel reserves. The United States is richly endowed with coal but has only modest reserves of oil and natural gas. More than 50% of the world's known reserves of oil are located in the Middle East compared with 19% in the Americas. Sub-Saharan Africa and China are critically short of oil. Natural gas, often a substitute for oil, is also unevenly distributed with nearly 40% of supplies located in the former Soviet Union and about 26% in the Middle East.

U.S. Energy Policy

According to some experts, the "energy crisis" of the 1970s occurred in the United States because a national energy policy was not a high priority. In western Europe, however, effective energy policies already existed. Following the Arab oil embargo, the United States began to form a national energy policy and enacted a major piece of legislation, the Energy Policy and Conservation Act of 1975. An important goal of this law is to reduce energy demand through conservation. Due to investments made in efficient technologies during the 1970s and early 1980s, energy conservation promises to continue despite lower oil prices.

FIGURE 4.17
Commercial energy consumption in industrialized countries. In panel A, energy consumption in all industrialized countries has increased with liquid fuels as a proportion going down and coal and gas going up, with an increase also in nuclear. Coal consumption has increased 22% since 1970 and represents a 30% total consumption in 1989. In panel B, OECD industrialized countries show a substantial reduction in liquid fuels because of the 1973 and 1979 Arab Oil Embargo and oil price hikes. These nations have also reduced their reliance on the import of foreign oil by reducing the amount of energy required to produce their gross domestic product. Panel C shows central Europe and the former Soviet Union countries. Here, there has been a dramatic increase in the use of natural gas and a sudden, sharp drop in coal.
(Source: World Resources Institute, 1992, p. 147.)

THE UNITED STATES' PRICE CEILING

Price ceiling is a price set by the government below the market price. In the long run, it produces shortages of the good in question. The shortage created by the Arab oil embargo and the higher prices that resulted, as well as higher prices from Iraq's invasion of Kuwait, culminated in America due to government-sponsored price ceilings on petroleum.

In 1971, the government put price controls on petroleum and natural gas. Consumers regarded this move as a real boon because it provided them with cheap mobility. These controls were part of Nixon's new economic policy in 1971, which was created to stop the general inflation in America. Price ceilings were lifted on most goods by 1981, but not on oil and gas. With prices frozen at an unreasonably low level, consumption increased. However, the costs of production were not frozen and continued to rise. Oil production in the United States, therefore, declined because oil producers reduced their exploration and drilling of new oil fields due to reduced productivity.

The effect of a price ceiling, which is set below the normal equilibrium quantity and price, lowers the price of the commodity but creates a shortage since the quantity demanded (Q_1) at a new price greatly exceeds the quantity supplied (Q_2) (Figure 4.19). Instead of allowing the price of gas and home heating oil to float upward and, thus, to provide suppliers with incentives to meet the shortage, America turned to overseas production centers, especially in and around the Persian Gulf. This oil was relatively less expensive and in an abundant supply until 1973.

FIGURE 4.18

Commercial energy consumption in developing countries, 1970–1990. In panel A, consumption of energy almost tripled in developing countries during the last 20 years. The demand for coal actually superseded the demand for oil, with the demand for natural gas also rising dramatically. In 1990, coal satisfied about 46% of total commercial energy demand, followed by petroleum with 38%. In panel B, oil-exporting developing countries maintain a heavy reliance on oil and natural gas, which has increased three-fold during the last 20 years. This was due to population growth, increased suburbanization, and low prices for internal oil and gas supplies. Panel C shows oil importing of developing countries. Developing countries rely on coal, followed by oil, with natural gas a distant third. Oil importing tapered off a bit with price hikes in the late 1980s. The greatest producers of coal are China, India, South Africa, and Korea, producing 95% of coal from developing countries.
(Source: World Resources Institute, 1992, p. 147.)

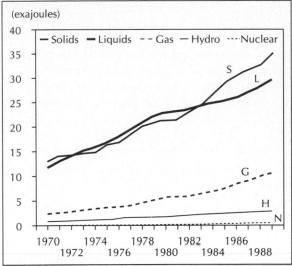

A. All Developing Countries

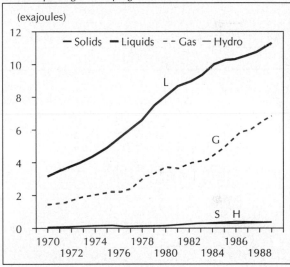

B. Oil-Exporting Developing Countries

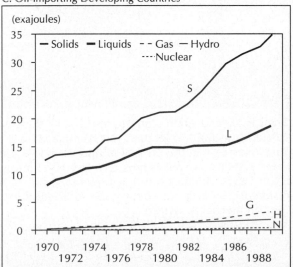

C. Oil-Importing Developing Countries

Table 4.4
Oil Consumers and Their Dependence on Persian Gulf Oil

	United States	Japan	Germany	France	Italy	United Kingdom
Total oil consumption (millions of barrels per day)	16.1	4.3	2.4	1.8	1.6	1.5
Percentage of total oil consumption imported	37	100	100	94	100	0
Percentage of total oil consumption imported from the Persian Gulf by tanker or pipeline	4	60	10	33	51	0

	United States	Japan	Western Europe
Percentage of total oil consumption passing through the Strait of Hormuz by tanker	4	60	11

Note: Britain is a net exporter of oil.
Source: Shipler, 1987, p. 1.

A Shell/Esso production platform in Britain's North Sea gas field. British oil exploration was stimulated by a dramatic increase in the price of oil in the mid-1970s and early 1980s, as well as by a recovery of oil prices in the late 1980s. Britain's North Sea oil and gas investment may keep the country self-sufficient until the end of the twentieth century.
(Source: Shell.)

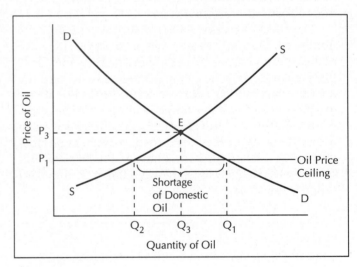

FIGURE 4.19
The U.S. oil price ceiling. The U.S. government established an oil price ceiling to keep prices artificially low. The price ceiling kept prices low for consumers, but did not allow the market to establish an equilibrium position at point E. It created a shortage because the quantity demanded at Q_1 was never supplied. At price P_1, the quantity supplied was Q_2. Thus, a shortage existed between the quantity Q_1, which the public demanded at the low oil price, versus Q_2, which suppliers could provide at such a price. Quantity demanded greatly exceeds the quantity supplied at the oil price ceiling. The shortage of domestic oil was supplied by foreign sources, which caused the United States to depend on imported oil.

Price controls precipitated, decreasing the United States' domestic oil supply, and increasing the supply of imported oil. Figure 4.20 shows the impact of the oil price controls on domestic and foreign suppliers in the United States in the 1960s and 1970s. The foreign sources filled the needed production void created by price controls of the U.S. government. These oil supplies were available at or below the ceiling prices and, therefore, consumers gobbled them up, showing little concern for the fact that local production, as a proportion of local consumption, was declining drastically.

The United States thus became tethered to the Middle East allowing for the energy crisis of the 1970s. In 1973, OPEC's first embargo occurred and, by 1978, it had increased the world price of a barrel of crude oil by 500%, eventually sending the world into general recession. The developed world created the prospects of long lines at the gas station, as well as much higher prices and regional shortages. The rising price of oil pushed the price of oil goods and services upward throughout the world, requiring belt tightening in the United States and falling standards of living worldwide. The effect in the Third World countries, especially for those governments without oil, was a disaster, plummeting them into high rates of debt and bankruptcy.

By the early 1980s, the U.S. government phased out price ceilings on the production of oil and gas, and domestic production began to increase once again. Fortunately, for the rest of the world, OPEC became less effective and successful at setting cartel oil prices because of internal bickering and get-rich-quick attempts. Various members would produce more than their quotas and set prices lower than agreed upon to sell more quantities quickly. Oil prices that were headed toward $40 a barrel suddenly went down and, by 1990, were again within the $15 to $20 a barrel range. However, the Kuwait/Iraq conflict and the Persian Gulf War reminded us once again that the developed world is too dependent on the Persian Gulf area, which is prone to internal conflict and political instability (Figure 4.21). (See box on page 152.)

THE UNITED STATES' FUTURE ENERGY POLICY

To ensure that an energy crisis does not recur, the United States must embrace a firm energy policy that advocates the following: the conservation of remaining oil and coal while renewable forms of energy are being developed; the elimination of industrial and home energy inefficiency; and the betterment of environmental quality. In addition, recurrent crises can only be prevented if the United States takes full account of world energy considerations. Energy is a worldwide problem that cannot be solved by confrontation among groups of countries. Sharing energy is essential to protect the interests of all producers and consumers.

Who was to blame for the energy crisis of the 1970s? The big oil and electric companies were at least partly responsible in their maneuvers to restrict production and imports in the manner of monopolies, oligopolies, and global cartels. The large, often excessive profits enjoyed by the oil companies were obtained at high cost to Americans, who saw no appreciable improvement in national energy self-sufficiency.

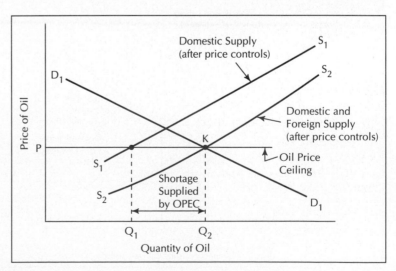

FIGURE 4.20
OPEC's stranglehold on the United States. Foreign sources of oil came to the American consumer's rescue. Supply curve S_1 shows domestic supplies after price controls. In order to fulfill domestic demand with the price ceiling at point K, imported oil had to be delivered. Curve S_2 shows the domestic *and* foreign supply of oil because of price controls. As long as the American consumer could get oil at such a low price, he or she did not care whether the source was domestic or foreign. The shortage of domestic supply was made up primarily by OPEC countries. Thus, the stage was set for the energy crisis of 1973 and 1978, when Arab nations reduced the flow of oil to America, thus raising prices and creating long lines at the pump.

OIL PRICES AFTER THE PERSIAN GULF WAR

FOLLOWED BY WORLD RECESSION

In the fall of 1990, Iraq invaded Kuwait, sending the world concern about oil dependency once again into a tailspin. By mid-1991, the reduction and supply from Kuwait and Iraq produced increasing prices in the world scene. The price of crude oil rose from $19 a barrel to $30 a barrel, affecting, most notably, gasoline and home heating oil.

As in the case of 1973 with the Arab oil embargo and again in 1979, the United States, western Europe, and most other industrialized nations faced the prospect of reduced oil supplies and its counterpart, fast-rising prices. The main question that most Americans were faced with was whether the United States and the developed world could face yet another world rise in energy prices without retreating back to the inflation and recessionary conditions that followed the OPEC embargo of the 1970s.

With the expectation of reduced future supplies of oil and higher prices in the supply curve, the price of oil increased. This shift occurred before there was actually a shortfall in world energy supply. Consequently, not only current costs and supplies but also expectations, are important in the equilibrium price and quantity that result immediately after a major world confrontation. In 1994, oil dropped to $15 per barrel due to low world demand and recession.

Who suffered from the energy crisis? Certainly most people in developed countries (especially those on fixed incomes), many small firms, and even independent oil companies. Non–oil-producing underdeveloped countries such as Jamaica, Guyana, Mali, and Zambia were hurt much worse. They could not afford to spend foreign exchange on expensive oil imports.

Adequacy of Fossil Fuels

In the next few decades, energy demands are expected to increase much faster than population increase. The question people are asking these days is, "How long can fossil fuel reserves last given our increasing energy requirements?"

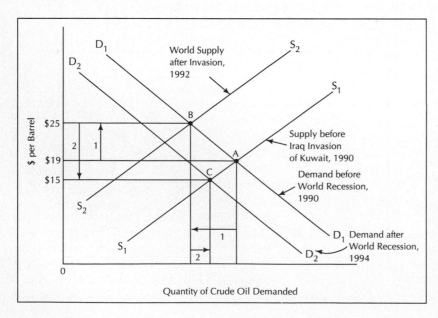

FIGURE 4.21
The Kuwait invasion. The Kuwait invasion by Iraq in 1990 had the immediate effect of knocking out world supply of oil by Kuwait and Iraq. With these supplies absent in the world flow of oil, as shown by S_2 above, the supply of crude oil demanded was reduced and prices rose (shift 1, from equilibrium point A to point B). Prices also rose in expectation of higher oil prices, even before a reduced supply hit the refineries. The oil price per barrel, which hit $35 during the Arab Oil Embargo of 1973 and 1978 and $25 a barrel during the Kuwait invasion, has dropped back down to $15 as of January 1994, due to world recession and low levels of demand (shift 2, from equilibrium point B to point C).

The vast areas of the world that have no fossil fuels and, consequently, are substantially limited in their ability to produce economic growth are also delineated. Other areas of the world have an abundance of fossil fuels. The darkly shaded countries indicate members of OPEC (Figure 4.16).

Unfortunately, the need for fossil fuels does not correspond very well with the production of fossil fuels. Most areas of South America have almost no fossil fuels, except for Venezuela and Ecuador. Most nations of Africa likewise are poorly endowed, except for Algeria, Libya in Muslim Africa, and Nigeria in Black Africa. In contrast, the developed nations of the world are moderately well-endowed with fossil fuels. North America has a large supply of coal, as shown by the fact that the United States contains approximately 29% of world coal reserves. Canada is likewise endowed proportional to its small population of 25 million.

OIL: BLACK GOLD

Europe, because of recent discoveries of petroleum in the North Sea and a moderate amount of coal in central Europe and Poland, is moderately well-endowed with fossil fuels. Large supplies, however, are imported from the Middle East to Europe. Mediterranean Europe, however, lacks all fossil fuels and is thus at a developmental disadvantage. The former Soviet Union has more than one-fourth of the world's proven coal reserves and is presently the world's top oil producer. However, its proven petroleum reserves are less than that of the Persian Gulf area.

Overall, and unfortunately, the developing world does not have a proportional share of energy resources. Developing nations possess only one-twelfth of the world's proven coal reserves, but when the Middle East is factored in, almost one-half of the natural gas and nine-tenths of the petroleum reserves of the world can be accounted for. The United States consumes nearly 25% of the world's production of energy, while the former Soviet Union countries consume another 15%.

Natural gas is somewhat limited overall, but plentiful in the western United States. In fact, the United States has 6% of the world's proven petroleum reserves, which includes mid-continent fields, gulf coastal fields, and the relatively new oil discovery on the north slope at Point Barrow, Alaska. However, the United States is a major net importer of petroleum. Natural gas is somewhat more problematic because of its difficulty to transport.

An enormous amount of petroleum is imported from the Middle East, where most of the world's proven reserves are concentrated. European and American companies originally controlled the Middle Eastern petroleum fields and exploited them. For these reasons, the United States and European nations have a poor image in certain locales throughout the Middle East, most notably Iran. American companies discovered the sources of oil, pumped and refined the oil, and transported it to energy thirsty developed countries around the world, yielding only a small proportion of the profits to the host countries in the Middle East. Most recently, in the 1970s, these countries nationalized their petroleum production and U.S. companies, such as Aramco, were expelled.

Current world oil reserves of 700 billion barrels are approximately 30 times the annual world oil production. U.S. oil reserves, however, are less than nine times its annual production. Probably some 500 billion barrels of new proved reserves will be added to the world reservoir in the next 40 years; however, the distribution pattern around the world indicates a shift of leverage that will become apparent in the next two generations. If nothing is done to change present trends, the global oil market will be in grave trouble by the year 2025. Exports from Africa and Latin America will peak by about the year 2000, and both continents will cease to be exporters before 2025. The Middle East will then be the only major exporter of oil. Import dependencies of North America, western Europe, and Japan/Far East will range from 52% to 98%. By 2025, demand will exceed production capacity. We could change this grim scenario through increased conservation, use of alternative fuels, and improved oil recovery techniques.

COAL: BLACK ROCKS THAT BURN

Coal is the most abundant fossil fuel and, at current production levels, world reserves will last about 500 years. Use of this resource, however, has been limited due to inefficient management by the international coal industry, the inconvenience of storing and shipping the fuel, and the environmental consequences of large-scale coal burning (Figure 4.22).

The principal fossil fuel in North America is coal (Figure 4.23). With the exception of the former Soviet Union, the United States has the largest coal reserves. Coal constitutes 67% of America's fossil fuel resources, yet it accounts for only about one-fifth of its energy consumption. If this share does not increase, the pro-

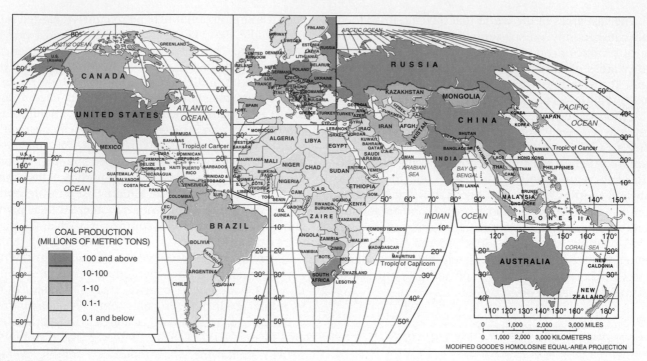

FIGURE 4.22
World coal production. The United States, followed by the former Soviet Union and China, produce more coal than any other countries. Australia, India, and South Africa also produce substantial amounts of coal. Since coal is bulky and more costly to transport than liquid oil, less coal is shipped internationally to supply world energy demands. Europe, which has a sparing supply of oil in the North Sea, is endowed with greater coal deposits, notably in Great Britain, Germany, and Poland. (See Color Insert page 1.7, bottom, for more illustrative map.)

jected life of coal is 200 to 400 years. If this share increases and more than one-half of the net energy is lost in mining, shipping, or by converting to more convenient forms of energy such as electricity, gas, and synthetic oil, the projected life is sharply reduced. Scientists say coal gasification and liquefaction could deplete U.S. supplies within 50 years.

Coal could provide some relief to the dependence on oil and gas (Figure 4.24). The United States has a 300-year supply of coal, mainly in the western Rocky Mountain states. The direct burning of coal and power plants and coal-generated electricity could substitute in part for petroleum, but its use in mobile demand units, such as automobiles, is not possible. The use of coal presents a number of problems that oil and natural gas do not, making it somewhat less desirable as an important fossil fuel. These problems are as follows:

1. Coal burning releases more pollution than other fossil fuels, especially sulfur. Low grades of coal, called bituminous coals, are accompanied by large supplies of sulfur, which are released into the atmosphere when coal is burned, along with the incipient smoke and soot. H_2O from moisture in the air, and SO_2 from the sulfur create H_2SO_4, which is acid rain (Figure 4.25).

2. Coal is not as easily mined as is natural gas or petroleum. Coal occurs in the solid form and must be mined with deep underground tunnels or with open-pit mining methods. Underground mining is costly and dangerous and open-pit mining leaves large scars on the earth's surface that are difficult to rehabilitate to environmental premining standards.

3. Coal is bulky and does not have a high value compared to its weight. It is expensive to transport and slurry pipelines are not nearly as efficient as oil pipelines. Coal is generally transported by railroad in the United States, but there are larger loading and unloading costs compared to oil and natural gas.

4. Coal is not a good fuel for mobile energy units such as trains, planes, and automobiles, and one

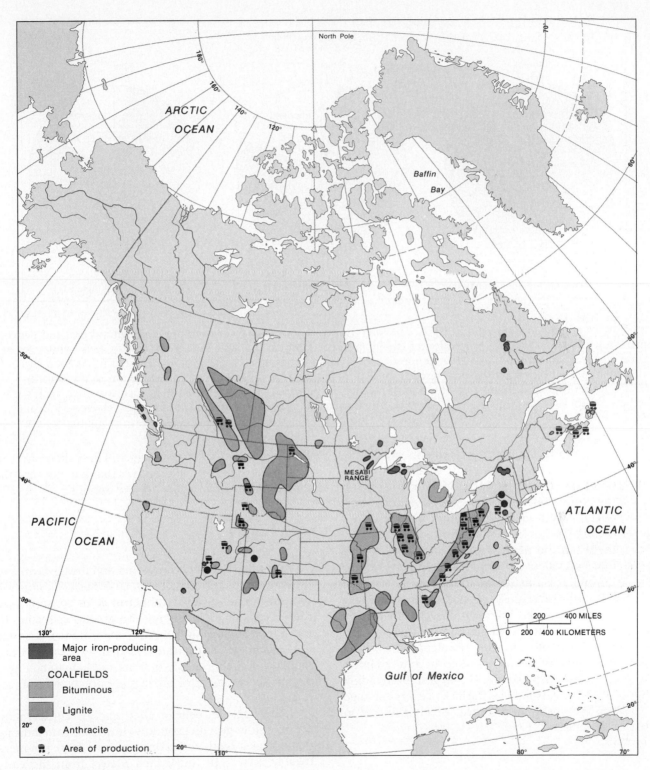

FIGURE 4.23
Major iron producing areas and coal fields of North America.
(*Source: Fisher, 1992, p. 121.*)

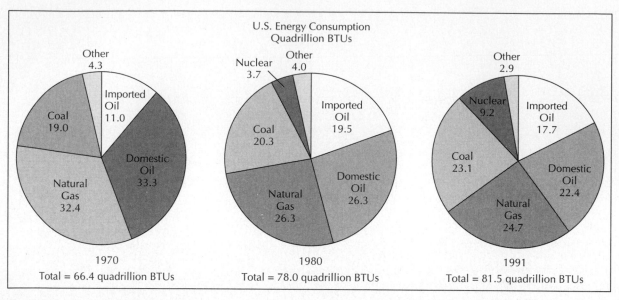

U.S. Energy Consumption
Quadrillion BTUs

1970
Total = 66.4 quadrillion BTUs

Other 4.3
Imported Oil 11.0
Coal 19.0
Domestic Oil 33.3
Natural Gas 32.4

1980
Total = 78.0 quadrillion BTUs

Nuclear 3.7
Other 4.0
Imported Oil 19.5
Coal 20.3
Domestic Oil 26.3
Natural Gas 26.3

1991
Total = 81.5 quadrillion BTUs

Other 2.9
Nuclear 9.2
Imported Oil 17.7
Coal 23.1
Domestic Oil 22.4
Natural Gas 24.7

FIGURE 4.24
United States energy consumption in BTUs. The three principal sources of fossil fuels are coal, natural gas, and petroleum. From 1970 to 1991, the proportion of energy use depending on coal increased from 19% to 23%, while that of natural gas declined from 32% to 25%. Domestic oil consumption declined from 33% to 22%, but it has been supported by imported oil, which has increased from 11% to almost 18% of total energy consumption in the United States. Another dramatic change, besides that of reliance on imported oil, is the increase of nuclear power, which was less than 1% in 1990 to more than 9% in 1991. The number of total BTUs jumped substantially between 1970 and 1980 by almost 14% in a 10-year-period; however, the increase between 1980 and 1991 was only approximately 4.5%.

of the most important requirements of a highly developed society is mobility. Coal, while it can be adapted through gasification techniques to the automobile, becomes expensive and is not, overall, well-adapted to motor vehicles. Coal could be a source of energy for gasoline via electricity. In the near future, electric cars will be more prevalent on American highways and in Europe. It is likely that, in the future, automobiles will also refuel at gas stations by connecting electric-powered cables to charging machines, as well as refueling at gas pumps. These battery chargers could supplant petroleum in the long run, but cars would need to be much lighter than they are presently. The biggest shortcoming of electric cars today is the lack of energy storage and their geographic range, which is limited to 100 miles.

Energy Options

The age of cheap fossil fuels is coming to an end. Americans are told by corporations and the government

that they must conserve energy and find alternatives to fossil fuels, especially alternatives that will not rape the environment. How viable are the options?

CONSERVATION

According to utility companies and the government, the way to reduce the gap between domestic production and consumption in the short run is for consumers to restrict consumption. Energy conservation stretches finite fuel resources and reduces environmental stress. Conservation can substitute for expensive, less environmentally desirable supply options and help to buy time for the development of other more acceptable sources of energy.

Many people believe that energy conservation means a slow-growth economy; however, data indicate that energy growth and economic growth are not inextricably linked. In the United States, from the early 1870s to 1950, GNP per capita increased sixfold, whereas energy use per capita only slightly more than doubled. Energy efficiency, the ratio of useful energy output to total energy input, increased substantially between 1921 and 1975.

FIGURE 4.25
Annual acid rain deposit levels in North America. When sulfur is released into the atmosphere from the burning of coal and oil, it combines with moisture to create acid rain. The worst inflicted areas of acid rain in North America occur downwind from the principal polluting regions of the industrialized Midwest. Ohio, western Pennsylvania, and northern New York State are the areas that are most heavily inflicted with acid rain deposits. Acid rain and snow deposits are also well documented in Europe, which is in a belt of prevailing wind coming from the west, as is the United States. The industrial regions of Central Europe, especially the Ruhr Valley in Northern Germany, have created strongly acidic precipitation in much of Scandinavia and Eastern Europe. Sulfur, released from the burning of coal, into the atmosphere, combines with water vapor to produce sulfuric acid. Such acid creates substantial air pollution and etches away at limestone buildings, monuments, and markers on the earth. Acid precipitation can also kill plant and animal life, especially aquatic life. Literally thousands of lakes in Sweden and Norway no longer support the fish they once did. Local governments dump large amounts of powdered limestone into these water bodies to neutralize the acid.

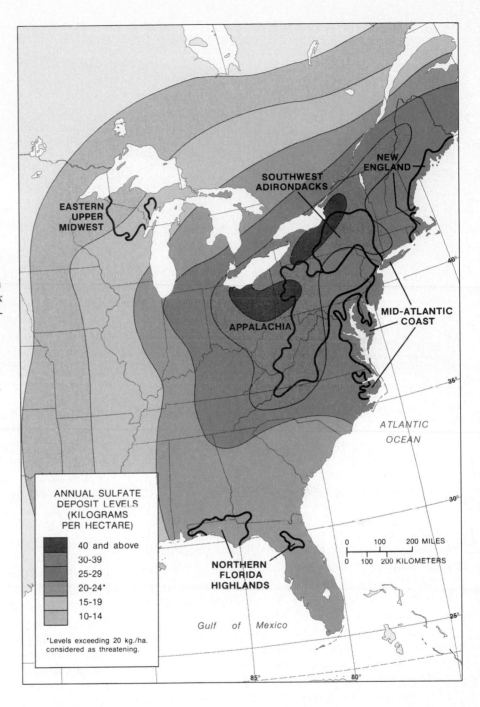

ANNUAL SULFATE DEPOSIT LEVELS
(KILOGRAMS PER HECTARE)

40 and above
30-39
25-29
20-24*
15-19
10-14

*Levels exceeding 20 kg./ha. considered as threatening.

At least two approaches to energy conservation have been suggested by the government and energy companies. One approach is to increase energy efficiency. Consumers can add insulation and storm windows to their homes, and they can drive more slowly, use smaller automobiles, and ride buses. Power plants can transmit "waste heat" to nearby plants. At best, utilities convert 27% of fuel energy into electricity; the rest escapes as heat in the form of warm air and gases. Consumers can lower thermostats, switch to lower wattage light bulbs, and take showers instead of baths. Industry could rely on less energy and more labor. The other approach is less attractive to most Americans—compulsory allocation and rationing. If consumers are unwilling to alter

The Wairakei geothermal facility in New Zealand produces electricity by drawing steam from a natural underground reservoir. The earth's interior heat is enormous, but it is still difficult to harness with present technologies. In general, geothermal resources can be economically exploited only when molten rock lies within 3000 meters of the earth's surface. Although the environmental impacts of geothermal energy is minor compared to those of many other energy sources, they do include possible pollution of surface waters and ground water.
(Source: United Nations—New Zealand Information Services.)

their styles of life voluntarily in order to save energy, then compulsory methods could be introduced to make sure that everyone shares the burden equally.

Alternative Energy Options

One alternative is nuclear energy. Atomic energy, however, can result in radioactive fallout to the environment, which is a major concern, especially since the nuclear accidents at the Three Mile Island plant in the United States in 1979 and at the Chernobyl station in the USSR in 1986. The wisdom of a commitment to nuclear energy depends ultimately on the ability of human beings—their technology and institutions—to manage a very hazardous enterprise. There has been heated debate as to whether human societies are capable of managing nuclear energy wisely. However, as long as industrial countries are locked into increased energy consumption, it seems inevitable that nuclear power will be required to help meet the demands. (See box on page 160.)

NUCLEAR ENERGY

Nuclear energy, although it provides a great advantage to conventional fuels, has not been as acceptable in America as it has in Europe. For example, 1 kilogram of enriched nuclear fuel packs more than 2 million times the energy of 1 kilogram of coal. Therefore, a large amount of energy is released from a very small amount of fuel, solving storage, transportation, and environmental problems of recovery.

Europe and Japan have relied on nuclear energy because of their lack of fossil fuels (Figure 4.26). In some countries and in Japan, two-thirds of the electrical energy produced comes from nuclear power plants. Belgium, France, Hungary, and Sweden produce more than one-half of their energy from nuclear power plants, while Finland, Germany, Spain, Switzerland, Japan, South Korea, and Taiwan are also major nuclear energy producers and users. In the United States and Canada, countries that are far less dependent on nuclear energy, eastern portions of the country are more receiving of nuclear power plants than the west. Illinois, for example, has 15 nuclear power plants alone; New England, as of 1993, drew most of its electrical power from nuclear power plants.

Similar to coal production and use, nuclear energy has its own set of built-in problems. Number one is safety. Nuclear power plants produce energy by splitting atoms in a controlled environment. The process is known as fission and it produces radiation and radioactive waste, which are lethal to animals exposed to it. We are familiar with the near meltdown at Three Mile

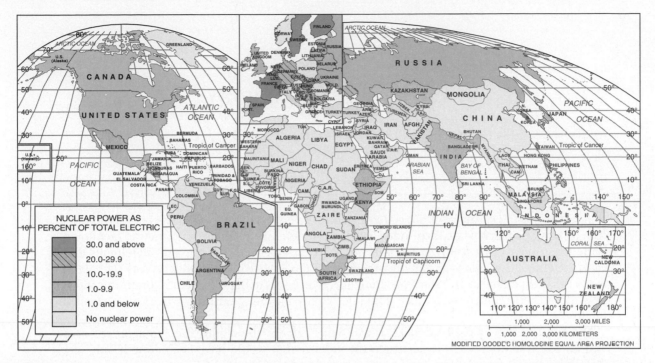

FIGURE 4.26

Nuclear power as a percentage of total energy use. The most important areas of nuclear energy production in the world include western Europe and Japan. These are areas that have a relatively small amount of fossil fuels to satisfy local demand for energy. In Europe, for example, France, Germany, and the Scandinavian countries of Sweden and Finland produce more than 50% of their electrical energy from nuclear sources. Nuclear power is much less prevalent in the developing nations of the world because of extremely high-scale economies, or start-up costs, and the need for expensive uranium fuels. (See Color Insert page 1.8, top, for more illustrative map.)

The large hyperbolic cooling tower and reactor containment dome of the Trojan nuclear power plant in Rainier, Oregon, add to the tranquility of this night scene. Safety issues surrounding the use of nuclear energy are fraught with turmoil. Most OECD countries expanded their nuclear energy production during the last 20 years, with France and Japan in the lead. Expansion of nuclear capacity had slowed by 1994 because of cost concerns and the chilling effects of the accidents at Three Mile Island in Pennsylvania and at Chernobyl in the Ukraine. New energy sources, such as geothermal, solar, biomass, and wind energy have increased and now provide up to 5% of total primary energy requirements in Australia, Austria, Canada, Denmark, Sweden, and Switzerland.
(Source: U.S. Department of Energy.)

STAR WARS AND CHERNOBYL

MELTDOWN HELP END

COLD WAR

Speaking in the spring of 1993, at a Princeton University conference on the end of the Cold War, Mikhail Gorbachev credited America's strategic defense initiative (SDI) and the meltdown of the Chernobyl nuclear power plant in northern Ukraine as the two major ingredients that led to the end of the Cold War and the backdown of the Soviet Union's military. Any attempt to match the United States' SDI Star Wars initiative, which was to build a satellite communications network over the United States that would detect any incoming missiles, would have crushed the Soviet economy.

We are fortunate that all-out nuclear war never came to the world. The Pentagon came up with an SDI initiative when it calculated the damage that would have been done if only one nuclear warhead would have penetrated a megalopolis in the northeastern seaboard of the United States. A first strike capability by the Soviets troubled the Pentagon. The motivation to pursue an SDI, rather than any calculated plan to force the Soviets to spend themselves into bankruptcy, was then initiated.

The Soviet defense ministers were absolutely paranoid about the possibility of a defensive network that would nullify a first or second nuclear strike move by the Soviet Union against the United States. Defense ministers at the conference indicated that they felt very vulnerable because due to the SDI, the United States could retaliate with a second strike and have it be dehabilitating without having received any major damage from the Soviet Union's first strike.

In addition, the Chernobyl nuclear power plant accident in April 1986, made people aware of what nuclear world war would entail. The Soviet Union finally realized the danger of anything nuclear. The accident was calculated to have had the effect of only one-quarter of a nuclear explosion, while many nuclear missiles are armed with multiple warheads.

Once the damage that occurred at Chernobyl was assessed, Gorbachev would not entertain any position based on the assumption that the Soviet Union may have to fight the United States. Gorbachev then assured President Ronald Reagan that the United States would never be attacked.

Island in Pennsylvania, as well as the Chernobyl meltdown in the Ukraine in the spring of 1986. The effects of the Chernobyl meltdown and radiation exposure to the surrounding countryside has increased the occurrence of a variety of cancers and birth defects by several thousand percent.

Between 1949 and 1989, the Soviet Union detonated 500 nuclear devices in Kazakhstan. Kazakhstan was a test site for nuclear armaments of the Cold War period in the Soviet Union. Tens of thousands of Kazakh people have paid a dear price (see "Kazakhstan: A Broken Empire," *National Geographic*, March 1993, pp.

23–35.) At the Chernobyl site, estimates of cancer victims range into the millions and an unknown number of birth defects have resulted from the accident, which affected 2 million people. Now that the Cold War is over, the West is learning of meltdowns and near meltdowns that occurred in countries behind the Iron Curtain. This "China syndrome" had been kept secret by the Soviet Union and Eastern Germany for 20 years.

The second problem associated with nuclear energy generation is the need to dispose of nuclear waste materials that have been spent and no longer are useful for energy generation. It seems that no one can design a leakproof container. Early radioactive wastes were dumped in the ocean in 50-gallon metal drums and soon began leaking into the seas. Likewise, many sites throughout America have contaminated ground water supplies and leak radioactive wastes, contaminating local water supplies and causing severe environmental problems. Love Canal, New York, and Times Beach, Missouri, are well-known cases. Most present and future sites suffer from the NIMBY ("not in my backyard") and LULU ("locally undesirable land uses!") effects; they are hotly protested by local residents. At the Stringfellow toxic waste dump near Riverside, California, for example, 10 companies have paid local residents $100 million so far in environmental impact settlements as of summer 1993. One strategy was to store radioactive waste in salt beds in the New Mexico desert, hundreds of miles from any town or city.

The last and most important problem associated with nuclear energy is that it is fissionable and, therefore, can be used to produce atomic weapons. In 1945, the United States used atomic weapons for the first time in the history of the world, which brought a rapid end to World War II. It dropped bombs on Hiroshima and, 3 days later, on Nagasaki, Japan; there was a massive loss of infrastructure and life.

Unfortunately, since that time, nuclear proliferation has been a major world concern because many nations, including nations hostile to the United States, now possess nuclear weapons. One concern is that terrorist nations, such as Libya, Iraq, Syria, Iran, North Korea, and Cuba, will develop such weapons to be used in punitive ways. In fact, terrorists have stolen small amounts of nuclear fuel to contruct their own weapons, which could wreak world havoc.

The last problem associated with nuclear energy is its very high-scale economy. A city just cannot build a small, inexpensive nuclear power plant for electrical generation. Each plant costs many billions of dollars to build and needs elaborate engineering and backup systems, as well as precautionary measures, which are very expensive. Due to a combination of high risk and high cost, some countries have decided to throw in the towel on nuclear power generation. Sweden, for example, is beginning to phase out its nuclear plants. Starting its phase-out in 1995, it plans to be completely nuclear-free by the year 2010.

GEOTHERMAL POWER

The development of geothermal power holds promise for the future in several countries that have hot springs, geysers, and other underground supplies of hot water that can easily be tapped. The occurrence of this renewable resource is highly localized, however. New Zealand obtains about 10% of its electricity from this source, and smaller quantities are utilized by Italy, Japan, Iceland, the former Soviet Union, and the United States.

If the interior of the earth's molten magma is sufficiently close to the surface (i.e., 10,000 feet), water beneath the surface and the water table may be sufficiently warm to produce steam that can be tapped by drilling geothermal wells. Geothermal energy is most producible in giant cracks or rifts in the earth's tectonic plate structure that occurs in earthquake or volcano country around the Pacific Rim. Wyoming and California are noted examples in the western United States.

HYDROPOWER

Another source of electric power, and one that is virtually inexhaustible, is hydropower—energy from rivers. Developed countries have exploited about 50% of their usable opportunities, the former Soviet Union and eastern Europe about 20%, and the Third World only 7%. In developed countries further exploitation of hydropower is limited mainly by environmental and social concerns. In the Third World, a lack of money and markets for the power are the main obstacles.

SOLAR ENERGY

Like river power, tidal, wind, and solar energy are inexhaustible. In the 1970s and early 1980s, solar energy caught the public eye through publicity of the relatively few solar homes and buildings constructed in the United States. Large-scale utilization of solar energy, however, still poses technical difficulties, particularly that of low concentration of the energy. It has been estimated that the energy of the sun's direct rays at sea level is slightly more than 1 horsepower per square meter. So far, technology has been able to convert only slightly more than 30% of solar energy into electricity; however, depending on the success of ongoing research programs, it could provide a large proportion of power needs in the twenty-first century.

Solar energy's positive aspects are that it does not have the same risks of nuclear energy, nor is it difficult, like coal, to transport. It is almost ubiquitous, but varies by latitude and by season. Solar energy and incoming solar radiation is highest in areas of the southwest

United States. It tapers off toward the east and to the north. The highest readings for incoming solar radiation in July are in Nevada, California, and Arizona. The highest incoming solar radiation levels in December, once again are in the southwest, centered on Nevada, Utah, Arizona, and New Mexico.

Passive solar energy is trapped rather than generated, by large glass plates, built into a building or a house. The greenhouse effect receives short-wave radiation from the sun. Once the rays penetrate the glass, they are converted to long-wave radiation and are trapped within the glass panel, thus heating the interior of the house or water storage tank.

The other type of solar energy system is *active solar energy*. One type of this form of solar energy is generated with photovoltaic cells, which are made from silicon. A bank of photovoltaic cells can be wired together and mounted on the roof with mechanical devices that maximize the direct sun's rays by moving at an angle proportional to the light received. Another type of active solar energy system is a wood or aluminum box filled with copper pipes and covered with a glass plate. Again, the solar insulation is trapped by the glass and temperatures reach several hundred degrees inside, converging the water inside the copper pipes for home water supplies and swimming pool heaters. The principal problem associated with solar energy is cost. High costs are associated with the generation of solar energy in cloudy areas of the country and in high latitudes or colder climates. But, unlike fossil fuels, solar energy is difficult to store for long periods of time without large banks of cells or batteries. At this point in time, solar energy production is still more expensive than other sources of fuel that are available. Perhaps this will not always be the case.

To promote the development of innovative energy supplies when the Arab oil embargo hit in the 1970s, the U.S. government offered tax incentives, including tax deductions for solar units mounted on housetops. While this initial tax deduction offset the high costs of constructing solar energy systems, maintenance and reliability became a problem in the not too distant future. Once an initial investment is made, solar systems can provide less expensive sources of electricity, primarily for water heating, if not for space heating, for many householders. However, families that are mobile and move from one house to another frequently will lose their investment. Most systems that are installed are not recoverable in the sale price of the structure.

Scientists continue to study ways to supply entire cities with all their energy from solar power. In the future, this will undoubtedly be possible. A major test for solar energy is *California's Solar 1*, a power plant located on Interstate 15 in the Mojave Desert, 200 miles north of Los Angeles. It has 1818 classroom-size mirrored panels that follow the direct ray of the sun throughout the day and year. The mirrors reflect sunlight into a boiler tank in the center. The resulting water is heated creating steam, which powers a steam turbine that creates electricity.

WIND POWER

Lastly, wind power provides an energy hope for a few areas of the world where there are constant surficial wind speeds of 15 mph or more. The amount of wind power available at the 50-meter height (or 164 feet), which is thought to be a favorable height for large wind machines, is measured in megawatt hours per square meter per year. The greatest majority of *wind farms* in the United States have sprung up in California. However, wind machines are an expensive investment and the initial costs and unsightliness of the wind machine has temporarily ended most wind farm projects. Wind farm potential in California has never matched the expectations, and presently it represents a stagnated industry.

BIOMASS

Still another form of renewable energy is biomass—wood and organic wastes. In 1980, biomass accounted for about 14% of global energy use. For Nepal, Ethiopia, and Tanzania, more than 90% of total energy comes from biomass. The use of wood for cooking—the largest use of biomass fuel—presents enormous environmental and social problems because it is being consumed faster than it is being replenished. Fuelwood scarcities—the poor world's energy crisis—now affects 1.5 billion people and could increase to affect 3 billion people by the year 2000 unless immediate corrective actions are taken.

With good management practices, biomass is a resource that can be produced renewably. It can be converted to alcohol and efficient, clean-burning fuel for cooking or transportation. Its production and conversion are labor-intensive, an attractive feature for underdeveloped countries that face unemployment problems. But the low efficiency of photosynthesis requires huge land areas for energy crops if significant quantities of biomass fuels are to be produced.

Many countries have expanded their use of biomass for fuel since the 1973 oil embargo. The United States

Fighting flames in Kuwait, 1992. Workers place a new well head that will enable the injection of chemical mud to kill the oil well. The lower base of the well has also been damaged by Iraqi explosives. When the chemical mud has been injected, the well oil pressure gushes out from this damaged area of the well, and the workers have to dismantle it further down to start all over again. They have worked on this well for about 1 week. Eventually, four Texas firms extinguished 600 burning Kuwait oil wells in a few months time.
(Source: Sebastiao Salgado/Magnum Photos.)

is using more wood-fired boilers for industrial and domestic purposes and is producing gasohol from corn. In 1985, 20 Third World countries formed the Biomass Users Network (BUN) that proposes, among other things, to convert unprofitable export crops such as sugar cane into biomass fuel for local consumption.

ENVIRONMENTAL DEGRADATION

◈

There are days in Los Angeles when the pollution levels reach what is called locally a *level three alert*. Everyone is advised to stay indoors, automobiles are or-

dered off the highways, and all strenuous exercise is discouraged. There is a town that was 50 miles south of St. Louis; it was Times Beach, Missouri. Here, dioxin levels from a contaminated plant became so high that the EPA required the town to be closed. The residents were moved, and the town is no longer inhabited. Similarly, nuclear wastes of plutonium have degraded the soil around Rocky Flats so that radioactivity levels are five times normal, and it is unhealthy to live there. Acid rain has become so bad in the northeast that the pH from the rivers and streams has been thrown off, and there have been massive fish die-offs.

Environmental awareness came to the forefront with the book *Silent Spring* by Rachel Carson (1962), which was aimed at awakening the population to rising levels of pollution. In 1969, the U.S. government enacted a piece of landmark legislation, the National Environmental Policy Act (NEPA), requiring environmental impact reports of major government improvements. This landmark event was followed by Earth Day in April 1970. Dennis Hayes organized a movement at the Harvard Law School to awaken Americans to the dreaded consequences of rapid industrialization. In 1971, California was the first state to enact major legislation to guard and preserve the environment with the California Environmental Quality Act (CEQA). This act did for the state of California and private projects what NEPA had done for government projects across the country. Massachusetts was next, and state-by-state followed suit with such environmental legislation. Recently, in 1990, Earth Day was celebrated again; organized by Dennis Hayes. This time it was a global event, involving 250,000,000 people in 150 countries. It was capped by the 1992 Rio de Janeiro conference on the environment, in which all but five countries of the world were represented.

President Clinton's administration was based heavily on his selection of Al Gore, the environmental candidate from Tennessee, as his running mate. Unfortunately, economic activity is the chief culprit of the environmental degradation that we have just described. Environmental concerns have required the drafting of numerous books, movies, and movements worldwide. These concerns can be categorized into four overlapping categories: (1) pollution, (2) wildlife and habitat preservation, (3) nonrenewable natural resources, and (4) environmental equity.

Pollution

Pollution is a discharge of unwanted gases and chemicals into both the air and water. Such discharge can reach levels that are sufficient to create health hazards to plants, animals, and humans, and reduce and degrade the natural environment. The natural environment has the capacity to regenerate and cleanse itself on a normal basis; however, when great amounts of gases and solids are released into it from industrial economic activity, recycling and purification needs are sometimes overwhelmed. Water, land, and atmosphere are polluted by industrial wastes, automobile emissions, power plants and other types of economic activity. Pollution occurs when nature's natural capacity for self-cleaning is overwhelmed. From that point on, the qual-

ity of the environment is reduced and becomes dangerous to human life, and dangers to animal and plant life increase. Gases, chemicals, and airborne solid waste contaminate and defoliate forests, inundate land surfaces, reduce fisheries, burden wildlife habitats, and cause great illness in human beings. Urban air pollution in low-income countries is especially bad. Usually the human body can rid itself of harmful substances, but when pollution occurs at a certain level, the body's ability to dispose naturally of the unwanted agents sometimes is exceeded, resulting in disability, illness, and even death.

The normal temperature drop as one rises in altitude is 3.5° per 1000 feet. This is called *the normal lapse rate*. Because air is cooler at higher elevations, warm air on the surface of the earth naturally rises and is dissipated through normal wind patterns. However, when a temperature inversion occurs, the normal lapse rate is temporarily disrupted up to an elevation of 3000 to 4000 feet, and hot air exhaust fumes from factories and other warm or polluted air sources actually sinks. Under these conditions, the earth and its inhabitants are under an even greater risk.

Wildlife and Habitat Preservation

Wildlife and habitat preservation for plants and animals called *renewable natural resources* are in danger throughout the world. These natural environments are critical reserves for endangered species of plants and animals. Wildlife, forestlands, and wetlands, including lakes, rivers and streams, and coastal marshes, are subject to acid rain, toxic waste, pesticide discharge, and urban pollution. They are also endangered by encroachment of land development and transportation facilities worldwide. The demand for tropical hardwoods, such as Philippine Mahogany, has already removed 50% of the tropical hardwoods necessary for the maintenance of the earth's ozone layer. In the United States alone, expanding economic activity has consumed forests and wetlands, depleted topsoil, and polluted at a rapid rate. Even certain species of plants and animals have been reduced, including the grizzly bear, American bison, whitetail deer, prairie dog, gray wolf, brown pelican, Florida panther, American alligator and crocodile, and a variety of water fowl and tropical birds, such as California's Least Bel Viro and Gnat Catcher.

Exxon-Valdez cleanup. Fifteen thousand birds were the first victims of the ecological catastrophe caused by the running aground of the Exxon-Valdez in March 1990, creating one of the largest oil spills in history. Five thousand sea otters soon followed suit in the Prince William Strait near Alaska. This oil spill actually increased the U.S. GNP because billions of dollars are being spent on cleanup, but the resource loss did not show up as negative income in the accounting system. A new world system of accounting must be practiced that includes natural resource loss, such as oil and timber. This system would incorporate the value of biological resources and biodiversity itself, where possible, as well as the costs of genetic resources, degraded water sheds, eroded soils, and depleted energy supplies. *(Source: Bill Nation/Sygma.)*

The problem of wildlife and habitat preservation is exacerbated by the need for economic gain. For example, the populations of the African tiger and elephant, each desired for a certain portion of its pelt, tusk, or skin, have been depleted. A variety of other questions beset wildlife managers and environmental farmers. Should farmers be permitted to drain swamps in Louisiana to farm the land, thus removing the habitat for American alligators? Should forest fires started by lightning be allowed to burn themselves out, as has been the practice on western U.S. forests and rangelands?

The enormous Yellowstone National Park fire in 1990 brought this practice into question, because it removed not only tourists but wildlife habitats of 90% of the park's animals. The trade-off of residential lands versus wetlands, wildlife migration versus forest management, highway safety versus habitat preservation, and conservation versus real economic development and growth of the U.S. economy are difficult issues that bring to mind the opportunity costs and production possibilities curve presented in Chapter 2. It is difficult to select the best alternative.

Nonrenewable Natural Resource Management

Mineral and geologic resources and extraction, as discussed in this chapter, represent an enormous set of environmental management questions. As we saw, the deposits of petroleum, iron ore, copper, bauxite, zinc, and other metallic deposits are nonrenewable. Present economic activity repletes world resources and the trade-off again besets us. Preservation of nonrenewable resources are short-run economic growth. Piles of tailings, deep scouring in the earth's surface from open-pit mining, pollution of ground water, supplies and streams, enormous garbage heaps, the filling of canyons with solid waste and oil spills, which are becoming more numerous are but a few of the nonrenewable natural management questions that must be addressed in the 1990s.

Environmental Equity

As we discuss in this chapter, as informed citizens, we need to enquire as to the equity of the costs of pollution and pollution abatement. Pollution, wildlife habitat destruction, and natural resource depletion affect the poor more than the rich. Who receives the benefits from environmental policy, and who incurs the cost?

Environmental Production Possibilities

Figure 4.27 shows the production possibilities curve again. This time, dollars worth of economic goods, both capital and consumer, are shown on the vertical axis, and dollars worth of pollution abatement is shown on the horizontal axis. Each society is confronted with getting one at the expense of the other. Currently, developing societies are not in on the production possibilities curve, meaning that they are receiving the total worth of other goods and spending 0 dollars worth of pollution abatement. U.S. and European nations have moved to position B on the production possibilities curve, meaning that they have sacrificed certain dollars worth of other goods, both capital and consumer, to achieve a level on the pollution abatement axis. Pollution abatement has been expensive. Economic goods must be sacrificed to protect the environmental commons that

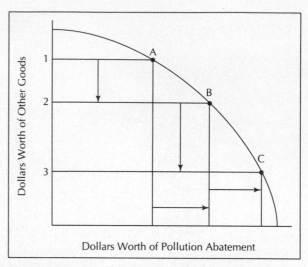

FIGURE 4.27

Production possibilities curve of pollution abatement cost. If a society adopts pollution abatement, other goods and services will have to be cut back. An initial level of a pollution abatement at point 1 can be purchased for a small reduction in the dollar's worth of other goods and services shown by the intersection on the production possibilities curve at point A. Increasing levels of pollution abatement will require greater proportions of sacrifice in the dollar's worth of other goods and services in a society at points B and C.

everyone can enjoy. The question is, what will be the level of trade-off? In the early stages, if a nation has no pollution abatement, and wants to achieve some, it may be able to trade $1 worth of goods for $2 worth of pollution abatement. The production possibilities curve is fairly elastic at the upper level. At middle levels, $1 of other goods can be traded equally for $1 of pollution abatement. At lower levels of the curve, which are below B, there is a so-called law of *increasing cost*. Simply put, a dollar's worth of sacrifice of other goods will only buy 50 cents worth of pollution abatement. The point at which society selects the trade-off is based on economic, social, cultural, and political values and perceptions, and it is not an easily resolved issue.

From a Growth-Oriented to a Balance-Oriented Life-style

It appears unlikely that energy availability will place a limit on economic growth on the earth; however, drastic changes in the use of energy resources seem certain. The ultimate limits to the use of energy will be

Ships are loaded with timber for export to Japan at the Weyehauser Docks, Longview, Washington. The timber industry represents a major economic activity in the northwestern United States and western Canada. Key issues center around how sustainable forest practices can contribute to both ecological restoration and soil quality. Loss of ecosystem habitats and endangered species, such as the Northern spotted owl, continue to raise questions about the logging industry. In dry areas, stripping of land vegetation for fuel wood leads to wind and water erosion. Worldwide overexploitation accounts for 10% of the degradated soils of the world. Africa has the highest percentage of degradated soils from this cause. The loss of tropical forest is currently a significant environmental and developmental issue as well. Loss of tropical forest diminishes biodiversity, contributes to climatic change by releasing stored carbon into the atmosphere, and often results in serious soil degradation, sometimes rendering the land unfit for future agriculture. (*Source: Martha Tabor/Impact Visuals.*)

determined by the ability of the ecosystem to dissipate the heat and waste produced as more and more energy flows through the system.

In countless ways, energy improves the quality of our lives, but it also pollutes. As the rate of energy consumption increases, so too does water and air contamination. Sources of water pollution are numerous: industrial wastes, sewage, and detergents; fertilizers, herbicides, and pesticides from agriculture; and coastal oil spills from tankers. Air pollution reduces visibility; damages buildings, clothes, and crops; and endangers human health. It is especially serious in urban-industrial areas, but it occurs wherever waste gases and solid particles are released into the atmosphere.

Pollution is the price paid by an economic system emphasizing ever-increasing growth as a primary goal. Despite attempts to do something about pollution problems, the growth-oriented life-style characteristic of Western urban-industrial society continues to widen the gap between people and nature. "Growthmania" is a road to nowhere. It is easy to see why. If the U.S. economy grew at a 5% annual growth rate, by about the year 2110, it would reach a level 50,000% higher than the present level. Problems of acquiring, processing, and disposing of materials defy imagination.

There are many who argue that we must transform our present linear or growth-oriented economic system into a balance-oriented system (Table 4.5). A balance-oriented economy explicitly recognizes natural systems. It recognizes that resources are exhaustible, that they must be recycled, and that input rates must be reduced to levels that do not permanently damage the environment. A balance-oriented economy does not mean an end to growth, but a new social system in which only desirable low-energy, high-labor growth is encouraged. It requires a deemphasis on the materialistic values we have come to hold in such high esteem. If current resource and environmental constraints lead us to place

◉

T a b l e   4.5

Comparison of Growth-Oriented and Balance-Oriented Life-styles

Growth-Oriented Life-style	*Balance-Oriented Life-style*
Essentially infinite resources and energy	Finite resources and infinite energy (if fusion or solar energy can be developed)
Linear flow of matter and energy	Linear flow of energy but recycling of matter
Increase flow rates of matter and energy and output (maximize throughput)	Stabilize flow rates of matter and energy by deliberately reducing throughput—a steady-state system with balanced inputs and outputs well below the limits of the system
Goals of efficiency, quantity, simplification, and cultural and physical homogeneity to attain short-term stability	Goals of quality and deliberate preservation of cultural and physical diversity to attain long-term stability at the expense of some efficiency
Output control of pollution (consequences of second law of thermodynamics can be avoided or minimized by cleaning up output)	Input and output control (consequences of the second law of thermodynamics can be decreased in the long run by decreasing input and flow rates along with controlling output)
Continued growth provides capital for output control and redistribution of wealth (trickle-down theory)	If growth continues, capital must be increasingly devoted to maintenance and repairs, thus decreasing life quality and preventing redistribution of wealth
Free enterprise, a competitive market system, or a centralized control economy that can respond to undesirable side effects	Market responds only if we find ways to include quality of life indicators into the price of goods and services
Short-term view and planning	Long-term view and planning
Local and national outlook	Global outlook

Note: The table suggests that we can transform our growth-oriented life-style into a balance-oriented life-style without restructuring our economic system. In striving to attain "balance," can we, at the same time, maintain our existing market system?
Source: Adapted from Miller, 1975, p. 25.

a higher premium on saving and conserving than on spending and discarding, then they may be viewed as blessings in disguise.

SUMMARY

◉

We introduce this chapter by restating the resources-population problem. It is possible to solve resource problems by: (1) changing societal goals, (2) changing consumption patterns, (3) changing technology, and (4) altering population numbers. In the Western world, much of the emphasis is on technological advancement and population control.

Following a review of renewable and nonrenewable resources, we explore the question of food resources. The food "crisis" is essentially a consequence of societal goals. Food production is increasing faster than population growth, yet more people are hungry. Socioeconomic conditions offer a more cogent explantation of why this is so than either population growth or environmental factors. In the course of transforming agriculture into a profit base for the wealthy, the Third World poor are being forced out of the production process.

Unlike food, which is replenished by the seasons, nonrenewable minerals and fossil fuels, once used, are gone forever. We discuss some of the alternatives to fossil fuels and point to energy conservation as a potent alternative with potential that remains to be fully exploited. In conclusion, the comparison between growth-oriented and balance-oriented life-styles underscores the importance of quality concerns as they relate to economic growth.

◈

KEY TERMS

acid rain
agriculture
balance-oriented life-style
biomass
California Environmental Quality Act (CEQA)
carrying capacity
conservation
deforestation
depletion curves
desertification
energy
fossil fuels
geothermal energy
Green Revolution
growth-oriented life-style
intermediate technology
level three alert
limits to growth
malnutrition
marine fisheries
maximum sustainable yield
mine tailings
minerals

National Environmental Policy Act (NEPA)
NIMBY and LULU effects
nonrenewable resource
normal lapse rate
Organization of Petroleum Exporting Countries (OPEC)
overpopulation
pollution
price ceiling
recycle
renewable resource
reserve
reserve deficiency minerals
resource
second law of thermodynamics
solar energy
stationary state
strategic minerals
tragedy of the commons
triage
undernutrition
wind farm

◈

SUGGESTED READINGS

Anderson, J. 1984. *Oil: The Real Story Behind the Energy Crisis.* London: Sidgwick and Jackson.

Bartelmus, P. 1986. *Environment and Development.* Boston: Allen and Unwin.

Brown, L. R. Printed annually, 1984 to 1993. *State of the World.* New York and London: Norton.

Brown, L. R., and Shaw, P. 1982. *Six Steps to a Sustainable Society.* Worldwatch Paper 48. Washington, DC: Worldwatch Institute.

Brown, L. R., and Wolf, E. C. 1985. *Reversing Africa's Decline.* Worldwatch Paper 48. Washington, DC: Worldwatch Institute.

Calzonetti, F. J., and Solomon, B. D. 1985. *Geographical Dimensions of Energy.* Dordrecht, The Netherlands: D. Reidel.

Commoner, B. 1976. *The Poverty of Power.* New York: Knopf.

Cutter, S. L.; Renwick, H. L.; and Renwick, W. H. 1991. *Exploitation, Conservation, Preservation: A Geographic Perspective on Natural Resource Use,* 2nd ed. New York: Wiley.

Darmstadter, J., and Landsberg, H. 1983. *Energy Today and Tomorrow: Living with Uncertainty.* Englewood Cliffs, NJ: Prentice Hall.

Durning, A. B., and Brough, H. B. 1991. *Taking Stock: Animal Farming and the Environment.* Worldwatch Paper 103. Washington, DC: Worldwatch Institute.

Ehrlich, A. H., and Ehrlich, P. R. 1987. *Earth.* New York: Franklin Watts.

Elsom, D. 1992. *Atmospheric Pollution: A Global Problem,* 2nd ed. Cambridge, MA: Blackwell.

Feshbach, M., and Friendly, A., Jr. 1992. *Ecocide in the USSR.* New York: Basic Books.

Frank, R. W., and Chasin, B. H. 1981. *Seeds of Famine: Ecological Destruction and the Development Dilemma in the West African Sahel.* Montclair, NJ: Allenheld, Osmun.

Goldsmith, E. P. B.; Hildyard, N.; and McCully, P. 1991. *Imperiled Planet: Restoring Our Endangered Ecosystems.* Cambridge, MA: MIT Press.

Goudie, A. 1992. *The Nature of the Environment,* 3rd ed. Cambridge, MA: Blackwell.

Goudie, A. 1993. *The Human Impact on the Natural Environment,* 4th ed. Cambridge, MA: MIT Press.

Harrison, P. 1992. *The Third Revolution.* New York: St. Martin's Press.

International Institute for Environment, Development and World Resources. 1988. *World Resources 1988–89.* New York: Basic Books.

Kemp, D. D. 1990. *Global Environmental Issues: A Climatological Approach.* New York: Routledge.

Knight, C. G., and Wilcox, P. 1975. *Triumph or Triage? The World Food Problem in Geographical Perspective.* Washington, DC: Association of American Geographers.

Lappé, F. M., and Collins, J. 1980. *Food First.* London: Abacus.

Mannion, A. M. 1991. *Global Environmental Change: A Natural and Cultural Environmental History.* New York: John Wiley & Sons.

Mounfield, P. R. 1985. Nuclear power in western Europe: Geographical patterns and political problems. *Geography,* 70:315–327.

National Geographic. 1981. *Energy: Special Report.* Washington, DC: National Geographic Society.

Pasqualetti, M. J., and Pijawka, K. D., eds. 1984. *Nuclear Power: Assessing and Managing Hazardous Technology.* Boulder, CO: Westview Press.

Pollack, C. 1986. *Decommissioning: Nuclear Power's Missing Link.* Worldwatch Paper 69. Washington, DC: Worldwatch Institute.

Rees, J. 1985. *Natural Resources: Allocation, Economics, and Policy.* New York: Methuen.

Repetto, R., ed. 1985. *The Global Possible: Resources, Development, and the New Century.* New Haven: Yale University Press.

Repetto, R. 1987. *Population, Resources, Environment: An Uncertain Future.* Population Bulletin, Vol. 42, No. 2. Washington, DC: Population Reference Bureau.

Schmandt, J., and Roderick, H., eds. 1985. *Acid Rain and Friendly Neighbors: The Policy Dispute Between Canada and the U.S.* Durham, NC: Duke University Press.

Schumacher, E. F. 1973. *Small is Beautiful.* London: Blond and Briggs.

Simon, J. L., and Kahn, H., eds. 1984. *The Resourceful Earth: A Response to Global 2000.* Oxford, England: Blackwell.

Stutz, F. P. 1995. Environmental impacts of urban transportation. In S. Hanson (ed.), *The Geography of Urban Transportation.* New York: Guilford.

U.S. Council on Environmental Quality. 1982. *The Global 2000 Report to the President.* New York: Penguin.

Warnock, J. W. 1987. *The Politics of Hunger.* New York: Methuen.

5

DECISION MAKING IN SPATIAL CONTEXTS

❖

OBJECTIVES

- To describe the differences between descriptive, rational, and prescriptive decision-making principles and to illustrate their use in locational decision making

- To explain how the fundamental conflict between labor and capital affect the locational decision making of firms

- To explain how locational decision making occurs on a local and global scale and involves multiple actors using GIS computer technology

- To discuss how the principle of environmental sustainability is leading some to question the ethical basis of conventional definitions of rational decision making for development

❖

Decision making with electronic maps. To advise the World Bank and other lenders, the UN Food & Agriculture Organization produced a computerized atlas of Africa.
(Source: Public Affairs, BP Exploration–Alaska, Anchorage.)

Decision-making processes are fundamental to understanding geographic patterns of economic and social activities, and those discussed in this chapter are necessary to understand the specific patterns discussed in succeeding chapters of this text.

Patterns of economic activity reflect human decisions. For example, cattle ranchers in Brazil hire bulldozers to clear tropical rainforest for cattle ranching; farmers in Kenya build terraces to fight soil erosion on sloping cropland. The first set of decisions leads to environmental degradation, the second to environmental conservation. What similar decision processes leads us to conclude that both groups are making "rational" decisions? For example, steel mills close in the older industrial regions of the developed world; semiconductor production moves to the newly industrializing countries of Malaysia and Thailand; high technology firms spring up along the M4 Corridor west of London and in Silicon Glen near Glasgow, Scotland. What rational principles of decision making guides these processes? In U.S. cities, major centers of retail and office activity known as "edge cities" spring up where major highway intersections occur beyond the suburbs of the 1970s, while blocks of apartments and townhouse communities locate close to subway systems, such as the Metro in suburban Washington, DC. Rational decision making? These outcomes of many independent decisions affect the well-being of people, alter the landscape, and set up new geographic patterns of factors that further affect the next set of location decisions that people make. Principles of decision making reflect the fundamental ideologies of the societies in which they take place. The ideology of most western societies today supports individualistic decision making with minimal state interference. This has not always been so and is not so in many other nonwestern societies.

When geographers examine spatial patterns of economic activities, they recognize two kinds of geographic contexts in which decisions are made. The first is represented by an individual or firm who has tentatively decided to construct a production plant or enterprise and is asking where would this project best be located. Here, the location context is an activity looking for a location. The second context is an individual or firm already occupying a location and asking what activity should occur at the location. In the first context, the activity is fixed and the decision concerns choosing a location for it; in the second, the location is fixed and the decision is to choose the best activity for it. In both contexts, these decisions occur in the context of multiple actors and factors and in the context of the wider economy. Governments, multinational corporations, international service and trading companies, national and international labor groups, intergovernmental organi-

IBM's manufacturing plant in Silicon Glen near Glasgow, Scotland, produces display systems, finance industry systems, and keyboards for customers in Europe, the Middle East, and Africa. IBM chose this Silicon Glen location to take advantage of the area's skilled labor, universities, and environmental attractions. *(Source: IBM.)*

zations, and special interest groups all play a part in economic decision making in an interactive mode.

Any geographic pattern of economic activity results from decisions of individuals, organizations, nation-states, and the broader international community. In many cases, all of these are involved. Often, the decisions of the larger entity become the constraints within which the smaller entity makes its decisions. At any time, the geographic pattern of the results of these decisions provides a unique pattern of opportunities to which decision makers react. On what principles do individuals base their decisions? Do all individuals, everywhere, use the same principles? Are these principles different from those used by organizations and states? In this chapter, we examine the principles that have been proposed to explain the economic behavior of each of these entities. Then we show how the development of geographic information systems (GISs) is beginning to change the way many decisions are being made and introduce spatial decision support systems (SDSS) as decision aids that are increasingly being used to make decisions.

DECISION-MAKING PRINCIPLES

◈

All decisions consist of individuals or groups making selections from alternatives. Decision-making principles, therefore, involve explanations of how alternatives are identified and measured, how they are evaluated, and how choices are made. We distinguish between how people make decisions, how "rational" people should make decisions, and how people can be assisted in making "better" decisions. This classification distinguishes between descriptive, normative, and prescriptive principles of decision making (Bell, Raiffa, and Tversky, 1988). *Descriptive principles* are generally inferred from real behavior. These inferred principles involve "people acting as if they are processing information according to the hypothesized principles." Sometimes the hypothesized principles are those used in the normative model. *Normative principles* are formulated as rules that "rational" people should use. The specific rational principles are usually statements that reflect the ideology of the society or person proposing the principle. Readers must judge for themselves whether they will accept the principle proposed. *Prescriptive principles* are principles of intervention in the decision-making process that are introduced to improve

the quality of decisions. The three principles can be distinguished by the criteria on which they are evaluated. For example:

> Descriptive models are evaluated by their *empirical validity,* that is, the extent to which they correspond to observed choices. Normative models are evaluated by their *theoretical adequacy,* that is, the degree to which they provide acceptable idealizations or rational choice. Prescriptive models are evaluated by their *pragmatic value,* that is, by their ability to help people make better decisions. (Bell et al., 1988, p. 17)

In studying the world economy, all three behavioral decision-making principles are encountered. Common to all three, however, is that they rely on geographic information. One objective of this chapter is to illustrate how the new world of digital GISs is transforming our understanding of the world economy and, indeed, is transforming how the world economy, itself, works. "Digital" GISs are replacing maps and tables—the traditional ways of storing spatial information (see box, "Why GIS?"). Since they are digital, they can be accessed and used directly. A computer can be given the decision principle and asked to find the geographic result from applying the principle to the geographic data. The whole field of transportation logistics (i.e., the selection of routes, the assignment of goods to different vehicles, computing optimal delivery routes) is rapidly being transformed as digital geographic information on the road, rail, and other transport networks becomes available for widespread use and global positioning systems (GPS) are used to keep track of the locations of vehicles in real time, and, as computer software and telecommunications networks become integrated for this purpose (National Research Council, 1993).

THE CLASSICAL LOCATION-THEORY APPROACH

◈

In the late 1950s and 1960s, a small band of self-proclaimed "new" geographers abandoned the old regional geography—attempts to understand the areal differences on the earth's surface by studying specific regions and their cultures—and pronounced geography as the science of location (Haggett, 1965). This science is based on a well-established body of classical location

WHY GIS?

Geographic Information Systems (or GIS) are becoming widely established in the commercial, government, and education sectors. The term "GIS" frequently is used to describe a number of applications and systems. For the beginner, the term may cause a great deal of confusion because it appears to have a wide variety of definitions and cover very different subject areas.

This section gives an introduction to the development of GIS, how GIS can be defined, and a short history of its evolution.

INTRODUCTION

Many organizations are now spending large amounts of money on GISs and on geographic databases. Predictions made by reputable firms suggest billions of dollars will be expended on these items over the next decade. Why should this be true now when only a few years ago such spending was a rarity?

There are two obvious answers to this question. The first is that the costs of computer hardware needed to do a particular job are decreasing rapidly, and so reaching a wider and wider audience. But more important still is that geography (and also the data that describe it) is part of our everyday world; almost every decision we make is constrained, influenced, or dictated by some fact of geography.

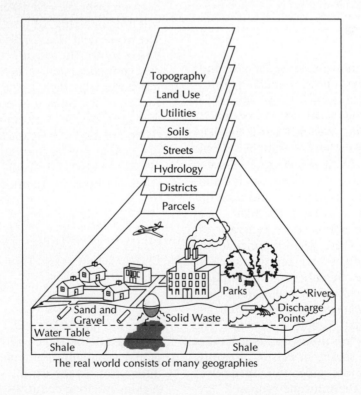

Text and graphic images provided courtesy of Environmental Systems Research Institute, Inc.

Fire trucks are sent to fires by the fastest routes available. Central government grants are often handed out to local government on the basis of the population in each area and we study diseases partly by measuring where they are prevalent and how rapidly they are spreading. In principle, then, there is now not only a need, but also an opportunity for GIS; from these have come the rapid growth in its popularity.

Such generalized explanations do not help you, our reader, to know why and how a GIS can help you. To bring you the benefits, we need to show you how to achieve results with a GIS.

First, however, it is vitally important to have some understanding of what a GIS actually is and what it can be used for—the latter is limited only by your imagination! We provide this understanding of GIS in several different ways.

◈

WHAT IS A GIS?

The use of GISs has grown dramatically in the 1980s to become commonplace in many businesses, universities, and governments. They are now used for an amazingly wide range of applications. As a result, there are many different definitions of what a GIS is and what it can or should do. We will describe a GIS as follows:

"A system of hardware, software, and procedures designed to support the capture, management, manipulation, analysis, modeling, and display of spatially referenced data for solving complex planning and management problems."

Although this definition is accurate, comprehensive, and widely accepted, we suspect that it does not help the newcomer to GIS. Instead, we can use a simpler definition for a GIS as follows:

"A computer system that can hold and use data describing places on the earth's surface."

◈

SPATIAL OPERATIONS

Many widely used computer programs—such as spreadsheets (e.g., Lotus 1-2-3), statistics packages (e.g., SPSS), or drafting packages (e.g., AutoCAD)—can handle some simple data of this kind (i.e., geographical or spatial data).

Why then are they not usually thought of as a GIS? The generally accepted answer is that

Name	Latitude	Longitude	GIS Population	Longitude	Latitude
London	80N	0	51	0	80N
Zurich	25N	8E	47	8E	25N
Utrecht	40N	5E	52	5E	40N
Redlands	50N	117W	34	117W	250N
Santa Barbara	50N	119W	34	119W	50N
Orono	30N	69W	45	69W	30N
Buffalo	30N	78W	42	78W	30N

Text and graphic images provided courtesy of Environmental Systems Research Institute, Inc.

a GIS is only a GIS if it permits spatial operations on the data. As a simple example, consider the file of data in the preceding table.

The preceding table shows the (very) approximate number of people working on all aspects of GIS in each of these centers of activity in the field in 1989.

If we ask, What is the average number of people working on GIS in each location?, this is an aspatial query; answering it does not use the stored value of latitude and longitude, describing where places are in relation to each other, and it is easily computed by many programs.

If, however, we ask, How many people are working in GIS in the major centers in Western Europe?, Which centers are within 1,000 miles of each other?, or What would be the shortest route if I had to visit all of these centers?, these are spatial queries and can only be answered using the latitude and longitude data and other information, such as the radius of the earth. Such questions are readily answered by GISs.

◈

DATA LINKAGE

It is also the case that GIS can usually link different data sets together. Suppose we want to know the death rate due to cancer among those people under 10 years old in each county. Suppose also that (as usual) we have the numbers of people of this age in each county in one file and the numbers of deaths in the group for each county in another file. We need to combine, or link, the two data files. After this is done, division of one figure by the other for the same county gives the desired answer.

If this seems trivial—and scarcely in need of a GIS—it is not always so. Consider the different ways in which data sets may need to be linked together.

Exact matching is when you have information in one computer file about many geographical features (e.g., counties) and additional information in another file about the same set of features. The operation to bring them together is easy and is achieved through use of a key that is common to both files—the county name. Thus, the record in each file with the same county name is extracted and the two are joined together and stored in another file.

Sometimes, however, some information is available for more detailed geographical areas than is other information. Typically, for instance, you get frequently collected (e.g., finance or unemployment) data only for large areas and infrequently collected data (e.g., census) for very small areas. If the smaller areas "nest" (i.e., fit exactly within) the larger ones, then the solution is to use hierarchical matching: add the data for the small areas together until the grouped areas match the bigger ones and then do an exact match.

On many occasions, however, the small areas do not match the larger ones. This is especially true when you are dealing with environmental data. Crop boundaries are usually defined by

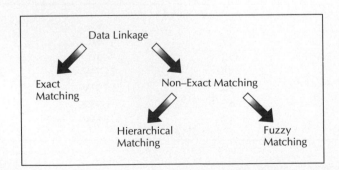

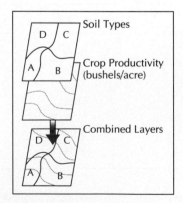

Text and graphic images provided courtesy of Environmental Systems Research Institute, Inc.

the edges of fields and these rarely match the boundary between types of soil. If we wish to answer questions such as, What soils are the most productive as far as wheat is concerned?, we need to overlay the two data sets and compute what crop productivity exists on each and every type of soil. In principle, this is like laying a map on tracing paper over another and noting the combinations of soil and crop productivity.

The important point is that GIS can do all these operations because it uses geography or space as the common key between the data sets—information is linked together if it relates to the same space as does another set of information.

Why is data linkage so important? Consider the situation in which you have two data sets for a given area, such as income for every county in the country and the average cost of housing for the same area. Each data set may be analyzed and/or mapped individually, Alternatively, they may be combined: one such combination exists. If, however, we have 20 data sets covering the country, rather than two, we have more than one million possible combinations. Not all of these may be meaningful (e.g., soil type and unemployment), but we will be able to tackle many more tasks than if the data sets were kept separate. By bringing them together, we add value to our database. To make this a reality, we need a GIS.

🔷

GENERIC QUESTIONS THAT A GIS CAN ANSWER

Thus far, we have described a GIS in two ways—through formal definitions and through its ability to carry out spatial operations and to link data sets together using space as the common key. We can, however, also describe what a GIS is by listing the type of questions that it can (or should be able to) answer. If we stand back far enough from a particular application, we can see there are five generic questions that a sophisticated GIS such as ARC/INFO can tackle.

The first of these generic questions seeks to find out what exists at a particular location. We can describe the location in different ways, for example, by place name, post or zip code, or geographic coordinates, such as latitude and longitude.

The second question is the converse and involves hunting through geographic space to find where certain conditions are satisfied, for example, a fishing lake without a public telephone, but no more than 50 miles from home.

The third question may involve both of the first two, but seeks the differences between the results for the two moments in time.

Questions four and five are more sophisticated. In asking question four, we may wish to know whether there is a cluster of deaths due to cancer among residents around a nuclear power station. Just as important, we will wish to know how many anomalies there are that do not fit the pattern and where they are located.

Finally, question five seeks to determine what happens, for example, if we add a new road

Questions	Type of Task
What is at . . . ?	Inventory and/or monitoring
Where is . . . true/not true?	Inventory . . .
What has changed since . . . ?	Inventory . . .
What spatial pattern exists?	Spatial analysis
What if . . . ?	Modeling

Text and graphic images provided courtesy of Environmental Systems Research Institute, Inc.

to the network, or if a leak of a toxic substance occurs into groundwater; by its nature, answering such a query requires both geographic and other information (and possibly even scientific laws) to answer.

A good GIS (especially ARC/INFO) can be used to answer all five types of query; however, some systems take much longer than others to produce a result and some are difficult to use. Indeed, many GISs at present have very limited capability to carry out spatial analysis or modeling.

◈

SOME APPLICATIONS OF GIS

The first applications of GIS varied between different parts of the world, depending on the local needs. Hence, in mainland Europe, the main effort went into the building of land registration systems and environmental databases. In Britain, however, the greatest expenditure in the 1980s was into systems for the utility companies and in the creation of a comprehensive topographic database for the whole country (mostly derived from maps at 1/1250 and 1/2500 scale).

In Canada, an important early application was in forestry for planning the volume of timber to be cut and access paths to the timber and in reporting all this to the provincial governments. In China and Japan, there has been heavy emphasis on monitoring and modeling possible environmental changes—unsurprising because of the catastrophic effects of flooding, earthquakes, and other natural hazards in these countries.

In the United States, all of these applications have also been important, but one other that deserves special mention is the use of GIS technology in the *TIGER* (Topologically Integrated Geographical Referencing) project by the U.S. Bureau of Census. This project produced a computerized description of the geography of the United States to facilitate taking and reporting the 1990 census and cost about $170 million. TIGER probably represents the largest-but-one collection of geographic data yet made—and ARC/INFO can read TIGER files.

The resulting geographic data files are on sale and can be used for a variety of purposes: when combined with demographic or other data from the 1990 U.S. Census, they can be used to target mail to suitable customers, underpin car guidance systems, and much else.

The most important point to note is that all these applications have been carried out using similar software and techniques. Thus, GIS are general-purpose tools.

The largest collection of geographic data yet assembled is the amazing volumes of satellite imagery collected from space. Unlike much other (vector) geographic data, these come in raster (or grid) form—small square areas of ground are each represented by one or more numbers that describe the properties of the ground area. Until recently, such data were invariably analyzed using special-purpose software, often on special hardware.

◈

WHAT A GIS IS NOT!

A GIS is not simply a computer system for making maps, even if these are drawn at a variety of scales and on a variety of different projections and in different colors. Maps are important to GIS because much information is stored in map form that needs to be converted into computer form; maps are also important as an effective means of demonstrating results.

The basis of a map—the coordinate system on which it is based—is also the framework on which all the nongeographical data are "hung." However, not all geographic information comes from maps (e.g., meteorological data) and not all results are produced in this form (e.g., statistical summaries).

Text and graphic images provided courtesy of Environmental Systems Research Institute, Inc.

Even more important, a true GIS never holds a map in any conventional sense. Thus, we would never hold the area shown as a road on a small-scale map—we want to hold the data rather than the pictorial representation of data. In this case, we would hold the centerline of the road and a note of the true width or type of route.

From this information, we would compute the plotted width as appropriate for any given map. Equally, we would not usually hold lots of "bird's eye views" of Mount St. Helens; we would hold a grid of heights of the ground and compute the particular view we wished, drawn in a way to suit a particular purpose and to please a particular individual.

In short, a GIS does not hold maps or pictures—it holds a geographic database from which we can (if we wish) produce the images, although we can also act on the data in other ways. To remove any confusion, ARC/INFO does not use the term "map" to refer to data sets but calls these "coverages."

It will be very clear from this that the database concept is central to GIS; in this, the GIS differs from simple drafting or computer mapping systems. Their role is only to produce good graphic output; thus, to produce a computer map, it is not strictly necessary that all lines meeting in a junction have the same coordinates. If the errors are small, the user will not be able to see them. Even small errors of this kind would, however, wreak havoc if the area of a polygon had to be computed.

Likewise, it is not essential that all the real world objects or entities or features making up a digital map are coded as such: provided that all of the lines are coded as to be drawn with a particular pen, it does not matter that the four lines making up the sides of a house are unrelated inside the computer. Once they are drawn, they will look to the human eye to form the real world feature.

However, if we want to go beyond just making pictures, such as if we wish to study water flow through a river system, we need to know three pieces of information about every feature stored in the computer: what it is, where it is, and how it relates to other features (e.g., which

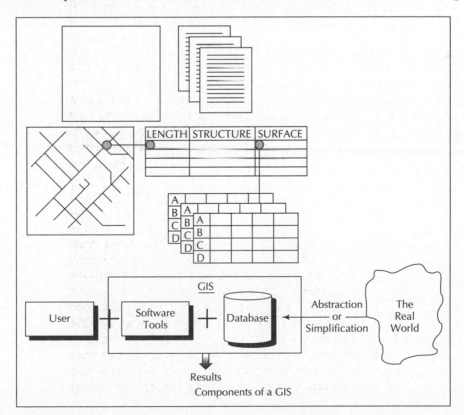

Components of a GIS

Text and graphic images provided courtesy of Environmental Systems Research Institute, Inc.

roads link together to form a network). Database systems provide the means of storing a wide range of such information and updating it without the need to rewrite programs as new data are entered.

All contemporary GISs incorporate a database system. In ARC/INFO, ARC handles the "where the features are" information while INFO is the database that handles the descriptions of what the features are and the relationships between features.

◈

THE COMPONENTS OF GIS

From everything said earlier, we see that a GIS is made up as shown in the following figure.

Some people would argue, however, that the user becomes part of the GIS whenever complicated analyses have to be carried out, such as spatial analyses and modeling. These usually require skills in selecting and using tools from the GIS toolbox and intimate knowledge of the data being used.

At present and for years to come, off-the-shelf and general-purpose GISs will rely on users to know what they are doing—pressing a button is not enough. *Getting Started With ARC/INFO*, the primer on which this article is based, cannot make you an expert, but it is designed to teach basics and good practice; you need to read more detailed textbooks and to explore the GIS to become one.

(Source: David Rhind. Why GIS? ARC News, October 1992 Issue, 11(3):1–4.)

---

theory built on the formulations of Johann Heinrich von Thunen (1826), Alfred Weber (1929), and Walter Christaller (1966). Within a few years, the theory had diffused into college textbooks (Abler, Adams, and Gould, 1971; Lloyd and Dicken, 1972).

The aim of location theory is to explain the location of economic and social activities in any area as the outcome of contemporary and past decision processes operating on the specific geographic factors of the area. Instead of focusing on absolute location (e.g., describing the industries found in Tokyo or the agricultural activities undertaken on the Canadian prairies), location theorists study geographic distributions as the outcomes of decision processes applied to unique environments of physical environmental, social, political, and economic factors. Given the values of these factors at one point in time and the conditions that determine the particular decision processes that are in use, what geographic pattern of activities should be found in the area? The location theorist sees current geographic patterns as predictable consequences of applying prevailing decision processes to the geographic pattern of variables considered by these processes. The classical location theorists saw the role of theory to be a pedogogic device—useful for gaining an understanding of how typical values of environmental, social, political, and economic forces would lead to typical spatial patterns of activities. Similar initial conditions and similar decision processes

would lead to similar spatial outcomes. In so far as such conditions often occurred, these typical outcomes would be found. This phase of location theory, very common in the 1950s and 1960s, emphasized spatial regularities or recurrent conditions and location theory in practice became indistinguishable for many people from the operational field of "spatial analysis." Spatial analysts, with the spatial regularities developed by the theorists in mind, looked at geographic data with the purpose of identifying spatial regularities, such as the common decrease in land values, rural population densities, and intensity of agricultural production with distance from cities. This explicit interest in searching for spatial regularities limited the depth of the explanatory power of theory. If all that location theory could answer was whether a particular spatial pattern occurred in a specific area, then little had been explained no matter what the answer. Should we care whether a particular geographic pattern is there? Eventually, the answer that many accepted was that if the pattern examined was simply one that was hypothesized, in an ad hoc way, to be there, then little to interest us could be found; but if decision processes had been applied to the facts of the area and then a pattern had been derived, which then was shown to be true, then a lot had been achieved because the fundamental aspects of the theory—the decision processses—had received support.

Currently, there is a resurgence of interest in *location*

theory. However, in this phase, the interest is not in theory as a pedagogic device for instruction but as a practical device for predicting the effects of changes in prevailing decision processes or changes in environmental, social, political, or economic conditions on the geographic pattern of activities and the welfare of people. The new location theory is also used as a basis for supporting improved decision making when it becomes incorporated into spatial decision support systems. This new phase is described after we examine the earlier phase on which current location theory is based.

Classical Location Theorists Predicted "Typical Spatial Patterns"

In the early, pedagogic phase of location theory, theorists identified the friction of distance—the cost of moving commodities, people, or information between places—as the key variable for explaining geographic patterns and, therefore, underscored the role of transport costs in location decision making. In order to isolate the effects of the distance variable and to construct models undisturbed by the distortions of the "real" world, location theory was often elaborated in an *isotropic environment*, an imaginary plain or surface with uniform environmental conditions, equal transport costs in all directions, and an equal distribution of population having identical capacities and preferences. All inhabitants on this plain employed the same decision process. They had perfect knowledge of all possible outcomes of a given action, had identical levels of resources, and acted solely to maximize their own utility. They were *optimizers* or *economic persons*. The objective of their decision process was to locate activities or to use a given piece of land to maximize returns to themselves.

AN EXAMPLE: LAND-USE PATTERNS

Imagine a region with a single market—a city. Demand for locally produced foodstuffs is concentrated in the city, where goods are manufactured, to be exchanged for agricultural commodities. Farmers in areas surrounding the city grow vegetables, potatoes, and wheat.

The fresh sweet corn this farmer is loading on his truck will be sold directly to consumers at the nearest central place—the farmers' market in Jackson, Mississippi.
(Source: USDA photo by David Warren.)

In order to isolate the effect of transportation costs on location relative to the city and land-use patterns, assume that the land surface is homogeneous in every respect. There are no barriers to movement, physical resources are evenly distributed, and soils are equally fertile. The farmers are equally distributed. They have identical incomes, demands, and tastes. Their production capacities are equal, and they all have perfect knowledge and act to maximize cash income. Prices for each commodity are stable and fixed in the city. With these assumptions, the only variable affecting the pattern of agricultural production is transport costs. These costs are a simple, linear function of distance. Costs are the same per kilometer regardless of distance traveled. Only one form of transportation exists.

Each crop brings a different market price per unit of land. The market price for vegetables is higher than the market price for potatoes, which in turn is higher than the market price for wheat. Differences in market prices occur in the process of reconciling the demands of the market for crops at different prices and the capacity of the region to supply a given amount of crops at different prices. The decision-making process that supports this reconciliation is described as follows.

Using hypothetical figures, the net returns per unit of land (*not* per unit of output) of different crops in different locations can be illustrated (Figure 5.1). In this diagram, the net returns per unit of land earned on vegetables fall off more rapidly with distance than that earned on potatoes because vegetables have a greater or bulkier physical yield per unit of land and, therefore, greater freight charges per unit of land. Consequently, as land becomes further from the market, more of its productive value is eaten away by freight costs. Farthest from the market, those activities whose freight costs per unit of land are small are found (Pred, 1967, pp. 67–75). This deduced spatial pattern is not, of course, the essence of this theory. What is truly fundamental is the description of the processes of human decision making that lead to the pattern. The particular deduced spatial pattern will vary according to the unique environmental context in which those decisions are made.

Such simplified worlds as that just described do not exist. We describe below a model, implemented on a computer, that allows more complex environments, corresponding more closely wth reality, to be analyzed. In this case, there is spatial variability of crop yields, production costs, market prices, and transportation rates. Since all these variables often do vary, the computer model is capable of generating a wide variety of land-use patterns rather than being restricted to the circles that result from simple conditions rarely or never

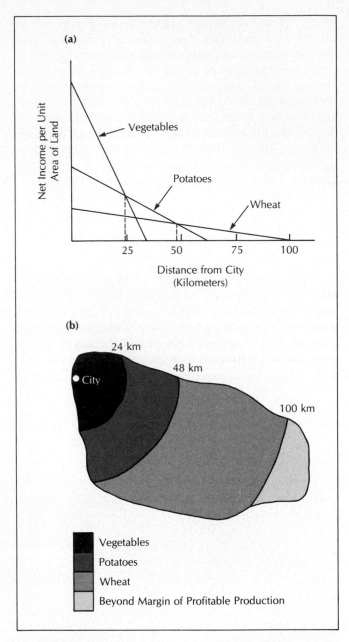

FIGURE 5.1
Land use in a hypothetical region: (a) net income from different crops at different distances from the capital city; (b) the geographic patterns of agricultural production.
(Source: Pred, 1967, p. 69.)

found in reality. The model allows each of the variables to be changed in controlled, experimental-type situations and makes possible an evaluation of how land-use patterns change as the pattern of the variables that describe the environment that decision makers consider. The return to the farmer at any location (economic rent)

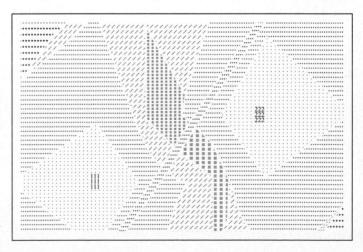

FIGURE 5.2
Simulation of land-use patterns: spatial variability in yields.
(Source: Rushton, 1969, p. 146.)

is defined as R and is shown to depend on the following equation (Dunn, 1954):

$$R = E(p - a) - Efk$$

where: E is yield per unit area

p is price of unit of commodity

a is cost for production of unit of commodity

f is transfer cost per unit distance per unit of commodity

k is distance to most profitable market

Figures 5.2 and 5.3 show two patterns of production that the model simulates for given hypothetical spatial patterns of yields, production costs, transfer costs, and distances to markets. Notice that these are no longer the simple patterns of Figure 5.1.

R. F. Dodson (1991) has developed this model further in an interactive computer program so that students can alter the geographic characteristics of a hypothetical area and then observe the effects on the land-use pattern generated by the decision-making principles. The program permits the user to locate many markets, set different prices at the markets, construct a railroad network, set transport rates differently for road and rail, and describe yields at various locations for different crops. The program is constructed on top of a GIS program (IDRISI, 1992). Such GIS programs are able to evaluate and display earth resources data from satellites. It is also possible to enter socioeconomic data such as observed yields of crops and market prices and to simulate how real world economic systems might change if natural environmental change occurs, such as might occur with global warming, or if national policies of crop price guarantees were changed. A student who wanted to see how such systems are now beginning to be developed could see it in the contents of recent issues of *Earth Observation Magazine*, *GIS World*, or *GeoInfosystems*. The Food and Agricultural Organization (FAO) has developed an Agro-Ecological Zone model to assess Africa's

FIGURE 5.3
Simulation of land-use patterns after increasing rate of decline in yields over that used in computing Figure 5.2.
(Source: Rushton, 1969, p. 147.)

agricultural suitability for many potential food crops (see box, "GIS Suitability Mapping and Modeling"). The model uses the Advanced Very High Resolution Radiometer (AVHRR) sensor on U.S. National Oceanic and Atmospheric Association (NOAA) satellites. From this data, computer maps supply a continuous overview, in time and space, of the entire continent of Africa's ecological conditions (van der Laan, 1992).

Location theorists are always concerned to understand the function of price and how decision makers will respond to changes in price and so change the production system. If the price of any commodity increases, all other variables remaining constant, then both the area in production and the total amount supplied to the market will increase. This result leads to positive sloping supply curves and, if we postulate that local demand, will be negatively sloping. Then we see that there is a point of equilibrium for which there is a corresponding spatial pattern of production. In Figure 5.4, both the activity supply curve and the local demand curve are shown. The equilibrium point represented in Figure 5.4 is known as the space-price equilibrium. It is an equilibrium point because any departure from the point will be accompanied by forces that lead to a return to the point. If, for example, in Figure 5.4, P_1 is the prevailing price, then S_1 would be the amount supplied while a smaller amount (D_1) would be demanded by consumers. This position is obviously not in equilibrium for it would lead to a surplus of the commodity in question. The most common method of disposing of a surplus is to offer it at a lower price and, as we have seen, a lower price would lead to a smaller supply by producers. Marginal producers would either go out of business or switch to some other activity.

How close to real life are the spatial patterns of production deduced from this decision-making model? A study by Wolpert (1964) made observations on the farming decisions and resource availability of a sample of Swedish farmers and computed the optimum return that each sample farmer could have achieved by using his resources differently. The optimum productivity values were determined by means of a linear programming analysis for representative farm situations with interpolation of the results to the circumstances of each sample farm. A comparison of actual productivity with optimum productivity "revealed that the average farmer achieved only two-thirds of the potential productivity that his resources would allow" (Wolpert, 1964, p. 544). (See Figure 5.5.) Wolpert concluded that rather than regarding men as optimizers, they should be regarded as searching for satisfactory outcomes and, he argued, they might better be called "satisficers."

Further study by Wolpert indicated that regional variations existed in the amount of knowledge possessed by the sample farmers and that variability in potential productivity due to vagaries in both climatic and economic factors might lead the sample population to diversify their activity even at the risk of incurring smaller profits. However, these differences did not appear strong enough to explain the large discrepancy between potential and actual productivity on the sample farms. This led him to conclude the following:

> The concept of the spatial satisficer appears more descriptively accurate of the behavioral pattern of the sample population than the normative concept of Economic Man. The individual is adaptively or intendedly rational rather than omnisciently rational. (Wolpert, 1964, p. 558)

Wolpert's study was a sophisticated quantitative analysis at the level of the individual decision maker. It was influential in a number of respects in that it focused attention on the applicability to classical geographic problems of decision-making models developed outside of geography; it illustrated the utility and power of mathematical programming analysis within the discipline; it focused attention on particular spatial biases in behavior deviation from model-norms; and it connected spatial biases in the communication network with variations in behavior patterns. In short, Wolpert's originality in that work was to combine place specific variables of the environment with a behavioral, decision-making process to derive a spatial configuration.

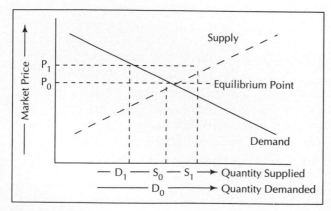

FIGURE 5.4
Space-price equilibrium.

GIS SUITABILITY MAPPING
AND MODELING

Land-use suitability mapping is a GIS technique that can help find the best location for a variety of land-use developmental actions, given a set of goals and other criteria. The mapping technique is based on environmental and human processes, and it analyzes the interactions among three sets of factors: location, land-use development actions, and environmental effects. The technique can yield three types of maps: (1) a map showing what land use will cause the least change in environmental processes; (2) a map showing qualitative predictions of environmental impacts of proposed land-use developments; given certain land-use developmental actions to be carried out and specific environmental actions to be controlled, and (3) a map showing the most and least suitable locations for those land-use actions.

At the heart of environmentally sensitive, systematic land planning and in the pivotal position between analyses and the definition of alternatives, mapped models, or suitability maps exist. A *suitability map* assesses the ability of each increment of land under study to support a given use. As the technique is now developing, the assessment of suitability is commonly based on predictions of the results likely to come about if a certain development is placed on a particular piece of land. Thus, in suitability mapping, environmental impact analysis and land planning can be effectively merged into a spatial system support system (SDSS).

The suitability mapping process, then, begins with a collection of information forming coherent descriptions to these three component sets of factors, and a means of defining the connections among them. These three sets of information—describing locations, developmental actions, and environmental effects—form the three legs of the tripod on which the suitability mapping process is built.

It is important to recognize that we do actually need all three. Since suitability mapping has become more widespread, efforts to simplify and hasten the process have often resulted in failure to take into account either developmental actions or environmental effects. Too often, locational maps are simply overlaid without definition of either the uses or environmental factors being considered. This can lead to meaningless conclusions. It happens partly because the collection on locational information is the most visible, usually more extensive and complex than the other two. This collection is essentially a map file showing geographic distribution of the locational variables that interact with developmental actions and environmental effects.

Generally, at the most basic level, these include the horizontal layers of the biosphere, starting with bedrock composition and other geological factors and proceeding upward through soil types, hydrology plant and animal communities, and microclimates. To this we often add human contributions to the environment, such as existing land uses, transportation routes, accessibility, and political and social boundaries.

Any or all of these land factors can be almost indefinitely expanded. Soil types can be grouped by various characteristics, such as bearing capacity, expansion potential, or porosity. Or they can be divided into capability classes according to the U.S. Soil Conservation Service system. Hydrology might include ground water basins and their capacity and recharge areas. Often, streams and tributaries are mapped to second, third, or fourth orders. Sometimes rates of flow are included. Man-made factors can likewise vary in their level and type of detail. Some developmental actions for which environmental effects can be estimated appear in Table 1.

The suitability modeling process is briefly described as follows:

Given: • Environmental effects to be minimized (stated in terms of transformations to be controlled) in priority order
   • Land-use developmental actions to be carried out (e.g., residential)

Find: Most or least suitable locations

Steps	Source Tools
1A List environmental processes or transformations related to given developmental actions.	Developmental action key charts linking process to development
1B List developmental actions related to given environmental transformations.	Transformation key charts
1C List effects (outputs) related to environmental transformations in 1A.	Transformation key charts
2A Match list of developmental actions in 1B with those given and record those that match.	Computer
2B Match list of effects (outputs) in 1C with those given and record those that match.	Computer
3A List locational variable, relative importance, and attribute sensitivity range related to developmental actions in 2A.	Transformation key charts
3B Determine where interactions occur between locational variables and transformations in 2A and 3B.	Computer
3C Assign a range to each variable according to its interactions; ranges must total 100%.	Scoring matrix
3D Assign a score to each attribute based on its sensitivity range.	Transformation key charts
4 Print weighted map based on these scores.	Data base, plotter

❖

Table 1

Developmental Actions for Which Environmental Effects Were Estimated

Cutting	Energy generation
Filling	Energy consumption
Excavation	Fertilizer application
Dredging	Groundwater extraction
Soil retention	Off-road vehicle use
Retaining walls	Active recreation
Dams	Passive recreation
Channels	Automobile operation
Walkways	Solid waste disposal
Demolition	Shoreline protection
Sewage disposal	structures
Outdoor lighting	Vegetation removal
Roof drainage	Vegetation introduction
Site drainage	Animal species removal
Fences	Animal species introduction
Paving	Settling and debris basins
Pest control	Spreading grounds
Weed control	Power transmission lines
Irrigation	Power transmission structures
Aquaculture	Building foundations
Soil cultivation	Building superstructures

(Source: Lyle and Stutz, 1983)

REGIONAL SCALE
URBAN SUITABILITY MODEL
MOST SUITABLE

LEAST SUITABLE

Suitability mapping is a type of GIS spatial decision support system that gives ratings to all pieces of land in a study area based on human and physical land characteristics. It helps answer question three of the world economy: Where is the best location for economic activity X?
(Source: Evans and Sutherland.)

These totals give the relative importance of each land variable in providing the related environmental effect in the transformation key chart. Once this is done, the scores are simply inserted in the modeling program to be totaled for each grid cell, and the results printed by the computer. The map that resulted from the matrix just described is shown in the photo. In this case, the purpose was to accurately identify specific lands with agricultural potential in a single watershed within the San Diego Coastal Plain, where urban development is progressing rapidly and agricultural uses are in direct competition with residential and recreational uses.

Models for urban suitability and fire hazards at the regional scale were derived by similar means. In these examples, each cell represents the full 1000-foot square. The urban suitability model is broad and inclusive, encompassing the consideration of a range of variables, while the fire hazard model is more limited in scope. The urban suitability map can provide a basis for urban growth policies and infrastructure locations and other long-range planning decisions. The fire hazard map can also plan a role in these or be used for such practical purposes as locating fire stations or areas where shingle roofs should be banned or fire retardant plants planted.

(Source: Lyle and Stutz, 1983.)

SPATIAL DECISION SUPPORT SYSTEMS

◈

Prescriptive decision-making principles are designed to help decision makers reach decisions about spatial problems that confront them. Many geographic problems involve the organization of activities or resources spatially to reach some desired objective. For example, much of the world economy involves traders who buy in one set of locations and sell in others. What decision principles do they follow? Long before textbooks in management science, such as that of Beer (1968), were written describing the mathematics of optimization methods for trade, individual traders throughout the world recognized that the key decision principle for involving themselves in trade was the principle that when the difference in prices of any commodity between any two markets is greater than the cost of transporting the good between the markets, then profit can be gained by buying in the market where the price is

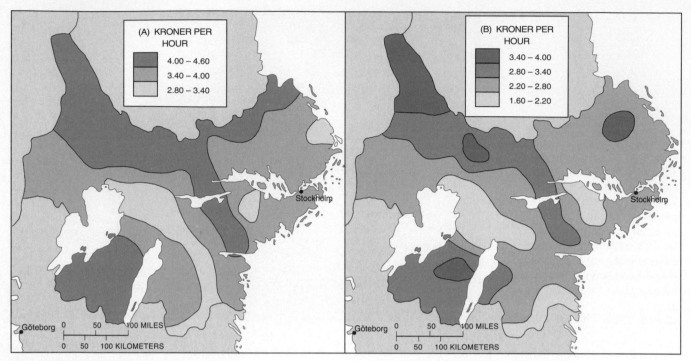

FIGURE 5.5
Contrast between (a) the potential productivity of farm labor (optimizer), and (b) the actual productivity of farm labor (satisficer) in middle Sweden.
(Source: Wolpert, 1964, pp. 540–541.)

low and selling in the market where the price is high. In 1938, the great French statistician, Cournot, formulated the law that the difference between prices in all markets should, in the absence of restrictions on trade, equal the cost of transporting the product between them. It is only comparatively recently that econometricians have developed the methods to determine, from information on potential production possibilities in each region at given relative prices, what the equilibrium price of each commodity will be in each market and what the pattern of trade will be between all markets. As the geographic information base improves, it becomes easier to compute these possible production levels in any region, given prices of all factors of production there. At this point, producers and traders begin to ask for advice on actions that will bring them highest returns on their efforts.

These optimization methods, increasingly, are being adopted and applied to the daily operation of the world economy. We illustrate by describing a SDSS called "TRAILMAN—Transportation and Inland Logistics Manager" developed by a research team at The University of Tennessee for the United States Agency for International Development (USAID) to assist in distributing

food aid in Africa (TRAILMAN, 1993). TRAILMAN is a microcomputer-based software package for logistics planning in Africa. That is,

> the system can be used to choose routes and schedules for shipping commodities from supply points (often overseas) to demand points. In addition to its programs for modeling the movement of goods in Africa, the system contains graphics and editing software for maintaining geographic data bases and building planning scenarios. The entire system is accessed through a series of menus. (TRAILMAN, 1993, p. 1.3)

The system addresses six questions:

> What is the least expensive way to move food aid from supply points to demand points so that all demands are met?
> What is the fastest way to move food aid from supply points to demand points so that all demands are met?
> What is the best combination of time and cost minimization?

What is the maximum amount of food aid that can be moved from supply points to demand points in a fixed amount of time?

What is the shortest distance, cost, time, or cost and time path between any two nodes by a given set of modes?

What is the best strategy for moving food aid from major distribution centers to outlying demand nodes? (TRAILMAN, 1993, p. 1.4)

The mathematical optimization methods used, known as linear programming, are quite complex. However, the software system calls the appropriate models as it decides the appropriate method that should be used to answer the question posed. These answers are determined from the questions it presents in its menus to the user. These prescriptive decision principles are those that an expert in food aid processing and distribution would use after many years of effort and experience in the field. The TRAILMAN software is trying to capture the knowledge of experts and embed it so that decision makers with far less experience will make decisions as good as those of the expert.

Figure 5.6, taken from the TRAILMAN manual, shows the major road system of the countries in the southern half of Africa. The box brought up on the computer screen illustrates how the system is first used to modify the road network. The illustration shows how a particular road link from Lusaka to Chipata can be deleted from the network for the purposes of a set of

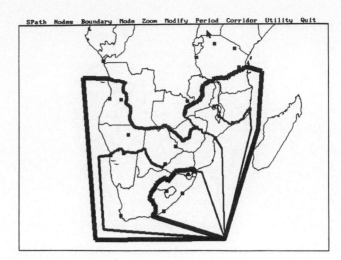

FIGURE 5.7
A linear programming flow map.
(*Source: TRAILMAN, 1993, p. 7.43*)

analyses. The user might want to delete this link if they have knowledge that the link is not available at the time of year when the food aid would be moving, or that it is broken by warfare and unsafe. Much of the work in using such decision support systems is the task of creating an accurate and relevant geographic data base for subsequent analysis. Figure 5.7 illustrates a solution to a particular problem of identifying the ports and the routes into the interior of South Africa where food aid is needed. Accompanying such a map are tables indicating the precise quantities of shipments that would move through each port and down each route. The program ensures that flows sent down any particular route are not more than the route can handle and that storage facilities exist, where they are needed, for the amounts of food aid that would arrive under each solution scenario.

Figure 5.8 shows the detailed distribution tours of food aid within one country in the region and shows the locations of the warehouses that would be used. This system is currently in use in South Africa where the confluence of several forces that have negatively affected the level of indigenous production of basic foodstuffs have left destitute large proportions of the populations of several countries in the region. These forces include a 5-year drought, attempts by governments in some areas of the region to control the production processes that have led to sharp reductions in production levels, fierce civil wars, and continued high rates of population growth. The distribution of food aid does not solve any of these fundamental problems; it merely averts catastrophe for the moment and gives these coun-

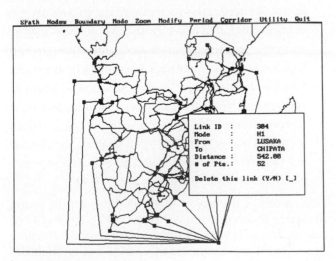

FIGURE 5.6
The delete link option.
(*Source: TRAILMAN, 1993, p. 7.37*)

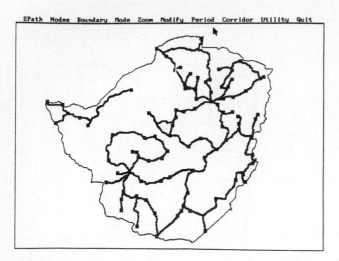

SPath Modes Boundary Mode Zoom Modify Period Corridor Utility Quit

FIGURE 5.8
A warehouse routing flow map.
(*Source: TRAILMAN, 1993, p. 7.46*)

tries some breathing room to solve these problems. The natural resource base of sub-Saharan Africa is clearly rich enough to support current levels of population but the infrastructure and institutions needed to support individual decision making that would raise overall levels of food production is absent. This, too, is a problem area where prescriptive, decision support tools could improve the geographic component of decision making, as described.

The Optimum Location of Infrastructure for Development

One of the important recognitions of the last decade is that if developing nations are to increase their production of food and other products, they must invest to develop their human resources: education, health, and general decision-making abilities. It is generally agreed that this should also include an increased emphasis on the role of women whose untapped potential for contributing to development is often ignored or, in some cases, consciously impeded. To improve human resources requires the development of an infrastructure, and this includes organizing resources, geographically, so that they are most effective. Schools and health centers should be geographically accessible to the people they are meant to serve, but in many countries the public funds needed to set up and operate these facilities are regarded as political spoils given to selected people or villages to reward them for their political support.

Consequently, when we examine the actual spatial distribution of these facilities, we find that the same levels of geographic accessibility could have been reached with far fewer resources if they had been located more carefully or that much higher levels of accessibility could have been realized by the same resources if they had been better located. As in the routing example discussed earlier, mathematical optimization methods have been developed that operate on a GIS that describes the amount of demand for each service at each location, the current location and size of facilities, and the network of roads over which people move. These methods, called *location-allocation methods*, were designed to answer questions such as how to:

find a set of locations that are optimal with respect to predefined objectives, such as locations for which the average distance of people to their closest facility is least; compare the performance of real geographical systems with estimates made for their normative counterparts—such as compare the average distance of people to their closest middle school with the average distance that they would be if the facilities had been optimally located; compute an optimal set of new locations to add to the existing set—that is, accept that decision makers are unlikely to close down existing schools, no matter how poorly they might be located, but compute the best new locations to add to the existing set of schools; assess the benefits and the costs of any constraints on location decisions that are present in real-life decisions—such as political constraints that defined political regions must have at least a given number of facilities; evaluate the quality of past (recent) location decisions—and thus determine whether recent location decisions have improved access as much as was possible given the location of facilities located at an earlier time; investigate alternative decision making principles and to illustrate, by simulation, the alternative location systems that would develop if these principles are employed. (Rushton, 1988, p. 100)

Discussions of the use of these methods can be found in Ayeni, Rushton, and McNulty (1987), Patel (1979), and Rushton (1984, 1988). These methods are now beginning to be adopted and used in many countries of the world as several commercially available GIS software begin to add location-allocation models to the many other spatial analysis functions in their systems (see box "GIS as a Megatrend").

Gis as a Megatrend

A decade ago, John Naisbitt authored a best-selling book titled *Megatrends: Ten New Directions for Transforming Our Lives.* This helped readers comprehend that the old industrial base was indeed fading away and that in its place a new information-electronics economy was springing forth. Naisbitt referred to this shift as the "end of denial" and the beginning of "America's new information economy." (p. 20).

To review the megatrends and Naisbitt's approach to developing them are listed and characterized. These trends are as follows:

Megatrend 1—from an industrial society to an information society
Megatrend 2—from forced technology to high-tech—high-touch
Megatrend 3—from a national economy to a world economy
Megatrend 4—from short term to long term
Megatrend 5—from centralization to decentralization
Megatrend 6—from institutional help to self-help
Megatrend 7—from representative to participatory democracy
Megatrend 8—from hierarchies to networking
Megatrend 9—from north to south
Megatrend 10—from either/or to multiple option industry

Let us explore the megatrends and see how each helps us precisely explain the effects of GIS. Some people with a more local perspective call it LIS, a land information system.

GIS TREND 1

GISs are being created and used to solve problems at all levels of business and government. This trend is supported by megatrend 1: from an industrial society to an information society.

GIS TREND 2

Hand geopositioning (GPS), laptop computing, and remote-sensing technologies are emerging that will make it possible to implement user-responsive GISs. This trend is supported by megatrend 2: from a forced technology to high-tech—high-touch, from using tapes and transits to establish geocoordinates to using satellites. And, overall, from thousands of dollars per data point to only hundreds.

GIS TREND 3

Networking among agencies, corporate branches, and levels of government has spawned multipurpose GISs. There has been a shift to intergovernmental and private-sector consortiums, or from individual technologies to the incorporation of multiple technologies. This trend is supported by megatrend 8: from hierarchies to networking, or from single-purpose to multipurpose systems.

GIS TREND 4

GISs have been designed to meet the needs of local government and individual citizens. GIS has shifted federal responsibility for innovation and modernization to responsibilities shared by state and local governments and the private sector. This trend is explained by megatrend 5, from centralization to decentralization, and megatrend 7, from representative to participatory democracy.

GIS TREND 5

GISs are designed to provide multiple future options. This trend is supported by megatrend 10: from either/or to multiple option, or from simple manual overlays to complex, sophisticated spatial analysis.

GIS TREND 6

To develop and implement multipurpose GISs, planning and design must focus on the long term, not a short-term, single-use scenario. This trend is supported by megatrend 4: from the short term to long term, or from the past to the future.

GIS TREND 7

GIS use has gone from the national level of use and development in the United States (with Hunstville, Alabama's Intergraph and Redlands, California's ARC/INFO) to use and development at the international level. Megatrend 3—from a national economy to a world economy— explains quite well how important the international sales of GIS software and hardware are to the vitality of the GIS industry.

Naisbitt was a GIS innovator a decade before he knew it. He makes us question the value of information and the future value of GIS.

"Information is power. Information has value. In the GIS community we know that intuitively, but we are struggling to have this truth accepted at all levels of use: in a world economy (megatrend 3), in a decentralized venue (megatrend 5), in a participatory government (megatrend 7), and in a multiple-option industry (megatrend 10)" (p. 67).

(Source: Adapted from Niemann, B. J., Jr., and Niemann, S. S. 1993, April. Geo Info Systems. Cleveland, OH: Advanstar Communications, pp. 64–67.)

THE MARXIST APPROACH

◈

Marxists differ from the other approaches we have discussed in developing their principles of decision making from a different philosophical position and a different understanding of the functioning of world production systems. They argue that decisions to develop new production systems reflect the competition between labor and capital and to decisions about new production processes that often use labor in new ways. The outcome of this process, they argue, in the capitalist system of production that currently dominates most of the world, leads to uneven development of regions as capital continually seeks new locations where its returns will be higher.

They argue that by focusing on decision making in this context their theories can respond to the transformation that began to sweep the world economy after the mid-1950s. In developed capitalist countries, this transformation involved the decline of the old basic industries—coal mining, steel making, and shipbuilding. It also involved a dispersal of industrial and service activities from major cities to smaller towns and suburbs, and from core regions to more peripheral ones. Much of these changing patterns occurred as a result of the increasing importance of large, multiplant companies. The variety of behavior exhibited by various multilocational companies is not easily accounted for in a classical or behavioral location-theory approach.

For Marxists, the sorts of characteristics that influence an entrepreneur's choice of where to build a factory, expand, or close, hinge on the *nature and demands of production*. In turn, changes in production and, consequently, in location factors are not the result of some autonomous choice by decision makers, but of wider economic and political forces, relations with labor within firms, and of firms' reactions to both. Thus, the decisions of firms to decentralize, to leave old manufacturing areas for new, and to abandon central cities for suburbs and beyond are a reflection of attempts to contend with changes in the broader economic environment.

Marxists disagree among themselves about how to explain the social organization of production. It can be argued that some versions of Marxism foster a rigid and oversimplified mind-set. There is a danger of viewing economic decisions as predetermined responses to a set of forces called the "demands of accumulation" and the "law of value." The Marxist approach is just as deterministic as traditional location theory. It normalizes particular decisions, which is particularly unfortunate in geography, a subject devoted to understanding unevenness, difference, place, and locality. It ignores geography, just as traditional location theory ignores social relations.

An alternate version of Marxism recognizes underlying causal processes, but recognizes, too, that such processes never operate in isolation. "The particular nature of capitalism in specific countries, the very different ways in which different parts of the economy respond to the general situation of economic recessions, the very different impact which the entry of particular forms of economic activity can have on different regions and local areas: all are products of many determinations" (Massey, 1984, pp. 6–7). Instead of viewing differences as deviations from a norm, this approach recognizes their significance as causal factors and appreciates their effects.

Geographers who accept this perspective argue that changes in the spatial organization of production are a response to changes in class relations—economic and political, national and international. The geography of economic activity involves a struggle between capital and labor. To understand the causes of location decisions, it is necessary to investigate relations between capital and labor and to examine their empirical form that varies among countries and over time.

The most interesting work in this version of Marxism so far concerns the location behavior of companies (Massey and Meegan, 1979; Scott and Storper, 1986). What are the building blocks for understanding the location strategies of firms? They include the nature of the labor process and the organization of capital, the social structure of capitalist production, and the relationship between the social and the spatial. These building blocks also help geographers appreciate the impact of location decisions on particular places at different times.

Characteristics of Industry

Industry is a collection of hundreds of different types of firms, which are reflected by each firm's location decisions. For example, market-seeking firms, banks, hotels, and locally oriented manufacturers locate within the market to serve it. Although it is vital to know about the location strategies of different types of firms (*where* should it be produced?), it is equally vital to know how the labor process and the organization of capital affect the geographic distribution of firms (*how* should it be produced?).

THE LABOR PROCESS

There are four phases in the development of the labor process (Aglietta, 1979). Each phase represents an increasing division of labor functionally and geographically. The geographic manifestation of each phase depends on the interaction between the requirements of the labor process and the inherited spatial structure.

The first phase, *manufacture*, consists of the gathering of workers into a factory system with firms widely dispersed throughout the countryside. Dispersal was a characteristic of British firms before the industrial revolution. It enabled entrepreneurs to avoid guild restrictions and high-cost labor in towns and to obtain access to water power (Perrons, 1981).

In the second phase, *machinofacture*, mechanization occurs and the division of labor within production develops. The use of mechanical principles and steam power frees industry from rural locations. Production is increasingly concentrated in towns. This phase was characteristic of industrial capitalist countries during the industrial revolution.

The third phase, *Fordism* (integrated production and assembly), together with *Taylorism* (application of scientific management principles to production), results in further job fragmentation, especially the separation of conception from execution. Fordism results in the geographic separation of control and production. It leads to the growth of office-based activities that often replace industry in central cities. Industrial activities move to the suburbs and, subsequently, in search of cheaper and less-organized labor, move beyond the suburbs to peripheral regions in the home country and the world.

The latest or fourth phase, *neoFordism*, results in further fragmentation of the labor force and the distilling of the traditional blue-collar class through the introduction of electronic information systems. NeoFordism reinforces the geographic pattern introduced by Fordism by increasing the physical separation of different production functions and by extending the possibility of decentralization of production to small-batch processes as well as large assembly runs.

These four phases represent different ways of com-

Production change or location change can reduce a firm's labor costs. The European Component Corporation opted for locational change when it decided to open a branch plant on a trading estate on the outskirts of Belfast, Northern Ireland. The facility, which manufactures automobile seatbelts, employs many older, married women—an abundant source of low-wage labor. Many manufacturing firms in the United Kingdom decentralized their activities in the 1970s and 1980s by opening plants in peripheral regions. Service firms adopted a similar strategy. They decentralized the more routine elements of clerical work out of London, to regions where wage rates and office rents were lower. *(Source: Industrial Development Board of Northern Ireland.)*

bining capital and labor in the production process. They lead decision makers to make different location choices. The introduction of each new stage, however, does not imply a complete reshaping of all location patterns. At any one place at any one time there are likely to exist a number of different production configurations.

THE ORGANIZATION OF CAPITAL

The adoption of a particular labor process is linked to the organizational structure of capital, especially the size of a company. Size distinguishes single-plant firms from multiplant firms or numerous small firms (small capital) from large firms (monopoly capital). It is also related to the development of the capitalist economy. Over time, the organization of the economy into larger units of capital, through merger and takeover (centralization) and through internal expansion (concentration), represents an increase of control by individual companies.

The spatial structures of capital are diverse. Three simple examples are concentrated, cloning, and part-process. The *locally concentrated structure* is characteristic of small firms. The *cloning branch-plant structure* is characteristic of multilocational companies manufacturing final consumer goods (e.g., bottled and canned soft drinks). The *part-process structure* is also characteristic of multi-location companies and is exemplified by Ford's world car with its worldwide part-process organization. Other structures include *conglomerate ownership*, in which the production of a wide range of different commodities is under the same financial control.

Social Structure of Capitalist Production

The labor process and the organization of capital attempt to link the day-to-day events in location decision making to the longer term development of capitalism. Without a framework for understanding the social structure of capitalist production, they only provide guidance as to the location strategies of firms. The defining classes of capitalist society are capital and labor. Capitalists control the accumulation process through decisions about investment, the means of production, and the authority structure within the labor process. The working class does not exert this type of control.

No capitalist society is so simple, however. For example, within the working class, divisions between skilled and unskilled workers figure prominently in location decisions. An industry may be rooted in a particular place because of the long experience of the area's workers. Changes in the labor process, however, may eventually free the industry from the labor market, and so also from its geographic ties. The release of an industry from its traditional labor source is an impetus to move production from core regions to peripheral ones and from industrialized countries to industrializing ones.

In addition to capital and labor, there are other classes in the capitalist social structure; for example, there are landowners and the self-employed. The *self-employed* have economic ownership and possession of the means of production, but exert no control over the labor of others. Like labor and capital, it is also differentiated. The classic example of the self-employed is the shopkeeper who retains a foothold in those parts of an economy where capitalist firms have yet to fully take over. In many industrialized capitalist societies, shopkeepers are on the decline—corner shops are under threat from supermarkets. But there are also sectors of the economy in which self-employment is expanding. Examples include the new professional and business service sectors.

This basic framework of the internal social structure of capitalist production is dynamic. It represents a set of social processes in which there is constant tension and conflict. It provides a basis for understanding location decision making.

The Social and the Spatial

Geography involves distance and closeness, variations between areas, and the character and meaning of particular places or regions. These ingredients are essential to the operation of social processes. The development of the social structure of capitalist production takes place in a geographic world—the social and the spatial are inseparable. Take an example that illustrates the decision-making conundrum. Production change and location change are alternative ways by which decision makers can achieve the same ends. Geographic differences in the labor force may give management greater flexibility in decisions about production. If production is potentially mobile, it may be easier to move to low-wage areas than to introduce a change in the labor process. Either strategy, production change or location change, can achieve the same result—a lowering of labor costs. The choice presents itself at a particular time; it generally serves to hasten a decision in a particular direction rather than to effect a departure from an existing trend. Nonetheless, results may be significant. What might have happened to the labor process in the clothing, textile, and electronic-assembly industries since the 1960s had multinational corporations not sought cheap labor reserves in the Third World?

DECISION MAKING ON A GLOBAL SCALE

◉

Old and new industries located phases of their production process in low-wage countries in the 1970s and 1980s as a response to the new realities of capitalism. The new realities had their origin in the end of the post-World War II boom in the late 1960s and early 1970s. A crisis of profitability in production in developed countries created a deepening internationalization of capital on a scale never before known. Through the interaction of production and money capital, internationalization emerged as a major force in the organization of production, work, and space in all countries (Scott and Storper, 1986; Storper and Walker, 1989). "Global competition is the battlefield; competitiveness and excellence are the battle cries" (O'Loughlin, 1988, p. 83).

The complexity and sophistication of the new economic geography calls into question the mechanistic conceptions of classical economic theory and Marxist crisis theory. Under classical criteria, factor endowments—land, labor, and capital—determine the location of economic activities in each country and among countries. Markets are left free to respond to supply and demand for products so as to allocate resources efficiently; but the relations of production defy this deterministic conception of economic behavior.

The new realities of capitalism also call into question Marxist crisis theory. In Marx's formulation, crisis, like the time of troubles in the 1970s, direct the long-term development of capitalism toward socialism (Figure 5.9). The crisis of the 1970s, however, did not result in a revolutionary "awakening"; instead, it led to yet another cumulative change in capitalism. During the 1980s, capitalism proved once again to be more technically dynamic and socially creative than predicted by Marx. For example, some Third World countries went beyond their initial role as cheap labor reserves and developed more complex patterns of industrialization, as the cases of Brazil, Hong Kong, and Singapore make clear.

In their reassessment of the new capitalism, a growing number of geographers accept the view that the relationship of capital and labor and the vast differences in prevailing wage rates around the world are keys for understanding location decision making about industrial activity. Marxist geographers, however, ignore the role played by other actors and factors—an essential

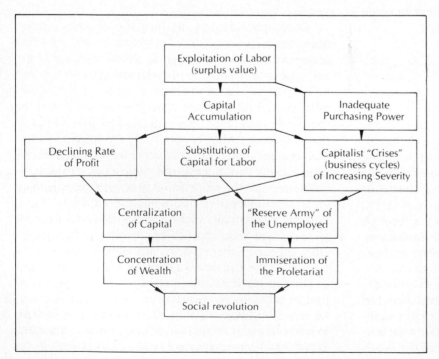

FIGURE 5.9
Model of Marx's crisis theory.
(Source: From The Age of the Economist, 5th ed. by Daniel R. Fusfeld. Copyright © 1986 by Scott, Foresman and Company. Reprinted by permission.)

aspect in the development of a comprehensive theory of location decision making. The increasing complexity and sophistication of the new economic geography can be appreciated, however, with recourse to a descriptive model of industrial decision making. Richard Robinson (1981), a professor of international management at the Massachusetts Institute of Technology, recognized that, since 1945, international business has moved through three general episodes and has started on a fourth. These episodes are defined by the number of actors relevant to location decision making.

The Two-Actor Era

The postwar years until 1955 were characterized by European and Japanese reconstruction. Technology, machines, and consumer goods that the U.S. dollar could buy were highly demanded. The market for U.S. exports exploded. Managers understood that to sell in volume to these markets required producing within those markets. They selected significant markets that they were in danger of losing if they depended solely on exports and those that could not be penetrated because of trade barriers, as was the case of Japan. During this postwar decade, the actors influencing industrial location were firms and their overseas commercial associates.

The Three-Actor Era

During the boom years, from 1955 to 1970, some government officials recognized that business was an important international actor. Increasingly, the political impact of corporate behavior entered the decision-making methodology.

In this era, reconstruction was complete in Japan and Western Europe, and their firms vigorously sought global markets. The Korean War ended, and the Japanese economy became a tower of economic strength. Colonialism collapsed like a house of cards, and the newly independent countries attempted to gain control over their development processes. An era of neonationalism gripped the world. Toward the end of the period, the United States expended enormous resources in Vietnam and accumulated massive balance-of-payment deficits as the goods and services priced in dollars became more expensive. Meanwhile, U.S.-based multinational firms created globally integrated production and marketing systems under headquarters administration

Europe returns to wind power. The Netherlands once used windmills to pump water off the land. The decision was made to turn to diesel pumps and nuclear power. Because of environmental side effects and dwindling fossil fuel supplies, the Netherlands is once again turning to wind power.
(Source: Regis Bossu/Sygma.)

and control. Increased international expertise at the headquarters and improved international communications systems made this headquarters/branch-plant structure feasible.

The appearance of giant enterprises first in the United States, then in Western Europe, and last in Japan intensified the sensitivities of host governments. By then, the dominance of U.S. power, technology, and capital were challenged. Alternative sources for needed capital, skills, machines, and technology could be found in Western Europe and Japan. Host governments became key actors whose policies directly affected the decisions of the multinationals.

The Four-Actor Era

The decade of the 1970s was a time of crisis. Industrial overcapacity was pervasive. The profitability of capital decreased first in Britain in the mid-1960s and then in the United States. France, Italy, and West Germany experienced stress between 1974 and 1978. Even Japan's economy began to falter in the early 1980s. Persistent U.S. balance-of-payments problems ended the fixed exchange-rate system and the value of the dollar dropped, especially in relation to the yen and deutschmark. The developing countries initiated efforts to restructure the world's economy and redistribute the world's wealth through the NIEO. One of the main targets of the Group of 77 was the large multinational firm, the chief allocator of goods and services internationally. The notion of a finite earth was dramatized by limits-to-growth rhetoric and by OPEC. An increasingly interdependent world economy became evident to all. As a consequence, parent governments acknowledged the economic and, hence, political impact of international business. The conduct of international business was too important to be left to the technostructure, the market, and Third World politicians. So began the four-actor era of the 1970s with the discovery of multinationals as political actors.

The Multiactor Era

International industrial location is no longer solely the province of multinationals, host and parent governments, and markets. A number of other actors are indirectly influential—national and international labor groups, intergovernmental organizations, and various special interest groups. Labor makes its desires felt through governments or multinationals. Intergovernmental organizations exert their influence on national governments. Special interest groups—consumers, conservationists, and political ideologists—act on governments or corporations to alter policies on safety, environmental protection, and products offered in different markets. These additional actors attempt to create a new international order in their own image.

The multiactor era of the late twentieth century introduces a new degree of uncertainty to corporate decision making. As the number and power of actors increase, so the cost of corporate decision making mounts, making it difficult for old-style multinationals to compete without more flexible methods of transacting international business. It appears that the multinational—a special form of international business that appeared in the 1950s and 1960s—is giving way to international service and trading companies. These organizations are engaged essentially in turnkey projects; they build and start up plants under contract, with an expanded training function (Robinson, 1981). Preeminent business organizations of the future may well be "those devoted to improving international markets in terms of special inputs—services, skills, knowledge, capital—and specific outputs—largely goods. The guts of such firms will be international information networks and data banks" (Robinson, 1981, pp. 18–19).

Managerial Response

Managerial expertise in "reading" the environment and responding appropriately is vital in the location of economic activities. How do decision makers perceive and respond to the complex and sophisticated international environment of the late twentieth century? "The perception of risk and uncertainty by decision makers is a direct function of their perception as to the accuracy and adequacy of the relevant data and of their familiarity with the environment within which they act. The greater the faith one has in the data, the lower the perceived uncertainty in relation to the environment" (Robinson, 1981, p. 19). This explains why U.S.-based firms invested first in Canada and England, countries culturally close to the United States. It also explains why decision makers are reluctant to build plants in culturally remote countries until they become familiar with the market, often via exports.

ECOLOGICAL PRINCIPLES AND DECISION MAKING

◈

Decision-making principles so far discussed have centered on optimizing the returns to individuals or groups, but there are many now who place nature as a power in its own right and with its own needs. They argue that any decisions that alter the endowments of nature should meet the principle of environmental sustainability. In the past decade, concerns about the permanent loss of many plant and animal species; the loss of habitats, such as wetlands, that maintain biodiversity; changes in the global climate; and the deteriorating quality and availability of safe drinking water over large parts of the earth have led many people to propose new principles of decision making. Any decisions made by individuals, organizations, or countries that diminish the capability of the earth to sustain mankind and preserve its rich heritage should be examined and made to meet the ecosensitivity test of preserving the quality of the environment. This principle is contrasted with other widely accepted principles of utility-maximizing or profit-maximizing behavior. Proposers of this point of view point to evidence that current decision-making processes are irreparably harming the earth and, since this is the only home for mankind, ethical principles must replace economic principles as the basis for actions. The Directors of the World Resources Institute (1992) explain the following theme:

> Wise management of natural resources and protection of the global environment are essential to achieve sustainable economic development and hence to alleviate poverty, improve the human condition, and preserve the biological systems on which all life depends. (p. ix)

Their conclusion is that

> we must seek a series of transitions or transformation to more sustainable paths of development, including: A technological transition away from today's resource-intensive, pollution-prone technologies to a new generation that places less stress on the environment; An economic transition to a world economy based on reliance on nature's ''income'' and not on depletion of its ''capital''; A demographic transition to a stable human population no more than twice the level of today; A transition in consciousness to a more profound and widespread understanding of global sustainability; An institutional transition to new arrangements—among governments and peoples—that can achieve environmental security. (Directors of the World Resources Institute, 1992, p. xi)

Through international organizations such as the United Nations, the Institute is attempting to persuade countries to agree to guarantee that development objectives be compatible with sustaining the resources of the world. This was the intended outcome of the 1992 Earth Summit in Rio de Janeiro, Brazil, sponsored by the United Nations. Proponents of the ecological view point to the need for an authority that will ensure that the decisions of individuals do not abrogate the agreements entered into with other countries by the state to which they belong. Most states do not acknowledge any such external authority. Many states lack the enforcement mechanisms to guarantee within their own territory the agreements concerning environmental conservation that they reach in international meetings. New decision-making principles will need to be developed and enforced if future patterns of resource use in the world economy is to meet the needs of this new ideology. The ideology that makes nature subservient to mankind and grants to mankind the powers of exploiting nature for his benefit, is a relatively recent development of western civilization. Glacken (1967) in his geographic classic traced the evolving views of nature by western society.

Summary

◈

The pace of economic and social change appears to be accelerating throughout the world and the changes that occur in one decade often become the factors that condition change in the next. Social scientists call these *endogenous factors* when results of one set of decisions become the major causes for the next decisions. In a major sense, the difference between our understanding of decision-making principles 20 years ago and today is that we now recognize that understandings based on theories of external conditions to which people respond are incomplete when we fail to consider how decisions at one time and place affect the context in which later decisions are made.

In examining different approaches to location decision making, we first consider traditional location theories. Classical location models assume the existence of *optimizers*. Such *normative models* are deterministic—a given set of data always yields a specific pattern. Today, with GISs, it is possible to represent in digital form the spatial pattern of the values of factors that influence economic decision making. The complexity of land-use patterns and of other geographic distributions of economic activities reflect the complexity of the location patterns of factors influencing decisions. The search for regularities in spatial patterns characteristic of economic geography 20 years ago is no longer a major objective of economic geography since it is now clear through simulations that a very large number of spatial patterns can exist. It is also clear now that a variety of decision-making motives drive human behavior in addition to the traditional profit motive.

We then turned our attention to prescriptive decision-making principles and noted that with the contemporary emphasis to develop methods to improve decision making about resource allocations, spatial decision support systems (SDSSs) have been developed to assist decision makers in selecting routes and choosing locations and activities to meet some agreed-upon objectives. The development of mathematical algorithms and their link to GISs is now leading to the widespread adoption of SDSSs.

A consideration of the work of Marxist geographers noted that many of them believe that location decision making is deeply structured by the capital-labor relation. Geographic differences in this relationship lead to the existence of a diversity of capitalist relations of production. The international or global perspective, we note, has become essential with the unprecedented internationalization of capital and associated shifts in the geographic distribution of economic activity that followed the end of the postwar boom.

In the last section of the chapter, we introduce the environmental perspective and note that environmental sustainability has become, for some, a principle to guide decision making across a broad set of economic activities, most of which consume or alter earth's natural resources.

◙

KEY TERMS

ARC/INFO
capital-labor conflict
environmental sustainability
equilibrium price
Fordism
geographic information system (GIS)
global positioning systems (GPS)
labor process
land-use gradient
location-allocation model
location theory
machinofacture
manufacture
megatrend

neoFordism
normative models
optimizer
organization of capital
rational, prescriptive, and descriptive decision-making processes
satisficer
social-spatial relations
spatial decision support system (SDSS)
spatial regularity
suitability modeling
Taylorism
TIGER files
TRAILMAN

◈

SUGGESTED READINGS

Dodson, R. F. 1991. VT/GIS: The von Thunen GIS Package. Technical paper 91-27. National Center for Geographic Information & Analysis, Santa Barbara, CA.

GeoInfo Systems: Applications of GIS and Related Spatial Information Technologies. Metuchen, NJ: Advanstar Communications. Various issues.

Glacken, C. 1967. *Traces on the Rhodian Shore.* Berkeley: University of California Press.

Haggett, P. 1965. *Locational Analysis in Human Geography.* London: Edward Arnold Ltd.

Lyle, J., and Stutz, F. 1983. Land use suitability modeling and mapping. *Cartographic Journal,* 18:39–50.

Massey, D. 1984. *Spatial Divisions of Labor: Spatial Structures and the Geography of Production.* New York: Methuen.

Parrott, R., and Stutz, F. 1992. Urban GIS applications. In D. Maquire, M. Goodchild, and D. Rhind (Eds.), *GIS: Principles and Procedures.* London: Longmans.

Pred, A. 1967. Behavior and location: Foundations for a geographic and dynamic location theory, Part 1. *Lund Studies in Geography,* Series B.27.

Rushton, G. 1988. The Roepke lecture in economic geography: Location theory, location-allocation models, and service development planning in the Third World. *Economic Geography,* 64:97–119.

Sayer, A., and Walker, R. 1993. *The New Social Economy: Reworking the Division of Labor.* Cambridge, MA: Blackwell.

Scott, A. J., and Storper, M., eds. 1986. *Production, Work, Territory: The Geographical Anatomy of Industrial Capitalism.* Boston: Allen and Unwin.

Storper, M., and Walker, R. 1989. *The Capitalist Imperative: Territory, Technology, and Industrial Growth.* New York: Basil Blackwell.

Wolpert, J. 1964. The decision process in a spatial context. *Annals, Association of American Geographers,* 54:537–558.

TRANSPORTATION AND COMMUNICATIONS IN WORLD ECONOMY

O B J E C T I V E S

- To develop an understanding of modern transportation and communication systems

- To consider the impact of transport costs on locational patterns

- To demonstrate the relationship between transport and economic development

- To examine communications innovations and on-line computer networks

- To examine several new developments and transportation policy

- To consider recent innovations in transport development of metropolitan areas

Traffic in Calcutta, India.
(Source: World Bank.)

For most of human existence, economic development was tied to natural conditions. People occupied narrowly circumscribed areas that were mostly isolated from other groups of people. Gradually, improvements in the efficiency and flexibility of growing transportation systems changed patterns of human life. Control and exchange became possible over wider and wider areas and facilitated the development of more elaborate social structures.

The course of human history was changed when European capitalism and its overseas progeny laid the foundations for technological culture. From the sixteenth century onward, there were great revolutions in science and trade, great voyages of discovery, and a consequent increase in productive, commodity, and financial capital. Capitalism required a world market for its goods; hence, it broke the isolation of the natural economy and of feudal society. The engine that drove this economic expansion was accumulation for accumulation's sake. In an effort to increase the rate of accumulation, all forms of capital had to be moved as quickly and cheaply as possible between places of production and consumption. To annihilate space by time, some of the resulting profits of commerce were devoted to developing the means of transportation and communication. "Annihilation of space by time" does not simply imply that better transportation and communication systems diminish the importance of geographic space; instead, the concept poses the question of how and by what means space can be used, organized, created, and dominated to facilitate the circulation of capital (Harvey, 1985, p. 37).

The transformation in transportation technology, together with capitalist development, served to integrate isolated producers. The integration of production points into a national or international economy does not change their absolute location (site), but it does alter their relative location (situation). Transport improvements increase the importance of relative space. The progressive integration of absolute space into relative space means that economic development becomes less dependent on relations with nature and more dependent on relations across space.

Most people no longer live in spatially restricted societies. Whether they live on farms or in cities, they can travel from place to place, communicate with each other over long distances, and depend on goods and information that come from beyond their immediate environment. Geographers refer to movements of goods, people, and ideas—by means ranging from walking to digital telephone networks—as spatial interaction.

Improvements in transportation promote spatial interaction; consequently, they spur specialization of location. By stimulating specialization, better transportation leads to increased land and labor productivity as well as to more efficient use of capital. As societies abandon self-sufficiency for dependency on trade, wealth and income rise rapidly.

Trade occurs when time and money required to move goods over geographic space are within limits to permit local specialization. The amount of trade is related to the location of specialized production, the cost and time it takes to overcome the friction of distance, and the demand for goods. Production costs set the

Container cargo handling at the Maersk Line Terminal, Port Newark, New Jersey. Containerization has greatly improved the operation, management, and logistics of conventional ocean-going freight. The impact of the container evolution has gone far beyond shipping and international trade alone. Newly designed cellular vessels have much faster ship turnaround times in ports, as well as improved cargo-handling productivity at ports. An expanded interface between water and land transportation has occurred. Container trains have also enhanced the economy and scale of rail transportation.
(Source: Photo courtesy of the Port Authority of New York and New Jersey.)

savings or additional wealth derived from local specialization and scale economies and influence the distance separating related activities. Specialization and trade may increase as long as production-cost savings exceed transport costs. For some activities, diseconomies occur at low levels of specialization; hence, production takes place at many locations. For other activities, concentration of production at a few locations is generally more profitable.

Transportation determines the utility or worth of goods. In today's world, almost nothing is consumed where it is produced; therefore, without transport services, most goods would be worthless. Part of their value derives from transport to market. Transport costs, then, are not a constraint on productivity; rather, transport increases the productivity of an economy because it promotes specialization of location.

Transportation is a key for understanding geographic patterns. How does the geographic allocation of transport routes affect development? How do transport networks shape and structure space? How do they modify location? What is the impact of transport costs and transit time on the location of facilities? This chapter provides answers to these questions in discussions on transport costs, routes, and networks; transport development; transportation and communications innovation; and metropolitan concerns in transportation policy.

TRANSPORT COSTS IN THE WORLD ECONOMY

◈

One of the major forces structuring the spatial organization of production is "the tyranny of distance": the fact that all movement costs. Societies have made a tremendous investment in both human and natural resources to overcome the friction of distance. Although transport innovations have reduced circulation costs, locational costs still exert a powerful influence on patterns of production. For that reason, we need to consider the following questions: What is the true form of transport costs? What determines specific transport rates? What effects do international regimes for shipping and aviation have on transport costs? What is the impact of transport costs on location? For what industries is transit time more crucial than cost?

General Properties of Transport Costs

Alfred Weber's industrial location theory emphasizes the cost of moving materials and finished products from place to place. Initially, it makes two normative assumptions about transport costs in order to concentrate on the idealized effects of distance. These assumptions are that: (1) transport costs are a linear function of distance, and (2) transport costs are exclusively a function of distance (zero distance equals zero cost) (Table 6.1). In reality, transport costs are much more complex.

Actual transportation costs can be categorized as either terminal costs or line-haul costs (Figure 6.1). Terminal costs must be paid regardless of the distance involved. They include the cost of preparation for movement, loading and unloading, capital investment, line maintenance, and other kinds of costs that are not a function of distance. Line-haul costs, in contrast, are strictly a function of distance. For example, fuel costs are proportional to the distance a load must be moved.

Terminal costs are fixed in the short-run, but are altered by technological changes. International shipping provides an example. In 1960, most merchant ships were general cargo vessels and high loading and unloading costs as well as long turnaround times were involved in their operation. Since that time, more and more ships have been built to handle specialized cargoes. The first of the new ships were oil tankers followed

◈

Table 6.1

Linear Transport Costs

Kilometers	Cost $
0	0
100	1
200	2
300	3
400	4
500	5
600	6
700	7
800	8
900	9
1,000	10

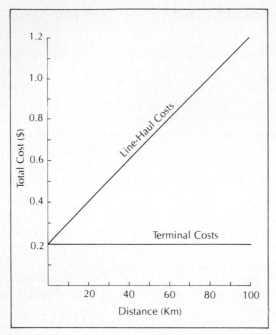

FIGURE 6.1
Terminal and line-haul costs. Terminal costs are also fixed costs. Line-haul costs incurred "over the road" are also variable costs.

by vessels designed to carry ores, grains, and containers. The reduction in handling costs in ports and the rapid turnaround of the ships more than offset the cost of building specialized handling facilities (e.g., gantry cranes costing more than $2 million).

Recent developments in cargo handling have changed the location and appearance of ports. In the Netherlands, for example, old, enclosed dock systems of ports such as Rotterdam have been joined by new, deep-water terminals such as Europoort. In the 1960s, oil terminals capable of handling tankers weighing more than 250,000 tons were constructed at Europoort. Subsequently, additional deep-water facilities have been developed to handle trade in grain, coal, and ore. The most recent development has been the provision of container-handling facilities and roll-on/roll-off terminals.

The world's first containerized service tied trucks and ships together in 1956. McLean, a U.S. trucking firm, organized this operation at Sea-Land and used converted tankers on trips from the port of Newark, New Jersey to Houston, Texas. Florida was added to this route in 1957 and Puerto Rico in 1958. By the mid-

1960s, Sea-Land initiated service by new cellularized containerships from New York to Europoort, Bremen, and Grangemouth in Great Britain. Three years later trans-Pacific service was established from Oakland, California to Hong Kong, Taiwan, and Singapore. By the early 1970s, numerous carriers entered into the containership business.

At first, the greatest appeal of the containership was its speed and economy in port. Moreover, it facilitated the multimodal transport of goods. For example, commodities from Japan and other Pacific Rim countries could be transported economically to Europe via North America. Later, container operations sought to speed up the ocean voyage as well—top usable speeds increased from 15 knots in the 1950s to 33 knots in the 1970s. In addition, the oil crisis of the 1970s led to efforts to make more economical use of fuel to stabilize line-haul costs.

With the emergence of a new international division of labor, ports continue to modernize their methods of handling cargo as they compete with each other for shares of global commodity traffic. In developed countries served by many ports, competition has decreased the relevance of the traditional concept of the port hinterland (i.e., the area served by the port). On the West Coast of the United States, for example, ports in California, Oregon, and Washington compete fiercely for the mounting trade with the Pacific Rim. In underdeveloped countries and in marginal zones within developed countries, limited port systems still serve particular hinterlands.

CARRIER COMPETITION

Competitive differences in transport media account for variations in terminal and *line-haul costs* (Figure 6.2). Trucks have low *terminal costs* partly because they do not have to provide and maintain their own highways, and partly because of their flexibility. If provisions for parking are adequate, they can load and unload almost anywhere. However, trucks are not as efficient in moving freight on a ton-kilometer basis as are railroad and water carriers. Of the three competing forms of transport, trucks involve the least cost only out to distance D_1. Railroad carriers have higher terminal costs than truck carriers, but lower than water carriers, and a competitive advantage through the distance D_1-D_2. Water carriers, such as barges, have the highest terminal costs, but they achieve the lowest line-haul costs, giving them an advantage over longer distances.

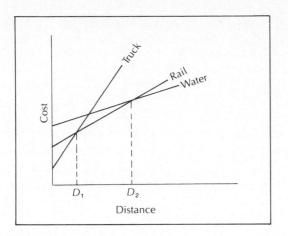

FIGURE 6.2
Variations in terminal and line-haul costs for air, truck, rail, water, and pipeline. Why do you suppose pipeline and water have the highest terminal costs? Why do air and truck have the highest line-haul costs?

CURVILINEAR LINE-HAUL COSTS

Thus far, line-haul costs have been portrayed as a linear function of distance. Actual line-haul costs, however, are curvilinear (Figure 6.3). As the graph illustrates, line-haul costs increase with distance, but at a decreasing rate. The distance from O to D_2 is twice the distance from D_1 to D_2, but does not involve twice the cost (C_1 to C_2). As the distance increases, the average cost per kilometer constantly decreases. This characteristic of actual transportation costs is often called "economies of the long-haul," which occurs for at least three reasons. First, terminal costs are the same regardless of the length of the trip. As line-haul costs increase, terminal costs become proportionally less of the total. Second,

line-haul rates are lower for longer hauls. Short hauls by rail, for example, are moved by "local trains"; longer hauls are moved by "through" freight trains, which stop less frequently and operate more efficiently. Third, tapered line-haul costs prevent rates from restricting long-distance hauls. Rates would soon become high enough to prevent traffic if they increased in direct proportion to distance.

STEPPED FREIGHT RATES

Theoretically, every station along a line from a given origin should pay a different rate based on its actual distance from the origin, but computing large numbers of rates is both time-consuming and expensive to administer. Consequently, zonal-rate systems are a common feature of transport companies. For example, railroads group stations into areas and charge a single rate for all stations within the same zone. In general, group rates are set in relation to control points, often the largest centers in each zone, thus reinforcing the urban dominance of these centers.

Railroads have stepped freight rates that retain the tapering principle and favor long-haul movements (Figure 6.4). The total transport bill per unit of delivered material from station R to Y should be only slightly more than to X. However, because of the nature of the rate zones, Y pays a much higher price than X. Station Z pays the same price as Y because it is in the same rate zone. Station X has a competitive advantage over Y, but Y does not have a cost advantage over Z despite the greater distance of Z from R. Historically, cities such as Chicago, St. Louis, and some Missouri and Ohio River crossings have occupied and benefited from strategic positions in railroad rate groupings.

FIGURE 6.3
Curvilinear line-haul costs make the longer trips less costly per mile. As we will see later in this chapter, information technology is redefining the commercial rail, motor and shipping marketplace, and may well result in a fully integrated, automatic, global system where *intermodal interface* associated with moving products and commodities is automatically arranged by artificial intelligence and other information technologies.

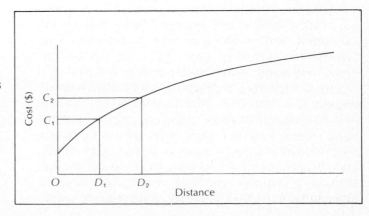

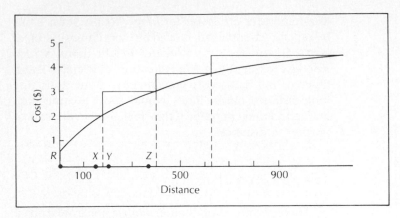

FIGURE 6.4
Stepped freight rates render ease of billing, but give advantages to cities located near the end of a flight zone.

Commodity Variations in Transport Rates

The transportation cost curve varies according to differences in transport modes—but what determines specific rates? One set of factors pertains to the nature of the commodity. Factors that enter into any determination of commodity rates include: (1) loading and packaging costs, (2) susceptibility to loss or damage, (3) shipment size, (4) regularity of movement, (5) special equipment and services, and (6) elasticity of demand.

LOADING AND PACKAGING COSTS

Of particular importance in determining the reasonableness of rates is the weight density of a commodity. Light, bulky commodities usually incur higher freight charges per carload or shipload than heavy, compact articles. This explains why rates generally favor "knocked-down" or "set-up" commodities. For example, parts for an automobile are shipped at a much lower rate than for a finished car.

A low weight-density factor is not the only reason why some commodities load cheaply. Ability to load commodities compactly must also be considered. Articles of odd shape such as furniture may not load efficiently. Sometimes containers cannot be filled without damage to commodities. Melons, for example, cannot be loaded more than a few layers deep without crushing those on the bottom. Furthermore, some articles cost more to load. Rubber latex can be piped to ship rapidly and cheaply, whereas television sets must be handled with care to avoid damage. Coal requires little advance preparation for shipment, but furniture requires special

crating and packing that add to terminal costs (Figure 6.5).

DAMAGE AND RISK VARIATIONS

Commodity rates reflect susceptibility to loss or damage. Except in the case of ocean carriers, most transport companies are liable for loss and damage during transit and must assume a greater risk for some commodities than for others. Sand, gravel, brick, and iron ore are not easily damaged, but fresh fruit and vegetables, television sets, and china run a high risk of damage because of perishability and/or fragility.

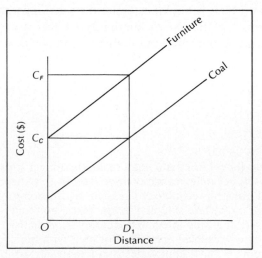

FIGURE 6.5
Variations in loading and packaging costs.

SHIPMENT SIZE

Some commodities are shipped in bulk, whereas others must be carried in small quantities. Railroads charge higher rates for less-than-carload lots than for carload shipments. Rates are lower for commodities transported in volume over a period because carriers can better organize operation and handling methods and reduce costs. A high volume of a single commodity lowers line-haul costs per ton. Striking examples are fully loaded trains carrying only coal or iron ore.

REGULARITY OF MOVEMENT

If traffic moves regularly, carriers can operate at lower costs and should charge lower rates. Schedules are worked out more easily, and vehicle and labor needs can be planned. Irregularity of movement increases rates. This is often true of seasonal movements of fruits, vegetables, and wheat. Many railroad cars must be supplied over a short period. These either have to stand idle much of the time or be diverted from other routes, disrupting regular service.

SPECIAL EQUIPMENT AND SERVICES

The type of equipment required for a commodity affects freight rates. Commodities that require refrigerator cars are more expensive to transport than articles that can be carried by ordinary boxcars. Some commodities require special services. For example, refrigerator cars may have to be precooled before being loaded with shipments of fresh fruits and vegetables, and carriers may charge extra for the costs incurred.

ELASTICITY OF DEMAND

Previous factors related to the relative cost of transporting different commodities, but the *elasticity of demand* for transportation must also be considered. Defined in general terms, the elasticity of demand is the degree of responsiveness of a good or service to changes in its price.

Carriers generally charge what the market will bear. Very often goods with a very high value per unit of weight, such as television sets, are able to bear a higher transportation rate than goods with a very low value per unit of weight, such as coal (Figure 6.6). Thus, the left-hand graph illustrates transportation price inelasticity for television sets. An increase in the rate from P_1 to P_2 produces only a slight change in the quantity of shipments. Coal, however, (in the right-hand graph) exhibits a great change in the quantity of shipments, with only slight change in the transportation rate (P_1 to P_2).

The value of an article does not completely determine a commodity's ability to bear a higher freight rate. Transportation services are not purchased simply for the sake of consuming ton-kilometers. Transportation is a means of distributing localized commodities. The most localized commodities can usually bear higher rates within the framework of loading, shipment size, and damage and risk characteristics.

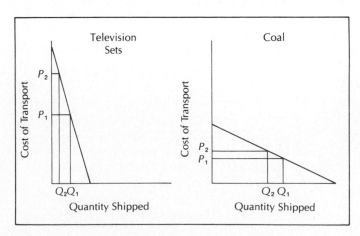

FIGURE 6.6
Demand elasticity for transportation. Higher valued television sets are more valuable and less elastic than quantities of coal. A large price increase to ship television sets results in a small reduction in the quantity shipped. A small price increase to ship coal results in a large reduction in the quantity shipped.

Freight Rate Variations and Traffic Characteristics

The characteristics of carriers and routes form a second set of factors determining specific transportation rates. Important factors include: (1) *carrier competition,* (2) *route demand,* and (3) *backhauling.*

CARRIER COMPETITION

An absence of competition between transport modes means a carrier can set rates between points to cover costs and, in the absence of government control, a carrier may set unjustifiably high rates. Intermodal competition and/or government regulation reduces the likelihood of such practices. The effect of competition between carriers is to reduce rate differences between competitors. For example, the opening of the St. Lawrence Seaway in 1959 resulted in lower rail freight rates on commodities affected by low water-transport rates.

ROUTE DEMAND

An important factor influencing the cost of haul is traffic density. High demand for transportation over a particular route can lower transportation rates. High demand lowers both line-haul and terminal costs per unit. The air shuttle between New York and Wasington, DC, is an example. Demand for this trip is so high that rates per passenger can be much lower than rates for trips over routes of similar distance where demand is low. High volume lowers the terminal costs per passenger. Fully loaded aircraft means lower line-haul costs per passenger.

BACKHAULING

Many carriers face heavy demand only in a specific direction. Consider the large volume of produce shipped from Florida to New York. Trucks must often return empty for the next load. The cost of the total trip, however, is used to determine the transportation rate. Because carriers must make return trips anyway, they are willing to charge very low rates on the backhaul. Any revenue on backhaul is preferred to returning empty. Rates are higher where there is little or no possibility of backhauling; most such runs occur in the transportation of raw materials from resource points to production points. An example is the railroad that carries iron ore pellets from Labrador to the port of Sept Illes, Quebec. This railroad may be likened to a huge conveyor belt that operates in one direction only. By contrast, the distribution of finished products generally involves traffic between many cities, creating a reciprocal flow and lower rates.

Regimes for International Transportation

In the international arena, transport rates and costs are affected by the nature of the regime governing the transport mode. To illustrate, let us consider the contrasting regimes of civil aviation and shipping. The international regime for aviation is dominated by the authoritative allocation of resources by states. By contrast, the international regime for shipping has been shaped by market-oriented principles. These different regimes were established by the industrialized countries. The regime for civil aviation developed in the early twentieth century and reflects a concern for national security. The regime for shipping evolved over more than 500 years and has been more concerned with facilitating commerce than with security.

CIVIL AVIATION

The fundamental principle governing aviation is that states have sovereign control over their own air space. From this principle, rules and procedures have developed that permit countries to regulate their routes, fares, and schedules. As a result, many countries, developed and underdeveloped, have secured a market share that is more or less proportional to their share of world airline traffic. Third World countries have been able to compete with companies based in the industrialized world on an equal footing. Air India, Avianca, and Korean Air Lines can challenge Delta, Air France, and British Airways.

SHIPPING

The international regime for shipping has left underdeveloped countries in a weak position with regard to establishing and nurturing their own merchant fleets.

The Rhine River is the main avenue of freight traffic for Europe. It enters the North Sea at Rotterdam, the world's busiest port. Although the Rhine River is heavily polluted from industrial wastes and chemical spills, it is still a scenic river and, along with castles such as this one, accounts for a large amount of tourism. The castle, Burg Katz, at Goarshausen recently sold to a Japanese businessman for $2.2 million, who will turn the historic landmark into a luxury hotel.
(Source: Reuters/Bettmann.)

In a world of markets, few underdeveloped countries have much influence when it comes to setting commodity rate structures. Lack of control over international shipping is an important area of concern in the Third World's quest for a NIEO.

Although the regime for shipping is characterized by the market, the market is inherently unfair—it favors developed countries over underdeveloped countries. Hence, Third World countries are faced with rate structures that work against them, inadequate service, a perpetuation of center-periphery trade routes, and a lack of access to decision-making bodies. Those Third World countries generating cargoes such as petroleum, iron ore, phosphates, bauxite/alumina, and grains cannot penetrate the bulk-shipping market, which is dominated by the vertically integrated MNCs based in developed countries. Cartels of shipowners, known as liner conferences, set the rates and schedules for liners (freighters that ply regularly scheduled routes).

Third World countries have attempted to change the international rules of shipping. They want to generate fleets of a size proportional to the goods generated by their ports. Their accomplishments have been limited, however. The UNCTAD Code of Conduct for Liner Conferences, which was adopted in 1974, was rejected by the United States. The Liner Code gives Third World country carriers a presumptive right to a share of the market; however, proposals to eliminate flags of convenience have not been accepted. Flags of convenience assume little or no real economic link between the country of registration and the ship that flies its flag. They inhibit the development of national fleets but for shipowners they offer a number of advantages, including low taxation and lower operating costs. Liberia and Panama are the most important open-registry, or flags-of-convenience, countries. Flags of convenience are used mainly by oil tankers and bulk-ore carriers controlled by MNCs.

Transport and Location

TRANSPORT COSTS AND LOCATION THEORY

With a knowledge of actual transport costs, it is possible to examine their implications on modifications of Weber's industrial location theory (Figure 6.7). Consider Weber's solution for one pure raw material (i.e., a raw material that loses no weight in processing) localized at M and sold as a finished product at MKT (Figure 6.7a). *Terminal costs* are zero and *line-haul costs* are linear. What happens to the Weberian solution when terminal costs are added? The solution is given in Figure 6.7b. We must always pay at least one set of terminal costs

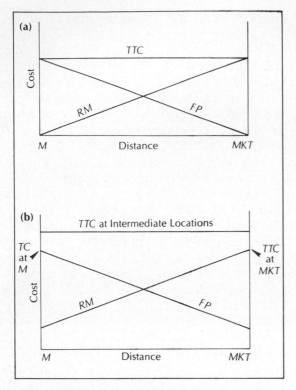

FIGURE 6.7
Weber's model: the effects of terminal costs. (M is site of raw material; MKT is the market; RM is raw material procurement costs; FP is finished product distribution costs; and TC and TTC are total transportation costs.)

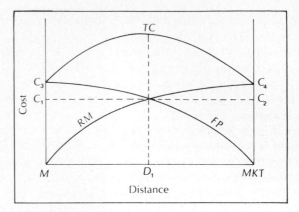

FIGURE 6.8
Weber's model: the effects of curvilinear line-haul costs favor the plant at the source of raw material (RW) or at the market (MKT), but not inbetween.

because either the raw material or the finished product must be moved. At either the mine or the market, one set of terminal costs is paid, but at any intermediate location, two sets of terminal costs must be paid. This raises total transportation costs by an amount equal to one set of terminal costs. Thus, mine or market locations have a clear advantage over intermediate points in terms of terminal costs.

Curvilinear line-haul costs also favor mine or market locations (Figure 6.8). For simplicity, the diagram eliminates terminal costs. It shows that curvilinear line-haul costs favor the long haul. Shipping the raw materials from M to D_1 costs C_1; shipping the finished product from D_1 to MKT costs C_2. Shipping the raw material all the way to MKT, however, only involves a cost of C_4. Total transport costs are minimized at either mine or market.

Commodity rates influence the location of economic activities. As a very general rule, transport rates are lower for raw materials than for finished products fa-

voring market locations (Figure 6.9). The graph retains linear transport costs for simplicity and shows that the lower raw material transport rate minimizes total transport costs (TTC) at the market.

Although tapering freight rates usually disfavor processing at intermediate locations because of additional terminal costs, these must be paid anyway at necessary transshipment or *break-of-bulk* points where a change in carrier must occur. This fact helps to explain why processing often takes place in port cities. Oil and sugar refineries, for example, often lie at tidewater. Iron and steel plants, the biggest and most visually impressive of

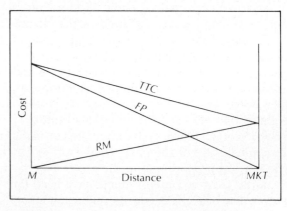

FIGURE 6.9
Weber's model: variations in commodity rates. Here, raw materials are cheaper to ship than finished products. Thus, total transport costs (TTC) are lower at the market (MKT).

all industrial establishments, are also attracted to coastal locations. The Ijmuiden works of Hoogovens in the Netherlands and the Mizushima works of Kawasaki steel on the north shore of the Japanese Inland Sea have deep-water access to ore and coal from international sources and can dispatch finished products to distant markets.

What is the effect of tapering freight rates on supply and market areas? They extend them. Consider for example, the market areas of producers. Suppose there are two producers of the same good (Figure 6.10). Firms A and B have the same terminal and line-haul costs, but A has lower production costs. With linear transport costs, the market between the two occurs at D_1 (Figure 6.10a). The situation changes, however, when curvilinear line-haul costs are introduced. Because of long-haul economies, A is able to capture some of B's market area (Figure 6.10b).

Thus far, we have examined the effects of transport rates on location in terms of *freight-on-board (FOB) pricing*. Consumers pay the plant price plus the cost of transportation; those close to the plant pay less than more distant consumers (Figure 6.11). However, many producers adopt a pricing policy known as *cost-insurance-freight (CIF) pricing*. In this pricing strategy, each consumer pays production costs plus a flat markup to cover transportation charges (Figure 6.12). Each consumer is charged a CIF price at C_1. Comsumers from A to B are charged more than the actual cost of transportation. Consumers from X to A and B to Y are charged less than the actual cost. Close-to-plant consumers pay the distribution costs of more distant consumers.

What effect does CIF pricing have on the market area of producers? The FOB prices of producers A and B are shown in Figure 6.13. The market-area boundary is at X_1 with FOB pricing. If B adopts a CIF pricing

FIGURE 6.10
Market areas: (a) with linear line-haul costs; (b) with curvilinear line-haul costs. *Magnetohydrodynamics* is a new technology being developed for ship propulsion based on the fundamental law of electromagnetism. Japanese technologists believe that ocean freighters will travel over 100 mph with such technology by the year 2000, shortening the trip from Japan to California to two days and flattening the curves. Regardless of advances in rail transportation and shipping, cooperation between and among carriers, customers and governments is moving ahead at a rapid rate. Market areas are being expanded because railroads, trucking firms and shipping companies are cooperating to produce new intermodal information and transportation efficiency and economy. Infrastructures are being developed to allow one to send most anything to any place in the world without talking to another person because of intermodal cooperation. Although one can now arrange for a freight forwarder to take care of all the details of a particular shipment, the intermodal arrangements that are made are ad hoc, designed for only one transaction. Information technology that is now making its way into the marketplace will allow the evolution of a permanent *international intermodal marketplace*. As the information needed for each step of the transportation process becomes standardized and available in digital form, it will open the door to worldwide automated transactions.

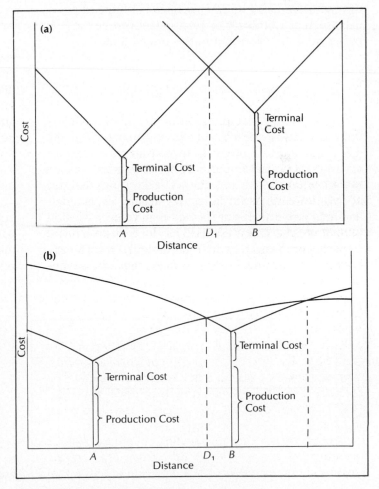

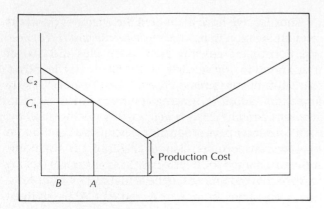

FIGURE 6.11
Freight-on-board pricing.

strategy, the market-area boundary shifts to X_2. Producer A can, of course, counter by also adopting CIF pricing. Thus, each consumer would pay the same price to each producer and price competition would disappear. Producers would then be forced to compete through advertising or other means. For finished products, such as clothing, CIF pricing tends to be the rule rather than the exception in the United States.

TRANSIT TIME AND LOCATION

Weber's industrial location theory and its modifications emphasize the cost of moving materials to the plant and finished products to consumers. Transport costs are of crucial importance for industries that are raw material seekers and market seekers, but they are of little importance for industries dealing in materials and final products that are of very high value in relation to their weight. This is especially so for high-tech firms.

High-tech firms rely on input materials from a variety of domestic and foreign sources; thus, the advan-

tages of locating a plant near any one supplier are often neutralized by the distance separating them from other suppliers. Their markets also tend to be scattered. Transport is a factor of some locational significance for these firms, but transit time is more crucial than cost. High-technology firms require access to high-level rapid-transport facilities to move components and final products, as well as specialized and skilled personnel. For this reason, they are often attracted to sites near major airports with good national and international passenger and air-cargo facilities. Concentrations of high-tech firms and research and development facilities are located in Silicon Valley near San Francisco, along the M4 motorway from Slough to Swindon to the west of London's Heathrow Airport, and in Tsukuba Science City, situated some 60 kilometers northeast of the center of Tokyo and 40 kilometers northeast of the Narita International Airport.

TRANSPORT IMPROVEMENTS AND LOCATION

Transport innovations have reduced circulation costs and fostered the new international division of labor. They have encouraged the decentralization of manufacturing processes in industrialized countries, both from major cities toward suburbs and smaller towns, and from central regions to those more peripheral. They have also encouraged the decentralization of manufacturing processes to those Third World countries with a free-market ideology and an abundance of weakly unionized, low-wage labor.

The "container revolution" and bulk-air cargo carriers have enabled MNCs based in the United States, Japan and western Europe to locate low-value–added manufacturing and high-pollution manufacturing processes "offshore" in more than 80 Third World free-

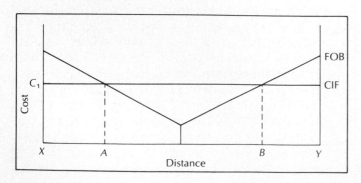

FIGURE 6.12
Freight-on-board and cost-insurance-freight pricing.

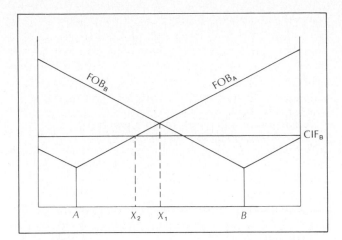

FIGURE 6.13
The effect of cost-insurance-freight on market-area boundaries.

The Mizushima works of Kawasaki Steel on the north shore of the Japanese Inland Sea has deepwater access for coking coal and iron ore from international sources. Major coking coal supply sources are Australia and Canada; major iron ore supply sources are the Philippines and Australia. Export shipments go mainly to Asia, the Communist Bloc, and North America.
(Source: Kawasaki Steel Corporation.)

trade zones. Almost one-half of these zones are in Asia, including Hong Kong, Malaysia, and south Korea. Free-trade zones are areas where goods may be imported free of duties for packaging, assembling, or manufacturing and then exported. These global workshops are geared to export markets, often with few links to the national economy or the needs of local consumers. They tend to be located near ports (e.g., La Romana, Dominican Republic), international airports (e.g., San Bartola, El Salvador), and in areas virtually integrated into global centers of business (e.g., Mexico's northern border or maquila zone) in Frederick Stutz's 1992 study of Tijuana-San Diego.

ROUTES AND NETWORKS

◈

Movements of goods, people, and information are highly channeled, but routeways do not exist by themselves. Rather, they are organized into networks. These individual networks—shipping lanes, railroads, highways, pipelines—service transport demand and bind regions together.

Networks as Graphs

A network is a highly complex system, and each different type has its own special characteristics. Networks differ in terms of density, shape, type of commodity or information carried, and type of flow (either continuous or intermittent). These widely varying characteristics make networks difficult to describe, evaluate, and compare. In order to uncover the basic spatial structure of networks, geographers reduce them to the level of graphs.

A network idealized as a *graph* consists of two elements of geographic structure: (1) a set of vertices (V) or nodes that may represent towns, railroad stations, or airports; and (2) a set of edges (E), lines, or links that may represent highways, railroads, or air routes. The reduction of a network to a system of vertices and edges illustrates topological position only (Figure 6.14). The location of vertices is considered in terms of their relative position on the graph regardless of their absolute location. Distance between vertices is determined in terms of intervals, not route length.

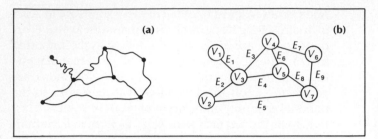

FIGURE 6.14
Reduction of a network (a) to a graph (b).
(Source: Haggett and Chorley 1969, p. 5.)

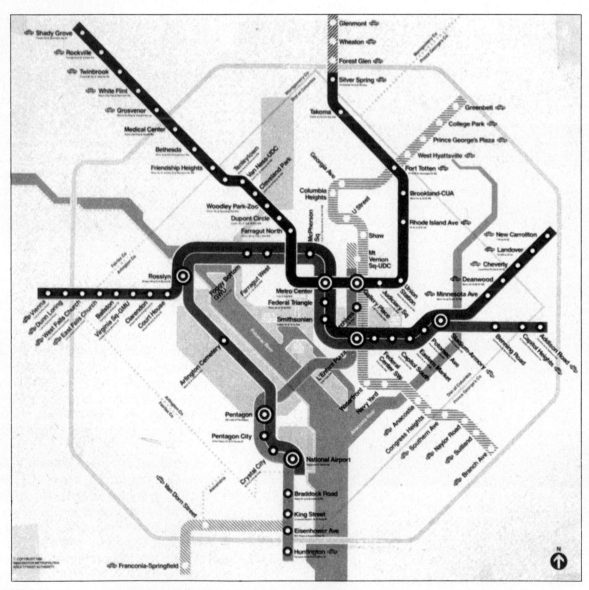

FIGURE 6.15
Metrorail, Washington, DC's subway system.
(Source: Washington Metropolitan Area Transit Authority.)

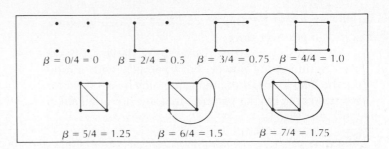

FIGURE 6.16
Beta values for seven four-vertex graphs. How is economic development related to connectivity and beta values for a country?

A familiar example of a network reduced to a graph is a subway or transit map (Figure 6.15). For the user of the Metrorail system in Washington, DC, a topological representation of the network is all that is required. On departing Dupont Circle, a passenger needs to know only whether the stop for Medical Center is before or after Bethesda. Neither Euclidean distance nor the shape of the route is important to the passenger. For this reason, all edges on the map can be represented as straight lines.

NETWORK CONNECTIVITY

We can evaluate the *connectivity* of a network simply by considering the system of edges and vertices. Connectivity means the ease of moving from one place to another within a network. Some networks are more successful in achieving ease of movement than others. The degree of success is known as the efficiency of the network, a property that we must be able to measure in order to compare networks.

The *beta index* is one of the simplest measures of network connectivity. It expresses the ratio between the number of edges in a system and the number of vertices in that system:

$$\beta = \frac{E}{V}$$

When the number of edges to vertices is large, the beta value is large, indicating a well-connected network. Conversely, more vertices than edges signifies a poorly connected network. A sequence of seven four-point graphs illustrates how we can measure differences in connectivity (Figure 6.16). In the simplest case, there are four unconnected vertices; therefore, the beta value is zero. The index reaches unity when all vertices are connected by the same number of edges. It exceeds unity when there are more edges than vertices. Although the maximum value in Figure 6.16 is 1.75, larger graphs would yield higher beta values. High beta values imply

that an economy is advanced and can afford bypass links around intervening places.

The beta index may be used to compare the structure of networks. For example, a nomogram portraying beta values for the railroad networks of several countries indicates that the index is high in developed countries, such as France, and low in underdeveloped countries, such as Ghana (Figure 6.17). In addition to comparing several different networks at the same time, the beta

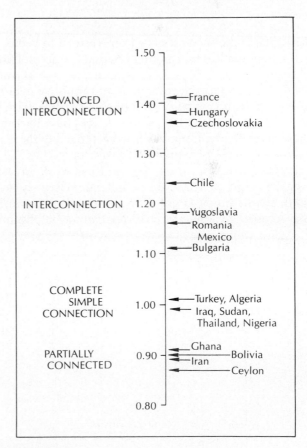

FIGURE 6.17
Beta values for the railroad networks of 18 countries. *(Source: Kansky, 1963, p. 99.)*

index may also be used to compare a single network as it changes over time.

Measures of network connectivity, however, have low discriminating power. For example, with a ratio like the beta index, the same value may be obtained for two networks having patterns that are not at all alike.

NETWORK ACCESSIBILITY

The search for indices of higher discriminatory power led to the development of graph-theoretical measures of *accessibility*. These include the accessibility index and the *Shimble or dispersion index*. The accessibility index measures the shortest paths from each vertex to every other vertex; the dispersion index computes the accessibility of a network as a whole.

The accessibility of a vertex is

$$A_i = \sum_{i=1}^{n} d_{ij}$$

where *dij* is the shortest path from vertex *i* to vertex *j*. For a hypothetical four-point network, the accessibility index for $V_1 = 3$, $V_2 = 4$, $V_3 = 4$, and $V_4 = 5$ (Figure 6.18). These values correspond to our intuitive notions about vertex accessibility. The most accessible place is V_1, the least accessible is V_4, and V_2 and V_3 have intermediate accessibility. If the index were applied to the U.S. railroad system, we would find that Chicago has a low accessibility index compared to New York or Los Angeles, both of which are peripheral. When we deal with graphs much larger than a four-point network, the accessibility value for a vertex cannot be obtained

by visual inspection. Computers are employed for large graphs, but for medium-size graphs we can use a shortest-path matrix. A matrix is an array of numbers ordered in rows and columns. The shortest-path matrix for the four-point network in Figure 6.18 is illustrated in Table 6.2.

The Shimble or dispersion index is defined as

$$D = \sum_{i=1}^{n} \sum_{j=1}^{n} d_{ij}$$

For the four-point network in Figure 6.18, the value of the dispersion index is 16 (Table 6.3). This value defines the graph's compactness in terms of all the paths within it and can be used to compare one network with another. For example, when the dispersion value is known, it can be used as a standard against which to measure the impact of new links on total accessibility.

Dispersion values are only an initial step in evaluating a transport network. Routes must be considered in terms of numerous criteria: characteristics of modes of

◼

Table 6.2
A Shortest-Path Matrix

To:	V_1	V_2	V_3	V_4	Row Sum
From:					
V_1	0	1	1	1	3
V_2	1	0	1	2	4
V_3	1	1	0	2	4
V_4	1	2	2	0	5

◼

Table 6.3
Connectivity Matrix and Dispersion Value

To:	V_1	V_2	V_3	V_4	Row Sum
From:					
V_1	0	1	1	1	3
V_2	1	0	1	2	4
V_3	1	1	0	2	4
V_4	1	2	2	0	5
				Total	16

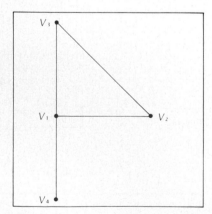

FIGURE 6.18
A four-vertex network, abstracted as a graph.

transportation (e.g., carrier capacity, cost, frequency of service, speed); vehicular capacity; technical quality (e.g., surface, curvature, gradient); and stress (e.g., overuse of certain links). The cost of building, improving, or maintaining links must also be taken into account, as well as the route's effectiveness in meeting given objectives. For example, the cost of improving a road to meet the capacity for peak demand must be balanced against the cost of congestion, time loss, and deterioration of the route from overuse.

Density and Shape of Networks

Graph theory is particularly useful in measuring accessibility, but it neglects important aspects of network structure. For example, graph theory fails to consider network density or shape.

NETWORK DENSITY

By *network density* is meant the total number of route miles or kilometers per unit area. This measure may be considered in several dimensions of space.

Examination of topographic maps reveals strong differences in road density at the local level. Villages have a denser pattern than the surrounding countryside, and downtown areas of cities have denser street patterns than suburbs. In the central area of Detroit, about 50% of the land is devoted to roads, but 3 kilometers from the central business district this figure drops to 34%. Distance-decay gradients, however, vary directly with city size. As city size increases, the need for interaction increases, and the proportion of land devoted to transport needs increases in linear fashion.

A study of the road pattern in Minneapolis-St. Paul by John Borchert (1961) provides much information on distance-density gradients for urban transportation networks. Because there was a high correlation between number of road junctions and road length, Borchert counted the number of road junctions on the map. Counting the number of junctions per unit area was much less tedious than measuring the number of miles of street per unit area. Borchert found a strong association between population density, as measured by the number of single-family dwellings, and network density, as measured by the number of intersections. In replicating Borchert's study in Dar es Salaam, Tanzania, in 1969, de Souza obtained similar findings.

An Amtrak conventional passenger train at Harper's Ferry, West Virginia. *(Source: Andrea Krause/ Photo Researchers, Inc.)* New *magnetic levitated* trains will shuttle passengers between American cities at over 300 mph in the not too distant future. Using far less energy and time than automobile and air travel, one will go by train from Los Angeles to San Francisco in an hour and a half, or between Washington D.C. and Boston in less than an hour. *Maglevs* are twice as fuel efficient as cars and four times as efficient as airplanes, while producing no pollution themselves. Trains are considerably more comfortable than cramped aircraft and as the French and Japanese trains have shown, could grow to be a significant portion of the public transportation market.

At the regional level, variations in network density are closely related to patterns of uneven development, as a map of the road density in Tanzania in 1970 shows. Densities for main and secondary roads were calculated by measuring the length of these roads in grid squares of approximately 740 square kilometers. The appropriate length was then assigned to the center of each square, and isolines were drawn to join places of equal density. Road density is positively associated with areas of high population density and of intense commercial activity. For example, high road densities occur around the primate city of Dar es Salaam and provincial towns such as Tanga and Iringa. They also occur in zones of export agriculture such as the cotton-growing area to the south of Lake Victoria and the coffee-growing area on the well-watered slopes of Mount Kilimanjaro.

At the world level, the distribution of network density is highly skewed (Table 6.4). Norton Ginsberg (1961) calculated that a few countries have very dense networks and many countries have sparse networks. Nearly two-thirds of the countries have distributions below the world mean. The distribution of countries with high and low densities is related to levels of economic development.

The greatest concentration of surface transportation facilities appears in western Europe, the United States and southern Canada, Japan, and in western parts of the former Soviet Union. In these regions, road and rail densities are so high that virtually no place is inaccessible. Somewhat less dense networks are found in parts of Uruguay, Argentina, eastern Brazil, eastern Australia, India, and Pakistan, and in parts of the Mediterranean Middle East. Most underdeveloped countries are poorly served by roads and railways; for example, the vast tropical heartlands of South America and Africa and the interior of China are not easily accessed.

NETWORK SHAPE

There is a striking contrast between developed and underdeveloped countries with regard to the shape and orientation of transport networks. In underdeveloped countries, these features are a reflection of their colonial history. Resulting networks often have a strong directional focus; they resemble drainage systems that converge on coastal ports. For example, railroad development in Brazil linked the port of Rio de Janeiro with São Paulo and the export-producing areas inland. In Argentina, railroad development centered on Buenos Aires and in Uruguay, on Montevideo. Port cities served as transshipment points for the export of primary products and the distribution of imported finished goods. Therefore, the networks of underdeveloped countries are typically fan-shaped. They distort and sharpen geographic and social inequalities because of an inadequate number of interlinkages.

In developed countries, the shape of transport networks is a fuller lattice, which allows a more even distribution of places by offering a degree of internal interchange. For example, Britain was crisscrossed with a dense network of main and branch railroads as early as 1900. The map does not reveal, however, that major routes converge on London. This tendency strengthened after World War II when the government nationalized and modernized the rail network.

Location of Routes and Networks

Spatial interaction depends on the existence of a demand-supply relationship. If a demand-supply relationship exists between two unconnected places and is profitable, then it is probable that a transport route will be constructed. Choosing the actual location for a new route is a political task, but the information used to aid decision making is based on economic principles. Of critical importance in deciding where to construct a new route is the balance between fixed and variable transport costs. Fixed costs are construction costs. Variable costs are operating costs that depend on the length of the routeway and the volume of traffic flowing along it.

■

Table 6.4
Distribution of Route Density

Route Media	Roads	Railroads
Number of countries compared	126	134
World mean density, km/100 km²	10.3	0.95
Maximum density, km/100 km²	302.0	17.90
Minimum density, km/100 km²	0.0	0.00
Percentage of countries below world mean	64	67

Note: Although these data are for the late 1950s, they are still an effective representation of world-scale network patterns.
Source: Ginsburg, 1961, pp. 60, 70.

TGV Express Train in France. In 1983, the Trans Grande Vitesse was introduced by the French Railway with service between Paris and Lyon at speeds of up to 200 mph on an entirely new track. By 1994, it had captured millions of new passengers from the highways and from domestic airlines. Proposed high-speed trains from Naples to Milan, from Lisbon to Marseille, from Bourdeaux to Glasgow via the Channel Tunnel, and from Geneva to Amsterdam are to be opened by the year 2005. Despite these advances, interurban rail will continue to occupy a subordinate role in the United States. But in China, Russia, and India, where private car ownership is low, the railway still carries the bulk of interurban traffic. *(Source: Rapho-Beaune/Photo Researchers, Inc.)*

A demand-supply relationship explains many, but not all, transport patterns. It does not, for example, account for the geographic pattern of Roman roads in Britain. Roman roads were built across the island to meet the government's need for fast communication between centers of civil administration in the south and east and defense lines and fortresses in the north and west. Postroads were constructed with little regard for construction costs and local economic needs.

MINIMUM-DISTANCE NETWORKS

As an example of how costs influence the geographic pattern of routes in a network, consider two extreme minimum-distance solutions to a problem in which a demand-supply relationship exists between five towns (Figure 6.19). In Figure 6.19a, the fixed costs of road construction are low, but operating costs are somewhat higher. The resulting network minimizes construction

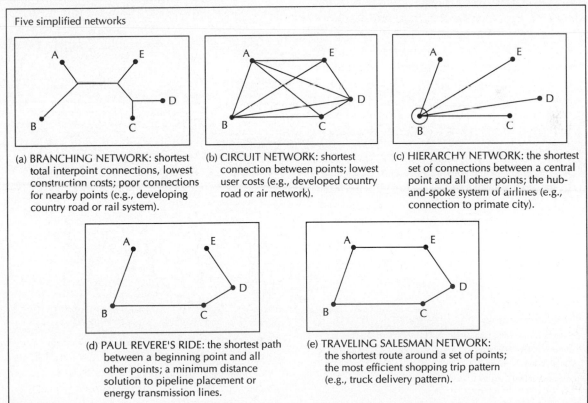

Five simplified networks

(a) BRANCHING NETWORK: shortest total interpoint connections, lowest construction costs; poor connections for nearby points (e.g., developing country road or rail system).

(b) CIRCUIT NETWORK: shortest connection between points; lowest user costs (e.g., developed country road or air network).

(c) HIERARCHY NETWORK: the shortest set of connections between a central point and all other points; the hub-and-spoke system of airlines (e.g., connection to primate city).

(d) PAUL REVERE'S RIDE: the shortest path between a beginning point and all other points; a minimum distance solution to pipeline placement or energy transmission lines.

(e) TRAVELING SALESMAN NETWORK: the shortest route around a set of points; the most efficient shopping trip pattern (e.g., truck delivery pattern).

FIGURE 6.19

Five graphs representing five simplified networks; each depicts a class of transport problems in its simplest form. *(Source: Adapted from Haggett, 1967, p. 31, and Fellman, Getis, and Getis, 1992, p. 68.)*

costs, and is called a *least builder's cost network*. This network has a lower degree of connectivity and is less convenient to users. In Figure 6.19b, operating costs are low, but fixed costs are high. The resulting network is maximum benefit to users because each of the five towns is directly linked to every other town. This is the *least user's cost network*. In Figure 6.19c, the *hierarchical network* shows the shortest set of connections between a central city and all other points. In Figure 6.19d, the network displays the shortest path between a beginning point and all other points in the system. It is called the *Paul Revere Network*. In Figure 6.19e, the shortest network interconnecting a set of points, where the origin and destination point are identical, is given. This is called the *traveling salesman network*.

The railroad pattern in the United States can be understood partly in terms of least-cost-to-use and least-cost-to-build motives. The least-cost-to-use network is characteristic of the eastern half of the country where cities are clustered and transport demands are high. In

◉

T a b l e 6.5

Difference in Connectivity Between User-Optimal and Builder-Optimal Networks

Network	Number of Edges	Number of Vertices	E/V	B
User optimal	10	5	10/5	2.0
Builder optimal	7	8	7/8	0.87

the West, where railroads preceded settlement and cities are scattered, the least-cost-to-build solution dominates. Two other examples of least-cost-to-build networks include Amtrak's National Rail Passenger System (Figure 6.20a) and the French Master Plan for the future TGV Network (Figure 6.20b).

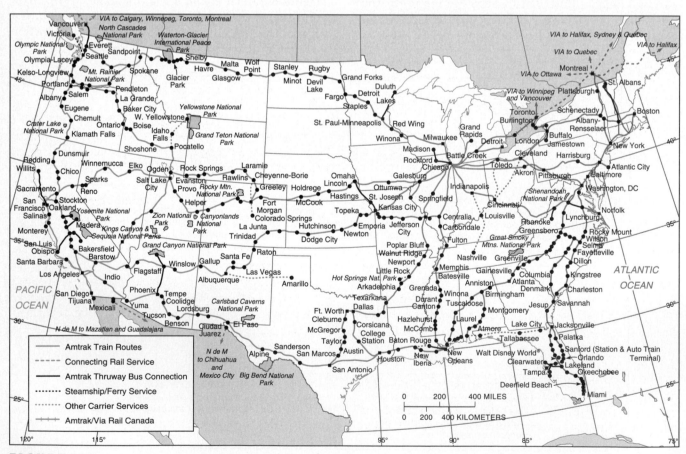

FIGURE 6.20a
Amtrak's national rail passenger system.

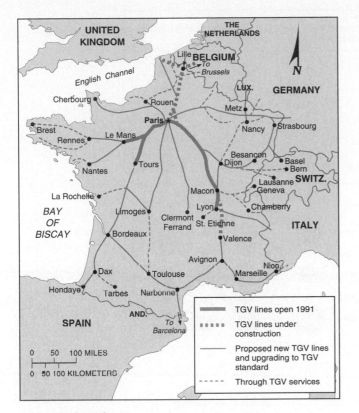

FIGURE 6.20b
The French masterplan for the future high-speed rail (TGV) network, 1994.

DEVIATIONS FROM STRAIGHT-LINE PATHS

Most transportation routes deviate from a direct straight-line connection. There are two main types of distortion from the straight-line connection; they are positive and negative deviations.

Positive deviations occur when routes are made longer in order to increase traffic. They are constructed to pick up as many settlements as possible. At one time, this type of deviation was common in developed countries. Adherence to on-line settlement, however, declined in importance with economic development. An extreme example is the U.S. Interstate Highway System. When it was built, many small towns, villages, and hamlets were bypassed in favor of larger settlements that generated the bulk of the traffic. In underdeveloped countries, linking as many settlements as possible played hardly any part in the construction of routes during the colonial period. The length of the routes was geared to a pattern of economic growth based on export production. Areas where export production was insignificant or where there was little demand for imports were bypassed by road and rail. As a result, these places stagnated and lost ground.

Negative deviations arise from the need to reduce the distance traveled through high-cost areas. A transport route is often distorted from a reasonably straight line because different areas have different building-cost characteristics. For example, differential building costs may be the result of terrain difficulties, such as the presence of a mountain barrier. But economic development necessitates tearing down physical barriers to exchange. In the nineteenth century, a great deal of trade between the east and west coasts of the United States was diverted via the Cape route—a diversion that added some 15,000 kilometers to the overland distance. When the time factor came to be more highly valued, the degree of distortion was reduced with the construction of the Panama Canal. Today, east-west surface transportation across the United States is hardly distorted at all by overland barriers.

Development of Transport Networks

Historically, the development of transport networks has reflected and induced settlement, industrialization, and urbanization. The impact of transport networks on regional economic development is demonstrated in the 1963 stage model of network change in underdeveloped countries created by Edward Taaffe, Richard Morrill, and Peter Gould. Studies in Nigeria and East Africa provided the basis for their model. They defined the extension of transport in underdeveloped countries explicitly in terms of penetration from the coast. "[Transport links reflect] (1) the desire to connect an administrative center on the sea coast with an interior area of political and military control; (2) the desire to reach areas of mineral exploitation; [and] (3) the desire to reach areas of potential agricultural export production" (Taaffe, Morrill, and Gould, 1963, p. 506).

AFRICAN TRANSPORT DEVELOPMENT

The Taaffe, Morrill, and Gould model illustrates how the interplay between the evolution of a transport network and urban growth is self-reinforcing (Figure 6.21). The ideal-typical sequence begins the first stage when early colonial conquest creates a system of settlements

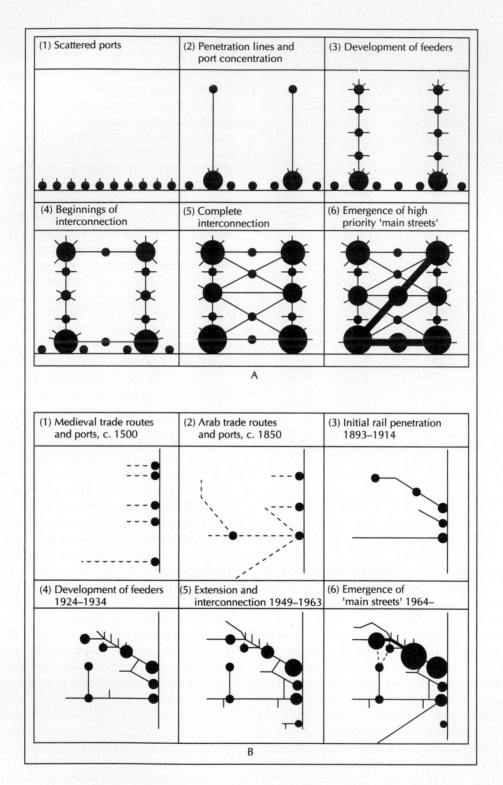

FIGURE 6.21
An idealized sequence of transportation development: (a) the Taaffe, Morrill, and Gould model; and (b) an adaption to East Africa by Hoyle. *(Source: Hoyle and Knowls, 1993).*

A passenger train pulls into the Terminus at Lagos, Nigeria. The Nigerian railway network is a colonial legacy. It serves the mines and the specialized crop-producing areas, carrying most of their products to the port of Lagos for export. *(Source: World Bank.)*

and berthing points along the seacoast. Gradually, a second stage evolves with the construction of penetration routes that link the best located ports to the inland mining, agricultural, and population centers. Export-based development stimulates growth in the interior, and a number of intermediate centers spring up along the principal access routes. This process results in the third stage of transport evolution—the growth of feeder routes and links from the inland centers. By the fourth stage, lateral route development enhances the competitive position of the major ports and inland centers. A few nodes along the original lines of inland penetration (i.e., N_1 and N_2) become focal points for feeder networks of their own, and they begin to capture the hinterlands of smaller centers on each side. The fifth stage evolves when a transport network interconnects all the major

centers. In the sixth and last stage, the development of high-priority linkages reinforces the advantages of urban centers that have come to dominate the economy.

According to Taaffe, Morrill, and Gould, high-priority linkages in underdeveloped countries are likely to emerge not along export-trunk routes, but along routes connecting two centers concerned with internal exchange activities. Nigerian geographer Akin Mabogunje (1980) questioned the logic of this assumption in that the sixth stage arises from earlier phases in which export-trunk routes receive the greatest attention. He argued that this contradiction can only be explained by the fact that the model is grounded in the history of transport development in developed countries. Thus, stage six of the model emphasizes the difficulty of transforming a colonial network into one suitable for more self-centered development (McCall, 1977).

The idealized model of network change describes one typical sequence of development. It shows that a transport network has the short-run purpose of facilitating movement, but that its fundamental effect is to influence the subsequent development and structure of the space economy through the operation of geographic inertia and cumulative causation. The term geographic inertia refers to the tendency of a place to maintain its size and importance even after the conditions originally influencing its development have changed, ceased to be relevant, or disappeared. The term cumulative causation refers to the process by which economic activity tends to concentrate in an area with an initial advantage. The stage model, therefore, illustrates how a space economy roots itself ever more firmly as initial locational decisions that shaped the system are subsequently reinforced by other decisions. The result is a concentrated and polarized pattern of development.

The evolution of transport systems is linked to the process of development. For thousands of years, most people walked and carried the goods they consumed. This time-consuming mode of transportation greatly limited the movement of commodities until after 1500 when major improvements in transportation began to take place.

At the time of Columbus, a mercantile revolution occurred in which nation-states replaced the chained economies of feudal society. The ideology of merchant capital, mercantilism, points to foreign trade as the source of a country's enrichment. To mercantilists, there existed a finite amount of trade in the world; consequently, the goal was to obtain the largest share. Mercantilism, therefore, was rooted in commercial expansion, for which improved transport was vital.

Commercial expansion first arose in Portugal and Spain; then, early in the sixteenth century, it became a characteristic of Western Europe. From many rival harbors, especially Antwerp, Amsterdam, and London, a commercial network spread out to embrace parts of sub-Saharan Africa and its adjacent Atlantic islands, the Americas, and parts of Asia.

Opposition to mercantilism increased in the late eighteenth century, gradually giving rise to a climate of economic liberalism. This new climate was especially evident in Britain, where economic life was being transformed by improvements in farming techniques and by the industrial revolution. From 1800 to the present, capitalism promoted the development of cheap and rapid forms of transport in an evolutionary process spurred by competition among the various transport modes. As described by James Vance (1986):

The basic technology of each [transport medium] was initiated when it stood as technically the most advanced for its time. When the deficiencies of a specific medium became obvious, efforts were made to overcome these, normally leading both to the change in the original form and to the creation of distinctly new forms of transport that avoided the previous failings. Railroads, for example, could greatly ramify the networks of movement possible with canals. In turn, however, the suburbanization of population and industry showed up sharply the failings of the steam railroad, leading to the rapid expansion of the use of automobile transportion. (p. 618)

Southeast Asian Transport Development

P. J. Rimmer (1977) identifies an alternate transport development strategy from his experiences in Southeast Asia. He terms it a hybrid transport system because the colonial powers transport and development system is superimposed through the colonization process on the economic and cultural system of the less developed region. The result is the colonial power exercises almost complete control over the exchange of goods internationally as well as the indigenous and imported dimensions of the transportation and economic system that results. Rimmer generalized four stages in the development of transport and trade between developed and less developed countries. These stages are outlined as follows.

1. A *precontact stage* in which no transportation or trade exists between the developed country or the Third World country. Within the Third World country, a rudimentary transportation system exists.

2. Beginnings of *colonialism stage*. Initial contact is made between regions, but the developed country's role in the social, political, and economic life of the undeveloped country is minimal. However, permanent trading posts and garrisons are established.

3. *High colonialism*. In this stage, the European power develops a set of railways, roads, and inland transportation systems with its trading post now established as the new capital of the developing region. Diversification of economic activity begins an importance of manufactured goods and exportation of natural resources moves into higher levels of intensity.

4. The *neocolonial stage*. While no radical adjustments are made from earlier stages, a greater modernization and diversification occurs in the Third World country in terms of transport and economic development.

A fifth stage which could be called *independence and codominance*, should now be added to the Rimmer model to coincide with Australia, New Zealand, and American developmental history. Here, a Third World nation or colony has developed into a regional economic and transport power on its own and has received full independence. With diversification and increased levels of international trade and transportation infrastructure development, links to the original developed country are strengthened and each region has developed a strong sense of identity as well as its own intensive levels of comparative advantage, as well as highly developed internal transportation networks.

FLOWS IN NETWORKS

Networks are constructed to carry flows of goods, people, and information. Geographers call this flow *spatial interaction*. Spatial interaction is the movement of goods, people, and ideas between areas, countries, cities, and even places within cities. These flows represent the exchange of supplies and demands at different locations. The flows are on networks. Geographic space is built with different availabilities of resources, commodities, information, opportunities, and populations. Because of this fact, movement occurs as a technique to satisfy human wants and needs with natural resources available and, finally, with the knowledge and skills that can convert the natural resources into usable items.

The California geographer, Waldo Tobler, has stated the concept of *distance decay* and called it "The First Law of Geography: Everything is related to everything else, but nearer things are more related to each other than are distant things." *Distance decay* is geographic concept that describes the attenuation or reduction in the flow, or movement, between places with increasing distance between them (Figure 6.22).

Most food shipments, natural resource flows, and commodity movements occur within regions and within countries, rather than between them. The underlying principle of *distance decay* is the *friction of distance*. There are time and cost factors associated with extra increments of distance for all types of flow or movement. For individuals, the out-of-pocket costs of operating a vehicle or truck are combined with the cost of a person's time. The California Department of Transportation calculates the cost of traffic jams by basing a person's time

at \$6 per hour. With longer distance, it is more expensive to ship commodities because of labor rates of drivers and operators, as well as over-the-road costs of vehicle operation. Telephone calls and parcel deliveries, likewise, can be more expensive for more distant locations.

Distant decay and the *friction of distance* are not exerted in a linear pattern. From observation of the figure, we can determine that interaction between places is related in an inverse way to the square of the distance, separating the two places.

The Gravity Model

Newton's law of gravitation states that any two objects in space attract one another according to a force that is proportional to the product of their masses and inversely proportional to the square of the distance separating them. Thus, Newton's law of gravitation can be expressed as the force of attraction F, which is equal to Mi, the mass of the first body, times Mj, the mass of the second body, divided by the distance separating i and j, which is given as:

$$F = \frac{Mi \times Mj}{dij^2}$$

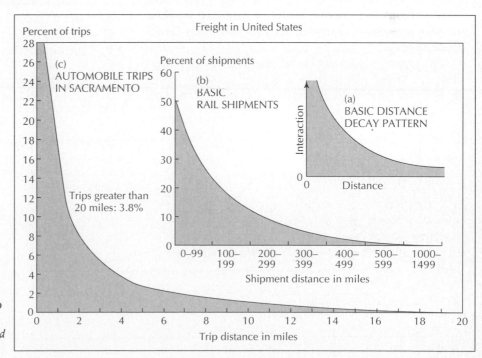

FIGURE 6.22
The distance-decay principle: (a) the basic pattern; (b) rail freight trips in the United States, 1990; and (c) auto trips in Sacramento, 1991.
(Source: Modified from Fellman, Getis, and Getis, 1992, p. 64.)

where K is the gravitational constant. Force equals mass of i times mass of j divided by distance between i and j.

This so-called *gravity model* has been applied to flows between two points in the transportation literature for more than 50 years. Geographers, planners, and engineers have realized that the gravitational model is useful in a social gravity concept and can be used to explain flows between two places, i and j. The flow, or interaction, Iij, is equal to the mass or population, Pi, of the first place, times the mass or population, Pj of the second place, divided by the distance between the two, raised to a power given by:

$$I_{ij} = P_i \times P_j \text{ divided by } d_{ij} \text{ raised to the power 2}$$

$$I_{ij} = \frac{P_i \times P_j}{d_{ij}^2}$$

(*Iij* equals population of i, times population of j, divided by distance between i and j squared.)

The gravity model has had perhaps the greatest use of any model in the field of transportation studies because it can be used to predict flows between two points for commodities, people traveling, information, telephone traffic, and radio and television messages. Frequently, distance is substituted by travel time or travel cost over a network, rather than by the straight-line path separating two places. Places have included, at one scale, continents and countries, and at the other scale, states or regions within countries, and even zones within cities. The gravity model, if properly weighed through regression analysis, has an extremely broad applicability.

The gravity model can be summarized by two principles: (1) larger places have a greater drawing power for flows of commodities, individuals, and information

than smaller ones; and (2) places that are more distant have a weaker attraction for one another than closer places. The gravity model is limited to flows between places, taking two places at a time. Using the principles of the gravity model, William J. Reilly (1931) developed the law of retail gravitation, which described the breaking point between two spheres of influence, of the border marking the outer edge of the trade areas of cities or regions.

The Law of Retail Gravitation

In the *law of retail gravitation*, Reilly (1931) uses the gravity model concept to identify the breaking point between two cities (Figure 6.23). The assumption is that people will travel to the most rewarding destination, based on nearness of the place and its size. In this case, as in the case of the gravity model, the size of the destination is a measure of the rewards, or value available. The model is given by the formula, *BP* equals *dij* divided by 1 plus the square root of P_2 divided by P_1, where

$$BP_j = \frac{a_{ij}}{1 + \sqrt{\dfrac{POP_i}{POP_j}}}$$

BP_j = Distance from the center of city 2 to the breaking point or boundary between city 1 and 2
d_{ij} = the distance between city 1 and city 2
P_i = the population of city 1
P_j = the population of city 2

Here, the law of retail gravitation has been applied to find the breaking point between San Diego and Los

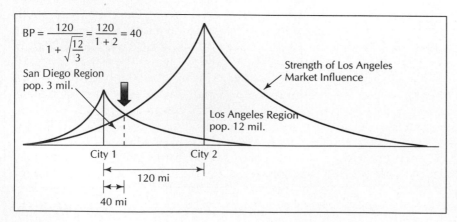

$$BP = \frac{120}{1 + \sqrt{\dfrac{12}{3}}} = \frac{120}{1 + 2} = 40$$

San Diego Region pop. 3 mil.

Strength of Los Angeles Market Influence

Los Angeles Region pop. 12 mil.

City 1   City 2

120 mi

40 mi

FIGURE 6.23
The law of retail gravitation applied to the breaking point between San Diego and Los Angeles. The breaking point (BP) between spheres is 40 miles north of San Diego's downtown and 80 miles south of Los Angeles' downtown.

Angeles. The two cities are approximately 120 miles apart, downtown to downtown. The population of the San Diego urban region is a little bit short of 3 million total people. The population of Los Angeles is 12 million, more or less depending on which subcities are included in the Los Angeles metropolitan region. The calculations show that the breaking point between the spheres of influence of San Diego and Los Angeles occur at 40 miles north of San Diego. This point coincides fairly closely with the boundary between San Diego County and Orange County and with a change of advertising media.

Most people south of the line receive the *San Diego Union* newspaper and listen to San Diego television channels for regular broadcasting and the evening news. They also follow the San Diego Padres baseball team rather than the Los Angeles Dodgers, San Diego Chargers football team, and the San Diego State University Aztecs athletic teams.

The majority of the people north of the breaking point, in Orange County, receive the *Los Angeles Times* newspaper, tune-in predominantly to Los Angeles television stations, and follow the myriad of Los Angeles professional athletic teams, including the Angels, the Dodgers, the Lakers, the Rams, the Clippers, and the Kings. Here, UCLA and USC have a strong following.

Figure 6.24 shows *areas of dominant influence* (ADI) for the United States as a whole in 1994, based on radio, television, and newspaper advertising. This remarkable map, created from actual data, provided by nationwide advertising companies, approximates the results of the law of retail gravitation if it were applied to every city pair adjacent to one another.

IMPROVED TRANSPORT FACILITIES

◈

Prior to the development of railroads, overland transportation of heavy goods was slow and costly. Movement of heavy raw materials by water was much cheaper than by land. For this reason, most of the world's commerce was carried by water transportation, and the important cities were maritime or riverine cities.

To bring stretches of water into locations that needed them, canals were constructed in Europe beginning in the sixteenth century, with the height of technology represented by the pound lock developed in the Low Countries and northern Italy. Until the nineteenth century, canals were the most advanced form of transportation and were built wherever capital was available. Road building was the cheap alternative where canals were physically or financially impractical.

The most active period of canal building coincided with the early industrial revolution. The vast increase in manufacturing and trade fostered by the canals paved the way for the industrial revolution (Mantoux, 1961). The canals were financed by central governments on the Continent and by business interests in England, where a complex network was built during the last 40 years of the eighteenth century and the first quarter of the nineteenth century. Somewhat later, artificial waterways were constructed in North America. They supplemented the rivers and Great Lakes, the principal arteries for moving the staples of timber, grain, preserved meat, tobacco, cotton, coal, and ores.

At sea, efforts before the industrial revolution concentrated on expanding the known seas and on improving ships (e.g., better hulls and sails) to allow for practical transport over increasing distances. By 1800, or a few decades later in the case of the technology of sail, the traditional technology of transport reached its ultimate refinement. Subsequently, the rapid expansion of commerce and industry overtaxed existing facilities. The canals were crowded and ran short of water in dry periods, and the roads were clogged when traffic in wet periods destroyed the surface on which it moved. The result was an effort to utilize mechanical energy as the motivating power.

The invention of the steam engine by James Watt in 1769 paved the way for technical advances in transportation. Its application to water in 1807 and to land in 1829, through the development of the locomotive, heralded the era of cheap transportation. The steamship reduced the cost of transportation by water, but the locomotive had a revolutionary effect on land transportation. In England, the railway served existing markets and provided urban populations with an excellent system of freight and passenger transportation. In the United States, the railroad was an instrument of national development; it preceded virtually all settlement west of the Mississippi, helped to establish centers such as Kansas City and Atlanta, and integrated regional markets. In Third World countries, railroads linked export centers more firmly to the economies of Europe and North America.

Eventually, mechanical power was used for localized urban transportation. Until the late nineteenth century, cities were mainly pedestrian centers requiring business establishments to agglomerate in close proximity to one

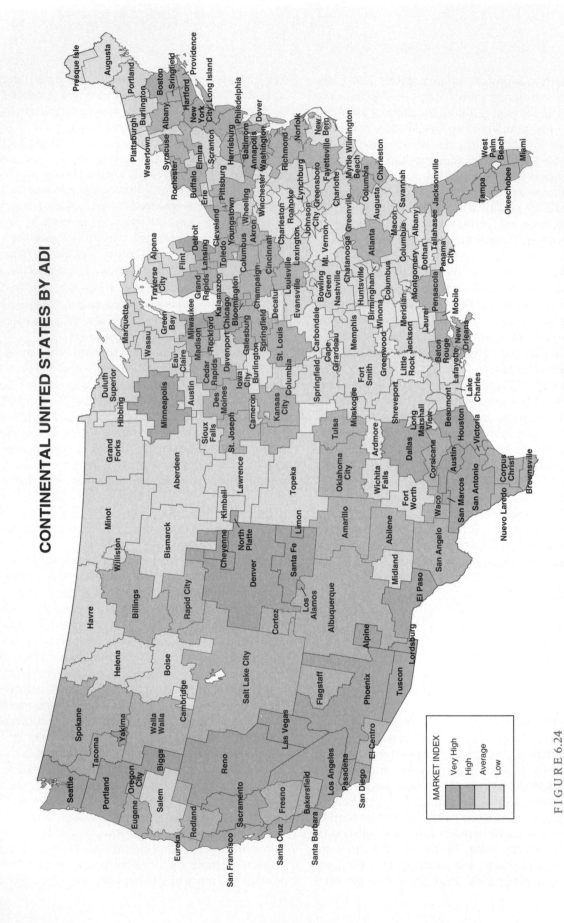

CONTINENTAL UNITED STATES BY ADI

MARKET INDEX

- Very High
- High
- Average
- Low

FIGURE 6.24

Areas of dominant influence (ADI). ADI is based on radio, television, and newspaper advertisements. For U.S. cities, ADI approximates the law of retail gravitation model if it were applied to adjacent pairs of cities.

another. This usually meant about a 30-minute walk from the center of town to any given urban point; hence, cities were extremely compact. The transformation of the compact city into the modern metropolis depended on the invention of the electric traction motor by Frank Sprague. The first electrified trolley system opened in Richmond, Virginia in 1888. The innovation, which increased the average speed of intraurban transport from about 5 to more than 15 miles per hour, diffused rapidly to other North American and European cities, as well as to cities in Australia, Latin America, and Asia.

The nineteenth century was a time when the road was reduced to a feeder for the railroad. Road improvements awaited the arrival of the automobile—"European by birth, American by adoption" (Rae, 1965, p. 1). In the United States, heavy reliance on the automobile is a cross between a love affair with the passenger car and a lack of alternatives. In cities such as Denver and Los Angeles, roughly 90% of the working population travels to and from work by car; in the less auto-dependent cities like New York, cars still account for two-thirds of all work-related trips. By comparison, in Europe, where communities are less extensively suburbanized and average commuting distances are half those of North America, only about 40% of urban residents use their cars. In Tokyo, a mere 15% of the population drives to work (Figure 6.25).

In the Third World, technical developments in transportation have created a crisis—the result of a mismatch between transportation infrastructure, services, and technologies and the need for mobility of the majority of the population (Replogle, 1988). Governments that favor private car ownership by a small but affluent elite distort development priorities. Importing fuels, car components, or already assembeld cars stretches import budgets thin. Similarly, building and maintaining an elaborate highway system devours enormous resources. The 1960s and 1970s saw a road-building boom in many Third World countries to the detriment of railroads and other forms of transport. With insufficient resources for maintenance, many Third World roads are in disrepair. In cities, bus systems and other means of public transportation are also in a poor state, meeting only a small proportion of transportation needs. And often the poor cannot afford public transportation at all. Walking still accounts for two-thirds of all trips in large African cities like Kinshasa and for almost one-half the trips in Bangalore, India. Pedestrians and traditional modes of transportation are increasingly being marginalized in the Third World (Figure 6.25).

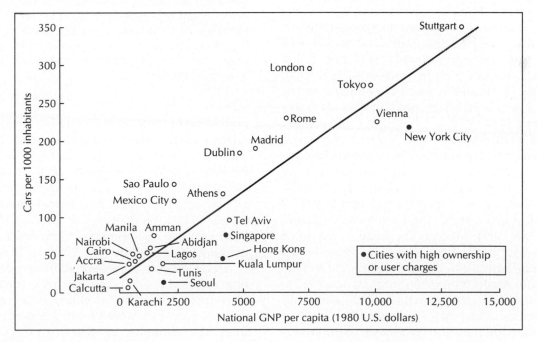

FIGURE 6.25
Private car ownership in selected major cities.
(Source: Hoyle and Knowles, 1993, p. 75.)

Transport changes in the last 175 years have not been confined to railroads and roads. At sea, ships equipped first with steam turbines and then diesel engines facilitated the rapid expansion of international trade. In addition, the opening of the Suez Canal in 1869 and the Panama Canal in 1914 dramatically reduced the distance of many routes. The trend in ocean shipping today is not so much increased size and speed of vessels as it is increased specialization. Bulk carriers of oil, grain, and ores are replacing break-bulk vessels. Containerships, which tie trucks and ships together, have become the basic transoceanic carrier. Planes have ousted passenger liners and trains as the standard travel mode for long-distance passengers. The shipment of cargo by air, however, is still in its infancy. Only perishable, high-value, or urgently needed shipments are sent by air freight.

Cost-Space and Time-Space Convergence

Transport improvements have resulted in what geographers call *cost-space* and *time-space convergence*—that is, the progressive reduction in cost of travel and travel time between places.

Transport improvements have brought significant cost reductions to shippers. For example, the opening of the Erie Canal in 1825 reduced the cost of transport between Buffalo and Albany from $100 to $10 and, ultimately, to $3 per ton. Railroad freight rates in the United States dropped 41% between 1882 and 1900. Between the 1870s and 1950s, improvements in the efficiency of ships reduced the real cost of ocean transport by about 60%.

Cheaper, more efficient modes of transport widened the range over which goods could be shipped economically. For example, the international trade in iron ore was negligible in the nineteenth century, but by 1950 exports of iron ore accounted for just under 20% of world production, and by 1967 for 36% (Manners, 1971, pp. 348–349). Much of the trade is accounted for by long-haul traffic, from Venezuela to the United States or from Australia to Japan. Similarly, steam coal, exported from Alaska, Colombia, South Africa, Australia, and China is shipped, on average, 6400 kilometers to its destination (Chisholm, 1982, p. 122).

Cheap transportation also contributed to the growth of cities. It enabled cities to obtain food products from distant places and facilitated urban concentration by stimulating large-scale production and geographic divi-

The *Concorde* travels at supersonic speeds between London and Washington, DC. But this status symbol does not fly cheaply; for example, it uses about four times as much fuel per passenger as wide-bodied jets. In this era of increasing fuel costs, there appear to be limits to the economical annihilation of space by time. *Source: British Airways.)*

sion of labor. Furthermore, transportation improvements changed patterns of urban accessibility. North American cities have grown from walking- and horsecar-scale cities (pre-1800–1890), to electric streetcar cities (1890–1920) and, finally, to dispersed automobile cities in the recreational automobile era (1920–1945), the freeway era (1945–1970), and the outer beltway and suburban downtown era (1970–present) (Figure 6.26).

Developments in transportation have also cut travel time extensively—to where relative distances between places melt away. The travel time between Edinburgh and London, a distance of 640 kilometers, decreased from 20,000 minutes by stagecoach in 1658 to under 60 minutes by airplane today (Figure 6.27). Time-space convergence was marked during the period of rapid transport development; for example, in the 1840s travel

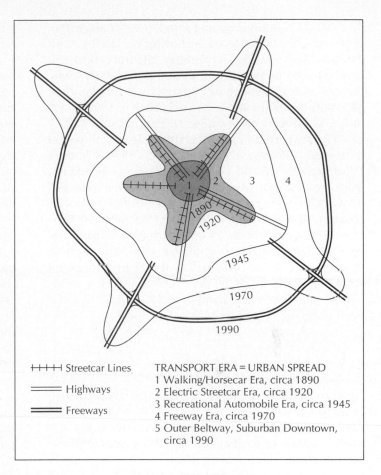

FIGURE 6.26
Stages of metropolitan growth and transport development in a North American city. Cities have grown from small monocentric, pedestrian cities to large, sprawling metropolitan areas, laced with beltways and suburban downtowns. Can cities spread much farther into the countryside? Unfortunately, American cities have not been planned as a system. Transportation decisions have often been made on the basis of a reaction to congested roads or the wishes of developers. More public transportation needs to be introduced, but stations need to be linked to residential and commercial development. Successful model transportation land use linkages occur in Toronto, Paris and Stockholm. Here, bus, rail, bike and pedestrian paths converge, giving convenience and efficiency to the intercity without inundating the countryside up to 50 miles away. In Portland, Oregon, and Corbita, Brazil, cities of 1.5 million, people use efficient mass transit systems designed on integrating land use and making provision for bicycle and pedestrian traffic, as well as express and local buses. The result is that these cities use 30 percent less gasoline per vehicle and a much lower percentage of personal disposal income is used on transportation (Stutz and Supernak, 1992).

┼┼┼┼ Streetcar Lines
═══ Highways
━━━ Freeways

TRANSPORT ERA = URBAN SPREAD
1 Walking/Horsecar Era, circa 1890
2 Electric Streetcar Era, circa 1920
3 Recreational Automobile Era, circa 1945
4 Freeway Era, circa 1970
5 Outer Beltway, Suburban Downtown, circa 1990

FIGURE 6.27
Time-space convergence between London and Edinburgh. *(Source: Adapted from Janelle, 1968, p. 6.)* Within the next few years, new transportation modes will accelerate time-space convergence. Magnetic levitation trains, traveling at 300 mph and supersonic air transports traveling at 3,000 mph are present reality. Zero emission automobile legislation is moving the United States towards electric cars and the possibility of a hydrogen economy. Fuel cells may become a major source of electrical energy production. Advanced information technology will, to some degree, eliminate much of the travel presently occurring today. Already, realistic *virtual reality* and *projection holography* allow businessmen to maintain long distance personable working relationships, thus reducing their need for travel. Many aspects of life, business, and communications will rely on moving information, instead of people. Virtual reality is already a significant aspect of work, learning, communications, business and entertainment. Using the power of the computer, individuals are able to transport themselves, virtually, to any place that has computer simulation. Virtual reality boardrooms will exist around the world, giving the effect of personal face-to-face communication, while the individuals involved are thousands of miles apart.

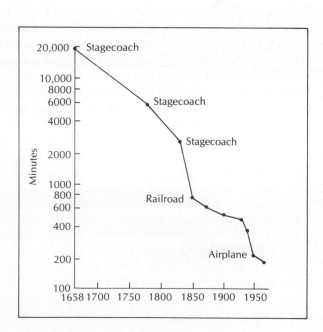

time between Edinburgh and London was longer than 2000 minutes by stagecoach, but by the 1850s, with the arrival of the steam locomotive, the travel time had been reduced by two-thirds, to 800 minutes. By 1988, the rail journey between Edinburgh and London took 275 minutes. When the line is electrified in 1995, travel time will be reduced to under 180 minutes.

Air transportation provides spectacular examples of time-space convergence. In the late 1930s, it took a DC-3 between 15 and 17 hours to fly the United States from coast to coast. Modern jets now cross the continent in about 5 hours. In 1934, QUANTAS/Empire Airways planes took 12 days to fly between London and Brisbane. Today the Boeing 747 SP is capable of flying any commercially practicable route nonstop. The result is that any place on earth is within less than 24 hours of any other place, using the most direct route. Reduction in travel times between London and Paris have likewise been dramatic (Figure 6.28).

TRANSPORTATION POLICY

Transportation policy and regulation has been well-established throughout the world and continued until the 1970s. The purpose of transportation national policy and regulation of air lines and rail carriers was to ensure quality control, protect companies and customers by closely guarding entry and exit from the market, and establishing quality and safety control standards throughout the industry. During this period, providers were not only providing basic transportation service but also meeting a social obligation. For example, Britain's Road Traffic Act of 1930 introduced a system of licenses and rates that effectively regulated the sporadic and unsafe market for bus services in that country. In addition, the Railway Act in Britain provided benefits of inexpensive travel to all sectors of the population.

DEREGULATION AND PRIVATIZATION

By the mid-1970s the international *theory of contestable markets* required that there be free entry of new transportation operators into the market to ensure efficiency and welfare maximization. The move toward *privatization* had begun. Regulation, on the contrary, was criticized as increasing inefficiency, limiting competition, and raising prices to consumers. The Swedish railways, for example, were deregulated by 1968 and British trucking also was deregulated in that year. U.S. domestic airlines began deregulation in the mid-1970s. In Great Britain, in 1980, the Transport Act removed all controls on the bus service and express service between cities. The 1985 Transportation Act deregulated local bus service inside and outside greater London. By the mid 1980s, the English government had sold nationalized transportation companies, including the National Freight Corporation, the British Transport Docks Board, the British Transport Hotels, Seaspeed Ferries, British Airport Authority, the National Bus Company, the Scottish Bus Group, and many other municipally owned companies.

Suddenly, in 1990 and 1991, a collapse of the communist economic system in central Europe and the former Soviet Union occurred. This collapse began a new phase in transportation deregulation and privatization, which has continued unabated throughout the world. The state-owned Soviet Unified Transport System was soon dismantled, and privatization set into eastern Europe and the former Soviet Union. In New Zealand, road freight deregulation has been completed, while in Australia interstate bus services has been deregulated.

Other privatization moves in developed countries have included Air New Zealand, Japanese National Railways, and Air Canada. In each case, an attempt has been made to increase efficiency and reduce public debt by balancing budgets.

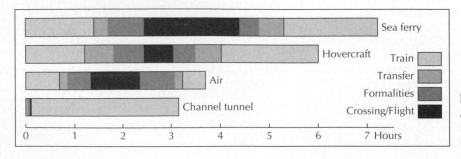

FIGURE 6.28
Journey times between London and Paris for ferry, air, hovercraft, and channel tunnel trails.

Boeing 747s line up at Terminal 4 of London's Heathrow Airport. British Airways alone operates 60 gates at Heathrow. Heathrow handled 35 million international passengers in 1992 and was the world's leading airport. It was followed by Frankfurt, Germany; London's Gatewick; New York's Kennedy; and Paris' Charles de Gaulle, which each handled more than 15 million passengers in 1991. Hong Kong, Amsterdam, Tokyo, and Zurich each handled between 10 and 15 million passengers. *(Source: British Airways.)*

Privatization and *deregulation* have been hampered in developing countries beause of a lack of foreign exchange to purchase necessary spare parts and replacement equipment. Sri Lanka, for example, has deregulated all bus routes, while communist China has deregulated long distance coach service, and fares are now allowed to vary for the first time. Nigeria has followed suit, by privatizing Nigeria Airways and its National Shipping Line, while Singapore privatized Singapore Airlines in 1985 and has offered to privatize its mass transit corporation.

DEREGULATION OF THE U.S. AIRLINES

The Civil Aeronautics Board (CAB) of the United States regulated the U.S. airline industry from 1938 until recently. During most of this period, the CAB's goal was to preserve the 16 trunk line airlines that existed in 1938 and to provide good service at fair prices with a high level of quality control. More recently, the 16 companies were reduced to 11 companies by mergers (American, Brannif, Continental, Delta, Eastern, National, Northwest, PanAm, TWA, United, and Western). Since deregulation, however, Brannif, Eastern, National, and Western have either gone completely out of business or been bought out by another carrier.

Because of the rapid economic growth of the United States, air passenger traffic increased 1000% between 1950 and 1970. The move had been from military planes to propeller planes and finally to modern jet aircraft. Airfares remained almost constant because of the lower cost of operating more efficient planes. However, the oil embargo of 1973/1974 and 1978 increased pressure for *deregulation* for U.S. domestic air services. In 1978, the United States Airline Deregulation Act limited the CAB's route licensing powers (eventually phasing them out) and its fare controls. The intention of this act was to:

1. make U.S. airlines more competitive
2. offer large reductions in average fares and distribute the benefits more equitably
3. provide new lower fare and quality operations
4. be more efficient
5. make airlines less likely to take part in cost-inflating competition
6. continue to serve preexisting networks
7. not subject the airline industry to severe financial distress

Domestic U.S. airlines are now open to any carrier who might venture into the market. The most important result of airline deregulation has been more competitive fares and survival of the most efficient companies. The development of a hub-and-spoke network has been a cost-saving measure. Most direct flights have been reduced and now air service requires at least one stopover in an airline hub city, unless the city pair are very large American cities. Service from smaller cities are directed into larger city airports or hubs and then are linked to final destinations by direct flights.

Privatization and deregulation have kept fares down. In 1976, only 15% of passengers on domestic air routes used discount coach fares; by 1987, 90% of the passengers used discounted tickets. However, as average fares have fallen on long-haul routes, fares on short routes have risen. Load factors have increased substantially with a hub-and-spoke system and the number of flights has declined, leading to lower overall costs.

After deregulation, a musical chairs occurred within the airline industry as eight former local service airlines (Hughes Airwest, North Central, Frontier, Ozark, Piedmont, Southern, Texas International, and US Air) grew rapidly and began to compete at regional levels. In the early 1980s, Alaska Air, Air Cal, Air Florida, PSA, and Southwest joined the competition. However, things had economically toughened by 1984 and the number of regional or national competitors had been reduced to only 10 airlines by 1988 and 7 by 1992 by financial failures, mergers, or takeovers. By 1991, Brannif, Continental, and Eastern were bankrupt and had stopped their operations, while National and Western had been taken over by Pan Am and Delta, respectively.

HUB-AND-SPOKE NETWORKS

In order to remain competitive, the airlines that did survive the shake-out of the 1980s restructured their networks so that they could reduce direct flights between most city pairs and operations could be more efficient and cost-effective with the hub-and-spoke network model. Hubs serve central locations that collect and redistribute passengers between sets of original cities. For example, it requires N (N-1) connections to provide direct linkages between N places and the network. The number of connections required to link these N places can be reduced to N-1 if a hub is established and direct flights are provided between the hub and the other nodes or places in the system. Therefore a hub-and-spoke network provides a certain level of economy.

Extremely large passenger volumes are funneled through hubs, and this allows the airlines to fly larger and more efficient aircraft and to offer more frequent flights between major hubs, increasing load factors (Figure 6.29).

However, *hub-and-spoke networks* can provide disadvantages, especially to the travellers who find their trips more lengthy, frequently with a change of planes, and fewer direct flights available. Also, great congestion is created at the main hub cities, and this affects efficiency both in the air and on the ground. It is important for airlines to make careful decisions as to the location and exact number of hubs so that their operation is competitive with other airlines. There have been a large number of optimum hub location studies in the literature. These mathematical optimization approaches have attempted to capture the real world realities of air passenger networks and the design problems that face most airlines (O'Kelly and Lao, 1991).

Not all cities have fared equally well. Of the 183 U.S. airports, 137 increased their number of flights between 1977 and 1988 by more than 50%. In contrast, the remaining 46 airports showed a precipitous decline on the order of 10% to 15% because of the order of deregulation. Resulting from this mad scramble to reduce fares and elevate efficiency for mega-hubs, Atlanta, Chicago, Dallas, and Denver have surfaced, each serving as a major connection for two or more airlines in Salt Lake City, Minneapolis, and St. Paul. Memphis and Detroit have also entered the market as major hubs. For example, American Airlines utilizes Dallas-Fort Worth and Chicago as national hubs, while Continental uses Houston, New York, Denver, and Cleveland. Delta Airlines' major hubs are Atlanta, Cincinnati, and Dallas; whereas for Northwest, Detroit, Memphis, and Minneapolis serve as hubs. Chicago is ranked well above all other nodes in the United Airlines network, and Pittsburgh and Charlotte are identified as major hubs for US Air (Shaw, 1993) (see Figure 6.29).

TRANSPORTATION OF NUCLEAR WASTES

◈

Nuclear wastes produced during the fission process include reactor metals, such as fuel rods and assemblies, coolant fluids, and gases found in the reactor. Fuel rods are the most highly radioactive waste found on earth

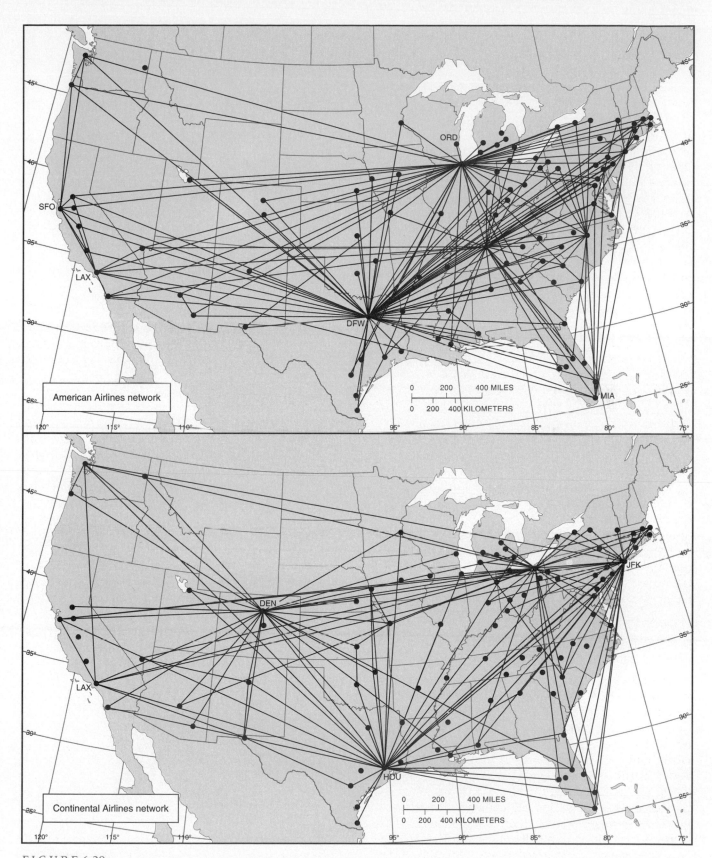

FIGURE 6.29

Hub-and-spoke networks for six major U.S. air carriers, 1993. *(These figures were first published in the Journal of Transport Geography, Vol. 1, No. 1, March 1993, pp. 51–54, and are reproduced here with the permission of Butterworth-Heinemann, Oxford, UK.)*

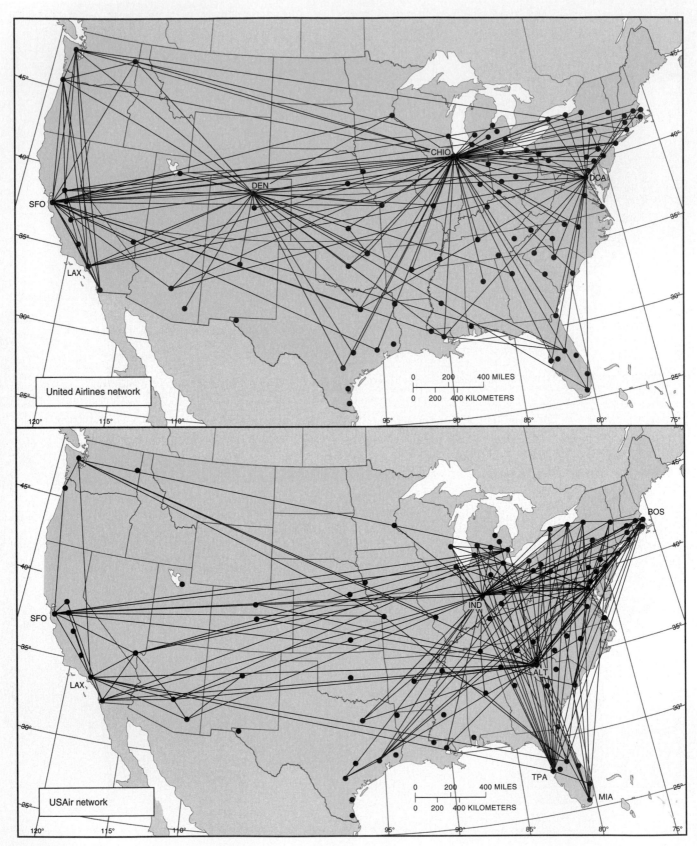

FIGURE 6.29
(Continued)

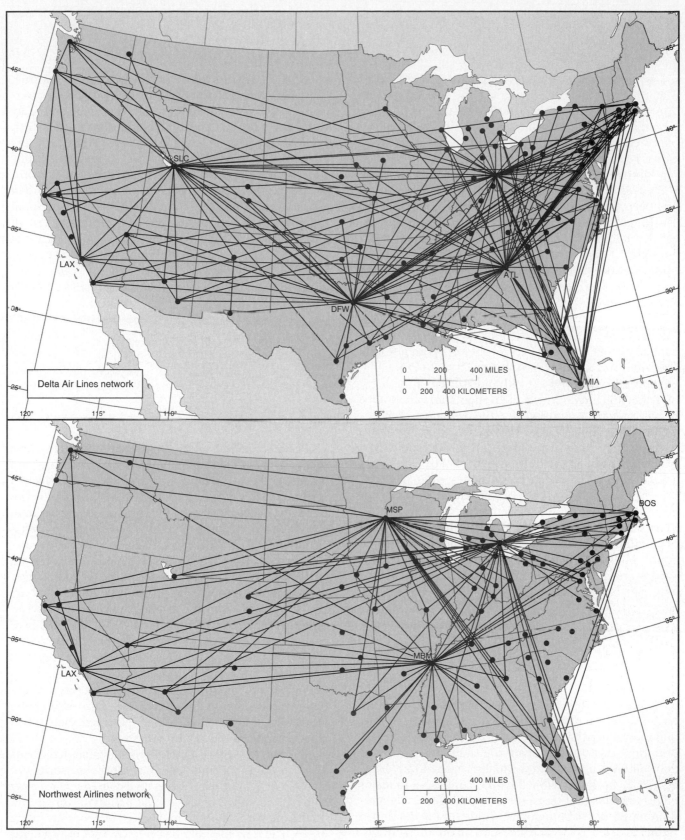

FIGURE 6.29
(Continued)

241

today and their dangerous level of radioactivity requires that they be transported to a special site for storage. The storage site must be located so that the radioactive material will not contaminate the ground water or the biosphere in any way. Geologic stability is a must. Most experts support deep underground geologic disposal in salt domes or other rock formations. Presently, the United States has 100 sites where radioactive waste has been temporarily stored. These include: Hanford, Washington; Livermore, California; Beatty and Las Vegas, Nevada; Idaho Falls, Idaho; Los Alamos and Albuquerque, New Mexico; Amarillo, Texas; Weldon Springs, Missouri; Sheffield, Illinois; Paducah, Kentucky; Oakridge, Tennessee; Aiken and Barnwell, South Carolina; and Niagara Falls and West Valley, New York. Recently, however, the federal government has selected Yucca Mountain, Nevada, as a permanent facility for the storage of high-level nuclear wastes from commercially operated power plants in America (Figure 6.30).

Special containers on rail and truck will be used, and the routes will avoid high population areas. One of the factors responsible for the selection of Yucca Mountain is the so-called NIMBY effect. The problem with nuclear waste deposition is that since no official or engineer can assure that each site will be completely safe, local residents want no possibility of an accident. Another more regional response to the removal of nuclear spent fuel is the so-called NIMTOO effect. NIMTOO stands for "not in my term of office." Politicians are quite sensitive to their constituencies, pleas, and concerns for safety, and usually vote to remove nuclear wastes and power plants from their districts.

TRANSPORTATION IN WORLD CITIES

◈

Until now, this chapter has concentrated primarily on flows of commerce, in the forms of goods, services, and information. A major portion of the study of transportation constitutes urban transportation problems and solutions in which individuals driving automobiles, especially in the developed world, contribute to major environmental and transportation difficulties. The predominance of the automobile in cities of the developed world have led to severe congestion on urban highways. At the same time, public transportation patronage seems to be declining.

In Third World cities, the reverse seems to be true. Most individuals cannot afford the operation or purchase of an automobile, and intercity areas are badly congested with inefficient public transportation, which is grossly inadequate in the inner areas. The inner areas are badly congested with a mixture of motorized traffic, pedestrian traffic, and animal drawn carts and wagons.

This section documents only one aspect of the urban transportation problems and solutions, the personal mobility changes in the United States during the last 30 years. Solutions to the tremendous increase in personal mobility in the developed world include new road construction, rail-based rapid transit systems, traffic management support programs, and transportation coordination.

PERSONAL MOBILITY IN THE UNITED STATES, 1990

◈

Personal mobility in the United States is at its highest point in history, with individuals making more and longer trips and owning more vehicles. Three factors account for this greater level of mobility in general. The first is the overall increased performance of the national economy. People have more money to spend on transportation, and this has led to greater automobile ownership and greater travel distances. The second is related to the increasing growth of cities and their spread over the surrounding countryside through a low-density urban expansion. On the average, distances between home and job have increased. Only recently has there been an increase in efforts to combine mixed-use activities in the same location and, thereby, reduce travel. A third major reason for increased mobility of Americans is the changing role of women in the work force. Many more women own their own vehicles, have entered the work force full-time, and have increased their travel demands during the last 30 years.

Because of increased mobility, individuals have benefited in the social and economic sense, but society as a whole may have felt the negative consequences. New concerns about rising levels of air pollution, congestion on the freeways, and the movement of goods are being posed. The new mobility has created a set of problems that have more difficult answers. Two techniques to address the issue of greater congestion and slower aver-

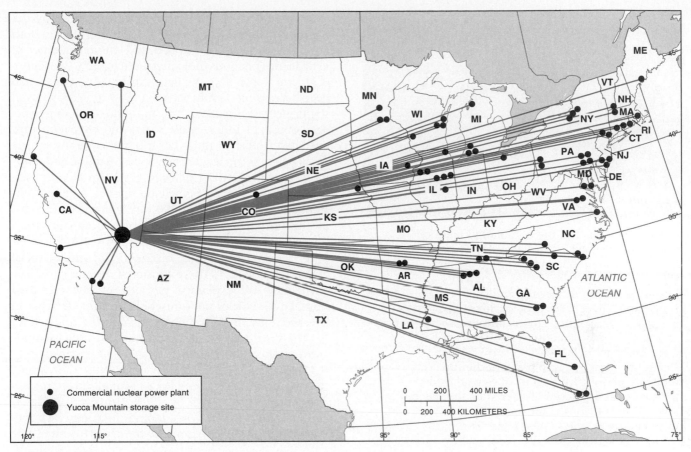

FIGURE 6.30
High-level nuclear waste from commercial power plants will be transported to Yucca Mountain, Nevada.

age speeds are being forwarded. One is to increase volumes on present roadways through *intelligent vehicle highway systems* (IVHS), and the other is to reduce travel demand by planning a land-use mix in localities so that trip origins and destinations are less separated. This approach is called *transit oriented development* (TOD). However, before we discuss these two measures of reducing congestion and increasing the greater volumes of flow, we first examine trends occurring in personal mobility in the United States.

The *Nationwide Personal Transportation Survey* (NPTS) has been conducted approximately every 7 years for the past 30 years. The results displayed here give important information regarding mobility of the American population. Between 1969 and 1990, the number of households, the number of drivers, the number of workers, the number of vehicles, the number of vehicle trips, the household vehicle miles traveled (VMT), the number of person trips, and the person miles of travel have

all increased at a much faster rate than the population (Table 6.6). During this period, the population increased by 21%; households increased at a rate of 49% in the same period; licensed drivers, 58%; workers, 56%; household vehicles, 128%; household vehicle trips, 82%; household vehicle miles traveled (VMT), 82%; person trips, 72%; and person miles of travel, 65%.

In addition, the number and percent of households that did not own a vehicle, dropped from 20% in 1969 to only 9.2% in 1990, a 33% reduction (Table 6.7). However, during the same period of time, the number of households with three or more vehicles increased by 535%. During this time period, the population increased by 21% and the number of households increased by 49%, but the number of household vehicles increased by 128% (Table 6.6).

The *journey-to-work trip*, both in terms of total miles of travel and in terms of number of trips, continued

Rush hour traffic fills the northbound lanes of the San Diego freeway in California. Rapid growth of automobile ownership in Western cities in the second half of the twentieth century has been met by unparallelled congestion. Greater levels of wealth in Western countries, more drivers, more auto ownership, and more women entering the labor force has contributed to high levels of car ownership. In California, auto ownership approaches one car for every person, whereas in cities worldwide, the figure rarely exceeds 10 per 100, and much lower figures than that for rural areas.
(Source: Spencer Grant/Photo Researchers, Inc.)

to account for the largest proportion of travel by the American household between 1969 and 1990. Both annual vehicle miles traveled and annual number of vehicle trips per household increased by 22% (see Figure 6.31 and Table 6.8). Vehicle trip lengths, which had been decreasing slightly between 1969 to 1983, showed slight increases in 1990. The home-to-work trip averaged about 11 miles, while social and recreation trips averaged almost 12 miles per trip. Other family or personal business trip lengths averaged 7.5 miles, and shopping trips averaged 5.1 miles in 1990. For all purposes, however, the average vehicle occupancy declined substantially from 1977 to 1990, an average of 16% for all trip purposes. The average vehicle occupancy for a home-to-work was 1.1; for all purposes, 1.6; for shopping, 1.7; for other family business, 1.8; and for social and recreation, 2.1. These factors of decline in vehicle occupancy are explained partially by the increased number of vehicles per household and the decrease in average household size in America during this period.

The distribution of journey-to-work trips by mode showed that public transit usage had dropped from 8.4% in 1969 to 5.5% nationwide in 1990. Conversely, the automobile accounted for 83% of all travel in 1969 and 91.4% of all travel by 1990. However, the average journey-to-work trip length increased 7% between 1983 and 1990, from 9.9 miles to 10.4 miles (see

Commuter traffic in Bejing. For half of the world's population, the bicycle is a principal means of transportation. In China, less than one person in a 1000 owns an automobile. Public buses are cheap and moderately efficient, but human power is still very important for intraurban movement by foot and bicycle. Pedestrian movement dominates urban areas in terms of the number of trips. If the price of gasoline or the price of parking doubled, would you be willing to travel by bicycle to get to work or school?
(Source: Paolo Koch/Rapho/Photo Researchers, Inc.)

◈

Table 6.6

Summary Statistics on Demographic Characteristics and Total Travel,
1969, 1977, 1983, and 1990 NPTS

	1969	1977	1983	1990	Percent Change 69–90*	69–90†
Households (000)						
All	62,504	75,412	85,371	93,347	1.9	49
1 person	10,980	16,214	19,354	22,999	3.6	109
2 persons	18,448	22,925	27,169	30,114	2.4	63
3 persons	10,746	13,046	14,756	16,128	2.0	50
4+ persons	22,330	23,227	24,092	24,106	0.4	8
Persons (000)						
All	197,213	213,141	229,453	239,416‡	0.9	21
Under 16	60,100	54,958	53,682	54,303	−0.5	−10
16–19	14,598	16,552	15,268	13,851	−0.2	−5
20–34	40,060	52,252	60,788	59,517	1.9	49
35–64	62,982	66,988	75,353	82,480	1.3	31
65+	19,473	22,391	24,362	26,955	1.6	38
All Male	94,465	102,521	111,514	114,441	0.8	21
All Male 16 and older	66,652	74,542	83,645	86,432	1.1	30
All Female	102,748	110,620	117,939	124,975	0.8	22
All Female 16 and older	73,526	83,721	92,080	96,371	1.1	31
All—5 and older	NA	198,434	212,932	222,101	0.9§	12§
Licensed Drivers (000)						
All	102,986	127,552	147,015	163,025‡	2.2	58
Male	57,981	66,199	75,639	80,289	1.6	38
Female	45,005	61,353	71,376	82,707	2.9	84
Workers (000)						
All	75,758	93,019	103,244	118,343‡	2.1	56
Male	48,487	55,625	58,849	63,996	1.3	32
Female	27,271	37,394	44,395	54,334	3.3	99
Household Vehicles‖ (000)						
	72,500	**120,098**	**143,714**	**165,221**	**4.0**	**128**
Household Vehicle Trips (000,000)						
	87,284	**108,826**	**126,874**	**158,927**	**2.9**	**82**
Household VMT (000,000)						
	775,940	**907,603**	**1,002,139**	**1,409,600**	**2.9**	**82**
Person Trips# (000,000)						
	145,146	**211,778**	**224,385**	**249,562**	**2.6**	**72**
Person Miles of Travel# (000,000)						
	1,404,137	**1,879,215**	**1,946,662**	**2,315,300**	**2.4**	**65**

Source: National Personal Transportation Survey, U.S. Department of Transportation, 1992.

◈

Table 6.7

Number of Households by Vehicles Available, 1969, 1977, 1983, and 1990 NPTS
(thousands)

Number of Vehicles Available	1969*	1977	1983	1990	Percent Change	
					69–90 †	69–90 ‡
No vehicle	12,876	11,538	11,548	8,573	−1.9	−33
	(20.6%)	(15.3%)	(13.5%)	(9.2%)		
One vehicle	30,252	26,092	28,780	30,654	0.1	1
	(48.4%)	(34.6%)	(33.7%)	(32.8%)		
Two vehicles	16,501	25,942	28,632	35,872	3.8	117
	(26.4%)	(34.4%)	(33.5%)	(38.4%)		
Three or more vehicles	2875	11,840	16,411	18,248	9.2	535
	(4.6%)	(15.7%)	(19.2%)	(19.5%)		
All Households	**62,504**	**75,412**	**85,371**	**93,347**	**1.9**	**49**
All Household Vehicles	**72,500**	**120,098**	**143,714**	**165,221**	**4.0**	**128**
Vehicles Per Household	**1.16**	**1.59**	**1.68**	**1.77**	**2.0**	**53**

* The 1969 survey does not include pickups or other light trucks as household vehicles.
† Compounded annual rate of percentage change.
‡ Percentage change rate.
Source: Household and vehicle data.

Figure 6.32). The average travel time for commuting trips declined for the same period, however, from 22 minutes in 1969 to 19.7 minutes in 1990, a reduction of 10% during the 21-year period. Consequently, the journey-to-work is somewhat longer in recent years but the average speeds are greater because the overall elapsed time is less due to the improvement of highway facilities; interstates, freeways, and beltways stretching

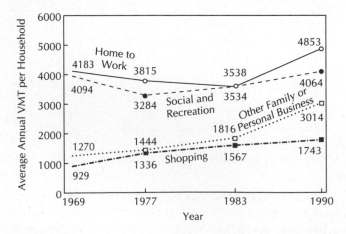
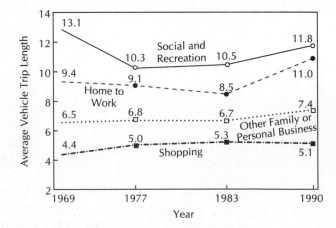

FIGURE 6.31
U.S. household vehicular travel for selected trip purposes, 1969, 1977, 1983, and 1990 NPTS: (a) average annual vehicle miles traveled (VMT), and (b) average vehicle trip length.

Table 6.8

Average Annual VMT, Vehicle Trips and Trip Length Per Household for Selected
Trip Purposes, 1969, 1977, 1983, and 1990 NPTS

Trip Purpose	1969	1977	1983	1990	Percent Change 69–90
Average Annual VMT					
Home to work	4183	3815	3538	4853	16
Shopping	929	1336	1567	1743	88
Other family or personal business	1270	1444	1816	3014	137
Social and recreation	4094	3284	3534	4064	−1
All purposes*	**12,423**	**12,036**	**11,739**	**15,100**	**22**
Average Annual Vehicle Trips					
Home to work	445	423	414	448	0.7
Shopping	213	268	297	345	62
Other family or personal business	195	215	272	411	111
Social and recreation	312	320	335	349	12
All purposes*	**1,396**	**1,442**	**1,486**	**1,702**	**22**
Average Vehicle Trip Length (Miles)					
Home to work	9.4	9.1	8.5	11.0	17
Shopping	4.4	5.0	5.3	5.1	16
Other family or personal business	6.5	6.8	6.7	7.4	14
Social and recreation	13.1	10.3	10.5	11.8	−10
All purposes*	**8.9**	**8.4**	**7.9**	**9.0**	**1**

* Includes other purposes not shown above, such as trips to school, church, doctor, dentist, and work-related business trips.
Source: Travel Day data.

into suburbia; and the development of employment centers near beltways in suburban locations. Lastly, an increase in automobile travel and a decrease in public transit has shortened average commute times as well.

Because of the rapid escalation in average vehicle price, Americans retain their vehicles for a longer period of time. For example, in 1969, 42% of household automobiles were 2 years old or less; by 1990, only 16% were 2 years old or less. During the same time period, the number of automobiles that were 10 or more years in age increased from 6% in 1969 to 30% by 1990. The usage of older vehicles, which have been shown to burn energy less efficiently and cleanly than newer vehicles, contributes to the energy and air pollution problems that America now faces.

Mobility and Gender

Personal mobility changes in America by gender between 1969 and 1990 have been even more dramatic than increases in trip length, vehicle miles traveled, and automobile ownership. Travel by women between 1983 and 1990 has increased 50% from 6382 annual miles to 9528 miles per female driver (see Figure 6.33 and

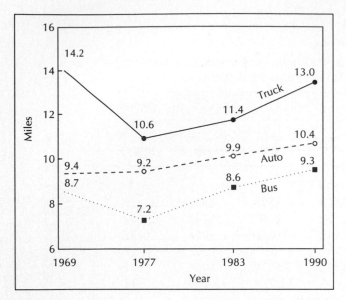

FIGURE 6.32
Average commute trip distance by mode, 1969, 1977, 1983, and 1990 NPTS.

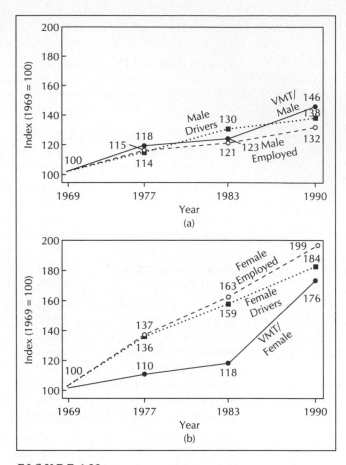

FIGURE 6.33
Changes in annual miles of travel (a) per male drivers, (b) per female drivers, for (1969, 1977, 1983, and 1990 NPTS. Recently, travel by females has increased much faster than travel by males because of increased car ownership by females and more females entering the labor force.

Table 6.9). The average annual miles per licensed male driver also increased dramatically between 1969 and 1990 by 46%. The most dramatic age group for both male and female was the 16 to 19 age group where a 75% to 106% increase occurred, followed by females in the 20 to 34 age period, where a 100% increase occurred in average annual miles driven per licensed driver. The enormous increase for females is primarily due to increased automobile ownership due to a more affluent society and a greater number of women who entered in the labor force requiring the use of an automobile. The increase in age groups 16 to 19 and 20 to 34 also reflects an affluent society with younger drivers receiving greater use of the family car and, in many cases, their own vehicle ownership. Finally, in 1969, the distribution of annual miles driven by males was 73% and by females, 27%. However, by 1990, although travel by males still accounted for the greatest proportion, 65%, the amount accounted for by female drivers increased to 35% of annual miles driven in America.

Due to the overall increases discussed and the number of trips females made for family trips and personal business as well as work-related business, they took, as a group, 70% more trips in 1990 than in 1983. The number of trips females took for family and personal business between 1983 and 1990 grew more than any other category, 37%. At the same time, 16% more work trips were taken by women because of increased employment outside the household.

Lastly, travel by individuals that are 65 years of age and older, compared to all age groups between the years 1983 and 1990 is shown in Table 6.10. Similar to trip-making for the entire population, individuals 65 years and older took approximately 6% more trips over the 7-year period. While this increase is comparable to all age groups, the average trip length of the population 65 years and older increased 19.4% during the 1983 to 1990 period, but the average trip length of all ages increased only 9.2%. When one multiplies the average trip length by the average number of person trips, the resulting average annual number of person miles of travel for individuals 65 years and older has increased by almost 26% during a 7-year period, a significant increase.

Table 6.9

Average Annual Miles per Licensed Driver by Driver Age and Sex, 1969, 1977, 1983, and 1990 NPTS

| | | | | | Percent Change | |
Age	1969	1977	1983	1990	69–90*	69–90†
			Male			
16–19	5461	7045	5908	9543	2.7	75
20–34	13,133	15,222	15,844	18,310	1.6	39
35–54	12,841	16,097	17,808	18,871	1.9	47
55–64	10,696	12,455	13,431	15,224	1.7	42
65+	5919	6795	7198	9162	2.1	55
Average	**11,352**	**13,397**	**13,962**	**16,536**	**1.8**	**46**
			Female			
16–19	3586	4036	3874	7387	3.5	106
20–34	5512	6571	7121	11,174	3.4	103
35–54	6003	6534	7347	10,539	2.7	76
55–64	5375	5097	5432	7211	1.4	34
65+	3664	3572	3308	4750	1.2	30
Average	**5411**	**5940**	**6382**	**9528**	**2.7**	**76**

* Compounded annual rate of percentage change.
† Percentage change rate.
Source: Driver's estimate of annual miles driven, including driving in all vehicles (personal and commercial).

Transit Oriented Development

Two major thrusts are being put forward for the year 2000 to accommodate travel demands in the city. The first of these is called TOD. The second is called IVHS. We first look at TOD and then examine IVHS. The idea behind TOD is to develop design guidelines to help the community to reduce dependency on automobiles and the distance of travel demands. Mixed use of residential employment, commercial and recreational, will bring trip-ends closer to the individual. This is the goal of TOD. When neighborhoods are designed for the comfort and enjoyment of people and their needs instead of

Table 6.10

Travel by Individuals 65 Years and Older Compared to All Age Groups, 1983 and 1990 NPTS

	Average Annual Person Trips			Average Annual Person Miles of Travel			Average Trip Length		
Age	1983	1990	Percent Change*	1983	1990	Percent Change*	1983	1990	Percent Change*
65 and older	672.3	713.5	6.1	4447.5	5596.4	25.8	6.7	8.0	19.4
All ages	977.9	1042.4	6.6	8483.9	9670.6	14.0	8.7	9.5	9.2

* Percentage change rate.
Source: Travel Day data.

just for people and their cars, it is reasoned that traffic congestion as well as the quality of life can be improved. At least two factors help reduce travel distances in Europe. One is higher density communities with shorter transportation and travel demands, and the other is very high costs of automobile ownership and gasoline expense. The European communities have employed concepts of TOD for generations, but America, with its low density urban sprawl and inexpensive land and gasoline, is just now coming to grips with the concept.

The TOD describes a scenario of land use with a compact pattern of mixed use designed to encourage pedestrian trips and support public transit. The emphasis is to provide public places and commercial traveler needs within walking distance of home. TOD presumes an understanding of links between land use and transportation and air quality. It is only one of the delicate long-term solutions to congestion in American cities. TOD has come about through the passage, in 1992, of the Federal Intermodal Surface Transportation Efficiency Act (called Ice Tea), which targets coordinated community planning as a prerequisite to the obtaining of federal transportation funds.

As we have just seen with the National Personal Transportation Survey of 1990, longer commuting distances from homes in the suburbs have contributed to a dramatic increase in vehicle miles driven and in the production of air pollutants. In addition, it is almost impossible to provide good transit service to these distant suburbs. Expectations for transit-oriented development are based on traffic surveys and forecasts, home price comparisons, regional air pollution and congestion modeling, ridership and consumer surveys, and other types of attitudinal techniques. All of these measurements indicate that a certain proportion of America's urban population would tolerate a pedestrian-oriented development that could reduce congestion, increase densities, and create more transit-oriented neighborhoods.

Since suburban communities in the outer city or edge city have lower densities, even trips to schools, stores, parks, and to visit friends have become more lengthy, and walking trips have become completely inconvenient and unsafe. This parallels the growing lack of the sense of community that has pervaded the orientation of the suburbs. The elimination of front porches, and preponderance of two-car garages dominating the facade of the single-family home and becoming the functional front door, and the location of neighborhood services being well beyond the reach of pedestrians have practically eliminated the chances of one meeting with a fellow neighborhood resident, as was once the case.

Naturally, the new emphasis on TOD would require amended zoning in the local region and changed general plans to ensure a greater mix of land uses, limited auto-oriented uses, the establishment of pedestrian scale walks and entrances. Further, there would be zoning for facilities that parallel public thoroughfares, for sidewalks and plantings, and for minimum, rather than a maximum, width of streets and a through traffic speed. The development of alleys and rear parking and the discouragement of the use of cul-de-sacs are some additional features of TOD.

IVHS

During the next 30 years, traffic volume in the United States is expected to double. Yet, each year, some 135 million drivers spend about 2 billion hours stuck in highway traffic. An estimated $46 billion is lost by American drivers trapped in traffic delays, by detours, and by wrong turns. However, IVHSs could greatly ameliorate this situation. The Clinton Administration is proposing to spend $200 million of next year's budget to encourage the development of high-tech highways that will use IVHS technology.

"Smart" cars are equipped with microcomputers, video screens, and other technologies that combine to take the frustration out of driving. Through the use of in-vehicle computers and navigation systems, drivers are guided step-by-step to their destinations. Fast, accurate information allows drivers to avoid accidents and congestion, while simultaneously offering information on restaurants, hotels, attractions, and emergency services—all available with the touch of a screen.

"Smart" highways are created by installing vehicle sensing systems. These sensing systems monitor traffic volume, speed, and vehicle weights. This information helps traffic engineers and transportation planners regulate signals to control traffic flow and plan for new roads. The radar-based collision warning systems will automatically signal a car to brake to avoid collisions. If successful, cars could someday safely travel faster and closer together, thus allowing more vehicles to use the road at the same time.

The current challenge that IVHS faces is the translation of these ideas, into applications that are practical, cost-effective, and user-friendly. IVHS will offer drivers much more data than previously available with paper maps and atlases, including data that can be updated on a continuous basis, such as status reports on traffic and environmental conditions.

Currently, freeways in the developed world can handle about 2000 vehicles per lane per hour. More traffic than this per freeway lane causes stop-and-go traffic, which leads to accidents and gridlock. If the average vehicle is traveling 60 miles per hour on a freeway, then the average density of automobiles per lane is one every 135 feet. If the vehicle is 16 feet long, then 118 feet of freeway is going to waste. One concept behind IVHS is to increase the number of vehicles traveling at high speeds, packing together into a platoon, so that up to 7000 vehicles per lane per hour could exist on modern freeway—one car every half second. If this could be accomplished, the present freeway system could be used in a much more efficient way, preventing the addition of extra freeway lanes and the double-deckering of freeways through the most congested urbanized areas. Double-deckering in a variety of U.S. cities, including San Francisco, Seattle, and New York, has always been met with a strong environmental opposition.

Automobile electronic components make up about 10% of the value of today's automobile. With smart streets and smart highways, this figure could jump to 25% by the year 2000 (see Figure 6.34). IVHS technologies range from real-time routing and congestion information being broadcast to the auto driver via radio to

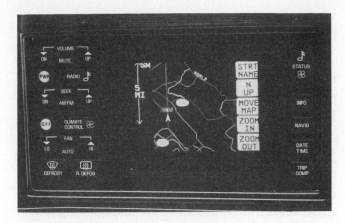

FIGURE 6.35
The Global Positioning System (GPS) satellite constellation is revolutionizing navigation. It is enabling smart cars, aircraft, and emergency and tactical vehicles to be equipped with real-time information on dashboard maps that result in major changes in commercial and private transportation efficiency.

allowing the car to drive by itself on an automated roadway. New electronics associated with IVHS provided real-time information on accident, congestion, and roadway incidents. Traffic controllers, which have information, beam it to motorists who can select new routing strategies or use roadside services (Figure 6.35). Collision avoidance systems using radar, lane tracking technologies that platoons or stack vehicles at high density, and readout terminals on the dashboard that display a map of the city, as well as locations of accidents and the shortest route between two points based on real-time traffic flow information, will be given (Figures 6.35 and 6.36).

IVHS technology has progressed the most in Europe and Japan. In Europe, a consortium of 12 European automakers, more than 75 research institutes and universities, and an additional 100 subsidiary electronics

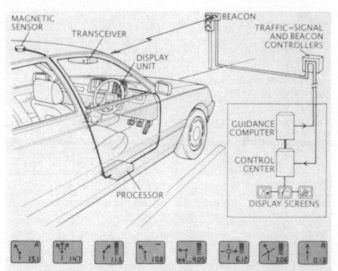

SMART CAR in London's Autoguide navigation system lets a motorist enter a destination on a hand-held remote unit (not shown); the car's processor then communicates with a control center by way of infrared signals and beacons. A dashboard display tells the driver how many kilometers remain in the journey (*numbers*), whether to go straight or to turn (*arrows*), how close a critical intersection is (*bars*) and whether the intersection is an ordinary one or a "roundabout" (*open circle*).

FIGURE 6.34
Intelligent Vehicle Highway Systems (IVHS) diagram. IVHSs provide in-vehicle navigation systems, speed control, and collision warning systems.
(*Source: Scientific American, May, 1990, p. 62.*)

FIGURE 6.36
Photo of dashboard in smart car.

and computer firms have combined in a project called Program for European Traffic with Highest Efficiency and Unparalleled Safety (PROMETHEUS).

This $1 billion experiment began in 1986 and has borne other programs, including the Dedicated Road Infrastructure for Vehicle Safety in Europe (DRIVE) and the Leitund Information System Berlin (LISB). In Berlin, for example, the LISB experimental route guidance information system operates more than 4000 kilometers of roadways, 5000 intersections, and 1500 traffic signals. Cars receive data from 250 infrared roadside signaling devices at the rate of 8000 characters per second.

In Japan, smart highways are operated under Advanced Mobile Traffic Information Communications Systems (AMTICS). The Japanese government and electronics firms operate mapping and navigation equipment built on the dashboard of the car with teleterminals connected by cellular radio to traffic control observation centers along the roadway.

The United States has gotten a late start in IVHS but has come on strongly in the last several years pledging $20 billion during the next 10-year period by the Department of Transportation in Washington, DC. The California Department of Transportation (CALTRANS) presently operates an experimental corridor on a 12-mile stretch of the Santa Monica freeway and surrounding major arterial streets. This smart corridor broadcasts through radio, using changeable message signs and menu driven telephone information systems. Squeezing cars closer together on the freeway at high speeds is the main approach to IVHS by California. The technology has been developed, but user acceptance and cost-effectiveness hurdles remain to be achieved. One of the biggest fears is that if something goes wrong, it could create a massive traffic incident involving more than several hundred cars at one time. Hospitals may be overloaded with demand. While America can tolerate 50,000 traffic fatalities per year from drunk drivers and human error, the public tolerance for deaths resulting from computer-operated vehicles on smart streets is almost zero.

Automatic Vehicle Identification

Even before the IVHS technology becomes fully operational, the *Automatic Vehicle Identification* (AVI) system will be operating. The concept behind AVI is to allow drivers to use express lanes or HOV lanes (*High Occupancy Vehicle*) and, thus, avoid congestion and gridlock by paying a toll. Toll booths for freeways in Pennsylvania and New York or bridge toll booths throughout the west often cause traffic delay. To enter the express lane or the HOV lane, a car needs to have an AVI tag attached to its rearview mirror. The tag costs $30 and is being developed by Texas Instruments. The tag is approximately the size of a credit card, contains a lithium battery, a microchip, and an antenna. When the car approaches an overhead radio device, fiber-optic cables transmit its identification to a control center that charges a congestion toll against the prepaid account of the motorist. If a vehicle enters the express lane without an AVI tag or without a prepaid balance on the motorist's account, surveillance cameras will alert a waiting police car or the motorist may be fined by being issued a warrant in the mail. Operators in the control centers, which are equipped with video cameras along the entire length of the freeway, raise and lower tolls based on levels of congestion, adjusting the signs equipped to flash numbers so that the maximum amount of cars can be processed without a slowdown.

Presently, a 10-mile stretch of freeway operates in Orange County, California. The $100 million roadway operated by the California Private Transportation company has leased new lanes that run down the median of state route 91 from Orange County to Los Angeles. It is expected that congestion pricing of $2 may save as much as 45 minutes in the commuting journey to work.

Transportation Software

The transportation sector of the world economy, from the planning of traffic flows on city streets to the international flow of commodities via tanker and air freight, is encountering challenges of increasing magnitude. Some of these challenges include increasing construction costs, greater fuel costs, greater environmental sensitivity, and even opposition by local special interest groups that are limiting further expansion of local to international transportation systems from highway to port to freight and rail. At the same time, traffic volume at all scales continues to grow steadily, resulting in lengthy traffic delays and increased total costs. At the same time, throughout the developed and developing world, the transportation infrastructure, at all scales, is in desperate need of improvement. The number of issues that transportation logistic managers and engineers must face is increasing rapidly.

Transportation planners, engineers, geographers,

and managers must work hard to get more mileage out of existing facilities and rolling stock. Decisions at the same time need to be made more quickly and efficiently. Yet, the amount of data on which decisions have to be made has been increasing exponentially since the 1950s. Many transportation organizations, from the private to the public sector, still rely on data analysis and hand mapping methods that have been used for decades. These methods now hinder, rather than enhance transportation companies' and public agencies' abilities to meet the transportation challenges.

For example, in the case of public transportation planning and management at the city and state level alone, endless hours have been spent by manually combining, calculating, and transferring data from spreadsheet to map. These analyses include: pavement characteristics, address matching of facilities, residence locations and intersections, base mapping, right-of-way mapping, cut-and-fill calculations required to build a new right of way, environmental impact assessment, accident factors analysis, hazardous material routing, and facility sighting repair crew and vehicle routing. Endless hours have been spent totalling property values by hand along proposed route alignments for which property needs to be purchased.

With the help of an integrated GIS (discussed in Chapter 5) transportation planners can eliminate these and the many other problems that they are faced with and produce plans quickly in a coordinated and efficient manner. Numerous levels of data are georeferenced to the same scale and stored in the computer for easy manipulation and combination, which had to be done previously by hand.

Typical GIS Applications for Transportation

GIS technology facilitates the coordination of many and varied functions of a transportation company. Traffic analysis; alignment studies; roadway design; rail, pavement and river route tracking systems; right-of-way or corridor analysis along the network; parking studies; optimum location of service facilities; optimum location of schools, fire stations and other public facilities; optimum routing through a system; and optimum allocation and flow modeling functions are accomplished through such geographic GIS software available today. Data can be pulled together from a variety of scales and sources, which before meant endless hours of matching by hand. Transportation industry uses in-

formation in tabular form, such as data from the U.S. Census, pavement summaries, accident locations, computer-assisted design data (i.e., roadway or rail design), survey data and public opinion information, market information and competition, image and remotely sensed data from satellites, surface data on roadway or routeway elevation, line drawings, scan documents (i.e., permits and boring logs), video backup images (i.e., photologging of network conditions) at every mile, and scan photographs. All of these and more can be integrated, managed, and mapped at identical scale and georeferenced using GIS software (see Table 6.11).

The value of GIS software lies in the ability to draw together and analyze tabular and map data from the nation, state, or local level, effectively cutting across functional divisions of agencies each with their own scale or data format. A GIS can store an entire digital, georeferenced network of rail, pavement, canals, rivers, fiber-optic telephone lines, or pipelines as a part of an executive information system that can support decisions on maintenance and improvements systemwide. The U.S. Census Bureau has digitized the road and highway system of the United States. This *TIGER File*, as it is called, is now widely used for transportation planning and management. Transportation planners and economic managers can use the GIS to see the entire system, analyze traffic flow, and compare the results against land use, economic projections, and demographic data in order to predict future levels of service that will be demanded. Engineers can use GIS to analyze

Table 6.11

Typical GIS Applications for Transportation

Facility Inventory and Maintenance
Optimum Routing and Scheduling
Emergency Management and Evacuation
Highway and Transit Planning and Traffic Forecasting
Environment Impact Assessment
Traffic Operations and Flow Speed
Accident Analysis and Prevention
Pavement Management and Summaries
Optimal Facility Location Modeling
Network Design and Evaluation
Market Analysis and Competition
Remotely Sensed Data from Satellite Mapping
Photologging of Network Conditions

simultaneously, geologic, hydrologic, topographic, climatic, and terrain-data features for transportation route structure design and maintenance. In addition, a GIS is well-suited for assessment of environmental, economic, political, and cultural impacts of new transportation projects. The major producers of such GIS software include the Environmental System Research Institute of Redlands, California, which produces ARC/INFO; Tydac Corporation, which produces SPANS; Caliper Corporation, which produces GIS PLUS and TRANSCAD; and Urban Systems Analysis Group, which produces TRANPLAN.

COMMUNICATION IMPROVEMENTS

◈

Modernization of transportation has integrated the economic world, but equally important are technical developments in communication. Traditional forms of communication such as the letter post have been joined by telecommunications and computer-based methods of information transfer. In many ways, communication is the invisible layer of transport supplementing the physical transport links between cities, regions, and countries (Daniels, 1985, p. 268).

In the nineteenth century, a major development in communication was that of the telegraph, which made possible the worldwide transmission of information concerning commodity needs, supplies, prices, and shipments—information that was essential if international commerce was to be conducted on an efficient basis. By 1886, a basic skeleton of international telegraph links was completed when a cable along the west coast of Africa was laid. Today, an international telecommunications network based on optical fibers and digital technology has replaced the telegraph. Breakthroughs in information technology not only increase the productivity of business, but also make it feasible to perform service tasks at a much wider range of locations than in the past. The "wired home" can now become the workplace as well as the base for many interactions that do not require travel (Asimov, 1978; Toffler, 1981). The *global office* is also becoming a reality. For example, in 1989, Texas Instruments opened a software development facility in Bangalore, India, that is linked by satellite to its headquarters in Dallas.

The most important improvement in global communications has been the development of satellite technology. The first communication satellites date from 1965, with the launching of Early Bird, able to carry 250 telephone conversations or two television channels simultaneously. Since then, more advanced communication satellites carry 100,000 circuits of simultaneous telephone communications or television channeling. This has allowed for the age of personal, mobile telephones and fax machines that can reach every corner of the globe instantly. In the commercial space, it appears that the planet will be completely covered by *satellite-based telephone* and message capability before the year 2000. The Russians have entered the commercial launch marketplace and have driven launch prices down. This has encouraged an expansion of the commercial use of space. Personal phones have also become miniturized (see photo, page 350).

On-Line Information Systems for Home Use

Several of the developed world's countries, Great Britain, Japan, United States, Germany, and France have nationwide videotex systems that provide on-line information including telephone, direct connections, travel services, retail, banking, weather, stockmarket quotations, and other information directly to the home consumer via dedicated terminal. The American system is known as Prodigy, a videotex system run jointly by Sears and IBM. France's *Transpac Network* seems to be the premier videotex in the world today, providing more than 12,000 information services to approximately 25% of French households. Through the network, users can chat with one another, get business information and quotations, make travel destination and airline reservations, do their banking, and leave messages.

A smart card reader on the terminal allows for purchase of services and goods from retail catalogues. France has been especially successful in promoting a nationwide Transpac Videotex program because they have made it extremely easy for a household to initiate the service. Terminals are given away free at the local telephone stores and, for approximately 15¢ per minute, France's telephone system, Telecom, provides a variety of services shown in Figure 6.37. The only thing that a household forfeits by initiating the service is receiving a 6-inch thick telephone book with included yellow pages!

COMPUTER NETWORKS OF MULTINATIONAL FIRMS

◼

Computer network technology has revolutionized the management and control of distributed locations of labor over a greater geographic area for multinational firms. Computer networks enhance capabilities for co-ordination and performance of geographically disbursed labor as well as process and reduce the need for face-to-face contact. Computer networks speed the process of business communications, not only within firms but also between firms, countries, and continents.

Mark Hepworth (1990) has written an entire book on the subject entitled the *Geography of the Information Economy.* In it, he states that:

The use of inter-organizational computer networks may reduce the optimum size of the firm, if the technology

FIGURE 6.37
France's Transpac videotex home communication system. *(Source: Scientific American, March 1990, p. 88.)* The value of the *microprocessor* in this new computer age of communications will enable the development of more knowledge being transmitted faster than can almost be imagined. It is generating important new scientific disciplines. Unlike past technologies, the microprocessor is feeding itself. Each new generation of chip is used to make more capable chips. Access via the home-based, personal computer, virtual reality technology will change entertainment, work, learning, travel and communications. Using the power of the microprocessor, a user will be able to "virtually" transport themselves to any place that can be simulated around the world. Information will be moved instead of people. Virtual reality will mature into *holography* in the next two decades that will allow full size, full color, three-dimensional images of people and objects to be transmitted over fiberoptic networks and projected onto physical space, allowing people situated around the world to "meet" with each other virtually. Just as cars, airplanes and televisions have shaped how we now think, perceive and behave, so will these new emerging technologies change the world economy in profound ways—only in much greater ways than ever before.

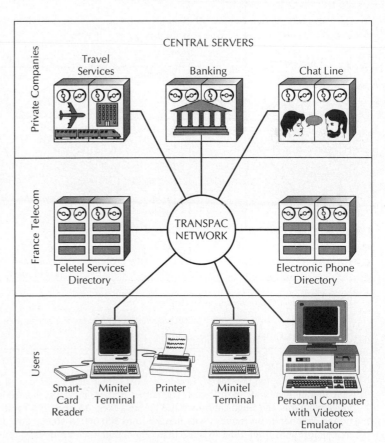

lowers the transaction costs associated with using the market more than it lowers the cost of organizing transactions internally. However, given the transactional difficulties that attend market exchange and information, we would expect inter-organizational networking to lead to further refinements to the interfirm or social division of labor, but with these tendencies being highly differentiated by function and spatially. In the case of order entry applications, such as "just in time" systems and manufacturing, the frequent need for changing product related information between contracting firms, may encourage spatial agglomeration tendencies. However, in the case of highly innovated industries, or the emerging on-line information industries, the need for spatial proximity between contracting firms, and the degree to which transactions are internalized would

have been particularly on information impactedness problems surrounding the development, manufacture and marketing of new products and their unfamiliar methods of utilization. (Hepworth, 1990, p. 96)

The Canadian I.P. Sharps Computer Network is shown in Figure 6.38. It produces and distributes information services that are for sale to transnational corporations. The integrated technologies include computer processing time, application software, public data bases, private storage, and network communications. The company's 100 data bases contain mostly time series statistics on energy, aviation, finance, economics, and actuary businesses. The information from the I.P. Sharp Network is processed with retrieval and analysis software to carry out management-related applications. Examples include economic forecasting, project evaluation, and market analysis.

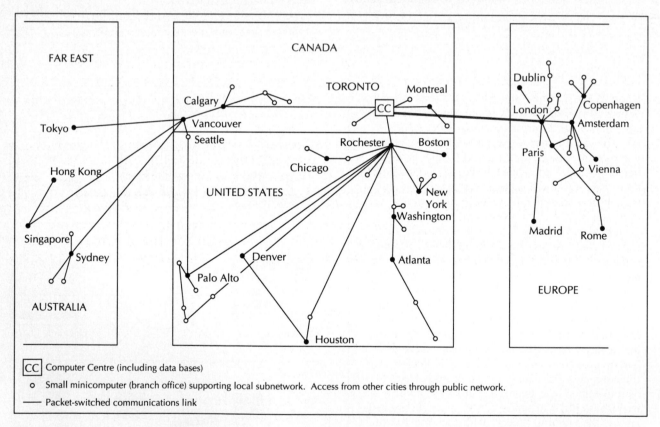

CC Computer Centre (including data bases)

o Small minicomputer (branch office) supporting local subnetwork. Access from other cities through public network.

— Packet-switched communications link

FIGURE 6.38

The I.P. Sharp network. (Source: Hepworth, 1990.) Huge data bases located at universities, federal agencies and research institutions are accessible to almost anyone at little cost. The largest of these networks is *Internet*, and it includes over 1,000 universities with databases of computer programs and huge consumer and business files. Between 1990 and 1995, it is estimated that the number of international, interconnected data banks on Internet will increase from 500,000 to 10,000,000. Transmissions of packets of information have gone from $50 million a month from 1988 to more than $20 billion a month in 1994. The population of users of Internet are increasing at 25 percent a month. At that rate, every person in the world would be connected by 1995.

Summary

◈

For simplicity, industrial location theory assumes that transport costs are proportional to distance; however, in the real world, transport costs are much more complex. In our review, we consider some of the factors other than distance that play a role in determining transport costs—the nature of commodities, carrier and route variations, and the regimes governing transportation. Transport costs remain critical for material-oriented and market-oriented firms, but they are of less importance for firms that produce items for which transport costs are but a small proportion of total costs. For these firms, transit time is more crucial than cost. Modernized means of transport and reduced costs of shipping commodities have also made it possible for economic activities to decentralize. Multinationals have taken full advantage of transport developments to establish "offshore" branch-plant operations, especially in Asia's economic "tigers" (Taiwan, South Korea, Hong Kong, Singapore, and Thailand).

Movements of goods, people, and information take place over and through transport networks. We begin this chapter by discussing how geographers analyze these networks by means of graph theory, reducing them to a set of vertices and a set of edges. Graph theoretic measures may be used to determine nodal accessibility and network connectivity. Geographers also examine other properties of networks—their shape and density. Using models of network change, they further demonstrate how the growth of transport media is inextricably tied to the process of economic growth.

In a discussion of transport development, we explain how improvements over the centuries have resulted in time-space and cost-space convergence. They integrated isolated points of production into a national or a world economy. Although the friction of distance has diminished over time, transport remains an important locational factor. Only if transportation were instantaneous and free would economic activities respond solely to aspatial forces such as economies of scale.

The prediction of flow in transportation networks consist of the estimation of the attraction of places based on their size and their distance apart. The gravity model is a good approximation for the prediction of commodity flow, information flow, and person movement between anchor points. The law of retail gravitation helps establish rules for the breaking point between cities and the edges of their spheres of influence. New developments in flow systems include spatially separated computer networks linking facilities of multinational corporations. Computer innovation now ties the home environment to remote information sources, including business and banking services, travel and commercial services, and library and telephone directory services.

Innovation in urban transportation systems is necessary because of the tremendous increase in travel demand in large cities of the developed world. For example, in the United States, vehicle miles traveled, automobile ownership, and total vehicle trips are increasing rapidly. IVHS technologies are aimed at accommodating this tremendous increase in travel with present roadways, while TOD seeks to redesign cities in higher densities to foster the use of public transportation systems. Because transportation systems, planning, construction, and management have become so complex, GIS computer software is now a common tool used by transportation decision makers and analysts.

◼

KEY TERMS

accessibility index
areas of dominant influence (ADI)
automatic vehicle identification (AVI)
backhauling
beta index
break-of-bulk point
communication
computer network
connectivity

cost-insurance-freight (CIF) pricing
cost-space convergence
deregulation
distance decay
elasticity of demand for transportation
freight-on-board (FOB) pricing
friction of distance
global office
graphs

gravity model
hub-and-spoke networks
Intelligent Vehicle Highway Systems (IVHS)
journey to work
law of retail gravitation
least builder's cost network
least user's cost network
line-haul costs
Nationwide Personal Transportation Survey (NPTS)
network density
Paul Revere network
privatization
route demand

Shimble index
smart cars
smart streets
spatial interaction
stepped freight rates
terminal costs
TIGER File
time-space convergence
Transit Oriented Development (TOD)
transit time
Transpac Network
transport costs
traveling salesman network

◻

SUGGESTED READINGS

Bird, J. H. 1971. *Seaports and Seaport Terminals.* London: Hutchinson.

Brunn, S. D., and Leinbach, T. R., eds. 1991. *Collapsing Space and Time: Geographic Aspects of Communications and Information.* London: Harper Collins.

Dempsey, P. S., and Goetz, A. R. 1992. *Airline Deregulation and Laissez Faire Mythology.* New York: Quorum Books.

Desta, E., and Pigozzi, B. W. 1991. Further experiments with spatial structure measures in gravity models. *Tijdschrift voor Economische en Sociale Geographie,* 82(3):220–226.

Dimitriou, H. T. 1990. *Transport Planning for Third World Cities.* London: Routledge.

Fleming, D. K. 1991. Competition in the U.S. airline industry. *Transportation Quarterly,* 45(2):181–210.

Gayle, D. J., and Goodrich, J. N., eds. 1990. *Privatization and Deregulation in Global Perspective.* London: Pinter.

Goetz, A. R. 1992. Air passenger transportation and growth in the U.S. urban system, 1950–1987. *Growth and Change,* 23(2):217–238.

Haggett, P., and Chorley, R. J. 1969. *Network Analysis in Human Geography.* London: Edward Arnold.

Hall, D. R., ed. 1993. *Transport and Economic Development in the New Central and Eastern Europe.* London: Belhaven.

Hayuth, Y. 1992. Multimodal freight transport. In B. S. Hoyle and R. D. Knowles (Eds.), *Modern Transport Geography* (pp. 199–214). London: Belhaven.

Hepworth, M. 1987. *Geography of the Information Economy.* New York: Guilford Press.

Hilling, D., and Browne, M. 1992. Bulk freight transport. In B. S. Hoyle and R. D. Knowles (Eds.), *Modern Transport Geography* (pp. 179–198). London: Belhaven.

Hoyle, B. S., and Hilling, D., eds. 1984. *Seaport Systems and Spatial Change: Technology, Industry and Development Strategies.* New York: John Wiley.

Hoyle, B. S., and Knowles, R. D. 1992. *Modern Transport Geography.* London: Belhaven.

Hoyle, B. S., and Smith, J. 1992. Transport and development. In B. S. Hoyle and R. D. Knowles (Eds.), *Modern Transport Geography* (pp. 11–31). London: Belhaven.

Janelle, D. G. 1969. Spatial reorganization: A model and concept. *Annals of the Association of American Geographers,* 59:348–364.

Jones, P., and Hervik, A. 1992. Restraining car traffic in European cities: An emerging role for road pricing. *Transportation Research,* 26A(2):133–145.

Kuby, M.; Ratick, S.; and Osleeb, J. 1991. Modelling U.S. coal export planning decisions. *Annals of the Association of American Geographers,* 81(4):627–649.

Leinbach, T. R. 1975. Transportation and the development of Malaya. *Annals of the Association of American Geographers,* 65:270–282.

Lo, L. 1991. Substitutability, spatial structure, and spatial interaction. *Geographical Analysis,* 23(2):132–146.

Lowe, J. C., and Moryadas, S. 1975. *The Geography of Movement.* Boston: Houghton Mifflin.

Mackett, R. 1992. Transport planning and operations in a changing economic and political environment: The case of Hungary. *Transport Reviews,* 12(1):77–96.

McCall, M. K. 1977. Political economy and rural transport: An appraisal of Western misconceptions. *Antipode,* 53:503–529.

McKinnon, A. C. 1989. *Physical Distribution Systems.* London: Routledge.

O'Connor, K., and Scott, A. 1992. Airline services and metropolitan areas in the Asia-Pacific region 1970–1990. *Review of Urban and Regional Development Studies,* 4:240–253.

O'Kelly, M. E., and Lao, Y. 1991. Mode choice in a hub-and-spoke network: A zero-one linear programming approach. *Geographical Analysis,* 23(4):283–297.

O'Kelly, M. E., and Miller, H. J. 1991. Solution strategies for the single facility minimum hub location problem. *Papers in Regional Science,* 70(4):367–380.

Oshin, O. 1991. Road transport and the declining fortunes of the Nigerian railway, 1910–1950. *Journal of Transport History,* 12(1):12–36.

Parolin, B. P.; Filan, S.; and Ilias, A. 1992. Spatial and economic effects of rail freight line closure: Conceptualisation and case study. *Impact Assessment Bulletin,* 10(1):33–46.

Parrott, R., and Stutz, F. P. 1992. Urban GIS Applications. In Maguire, D. J., Goodchild, M. F., and Rhind, D. W. (Eds.), *Geographical Information Systems: Principles and Applications,* (pp. 247–260) (Vol. 2). London: Longman.

Rimmer, P. J. 1985. Transport geography. *Progress in Human Geography,* 9(2):271–277.

Rimmer, P. J. 1988. Transport geography. *Progress in Human Geography,* 12(2):270–281.

Schaeffer, K. H., and Sclar, E. 1975. *Access for All: Transportation and Urban Growth.* Baltimore: Penguin Books.

Slack, B. 1990. Intermodal transportation in North America and the development of inland load centres. *Professional Geographer,* 42:72–83.

Smith, D. M. 1981. *Industrial Location, 2nd ed.* New York: John Wiley.

Sorenson, N. 1991. The impact of geographic scale and traffic density in airline production costs: The decline of the no frills airlines. *Economic Geography,* 67:333–345.

Stutz, F. P. 1977. *Social Aspects of Interaction and Transportation.* Washington, DC: Association of American Geographers.

Stutz, F. P. 1992. Maquiladoras: Transportation-labor cost substitution along the U.S.-Mexican border. In Janelle, D. (Ed.), *Snapshots of North America.* Washington, DC: 27th Congress of the International Geographical Union.

Stutz, F. P. 1995. Environment Impacts of Urban Transportation. In S. Hanson (Ed.), *Urban Transportation Geography.* New York: John Wiley.

Stutz, F. P., Parrott, R. 1992 and P. Kavanaugh. Charting Urban Space-Time Population Shifts Using Trip Generation Models. *Urban Geography,* 13:468–475.

Stutz, F. P., and Supernak, J. 1992. *Understanding Land Use and Transportation Linkages.* Final Report, Project No. 90190–004, California Department of Transportation, Sacramento, California.

Taaffe, E. J.; Morrill, R.; and Gould, P. R. 1963. Transport expansion in underdeveloped countries: A comparative analysis. *Geographical Review,* 53:503–529.

Williams, A. F. 1992. Transport and the future. In Hoyle, B. S. and Knowles, R. D. (Eds.), *Modern Transport Geography,* (pp. 257–270). London: Belhaven.

WORLD AGRICULTURE AND RURAL LAND USE

⬥

OBJECTIVES

- To discuss the origin and diffusion of agriculture

- To help you appreciate the effects of agricultural practices on the land

- To acquaint you with world subsistence agricultural practices, associated crops, and regions

- To acquaint you with commercial agricultural practices, associated crops, and world regions

- To describe the agricultural policies of the United States and the former Soviet Union and the shortcomings of these policies

- To examine von Thünen's deductive model of agricultural land use

⬥

Peasants plowing rice fields prior to planting in central Luzon, Philippines.
(Source: World Bank.)

Agriculture, the world's most space-consuming activity and humanity's leading occupation, is the science and art of cultivating crops and rearing livestock in order to produce food (and fiber) for sustenance or for economic gain. It is the basis for the development and betterment of humanity. Throughout most of our existence as a species, we were hunters and gatherers, subsisting on what nature chanced to provide. Agriculture made possible a nonnomadic existence; it paved the way for the rise of cities and fostered the development of new technologies. Until the nineteenth century, however, agriculture produced little food per worker, so most of the population worked full time or part time on the land. The small surplus released few people for other pursuits. Not until the agrarian revolution that occurred in European settlement areas during the last 200 years did large-scale employment in manufacturing and service activities become possible. The shift of labor from the agricultural sector to other sectors constitutes one of the most remarkable changes in the world economy in modern times. In the United States and the United Kingdom, only 2% of the economically active population now work directly in agriculture. In contrast, about 90% of the population in a number of African and Asian countries are engaged in the agricultural sector.

Economic geographers are concerned with problems of agricultural development and change as well as with patterns of rural land use. Where was agriculture discovered? How did it diffuse? Why do farmers so often fail to prevent environmental problems? What are the characteristics of the main agricultural systems around the world, and what are their goals? What is the effect of industrialized agriculture on farmers and the traditional rural countryside? What principles can help us understand the spatial organization of rural land use? In this chapter, we seek answers to these questions.

Of critical importance to many of the issues addressed in this chapter is the decision-making environment of land users and land managers. Who makes decisions to manage land, how are they made, and what are their consequences? Frequently, individual farmers make direct land-use decisions, but they often must choose from a predetermined range of options. Farmers may be denied access to common property resources, such as water or grazing land. Landlords, multinationals, the state, or social or market demand may force them to grow certain crops. They may be faced with fluctuations in prices for export commodities. It is incumbent on land managers to devise strategies to cope with such pressures and apply these strategies to their land, which, itself, is subject to changes in nature. To appreciate the response of land managers to changes in their circumstances, we must recognize the significance of different scales. Patterns of production and land use are the outcome of a series of forces operating at a series of scales.

TRANSFORMING ENVIRONMENTS THROUGH AGRICULTURE

◈

The course toward a technological culture was marked by the rise of farms at the expense of the wilderness and by the rise of cities at the expense of the countryside. Agriculture was the first instance of human land use that significantly altered the natural environment. Before agriculture, landscapes evolved according to the laws of nature.

Revolutions in Agriculture

Most likely through a series of accidents and deliberate experiments people eventually learned how to produce food and fiber plants by using the components of soil, moisture, and the atmosphere. They also learned how to herd animals and to control animal breeding. Domestication of plants and animals probably emerged as an extension of food-gathering activities of preagricultural hunters and gatherers and as a response to a slow, sustained increase in population pressure.

Although scholars have been unable to determine exactly where and when the earliest experiments in food production occurred, they suspect that the first agricultural revolution began in the *Fertile Crescent* of the Middle East nearly 10,000 years ago (Figure 7.1 and Table 7.1). This was a well-watered area, extending from the highlands of the eastern Mediterranean through the foothills of the Taurus and Zagros mountains. Archaeological finds also indicate that domestication began early in parts of Central America and Southeast Asia.

A reliable food supply liberated people from food gathering. Increased security and leisure, resulting from the new way of life, allowed time for arts and crafts. Communities became involved in spinning, weaving, and dyeing cloth from vegetable fibers, cotton, silk, and wood and in manufacturing pottery and containers. Adequate food supplies also allowed for the exchange

FIGURE 7.1

The fertile crescent. This area stretches from the Persian Gulf in the southeast, north to the southern border of Turkey, and to the Mediterranean Sea in the southwest. The Nile Valley of Egypt, a rich agricultural region, and its Delta, are sometimes included in the Fertile Crescent. The territory was one of the most important in terms of successions of great empires throughout world history, including the Assyrians, Babylonians, Medes, Persians, Egyptians, Israelites, Venetians, and Turks. Many important early developments in the domestication of agricultural plants originated in the region between the Tigres and Euphrates Rivers, which comprise present-day Syria, Iraq, Turkey, and Iran.

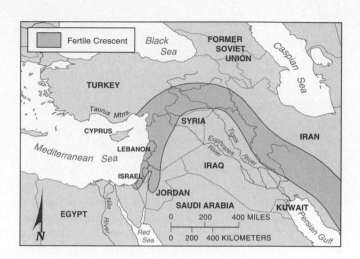

Table 7.1

Three Agricultural Revolutions

	Beginnings and Spread	Subsistence to Market	Industrialization
Time	Pre-10,000 B.P. to twentieth century	C. A.D. 1650 to present	1928 to present
Key Periods	Neolithic Medieval Europe	Eighteenth-century England Nineteenth–twentieth century in European settlement areas	Present
Key Areas	Europe South and East Asia	Western Europe and North America	Former Soviet Union and Eastern Europe North America and Western Europe
Major Goal	Domestic food supply and survival	Surplus production and financial return	Lower unit cost of production
Characteristics	Initial selection and domestication of key species Farming replaces hunting and gathering as way of life and basis of rural settlement and society Agrarian societies proliferate and support population growth Subsistence agriculture: labor intensive, low technology, communal tenure	Critical improvements, mercantilistic outlook, and food demands of industrial revolution replace subsistence with market orientation Agriculture part of sectorial division of labor: individual farm family becomes "ideal" for way of life and for making a living Commercial agriculture develops growing reliance on technological inputs and infrastructure	Collective (socialist) and corporate (capitalist) ideologies and common agrotechnology favor integration of agriculture production into total food-industry system Emphasis on productivity and production for profit replace agrarian structure and farm way of life Collective/corporate production uses economies of scale, capital intensity, labor substitution, and specialized production on fewer, larger units

Source: Troughton, 1985, p. 256.

of specialized goods in markets. In addition, plant cultivation weakened the forces that scattered populations and strengthened the forces that concentrated them. The new way of life allowed people to live in villages and towns, which reached population densities far higher than those of preagricultural communities.

Farming practices that emerged during the Neolithic period changed little until the creation of a feudal hierarchy in medieval Europe. In this hierarchy, secular or religious overlords protected the serfs who farmed fields and paid taxes in *kind* (goods or commodities) or money according to the custom of the manor. English religious manors extracted the *tithe*—one-tenth of a farmer's annual production. Bishops and abbots were bedfellows who put nothing into the farming business and took none of the risks but harassed farmers at harvest time.

The most important innovations associated with farming in medieval Europe were the heavy plow, the replacement of oxen with horses for plowing, and the development of the open-field system, consisting of two or three large fields on each side of a village. These advances increased agricultural production, intensified human concentration in villages and towns, generated commerce, and changed patterns of environmental exploitation. For example, the forested lowlands of Western Europe were gradually cleared when the heavy plow was invented. Clayey lowland soils could not be cultivated with the old Mediterranean scratch plow, which was suitable only for light limestone soils.

Medieval farming methods prevailed in Western Europe until capitalism invaded the rural manor. This resulted from a vast population increase in the new trading cities that depended on the countryside for food and raw materials. Another force that brought the market into the countryside was the alienation of the manorial holdings. Lords, who needed cash to exchange for manufactured goods and luxuries, began to rent their lands to peasants rather than having them farmed directly through labor-service obligations. Thus, they became landlords in the modern sense of the term. The breakup of the manorial system, however, stemmed more directly from the Hundred Years' War (1337–1453) and the Black Death (1348–1349). The depopulation that resulted from these devastating events meant a shortage of labor. Wages rose, and land, relatively more plentiful, began to rent for less. Lords wanted to reestablish the labor-service obligation, but they were unable to turn back the clock. With the extension of the market into the countryside, peasants enjoyed greater independence and prosperity. Efforts to reinstate the old obligations were resisted in a series of peasant revolts that broke out across Europe from the late fourteenth century to the early sixteenth century.

A second agricultural revolution that began with the demise of the manorial system replaced subsistence agriculture with market-oriented agriculture (see Table 7.1). Open fields were enclosed by fences, hedges, and walls. Crop rotation replaced the medieval practice of fallowing fields. Seeds and breeding stock improved. New agricultural areas opened up in the Americas. Farm machines replaced or supplemented human or animal power. The family farm came to represent the core model of commercial agriculture.

Since the late 1920s, a third agricultural revolution has been taking place (see Table 7.1). This revolution, which some observers believe is the logical extension of the second agricultural revolution, points to the resolution or rationalization of the distinction between family and corporate models of agriculture (Vogeler, 1981). In other words, it signifies the elimination of distinct agrarian economies and communities. Although the third agricultural revolution is incomplete, industrial agriculture has become the dominant form in most developed countries, capitalist and socialist, and is being applied to export enclaves of Third World countries. Key elements of industrial agriculture are capital intensity, technological inputs, high energy use, concentration of economic power, and a quest for lower unit costs of production. Although industrial agriculture has increased output per unit of input, it has also depleted water and soil resources, polluted the environment, and destroyed a way of life for millions of farm families. During the 1960s and 1970s, many American family farmers who could avail themselves of the new technologies and expand their acreages were able to survive. But in the 1980s, foreclosures and bankruptcies became common, especially in the farm-dependent counties of the U.S. Midwest. Indebted farmers were unable to remain solvent in a period of reduced export demand.

Industrial agriculture has drastically reduced the number of farmers in North America. In the United States, the number of farmers declined from 7 million in 1935 to around 2 million in 1990. In Canada, 600,000 farm operators existed in 1951 but only half that number were still in operation in the late 1970s. Europe has witnessed similar trends. In Great Britain, for example, an annual 1.5% decline in the number of farm workers occurred during the 1980s.

The Diffusion of Agriculture

The Fertile Crescent was one of several locales for plant and animal domestication (Table 7.2 and Figure 7.2). The spread of agriculture from these centers was slow. For example, archaeologists have calculated that it took from 6000 B.C. to 3000 B.C. for a form of shifting cultivation to spread along the Danube and Rhine corridors. (Shifting cultivation is a type of agriculture in which clearings are used for several years then abandoned and replaced by new ones.) Another 1000 years elapsed before agriculture reached southern England.

By A.D. 1500, on the eve of European overseas expansion, agriculture had spread widely throughout the Old World and much of the New World. In Europe, the Middle East, North Africa, central Asia, China, and India, cereal farming and horticulture were common features of the rural economy. Nonagricultural areas of the Old World were restricted to the Arctic fringes of Europe and Asia and to parts of southern and central Africa. Agriculture had not spread beyond the eastern Indian islands into Australia.

By the time of the first European voyages across the Atlantic, the cultivation of maize, beans, and squash in the New World had spread throughout Central America and the humid environment of the eastern half of North America as far north as the Great Lakes. In South America, only parts of the Amazon Basin, the uplands of northeastern Brazil, and the dry temperate south did not have an agricultural economy.

These patterns of agriculture persisted until the era of European overseas settlements. From the Age of Discovery to the mid-seventeenth century, Europeans did not attempt to establish large overseas settlements. Eventually, European settlement assumed two forms: (1) farm-family colonies in the middle latitudes of North

Table 7.2

Probable Areas of Origin of Selected Crops and Domesticated Animals

Area	Crops	Animals*
Fertile Crescent	barley, beets, cabbage, carrots, date, fig, grapes, oats, olive, onion, pea, rye, turnip, rutabaga, wheat	camel, cattle, dog, duck, goat, pig, pigeon, horse, sheep
Central Asia	almond, apple, carrot, cherry, flax, hemp, lentil, melon, pea, pear, turnip, walnut	camel, cattle, chicken, dog, horse?, reindeer, sheep, yak
North China	apricot, cabbage, millet, mulberry, peach, plum, radish, rice, sorghum, soybean, tea	chicken?, dog, horse, pig?, silkworm
Southeast Asia	bamboo, banana, black pepper, citrus, eggplant, mango, sugarcane, taro, tea, yam	cat?, cattle, chicken, dog, duck, goose, pig, water buffalo
Ethiopia	coffee, barley, okra, wheat	
Nile Valley	cotton, cucumber, lentil, millet, melon, pea, sesame, sorghum	cat, dog, donkey
West Africa	kola nut, rice, watermelon	
Central America	avocado, beans, cocoa, corn, cotton, sweet potato, pumpkin, red pepper, squash, sunflower, tobacco, tomato, maize	dog, turkey
Northern Andes	beans, potato, pumpkin, squash, strawberry, tomato	alpaca, guanaco, guinea pig, llama, vicuña
Eastern South America	beans, cassava, cocoa, peanut, pineapple, potato, sunflower, squash, sweet potato	dog, duck

* Question mark indicates uncertainty as to area or areas of origin. Occurrence of crops and animals in more than one area points to the likelihood of independent invention.

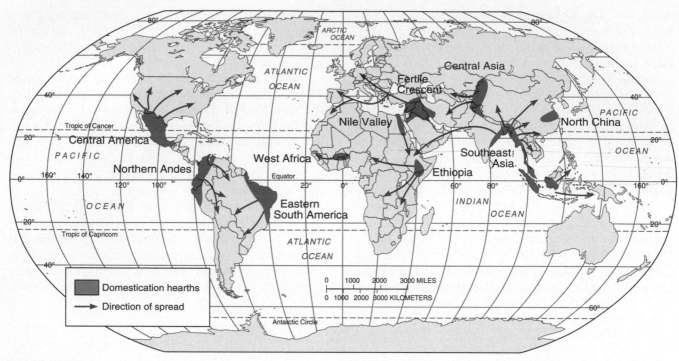

FIGURE 7.2

Origins of plant and animal domestication. Animals were probably first domesticated as household pets by prehistoric peoples. The domestication of plants came from two sources. The first was *vegetated planting,* which was the planting of pieces of existing plants, such as stems and roots. Plants first found growing wild that were useful to the household were cut up and transplanted. *Seed agriculture* was the second source, and it inplanted. *Seed agriculture* was the second source, and it involved the planting of seeds, which were the direct result of natural, annual fertilization of plants.

America, Australia, New Zealand, and South Africa; and (2) plantation colonies in the tropical regions of Africa, Asia, and Latin America. These two types of agricultural settlements differed considerably.

For example, farm colonization in North America depended on a large influx of European settlers whose agricultural products were initially for a local market rather than an export market. Europeans introduced the farm techniques, field patterns, and types of housing characteristic of their homelands; yet, they often modified their customs to meet the challenge of organizing the new territory. For example, the checkerboard pattern of farms and fields that characterizes much of the country west of the Ohio River resulted from a federal system of land allocation. It involved surveying a baseline and a principal meridian, the intersection of which served as a point of origin for dividing the land into 6-by-6-mile townships, then into square-mile sections, and, still further, into quarter sections a half-mile long. This orderly system of land allocation prevented many boundary disputes as settlement moved into the interior of the United States.

On the world's largest rubber plantation at Harbel, Liberia, more than 36,000 hectares, or 30% of the total land area of Liberia, are cultivated by Firestone. The company has also established plantations in Brazil, Ghana, Guatemala, and the Philippines. How do plantations benefit host societies? (*Source: Firestone Tire and Rubber Company.*)

A tapper on the Firestone plantation in Liberia makes an incision in a rubber tree. The latex will flow down the incision through a spout and into a cup attached to the tree. Some of the latex is carried in pails by women to collecting stations. What would this tapper do if he were not working for Firestone?
(Source: Firestone Tire and Rubber Company.)

In tropical areas, Europeans, and later Americans and Japanese, imposed a plantation agricultural system that did not require substantial settlement by expatriates. Plantations are large-scale agricultural enterprises devoted to the specialized production of one tropical product raised for the market. It is believed that they were first developed in the 1400s by the Portuguese on islands off the tropical West African coast. Plantations produced luxury foodstuffs, such as spices, tea, cocoa, coffee, and sugarcane, and industrial raw materials, such as cotton, sisal, jute, and hemp. These crops were selected for their market value in international trade, and they were grown near the seacoast to facilitate shipment to Europe. The creation of plantations sometimes involved expropriating land used for local food crops. Sometimes, by irrigation or by clearing forests, new lands were brought into cultivation. Europeans managed plantations; they did no manual labor. The plantation system relied on forced or poorly paid indigenous labor. Very little machinery was used. Instead of substituting machinery for laborers when local labor supplies were exhausted, plantation managers went farther afield to bring in additional laborers. This practice was especially convenient because world demand fluctuated. During periods of increased demand, production could be accelerated by importing additional laborers. This practice made the need for installing machinery

during booms unnecessary and minimized the financial problems of idle capital during slumps.

The effect of centuries of European overseas expansion was to reorganize agricultural land use worldwide. Commercial agricultural systems have become a feature of much of the habitable world. Hunting and gathering, the oldest means of survival, has virtually disappeared, although it still sustains groups such as the Bushmen of the Kalahari and the Pygmies of Zaire. Pastoralists, such as the Masai of Kenya and Tanzania who drive cattle in a never-ending search for pasture and water, have declined in numbers. Subsistence farming still exists, but only in areas where impoverished farmers, especially in underdeveloped countries, barely make a living from tiny plots of land. Few completely self-sufficient farms exist; most farmers, even in remote areas of Africa and Asia, trade with their neighbors at local markets.

Human Impact on the Land

The emergence of agriculture and its subsequent spread throughout the world has meant that little if any land still can be considered natural or untouched. Vegetation has been most noticeably changed. Virtually all vegetation zones show signs of clearing, burning, and the browsing of domestic animals. The impoverishment of vegetation has led to the creation of successful agricultural and pastoral landscapes, but is has also led to land degradation or a reduction of land capability. Land degradation is a social problem of major significance—the "quiet crisis" that erodes the basis of civilization (Brown, 1981).

Hunters and gatherers hardly disturb vegetation, but farmers must displace vegetation to grow their crops and to tend their livestock. Farmers are land managers; they upset an equilibrium established by nature and substitute their own. If they apply their agrotechnology with care, the agricultural system may last indefinitely and remain productive. On the other hand, if they apply their agrotechnology carelessly, the environmental base may deteriorate rapidly. How farmers actually manage land depends not only on their knowledge and perception of the environment, but also on their relations with groups in the wider society—in the state and the world economy.

As agriculture intensifies, environmental alteration increases. Ester Boserup (1965) proposed a simple five-stage model of agricultural systems based on frequency of land use. Stage 1, forest-fallow cultivation, involves cultivation for 1 to 3 years followed by 20 to 25 years of fallow. In Stage 2, bush-fallow cultivation, the land is cultivated for 2 to 8 years, followed by 6 to 10 years of fallow. In Stage 3, short-fallow cultivation, the land is fallow for only 1 to 2 years. In Stages 4 and 5, annual cropping and multicropping, fallow periods are either very short—a few months—or nonexistent. Boserup noted that the transition from one form of agriculture to another was accompanied by an increasing population density, improved tools, the increasing integration of livestock, improved transportation, a more complex social infrastructure, more permanent settlement and land tenure, and more labor specialization.

Forest-fallow, or shifting cultivation, survives in areas of the humid tropics that have low-potential environmental productivity and low population pressure. Under ideal conditions, this form of agriculture leaves much of the original vegetation intact. Farmers make small, discontinuous clearings in forests. They girdle some trees and cut down others, burn the debris, and prepare the soil by digging holes in a pattern of points for a variety of crops—groundnuts, rice, taro, sweet potato. Because no fertilizer is used, soil nutrients are quickly depleted. Thus, farmers abandon their plots and establish new gardens every few years, but they rarely move their residences. Except on steep slopes, where soil erosion can be a serious problem, shifting cultivation can be a sustainable system of agriculture (Clarke, 1977; Grandstaff, 1978). It allows previous plots to re-generate natural growth. In Papua New Guinea, for example, about one-quarter of the country's forested area is well-developed secondary forest created and maintained by shifting cultivation.

However, shifting cultivation can lead to degradation when an increasing population demands too much of the land or when new forces intrude into the farming system. In one sequence, common in Latin America, shifting cultivation agriculturalists follow loggers and oil prospectors into an area. After cropping is finished, the land is seeded with grass and sold to commercial ranchers who produce beef for the North American and European markets. Heavily grazed, the land quickly declines in carrying capacity and is then abandoned as the ranchers move to new areas (Nations and Komer, 1983).

In contrast, permanent agriculture (annual cropping and multicropping) usually occurs in areas of high-potential environmental productivity and of high population pressure. Under permanent cultivation, the land becomes totally transformed. Yet the beauty, fertility, and endurance of the land may not be impaired. Soils of the Paris Basin have been intensively cultivated for hundreds of years, and still they remain highly productive. In many parts of the Orient, carefully terraced hillsides have maintained the productivity of valuable soil resources after thousands of years. These agricultural landscapes are in harmony with nature.

In general, modern farming practices pose the main danger to land. Clean tillage on large fields, monocul-

A scene showing the deforestation in the rainforest in Acro, Western Brazil. Forests have been burnt to the ground to create temporary pastures for cattle. The nation's rainforests are being cut down at a rate 50 percent faster today than they were 10 years ago. Rainforest loss creates a number of intractable problems: a) contributes to greenhouse warming, b) eliminates the cleansing of the atmosphere, c) creates new semi-deserts, d) increases large-scale flooding, and e) threatens wildlife habitats. (*Source: UN Photo 15744./ P. Sudhakaran.*)

ture (the cultivation or growth of a single crop), and the breaking down of soil structure by huge machines are a few factors that may destroy the topsoil. Droughts and dust storms during the 1930s, 1970s, and 1980s in the Great Plains of the United States gave testimony of how nature and industrial agriculture can combine to destroy the health of a steppe landscape and transform it into a desert.

Whether farmers achieve a harmonious relationship with nature does not necessarily depend on either their technologies or their political philosophies. Farmers with simple tools and technologies can destroy the long-run food-producing capacity of the land. Mechanical agriculture in both capitalist and socialist countries alike can degrade the land.

Agriculture threatens ecological balances when people begin to believe that they have freed themselves from dependence on land resources. In capitalist countries, there is an inherent tendency to exploit the land as a result of pressure to reproduce economic conditions of production or to maximize profits. Household and corporate producers want to make land use more efficient and land more productive; thus, farming is often viewed as just another industry. However, we must remember that land is more than a means to an end; it is finite, spatially fixed, and ecologically fragile. If we desecrate the land, human life cannot continue. As Ernest Schumacher (1973) pointed out in his book *Small is Beautiful*, there are three important goals of agricultural land use: health, beauty, and permanence. If these are not the objectives of agriculture, how can we produce the foodstuffs that sustain us on any long-term basis?

FACTORS AFFECTING RURAL LAND USE

◈

Rural land-use patterns, which are arrangements of fields and larger land-use areas at the farm, regional, or global level are difficult to understand. Worldwide, hundreds of farm types exist. When faced with such diversity, geographers frequently divide the world into parts or regions to simplify the problem of description. A map of nine agricultural regions, ranging from labor-intensive rice-paddy farming to nomadic herding, is one of many that geographers have proposed to break down varied farm types into a few generalized patterns.

The most interesting aspect of the world's agricul-

tural regions is not their number or extent, but the uniformity of land-use decisions farmers make within them. Given any farming region, why do farmers make similar land-use decisions? For example, why does one farmer on the slopes of Mount Kilimanjaro decide to mix coffee bushes with banana stands, and likewise all other neighbors? The land-use pattern on Kilimanjaro, as elsewhere, reflects a host of factors. Geographers identify at least four groups of variables that determine land use: site characteristics, cultural preference and perception, systems of production, and relative location. We discuss these four groups of variables in more detail next.

SITE CHARACTERISTICS

◈

Variations in rural land use depend partly on site characteristics, such as soil type and fertility, slope, drainage, exposure to sun and wind, and the amount of rainfall and average annual temperature. As an example, consider the climate milieux in which crops grow. Plants require particular combinations of temperature and moisture. An optima-and-limits schema can show the range for a hypothetical crop. Increasing rainfall is plotted on the horizontal axis and inceasing temperature on the vertical axis. Absolute physical limits of the crop are "too wet," "too dry," "too cold," and "too hot." A series of isopleths, which connect points of equal dollar yield her hectare, mark optimum conditions. A diagram can show that a particular combination of temperature and moisture conditions characterizes each site. Absolute climatic limits are wide for some crops, such as maize and wheat, but narrow for others, such as pineapples, cocoa, bananas, and certain wine grapes.

WORLD CULTURAL PREFERENCE AND PERCEPTION

◉

Food preferences and prejudices are one of the most important variables in determining the type of agricultural activity at a given site. Some cultural groups would rather starve than eat edible but taboo food (Simoons, 1961). Many Africans avoid protein-rich chickens and their eggs. Certain Hindus abstain from eating all meat,

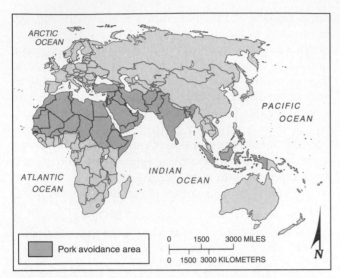

FIGURE 7.3

Pork avoidance areas of the world are shown. Cultural preferences and perceptions against certain foods by a particular culture are called *food taboos*. The pork avoidance, or pork taboo, for North Africa and the Middle East occurred in early biblical times. The Semitic peoples were nomadic herders; pigs were more conducive to sedentary agricultural regions. Pigs were considered unclean because of their environmental setting. Today, the Muslim areas of the world, which subscribe to some Old Testament biblical laws, are the largest areas of pork avoidance. The Muslim faith spread throughout the Middle East to India and Southeast Asia, areas that are not nomadic herding regions. Nonetheless, they have also adopted the pork taboo because of religious practices. While India is only 15% Muslim and, therefore, does not have a taboo against pork by the majority of the population, beef taboos are practiced in this world region by the majority.

but particularly beef. Muslims do not eat pork; hence, pig raising is absent from the Muslim world, which stretches from Mauritania and Morocco to Pakistan and Bangladesh and to parts of Indonesia (Figure 7.3). The Chinese and some other people of East and Southeast Asia abstain from drinking milk or eating milk products. In the United States, a consumer preference for meat leads American farmers to put a greater proportion of their land in forage crops than European farmers, who grow more food crops.

People interpret the environment through different cultural lenses. Their agricultural experiences in one area influence their perceptions of environmental conditions in other areas. Consider the settlement of North America. The first European settlers were Anglo-Saxons accustomed to moist conditions and a tree-covered landscape. They equated trees with fertility. If land was to be suitable for farming, it should, in its natural state, have a cover of trees. Thus, the settlers of New England and the East Coast realized their expectations of a fertile farming region. When Anglo-Saxons edged onto the prairies and high plains west of the Mississippi River, they encountered a treeless, grass-covered area. They underestimated the richness of the prairie soils, in particular, and the area became known as the "great American desert." In the late nineteenth century, a new wave of migrants from the steppe grasslands of Eastern Europe appraised the fertility of the grass-covered area more accurately than the Anglo-Saxons who preceded them did. The settlers from Eastern Europe, together with technological inventions such as barbed-wire fencing and the moldboard plow, helped to change the perception of the prairies from the "great American desert" to the *great American breadbasket*.

In areas of new settlement, a succession of good farming years often engenders a false optimism about the environment. Until the disasters of the 1930s, farmers of the American Great Plains did not realize that the land they worked was highly sensitive. In fact, there was a belief that occupation of the Great Plains increased rainfall and could ban the specter of drought (Webb, 1931). In Australia, the hazards of farming the semiarid regions were first ignored, then harshly recognized, and later only partly accepted (Meinig, 1962; Williams, 1979).

Ignorance of land degradation and its perception are a function of the rate and accumulated degree of degradation as well as the intelligence of land managers. In the mountains of Ethiopia, where cultivation has been occurring for 2000 years with a fairly low rate of soil loss, the cumulative erosion of good soil has resulted in a serious decline in the capability of the land. In comparison, in the hills of northern Thailand, where rates of soil loss are much higher, the local land-management system has compensated for soil erosion, and the capability of the land has been maintained (Hurni, 1983).

However, land is sometimes devastated by land managers—not because of ignorance or stupidity but because of calculated human agency. A strong market imperative, a need to occupy new land for cropping, or a belief that man can and must master nature can ruin land in sensitive environments. Much land in the former Soviet Union has been degraded as a result of attempts by the state to "transform nature" (Komorov, 1981). One of the most disastrous efforts to revive agriculture's lagging production was President Nikita Khrushchev's hasty, grandiose *Virgin and Idle Lands Program* (Jackson, 1962). It involved massive plowing of the dry steppe east of the Volga River that resulted in increased corn and wheat production. Elimination of fallowing in the steppe reduced soil moisture reserves, encouraged weed and insect infestations, and depressed yields, while frequent moldboard plowing pulverized the soils and led to enormous dust storms (Stebelsky, 1983).

SYSTEMS OF PRODUCTION

◈

Systems of agricultural production set their imprint on rural land use. Like manufacturing, the agricultural endeavor is carried out according to three systems of production: peasant, capitalist, and socialist (Table 7.3). The major distinction among these systems is the labor commitment of the enterprise. In the peasant system, production comes from small units worked entirely, or almost entirely, by family labor. In the capitalist system, family farming is still widespread; but, as in the socialist system, labor is a commodity to be hired and dismissed by the enterprise according to changes in the scale of organization, the degree of mechanization, and the level of market demand for products.

In any geographic region, one system of production dominates the others. For example, capitalist agriculture dominates parts of South America, whereas peasant agriculture dominates other parts of the continent. Capitalist agriculture finds expression in a vast cattle-ranching zone extending southwest from northeastern Brazil to Patagonia; in Argentina's wheat-raising Pampa, which is similar to the U.S. Great Plains; in a mixed livestock and crop zone in Uruguay, southern Brazil, and south central Chile, which is comparable to the U.S. Corn Belt; in a Mediterranean agriculture zone in middle Chile; and in a number of seaboard tropical plantations in Brazil, the Guianas, Venezuela, Colombia, and Peru. Peasant agriculture dominates the rest of the continent. There is shifting cultivation in the Amazon Basin rain forest, rudimental sedentary cultivation in the Andean plateau country from Colombia in the north to the Bolivian Altiplano in the south, and a wide strip of crop and livestock farming in eastern Brazil between the coastal plantations and livestock ranching zones.

Subsistence, or Peasant Mode, of Production

Subsistence agriculture, also called *peasant agriculture,* is associated with underdeveloped countries, and it is labor intensive (labor centered). Farmers are small-scale producers who invest little in mechanical equipment or chemicals. They are interested mainly in using what they produce rather than in exchanging it to buy things that they need. Food and fiber are exchanged, particu-

Table 7.3
Systems of Production

	Peasant	*Capitalist*	*Socialist*
Labor Commitment of the Enterprise	Total	Partial	Partial
Institutional Basis	Family	Family Joint stock	Combine
Control and Direction	Family	Family-managerial	Managerial
Means of Distribution	Barter-market	Market	Prescription-market
Media of Distribution	Kind-money	Money	Money
Mechanization	Possible	Usual	Usual
Regulator	Labor supply	Market	State

Source: Adapted from Franklin, 1965, p. 149.

larly through interaction with capitalist agriculture at global, national, and local scales, but farm families consume much of what they produce. Karl Polanyi (1971) called this *use value* rather than *exchange value*. To obtain the outputs required to be self-supporting, peasant farmers are frequently willing to raise inputs of labor to very high levels, especially in crowded areas where land is rarely available. Highly intensive peasant agriculture occurs in the rice fields of South, East, and Southeast Asia. Most of the paddies are prepared by ox-drawn plow, and the rice is planted and harvested by hand—millions of hands. Clifford Geertz (1963) coined the term *agriculture involution* to refer to the ability of the agricultural system in the densely populated parts of Asia, including Japan, to absorb increasing numbers of people and still provide minimal subsistence levels for all in rural communities.

An example of the peasant mode of production exists in the semiarid zone of East Africa. This zone includes the interior of Tanzania, northeast Uganda, and the area surrounding the moist high-potential heartland of Kenya. As in most parts of the Third World, peasant agriculture in this region has been complicated by the colonial and postcolonial experience.

According to Philip Porter (1979), people in the semiarid area of East Africa earn a living by combining several activities. They eat their crops and livestock and sell or exchange agricultural surpluses at markets. They grow cash, or export, crops such as cotton. They maintain beehives in the bush and sell part of the honey and wax. They brew and sell beer. They hunt, fish, and collect wild fruits. They earn income by cutting firewood, making charcoal, delivering water, and carrying sand for use in construction. Some of them have small shops or are tailors. Most important, people sell their labor, both short term and long term, nearby and far away (Figure 7.4).

To farm and herd successfully in the semiarid zone, land managers must meet certain requirements set by the environment and by the nature of crops and animals. Livestock require water, graze, salt, and protection from disease and predators. To meet these needs day after day, year after year, land managers must have considerable skill and knowledge. They must know a great deal not only about the ability of animals to withstand physiological stress, but also about environmental management—which grass to save for late grazing, where and when to establish dry-season wells to enable the stock to withstand the rigor of the daily journey between water and graze. With respect to crops, land managers must know about plant-moisture and nutrient needs.

They must also be sensitive to the variability of rainfall.

Most of the time, this system of agriculture in East Africa provides peasants with an adequate and varied food supply. In bad times, there are mechanisms for sharing hardship and loss so that those farmers who are hardest hit can usually rebuild their livelihoods after bad times end. However, the peasant mode of production has been forced to adjust to pressures from governments during colonial and postcolonial periods.

For a long time it was fashionable to decry the conservatism of peasant farmers. But conservatism does not mean an unwillingness to change. Peasant farmers who live in environments of high risk and uncertainty, such as those in the semiarid zone of East Africa, do adopt risk-aversion behavior; in fact, they are more likely to

Feed lots for beef cattle at Grosford, California. According to the "Code of the West," cattle ranchers owned little land, only cattle, and grazed open land wherever they pleased. New cattle breeds introduced from Europe, such as the Hereford, offered superior meat, but were not adapted to the old ranching system of surviving the winter by open grazing. In moist areas, crop growing supplanted ranching because it generated a higher income per acre. Some cattle are still raised on ranches, but most are sent for fattening to feed lots along major interstate highways or railroad routes. Many feed lots are owned by agribusiness and meat-processing companies, rather than by individuals.
(Source: Joe Munroe/Photo Researchers, Inc.)

FIGURE 7.4

The structure of the semiarid peasant agricultural system in East Africa. *(Source: Porter, 1979, p. 33.)* Can the delicate nature of this semi-arid peasant agricultural system keep pace with the rapid population growth of Africa? Conventional wisdom says no. African countries continue to report a decline in per capita food production. Inadequate rainfall, plunging world prices, ethnic unrest, and civil war contribute to the decline. If the situation looks bleak in 1994, the high rate of population growth and slow to negative economic growth may spell disaster by the year 2020, with global plagues, poverty and military violence. While Africa had only 50 percent of the population of Europe in 1950, by the year 2020, it will have 300 percent of the population of Europe! Great pressure is being placed on African environmental systems because of net capital flows which are insufficient to pay for imported energy or environmental technology. The developing world relies on bulk commodities, which are exported in exchange for foreign capital. As described later in this chapter, Africa is suffering from severe commodity deflation. Most exports are dwindling in value per ton. Timber is one of the only commodities that is increasing in value on the world market. The result is clear cut forests, floods, declining revenues from food production and tropical forests being used for firewood. Because of lack of capital, transportation systems, and political stability, poor food distribution will continue and mass starvation, on an unprecedented scale, could result. Disease and political chaos may result. Millions have already died of AIDS because of a lack of capital to fight the spread.

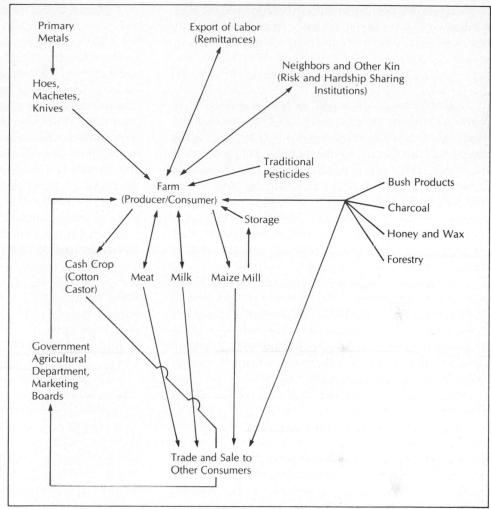

behave in a risk-averting manner than can wealthy, large-scale commercial farmers who have the resources to better withstand failure. Given proposals for change that will work in the environments in which they live, peasant farmers are just as willing to adopt new ideas and technologies as their American or European counterparts are.

SUBSISTENCE AGRICULTURE: CROPS AND REGIONS

Most of the world's farmers, including the people of Latin America, Africa, and Asia, practice subsistence agriculture. These regions have several characteristics in common:

1. The majority of workers are engaged in agriculture instead of manufacturing, services, and processing information.

2. Agricultural methods and practices are primitive. Farms and plots are small in comparison with those of the developed world, labor is used intensively, and mechanization and fertilization are used only infrequently.

3. Agricultural produce that is harvested on the farms is used primarily for direct consumption. The family, or the extended family, subsists on the agricultural products from the farm. Although in certain years surpluses may be produced, this is rarely the case.

James Rubenstein (1994) divides subsistence agriculture into three categories: shifting cultivation in the tropics, pastoral nomadism in North Africa and the Middle East, and intensive subsistence agriculture in South and East Asia, where rice is grown (Figure 7.5).

Shifting Cultivation

Shifting cultivation is a type of primitive agriculture practiced in three main tropical rain-forest areas of the world: (1) the South American Amazon region, (2) the central African Congo region, and (3) Southeast Asia, Indonesia, and New Guinea (Figure 7.5). Rainfall is heavy in these regions, vegetation is thick, and soils are relatively poor quality.

When shifting cultivation is practiced, the people of a permanent village clear a field adjacent to their settlement by slashing vegetation. After the field is cleared with axes, knives, and machetes, the remaining stumps are burned. Daily rain returns the ash and nutrients to the soil, temporarily fertilizing it. (Because of this clearing technique, shifting cultivation is sometimes called *slash-and-burn* agriculture.) The field is used for several years. At the end of this time, the soil is depleted, and the village turns elsewhere to clear another field. Eventually, the forest vegetation again takes over, and the area is refoliated. The soil is thus allowed to replenish itself.

Using hoes or knives, the farmers plant the fields by hand with tubers or seeds. An indentation is made in the soil. A stem of a plant is submerged or a seed is dropped into a hole, and soil is pushed over the opening by hand. Mechanization and animals are not used for plowing or for harvesting. The most productive farming occurs in the second or third year after burning. Following this, surrounding vegetation rapidly regenerates, weeds grow, and soil productivity dwindles. The plot, sometimes called a *swidden* or *milpa*, is abandoned. Then, a new site is selected nearby. Usually, the village does not permanently relocate. The villagers commonly return to the abandoned field after 6 to 12 years, by which time the soil has regained enough nutrients to grow crops again.

The predominant crops grown in shifting agricultural areas include corn and manioc (cassava) in South America, rice in Southeast Asia, and sorghum and millet in Africa. In some regions, yams, sugarcane, and other vegetables are also grown.

The patchwork of a swidden is quite complex and seemingly chaotic. On one swidden, a variety of crops can be grown, including those just mentioned, as well as potatoes, rice, corn, yams, mangoes, cotton, beans, bananas, pineapples, and others, each in a clump or small area within the swidden.

Only 5% of the world's population engages in shifting cultivation. This low percentage is not surprising because tropical rain forests are not highly populated areas. However, shifting cultivation is practiced on about 20% of the world's land surface and therefore is an important type of agriculture. The amount of land devoted to this type of agriculture is decreasing because governments in these regions deem shifting cultivation to be economically unimportant to the government and to the country as a whole. Consequently, they are selling and leasing land to commercial interests that destroy the tropical hardwoods and rain forests.

These forests are important for oxygen production and a global, ecologically balanced environment. Many scientists believe that maintenance of the tropical rain forests contributes to a healthy atmosphere and guards against global warming. The fewer rain forests, the more carbon dioxide builds up and causes the greenhouse effect by trapping solar radiation in the atmosphere. Species extinction from rain forest depletion is also a serious problem. Therefore, even though shifting cultivation is an inefficient form of agriculture for large populations, it helps maintain the tropical forests.

One principal agreement of the Rio de Janeiro United Nations Conference on Environmental Development, held in the summer of 1992, was the preservation of tropical hardwoods. Presently, the World Bank and the International Monetary Fund (IMF) will loan monies to developing nations only if those nations practice certain environmental protection measures. One such measure is maintenance of tropical hardwoods.

Pastoral Nomadism

Shifting cultivation and *pastoral nomadism* can be classified as extensive, or nonintensive, subsistence agriculture. Areas in which pastoral nomadism is practiced include North Africa and the Middle East, the eastern plateau areas of China and Central Asia, and Eastern Africa's Kenya and Tanzania (Figure 7.5). According to Rubenstein (1992) only 15 million people are pastoral nomads, but they occupy 20% of the earth's land area. Combining this area with that in which shifting cultivation is practiced, we can see that almost 50% of the world's area is included. The pastoral nomads occupy areas that are climatically opposite those of shifting cultivators. The lands occupied by pastoral nomads are dry, usually less than 10 inches of rain accumulate per year, and typical agriculture is normally impossible, except in oases areas.

Instead of depending on crops as most other farmers do, nomads depend on animal herds for their sustenance. Everything that they need and use is carried with them from one forage area to another. Tents are constructed of goats' hair, and milk, clothing, shoes, and implements are produced from the animals. Pastoral nomads consume mostly meat and grain. Sometimes, in exchange for the meat, other needed goods are obtained from sedentary farmers in marginal lands near the nomads' herding regions. It is common for pastoral nomads to farm areas near oases or within floodplains that they occupy for a short period of the year. Nomadic parties usually include 6 to 10 families who travel in a group, carrying bags of grain for sustenance during the drier portions of the year.

A set cyclical pattern of migration is entrenched in the nomadic way of life, and it lasts for generations. Pastoral nomads are not wandering tribesmen; they follow a 12-month cycle in which lands most available with forage are cyclically revisited in a pattern that exhibits strong territoriality and observance of the rights of adjacent tribes. The exact migration pattern of today's pastoral nomads have developed from a precise geographic knowledge of the region's physical landforms and environmental provision.

Nomads must select animals for their herds that can withstand drought and provide the basic necessities of the herdsmen. The camel is the quintessential animal of the nomad because it is strong, can travel for weeks without water, and can move rapidly while carrying a large load. It is almost completely impervious to driving desert sandstorms because it has extra skin folds over its eyes. The goat is the favorite small animal because it requires little water, is tough, and can forage off the least green plants. Sheep are slow moving and require more water, but they provide other necessities: wool and mutton. Small tribes need between 25 and 60 goats and sheep and between 10 and 25 camels to sustain themselves.

In early times, before railroad and telegraph, pastoral nomads were the communication agents of the desert regions, carrying with them innovation, information, and adaptation. This is no longer the case, now that their host governments have joined the information and technology age. Many of these governments have modern weapons and can control vast territories. However, nomadic herding has been allowed to remain because these vast dry areas of the world cannot be used for other economic activity. Furthermore, government attempts to settle pastoral nomads have met with little success, although the former Soviet Union and China have settled large numbers of them. In the future, pastoral nomads will be allowed only on lands that do not have energy resources or precious metals beneath the surface, or on lands that cannot be easily irrigated from nearby rivers, lakes, or groundwater aquifers. In any case, the number of pastoral nomads is declining because of increasing population pressures on the countries in which they live.

Intensive Subsistence Agriculture

Intensive subsistence agriculture is practiced by large populations living in East Asia, South Asia, Southeast Asia, Central America, and South America (Figure 7.5). Whereas shifting cultivation and pastoral nomadism are extensive low-density, marginal operations, intensive subsistence agriculture, as the term implies, is a higher intensity type of primitive agriculture in the majority of the densely populated developing areas of the world. Rice is the predominant crop because of its high levels of carbohydrates and protein. Most farmers using intensive subsistence rice agriculture use every available piece of land, however fragmented, around their villages. Most often, a farm encompasses only a few acres.

Intensive subsistence agriculture is characterized by several features:

1. Most of the work is done by hand, with all family members involved. Occasionally farm animals are used, such as water buffalo or oxen. Almost no mechanization is used because of lack of capital to purchase such equipment and because plots are tiny.

2. Plots of land are extremely small by Western standards. Almost no piece of land is wasted. Even roads through agricultural regions of intensive subsistence are made narrow so that all cultivatable areas can be used.

3. The physiological density (that is, the number of people that each acre of land can support) is very high.

4. Principal regions that are cultivated are river valleys and irrigated fields in low-lying, moist regions in the middle latitudes.

Because rice is a crop that has a high yield per acre and is rich in nutrients, it is a favorite in intensive subsistence agricultural regions (Figure 7.6). First, the field is plowed with a sharpened wooden pole that is pulled by oxen. Next, the field is flooded with water and planted with rice seedlings by hand. Another method is to spread dry seeds over a large area by hand. When the rice is mature, having developed for three-fourths of its life underwater, it is harvested from the rice *paddy*, or *sawah*, as it is called in Indonesia. To separate the

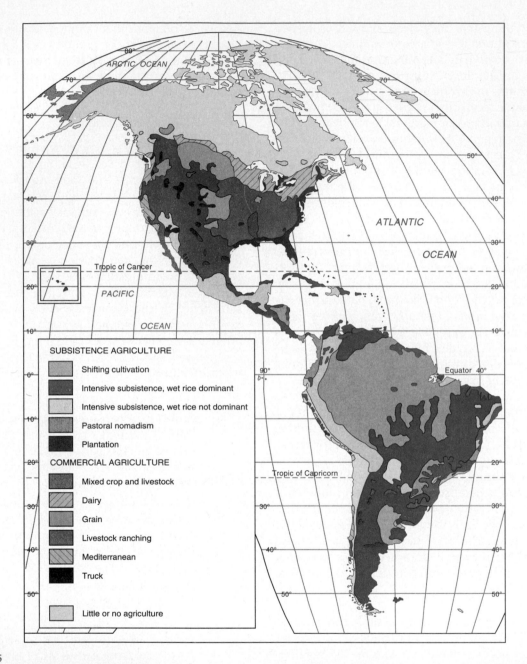

FIGURE 7.5
World agricultural regions. Geographers and agricultural economists divide the world into three agricultural regions. The first is subsistence, or peasant, agriculture. The second is commercial, or capitalist, agriculture, and the third is the socialist, or command economy, agricultural system. On this map, commercial and socialist systems are shown as commercial agriculture. Subsistence agriculture includes nomadic herding, slash-and-burn agriculture, and intensive sedentary subsistence agriculture. (See Color Insert 2 for more illustrative map.)

Africa, Southeast Asia, and the Amazon Basin are the principal regions of shifting agriculture. North Africa, Southwest Asia, and central East Asia are the principal areas of nomadic herding, or pastoral nomadism. Intensive subsistence agriculture includes rice-dominant cultivation and rice mixed with other crops. These regions include East Asia, South Asia, and Southeast Asia. Plantation agriculture is primarily in tropical and subtropical regions of Latin America, Asia, and Africa.

Commercial regions, on the other hand, include mixed crop and livestock farming, which exists primarily in the northern United States, southern Canada, and central Europe. It also includes dairy farming near the population cen-

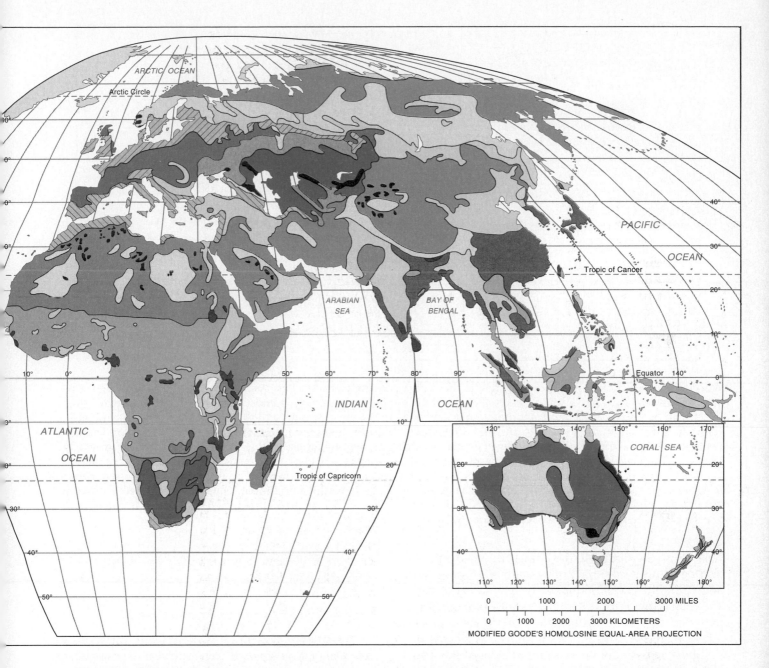

MODIFIED GOODE'S HOMOLOSINE EQUAL-AREA PROJECTION

ters of the northeastern United States and northwestern Europe. Grain cultivation exists in Argentina, the American Great Plains, the central Asian Plains of the former Soviet Union, and in Australia.

Livestock ranching includes areas too dry for plant cultivation, including the western mountain and plain regions of Canada and the United States; southeastern South America; southwestern regions of the former Soviet Union, centered on Kazakhstan; and large portions of Australia.

Mediterranean agriculture specializes in horticulture—fruit and vegetable regions—and includes areas surrounding the Mediterranean Sea, regions of the southwestern United States, central Chile, and the southern tip of Africa.

Finally, commercial gardening and fruit farming, also called truck farming, exist in the southeastern United States to supply the northeastern population center of America. This type of farming also exists in southeastern Australia.

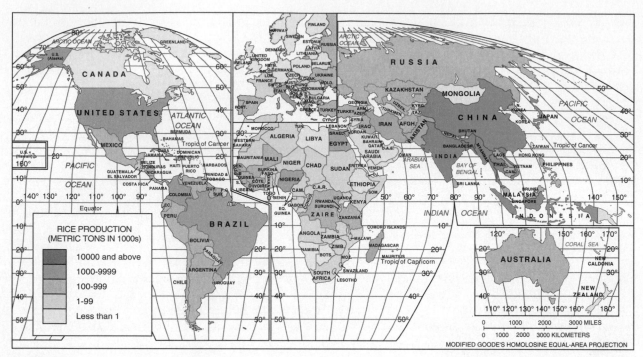

FIGURE 7.6
World rice production. Anthropologists tell us that rice was domesticated in East Asia more than 7000 years ago. Unlike corn in America, rice is almost exclusively used for human consumption. Almost 2 billion people worldwide are fed chiefly by rice. It is the most important crop cultivated in the most densely settled areas of the world, including China in East Asia, India in South Asia, and Southeast Asia. These areas produce more than 90% of the world's rice. Populations in these regions use rice for between one-third and one-half their total food intake. Rice can be grown in only very humid and tropical regions because it depends on water to develop. Rice requires a large amount of labor and tedious work, but the returns are bountiful. Rice produces more food per unit of land than any other crop, thus it is suitable for the most densely populated areas of the world, such as China and India. Outside Asia, Brazil is now the leading rice producer, followed by the United States. Each of these two countries provides less than 2% of the world's rice supply. (See Color Insert 2 page 2.2, top, for more illustrative map.)

husks from the rice itself, the farmers thrash the rice by beating it on a hard surface or by trampling it underfoot. Sometimes it is even poured on heavily traveled roads. The chaff is thus removed from the seeds, and sometimes the wind blows the lightweight material far from the pile of rice itself. This process is known as *winnowing*.

Some year-round, tropical, moist areas of the world allow *double cropping*. This means that more than one crop can be produced from the same plot throughout the year. Occasionally in wet regions two rice crops are grown, but more frequently a rice crop and a different crop, which requires less water, are produced. The field crop is produced in the drier season on nonirrigated land.

In the higher-latitudes of East Asia, rice is mixed with other crops and may not be the dominant crop. In western India and the northern China plain, wheat and barley are the dominant crops, with oats, millet,

corn, sorghum, soybeans, cotton, flax, hemp, and tobacco also produced.

Problems Faced by Subsistence Agriculturalists

Subsistence agriculture is subjected to variations in soil quality, availability of rain from year to year, and, in general, environmental conditions that can harm crop-production levels and endanger life. Chapter 4 discussed the problems associated with dry and marginally agriculturally sustainable regions of Africa, especially Ethiopa and Somalia.

In addition, subsistence agriculturalists lack tools, implements, hybrid seeds, fertilizer, and mechanization that developed nations have enjoyed for nearly 100 years. With such drawbacks, subsistence agriculturalists can barely provide for their families, and net yields have not increased substantially for many generations. These families and countries do not have enough capital to purchase the necessary state-of-the-art equipment to improve their standard of living.

Finally, all too often developing countries turn to their only source of revenue to generate the cash flow needed for infrastructure, growth, and military equipment. They must produce something that they can sell in the world market. Occasionally, they sell mineral resources and nonmineral energy resources or fuels. Most frequently, however, developing countries generate funds from the agricultural sector, which also needs further development. Often, these countries sell cash crops on the world market to generate foreign revenue, thus the food is not used to sustain its own population. Fruits and vegetables are examples.

Another category of agricultural products that can generate the needed revenue is nonfood crops, such as sugar, hemp, jute, rubber, tea, tobacco, coffee, and a growing harvest of cotton to satisfy the world's need for fabric and denim. How can starving nations feed themselves when a large proportion of their agricultural

productivity and acreage is devoted to nonfood crops? This is the plight of many African, South American, Central American, and Asian countries today. As a result, sometimes alternative sources of income are inviting, even if they are illegal.

Illegal Drug Trade The peoples of South America and Asia sometimes produce crops that are sold on the world market and that bring much higher profits than conventional crops do. These high-profit crops are the coca leaf, from which cocaine and crack cocaine are produced; marijuana; opium; and hashish. Even though they are illegally grown, these crops provide farmers with hundreds to thousands of times the monetary return of the same acreage planted with conventional crops.

There is a geographic setting and contiguity to most major drug-producing areas of the world (Figure 7.7). For example, in South America, the countries of Bolivia, Peru, Ecuador, and Colombia produce the coca leaf. Half the supply comes from Peru alone, and the next largest amount comes from Colombia. However, Co-

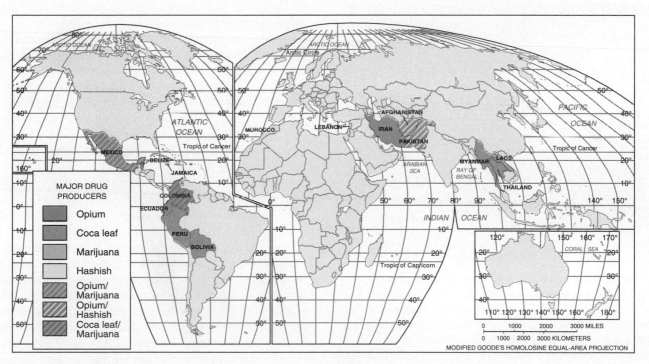

FIGURE 7.7
Sources of drugs worldwide. Drugs flow from the impoverished Third World countries to the demand centers in the developed world of North America, Europe, and cities throughout the remainder of the world. The flow of marijuana from South America has decreased, whereas the flow of hard drugs from South America, primarily the coca leaf, from which cocaine and crack cocaine are made, has increased substantially. Sources of the coca leaf include Colombia, Ecuador, Peru, and Bolivia. Morocco, Afghanistan, and Pakistan are the chief sources of hashish, whereas Iran, Afghanistan, Pakistan, and Southeast Asia are the principal supply regions of opium.

lombia is the target of U.S. DEA (Drug Enforcement Agency) activity because it is the refining center and distribution point of 85% of the cocaine from South America that enters the United States. Marijuana, the illegal drug used most widely in the United States, comes primarily from Mexico. Smaller amounts come from Colombia, Jamaica, and Belize (see box on page 281).

Some of the most remote and hostile regions of the world produce opium from the juice of opium poppies. Iran, Afghanistan, Pakistan, Myanmar, Thailand, and Laos are principal supply regions. Pakistan, Afghanistan, Lebanon, and Morocco are principal producers of hashish.

Developing countries are now beset with a great problem. On the one hand, the world frowns on the production of illegal drugs, and the IMF, the World Bank, and the United Nations attach conditions to their loans and bail-out programs according to the amount of law enforcement against drug production. On the other hand, such governments face tremendous interna-

Harvesting cocaine in Peru. This peasant gathers cocoa leaves four or fives times per year. One hectare furnishes 2 tons of leaves per year, which makes it possible to manufacture 40 kilos of pâte. This pâte is smoked in a form of a stock, or transformed into cocaine. Most of the production occurs in Colombia, South America. The traffic in coca leaves is one of the major problems in Peru. Under American pressure, the government set up a plan for tearing up the plants, calling for the destruction of 600 hectares per year. Even so, this is a small amount considering there are more than 200,000 hectares now devoted to producing coca leaves in Peru. (Source: J. C. Criton/Sygma.)

tional debt and a lack of products that generate foreign exchange. Consequently, although most of these countries' official policies disallow drug production, in reality enforcement against illegal drug production is impossible in certain regions of each country because of the potential for insurrection and the political power of drug money.

Commercial Mode of Production

Agriculture in the United States epitomizes the commercial system (see Figure 7.8). Modern American farming is quick to respond to new developments, such as new productiontechniques. Consequently, farmers with sizable investments of money, materials, and energy can create drastic changes in land-use patterns. For example, farmers in the low-rainfall areas of the western United States have converted large areas of grazing land to forage and grass production with the use of center-pivot irrigation systems. Other farmers grow sugar beets and potatoes in western oases through federally subsidized water projects.

American farmers are more vulnerable to catastrophic events than their peasant counterparts are. For the most part, peasant farmers can provide their families with food, clothing, and shelter. Most American farmers are completely tied to an elaborate marketing system. If their communication lines with the wider space economy (Figure 7.8) were cut, they would quickly run out of the essentials: fuel, spare parts, fertilizer and seeds, and store-bought food and clothing.

At the frontier of American farming is *agribusiness*, which is associated with the trend on the part of such giant food companies as Ralston Purina, General Mills, General Foods, Hunt-Wesson, and United Brands to control the whole food chain from "seedling to supermarket." The concept that describes the food companies' control of production, processing, and marketing is *vertical integration*. The promise of high profits and a favorable tax structure has also attracted nonfood companies to move into food production. These companies include tractor firms, fertilizer and pesticide manufacturers, oil companies, and aircraft companies.

At the farm level, agribusiness is *capital intensive* and *energy intensive*. The very high per capita productivity results in rural farm depopulation. Although the family farm remains the basic unit in the American agricultural system, the direct role of agribusiness is increasing. The importance of corporate farming is growing in *market*

Marijuana use on

Campus Dwindles

The U.S. DEA reports that a *lid* (1 ounce) of marijuana sold on American college campuses in 1994 for $300 to $400. In comparison, gold sold at $365 an ounce. The DEA estimates that approximately one-fourth of the American public has used marijuana at one time or another, and it is the most widely used illegal drug in history. In 1975, the DEA reported that 35% of all college-age students used marijuana at least once a month; by 1994 the figure slipped to 10%, partly because of a flood of information citing marijuana as an agent that kills brain cells. According to the theory of supply and demand, declining use levels should mean lower prices worldwide, especially in the United States.

However, the supply has been cut back at the same time that demand has dwindled. One reason for the reduction in supply is that law enforcement in Mexico and Central America has improved substantially, and thus the number of acres devoted to marijuana has declined precipitously. Another reason is that more lucrative forms of illegal drugs can now be produced, most notably cocaine. Because producers have shifted to these more lucrative forms of drugs, the marijuana supply has dwindled, as shown in the diagram. Marijuana is also comparatively bulky, so a cargo of marijuana leaves is easier for authorities to identify than highly valued, much smaller compartments of cocaine. The interception of marijuana smugglers at the border and on the high seas has improved substantially as a result of the efforts of the Border Patrol and the Coast Guard. Therefore, how can we explain the high price of pot on campus? The answer is simply this: Supply has dwindled faster than demand.

Marijuana use on campuses across America. The use of marijuana on college campuses in 1975 was much more prevalent than it is today. Three reasons account for the reduction in marijuana use on campus. First, the supply in 1994 was less than the supply in 1975 because the U.S. Drug Enforcement Agency (DEA) has been successful in reducing the acreage devoted to marijuana production in such countries as Colombia and Mexico. In addition, the Border Patrol, the Coast Guard, and other government agencies have been more successful in intercepting contraband drug flow into America. These factors have reduced the supply substantially. Second, valuable and undetectable lands devoted to the growth of illicit drugs have been converted to coca leaf production, which is more profitable per unit area. Third, new evidence from the U.S. Surgeon General's office suggests that marijuana can cause reproductive damage and brain damage. For these reasons, both the supply and the demand have declined. Therefore, the quantity demanded on campus is less, but the price is higher.

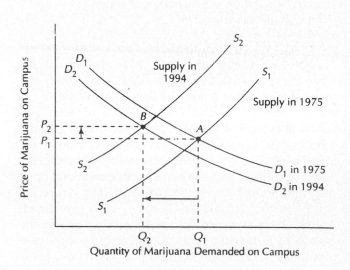

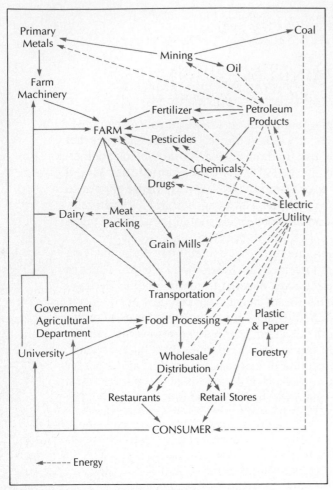

FIGURE 7.8
The structure of the U.S. agricultural system.
(Source: Knight and Wilcox, 1976, p. 23.)

gardening, which is sometimes called *truck farming*. Modern food-production truck farms specialize in intensively cultivated fruits, vegetables, and vines, and they depend on migratory seasonal farm laborers to harvest their crops. Other examples of modern food production include poultry ranches and egg factories. Agribusiness has also extended livestock farming immensely. At one time, livestock farming (for example, in western Iowa) was associated with a combination of crop and animal raising on the same farm. In recent years, livestock farming has become highly specialized. An important aspect of this specialization has been the growth of factorylike feedlots, where companies raise thousands of cattle and hogs on purchased feed. Feedlots are common in the western and southern states, in part because winters there are mild. These feedlots raise more than 60% of the beef cattle in the United States.

American corporate farming is also extending over-

seas to become a worldwide food-system model. Family farming is still dominant in Western Europe, but beef feedlots are found in the Italian Piedmont. Poultry-raising operations in Argentina, Pakistan, Thailand, and Taiwan are like those in Alabama or Maryland. Enterprises such as United Brands, Del Monte, Unilever, and Brooke Bond Oxo are diverting more and more food production in underdeveloped countries toward consumers in developed countries.

U.S. COMMERCIAL AGRICULTURE: CROPS AND REGIONS

The main characteristic of *commercial agriculture* is that much of it is produced for sale off the farm, at the market. Commercial agricultural areas include the United States and Canada, Argentina and portions of Brazil, Chile, Europe, the former Soviet Union countries, South Africa, Australia, New Zealand, and portions of China.

Following are some of the characteristics of commercial agriculture:

1. Populations fed by commercial agriculture are normally nonfarm populations who are living in cities and engaged in other types of economic activity, such as manufacturing, the services, and information processing.

2. Only a small proportion of the countries' population is engaged in agriculture. We saw, in Chapter 3 (Figure 3.27), that in the United States less than 2% of the population is engaged in agriculture, and this figure is less than 1% in some European countries.

3. Machinery, fertilizers, and high-yielding seeds are used extensively.

4. Farms are extremely large and the trend is toward even larger farms.

5. Agricultural produce from commercial agriculture is integrated with other agribusiness, and a vertical integration exists that stretches from the farm to the table.

Let us look more closely at the last four points just mentioned.

Commercial Agriculture and the Amount of Farmers

The percentage of laborers in developed countries working in commercial agriculture is less than 5% overall. In contrast, in some portions of the developing world where intensive subsistence agriculture is practiced,

Corporate farming in the United States. (Top) One of the 120 employees watches a television monitor to see when a truck is in position to receive its load of computer-calculated feed ingredients at the Montfort feedlot in Greeley, Colorado. She will then release the ingredients into the truck and tell the operator by radio which pen gets the feed. (Bottom) Trucks mix the feed on the way to 265 separate feeding pens. The pens hold about 100,000 head of cattle at any one time, a number 400 times greater than that required for efficient energy and resource use.
(Source: USDA photos by Michael Lawton.)

90% of the population is directly engaged in farming, and the average is 60% overall. Today, America's farmer can produce enough food for his family and 70 other families (see Table 7.4).

In 1990, the United States had approximately 2 million farms, compared with 5.5 million in 1950 (Figure 7.9). This reduction in the number of farm families as a percentage of the population is a result of *push factors* and *pull factors. Push factors* are economic factors (such as the high cost of equipment) that push families off the farms. *Pull factors* include the advantages of urban life in America, in Europe, and in other developed countries. The opportunity for college education, specialized occupations in the services, finance, insurance, real estate, and telecommunications has lured farm children off the land. The attraction of these alternatives is the promise of a higher standard of living and a shorter working day. However, according to the 1990 census, for the first time in American history more people have moved from the cities to the countryside. But most of these urban-to-rural migrants have moved to enjoy a relaxed pace of life and retirement, not the arduous

The development of the center-pivot irrigation system in the 1950s enabled large-farm operators to transform huge tracts of land in sandy and/or dry regions of the United States into profitable cropland. Here, alfalfa is being irrigated in Montana.
(Source: USDA-SCS photo by Tim McCabe.)

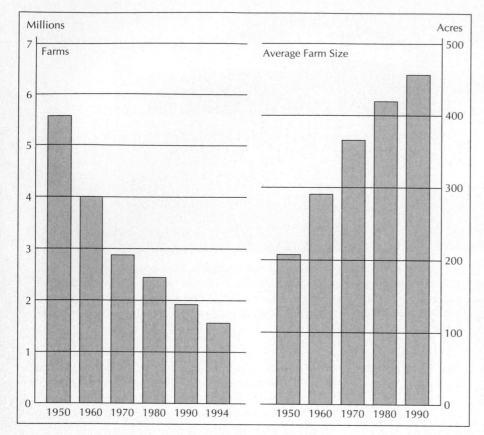

FIGURE 7.9
The number of U.S. farms compared with the average farm size. For the last 40 years, the number of U.S. farms has decreased by almost two-thirds, to approximately 2 million. At the same time, the average farm size has increased two and one-half times from 200 acres to almost 500 acres.
(Source: U.S. Bureau of the Census, 1994, p. 241.)

work of the farm. One serious problem in the United States, and a push factor, is the encroachment of the metropolitan area onto the best farmland, directly adjacent to the urban area. Suburban sprawl, brought by interstate highways that reduce the commute and penetrate into the flat countryside, has usurped viable topsoil and farmland around Los Angeles, Chicago, Amsterdam, Paris, and Buenos Aires.

Machinery and Other Resources in Farming

The second aspect unique to commercial agriculture, besides the small percentage of farmers in the population, is the heavy reliance on expensive machinery, tractors, combines, trucks, diesel pumps, and heavy farm equipment, all amply fueled by petroleum and gasoline resources, to produce the large output of farm products. To this has been added miracle seeds that are hardier than their predecessors and that produce more impressive tonnages. Commercial agriculture is also fertilizer intense. Improvements in farm-to-city transportation have resulted in less spoilage. Products arrive at the canning and food-processing centers more rapidly than they did in previous generations. By 1850, the farm was well connected to the city by rail transportation. More recently, the motor truck has supplanted rail transportation, and the advent of the refrigerator car and the refrigerator truck means that freshness is preserved. Cattle also arrive at packing houses by motor truck as fat as when they left the farm, unlike 100 years earlier, when long cattle drives were the order of the day, connecting cattle fattening areas in Texas, Oklahoma, and Colorado with the Union-Pacific rail line, stretching from St. Louis to Kansas City to Denver.

Agricultural experiment stations are now part of every state and are usually connected with land-grant universities. These stations have made great strides and improvements in agricultural techniques, not only in improved fertilizers and hybrid plant seeds, but also in hardier animal breeds and new and better insecticides and herbicides, which have reduced pestilence. For example, conquering the boll weevil in the 1940s tripled cotton production and yields. In addition, local and state government farm advisors can provide information about the latest techniques, innovations, and prices so that the farmer can make wise decisions concerning what should be produced, when it should be produced, and how much should be produced.

Harvesting wheat by combine in the United States exemplifies capital- and energy-intensive agriculture. Grain, such as the wheat shown here, is often a major crop on most farms. Commercial grain agriculture is different from mixed crop and livestock farming in that the grain is grown primarily for consumption by humans, rather than by livestock. In developing countries, the grain is directly consumed by the farm family or village, whereas in commercial grain farming, output is sold to manufacturers of food products.
(Source: USDA photo by Doug Wilson.)

Commercial Agriculture and the Size of Farms

Commercial agriculture has a scale economy associated with it. In 1990, the average farm in the United States encompassed nearly 500 acres (Figure 7.9), and this size is increasing. This increase means that a lower production cost per acre is expended on a larger farm. Although the productivity per acre is not as high as that of small farms, the difference between cost and revenue is highest for large farms. In the United States, 90% of the farmers own their farms; the remaining 10% of farms are absentee agribusiness and incorporation farms. On the other hand, in France, the United Kingdom, and Canada, only 50% of the farmers own their farms.

Large farm equipment such as tractors, combines, threshers, pickers, and reaping devices are most efficient when they can run long hours over flat terrain on extremely large farms. Because the equipment is so expensive, farming today is a capital-intensive activity. The need for so much capital also helps to push farmers out of business. Frequently a farmer needs a large piece of equipment but cannot use it intensively enough to amortize it or pay for its value.

Farms and Their Relationships with Other Businesses

Farming in the developed world is an agribusiness venture. Large food-processing companies, such as General Mills, General Foods, Ralston Purina, and Camp-

bell, purchase most of the farm products directly from the farmer. Therefore, the farmer is integrated into a large variety of economic activity, which features inter-industry cooperation to provide food to the tables of not only Americans, but also other citizens of the world. These activities include food transportation, processing, canning, packaging, inspection, sorting, storing, wholesaling, and retailing. However, agribusiness includes capital goods production as well, including fertilizer producers, seed producers and distributors, tractor and combine manufacturers, and energy companies.

TYPES OF COMMERCIAL AGRICULTURE

James Rubenstein (1994) divides commercial agriculture into six main categories: mixed crop and livestock farming, dairy farming, grain farming, cattle ranching, Mediterranean cropping, and horticulture and fruit farming (see Figure 7.5).

Mixed Crop and Livestock Farming

Mixed crop and livestock farming is the principal type of commercial agriculture, and it is found in Europe, Ireland, Russia, Ukraine, North America (west of the Appalachian Mountains and east of 100° west longitude), South Africa, central Argentina, eastern Australia, and New Zealand.

The primary characteristic of mixed crop and live-

In Indonesia, harvesting rice is an example of labor-intensive peasant culture.
(Source: World Bank.)

stock farming is that the main source of revenue is livestock, especially beef cattle and hogs. In addition, income is produced from milk, eggs, veal, and poultry. (See Figure 7.10.) Although the majority of the farmlands are devoted to the production of crops such as corn, most of the crops are fed to the cattle. Cattle fattening is a way of intensifying the value of agricultural products and reducing bulk. Because of the developed world's dependence on meat as a major food source, mixed crop and livestock farmers have fared well during the last 100 years. However, widespread acceptance of the heathfulness of the low-fat diet may affect this type of farming in the future.

In developed nations, the livestock farmer maintains soil fertility by using a system of crop rotation in which different crops are planted in successive years. Each type of crop adds different nutrients to the soil. The fields become more efficient and naturally replenish themselves with these nutrients. Farmers today use the *four-field rotation system*, wherein one field grows a cereal, the second field grows a root crop, the third field grows clover as forage for animals, and the fourth field is fallow, more or less resting the soil for that year.

Most cropping systems in America rely on corn (Figure 7.11) because it is the most efficient for fattening cattle. Some corn is consumed by the general population in the form of corn on the cob, corn oil, or even margarine, but most is fed to cattle or hogs. The second most important crop in mixed crop and livestock farming regions of central North America and the eastern Great Plains is the soybean. The soybean has more than 100 uses, but it is used mainly for animal feed. In China and Japan, tofu is made from soybean milk and is used as a major food source. Soybean oil is also used. Children with galactosemia must drink soy milk to avoid the lactic acid in cow's milk.

Dairy Farming

Dairy farming accounts for the most farm acreage in the northeastern United States and northwestern Europe. It also accounts for 20% of the total value of agricultural products from commercial agriculture. Ninety percent of the world's milk supply is produced in these few areas of the world. Most milk is consumed locally because of its weight and perishability. Figure 7.12 shows the distribution of milk production in the world.

Dairy farming is an intensive land-use activity, as the von Thünen model, discussed later in this chapter, shows. Because milk is heavy and highly perishable, dairy farms are near cities, and the milk is trucked into the cities daily. The area around the city from which milk can be shipped in daily without spoilage is known as the city's *milkshed* region. Most farms in Australia, New Zealand, Europe, and North America are within the milkshed of a consuming city because of the rapid transportation of refrigerated trucks on interstate highways and railroad cars on railroad lines.

Some dairy farms produce butter and cheese as well as milk. In general, the farther the farm is from an urban area, the more expensive the transportation of fluid milk, and the greater proportion of production in more *high value-added* commodities, such as cheese and butter. For example, the Swiss have discovered ways of concentrating their milk products into high value-added chocolates, cheeses, and spreads that are distributed worldwide. These processed products are not only lighter, but also less perishable. On the other hand, in the United States, the proximity of farms to Boston, New York, Philadelphia, Baltimore, and Washington, DC, on the East Coast, and to Chicago and Los Angeles in the Midwest and West mean that these farms primar-

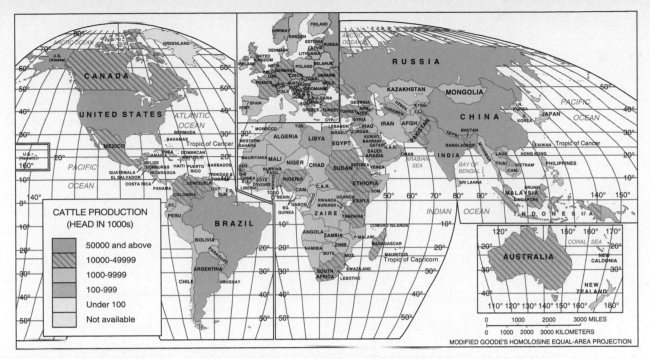

FIGURE 7.10

World beef and veal production. The developed countries produce the most beef and veal products because a large amount of the grain crops can be fed to cattle to fatten them. Poorer nations must consume all available food supplies directly or use them as revenue-producing exports. The United States, western Europe, the former Soviet Union, Brazil, Argentina, and Australia are the leading producers of beef and veal worldwide. (See Color Insert 2 page 2.2 bottom, for more illustrative map.)

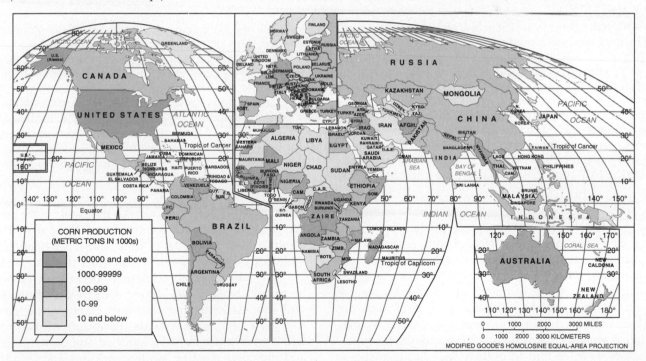

FIGURE 7.11

World corn (maize) production. Corn was domesticated in Central America more than 5000 years ago and exported to Europe in the fifteenth century. The United States accounts for more than 30% of the world's corn production. Ninety percent of this corn crop is fed to cattle and livestock for fattening and meat production. Outside the United States, corn is called maize. China is the second-leading producer of corn, but in this case, the majority of the crop is consumed by humans. Because meat produces a greater market value per pound than selling corn does, U.S. farmers convert corn into meat by feeding it to livestock on farms and feedlots. In the United States, the Corn Belt is also the livestock region of North America, and it is located in the western Midwest and the eastern Great Plains, centered on the state of Iowa. Argentina and Brazil, as well as Europe, also have sizable corn-production areas. (See Color Insert 2 page 2.3, top, for more illustrative map.)

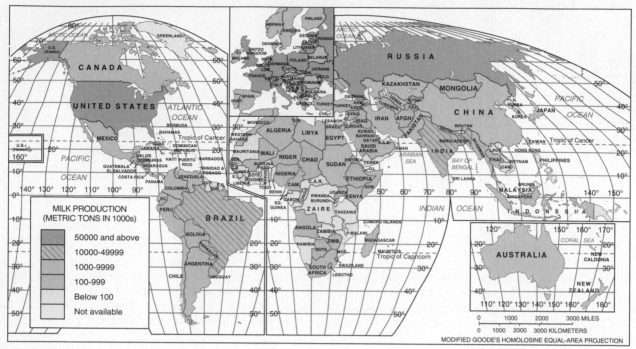

FIGURE 7.12

World milk production. There is a high correspondence between levels of economic development and the amount of per capita fluid milk production. Dairy farms are expensive to operate; thus, milk is a luxury in most areas of the world. Note Africa's paucity of milk production, except for South Africa. Most large cities of developed countries have milk production close by because of its heavy weight and perishability. Dairy farms exist further away from large cities, but in these cases most milk products are converted to less perishable and less heavy commodities, such as cheese and butter. For example, almost all the milk produced in Wisconsin is converted to cheese and butter, while 99% of the milk produced in Pennsylvania and New York is for direct fluid milk consumption. Countries such as New Zealand that are noted for specialized milk commodities but are a distance from the world's market, must also convert the majority of their milk products into less perishable forms in order for it to be shipped to the world markets. New Zealand, for example, produces only 5% liquid milk from its dairy products, compared to 70% for the United Kingdom. (See Color Insert 2 page 2.3, bottom, for more illustrative map.)

ily produce fluid milk. Farms throughout the remaining areas of the United States primarily produce butter and cheese. For example, only 10% of dairy farms in Wisconsin produce fluid milk because of their distance from the market, whereas only 10% of New York and Pennsylvania farms produce butter and cheese because of their proximity to Philadelphia, New York and the northeastern seaboard, Pittsburgh, and Detroit. Worldwide, remote locations such as New Zealand, for example, devote three-fourths of their dairy farms to cheese and butter production, whereas three-fourths of the farms in Great Britain, with a much higher population density at close proximities, produce fluid milk.

The cow is an amazing conversion machine that produces large amounts of consumable food products that are vitamin and protein rich. Certain types of cows, such as the holstein, produce enormous quantities of milk twice daily. Other types of cows, such as the jersey,

produce lower but richer quantities of milk with more cream. Most dairy farms have a variety of cows that produce both high-quality milk and large quantities. Frequently the milk is mixed to produce the best results.

Dairy farms are labor intensive because cows must be milked twice a day. Most of this milking is done with automatic milking machines. However, the cows still must be herded into the barn and washed, the milking machines must be attached and disassembled, and the cows must be herded back out and fed. The difficulty for the dairy farmer is to keep the cows milked and fed during winter, when forage is not readily available and must be stored.

Grain Farming

Commercial grain farms are usually in drier territories that are not conducive to dairy farming or mixed crop and livestock farming. Most of the grain, unlike

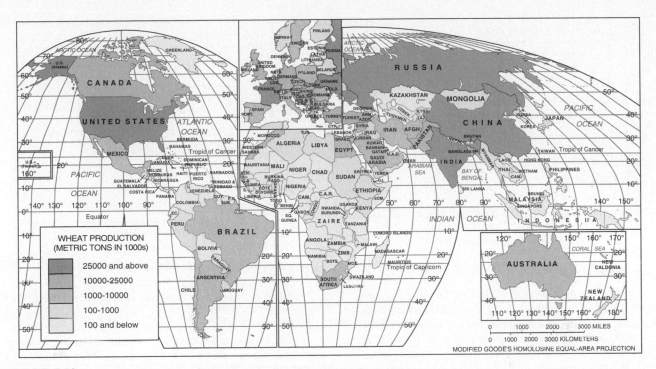

FIGURE 7.13
World wheat production. The United States, Canada, Australia, and Argentina are the primary wheat exporters, whereas the former Soviet Union countries, especially Kazakhstan, and India and China import the most wheat. China is the world's leading wheat producer, followed by the former Soviet Union and the United States.

Wheat can be stored in grain elevators. Therefore, current wheat prices worldwide reflect not only growing conditions for that year, but also supplies from commercial and subsistence operations that have been stored throughout the World. (See Color Insert 2, page 2.4, top, for more illustrative map.)

the products of mixed crop and livestock farms, is produced for sale directly to consumers. Only a few places in the world can support large grain-farming operations. These areas include China, the United States, Canada, the former Soviet Union, Argentina, and Australia (Figure 7.13). Wheat is the primary crop and is used to make flour and bread. Other grains include barley, oats, rye, and sorghum. These grains are less perishable than fluid milk or corn and can be shipped long distances. Of the group, wheat is the most highly valued grain per unit area and is the most important for world food production. Figure 7.14a shows that grain yield and production have increased markedly in developing countries between 1970 and 1990, while cropland area has increased only slightly. However, production per capita is much more disappointing in developing countries (Figure 7.14b). Africa is declining.

In the United States, the Spring *Wheat Belt* is west of the mixed crop and livestock farming area of the Midwest and is centered in Minnesota, North Dakota, South Dakota, and Saskatchewan (Figure 7.15). Another region, just south, near the 100th parallel of longitude, is the Winter Wheat Belt, which is centered in

Kansas, Colorado, and Oklahoma. Because winters are harsh in the Spring Wheat Belt, the seeds would freeze in the ground, so instead *spring wheat* is planted in the spring and harvested in the fall: the fields are fallow in the winter. *Winter wheat,* however, is planted in the fall and moisture accumulation from snow helps fertilize the seed. It sprouts in the spring and is harvested in early summer.

Like corn-producing regions, wheat-producing areas are heavily mechanized and require high inputs of energy resources. Today the most important machine in wheat-producing regions is the combine, which not only reaps but also threshes and cleans the wheat.

Large storage devices called *grain elevators* are the most prominent landscape feature as one traverses the Great Plains of America and Canada. Major cities in the Great Plains, such as Minneapolis and St. Paul, built their fortunes off flour milling and distribution.

Wheat is the international commodity because it leads the list of world food products that are transported between nations. The United States and Canada are the leading export nations for grains and together account for 50% of wheat exports worldwide. Although the large

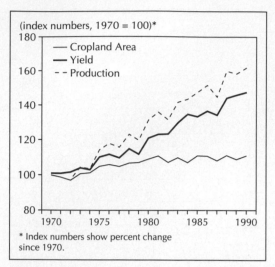

FIGURE 7.14a

The world's output of major food crops has increased dramatically during the last 20 years. The most dramatic increase has been in cereals, from 1.3 billion metric tons in 1970 to almost 2 billion metric tons in 1990. Milk, meat, fish, fruit, and vegetables have also made gains in production worldwide.

In the last 20 years, every region of the world has increased production. Most notable has been the Asian centrally planned economies, which have doubled their production, whereas the Near East and Latin America have produced a 60% to 80% increase. Production in Africa has increased more than 40 percent during the last 20 years, even though the per capita production has decreased. The figure shows that the index of grain production has increased substantially during the last 20 years primarily as a result of an increase in yields, instead of an ever-increasing cropland.
(Source: World Resources, 1992–1993. A Guide to Global Environment, 1992, p. 95.)

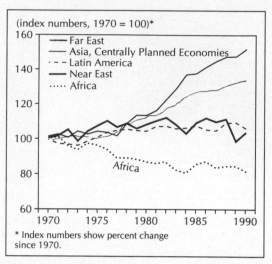

FIGURE 7.14b

Index of per capita food production in developing regions, 1970–1990. While the index of grain production and yields in developing countries showed notable increases between 1970 and 1990, the prognosis is much poorer when one includes the effect of population growth. As this figure indicates, African countries showed a per capita decline in food production, with the worst declines occurring in Angola, Botswana, Gabon, Mozambique, Rwanda, and Somalia. Sudan also fell dramatically. As discussed in Chapter 6, many factors contribute to these fluctuations, including inadequate rain fall, plunging world prices, ethnic unrest, and civil war.
(Source: World Resources, 1992–93, p. 568.)

grain trade agreements between the United States and the Soviet Union in the early 1970s are no longer in effect, the North American wheat-producing areas have been appropriately labeled the *world's breadbasket* because they still provide the major source of food to many deficit areas of the world, including the starving nations of Africa.

Cattle Ranching

Cattle ranching is practiced in developed areas of the world where crop farming is inappropriate because of aridity and lack of rainfall. Cattle ranching is an extensive agricultural pursuit because many acres are

needed to fatten cattle. In some instances, cattle are penned near cities, and forage is trucked to these cattle-fattening pens, which are called *feedlots*.

Amerindians and native Americans were agriculturalists and hunters, not cattle ranchers. America received its first domesticated cattle from the Iberian Peninsula as a result of the second voyage of Christopher Columbus and the succeeding voyages of other explorers (Rubenstein, 1992). Animal husbandry was part of these explorers' cultures, so cattle ranching was introduced to the New World and was successful because of the hardiness of the animals and the large, extensive areas of rangeland.

Major cities grew up across the western United States because of the services provided by their slaughter-houses and stockyards. Denver, Dallas, Kansas City, and St. Louis are examples. If a cattleman could get a steer to one of these cities, it was worth ten times as much

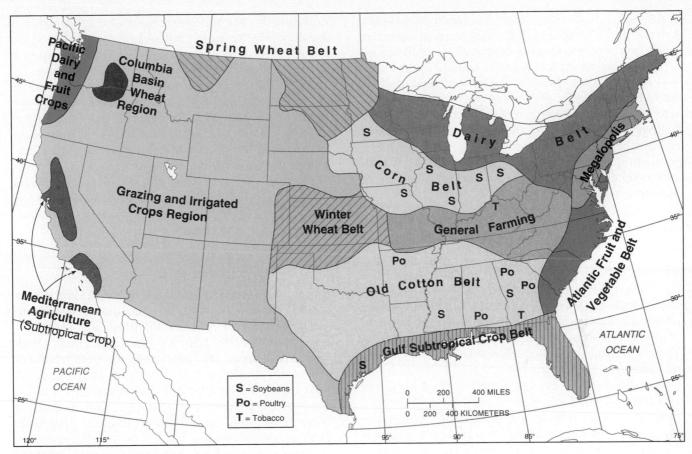

FIGURE 7.15
Major agricultural regions of the United States.

as the $5 it was worth on the range. Early American ranchers were not as concerned about owning territory as they were about owning heads of cattle. Consequently, the range was open and the herds grazed as they went toward market. Later, farmers bought up the land and established their perimeters with barbed-wire fences. Until about 1887, the ranchers cut the barbed-wire fences and continued to move their herds about wherever they pleased. However, after that point, the farmers seemed to win the battle, and ranchers were forced to switch from long cattle drives and wide territories of rangeland to stationary ranching. The land was divided according to the availability of water and the amount of rainfall. Farmers used the land that was productive for farm crops, such as grains and wheat, whereas the ranchers received the land that was too dry for farming. Rubenstein (1994) points out that, ironically, today 60% of cattle grazing occurs on land leased from the U.S. government. (Beef and veal production are shown in Figure 7.10.)

The most popular variety of beef cattle today is the Hereford. It was introduced from Europe, was not as hardy, and could not withstand the long, cold winters of the American Great Plains as well as the longhorn cattle that were first raised. However, the Hereford had a greater proportion of beef, and, if properly cared for with stockpiled forage in the winter, could produce a good profit to the rancher.

Today ranches in Texas and the West cover thousands of acres because the semiarid conditions mean that several acres alone are required to fatten one head of cattle. In addition, extremely large ranches are owned by meat-packing companies that can fatten the cattle, slaughter them, and package the meat all on the same ranch (see Figure 7.15).

South America, Argentina, Uruguay, and Brazil each have a major cattle-ranching industry (see Figure 7.5). These regions, as well as Australia and New Zealand, followed a similar pattern of cattle-ranching development. First, cattle were grazed on large, open, government tracks with little regard for ranch boundaries. Later, when a conflict with farming interests occurred, cattle ranches moved to the drier portions of the country. When irrigation first began to be used in the 1930s and 1940s, farms expanded their territory, and ranchers moved to even drier portions of the country and centered much of their herds on feedlots near railroads or highways directed toward the market. Today, ranching worldwide has become part of an agribusiness meat-processing industry and is vertically integrated with commercial ranching and the meat-distribution part of the same companies.

Mediterranean Cropping

The Mediterranean regions of the world grow specialized crops, depending on soil and moisture conditions. These regions include the lands around the Mediterranean Sea, the coastal lands of southern California, central Chile, South Africa, and southern Australia. In these regions, the summers are dry and hot, and the winters are mild and wet. All areas are located in the midlatitudes.

The Mediterranean Sea countries produce olives and grapes. Two-thirds of the world's wine is produced from the Mediterranean countries of Europe, especially Spain, France, and Italy. In addition, these countries and Greece produce the world's largest supply of olive oil for cooking. In these regions, wheat is also grown for the production of staple bread products and pasta.

In California, the crop mix is slightly different because of consumer demand and preference. Most of the land devoted to *Mediterranean agriculture* is taken up by citrus crops, principally oranges, lemons, and grapefruit. Nut trees, tomatoes, avocados, and even flowers are produced in the balmy Mediterranean climates of California. San Diego county alone produces 80% of the North American supply of poinsettias, for example (Stutz, 1993). Because of its high value-added Mediterranean crops, San Diego county ranked fifth in the United States in 1992 in value agricultural products. Similar products are grown in Chile, South Africa, and Australia. Australia also produces kiwifruit and the jojoba nut (see Figure 7.5).

Unfortunately for Mediterranean farmers, these areas of the world are some of the most prized for their wonderful climates. Northwestern Europeans have discovered the Mediterranean lands and turned them into a series of rivieras. The closest, and most expensive, is the French Riviera, centered on Nice. The next closest, and next most expensive, is the Italian Riviera, centered on Portofino. The Europeans have also discovered the less expensive Costa del Sol and Costa Brava in Spain and the Algarve in southern Portugal. Little discussion is necessary to describe the population pressure of tourism and the burgeoning growth of southern California. Ninety percent of the Chilean population lives in the Mediterranean lands in the central one-third of the country, centered on Santiago. Cape Town is the most desirable locale for South Africans from a climatic standpoint, and in Australia Adelaide shares the climatic abundance. Condominium projects, time-shares, and burgeoning suburban developments for major cities, especially Los Angeles, are rapidly dwindling our Mediterranean agricultural lands.

Horticulture and Fruit Farming

Because of taste and preferences and a severe winter season, there is a tremendous demand in the Eastern Seaboard cities of America for fruits and vegetables not grown locally. Shoppers in Philadelphia; New York; Washington, DC; Baltimore; and Boston are willing to pay dearly for *truck farm* fruits and vegetables, such as apples, asparagus, cabbage, cherries, lettuce, mushrooms, peppers, and tomatoes. Consequently, a horticulture and fruit-farming industry exists as close as possible to this portion of the United States, as temperature and soil conditions allow. Stretching from southern Virginia through the eastern half of North Carolina and South Carolina to coastal Georgia and Florida is the *Atlantic Fruit and Vegetable Belt* (Figure 7.15). This is an intensively developed agricultural region with a high value per acre. The products are shipped daily to the northeastern cities for direct consumption or for fruit and vegetable packing and freezing.

As in the case of Mediterranean agriculture and subtropical cropping in southern California, the Atlantic Fruit and Vegetable Belt of horticulture and truck farms relies on inexpensive labor. In California, the laborers are primarily from Mexico and Central America and enter the United States illegally. On the Atlantic Coast, the laborers are primarily from the Caribbean and Puerto Rico, and their immigration status is also often questionable. Inexpensive labor is one way for specialized agriculturalists to maintain their production in areas that are under pressure for urban growth and expansion. In southern California, the retirement and entertainment industries apply pressure, whereas on the Atlantic Coast, pressure results from relocated manufacturing plants from the Northeast and the incipient laborers and populations that they generate.

U.S. AGRICULTURAL POLICY

In the early days of America, farms were family owned, were small, and served local markets. In those days, farm prices were stable and predictable. Nature accounted for sudden weather changes and soil conditions, which led to price fluctuations. From time to time, a certain region of the country's farms enjoyed bumper crops; other times, it suffered through droughts.

More recently, farming has been highly mechanized and technological improvements have revolutionized agriculture. By the beginning of the twentieth century, farms had become much larger. An individual farm family could manage as many as a thousand acres with new mechanized equipment. More acres were cultivated and high yields were produced. With improved transportation to the markets and between countries, the American farmer now served a much wider market area. The early years of the twentieth century were fairly prosperous for farmers, especially during World War I, when American farmers provided a large amount of food for Allied troops and the rest of the nation worked to produce war material. However, many farmers lost their fortunes during the 1920s and 1930s with the Great Depression, and many farms ceased to operate. World War II created another upswing for agricultural pursuits as farmers once again provided food for a much larger army, the Western allies, and a hungry nation.

After the war, the farmers' fortunes dwindled in the 1950s and 1960s until the U.S. government agreed to major grain trade agreements with the Soviets. As a result of these agreements, farms prospered even more until the early 1970s. Since then, the national economy has slowed, and farms have felt the effect. At the same time, world markets for U.S. grain have dwindled as foreign countries have become better able to produce more of their own food. For example, as a result of Green Revolution technology, India, formerly a net food importer, is now a net food exporter. At the same time, the prices of farm operation—including machinery, fertilizer, land, and transportation—have increased drastically. These less profitable times for farmers, in which costs have outrun income, seem to be continuing into the 1990s. Compared with other sectors of the economy, the farm sector has faced higher operating costs and lower revenues and is a problem industry in America.

The Farm Problem in America

One reason that agricultural markets are currently in such desperate straits is that the demand for farm products is inelastic. Consumers do not demand more food when farm prices are low, so the reduction in price does not lead to a substantial increase in the quantity demanded. This phenomenon is coupled with the fact that the yield from American agriculture has increased manyfold during the last 100 years. Technological and mechanical improvements and hybrid seeds have increased yields more than anyone expected. These innovations make U.S. farm productivity the highest in the world. Finally, the quantity of farm products has increased much more rapidly than the demand has. These three factors have pushed down prices, as shown in Figure 7.16.

FIGURE 7.16
Falling U.S. agricultural prices. During the last 100 years, American farm production has burgeoned remarkably because of increased productivity, increased mechanization, and improved fertilizers, pesticides, and hybrid seeds. The U.S. farm supply in 1994 was substantially more than it was in 1950, despite the Soil Bank program and other methods used to keep land out of production. At the same time, because food is an inelastic commodity, demand has increased, but not as much as supply. The result has been increased quantities and reduced prices. There are more than enough agricultural commodities to supply America and export quotas.

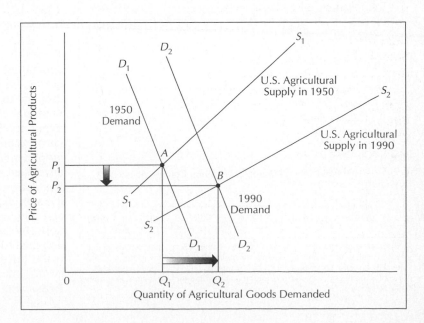

By looking at Figure 7.16, we see the three tendencies of American farming during the last 100 years: drastically increased supply, moderately increased demand, and falling prices. The result has been marginal returns to farm families and has spelled disaster for many farmers. With lower prices and increased quantities, more and more farmers cannot afford the rapidly rising costs for machinery, fertilizer, transportation, and labor. World farm prices have likewise fallen (Figure 7.17). The result to American farmers has been a continuing reduction in return for their investment. Considering our production possibilities curve (see Chapter 2, Figures 2.8 and 2.9), farmers should now move their productivity to another, more profitable industry. However, unlike a store that can change hands and change function, or a high-tech manufacturing plant that can change products, a farm is difficult to adapt to any new economic use. Besides farming, what else can a farmer do with a thousand acres of land in the middle of Nebraska?

There has been a large movement of farm families and farm labor away from the farm (Table 7.4). In 1910, 35% of the American population lived and worked on farms. By 1994, this figure had dropped to less than 1.5% of the total population. However, considering present production, prices, and consumption, we still have too many farmers in America today. In a normal market situation, resources would have shifted away from agriculture into other categories of economic use. However, because of American government price supports for farms, this has not been the case and there has been no movement along the production possibilities curve.

The U.S. Farm Subsidy Program

As early as 1933 Congress passed the Agricultural Adjustment Act to aid American farmers. This act was designed to help a large proportion of the population (as much as 33%) (see Table 7.4). The main foundation of this act was to artificially raise farm prices so that farmers could enjoy a "fair price," or *parity price*, for their products. A parity price was defined as "equality between the prices farmers could sell their products for, and the price they would spend on goods and services to run the farm." The parity period was from 1910 to 1914 when farm prices were relatively high in comparison with other products. Let us illustrate the concept of parity price: If in 1914 a farmer could sell a bushel of corn and with the income from it buy 5 gallons of gas, the ratio between the price of farm products and the consumer price index would be maintained into the future.

Since 1933, however, the parity ratio declined for farmers until 1990, when it was approximately 50% of the original 1914 parity established in 1933. In other words, without parity a farmer could sell products and purchase only 50% of what he or she could in the earlier period. As Figure 7.18 shows, real farm income, even in the short run, has been on a downward trend since

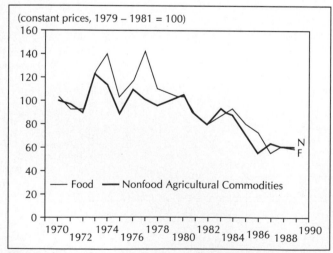

(constant prices, 1979 – 1981 = 100)

— Food — Nonfood Agricultural Commodities

Note: *Food commodities* include beverages (coffee, cocoa, tea), cereals (maize, rice, wheat, grain sorghum), fats and oils (palm oil, coconut oil, groundnut oil, soybeans, copra, groundnut meal, soybean meal), and other food (sugar, beef, bananas, oranges). *Nonfood agricultural commodities* include cotton, jute, rubber, and tobacco.

FIGURE 7.17
Trends in agricultural commodity prices. The trends in agricultural commodity prices show declines worldwide during the past two decades. Most farm prices have dropped to 60% of their 1970 levels. The decline in agricultural commodity prices has negatively affected many developing countries that base their economies on farm exports. This worldwide decline in farm commodity prices is a result of the inelasticity of food demand in developed nations, increased food supplies from Green Revolution techniques, and increases in food productivity, subsidies to producers in industrialized economies, and low income growth of farmers in developing nations. In the United States, for example, export subsidies designed to use farm overproduction abroad has kept world prices down by increasing the supply.
(Source: World Resources, 1992–1993, A Guide to Global Environment, 1992, p. 97.)

◼

Table 7.4

The Decline of the American Farm Population

Year	Farm Population (millions)	Farm Population as a Percentage of the Total Population
1910	32.1	35
1920	31.9	30
1930	30.5	25
1935	32.2	25
1940	30.5	23
1945	24.4	18
1950	23.0	15
1955	19.1	12
1960	15.6	9
1965	12.4	6
1970	9.7	5
1975	8.9	4
1980	7.2	3
1985	5.4	2
1987	5.0	2
1990	4.4	1.7

Source: Statistical Abstract of the United States and Economic Report of the President 1992, U.S. G.P.O. p. 69.

the high prices of the early 1970s during the Soviet grain trade agreements.

The federal government stepped in to establish a subsidy program, or a price floor. The government established price supports for key agricultural commodities. These supports were minimum prices that the government could assure farmers. The *price floor* is a guaranteed price above the market price. For example, the government bought all corn and wheat from farmers and sold it at what the market would bear. It stored many of these commodities in its own storage facilities. In 1994, the U.S. government offered farmers *target pricing*, which is similar to the price supports of the 1950s through the 1980s. With target pricing, the government pays directly to the farmer the difference between the market selling price and the target price that the government has set. The government no longer takes control of the product.

Figure 7.19 shows the effect of price supports on agricultural products. The subsidy process and its results are outlined next:

1. The market cannot arrive at an equilibrium price through its normal market mechanism.

2. Farmers produce a larger amount of surplus goods.

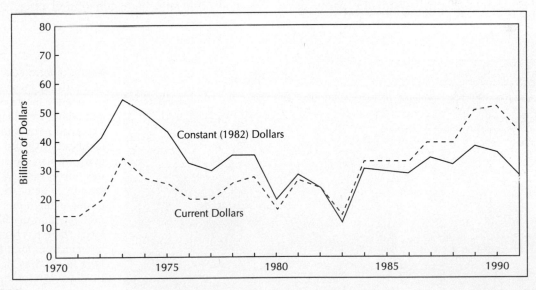

FIGURE 7.18

Net income of U.S. farmers, 1970–1991. According to the U.S. Bureau of the Census, the net income of American farmers during the last 21 years has been relatively flat, with a noticeable trough in 1983 and a major upturn in 1973. The upturn was related to grain trade agreements between the U.S. government and the then Soviet Union.
(Source: U.S. Bureau of the Census, 1992a, p. 107.)

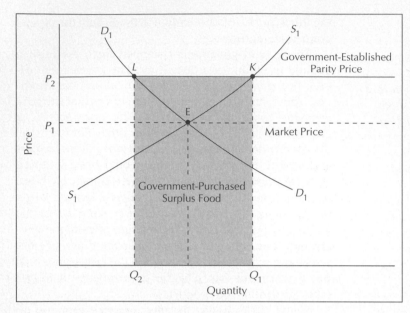

FIGURE 7.19
U.S. agricultural price supports. The U.S. government has supported farmers by establishing a parity price above the equilibrium price, according to supply and demand factors. For the last 60 years, the effect of the price support has been to establish prices higher than they would normally be, thus producing a surplus that the government was required to purchase with tax dollars. The market cannot obtain an equilibrium at E because surplus goods are produced and too often wasted. The farmers' incomes are artificially raised, but buyers in the marketplace must pay more than the goods would warrant under normal conditions. Unfortunately, resources are artificially allocated and therefore misallocated as price shifts from P_1 to P_2, demand drops back to point L, while supply moves up to point K.

3. Buyers pay more than they would if market conditions prevailed.

4. Farmers' incomes are artificially raised by government subsidies.

5. Resources are poorly allocated and some are wasted.

As shown in Figure 7.19, the parity price is established above the market price. With the parity price artificially high, farmers will supply the intersection of the price line and the supply curve at K for a total quantity of q_1. However, with higher prices, the consumers will demand q_2. The difference between q_1 and q_2 is the surplus that the government would purchase under the old price-support plan. Regardless of whether the subsidization is in the form of price supports or target pricing, the result is an extra cost to the taxpayer.

These price-support and target-price programs relegated artificially high agricultural prices to American

Nebraska farm auction. Because of drastically increased supply, moderately increased demand, and falling world farm prices, margined returns to farm families has spelled disaster for many farmers. Auctions, such as this one in Nebraska, allows farmers to liquidate in hopes of raising enough money to cover mortgages on machinery and land. There has been a large movement of farm families and farm labor away from the farm. In 1910, 35% of the American population lived and worked on farms; by 1994, this figure had dropped to 1% to 1.5%.
(Source: Andy Levin/Photo Researchers, Inc.)

agriculture for the last 40 years. The hope, of course, was that market prices would rise to parity, and they did during World War II and during the Soviet grain trade agreements of the early 1970s. However, most of the time the price of farm products was much less than the parity price. The government also attempted to reduce production with the *Soil Bank program*, which paid farmers to keep acreage out of production. Initially, this approach worked, but the per-acre yields increased amazingly and completely overshadowed the lost acreage in terms of total yield.

Unfortunately, the small American farmer as a cultural institution is an endangered species. For years, the government price-support programs kept inefficient farmers in business. Now, an even more terrible conclusion to the farm problem is resulting. It appears that the subsidy program has and continues to benefit the larger farmers, the agribusinesses, and not the small family farms as originally expected (Figure 7.20). In essence, the large corporate agribusiness farms have become richer, and, with their production and the lion's share of U.S. government subsidy, forced food prices even lower. This has, in effect, continued to force the small farmers off the land.

The obvious solution to America's farm problems is to design new uses for farm products that are not currently demanded in America. One example is an attempt to generate gasohol from corn and other agricultural products to fuel automobiles. A second use of the food surplus is *Food-for-Peace programs*, which allow agricultural surpluses to be distributed to starving nations in-stead of being liquidated or exterminated by dumping or destroying storehouses of food. Locally, the *food-stamp program* for America's poor operates off the large agricultural surplus.

Socialist Mode of Production

The former Soviet Union is one example of a country with a socialist system of agriculture. This mode of production is based on the labor theory of value, in which the state, representing peasants and workers, distributes wealth according to need rather than ownership of land, factories, or stores.

Before the Bolshevik Revolution, agricultural land consisted of a mixture of small peasant holdings and estates of the rich. The Communists subsequently organized the land into kolkhozes and sovkhozes in response to the poorly organized peasant holdings that they inherited from the Bolsheviks. *Kolkhozes* are collective farms resulting from the merger of land, livestock, and implements by peasants who delegate management to elected officials and derive their income from the proceeds of the operation. *Sovkhozes* are state-owned enterprises whose managers, workers, and employees are paid wages and salaries from a state budget on the basis of the type of work that they do. Sovkhozes are generally larger and better equipped than kolkhozes and tend to specialize. In 1980, the average size of a sovkhoz was 17,000 hectares compared with 6500 hectares for a kol-

FIGURE 7.20
The proportion of farms, the proportion of farm sales, and the percent of government support payments by farm size and dollar sales. Most American farms are small and produce small proportions of total farm sales. However, most government support payments go to large farms. With regard to farming and farm policy, the rich appear to be getting richer, whereas the poor, or small farms, who were the original focus of price supports, are getting relatively poorer and scarcer.
(Source: U.S. Bureau of the Census, 1993, p. 24.)

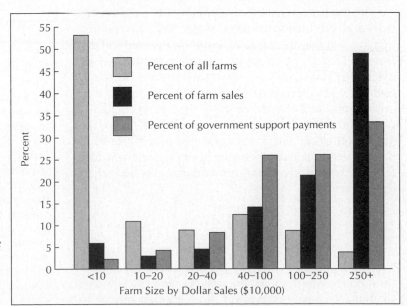

khoz. In the 1970s, cultivated land was fairly evenly divided between kolkhozes and sovkhozes. However, by 1980, sovkhozes represented nearly 70% of the total agricultural area. The government of the former Soviet Union intends eventually to convert the remaining kolkhozes into state farms that will be cultivated not by peasants, but by workers who will receive the same regard as their industrial counterparts.

Tiny private plots or, in official Soviet parlance, "personal subsidiary holdings" exist alongside the giant socialized farms. These plots consist of small gardens in which a typical collective farmer or state farm worker may keep a cow, a few pigs, and some chickens. The private plot helps compensate for the deficiencies of socialized farming in the labor-intensive operations of animal husbandry and fruit and vegetable production.

Compared with the transformation of Chinese agriculture, the organization of socialist agriculture in the former Soviet Union was not strikingly successful. Soviet agricultural achievements also were less impressive than their industrial accomplishments. Between 1930 and 1970, agricultural production increased by only 70% to 80%, whereas industrial output increased more than tenfold. According to Rhoads Murphy (1978), "[a major reason] agriculture has failed to match the gains of manufacturing and faced recurrent crises over food production has been the difficulty of changing archaic systems of land use in an immense country of nearly [285] million people. It has been much easier to change industrial techniques because there was less resistance to change, and fewer individuals, groups, or traditional regional structures were involved" (p. 172).

The former Soviet Union attempted to increase agricultural production in three ways: first, by opening up new, but mainly marginal, lands on the cold and dry fringes; second, by improving farming methods (e.g., irrigation) and crops (e.g., drought-resistant varieties); and third, by mechanizing, especially its wheat and other grain lands. None of these methods was totally successful. Aside from recurring weather problems, the food-production fiasco was attributed to a low level of past agricultural investments, to poor management, and to a lack of incentives for farm workers to increase their output.

SOVIET AGRICULTURAL POLICY

In the former Soviet Union, another type of agricultural policy was in effect. Prices were set artificially low so that all consumers would have enough money to purchase the food that they needed. The government fixed input and output prices, and these prices held for many years, bearing no relationship either to their economic value or to the prices that a free and competitive market would dictate. Such low prices meant that the demand was much greater than the supply. Consider, for example, Figure 7.21. The perfectly inelastic supply curve, S_1, is vertical in a command economy. In this case, agricultural products are provided at a particular price and quantity. Prices and supplies are set by government quotas. A normal demand curve slopes down to the right, as D_1 does in this figure. Given the inelastic supply S_1, the equilibrium price is p_3 at Point B. But, the new price is established by the government,

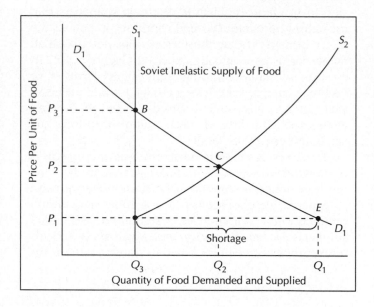

FIGURE 7.21
Soviet food price-fixing dilemma. The former Soviet Union's centrally planned economy tampered with food prices. An *inelastic supply* was established, shown by supply curve S_1. The government provided food at a particular price and quantity well below market equilibrium at Point C. The price was established at p_1 and, consequently, the demand increased to Point E. The amount supplied was shown at the intersection of S_2 and q_3. A massive shortage developed and resulted in long food lines and disgruntled populations. Not everyone who wanted to purchase food at the artificially low price could do so because of the shortage. Since the Soviet Unions collapse, prices have floated up to the equilibrium position at C. These prices are much higher than they were under the old system. The shortage has been reduced substantially, but prices have increased dramatically.

below the equilibrium price, at p_1. Food is available to everyone, even the poor. The problem is that demand now shifts far to the right, and not everyone who wants to purchase food at the artificially low price can do so because of the shortage. At p_1, the quantity demanded, q_1 at Point E, is much greater than the amount supplied. This explains the long lines and empty shelves for food items and many consumer products in the former Soviet Union.

It has been said, and aptly so, that one-third of a Russian's life is spent sleeping, one-third working, and one-third standing in line. From this type of pricing mechanism, black markets emerge, which provide people with food and other commodities at a higher quality, and the people need not stand in line. However, the goods are much higher priced. Since the Soviet economy collapsed, prices have necessarily floated up to an equilibrium position, which are much higher than they were under the former Soviet system. The new equilibrium position at C would be at the intersection of S_2 and D_1, with the price p_2 and the quantity q_2. Note that the shortage has been reduced substantially, but prices have increased.

The restructuring of the Soviet economy has a serious inflationary problem built in. In January 1992, Boris Yeltsin single-handedly decontrolled government prices in the Russian republic. This allowed prices to triple and quadruple overnight. He then had to adopt microeconomic policies to control hyperinflation so that people wouldn't rebel and revert to the old-guard Communist system. His decontrol was based on the idea that farms now going through a process of privatization would respond to higher market prices with greater incentives. Higher prices would mean more output and eventually a supply that would keep prices reasonable and ease the food shortages. However, privatization suggests that as farm prices rise dramatically produce and consumer goods are withheld in expectation of immediately higher prices in the future; therefore, shortages and social and political unrest result.

Comparison of the Three Systems of Production

We can make some general observations about peasant, capitalist, and socialist agriculture. The peasant system of production is the most efficient in terms of value of output per hectare. Capitalist agriculture, epitomized by American agribusiness, is the most productive, but it uses costly inputs. Finally, socialist agriculture, as in the former Soviet Union, is less efficient than peasant agriculture and less productive than capitalist agriculture.

RELATIVE LOCATION OF FARMS

🔲

Despite the growing importance of public companies and corporations, farming is still, for the most part, a family business. An important factor that shapes individual farmers' land-use decisions is the relative location or situation of a place in terms of its access to other places. Worldwide, the importance of situational components in agriculture increased as market exchange economies grew and developed. At one time, before commercial agriculture, a farmer's site relations—links with soil, sun, rain, and crops—were overwhelmingly important considerations in earning a living. Today, site relations have not ceased to be important; farmers still depend on the weather. However, site relations have weakened as farmers have been drawn increasingly into situational relationships, with transport lines between farms and the market linking them ever more strongly to a wider spatial economy.

VON THÜNEN'S MODEL

🔲

Relative location determines agricultural land use in several dimensions of space. The importance of relative location in rural land use was first discussed by Johann Heinrich von Thünen, a north German estate owner interested in economic theory and local agricultural conditions. From his experiences as an estate manager, he observed that identical plots of land (sites) would be used for different purposes, depending on their accessibility to the market (situation). The meticulous records that he kept provided a framework for his book, *The Isolated State*, which was published in 1826. Von Thünen's aim was to uncover laws that govern the interaction of agricultural prices, distance, and land uses as landlords seek to maximize their income. His methods in many ways constitute the first economic model of spatial organization; his conclusions continue to be discussed and debated by modern economic geographers.

The Law of Diminishing Returns and the Concept of Rent

Von Thünen's principles of agricultural land use are based on traditional economic theory. To understand his main ideas, we must first review two classical concepts: the law of diminishing returns and the concept of economic rent.

THE LAW OF DIMINISHING RETURNS

The *law of diminishing returns* relates to the situation that confronts farmers in the short run. It considers existing possibilities of managing land, labor, and capital inputs. It considers the state of technical knowledge as given and assumes no fundamental cost-reducing production changes. This law is as follows: As successive units of a variable input (say, labor) are applied to a fixed input (say, land), total product (output) passes through three stages. First, the total product increases at an increasing rate; second, it increases at a declining rate; third, it declines.

A standard example illustrates the principle of diminishing returns (Figure 7.22 and Table 7.5). Assume one fixed input (land) and one variable input (labor). Average productivity (AP) of labor is the total product (TP) divided by the number of labor units. Marginal productivity (MP) of labor is the addition to total output attibutable to the last labor input employed. Throughout Stage 1, marginal product exceeds average product. The intersection of the marginal-product curve with the average-product curve marks the end of Stage 1 and the beginning of Stage 2. During Stage 2, the marginal-product curve declines until it finally becomes zero. This marks the end of Stage 2 and the beginning of Stage 3.

Knowledge of total, average, and marginal productivity establishes some general boundaries for rational zones of agricultural production. If famers are trying to obtain a maximum return for their investments, they will never operate in Stage 1. The level of intensity is too low; that is, the amount of variable inputs (labor) per unit of land area is too small. Land is used too extensively. Farmers would want to take advantage of increasing returns to scale and add more variable inputs to intensify their operations. The boundary between Stages 1 and 2 is termed the *extensive margin of cultivation.*

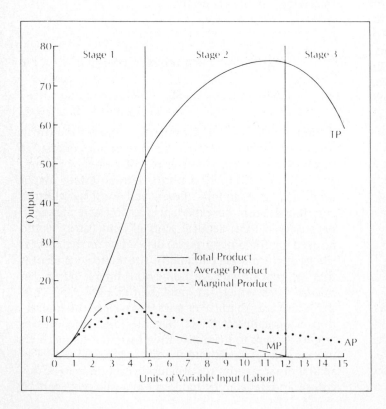

FIGURE 7.22

The stages of production and the law of diminishing returns. The *law of diminishing returns* confronts farmers in the short run in their attempt to manage land labor and capital inputs. As successive units of a variable input are applied to a fixed output, total product produced increases and then begins to decline. Efforts are now underway to change the law of diminishing returns through *biotechnology.* Biotechnology is about changing organic life—plants, animals, and even people, by manipulating the genetic code that determines physical quality and characteristics. Since the inception of the Green Revolution three decades ago, a number of genetically engineered seed stocks have been developed for corn and sunflowers that offer much better resistance to pests and disease and produce products within enhanced natural characteristics. The first gene-spliced tomato hit the supermarkets in 1993. It has an extended shelve life, resists softening, takes less water irrigation to produce, and is much tastier than conventional tomatoes. At LSU, biochemists are producing engineered potatoes, rice and cassava that will have the protein value of meat. Apples are now available that will not brown when exposed to air. Pest and frost-resistant fertilizers are now on the market and genetically engineered seeds for alfalfa plants have more protein and require less fertilizer. Biopesticides are also now being produced, which do not destroy the environment as do traditional chemical weapons. Pure bred calves are being produced from man-made embryos and thousands of high-quality identical items can be produced through cloning. Genetically altered cows in England are producing more milk with less feed. Will these biotechnological advances in agriculture be forthcoming on a large scale basis in time to save Africa?

Table 7.5
An Illustration of the Law of Diminishing Returns

Variable Input	Total Product	Average Product	Marginal Product	Stage of Production
0	0	0.00	0	
1	5	5.00	5	
2	16	8.00	11	1
3	30	10.00	14	
4	45	11.25	15	
5	55	11.00	10	_____
6	61	10.17	6	
7	66	9.43	5	
8	70	8.75	4	2
9	73	8.11	3	
10	75	7.50	2	
11	76	6.91	1	
12	76	6.33	0	_____
13	73	5.62	−3	
14	69	4.93	−4	3
15	60	4.00	−9	

Farmers who are trying to maximize their returns will also never operate in Stage 3. Obviously, no rational farmer will operate in the range in which additional units of labor decrease total production, causing negative marginal-product values. The boundary between Stages 3 and 2 is regarded as the *intensive margin of cultivation*. This leaves Stage 2 as the *zone of rational production*. In the real world, however, many enterprises—particularly large ones—operate successfully in Stage 3 because of government regulations, subsidies, and lack of true economic competition.

Radicals find fault with the law of diminishing returns. Given the law's assumption of profit maximization, they claim it to be tautological in that the conclusions are concealed in the definitions. Farmers, for example, hire workers as long as they produce a surplus above their wages. When the additional profit falls to zero (i.e., when the marginal product from the last unit of labor added equals zero), farmers stop adding workers. Radicals admit that the law shows farmers how to manipulate labor and capital to maximize profits but argue that in a capitalist society the law operates to the disadvantage of workers.

ECONOMIC RENT

The concept of economic rent is central to von Thünen's discussion of agricultural land use. *Economic rent* is a relative measure of the advantage of one parcel of land over another. More precisely, it is the difference in net profits between two units of land. Net profit per unit area of land is equal to the total value of production minus the total costs involved in bringing forth the product. Differential rents may result from variances in productivity of different parcels of land and/or variances in the distance from the market.

At the beginning of the nineteenth century, British economist David Ricardo (1912) presented the idea that rent variations result from the effect of physical factors on productivity. We can illustrate Ricardo's ideas of rent variations attributable to fertility conditions in a productivity schema for a spatially restricted area (Figure 7.23). As we move away from a crop's optimum physical conditions, costs per hectare increase and rents decrease. A cross section is drawn through the line *A-A'*. The side view is a space-cost curve, which graphs changes in cost across distance. Assume that the market

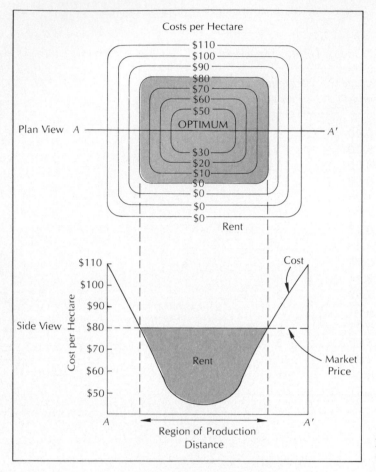

FIGURE 7.23
Optimal and marginal limits: the space-cost curve.

price of a crop is $80 for 1 hectare of production. In this imaginary case, limits of production are determined by the intersection of the market-price line and the space-cost curve. No production occurs outside the $80 isoline, but rent increases toward the optimum.

What happens if the market price for a crop rises to $100 because of increasing demand? (See Figure 7.24) Spatial margins to profitability (SMP) spread out. Previously submarginal land is brought into production, and higher-rent land is used more intensively. On the other hand, if the market price falls to $60, spatial margins to profitability draw back. Lower-quality land is abandoned, and superior-quality land is used less intensively.

Von Thünen provided an alternative view of economic rent. Holding land quality constant, he demonstrated that rent is the price of accessibility to the market. In other words, rents decline with the distance from a market center. Geographers often use the term *location rent* as opposed to *economic rent* to express the concept

of decline in rents with an increase in distance from the market.

The Isolated State

FEATURES OF THE ISOLATED STATE

To explain agricultural land use, von Thünen described an idealized agricultural region about which he made certain assumptions. He envisioned an isolated state with a large central city serving as the only marketplace. A uniform plain surrounded the city. The farmer used a single mode of transport—the horse and cart—to supply the market with produce. The farmers were price takers, who attempted to maximize their profits. There were no extraneous disturbances in this ideal landscape; social classes and government intervention were absent. In addition to these constraints, von Thünen introduced

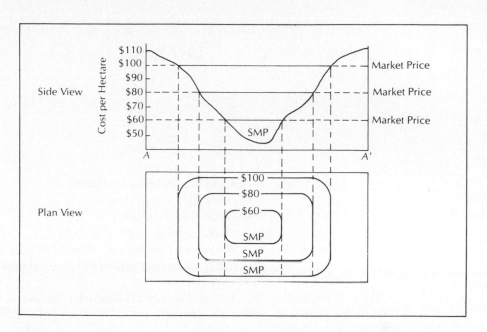

FIGURE 7.24
Spatial margins to profitability.

one variable: transport to the central town—its costs increased at a rate proportional to distance.

Von Thünen's conditions are not representative of actual conditions in the early nineteenth century or in this century. Indeed, von Thünen regarded the Isolated State as an Ideal State—the ultimate stage in the development of bourgeois society. In his view, this Ideal State represented a goal that humankind should strive toward. When it is attained, no further change is necessary. People live in a harmonious society free of exploitation.

THE PROBLEM

After stating his assumptions in *The Isolated State*, von Thünen posed the problem that he wanted to investigate:

The problem we want to solve is this: what pattern of cultivation will take shape in these conditions?; and how will the farming system of the various districts be affected by their distance from the Town? We assume throughout that farming is conducted absolutely rationally.

It is on the whole obvious that near the Town will be grown those products which are heavy or bulky in relation to their value and which are consequently so expensive to transport that the remoter districts are unable to supply them. Here also we find the highly perishable products, which must be used very quickly. With increasing distance from the town, the land will progressively be given up to products cheap to transport in relation to their value. For this reason alone, fairly sharply differentiated concentric rings or belts will form around the Town, each with its own particular staple product.

From ring to ring the staple product, and with it the entire farming system, will change; and in the various rings we shall find completely different farming systems. (Hall, 1966, p. 7)

Thus, Von Thünen suggested that in a landscape free from all complicating factors, locational differences were sufficient to produce a varied pattern of land use. After he observed the role of transport costs (See box on page 304) von Thünen relaxed his rigid assumptions and introduced other variables to see how they modified his ideal pattern of land use.

LOCATION RENT FOR A SINGLE CROP GROWN AT ONE INTENSITY

To illustrate von Thünen's concept of differential rent, let us assume an isolated state producing one commodity (say, wheat) grown at a single intensity on yield

LOCATION RENT

Location rent for any crop can be calculated by using the following formula:

$$R = E(p - a) - Efk$$

where: R = location rent per unit of land
E = output per unit of land
k = distance to the market
p = market price per unit of output
a = production cost per unit of land (including labor)
f = transport rate per unit of distance per unit of output

Thus, if we assume that a wheat farmer 20 kilometers from the market obtains a yield of 1000 metric tons/km^2, has production expenses of \$50/ton/km^2 to transport grain to the market, and receives a market price of \$100/ton at the central market, the location rent accruing to 1 square kilometer of the farmer's land can be calculated as follows:

$$R = 1000(\$100 - \$50) - 1000(\$1 \times 20)$$
$$= \$50,000 - \$20,000$$
$$= \$30,000$$

At 50 kilometers from the market, the location rent per square kilometer of land in wheat is \$0. Obviously, no rational farmer in a competitive market economy would grow wheat beyond 50 kilometers from the market.

---

per acre per year. Let us further assume that the market price of wheat is \$100 per hectare per year, that it costs every farmer in the state \$40 to produce a hectare of wheat, and that transport costs are \$5 for each hectare of wheat (Figure 7.25). Under these conditions, what would be the net profit per hectare for farmers located 0, 1, 6, and 12 kilometers from the market? Farmers adjacent to the market pay no transport costs; therefore, their net profits would simply be market price (\$100) minus production costs (\$40)—or \$60. Farmers 1 kilometer from the market pay \$5 in transport charges; thus, their net profits would be \$55. At 6 kilometers from the market, farmers would earn a net profit of \$30, and at 12 kilometers, net profits would be zero. Beyond 12 kilometers it would be unprofitable to grow a crop for the market. In this outer area, only subsistence cultivation could be pursued, and cash would have to be earned by migrant labor.

Our example has shown that farmers near the central market pay lower transport costs than farmers at the margin of production. Clearly, the net profits of the closer farmers are greater, and the difference is known as *economic rent*. Farmers recognize this condition, and they know that it is in their best interest to bid up the amount that they will pay for agricultural land closer to the market. Bidding continues until bid rent equals location rent. At that price, farmers recover production and transport costs, and landowners receive location rents as payments for their land. Competitive bidding for desirable locations cancels income differentials attributable to accessibility. The *bid rent*, or the trade-off of rent levels with transport costs, produces a spatial-equilibrium situation. It declines just far enough from the market to cover additional transport costs; hence, farmers are indifferent to their distances from the market.

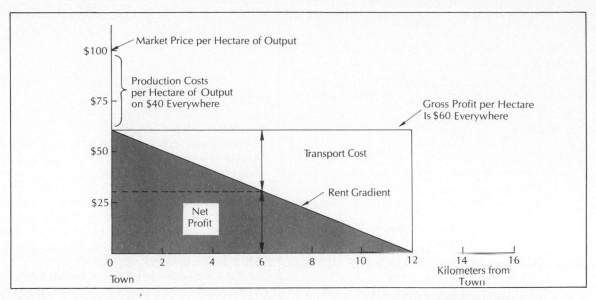

FIGURE 7.25
Net income from wheat production. Von Thünen suggested that the net income would decline with increasing distance from the town where the product had to be sold. Transportation costs would eat into the net income as one moved farther away from the town. In this example, production costs are $40.00 per hectare at every location, and the margin of profitability is 12 kilometers.

We can simplify Figure 7.25 by including production costs in a single expression with market price. This is illustrated in Figure 7.26a, which shows a rent gradient sloping downward with increasing distance from the central market. When the *rent gradient* is located around the market town, it becomes a rent cone, the base of which indicates the extensive margin of cultivation for a single crop grown at a single intensity (Figure 7.26b).

LOCATION RENT FOR A SINGLE CROP GROWN AT DIFFERENT INTENSITY LEVELS

Now let us suppose that wheat is grown at two intensity levels, reflecting two farming systems (Figure 7.27). The more intensive farming system has a steeper rent curve and is the most profitable system as far as 36 kilometers from the market. The less-intensive system is most profitable from 36 kilometers to the limits of wheat farming, at 70 kilometers. At the margin of transference, the location rent for the two farming systems is the same. Separation between more-intensive and less-intensive systems illustrates the principle of *highest and best use*.

According to this principle, land is used for the purpose that earns the highest location rent for its owner but not necessarily the highest wage for the workers.

LOCATION-RENT GRADIENTS FOR COMPETING CROPS

In von Thünen's analysis, patterns of agricultural land use form acccording to the principles of highest and best use as measured by the location rent at each distance from the market. Consider location-rent gradients for an isolated state in which farmers have three land-use choices: vegetable production, dairying, and beef production (Figure 7.28). A farmer close to the market could profitably carry on any one of the three activities, but which activity would maximize the farmer's income? Vegetable production has the highest rent-paying capability. All farmers seeking to maximize their incomes make the same decision: They grow vegetables between 0 and 10 kilometers from the market. Dairying is the choice between 10 and 25 kilometers, and beef production is the choice between 25 and 50 kilometers from the market. Beyond 50 kilometers, no commercial land use is feasible.

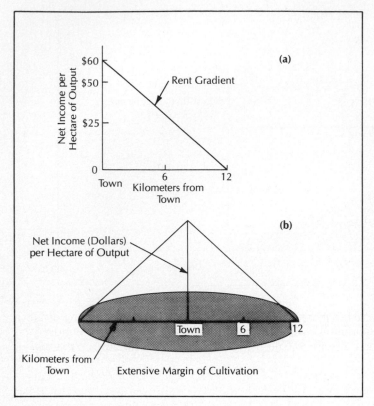

FIGURE 7.26
The rent gradient, when displayed in three-dimensions, becomes a rent cone or demand cone. Figure 7.28 shows rent gradients for competing crops according to Von Thunen's classic model. While rent gradients are the basis of land value, both in rural areas and within cities, the electronic intermodal marketplace has revolutionized buying and selling of goods and is blurring the Von Thunen rent gradient. Via computer, one is now able to access most any marketplace. Shipping services for any commodity are offered in the marketplace. Automatically, all of the shippers in the marketplace bid on the business. The client's computer analyzes the offers and automatically selects one option. At the least, offers are presented to the client and he or she decides on which option to take. The rest of the process is completely automatic. Production of shipping documents, intershipper coordination, customs clearance, billing, exchange of funds and fees, tracking of shipments, etc.

VON THÜNEN'S ORIGINAL CROP SYSTEM

In his theoretical Isolated State, von Thünen described six farming systems arranged in a series of concentric circles around the central city. The innermost zones produced perishable products (fluid milk and fresh vegetables) and heavy, bulky commodities in proportion to their value (fuelwood and lumber). On land most distant from the market, where transport costs were highest, land was used only for animal husbandry, which requires little investment but large amounts of

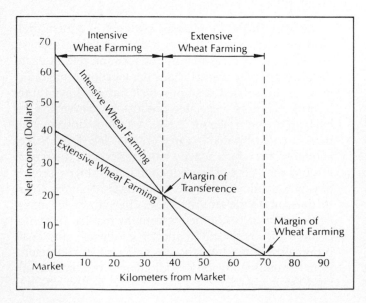

FIGURE 7.27
Rent gradient for a single crop grown at different intensities. Originally, financial transactions between individuals in time was the marketplace. Initially, all aspects of the business, offering to buy, to sell, recordkeeping, transactions, billing, analysis and knowledge of the market were manually produced. With the advent of *information technology*, every piece of the marketplace is now automated. The client interfaced with the marketplace is also completely electronic in the largest and most sophisticated cases. With artificial intelligence and rule-based decision-making, the client's trading decisions are made by computers and the complete transaction is initiated, confirmed and reported without any human intervention. This seemingness automatic purchase or sale of thousands of varieties of products that are bought and sold in the marketplace will be discussed further in Chapters 10 and 11.

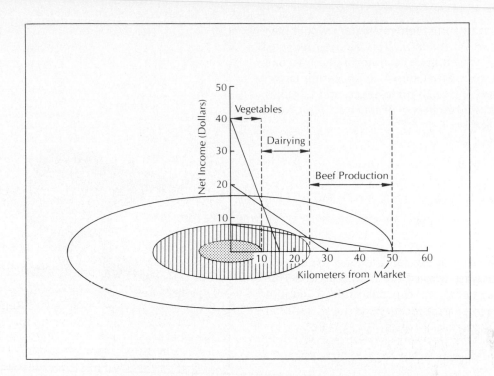

FIGURE 7.28
Location rent gradients for competing crops. Because of the different sloping bid rent curves based on market prices and transportation costs for various crops, the *highest and best use* and the highest level of net income will result from a combination of crops being grown at different distances from the market. Vegetables have the highest rent-paying ability because of their relatively high yield per hectare. Due to their weight, however, the bid rent curve drops off dramatically, as transportation costs eat into profits. Vegetables are the best choice, up to 10 kilometers from the market, beyond which dairying becomes a better choice. At approximately 24 kilometers from the market, dairying and its associated relatively heavy and perishable products become more expensive to ship than the less expensive beef production. From this point out to the margin of production at 50 kilometers, beef is the wisest choice. Beyond that point, no commercial land use is feasible.

space (livestock ranching). Between these inner and outer rings, agriculture consisted of intensive and extensive arable farming.

At first, it seems odd that von Thünen put a forestry zone close to the market. This arrangement does not fit with our image of reality. However, timber and fuel were in great demand in early nineteenth-century Germany. Consumers were not willing to pay high prices for items that were expensive to haul over long distances. The fact that patterns of agricultural land use in developed parts of the world in the late twentieth century differ from those of the early nineteenth century does not undermine von Thünen's methodology; they simply reflect higher levels of transport efficiency and time-space convergence (see Chapter 6).

MODIFIED PATTERNS OF AGRICULTURAL LAND USE

Von Thünen was acutely aware that many conflicting factors—physical, technical, cultural, historical, and political—would modify the concentric patterns of agricultural land use. He modified some of his initial assumptions—the transportation assumption, for example—to approximate actual conditions more closely. Although he retracted the condition of a single-market town, he did not elaborate on the effects of several competing markets and a system of radiating highways. We can presume, however, that the tributary areas of competing markets would have had a variety of crop zones enveloped by those of the principal market town and that a radiating highway system would have produced a "starfish" pattern. Von Thünen retracted other conditions as well, such as uniform physical characteristics, and considered other complicating factors such as the effects of foreign trade, taxes, and subsidies. He also emphasized the effect of distance on agricultural land use at all scales.

VON THÜNEN'S MODEL AND REALITY

◈

Does the intensity of agricultural land use and the price of land increase toward the market as von Thünen's model suggests? We can answer this question by examining agricultural locations at local, regional, national, and international scales.

Local Scale

Thünian effects at the local scale can be observed in the Third World, where localized circulation systems resemble those of early nineteenth-century Europe. Ronald Horvath (1969) found such a pattern of land-use around Addis Ababa, Ethiopia. Von Thünen's original farming system placed forestry in the second land-use ring, from which the city drew wood for building and fuel. Horvath described an inner wood-producing zone of eucalyptus forest that surrounded the Ethiopian capital (Figure 7.29). The zone was wedge-shaped rather than a ring, reflecting the greater accessibility to the city along major roads. Horvath also showed the expansion of the eucalyptus zone between 1957 and 1964, indicating transport improvements in the Addis Ababa area. The improvements permitted wood to be shipped to the city over increasingly greater distances and released more land near the city to be used for vegetable production. Horticulture was a major activity of the innermost ring in von Thünen's ideal schema.

Additional studies indicated distance-related adjustments in land use in the Third World. Piers Blaikie (1971) observed that small farmers in north India adjust land use to distance from their villages in order to reduce the total amount of work to be completed. Farmers living in these villages must walk to the land that is under cultivation; therefore, the greatest effort is applied

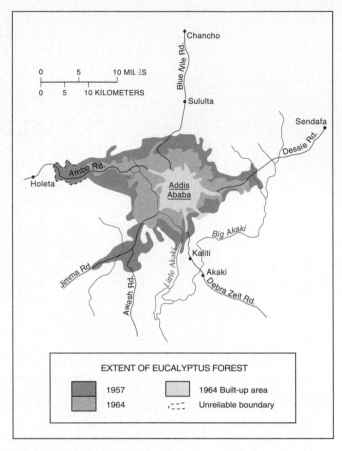

FIGURE 7.29
The forest zones surrounding Addis Ababa, Ethiopia. *(Source: Based on Horvath, 1969.)*

to land near the village, and farming becomes less intensive in the outlying fields (Figure 7.30).

Regional Scale

We have seen that Thünian production patterns exist at the local scale. But does von Thünen's model work at other scales? Let's move up the scale from the local level to the regional level, and take as our example the Whiskey Rebellion of western Pennsylvania farmers in 1794.

In the late eighteenth century, Eastern Seaboard cities—New York, Philadelphia, and Baltimore—were supplied with agricultural commodities by inland farm-

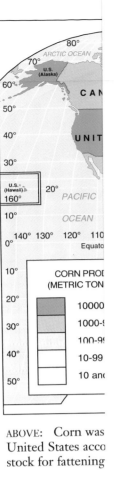

ABOVE: Corn was
United States acco
stock for fattening

BELOW: There is
tion. Dairy farms a
except for South A
and perishability.

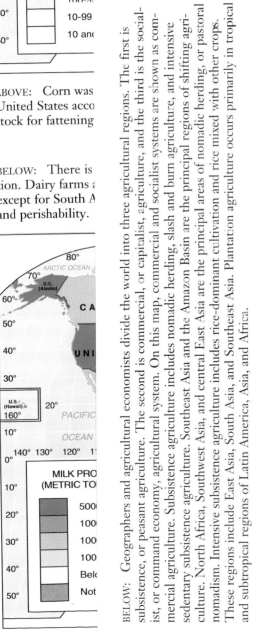

MILK PRO
(METRIC TO

5000
100
100
100
Belo
Not

BELOW: Geographers and agricultural economists divide the world into three agricultural regions. The first is subsistence, or peasant agriculture. The second is commercial, or capitalist, agriculture, and the third is the socialist, or command economy, agricultural system. On this map, commercial and socialist systems are shown as commercial agriculture. Subsistence agriculture includes nomadic herding, slash and burn agriculture, and intensive sedentary subsistence agriculture. Southeast Asia and the Amazon Basin are the principal regions of shifting agriculture. North Africa, Southwest Asia, and central East Asia are the principal areas of nomadic herding, or pastoral nomadism. Intensive subsistence agriculture includes rice-dominant cultivation and rice mixed with other crops. These regions include East Asia, South Asia, and Southeast Asia. Plantation agriculture occurs primarily in tropical and subtropical regions of Latin America, Asia, and Africa.

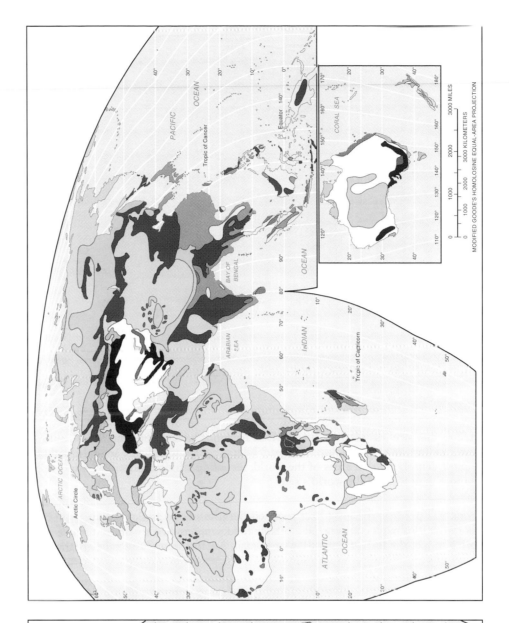

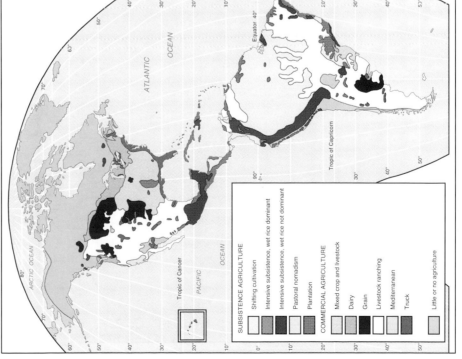

SUBSISTENCE AGRICULTURE
Shifting cultivation
Intensive subsistence, wet rice dominant
Intensive subsistence, wet rice not dominant
Pastoral nomadism
Plantation

COMMERCIAL AGRICULTURE
Mixed crop and livestock
Dairy
Grain
Livestock ranching
Mediterranean
Truck
Little or no agriculture

2.1

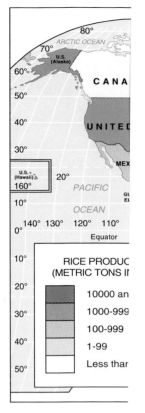

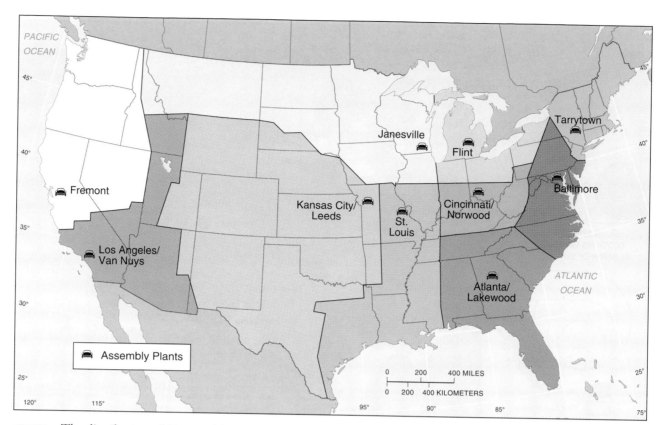

ABOVE: The distribution of 10 assembly plants across the United States in 1983 helped Chevrolet minimize the cost of distributing bulky products to consumers in each region. Recently, Chevrolet and other automobile manufacturers have reconcentrated their plants in the Midwest. Interior locations near Detroit are a result of the large increase in the variety of automobile models produced in North America. Automobile companies now operate a single assembly plant specializing in the production of one model for distribution throughout the United States and Canada, and therefore take advantage of scale economies.

BELOW: There has been a marked national shift from a disbursed coastal pattern during the last 20 years to a concentrated pattern near the original automobile core. Japanese-owned automotive parts manufacturing plants have followed U.S. motor vehicle assembly plants and clustered in the Midwest.

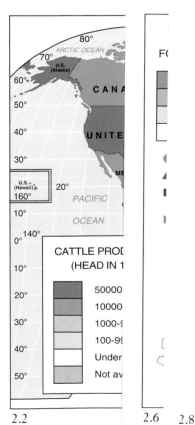

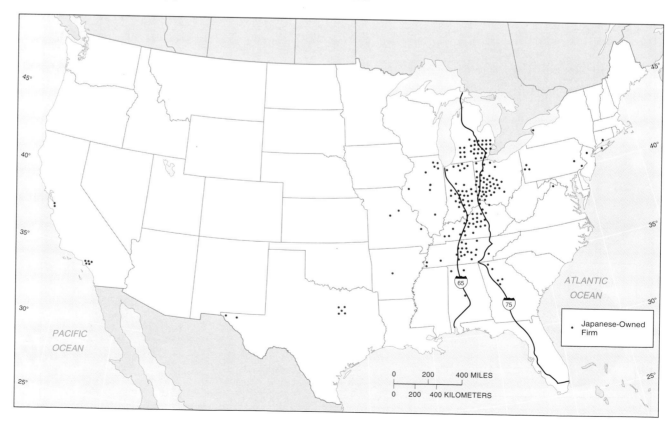

2.2   2.6   2.8

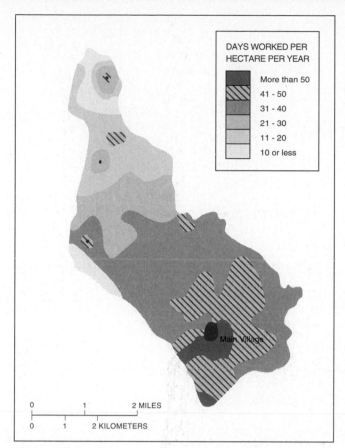

FIGURE 7.30
Intensity of farming around a village near Jaipur in Rajasthan, India.
(Source: Based on Blaikie, 1971.)

ers. Close to the national market were dairy farms, market gardens, and woodlots. Beyond the woodlots were grain- and meat-producing areas. Still farther from the Eastern Seaboard, frontier farmers could profit only by raising grain and converting it to whiskey. Whiskey, which has a high value per unit of weight, was easy to transport. A few kegs were lashed onto the backs of mules and moved to the market at low kilometer costs.

Western Pennsylvania whiskey producers fared well until 1794, when the U.S. government levied a special tax on inland whiskey. This tax effectively reduced the net profit for whiskey so that the zone of profitable farm production shrank eastward. Frontier farmers, having lost their source of income, rebelled. Federal troops were called in to restore order. As you know, the discriminatory tax was not permanent; it was repealed during Thomas Jefferson's administration.

National Scale

Agricultural land use at the national level represents another change of scale. Suppose that we consider U.S. agricultural production going from the hypothetical to the real. Figure 7.31a is a map of hypothetical land-use rings. It assumes that the United States is a homogeneous plain, that New York City is the only national market, that transport costs are uniform in all directions from New York City, and that crops are ranked by rent-paying ability. These land-use zones, of course, are not consistent with reality. Other assumptions, such as a north-south temperature gradient, result in a more complex and realistic pattern (Figure 7.31b).

Now consider the map depicting the actual regionalization of U.S. agricultural production (see Figure 7.15). The major agricultural regions, established for more than a century, developed largely within the framework of von Thünen's model. By 1900, early nineteenth-century crop zones had expanded with improving transport technology from local isolated states to the entire country. As the agricultural structure changed, the enlarged original Thünian zones were modified: (1) the first ring developed a distinct horticultural zone and a surrounding Dairy Belt, (2) the forestry ring was displaced to the marginal areas of the system because the railroad could haul wood cheaply, (3) the crop ring subdivided into an inner mixed-crop/livestock belt that produced meat (the Corn Belt) and an outer cereal-producing area, and (4) the ranching area remained a peripheral grazing zone that supplied young animals to be fattened in the Corn Belt. This super-Thünian regional system was anchored by a supercity—the northeastern Megalopolis.

Although the map of U.S. agricultural regions does not exhibit the classic rings, certain regularities are apparent. Of most importance, the intensity of farming declines with distance from the national market. Thus, the Atlantic Fruit and Vegetable Belt, Dairy Belt, Corn Belt, Wheat Belts, and Grazing Belt conform to the model's structure. Deviations from the schema are the result of environmental variations, and special circumstances. Central Appalachia supports only isolated valley farming (general farming). Areas of the dry western mountains that have been reclaimed through hugh federal investments in irrigation projects support oasis farming. California and the Gulf Coast-Florida region have mild winters and, with the help of irrigation and refrigerated transport, produce large crops of fruits and vegetables. The farms of the Pacific Northwest serve the

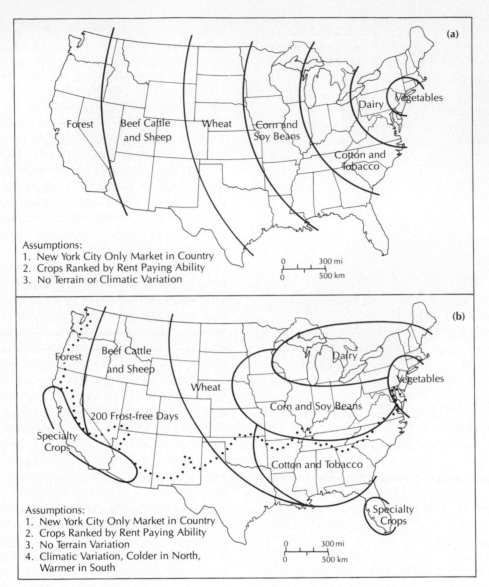

FIGURE 7.31
Hypothetical land-use rings in the United States.
(Source: Kolars and Nystuen, 1974, p. 258.)

local population—the nation—with potatoes, apples, and other specialty crops, and the Pacific Basin countries with wheat. The old Cotton Belt, once poorly integrated into the national economy, specializes in the production of beef, poultry, soybeans, and timber (de Blij and Muller, 1993).

International Scale

Finally, we can increase our scale of observation to the international level. In Europe, the intensive cash-cropping areas that extended only a few miles from the market have expanded far beyond von Thünen's estate, southeast of Rostock, in Mecklenburg, Germany. We can now visualize Europe as a set of von Thünen rings. Production is most intense in the area centered on the Low Countries, Denmark, north Germany, northern France, and southeastern England.

The world itself may also be viewed as a set of von Thünen rings. At this scale, the world is the isolated State and Europe-North America is the Thünian "Town."

SUMMARY

◈

For many thousands of years a complex relationship has evolved between people and the natural environment. All people depend on agriculture for their well-being, but in our agricultural pursuits, we necessarily modify the land. Good land managers give back to nature what they take; poor land managers degrade the environment.

Collections of plants and animals define fields that are organized around farms. Collections of farms make up farming regions. When geographers speak of agricultural regions, they refer to the artificial division of the world into homogeneous farming types.

The most intriguing aspect of farming regions is not their number or extent but the similarity of land-use decisions farmers make within them. After reviewing agricultural origins and dispersals and the effects of food production on the land, we identified four basic factors that influence agricultural land-use patterns. These factors are site characteristics, cultural preference and perception, systems of production, and relative location.

Agriculture in developing countries is primarily of the subsistence variety. Subsistence agriculture includes shifting cultivation, intensive farming, and pastoral nomadism. Developing countries have usually more than 50% of their labor force engaged in agriculture and use few pieces of mechanized equipment.

By contrast, agriculture in developed countries employs a small percentage of the labor force and uses large-scale mechanized equipment and large inputs of energy and fertilizers. While outputs per hectare are comparable to intensive farming and even somewhat less, outputs per worker are as much as 50 times greater. Farmers who raise crops and livestock on huge farms are part of a vast agricultural system that includes machinery manufacturers; fertilizer, pesticide, and energy supplies; grain mills and slaughterhouses; food processing and wholesale and retail distribution.

Although mixed crops and livestock farms are the most common in developed countries, other types of commercial agriculture also exist, including dairy farming, commercial grain farming, usually centered on wheat, cattle ranching, Mediterranean horticulture, and tree farms.

One theory that helps us to understand the distribution and location of agriculture was formalized by Johann Heinrich von Thünen in the early nineteenth century. We described the normative model that von Thünen developed to explain patterns of land use around the town in north Germany where he lived. We then presented some of the conclusions that can be drawn from this model: (1) There is an inverse relationship between location rent and transport costs; (2) there is a limit to commercial farming on a homogeneous plain with an isolated market town at its center; (3) land values and intensity of land use increase toward the market; and (4) crop types compete with one another and are ordered according to the principle of the highest economic rent.

In the last section of the chapter, we saw how the basic Thünian principles can be applied to agricultural land-use patterns at scales ranging from the village to the world. Contemporary Thünian effects at the microscale are best observed in the Third World, where localized circulation systems provide a transport setting similar to that of early nineteenth-century Europe. Improvements in transport technology and the development of refrigeration have permitted the Isolated State to expand from the micro- to the macroscale. Thus, in the United States and Europe the model is no longer centered on a single city but on a vast urbanized region. At the global level, core nations are the market around which production zones develop (Chisholm, 1979; Schlebecker, 1960).

◈

KEY TERMS

agribusiness
Atlantic Fruit and Vegetable Belt
average product
capital intensive
commercial agriculture
corn belt
cultural preference
double cropping
environmental perception
extensive margin of cultivation
feedlots
fertile crescent
Food-for-Peace programs
food-stamp program
four-field rotation system
grain elevators
highest and best use
high value added
inelastic supply curve
intensive margin of cultivation
intensive subsistence agriculture
Isolated State
Kolkhoze
labor intensive
location rent
marginal product
margin of cultivation
Mediterranean cropping
milkshed
milpa farming

mixed crop and livestock farming
paddy
parity price
pastoral nomadism
peasant agriculture
price floor
price supports
relative location
rent
sawah
shifting cultivation
site characteristics
slash and burn
sovkhozes
space-cost curve
spring wheat
stages of production
subsistence agriculture
swidden
target pricing
total product
truck farming
use value
vertical integration
virgin and idle lands program
Von Thünen's isolated state
wheat belts
winnowing
winter wheat
world's breadbasket

◈

SUGGESTED READINGS

Babbington, A., and Carney, J. 1990. Geography in the international agricultural research centers: Theoretical and practical concerns. *Annals of the Association of American Geographers,* 80:34–48.

Bascom, J. B. 1990. Border pastoralism in eastern Sudan. *Geographical Review,* 80:416–430.

Blaikie, P., and Brookfield, H. 1987. *Land Degradation and Society.* New York: Methuen.

Boserup, E. 1981. *Population and Technology.* New York: Blackwell.

Brown, L. R., and Young, J. E. 1990. Feeding the world in the nineties. In *State of the World* (pp. 101–141). New York: Norton & Company.

Chisholm, M. 1979. *Rural Settlement and Land Use: An Essay in Location*, 3rd ed. London: Hutchinson.

Cochran, W. W., and Ryan, M. E. 1976. *American Farm Policy, 1948–73*. Minneapolis: University of Minnesota Press.

Cromley, R. G. 1982. The von Thünen Model and Environmental Uncertainty. *Annals of the Association of American Geographers*, 72:404–410.

Dahlberg, K. A., ed. 1986. *New Directions for Agriculture and Agricultural Research: Neglected Dimensions and Emerging Alternatives*. Totowa, NJ: Rowman and Allanheld.

Dove, M. R. 1985. *Swidden Agriculture in Indonesia: The Subsistence Strategies of the Kalimantan Kantu*. Amsterdam, The Netherlands: Mouton.

Ebeling, W. 1979. *The Fruited Plain: The Story of American Agriculture*. Berkeley: University of California Press.

Found, W. C. 1971. *A Theoretical Approach to Rural Land-Use Patterns*. London: Edward Arnold.

Furuseth, O. J., and Pierce, J. T. 1982. *Agricultural Land in an Urban Society*. Washington, DC: Association of American Geographers.

Gregor, H. F. 1982. *Industrialization of U.S. Agriculture: An Interpretive Atlas*. Boulder, CO: Westview.

Grigg, D. B. 1984. *An Introduction to Agricultural Geography*. London: Hutchinson.

Hall, P. G., ed. 1966. *Von Thünen's Isolated State*. Translated by C. M. Wartenberg. Oxford, England: Pergamon.

Hart, J. F. 1986. Change in the Corn Belt. *Geographical Review*, 76:51–73.

Hedlund, S. 1984. *Crisis in Soviet Agriculture*. London: Croom Helm.

Ilbery, B. W. 1985. *Agricultural Geography: A Social and Economic Analysis*. New York: Oxford University Press.

Raven, P. H., Berg, L. R., and Johnson, G. B. 1993. *Environment*. Philadelphia: Saunders College Publishing.

Reganold, I. P., Papendick, R. I., and Parr, J. E. 1990. Sustainable agriculture. *Scientific American*, June, 88–95.

Rhoades, R. E. 1991. The world's food supply at risk. *National Geographic*, 179(4): 81–94.

Rubenstein, J. M. 1994. *The Cultural Landscape: An Introduction to Human Geography*. New York: Macmillan.

Smith Everett, G., Jr. 1980. America's richest farms and ranches. *Annals*, Association of American Geographers, 70:528–541.

Turner, B. L. II, and Brush, S. B. eds. 1987. *Comparative Farming Systems*. New York: Guilford.

World Resources Institute. 1993. *World Resources: A Guide to the Global Environment, 1992–93*. New York: Oxford University Press.

URBAN LAND USE: THEORY AND PRACTICE

◈

OBJECTIVES

- To explore the relationship between urban growth and development
- To explain how the process of city growth operates under free-market conditions
- To extend von Thünen's model to urban land-use configurations
- To introduce land-use models that describe the spatial dispersion of activities in cities
- To help show that the free market for space in the metropolis has produced a pattern of sprawl and social problems

◈

The heart of Amsterdam, Netherlands.
(Source: KLM Aerocarta.)

A city is a built environment—a tangible expression of religious, political, economic, and social forces that houses a host of activities in proximity to one another. Cities, the foundation of modern life, represent humanity's largest and most durable artifact (Vance, 1977). They are living systems—made, transformed, and experienced by people.

Although the world pattern of cities is primarily the result of events triggered by the nineteenth-century industrial revolution, the city originated thousands of years ago. The first cities emerged in the Mesopotamian area of the Middle East about 7000 years ago. Cities also developed early in the Nile Valley (about 3000 B.C.), in the Indus Valley (by 2500 B.C.), in the Yellow River Valley of China (by 2000 B.C.), and in Mexico and Peru (by A.D. 500). The raison d'être of cities from the start was to exchange goods and services with surrounding communities. As urbanization spread from its ancient hearths, it was incorporated into the cultures of various regions.

The manifestations of the urban process display dazzling diversity. Because the historical antecedents of modern patterns of daily living differ from one part of the world to another, the structure of the city differs from region to region. For example, North American cities contrast strikingly with those of Europe or Asia. North American cities are largely the creation of the last 200 years, a period of free-market capitalist activity politically based on the concepts of democracy and a relatively egalitarian spirit. Most European cities have grown since the start of the nineteenth century, but the tradition of privatism has not been the only structural influence on their urban growth. For the majority of European cities, other socioeconomic structures (e.g., feudalism, absolutism, mercantilism), never significantly present in North America, have also played a role.

In Europe, urban life began more than 2000 years ago. Few European cities were created on virgin territory; most evolved from rural settlements. Some European cities existed before the growth of the Roman Empire. Apart from their own city-states, the Ancient Greeks were responsible for the foundation of other Mediterranean cities such as Naples, Marseilles, and Seville. By the end of the Roman Empire, many of Europe's largest present-day cities had been established.

From the fall of the Roman Empire to the early modern period, cities in Europe grew slowly or not at all. They ceased to be important during the period loosely referred to as the Dark Ages, a time when long-distance trade and rural-urban interaction drastically declined.

Cities revived from the sixteenth century onward with the pursuit of profit in a period of incipient and later burgeoning capitalist economic activity. In commerce, a new middle class developed, and the revolution in the countryside reduced the peasant class and helped establish the working class. The accumulation of capital, the growth of new social classes, the use of inexpensive labor in the colonies, and scientific and technological breakthroughs destroyed the feudal fetter on production and created a new function for the city—industrialization. The emergence of the *industrial city,* a product of capitalism, resulted in lower transportation and communication costs for entrepreneurs who needed to interact with one another; hence, most commercial and industrial enterprises concentrated in and around the most accessible part of the city—the *central business district* (CBD).

During the period of urban decline and rebirth in Europe, the urban process of the rest of the world exhibited different patterns. Before A.D. 1500, Europe was a mere upstart in a world system that included major interlocking subsystems of central places stretching from the Mediterranean region to China. These subsystems were dominated by cities such as Constantinople, Baghdad, Samarkand, Calcutta, and Hangchow that had greater continuity and played a more permanent role in the world economy than their European counterparts did (Abu-Lughod, 1987–1988). Not until the commencement of European colonization were the urban civilizations of Asia, Africa, and the Americas threatened. Centuries of European penetration and occupation resulted in the growth of many cities that owe their origins to colonial foundations or to trading requirements.

Eventually, *colonial cities* dominated the urban patterns of Africa, Asia, and Latin America. Political independence and the development of the new international division of labor allowed underdeveloped countries to experience a transformation of the urban process as profound as that in nineteenth-century Europe and North America. Indeed, urban growth is now occurring more rapidly in the underdeveloped world than it did in Europe during its period of fastest growth in the late nineteenth century. During the second half of the twentieth century, increasing affluence and the technologies of mass transportation and modern communications began a trend toward urban decentralization in Europe and North America.

Waves of change have washed through cities, remodeling and redefining their shapes and details, but rarely have the traces of their historical legacies been completely obliterated. The legacy of history is of immense importance to economic geographers who study cities and attempt to find solutions to urban problems and crises. Questions of interest to the economic geographer include the following: What types of societies and associated modes of economic exchange give rise to cities? What economic factors account for cities? What are the most vital influences on urban structure? What are the issues at the core of the urban process? Answers to these questions are the concern of this chapter.

CITIES AND SOCIETIES

◈

Basic Forms of Society

Cities require the existence of a particular type of society in order to grow and develop. In the context of our discussion, a *society* refers to a group of people organized around a self-sufficient operating system that outlives any individual member. To maintain conditions of self-sufficiency, human groups must have forms of social organization capable of producing and distributing goods and services.

We can identify three main types of societies with associated forms of economic exchange (Fried, 1967). First, *egalitarian societies* are established through voluntary cooperative behavior. The economies of these societies are dominated by *reciprocity*, of which market barter is an example. Reciprocity involves trading without the use of money in a mutually beneficial exchange of goods.

Second, there are *rank societies*, examples of which are tribal and feudal societies. The economy of a rank society is dominated by *redistribution*. For example, African chiefs would exact gifts in kind (goods or commodities) and/or money from their tribes according to custom. And, under feudalism in Europe, serfs, who were bound to the land of some estate, owed the overlord (by tradition, or by force if necessary) food, labor, or military allegiance.

Third, there are *stratified societies*, in which members do not have equal access to the resources that sustain life. The economies of these societies are dominated by *market exchange*. A market-exchange society adapts to scarcity by selling goods and services at a price. Pricing is the mechanism that connects the economic activity

of large numbers of individuals and controls many decentralized decisions. Market exchange facilitates division of labor, specialization of production, and technological and organizational advances. It produces wealth for society out of scarcity, but often at the cost of even greater scarcity for the already poor. Socially created scarcities cannot be eliminated in market-exchange economies.

Cities do not evolve in egalitarian societies dominated by reciprocity. However, reciprocal forms of interaction, such as the mutually beneficial exchange of goods and services, do occur in cities. Everyday examples of reciprocity in an urban setting are exchanges among neighbors: lending a snowblower, gossiping, helping out when life crises occur.

Cities evolve in societies that can organize the exploitation of a surplus product. Rank and stratified societies have an especially suitable hierarchical structure to extract, appropriate, and redistribute a socially derived surplus product. A *social surplus product* is the part of the annual product of any society that is neither consumed by the direct producers nor used for the repro-

A canal in the merchant city of Bruges, Belgium. This Hanse town was the north European counterpart to Venice during the mercantile period.
(Source: Belgian Tourist Office.)

duction of the stock or the means of production. In rank and stratified societies, the social surplus product is appropriated by the ruling group. Surpluses are extracted from outside the confines of a city, as in the case of agriculture, and from inside a city, as in the case of manufacturing.

Stratified societies provide the most favorable conditions for the growth of cities. These conditions include unequal access to resources that sustain life, socially created resource scarcities, and institutions of market exchange. Except in countries that claim to have socialist economies (e.g., North Korea, China, and Cuba), contemporary cities exist in stratified societies.

Transformation of Market Exchange

Prior to the industrial revolution, market exchange was an appendage to the redistributive economy of the rank society. Under feudalism, European cities were usually extensions of the personalities of those who governed them. For example, Venice, Italy, was the city of the doges. Located at the seaward margins of the marshy Po Delta, Venice became one of Europe's most important centers of manufacturing and long-distance trade during the Middle Ages and early modern period. The dominant economic institutions of Venice and other European towns were the *guilds*—craft, professional, and trade associations. In Europe, before the industrial revolution, anyone who wanted to produce or sell any good or service was required to join a guild, which regulated members' conduct in all their personal and business activities. With the industrial revolution came a steady penetration of market exchange through the fabric of society. Cities ceased to be reflections of individual rule; they became instruments of industrial growth.

Individual capitalism was the hallmark of the early stages of the industrial revolution. Indeed, the period from the mid-1840s to 1873 has been called the golden age of individual or competitive capitalism. Under competitive capitalism, cities registered high rates of industrial innovation and prodigious increases in productive power. Their standards of achievement were based on industry and technology. If both prospered, the city was considered to be good. The best city was the busiest one—the one that was growing most quickly and recording the largest increases in bank clearings. However, these producer cities were ugly creations and hor-

rifying environments for the laboring poor. The British coined the term *Black Country* to refer to the grimy industrial cities of the English Midlands. Interestingly, the industrial city, which functioned as a workshop for production and capital accumulation, does not attract twentieth-century tourists in search of urban beauty. Tourists avoid rich industrial cities such as Toledo, Ohio, and overrun poor preindustrial cities such as Toledo, Spain.

In the late nineteenth century, capitalism took on a different form. There was a drift from competitive capitalism to monopoly, or corporate, capitalism. Through the elimination or absorption of small competitors, large industrial and financial corporations emerged. Their emergence diminished the community of competition. In today's developed countries (and in many underdeveloped countries) important areas of manufacturing and strategic industries are dominated by a relatively small number of multinational corporations.

Large corporations have had a major influence on the twentieth-century Western city. Corporate administrative buildings and home plants dominate skylines and extensive land areas. For example, the organizational headquarters of such corporations as Standard Oil of Indiana and Sears Roebuck have helped to shape the image of Chicago.

The geography of contemporary Western cities has also been affected by the need of corporate enterprises to find ways to absorb their surpluses. An American example is the corporate penchant for disposing of their surpluses through urban renewal projects. Funds are sometimes used in projects sponsored by local governments to replace run-down, low-income housing with luxury office and residential buildings. Corporations and the federal government have poured resources into urban renewal projects in cities including Atlanta, Boston, Dallas, Houston, Minneapolis, New York, and Philadelphia.

In addition, American cities have been affected by the need for corporate enterprises to increase demand for their products and services. *Need creation*, a process in which luxuries are marketed as necessities, is exploited by corporations through daily appeal to potential customers. Need creation also operates as a consequence of urban spatial organization. For example, low-density metropolises, such as Kansas City, Dallas, Houston, and Los Angeles, make a car, or two cars, a necessity. Residents are literally forced to drive the cars that the automobile industry produces.

Relative Importance of Different Modes of Exchange

All three modes of economic exchange (*reciprocity, redistribution,* and *market exchange*) operate in most cities, but the emphases have varied with time. The cities of medieval Europe reflected the dominant influence of redistribution, but market exchange also operated. In general, cities in the zone between the North Sea and Italy were more supportive of the market than those on the margin of the region were. In the commercial area, as the old feudal ordering of society declined, the social and political influence of merchants grew. When commerce was permitted to operate freely, as in Venice and Florence, the market became a notable feature of city structure. Yet, the disposal of wealth through the construction of massive cathedrals, public buildings, and universities emphasized the preeminence of cultural values over worldly economic concerns. The imprint of cultural values is also unmistakable in other places with a long history of urbanization. For example, Lahore, the cultural focus of Islamic Pakistan, founded in the first or second century A.D., is adorned with palaces and mosques.

From the late medieval period onward, the importance of market exchange increased. Large commercial cities such as London, Amsterdam, and Antwerp boasted the triumph of the market over redistribution. By the nineteenth century, market exchange dominated life in western Europe and in its overseas progeny.

In North America, where the medieval order did not exist, the nineteenth-century city was an expression of economic influence. The power of the American city did not rest in the nominal government; rather, it was based in the dominant economic institutions, which were usually industrial establishments. Nonetheless, city government did play a redistribution role that grew more important as the industrial revolution progressed. Urban bureaucracies collected taxes and provided a range of public services. Although much less prominent than the other modes of integration, reciprocity existed at every level of society, especially in working-class neighborhoods, where it provided residents with a degree of social solidarity and security.

In the modern Western city, the role of reciprocity is abridged. Market exchange prevails, but it is challenged by redistribution. Because of the growth of big business and government, redistribution is more im-

Typical Moscow apartments at night. There is a light burning almost everywhere because entertainment possibilities at night are very rare. In this city of 10 million inhabitants, only hard currency facilities are open after 11:00 p.m. Apartments are typically small and noisy. Single-family dwellings in Soviet cities are very rare.
(Source: Wim Van Cappellen/Impact Visuals.)

portant now than it was in the nineteenth century. The hierarchical status of employees in modern institutions is reminiscent of the structure of rank societies. Corporate and government bureaucracies have become major agents of redistribution in urban areas. For example, governments appropriate resources and return them to the populace at large in the form of various public services, welfare programs, public projects, and subsidies. The provision of funds for elementary schools and high schools is a good example of government redistribution at the local level. Most of the money for schools, which usually represent the largest expense for local government, is generated from property taxes.

THE PROCESS OF CITY BUILDING

What general forces attract business and industry to cities? In a purely competitive market, we can account for the attraction of firms to cities in terms of two opposing forces. These forces are *scale economies* and *transportation costs*. The influence that they exert on city building becomes apparent as we survey the classical economic principles that relate to the production and cost behavior of the single firm.

Cost Behavior of the Single Firm

Firms have short-run and long-run planning periods relative to the production function. The *production function* is a mathematical statement of the relationship between the inputs (land, labor, and machines) used by a firm and the flow of output (goods and services) that results in a particular time period (week, month, year). By definition, *long run* is a period long enough to permit a firm to vary the quantity of all the inputs in its production function; *short run* is a period short enough for at least one input to be fixed in amount and invariable.

Suppose that we have a simplified production function consisting of two inputs—machines and human labor. How would we illustrate the firm's production cost? A common device in economic analysis is to use the relationship between the level of output and the cost *per unit of output* (*average cost*). Some basic data are presented in Table 8.1 for a hypothetical firm manufacturing Frisbees.

The relationship between the inputs (labor and ma-

Table 8.1
Cost Relationships for a Firm

Labor (1)	Machines (2)	Output (3)	Total Cost (4)	Cost per Unit of Output (5)
10	5	6000	$1200	$0.20
20	10	12,000	$2400	$0.20
40	20	24,000	$4800	$0.20
80	40	48,000	$9600	$0.20

chines, or Columns 1 and 2) and the output (Frisbees, or Column 3) is given by the firm's production function. If 10 units of labor are employed (10 people for 1 day each) and 5 machines are used (1 day each), the output is 6000 Frisbees. If each day of labor costs the firm $100 per employee and each day's use of one machine costs $40, the firm's total cost of producing 6000 Frisbees is $1200 (Column 4). Cost per unit of output, or average cost, is $0.20 (Column 5).

In this case, if the firm decides to expand its output, its production function tells it that the optimal way to do so is to increase both inputs by the same proportion (e.g., doubling both, tripling both, increasing both by 50%, etc.). Suppose that the firm wants to double its output (to 12,000) and does this by doubling its use of both labor and machines (to 20 and 10, respectively). If the price of each input remains the same, the firm's total costs double to $2400. However, the cost per unit of output (average cost) remains constant at $0.20. In this case, continued increases in output have the same effect. As output doubles, total costs double and cost per unit of output remains unchanged at $0.20. This phenomenon is called *constant returns to scale*. Figure 8.1a shows the relationship between average cost and the level of output. Economists refer to this graph as the *long-run average-cost* (*LRAC*) *curve*.[1]

Two types of agglomeration economies (described in more detail in the next section of this chapter) can

[1] Constant returns to scale is not the only possibility. For some firms in some industries, output rises by a greater proportion than inputs are increased (*increasing returns to scale*, or *economies of scale*), and average cost decreases as output increases. In other cases, output rises by a smaller proportion than the increase in inputs (*decreasing returns to scale*, or *diseconomies of scale*), and average cost rises as output rises. These cases are presented and discussed in the next section of this chapter and in more detail in Chapter 10.

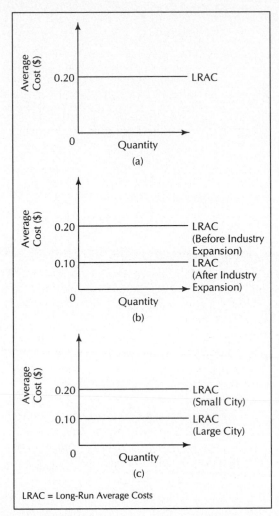

FIGURE 8.1
Constant returns to scale for a firm: (a) no agglomeration or internal scale economies; (b) localization economies; (c) urbanization economies.

also have constant returns to scale: *Localization economies* refer to declining average costs for firms as the output of the industries of which they are a part increases (Figure 8.1b). *Urbanization economies* refer to declining average costs for firms as cities increase their scales of activity (Figure 8.1c).

Scale Economies and Diseconomies of the Single Firm

SCALE ECONOMIES

Scale economies are a key for understanding why economic activities concentrate in cities. The concept refers to a set of conditions in which average costs of a firm decrease as the scale of production increases. Changing the scale of production means altering proportionately all inputs used in production. Costs of production under these conditions are called long-run costs. Dividing long-run costs by output yields the long-run average costs of a firm.

Two sets of forces influence a firm's long-run costs: internal scale economies and external scale economies.

Internal Scale Economies

Internal scale economies are subject to direct management control. Managers may be able to take advantage of labor economies (more efficient labor specialization), technical economies (larger, more efficient machines), market economies, and managerial economies. Internal economies come into play because many production factors (inputs) are indivisible and can be used more efficiently at larger scales of output. Thus, the concept of internal scale economies refers to cost-reducing changes that tend to lower the average costs of firms as they grow in size (Figure 8.2a).

External Scale Economies

External scale economies represent two forms of *agglomeration economies:* (1) localization, or industry, economies and (2) urbanization economies. *Localization economies* refer to declining average costs for firms as the output of the industries of which they are a part increases (Figure 8.2b). These economies stem from benefits that industries derive within restricted geographic areas, such as the development of a large labor pool with skills needed by the industry.

Urbanization economies refer to declining average costs for firms as cities increase their scales of activity (Figure 8.2c). Cost reductions stem mainly from technologies that stimulate production on a scale that can be achieved only with firm specialization; that is, when plants perform only one or a few functions in the overall production process. As a result of transportation costs, firm specialization leads to geographic clustering, which, in turn, promotes more geographic specialization and concentration. The garment industry of New York and London and the metal trades of Ohio and the English Midlands are outstanding examples of geographic clustering of specialized firms.

J. Vernon Henderson (1988) extensively investigated localization and urbanization economies. He used sophisticated statistical analyses to estimate the relationships between output per worker (labor productivity)

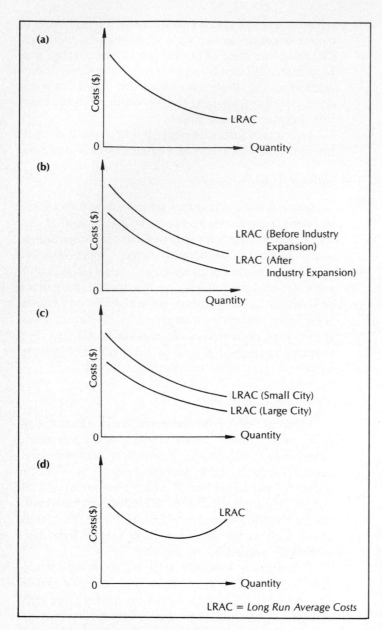

FIGURE 8.2
Scale economies and diseconomies for a firm: (a) internal economies; (b) localization economies; (c) urbanization economies; (d) internal economies and diseconomies.

in particular industries in urban areas and two variables: (1) the total output of the same industry in urban areas and (2) the total population of urban areas.

The first relationship provides evidence of localization economies. If higher labor productivity in, say, garment manufacture, occurs in urban areas having a high rate of garment output, then, other things being equal, garment manufacturers in urban areas near other firms in the same industry will have lower costs per unit of output. On the other hand, a positive (direct) relationship between labor productivity in an industry and total

urban population suggests that firms in that industry reap lower unit costs from being located in larger urban areas, regardless of the types of firms located there—an urbanization economy.

Henderson studied two countries, the United States and Brazil, and his results, along with those of a study of Japan by R. Nakamura, are summarized in Tables 8.2 and 8.3.[2] Table 8.2 shows that localization econo-

[2] The Nakamura results originally appeared in Nakamura (1985) but are given here as reported in Henderson (1988, p. 96).

◈

Table 8.2
Localization Economies

United States*	Brazil	Japan*
Primary metals	Iron and steel	Iron and steel
Electrical machinery	Nonelectrical machinery	Nonferrous metal
Machinery	Transport equipment	Nonelectrical machinery
Petroleum	Chemicals (including petrochemicals)	Electric machinery
Apparel	Textiles	Transport equipment
Leather products (?)		Precision machinery
Wood products (?)		Textile products
Pulp and paper		Apparel
Food products		Pulp and paper products
		Food products (?)
		Metal products
		Rubber and plastics
		Chemicals
		Printing and publishing (?)

* A question mark (?) indicates that the result is of marginal significance.
(Source: Henderson, 1988.)

mies are evident in many industries in each country. However, it is clear that the results are not identical in all three countries. Table 8.3 shows the significant cases of urbanization economies. This second category of external economies is far less common than localization economies.

◈

Table 8.3
Urbanization Economies

United States*	Brazil	Japan*
Nonmetallic minerals	Printing and publishing	Nonelectrical machinery (?)
Primary metals (?)		Textile products
		Food products
		Lumber products
		Furniture
		Printing and publishing

* A question mark (?) indicates that the result is of marginal significance.
(Source: Henderson, 1988.)

Henderson's results must be interpreted with caution, however. Data limitations and significant statistical problems exist with any studies of this sort. Furthermore, as pointed out by Henderson, these studies do not deal with the possibility of external economies being realized from the scale of *related* industries as opposed to the industry itself (a localization economy) or the scale of the whole urban economy (an urbanization economy). Nonetheless, the finding of limited urbanization economies is significant. It suggests that the productivity-enhancing (cost-saving) advantages in urban areas arise from concentrations of firms in the same industry rather than from large urban size.

SCALE DISECONOMIES

Internal and external economies accrue only up to a point. Consider internal diseconomies. At first, firms experience cost-reducing internal economies, but after a certain scale of production is attained, it becomes impossible to vary proportionately all inputs used in the production process (Figure 8.2d). Management, for example, does not grow proportionately as firms expand. Managers are forced to spread themselves ever more thinly over wider areas of decision making. Decreasing returns set in, with an eventual decrease in efficiency.

External diseconomies must also be accounted for. For example, urbanization diseconomies—rising average costs accompanying an increasing scale of activity within a city—may arise for at least three reasons: First, firms may experience higher costs as a result of land scarcity. Second, competition for labor and high living costs may force firms to pay workers higher wages. Third, firms may encounter transportation congestion, parking problems, pollution, crime, and financial difficulties.

Transportation Costs of the Single Firm

There would be no need to worry about transportation costs if resources were ubiquitous, if production technology were the same everywhere, and, of course, if movement were instantaneous and free. But resources are rarely ubiquitous, technical aspects of production are highly variable, and movement over geographic space always encounters resistance. Transportation costs represent the alternative output that we relinquish when we commit inputs to the movement of people, goods, information, and ideas over geographic space. They are the swimming pools and libraries that must be surrendered for roads and railways.

What effect does the cost of overcoming the friction of distance have on the location of economic activities? Because transportation costs are directly correlated with distance, profit-maximizing firms select sites close to their inputs, to other firms, or to consumers who buy their products. Workers decide to live near their places of employment. Accessibility pays off in the form of transportation-cost savings that concentrate firms and workers. Moreover, incentives to concentrate activities are intensified by existing transportation systems, which provide a high degree of access to only a limited number of geographic areas.

Economic Costs and City Building

Having explored the meaning of scale economies and transportation costs, we are now in a position to see how these forces influence city building. First, let us consider an area in which people are dispersed geographically and a production technology in which economies of scale are absent. As the sizes of firms increase, they experience only constant returns to scale; that is, their output increases proportionately as the amount of all inputs increases. Firms could choose to locate in proximity to one another, but if there were no scale economies, such a choice would result in rising unit costs and falling profits. Geographically concentrated production would increase the distance, and hence the cost of transporting goods and services, from producers to consumers. With scale economies absent, there would be no incentive to profit-maximizing firms to concentrate production.

Now let us alter the situation. Suppose that a new technology is developed for the garment industry that allows a specialized machine to make buttonholes in coats cheaply and in large quantities.[3] Suppose also that no single coat manufacturer can keep the machine busy all the time, but if the coat manufacturer were located near other coat manufacturers, their total demand for buttonholes would make it profitable for an entrepreneur to invest in such a machine and rent time on it to each manufacturer. Geographic concentration of garment firms would reduce their cost per unit (a localization economy).

If consumers remained dispersed geographically, such concentration would again increase transportation costs. But this time, transportation-cost increases could be offset by a reduction in another cost (e.g., skilled labor). If so, profit-maximizing garment firms would locate near one another and their employees would live nearby. The buttonhole firm and other suppliers of goods and services to these households would also locate nearby. A city would be created. In this way, city building is cumulative; concentration leads to more concentration.

Cities grow when they gain firms and population. To illustrate this process, geographers sometimes use the principle of *cumulative causation*. This principle states that increases in urban economic activity create an increase in population. In the case of urban decline, the reverse holds true. Cities decline when they lose firms and population, conditions that create negative cumulative causation.

---

[3] This example is taken from Hoover (1984, p. 110).

INTRAURBAN SPATIAL ORGANIZATION

◈

We have seen that activities locate in cities for sound economic reasons. But what factors influence where the various activities will locate in a city? Why are some parts of a city zoned for commercial land use, others for industrial use, and still others for mixed single- and multifamily housing? Classical urban location theory provides one answer. This theory concerns the private land-use decision process; it is based on von Thünen's concept of location rent. Assumptions embodied in urban location rent theory are these: First, the central business district (CBD) is the most economically productive location because of its concentration of transportation facilities; second, rent falls to zero at the fringe of the city (it falls to a level of agricultural value); third, firms are competitive price takers, not price makers; and, finally, cities exist in competitive market-exchange economies without government and social classes. Although the concept of differential rent is a useful arranger of land uses, a word of warning is in order. In capitalist societies, the pursuit of the most profitable use of urban land is inhibited, to varying degrees, by monopoly, by societal class divisions, by racial discrimination, and by public authority. However, despite its deviations from real-world conditions, urban location theory is still used by many economic geographers to indicate and interpret problems of land use in cities.

The Competitive-Bidding Process

Classical location theory states that activities locate in cities according to the outcome of the *competitive-bidding process*. People willing and able to pay the highest price for a particular site win the competition and put the land to the economically highest and best use. Highest and best use, of course, can change as external market forces change. These forces include effective demand, public tastes and standards, and land-use regulations.

To illustrate the competitive-bidding process, imagine a city on a featureless plain in which there are only two demanders of land, Jason and Sam, who bid for sites that stretch from the CBD to the perimeter of the city (Figure 8.3). Each is willing to pay more for some sites than other sites. At site D_1, Jason is willing to pay $25 and Sam only $20. On the other hand, Jason has no interest in land at D_3, but Sam is willing to pay $15 for it. If the bid-rent curves for Jason and Sam represented their actual behavior in the urban land market, the outcome of the competitive-bidding process would place Jason between the CBD and D_2 and Sam beyond site D_2.

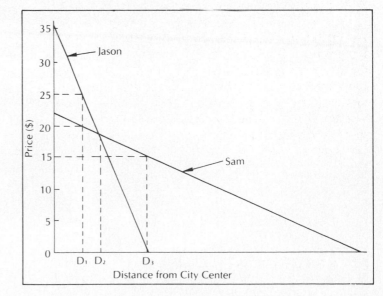

FIGURE 8.3
The bidding process for two entrepreneurs results in overlapping bid rent curves. The maximum rent that a user is willing to pay for a site is the *ceiling rent*. Why is the ceiling rent for Jason higher than that for Sam? Why is Jason's bid rent function steeper than that of Sam's bid rent curve?

Our hypothetical example raises a fundamental question: Why do users bid for particular parcels of land? In some instances, a user may value the inherent characteristics of a site. For a residential user, a scenic vista may be desirable; for a commerical user, nearness to potential customers may be crucial. In other instances, site attributes such as natural hazards may detract from the value of a tract to all potential developers or bidders.

Although part of every tract's value depends on site characteristics, relative location is usually more important. For particular activities, some land parcels may be more desirably located than others because they are more accessible; that is, they reduce users' transportation costs. For example, if accessibility to work is important to residential users, bid-rent curves reflect higher bids near places of employment.

Ceiling Rents

According to classical economic theory, the competition for the use of available locations results in the occupation of each site by the user able to derive the most utility or profit from it, and therefore able to pay the highest rent. The maximum rental that a particular user pays for a site is called the *ceiling rent*.

Consider a hilly tract of land, commanding excellent views, on the outskirts of a city. Ceiling rents for this parcel of land might be $9000 for residential, $6000 for retailing, and $5000 for manufacturing. Clearly, this tract of land is likely to be sold or leased for residential land use. But if the tract owner thinks that the site is worth more than $9000, the land will remain vacant.

Another tract is for sale a few kilometers away from the parcel put to residential use. It is relatively flat and located adjacent to a major highway. Ceiling rents might be $3000 for residential, $10,000 for retailing, and $7000 for manufacturing. In this case, the tract is sold or leased for retailing—say, a shopping center.

The Residential Location Decision

An important criterion for most people in selecting a home is accessibility to where they work in the city. The choice of a residential location depends, in part, on how much money a family can afford to spend on overcoming relative distance. For purposes of our discussion, we assume a single-centered city; that is, a city with only one center of employment—the CBD.

First, let's consider patterns of residential land use and the cost of commuting to work. A family's budget must account for living costs, housing costs, and trans-

Stamford Town Center, Connecticut. Beyond the "zone of better residents" is a broad commuter zone. It is an incompletely built-up area of small satellite towns and middle- and upper-class residences, with major malls and shopping centers at the intersection of beltways. *(Source: John Bunting/Impact Visuals.)*

portation costs. Assume that people are either rich or poor. Poor families, who have little money to spend on commuting after living and housing expenses are deducted from their income, have sharply negative bid-rent curves. They attach much importance to living close to where they work. The only way the inner-city poor can afford to live on high-rent land is to consume less space. On the other hand, rich families have plenty of money to spend on transportation. Proximity of residential sites to places of employment is of little consequence to them. They can trade access for agreeable lots away from the center of the city.

But now let's consider the effect of time costs on the residential decision. Time spent commuting is time that could be devoted to earning income. For this standpoint, distance is more critical for the rich, whose time is more valuable than that of the poor. Rich households have steep bid-rent curves, and they are located near the center of the city. Meanwhile, the poor, with shallow bid-rent curves, live farther away. This land-use pattern is characteristic of many Third World cities; the poor often live in peripheral squatter settlements, whereas the rich occupy high-rent city housing.

To this point, a single mode of travel to work has been assumed. A more realistic situation would involve two modes of travel—walking and driving. The steepest bid-rent curve is for the rich walking to work, followed by the poor walking, the rich driving, and the poor driving.

Although cost, time, and mode of travel to work have important implications for residential location, many other dimensions to accessibility, such as nearness to services, and general supply and demand factors must be considered. These and other factors influence bid prices. In every situation, however, the rich can outbid the poor. The results of the competitive-bidding process in market societies are always relatively advantageous to the rich and relatively disadvantageous to the poor. (See "Housing Price Differential" box.)

Site Demands of Firms

Firms also compete for urban space, but because of the nature of their activities, the criteria that they use in making locational decisions are not the same as those for households. Given a rational market-exchange economy, firms want to maximize profits and households want to maximize satisfactions. If intraurban accessibility is important to sales, firms should be willing to make higher bids for locations that are central to all potential customers. Increasing distance from the more productive locations in the urban area should increase costs to customers and therefore reduce sales. This would mean decreasing revenues, and, hence, lower profits. For *nonbasic firms* this is the case, but for basic firms it is not. *Basic firms* export what they produce to surrounding areas; nonbasic firms sell goods or provide services to city residents and businesses.

Revenues of nonbasic firms decline as the firms move away from downtown or from other central locations. For example, department stores have high revenue requirements for profitable scales of operation. Traditionally, these firms required access to all parts of a city. They were willing to pay high rents for downtown sites where intraurban transportation lines converge. Many nonbasic firms, such as grocery stores and beauty parlors, have much lower revenue requirements. Their revenue conditions allow smaller geographic scales of operation in the city.

Location within the city has little effect on the revenues of basic firms, but more of an effect on some of their costs. Firms requiring a lot of space might purchase sites at marginal locations where land costs are lower. Those drawing labor from residential areas throughout the city might be willing to pay high rents for central locations. Movement away from central locations could result in higher wage bills. To attract necessary labor, firms might be forced to increase wages to compensate for higher journey-to-work costs.

Market Outcomes

We have looked separately at locational decisions of households and firms as they deal with distance frictions. Now let us fashion a model, analogous to von Thünen's crop model, that shows how a multitude of individual decisions combine to produce a pattern of urban land use in which rents are maximized and all activities are optimally located.

Consider three land-use categories: manufacturing, commercial, and residential. Figure 8.4a shows distinctive bid-rent curves for the three types of land use in our hypothetical single-centered city. Commercial activities that require the most productive central sites have steeply sloping rent gradients. Manufacturing firms have shallower bid-rent curves. They cannot afford to pay the high costs of a central location. Residences have gently angled bid-rent curves and are relegated to the

HOUSING PRICE

DIFFERENTIALS, 1993

Frederick Stutz and Art Kartman provide a method of explaining the basis of housing price differentials using the supply-demand framework. The approach is based on the idea that the actual price at which any item is sold is the outcome of a complex set of factors that determine the behavior of buyers and sellers. Demand factors are those that determine the number of potential buyers, the amount each wants to buy, and the maximum price each is willing to pay. Supply factors determine the number of sellers, how much each will offer for sale, and the minimum price necessary to induce each seller to offer one item for sale. Except in special cases, neither set of factors is the sole determinant of the price at which an item is sold. For example, even if there is only one seller, a monopolist, the ability of the monopolist to set the price is limited by how much money or income buyers have ("what the market will bear").

Key demand factors in the housing market are population (both the number of people and the household size); inflation-adjusted, or "real," income per person or per household; and, in the case of owner-occupied housing, the home buyers' expectations of the future change in home prices. Important supply factors are the availability of items needed in building new housing units (land, labor, and construction equipment and materials) and construction standards or building codes. Availability of financing may be viewed either as a demand factor (long-term mortgages) or as a supply factor (construction loans).

As an example of the effect of a demand factor, consider an increase in the number of households in an area as a result of in-migration. If vacant housing of the desired kind is limited, the price of existing housing will be bid up. This will induce new construction and create new demand for land, labor, and raw materials. If these items are abundant, their prices should remain constant. However, if supplies are limited, their prices will be bid up. This increase in builder cost will lead to even further increases in housing prices, with the amount depending on how willing home buyers are to pay the higher prices. Increases in income and a heightened expectation of future increases in home prices will have similar effects.

On the supply side, consider a case of vacant land where the local authorities suddenly change the zoning from residential to nonresidential. The reduction in available supply will raise land prices and, hence, builder costs. The ability of builders to pass on the higher costs depends on the willingness of buyers to pay them. The more willing the buyers are to pay, the higher the demand pressures remain on land, labor, and so forth, and the more limited these items are relative to the demand, the greater the upward pressure on home prices. Similar responses occur for reduced vacancies; higher labor, equipment, and material prices; and stricter building codes.

Better access to amenities—the CBD, jobs, shopping, schools, and high-rent districts—as shown in the top rectangle of part (a) of the diagram, adds to the willingness of buyers to pay higher prices and to overall demand. The three graphs at the bottom describe how supply and demand curves shift upward, thus raising the price of housing. At the bottom left, the demand curve shifts to the right, raising the price of housing, whereas the supply curve remains fixed. The graph at the lower right describes a situation in which the supply curve shifts upward to the left, raising the price of housing, whereas the demand curve stays fixed. When these processes occur simultaneously, the center graph describes an even larger increase in price. Part (b) of the diagram shows average U.S. home prices in 1993.

(Source: Stutz and Kartman, 1982.)

(a) The economic geography of housing prices increases. (b) Average home prices in the United States in 1993. The 71 largest cities are shown.

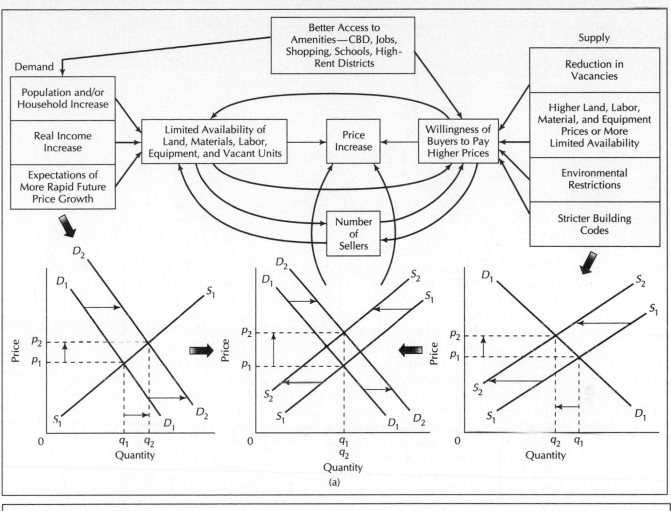

(a)

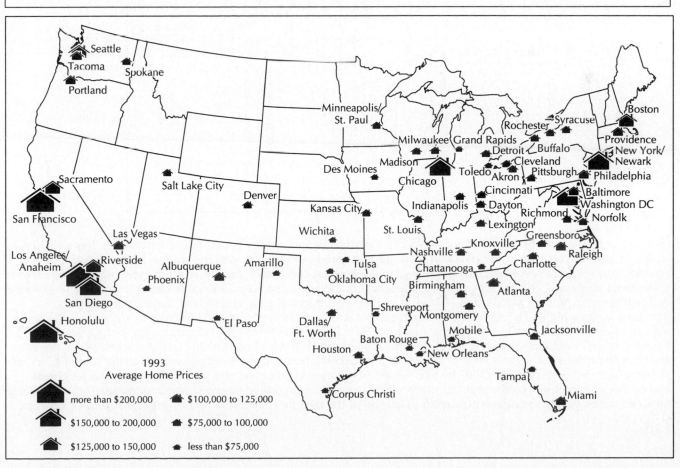

1993
Average Home Prices

more than $200,000 $100,000 to 125,000

$150,000 to 200,000 $75,000 to 100,000

$125,000 to 150,000   less than $75,000

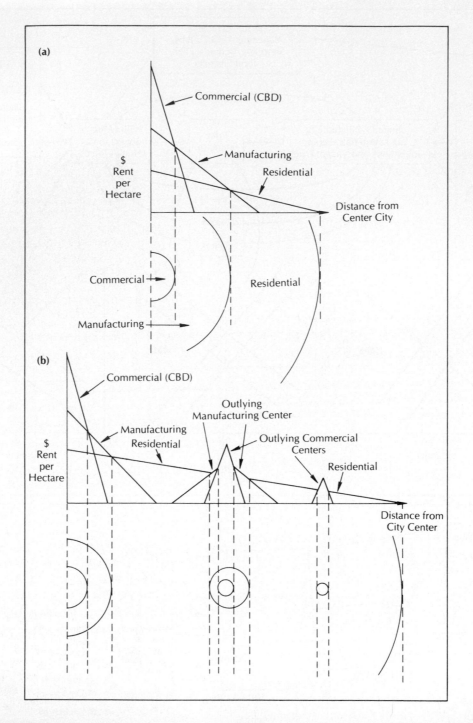

FIGURE 8.4

Multiple land-use patterns: (a) single-centered city. Commercial space, such as that found in the CBD, has a higher intensity of land use because of the potential mark-up of its goods and services and the volume of business that it can produce. Mark-up times volume, called turnover in the business community, results in a relatively high ceiling rent for commercial land uses. The bid rent curve for manufacturing is less steep because manufacturing is not able to generate as much revenue off each square unit of land. It can produce more off each unit of land than can residential; therefore, it has a higher ceiling rent. The residential bid rent curve is even less steep because of a lower ceiling rent at the center of the city, as well as a lower use intensity on a low sensitivity to travel distances. (b) multicentered city. In a multicentered city, more than one location affords the user high levels of accessibility to the market. While the commercial CBD retains the highest level of accessibility and, therefore, the highest ceiling rents, outlying shopping centers or manufacturing centers, perhaps at the intersection of beltways in suburbia, also provide relatively steep bid rent curves. Because exposure to the regional market increases at such accessible locations, the opportunity for volume and turnover increases, increasing the maximum utilization of the land by commercial and manufacturing entrepreneurs.

outer ring, where land prices are lower. We can complicate matters by considering a land-rent profile in a multicentered city (Figure 8.4b). Apart from secondary peaks, perhaps at intersections of main traffic routes, the rent gradient still shows price bids declining outward from the CBD.

CLASSICAL MODELS OF URBAN LAND USE

◈

So far, our study of urban structure has been static. Now let us turn to an urban land-use model that helps explain city-building processes in North America. It is the concentric-zone model of Ernest Burgess (1925), a sociologist. This is an historical generalization about the layout of the city; therefore, no particular city fits this type exactly.

The Concentric-Zone Model

Burgess's *concentric-zone model* emphasizes centripetal forces that focus economic activity on the CBD, which was the dominant center of urban spatial organization in the industrial city. For simplicity, the model assumes a uniform land surface, universal accessibility, and free competition for space. Under these assumptions, cities expand symmetrically in all directions. Burgess suggested a sequence of five zones from center to periphery (Figure 8.5 See also Color Insert 2.)

1. *The central business district.* This zone is the focus of commerce, transportation, and social and civic activity. It encompasses department stores, specialty shops, office buildings, banks, headquarters of organizations, law courts, hotels, theaters, and museums. Encircling the downtown retail district is a mixture of wholesaling and light-manufacturing operations and truck and retail depots.

2. *The zone of transition.* This area reflects residential deterioration. Older private homes have been subdivided into rooming houses. Mansions have been taken over for offices and light manufacturing (functional change). Abandoned dwell-

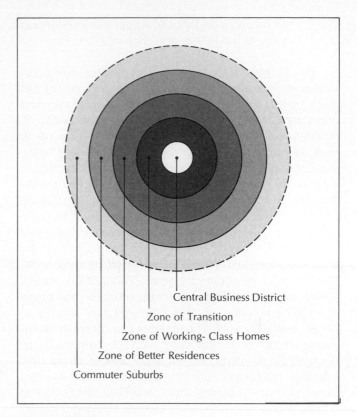

Central Business District
Zone of Transition
Zone of Working-Class Homes
Zone of Better Residences
Commuter Suburbs

FIGURE 8.5
Burgess's concentric-zone model of urban structure. (See color insert 2, page 2.4.)

ings have been torn down to provide space for urban renewal (morphological change). According to Burgess, this is the zone of slums, with their attendant disease, poverty, illiteracy, unemployment, and underworld vice.

3. *The zone of "independent workers' homes."* This ring is characterized by decreasing residential density and increasing quality and cost of homes. It is inhabited by blue-collar workers who have "escaped" the zone of residential deterioration but who need to live close to work. It is regarded as an area of second-generation immigrants who have had enough time to save the money to buy homes of their own.

4. *The zone of better residences.* Still farther from the CBD, working-class residences give way to newer, more spacious single-family dwellings and high-rise apartment buildings occupied by middle-class families.

5. *The commuter suburbs.* Beyond the zone of better residences is a broad commuter area. It is an incompletely built-up area of small satellite

towns and middle- and upper-class residences along railway lines and major highways.

The Burgess model suggests that as cities grow resistances are encountered. Characteristic land uses of one zone exert pressure on future land uses of the next outer zone. This process is called *invasion and succession.* Residents of one zone try to improve their situation by moving outward into a zone of better housing units. New housing constructed at the edge of the city triggers a complex chain of moves. Dwellings vacated by the out-migration of middle- and high-income families are filled by lower-income families moving from the next inner zone. At the end of the chain, the working poor move out of the zone of transition, leaving behind the least fortunate families and abandoned housing units. The result is an inner-city slum. This *filtering process,* which exerts downward pressure on rents and prices of existing housing, enables lower-income families to obtain better housing. The major reason the filter-down process occurs is that the poor, with the strongest latent demand for housing, are the least able to afford new housing. In contrast, the rich can most easily afford to move into new housing and leave their old homes to others. The demand for high-income housing is generally elastic—a new demand generates a quick response from the private housing industry.

The Sector Model

The *sector model* takes into account differences in accessibility and, therefore, in land values along transport lines radiating outward from the city center. According to Hoyt's model, a city grows largely in wedges that radiate from the central business district. One wedge may contain high-rent residential; another, low-rent residential; and still another, industrial. Hoyt believed the contrasts in activity along various sectors usually became apparent early in the city's history, and continued to be marked as the city grew. (See the color insert page 2.5, top.)

The Multiple-Nuclei Model

The concentric and sector models describe single-centered cities. However, most modern cities have *multiple nuclei:* a downtown with satellite centers on the periphery. In 1945, Harris and Ullman described a model city that develops zones of land use around discrete centers. Their model of urban structure encompasses five areas: (1) the central business district, (2) a wholesaling and light-manufacturing area near interurban transport facilities, (3) a heavy industrial district near the present or past edge of the city, (4) residential districts, and (5) outlying dormitory suburbs.

Harris and Ullman recognized that the number and location of differentiated districts depends on the size of the city and its overall structure and peculiarities of historical evolution. They also gave reasons for the development of separate land-use cells. The pattern of multiple cells might result from specialized requirements of particular activities, repulsion of some activities by others, differential rent-paying ability of activities, and the tendency of certain activities to group together to increase profit from cohesion. (See the color insert page 2.5, bottom.)

MODELS OF THIRD WORLD CITY STRUCTURE

◈

The classical models are based on North American experience and are not universally applicable. They are tied to a particular culture. Although the forces of urban change may eventually result in closer similarity of city structure in the non-Communist world, attitudes toward density, land-use arrangements, open spaces, and architectural preferences will continue to vary. In addition, institutional factors—zoning laws, building codes, the role of government in the housing market—will vary with the culture and the level of technology. Models of the structural elements of cities in Latin America and Southeast Asia exemplify different patterns of land use in different regions.

Latin American City Structure

Ernest Griffin and Larry Ford (1980) proposed a model of the Latin American city. Blending traditional elements of Latin American culture with modernizing processes, the framework of the idealized city is a composite of sectors and rings. The heart of the city consists of a vibrant and thriving CBD. A reliance on public transportation and nearby concentrations of the affluent ensure the dominance of the inner city, with a landscape that increasingly exhibits skyscraper offices and condominium towers.

Outward from the inner city is a *commercial/industrial spine* surrounded by a widening *elite residential sector*. The spine/sector is an extension of the CBD, characterized by offices, shops, high-quality housing, restaurants, theaters, parks, zoos, and golf courses, which eventually gives way to wealthy suburbs. Within the spine/sector, the centrifugal forces are similar to those operating in North American cities.

Three zones, which reflect traditional Latin American characteristics, are home to the less fortunate, who account for the majority of city residents. The *zone of maturity*, attractive to the middle classes, features the best housing beyond the spine/sector. Filtered-down colonial hoes and improved self-built dwellings are common. In the *zone of in situ accretion*, the housing is much more modest, interspersed with hovels and unkempt areas. It is a transition zone between inner-ring affluence and outer-ring poverty. The outermost *zone of peripheral squatter settlements* houses the impoverished. Although this teeming, high-density ring looks wretched to a middle-class North American, the residents perceive that neighborhood improvement is possible; they hope, in time, to transform their communities.

The final structural element of the Latin American city is the *disamenity sector*. In this sector, we find slums, known as *favelas* in Brazil. Open sewers line streets; residents live in tiny huts built illegally and lacking sanitation. The worst of these poverty-stricken areas include people so poor that they live on the streets, often in doorways or in cardboard boxes that they carry with them.

Rio de Janeiro—Favela de Roanhia. Here in Brazil, many favelas are on the outskirts of town. Open sewers line the streets and residents live in tiny, illegally built huts, lacking sanitation and fresh water. The worst of these poverty stricken areas include people so poor that they live on the streets, often in doorways or in cardboard boxes they carry with them. Because of total denuding of the landscape in search of firewood for cooking and warmth, when rains come, mud slides generally take lives.
(Source: Alain Keler/Sygma.)

Southeast Asian City Structure

If the Griffin-Ford model provides an interpretation of the organization of a Third World city, then Terry McGee's (1967) generalization about the Southeast Asian city provides a departure that occurs in colonial port cities that have continued to grow rapidly in the postindependence era. McGee's land-use diagram illustrates the old port zone, which is the city's focus, together with a surrounding commercial district. A formal CBD is absent, but its elements occur as separate clusters: a sector of government buildings; a European commercial area; a crowded alien commercial zone, where the bulk of the Chinese merchants live and work; and a mixed land-use strip of land along a railway line for various economic activities, including light industry. Other nonresidential zones include a peripheral market-gardening ring and, still farther from the city, a new industrial park. The residential zones in McGee's model are reminiscent of those in the Griffin-Ford model: a new high-class suburban residential area, an inner-city zone of comfortable middle-class housing, and peripheral areas of low-income squatter settlements with substandard sanitation and inadequate water supplies.

SPRAWLING METROPOLIS: PATTERNS AND PROBLEMS

◈

The Spread City

The classical models of land use fitted earlier patterns of North American city growth better than present-day patterns. The concentric-zone model, developed in the 1920s, emphasized centripetal forces that concentrated economic activity in the downtown of the inner city. Subsequently, the sector model and then, even more so, the multiple-nuclei model stressed centrifugal forces that have decentralizing influences. In the second half of the twentieth century, centrifugal forces have gained the ascendancy. As a result of automobile-based intraurban dispersal, the city has evolved into a restructured form variously called the *spread, suburban,* or *multicentered metropolis.* The classical models cannot accommodate this new urban reality.

James Wheeler and Peter Muller (1981) diagrammed the general characteristics of the contemporary multinodal north American metropolis, which may be regarded as an updating and extension of the classical models of intraurban structure. Their "pepperoni pizza" model consists of a traditional CBD and a set of coequal suburban minicities, serving a discrete and self-sufficient

Cut off from the city's mainstream and many of its services, the urban poor live in makeshift shelters. In many Third World cities, more than half the residents live in slums such as this squatter settlement on the urban fringe of Djakarta, Indonesia.
(Source: World Bank.)

area. James Vance (1977) called these new tributary areas *urban realms*, in that each maintains a distinct economic, social, and political significance and strength.

The rapid outward spread of urban North America owes much to the completion of the radial and circumferential freeway network, which resulted in near-equal levels of time convergence across the metropolitan area. In effect, the freeway system destroyed the regionwide advantage of the CBD, making most places along the expressway network just as accessible to the metropolis as the downtown was before 1970. No longer on the cutting edge, the downtown gave way in the 1970s and 1980s to an ever-widening suburban city that was being transformed—new neighborhoods, new business centers, and new shopping malls. Many Americans now live, work, play, shop, and dine within the confines of this freeway culture.

The spreading out of the American city has captured the imagination of geographers. In the early 1960s, an extreme form of a spread city was described by Jean Gottmann (1964), who coined the term *megalopolis* to describe the coalesced metropolitan areas on the Atlantic Seaboard. This superurban region stretches from Boston to Washington; hence, it is sometimes referred to as *BoWash*. It includes a network of cities fused by expressways, tunnels, bridges, and shuttle jets. Another evolving supercity is the loosely knit lower Great Lakes urban region, also known as *ChiPitts*, centered on Chicago, Detroit, Cleveland, and Pittsburgh.

By the year 2000, trend projections indicate that the United States will consist of four superurban regions:

1. *BoWash*, extending along the Atlantic Seaboard
2. *ChiPitts*, stretching from Chicago to Pittsburgh, and merging with BoWash via the "Mohawk Bridge" to form the Metropolitan Belt
3. *SanSan*, a belt from San Francisco to San Diego
4. *JaMi*, a strip from Jacksonville to Miami

These megalopolitan networks will be supplemented with about 22 other major urban regions, each containing at least a million people (Figure 8.6). According to Jerome Pickard (1972), five-sixths of the population will be concentrated on one-sixth of the country's land area.

Outside the United States, *conurbations*, or "systems of contiguous cities," are also evident. In Canada, there is the Windsor-Quebec city axis, which geographer Maurice Yeates (1975) called *Main Street* (Figure 8.7). More than half of all Canadians live in this multicultural megalopolis, many of whom make their homes in Toronto and Montreal. In Great Britain, megalopolitan England developed as an axial belt from London through Birmingham to Liverpool, Manchester, and Leeds (Figure 8.8). The five conurbations of megalopolitan England—Greater London, West Midlands, Southeast Lancashire, West Yorkshire, and Merseyside—as well as those of Tyneside and Central Clydeside, are home to one-third of the British population of 57 million. In the western Netherlands, the *Randstad* (or Ring City), runs in a horseshoe-shaped line approximately 170 kilometers long (Figure 8.9). It centers on major conurbations grouped around the four cities of Rotterdam, The Hague, Amsterdam, and Utrecht. From this complex, the E36 motorway joins the Netherlands to the heart of Europe, linking the Randstad with another vast urban agglomeration of continental Europe—the Rhine-Ruhr. The Dutch Randstad and the cities of the Rhine-Ruhr coalesced in the 1980s into a gigantic urban region: a European megalopolis stretching down the river Rhine from Bonn to the Hook of Holland. In Japan, too, there is an enormous, high-density megalopolis. Half of Japan's more than 120 million people are crowded into three areas—the conurbations around Tokyo, Osaka, and Nagoya. One-third of all Japanese live within 150 kilometers of their emperor's palace in central Tokyo.

The formation of regional and urban systems also characterizes Third World urban processes. The rapid increase in the number, population, and expansion of urban agglomerations in some underdeveloped countries is leading to the growth of megalopolises. Such systems are developing in Brazil, where the major nodes are Rio de Janeiro–Belo Horizonte–Sao Paulo; in Mexico, where Mexico City–Puebla–Vera Cruz form the major centers; and in Egypt, where Alexandria and Cairo are the major cities. Elsewhere, urban growth is concentrated around one or two cities, as in Lagos and Ibadan, Nigeria; in Djakarta and Surabaja, Indonesia; and in Seoul, South Korea. Nearly 40% of South Korea's 42 million people live in or near Seoul, the nerve center of the nation.

The geographer Peirce Lewis (1983) provided a provocative description of the outward spread of cities. For the United States, he coined the term *galactic metropolis* to refer to a vast continuum of urbanization stretching from coast to coast. In his national vision, huge urban concentrations are interspersed with small towns and cities, as well as with loosely separated clusters of houses and businesses around freeway interchanges. Lewis's vision can be extended to the global level, where im-

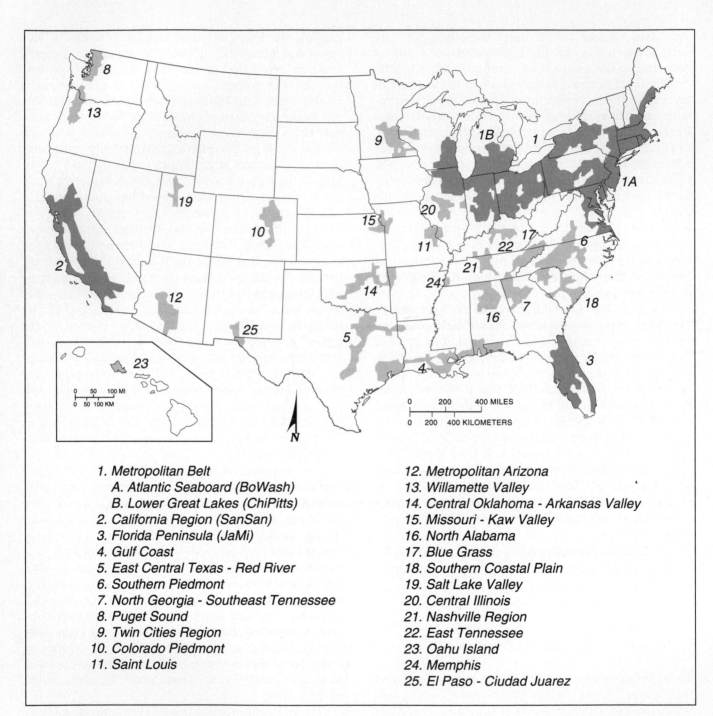

1. Metropolitan Belt
   A. Atlantic Seaboard (BoWash)
   B. Lower Great Lakes (ChiPitts)
2. California Region (SanSan)
3. Florida Peninsula (JaMi)
4. Gulf Coast
5. East Central Texas - Red River
6. Southern Piedmont
7. North Georgia - Southeast Tennessee
8. Puget Sound
9. Twin Cities Region
10. Colorado Piedmont
11. Saint Louis

12. Metropolitan Arizona
13. Willamette Valley
14. Central Oklahoma - Arkansas Valley
15. Missouri - Kaw Valley
16. North Alabama
17. Blue Grass
18. Southern Coastal Plain
19. Salt Lake Valley
20. Central Illinois
21. Nashville Region
22. East Tennessee
23. Oahu Island
24. Memphis
25. El Paso - Ciudad Juarez

FIGURE 8.6
Projected growth of U.S. urban regions with populations of 1 million or more by the year 2000. The four superurban regions are shown in a darker shade.
(Source: Pickard, 1972, p. 143.)

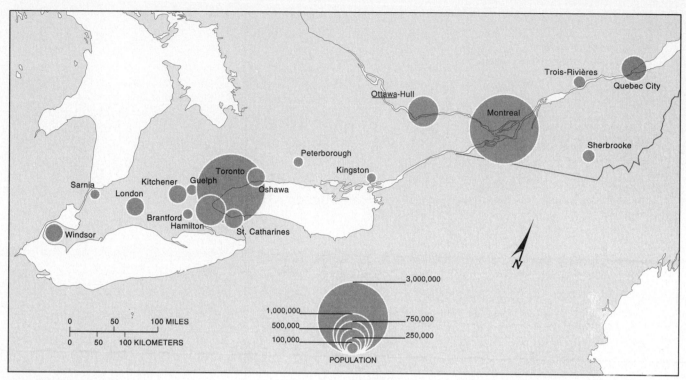

FIGURE 8.7
Canada's Main Street.
(Source: Yeates, 1984, p. 242.)

proved transportation systems and modes of communication are leading to the ultimate form of human settlement—the *ecumenopolis*. According to the late Greek planner, Constantine Doxiadis (1970), an ecumenopolis, consisting of most of the world's population, will be highly integrated into a global urban network in the twenty-first century.

Causes of Urban Spread

What is at the heart of this spreading out of the American city? A number of economic and noneconomic factors are involved. Let us now look at one or two of them with reference to the locational decisions of households and firms.

Suburbanization of households is closely associated with intraurban transportation improvements (Figure 8.10). With each revolution in transportation, travel costs were lowered, and families become less willing to pay high rents for central locations. Since 1945, the

desire for a single-family home in the suburbs has resulted in rapid suburban expansion. Low-mortgage interest rates, loan guarantees provided under federal housing and veterans' benefit programs, property-tax reductions for owner-occupied homes, cheap transportation, and massive highway subsidies have reinforced this trend. The freeway-dominated automobile era has removed virtually all restrictions on intraurban population mobility so that residential land use is feasible almost anywhere in a metropolitan area, especially with automobile companies buying and closing down intraurban streetcar lines across the country.

THE ECONOMICS OF COMMUTING

The economics of residential land and commuting time are attributed to Alonso (1964) and Muth (1969). According to these theorists, residential location choice is a utility-maximization process. In the simple model, the assumptions include these: (1) each household has one laborer, (2) housing is a homogeneous factor

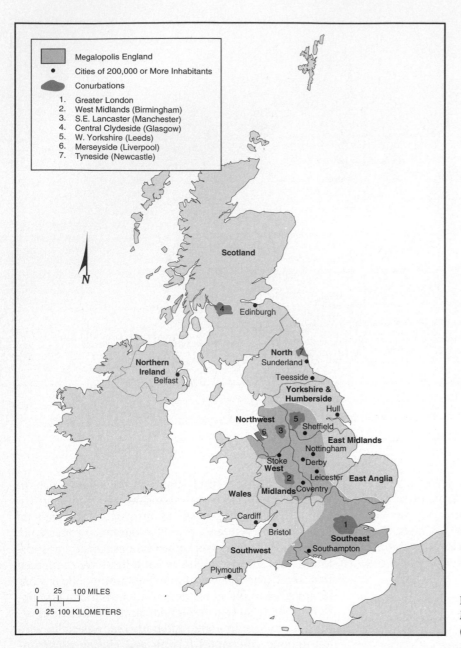

FIGURE 8.8
Megalopolitan Great Britain.
(Source: Based on Herbert, 1982, p. 234.)

and only location varies, (3) transportation costs are based solely on the commuting distance to work, and (4) all employment is fixed at the center of the city. Each householder chooses the location where the best combination of land, rent, and transportation costs (as well as a set of other factors) occurs.

In the residential land theory, costs of housing and land decline farther from the center of the city, as land becomes less in demand. All commerce and business occur in the center of the city, where the price of land is bid up. With increasing distance from the city, there is less opportunity for commerce and less demand for space as a function of area, or πr^2 (pi times radius squared). For example, if all housing were the same price—a uniform price for land at every location—all business owners and householders would choose the same location, the center of the city. On the other hand, transportation costs increase with distance from the city, as a direct function of time in movement.

The optimal location for a householder is the point

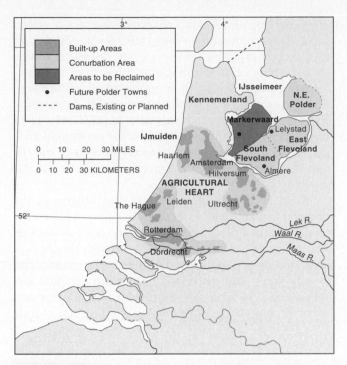

FIGURE 8.9
Randstad, Holland: a horseshoe-shaped ring of cities, each performing specialized functions—government in The Hague, commerce in Rotterdam, shopping and culture in Amsterdam—with a central agricultural, or green, heart.
(Source: Based on Hall, 1982, p. 236.)

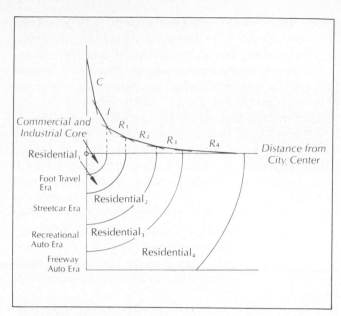

FIGURE 8.10
Passenger transportation improvements and housing density. With each innovation in transportation, travel costs were lowered, and families became less willing to pay high rents for central locations.
(Source: Abler, Adams, and Gould, 1971, p. 358.)

where the marginal savings in housing are equal to the marginal increase in transportation costs. That is, householders will, according to their preferences for transportation and housing space, try to maximize both by finding the place away from the center of the city, where the decrease in housing costs is just offset by an increase in the commuting costs. Studies have shown that the housing preference is the stronger of the two. That is, people are willing to offset extra transportation costs to consume a larger *market basket* of housing, even if doing so means a longer commute. The theory continues by postulating that with increased incomes more housing will be consumed farther from the city, where the unit cost of consumption is less.

What if transportation costs decline because highway improvements or a mass-transit line reduces travel time? According to Figure 8.11, as transportation costs decline from T_{D_1} to T_{D_2}, the optimum, or equilibrium, location for housing moves from D_1 to D_2, outward toward the suburbs, as a larger market basket of housing can be consumed for the same transportation cost.

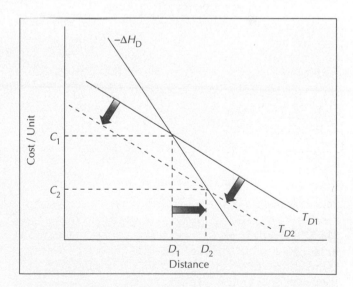

FIGURE 8.11
The effect of reduced transportation costs (T_{D_2}) on residential location (D_2).
(Source: Guliano, 1986, p. 251.)

$-\Delta H_D$ is the householders' savings on housing costs by moving away from the center of the city. The original equilibrium location is D_1, where the housing-cost decline curve intersects the transportation-cost decline curve. The new equilibrium location is D_2, where the housing-cost decline curve, $-\Delta H_D$, intersects the new transportation-cost curve, T_{D_2}, according to Guliano.

Since World War II, gasoline prices in the United States have been extremely low compared with those of other highly developed nations around the world. For example, in the 1950s, a gallon of gasoline averaged $0.20. In the 1960s, it averaged $0.35. During the 1970s, a gallon of gasoline remained at $0.35, only creeping up to $0.65 by 1978. During the 1950s through the 1970s, America saw its most dramatic suburbanization push, associated with freeway building and inexpensive gasoline, relative to other commodities and high demand.

So far, two types of costs have been discussed: out-of-pocket gasoline costs and time costs. Each affects social classes differently. From a business standpoint, an increasingly rapid movement toward decreased travel-time costs benefits the wealthy more than the low-income groups because their time is worth more. Keeping the price of gasoline low also benefits the wealthy more because, compared with other family needs, gasoline is a lower overall proportion of the household budget. Other things being equal, travel-time costs and the cost of gasoline have more of an effect on higher-income groups.

Now, according to residential rent theory, as the demand for suburban residential locations increases, the relative price of properties closer to the city will decline. Regardless of lower prices, residential rent theory predicts declining population densities in the central and nearby areas, and increasing population densities farther away, which has been the case in American cities. Improvements in transportation that reduce commuting

Southdale Center, which opened in 1956 as the first enclosed, climate-controlled shopping center in the United States, is in the Minneapolis suburb of Edina, Minnesota, a typical edge city.
(*Source: The Center Companies.*)

time have a strong decentralizing effect on a city, especially for the higher-income groups.

The flight of households to the suburbs, the inhabitants of which outnumbered those of the central city by 1970, may also be a consequence of rising real incomes, population growth, and the postwar movement of rural blacks to central cities (Table 8.4). However, although it is true that upper-income households are concentrated in the suburbs, there is an unresolved debate as to whether this is the result of income per se or some other variable. In the 1960s, Richard Muth (1969) argued that income is the cause. He argued that higher income led to a higher demand for housing (a positive-income elasticity), and this higher demand for housing led to a utility-maximizing move away from the city. Although higher income also meant an increased commuting-time cost (the time cost is estimated as a fraction of a person's explicit or implicit hourly wage) and would tend to make the householder more interested in remaining near the job site, Muth's statistical studies led him to conclude that the added push away from the CBD exceeded the added pull toward it. In 1987, William Wheaton published another study on the same question. His results showed that the push effects and the pull effects were almost the same. Thus, his work suggests that higher income per se is not the reason for the suburban concentration of upper-income individuals.

GENTRIFICATION
OR SUBURBANIZATION

Between 1940 and 1970, many southern blacks were displaced from mechanized farms and moved to northern cities. Black migration from the rural South

to the urban North peaked in the late 1950s. As blacks moved into city neighborhoods, white middle-class families experienced property devaluation, often spurred by the blockbusting of real-estate brokers. Meanwhile, valuations of suburban locations increased. The number of whites who moved to the suburbs in order to maintain a social distance from the immigrant blacks of the inner city has not been documented, however.

During the 1970s and 1980s, reverse migration occurred; middle-class families moved from the suburbs to the inner cities. The number of families involved was relatively small, however. For every family that moved back to the inner city, eight moved to the suburbs. Residential revitalization in and around the CBD clearly did not spawn a return-to-the-city movement by suburbanites. In fact, most reinvestment was undertaken by those already living in the central city. Such inner-city neighborhood redevelopment involves *gentrification*—property upgrading by high-income settlers—which frequently results in the displacement of lower-income residents.

Suburbanization of retailing was a response to the residential flight to the suburbs, new merchandising techniques, and technical obsolescence of older retailing areas. The automobile provided customers with a convenient mode of transportation to shopping places, but downtown parking facilities were scarce and expensive. A need to improve the parking situation and to increase profits impelled retailers to the suburbs.

The decentralization trend began in the 1920s as stores began spreading out from the downtown along main thoroughfares. Yet, it was not until the postwar years that retailers moved to the suburbs in large numbers. First came the strip center, or neighborhood shopping center, consisting of a string of 10 to 30 shops,

◈

Table 8.4
U.S. Population Change, 1980–1990

	U.S. Population		
	1980	*1990*	*Change (%)*
Metropolitan areas	170,540,000	189,877,000	+ 11.3
Inside center cities			
Outside center cities			
Nonmetropolitan areas	57,217,000	61,646,000	+ 7.7
Total	227,757,000	251,523,000	+ 10.4

usually anchored by a supermarket. Then came the larger community center with a small department store or a variety store as the principal tenant. The success of these early centers, which catered to a limited trade area, depended on a main-road location, free parking, and the persuasiveness of "super" everything, "drive-in" everything, self-service stores, and discount outlets.

Neighborhood and, later, larger community shopping centers became vulnerable to more attractive regional shopping centers that appeared after 1955. The newest and biggest of these centers in distant suburbs have several floors, three or more department stores, and scores of specialty shops. Surrounded by huge parking lots, these shopping complexes are usually enclosed so that customers can shop in climate-controlled comfort. Unlike early suburban shopping centers, the giant regional shopping centers are catalysts attracting a variety of activities to the area.

Decentralization of manufacturing began before the turn of the century. Technical advances, such as the development of continuous-material flow systems, induced many manufacturers, especially those engaged in large-scale production of industrial goods, to spread out along suburban railway corridors where land was relatively cheap and abundant. Nonetheless, most manufacturers, despite truck transportation, decided to remain in or near the central city until the 1960s, when two technological breakthroughs occurred. Peter Muller (1976) describes these breakthroughs:

> These post-1960 breakthroughs involved the completion of the intraurban expressway system and the long-delayed attainment of scale economies in local trucking operations. Completing the freeway network made it possible to assemble goods at any number of points equally accessible to the rest of the metropolis, and newly economical short distance trucking helped to neutralize the transportation cost differential between inner city and suburb. With the near equalization of these costs across much of the metropolis, intraurban goods movement via truck became as efficient as inter-regional freight transport. And by eliminating the locational pull of central city water and rail terminals, most of the remaining urbanization economies of downtown were quickly nullified. (p. 33)

In the freeway metropolis, the economic advantages of a central-city location have disappeared. Consequently, the spatial organization of the manufacturing industry is responding increasingly to noncost factors.

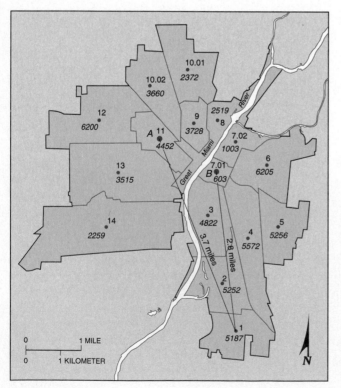

FIGURE 8.12

Geographers can compute the relative potential for a service at various locations. For example, to determine whether a service should be located in Tract 7.01 or Tract 11 in Hamilton, Ohio, follow these steps: (1) Determine the potential population of patrons in each of the other neighborhoods; these figures are shown in italics. (2) Measure the distance from each neighborhood to one of the alternative locations; for example, the distance from Tract 1 to Tract 7.01 (location *B*) is approximately 4.5 kilometers (2.8 miles). (3) Divide the population in each neighborhood by the distance from that neighborhood to the proposed location of the service. (4) Sum all the populations and divide by the distance; this figure is the relative potential of a service at a particular location. (5) Repeat steps 2 through 4 for alternative location *A*. The optimal location for a service is the tract with the highest relative potential.

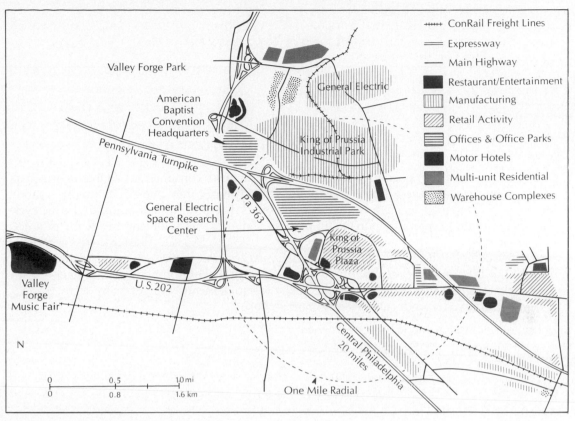

FIGURE 8.13
Internal economic geography of the suburban minicity: King of Prussia, Pennsylvania.
(Source: Based on Muller, 1976, p. 41.)

Manufacturers are relatively free to select the most prestigious sites that they can find in the outer city.

Expansion of offices into the suburbs began in the early postwar years, when large corporations began looking for new office headquarters. For example, General Foods, IBM, Reader's Digest, Union Carbide, and ESSO-Standard Oil left New York for the suburban countryside. This trend of the large corporations prompted an avalanche of similar moves by a host of small office firms. In that they were unable to create their own environments in the manner of the large corporations, the small firms began to rent or lease space in office parks. Tenants of these office buildings were attracted by the convenience, amenity, and prestige of an office-in-a-park address. The major factor in office-site selection is accessibility to an expressway.

Initially, suburban business and commerce located at any convenient highway intersection or at a site near a freeway. Today, geographers can compute the relative potential for a business at several locations to determine the optimal location (Figure 8.12). (See "Microvision" box.)

Suburban economic activities have a growing locational affinity for one another. Without doubt, the focal point of the outer city is the huge regional shopping center. Super shopping malls are catalysts for other commercial, industrial, recreational, and cultural facilities. The result is the emergence of miniature downtowns called *minicities* (Figure 8.13). In many metropolitan areas, minicities are unplanned, loosely organized, multifunctional nodes, and they are strongly shaping the geography of suburbia.

Urban Realms Model

James Vance (1964, 1977) put forward the urban realms model, which he constructed from his observations of the San Francisco Bay area and its sprawling metropolis. Peter Muller (1981, 1989), and others, ap-

MICROVISION

WHAT IS MICROVISION

MicroVision is a micro-geographic targeting system that uses consumer, as well as census data to accurately classify every household in the United States into one of 50 unique market segments. Each market segment consists of households that are at similar points in the life cycle and share common interests, purchasing patterns, financial behavior and needs for products and services.

To give complete flexibility in consumer segmentation strategies, MicroVision further assigns each of the 50 market segments to one of nine groups. Each group contains segments with similar characteristics or habits, giving the ability to simultaneously target many segments that will respond alike to product, service or market efforts.

UNLIMITED APPLICATIONS

MicroVision can be used in many ways.

Customer Profiling. More precisely identify the purchasing behaviors and lifestyles of customers and prospects to develop the most profitable marketing strategy possible.

Product and Service Demand. More accurately determine the products and services consumers use and need, then design an effective cross-selling strategy.

Market Analysis. Better pinpoint where consumers with the highest potential for sales and profits are located, and target as few as five to 15 households.

Media Selection. More confidently select the advertising media that will entice customers and prospects to respond to promotions.

Direct Marketing. Better maximize the response and return on direct marketing investment, and obtain a higher response rate while mailing fewer pieces.

HOW MICROVISION WAS BUILT

MicroVision was built by combining aggregated consumer demand data from Equifax National Decision Systems of San Diego, California, with the most current census data. Over 100 unique characteristics for more than 160 million consumers were used, including demographic, socio-economic, housing, purchasing activity, consumption pattern and consumer financial information.

The data was then statistically clustered at the ZIP + 4 level of geography. Over 23 million ZIP + 4s, each consisting of only five to 15 households, were used in the MicroVision clustering process. This gives the ability to target the lowest possible level of geography of any segmentation system. From this clustering process, 95 unique and homegeneous sub-segments were identified.

MICROVISION GROUPS

ACCUMULATED WEALTH (MVG1)

SEG. #	NAME
1	Upper Crust
2	Lap of Luxury
3	Established Wealth
4	Mid-Life Success
5	Prosperous Ethnic Mix
6	Good Family Life
14	Middle Years

MAINSTREAM FAMILIES (MVG2)

SEG. #	NAME
10	Home Sweet Home
11	Family Ties
16	Country Home Families
17	Stars and Stripes
18	White Picket Fence
22	Aging America
23	Settled In
35	Late-Life Laborers
38	Back Country

YOUNG ACCUMULATORS (MVG3)

SEG. #	NAME
9	Building a Home Life
19	Young and Carefree
25	Bedrock America
28	Building a Family

MAINSTREAM SINGLES (MVG4)

SEG. #	NAME
8	Movers and Shakers
12	A Good Step Forward
15	Great Beginnings
32	Metro Singles
34	Books and New Recruits
39	On Their Own
40	Trying Metro Times

CONSERVATIVE SENIORS (MVG6)

SEG. #	NAME
7	Comfortable Times
20	Social Security
21	Sunset Years
30	Retirement Age
31	Golden Times

ASSET-BUILDING FAMILIES (MVG5)

SEG. #	NAME
27	Middle of the Road
29	Establishing Roots

SUSTAINING ETHNIC FAMILIES (MVG8)

SEG. #	NAME
24	Metro Minority Families
41	South of the Border
42	Hanging On
43	Low-Income Blues
44	Hard Years
46	Difficult Times

CAUTIOUS YOUNG COUPLES (MVG7)

SEG. #	NAME
26	The Mature Years
33	Living Off The Land

SUSTAINING SINGLES (MVG9)

SEG. #	NAME
13	Successful Singles
36	Metro Ethnic Mix
37	Moving Ahead Minorities
45	Struggling Minority Mix
47	University U.S.A.
48	Innercity Singles

*Segments 49 and 50 were not placed in a group due to their non-homogeneous nature.

MicroVision is a GIS computer marketing system that targets microgeographic segments of the population by using census data. It can be used for a variety of applications, including customer profiling, media selection, direct marketing, and market analysis. For the latter, it is used to detect the areas of highest retail sales and the most profitable retail locations. Equifax National Decision Systems of San Diego, the MicroVision creator, is the largest market area firm in the United States.

MicroVision then classifies every household in the United States into one of 50 market segments based on the unique characteristics of its ZIP + 4. This extensive segmentation process makes MicroVision an accurate segmentation and targeting system for any market, of any size and shape, anywhere in the United States. MicroVision gives the ability to precisely quantify, locate and target the most profitable customers and prospects.

◈

EASY-TO-USE ANALYSIS TOOLS

MicroVision provides a variety of effective analysis tools including reports, bar graphs, and game plans to help thoroughly understand customers and prospects.

The MicroVision Profile Report shows what percentage of total customer households are in each MicroVision market segments. It then compares this composition to the total market area, allowing one to calculate customer penetration per segment. This report also provides indices to help determine the propensity of each segment to be a customer.

TheMicroVision Game Plan clearly identifies core and developmental market segments. This allows one to tailor marketing efforts on key developmental segments to help attain increased market share and profits.

The MicroVision Bar Graphs allows one to quickly profile and identify the purchasing, media and lifestyle behaviors of customers. This information is critical to developing targeted and profitable marketing programs.

---

plied this model to New York City and the Los Angeles metropolitan area. The urban realms model identifies suburban regions that have independent suburban downtowns as their foci, and yet are within the sphere of influence of the central city and its metropolitan CBD. Each suburban downtown coexists with other suburban downtowns, as well as the principal CBD, each being self-sufficient in foreman function. Hartshorn (1992) calls this model the "culmination of the impact of the automobile on urban form in the 1990s (p. 234)."

According to Vance, the existence and form of each urban realm, in modern Anglo-American cities today, depends on four factors: (1) the overall size of the metropolitan region, (2) the amount of economic activity in each urban realm, (3) the topography and major land features, which can help to identify urban realms, and (4) internal accessibility of each realm with regard to daily economic functioning and travel patterns. Also according to Vance, a region has a high probability of becoming a self-sufficient urban realm if the following are true: (1) the overall size of the metropolis is large,

(2) there is a large amount of decentralized economic activity in the region, (3) the topography and barriers isolate the suburban region, and (4) it has good internal accessibility for self-sufficient daily commerce and functioning (especially if it is tied to an airport or metropolises).

Somewhat later than in North America, European cities expanded outward from the inner cities to the suburbs and beyond. In the 1950s, for the first time the population of major British cities started to decline. Often inner-city depopulation was a result of an official policy to relieve overcrowding. By the 1960s, these major cities began to lose business. Old industries around which the cities had grown up, and that supported the economy of the inner cities, were in decline. The newer growth industries could not make up the job losses and were often developed on greenfield sites far from the central cities, where building and land were less expensive. Although large European cities are beginning to resemble expanding doughnuts as they decentralize, their CBDs remain more vibrant than many in North America.

JAPANESE SPRAWL

Urban sprawl is also a feature of Japanese cities. Tokyoites who want to purchase their own homes have been pushed farther and farther from the middle of the city by high land prices. Of Tokyo's 5 million or more daily commuters, 2.75 million live outside the city, itself an area larger than Luxembourg. Even though land prices in central Tokyo are astonishingly high by New York and London standards, Japanese companies still want their headquarters near the ministries and banks of the capital. Eventually, Tokyo—a megalopolis with the profile of a pancake—may become so big that it decentralizes. Technology is the key to decentralization.

Tokyo's Murunouchi business district with its row upon row of modern office buildings. Tokyo and its neighbors are home to more than 20 million people. In contrast, the 2 million residents of Phoenix, Arizona, live in a metropolis that sprawls over 2000 square miles. (*Source: Japan Information Service, Consulate General of Japan at Chicago.*)

Telecommunications and high-speed, magnetically levitated trains would make Japan's second city, Osaka, a 60-minute ride from Tokyo against today's 3.5-hour ride in a "bullet train." The line would pass through Nagoya and create an urban corridor along central Japan's Pacific coast. Away from this spine would lie suburban centers linked by advanced telecommunications networks. Tokyo would become a vast, wired megalopolis of more than 60 million people stretched over 500 kilometers. This vision is less odd to the Japanese than to Europeans. Japanese cities do not have centers such as Paris or London, but a series of subcenters, more like a grand-scale, high-density Phoenix or Tucson.

By European or American standards, Japanese cities are overcrowded to Dickensian proportions, but so too are the large Third World cities. In many a Third World country, the largest city is growing uncontrollably. Rapid growth is linked to what economic geographers call the *economies of agglomeration*. Firms locate in the large city because of the existence of modern infrastructure. When a plant locates in the city, it brings with it new jobs. And industry is not the only source of work in the metropolis. The growing bureaucracy needed to administer public investment in schools, transportation, communications, water, and sanitation provides many jobs, as does the semilicit service economy. Work in the industrial plant, bureaucratic office, or black market offers a higher standard of living than that available in the provincial town or village. The superior standard of living has a powerful attraction for the people of peripheral regions, who flock to the large, crowded cities.

Problems of the City

The free market for space in the metropolis has produced a pattern of suburban sprawl in advanced capitalist societies. From a rare social entity at the beginning of the twentieth century, suburbs have evolved into major growth centers for industrial and commercial investment, and a suburban way of life has been adopted by millions of people. The decentralized metropolis fostered large-scale consumption and prosperity in the past, but it is causing real problems now. In some instances, the urban fringe has pushed out farther than workers are willing or able to commute. Urban sprawl has generated externalities such as uneven development, pollution, and the irrational use of space, which increasingly impinge on the life of urban residents. Furthermore, recurrent fiscal crises threaten to bankrupt central cities.

In the United States, the rationalization of the metropolis for the purpose of planned development is blocked by the political independence of the suburbs. The suburbs have resulted from the differential ability of various groups to organize and protect their advantages. They are not willing to abdicate clear-cut, short-run benefits for less certain long-run gains. Thus, metropoliswide planning in the face of a bewildering multitude of rigid and outdated municipal boundaries—1200 of them in New York—is extremely difficult, if not impossible, to implement. Yet without planning, without redrawing areas of municipal authority, the continued profitability and stability of the metropolis and capitalist society are threatened.

Most cities in North America and Western Europe are now faced with a roughly similar situation—they are dying in the middle. Jobs are moving out with modern technology and communications, and so is shopping and entertainment. Violence is moving in. The need for the city, as far as the middle class is concerned, has diminished.

To be sure, there have been attempts to revitalize inner cities. For example, in England there are tax-incentive plans for the rebirth of blighted areas. The intent is to create jobs out of urban wastelands and to transform old warehousing and waterfront districts. In London, dock-land revival involves some light manufacturing, but it is dominated by office and commercial development as well as the construction or refurbishment of housing units (gentrification). The residen-

In Liverpool, England, high-rise housing estates replace nineteenth-century row houses in an attempt at urban renewal.
(Source: WHO photo by E. Spooner.)

tial units are for the rich up-and-comers; they cost too much for the majority of the original Eastenders. Small schemes aimed at revitalizing inner-city areas are narrow technical solutions to a broad problem created by capitalist development.

Most governments of Western Europe and North America have concentrated, often for decades, on relieving congestion and welfare pressures by demolishing block upon block of old housing, factories, and other buildings. A major problem for local governments has been where to rehouse the people affected by clearance. One solution has been to replace crowded terraced streets with blocks of tall apartments. But besides being more expensive to build than houses, high-rise housing developments are generally regarded as dehumanizing environments.

Most redevelopment schemes can rehouse only about half the displaced population. The so-called overspill must move out. Governments have tried a variety of methods to relieve the overspill problem. For London, in the 1940s, it was proposed that a green belt of open space be preserved around the built-up area, and that a number of new towns to house people from central London be developed beyond the green belt. The eight new towns that were built in the 1950s and 1960s were fashioned after the Garden City model, advocated in Ebenezer Howard's (1946) book, *Garden Cities of Tomorrow*, first published in 1902. This model called for self-contained, medium-sized cities with large areas of public open space separating urban functions.

New towns have been built in other parts of Great Britain as well, especially northern industrial areas (Figure 8.14). The British new-town model has also been adopted in the United States, Japan, and other European countries. In the United States, examples include Columbia, Maryland; Reston, Virginia; and Irvine, California.

New towns and other population redistribution schemes, such as planned public-housing estates, have not solved big-city problems. For example, a deep-seated polarization between inner and outer city remains. Increasingly, the center city is home to the metropolitan disadvantaged and includes a few specialized services, whereas suburb and satellite cities house the affluent and support a range of activities that were previously city bound. This pattern of spatial organization favors rich people, who collect a disproportionate share of the surplus product with respect to the location of services and job opportunities. Examples of how the rich tend to be favored in U.S. metropolitan areas follow.

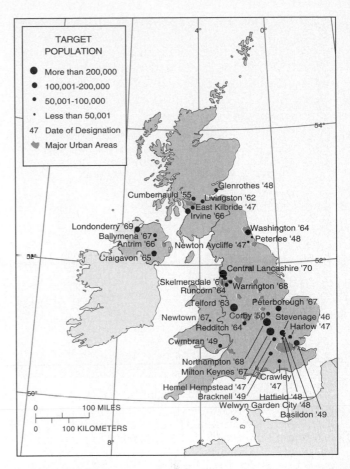

FIGURE 8.14
New towns in Great Britain, 1946–1980.
(Source: Based on Hall, 1982, p. 167.)

RETAIL STORES

Shop location is a reflection of the economic behavior of entrepreneurs. However, their decisions are usually subject to some public control through zoning. Decision makers select locations with a high demand potential. And because demand is income related, it is natural for entrepreneurs to choose affluent suburban areas first. For example, many large supermarkets locate in the suburbs and sell their produce at lower prices than inner-city neighborhood stores do. Differential prices and accessiblity to retail outlets contributed to the urban riots of the 1960s and 1970s.

MEDICAL CARE

Health care services provided by general practitioners, internists, and pediatricians are located mainly

Shopping in Tysons Corner, Virginia, the archetypal *edge city*, on the outskirts of Washington DC. It is the largest retail concentration on the East Coast (after Manhattan, New York).
(Source: Frederick P. Stutz.)

by private action. Because they, too, are sensitive to demand potential, they tend to locate in affluent areas even though the need for medical care is likely to be higher in low-income neighborhoods. In the inner city, the needy sick are taken care of in public hospitals, which are often poorly equipped and understaffed.

PUBLIC UTILITIES

Provision of water, electricity, sewage and sanitation, and transportation services provides additional examples of the inequitable appropriation of the surplus. For instance, consider water. In some metropolitan areas, water prices are not seasonally adjusted, yet the peak demand for water in summer comes mainly from suburban families, who use it to sprinkle lawns and fill swimming pools. Inner-city residents have neither yards to sprinkle nor pools to fill. When pricing systems for water fail to reflect seasonal demands, they effectively subsidize the already wealthy.

NOXIOUS ATTRIBUTES

The value of a dwelling varies according to proximity to noxious attributes such as smoke, dust, noise and water pollution, and traffic congestion. The affluent, who wield political clout, usually manage to exclude noxious facilities from their neighborhoods. But these facilities must go somewhere. Traditionally, facilities such as power stations have been located in inner-city communities and in rural areas.

JOBS/HOUSING BALANCE

A relatively new solution to the problem of increased suburban traffic congestion caused by explosive employment growth gained credibility in the late 1980s in

A homeless pair begging on the streets of New York in front of a Manhattan storefront.
(Source: Thomas Hoepker/Magnum Photos.)

many areas of the United States. This problem resulted from the increased commuting times to these work centers from low-density residential subdivisions that shifted farther into the suburban fringe. Some observers (Porter, 1985; Porter and Lasser, 1988) have noted that if nearby affordable housing development had accompanied job center growth, perhaps less auto traffic would have resulted (Porter, 1985). This led to a ground swell of support for the concept of *jobs/housing balance*. Local and regional planners increasingly support the notion of expanding the supply of housing in job-rich areas and the quantity of jobs in housing-rich areas. Ideally, a ratio of one job per dwelling (a ratio of 1 : 1) would represent a balance. However, in many households more than one person is employed, so more jobs than housing units would provide a better balance.

The Southern California Association of Governments (SCAGS) has studied this issue for nearly 20 years and projected in the mid-1980s that, between 1984 and 2010, a growth of nearly 6 million people would occur in a particular region, along with the addition of 3 million jobs (Porter and Lasser, 1988). Moreover, the projections indicated that most of the job growth would occur in Los Angeles and Orange County, whereas housing growth would occur in the fringe counties of San Bernardino, Riverside, and Ventura. The projections indicated that this imbalanced growth would further overload freeways and average speeds on them would drop 50% to 19 mph. The SCAGS growth-management plan, adopted in 1989, recommended a jobs/housing ratio of 1.22 to 1 within each subregion of the area. The ratio represents the projected regionwide balance between jobs and housing in 2010. Now the question becomes how can one achieve such a balance? What is the appropriate geographic area in which to achieve balance? What price ranges should be encouraged? As answers to these and other questions are worked out in California, and elsewhere in the coming years, evidence mounts that the jobs/housing crisis is worsening.

OUT IN THE BOONDOCKS

Affordable housing for most workers is not being provided in adequate quantities near growing suburban employment centers, commuting trips are becoming longer, and pollution levels from automobile emissions continue to increase. The problem is graphically portrayed by the experience of commuters from Moreno Valley, in Riverside, the fastest-growing county in California, according to the 1990 census. A decade ago, only 28,309 people lived there; now the population is 116,427. The nearest major employment centers are in Orange County, 45 miles to the west, and in Los Angeles, 70 miles to the northwest. According to one commuter (Ferguson and Carlson, 1990, p. 91), "The drive to L.A. takes two hours on a good day, three when an accident ties up traffic on the Pomona Freeway."

In their article, Ferguson and Carlson (1990) call rapidly growing communities like these the *boondocks* because they lack urban amenities and are "boomtowns" in remote boondock areas for only one reason—access to affordable housing. The article discusses the stress of the long commute and the strain it places on family relations. This problem has now spread to most metropolitan areas of the country, including New York, Chicago, and San Francisco, and to many areas in Florida. Long work commutes have fueled the clamor for growth management in which the jobs/housing balance issue and traffic congestion play an important role.

EMPLOYMENT MISMATCHED FOR MINORITIES

Private and public discrimination (e.g., redlining by lending institutions, actions of realtors, screening devices adopted by subdivision developers) and exclusionary zoning practices give the poor, especially minorities, little recourse but to locate in inner-city areas. Meanwhile, most new employment opportunities matched to the work skills of these people are created in the suburbs. This is known as the *spatial mismatch theory*. Thus, the poor are faced with the problem of either finding work in stagnating industrial areas of the inner city or commuting longer distances to keep up with the dispersing job market. Although *reverse commuting* has increased, barriers abound. These barriers include *transportation constraints*—such as increased time and cost of the daily journey to work, and inadequate public transportation for those without cars—and *communication constraints*—such as difficulty in obtaining timely information concerning new job opportunities. Other serious obstacles to suburban employment faced by the inner-city poor include few and substandard work skills and biased hiring practices. In the face of these problems, many otherwise employable persons give up job hunting altogether and contribute instead to the growing number of unemployed in inner-city neighborhoods.

The city of Philadelphia suggests that the spatial mismatch theory is an important factor in the high unemployment levels of black youths. Overall, unemploy-

In the late 1970s, a decision was made to move Union Carbide's headquarters from New York City (at right) to Danbury, Connecticut (below). *(Source: Union Carbide Corporation.)*

ment levels for both black and white youths increase with greater distances to job opportunities. The principal reason for higher black unemployment rates is that the commuting time for blacks was 26 minutes, compared with 19 minutes for whites. Although 50% of the white youths were employed, only 27% of the black youths held jobs. However, the mismatch hypothesis accounts for only approximately half the unemployment, leaving another 50% to be explained by labor-market discrimination, motivation, differences in education, and so forth.

In another study, which compared 50 metropolitan areas in 1991, Ihlanfeldt and Sjoquist (1990) conclude that (1) the mismatch hypothesis explains 25% of the gap between black and white employment rates and 35% of the gap between hispanic and white employment rates, and (2) the spatial mismatch theory is more strongly operative in larger urban areas. The smaller the city, the lower the gap between black and white unemployment rates explained by poor access. Ihlanfeldt found in the 50 metropolitan areas only a 3% gap in small cities but a 14% gap, which resulted from inferior access, in medium-sized cities.

The research just mentioned suggests that some questions still need to be answered to explain unemployment in the ghetto and in poor sections of the city. The spatial mismatch theory cannot answer these questions.

However, any government can promote the suburbanization of minorities in a number of ways and thus reduce access problems and the long commutes to available job opportunities. Governments need to enforce fair housing laws that reduce housing discrimination and poor treatment of minorities in suburban housing markets. Zoning laws also play a key role in blocking from suburbia multifamily housing that minorities can afford. Consequently, local governments must consider providing a full range of government and social services to suburban communities, reducing exclusionary zoning, and providing for a full range of housing types in suburbia.

Visions of Future Metropolitan Life[4]

According to Anthony Downs, Senior Fellow at the Brookings Institution, the current vision of a desirable metropolitan area includes four elements:

[4] This subsection is adapted from Stutz (1992).

1. ownership of single-family homes on spacious lots
2. ownership and use of personal motor vehicles
3. low-density suburban office or industrial workplaces and shopping centers
4. residence in small communities with self-governance

However, inconsistencies in these key elements result in four corresponding flaws in the vision:

1. Low-density residential and work patterns generate a tremendous amount of vehicular travel and traffic congestion.
2. There is no provision for housing for low- and moderate-income families.
3. There is no consensus regarding how to finance the required infrastructure.
4. No mechanism exists to resolve disagreements about facility locations (a result of NIMBY and LULU syndrome).

According to Downs, a new vision for suburban America can be crafted from key elements of existing visions, if residents begin to think and behave more in terms of community and the collective impacts of individual decisions, rather than the way they currently think and behave. Key elements of the new vision are as follows:

1. Sizable areas must be set aside for moderately high-density residential and workplace uses.
2. Residents must live closer to work.
3. The governance structure must include provisions for local authority administered in the context of areawide needs.
4. Incentive arrangements are required to encourage individuals and households to take into account more realistically the collective costs of their decisions. (Examples include peak-hour pricing on highways and linkage zoning requiring the simultaneous development of housing and workplaces.)
5. Equitable strategies to finance the infrastructure must be developed.

Any serious effort to eliminate the polarized or dualistic metropolis must involve planning on a metropoliswide basis. Whether such an effort can succeed remains an open question; certainly, it will be made more difficult by governments reactive to the needs of dominant economic interests.

If the dynamics of capitalist development have created urban problems in developed countries, they have created even more severe urban problems in the non-Communist countries of the underdeveloped world. The rapid growth of Third World cities creates not only social divisions and tensions within them, but also a polarization of metropolis and periphery. For Third World countries, this polarization can lead to political and environmental disaster.

Policies to curb the expansion of major cities, which is largely a product of economic growth, are not easily established. It is more efficient from an economic standpoint to invest in the large city than to invest in the periphery. Thus, public and private capital tend to concentrate in the major city. The cost of providing public services—schools, roads, transportation, communications systems, water, and sanitation—is high in the metropolis, but the government of an undeveloped country is under considerable pressure to invest its capital there. Part of the pressure is political. The stability of the country often depends on preventing unrest in the major

Oxford Street is a major shopping district in London's West End. *(Source: The British Tourist Authority.)*

London is not only the seat of government, it houses the headquarters of 80% of major British transnational corporations. It is the center of banking, insurance, publishing, fashions, advertising, and the legal system for Britain. London's influence stretches far beyond the city, to dominate all of the British Isles and even northwest Europe.

city. So that all runs smoothly, public services are often provided in the metropolis before they are provided in the periphery.

The relatively high standard of living in the major city is the force that drives the concentration of population. To reduce the flow of people toward major cities, the differential in living standards between city and countryside must be reduced. This can be accomplished by slowing the pace of national economic growth and/or raising the standard of living in the countryside.

Migration toward major urban areas has been limited by economic depression, as in the case of Peru and Chile. It has also been curbed in socialist countries: Stringent policies have reduced the growth of Havana, Cuba, and Ho Chi Minh City, Vietnam. More interesting to policymakers are countries in which population flow to the bright city lights has been checked by improving the quality of life of those who live in the periphery. Examples include Argentina and Venezuela, countries that have achieved a high level of economic development. The case of Sri Lanka illustrates that even a poor country can upgrade living conditions in the countryside. However, in this case, national economic growth and social cohesion were sacrificed.

In the foreseeable future, most public investment will take place in the major cities of underdeveloped countries. Without this investment, the stability of many of these countries may be threatened. However, some of the adverse effects of rapid concentration can be countered by governments who also pay attention to areas beyond the traffic-choked, smog-wrapped cities.

SUMMARY

◉

Cities exist in societies that create the conditions necessary for the appropriation of the *surplus product*. These conditions are met in *stratified market-exchange societies*. In the nineteenth century, the stratified societies of Europe and North America experienced an urban transformation. During this period of widespread innovation, cities, especially large manufacturing ones, were ugly creations and horrifying environments for the poor. Denied access to the fruits of rapid economic growth, the worker bore the social costs of urban industrialization. The early nineteenth-century industrial city was characterized by many small, relatively powerless enterprises. Toward the end of the nineteenth century, however, the market mode of economic integration took on a different appearance. There was a drift from individual to monopoly capitalism. As a result, control of the most important industries became more and more concentrated. Today, large corporations have a pervasive influence on cities throughout the capitalist world.

To explain how certain general forces tend to concentrate activities in cities, we considered the model of *pure competition*. This model, which approximates nineteenth-century capitalism, shows that profit-maximizing decisions lead to concentrated clusters of firms at nodes where production and assembly costs are minimized. In addition, the location of many firms in proximity to one another helps to reduce the transportation costs of shifting secondary inputs and outputs among them. Workers live close to their places of employment, in dense residential districts scattered around the industrial and commercial heart of the city.

In a capitalist society, urban land-use arrangements are structured by a *rent-maximizing land market*. We used classical urban location theory to illustrate why land-using activities are located where they are. Although the private appropriation, exchange, and use of urban land are steadily being eroded by the progressive socialization of space through planning, urban land use in contemporary North America and Western Europe is governed primarily by market exchange.

From the operation of the private land market emerge characteristic patterns of land use: a commercial core, a scattering of industry, and socially segregated neighborhoods. We described three widely accepted models that capture the essence of the urban land-use system in North America before the advent of suburbia: the *concentric-zone, sector, and multiple-nuclei models*. Departures from these patterns appear in cities in different cultural realms, as exemplified by the models of Latin American and Southeast Asian cities.

The focus of the last part of the chapter was on the patterns and problems of urban sprawl in developed and underdeveloped countries. The growth of cities, which is the inevitable concomitant of economic growth, has witnessed a host of deleterious breakdowns and conflicts. In developed and underdeveloped countries, the predicament-laden course of urban expansion and land-use development highlights the need for social control and management.

◈

KEY TERMS

agglomeration economies
average total costs
basic firms
boondocks
BoWash
ceiling rent
center city
central business district (CBD)
ChiPitts
colonial city
competitive-bidding process
concentric-zone model
constant returns to scale
conurbation
cumulative causation
ecumenopolis
egalitarian societies
filtering process
fixed costs
functional change
galactic metropolis
gentrification
guilds
income elasticity
industrial city
invasion and succession
jami
jobs/housing balance
localization economies
LRAC curve
Main Street
market basket
market exchange

megalopolis
minicity
morphological change
multicentered metropolis
multiple-nuclei model
need creation marketing
new-town model
nonbasic firms
production function
pure competition
Ranstad
rank societies
reciprocity
redistribution
rent-maximizing land market
SanSan
scale diseconomics
scale economies
sector model
short run
social surplus product
spatial mismatch theory
spread city
squatter settlement
stratified societies
suburb
transportation costs
urban land-use models
urban realm
variable costs
zone in transition
zone of working-class homes

◈

SUGGESTED READINGS

Aitken, S.; Stutz, F.; Chandler, R.; and Prossov, R. (1992). Neighborhood integrity and residents' familiarity: Using a geographic information system to investigate place identity. *TIJDSCHRIFT VOOR ECONOMISCHE EN SOCIALE GEOGRAFIE*, 34:1–12.

Alonso, W. 1964. *Location and Land Use*. Cambridge, MA: Harvard University Press.

Armstrong, W., and McGee, T. G. 1985. *Theatres of Accumulation: Studies in Asian and Latin American Urbanization.* New York: Methuen.

Benevelo, L. 1991. *The History of the City,* 2nd ed. Cambridge, MA: MIT Press.

Bourne, L. S., ed. 1971. *Internal Structure of the City.* New York: Oxford University Press.

Brunn, S., and Williams, J., eds. 1983. *Cities of the World: World Regional Urban Development.* New York: Harper & Row.

Castells, M. 1977. *The Urban Question: A Marxist Approach.* London: Edward Arnold.

Dear, M., and Scott, A. J., eds. 1981. *Urbanization and Urban Planning in Capitalist Society.* New York: Methuen.

Drakakis-Smith, D. 1987. *The Third World City.* New York: Methuen.

Ford, L. R. 1992. Reading the skylines of American cities. *Geographical Review,* 82:180–200.

Friedan, B. J., and Sagalyn, L. B. 1989. *Downtown Inc.: How America Rebuilds Cities.* Cambridge, MA: MIT Press.

Gale, S., and Moore, E., eds. 1975. *The Manipulated City: Perspectives on Spatial Structure and Social Issues in America.* Chicago: Maaroufa Press.

Garreau, J. 1991. *Edge City: Life on the New Frontier.* New York: Doubleday.

Golany, G., ed. 1978. *International Urban Growth Policies: New-Town Contributions.* New York: Wiley.

Gos, J. 1993. The "magic of the mall": An analysis of form, function, and meaning in the contemporary retail built environment. *Annals of the Association of American Geographers,* 83:18–47.

Gottmann, J. 1964. *Megalopolis.* Cambridge, MA: The MIT Press.

Hart, J. F., ed. 1991. *Our Changing Cities.* Baltimore: Johns Hopkins University Press.

Hartshorn, T. A., and Muller, P. O. 1989. Suburban downtowns and the transformation of Atlanta's business landscapes. *Urban Geography,* 10:375–395.

Harvey, D. 1973. *Social Justice and the City.* London: Edward Arnold.

Jones, K. G., and Simmons, J. W. 1990. *The Retail Environment.* London and New York: Routledge.

Kain, J., ed. 1975. *Essays on Urban Spatial Structure.* Cambridge, England: Ballinger.

Knox, P. L. 1991. The restless urban landscape: Economic and sociocultural change and the transformation of metropolitan Washington, DC. *Annals of the Association of American Geographers,* 81:181–209.

Knox, P. L. 1994. *Urbanization: An Introduction to Urban Geography.* Englewood Cliffs, NJ: Prentice Hall.

Lawrence, H. W. 1993. The greening of the squares of London: Transformation of urban landscapes and ideals. *Annals of the Association of American Geographers,* 83:90–118.

Longley, P. A.; Batty, M.; and Shepherd, J. The size, shape, and dimensions of urban settlements. *Transactions of the Institute of British Geographers,* 16:75–94.

Lowder, S. 1988. *Inside Third World Cities.* London: Routledge.

Muller, P. O. 1981. *Contemporary Suburban America.* Englewood Cliffs, NJ: Prentice Hall.

O hUallachain, B., and Reid, N. 1991. The location and growth of business and professional services in American metropolitan areas, 1976–1986. *Annals of the Association of American Geographers,* 81:254–270.

Palm, R. 1981. *The Geography of American Cities.* New York: Oxford University Press.

Papageorgiou, G. J., ed. 1976. *Mathematical Land Use Theory.* Lexington, MA: D. C. Heath.

Parrott, R., and Stutz, F. P. (1992). Urban GIS applications. In Maguire, Goodchild, and Rhind (Eds.), *GIS: Principles and Applications* (pp. 247–260). London: Longman.

Rushton, G. 1978. *Optimal Location of Facilities.* Wentworth, NH: Compress, Inc.

Stutz, F. P. 1992. Maquiladoras branch plants: Transportation—labor cost substitution along the U.S./Mexican border. In 27 Congress of the International Geographical Union (Ed.), *Snapshots of North America.* Washington, DC: I.G.U.

Stutz, F. P. 1992. Urban and regional planning. In T. Hartshorn (Ed.), *Interpreting the City: An Urban Geography Textbook* (pp. 445–476). New York: John Wiley & Sons.

Stutz, F. P.; Parrott, R.; and Kavanaugh, P. 1992. Charting urban space-time population shifts using trip generation models. *Urban Geography,* 13(5):468–475.

Tabb, W. K., and Sawers, L., eds. 1978. *Marxism and the Metropolis: New Perspectives in Urban Political Economy.* New York: Oxford University Press.

United States National Advisory Commission on Civil Disorders. (Otto Kerner, chairman). 1968. *Report.* New York: Dutton.

Vance, J. E. 1977. *This Scene of Man: The Role and Structure of the City in the Geography of Western Civilization.* New York: Harper & Row.

White, P. 1984. *The West European City: A Social Geography.* New York: Longman.

Whyte, W. H. 1988. *City: Rediscovering the Center.* New York: Doubleday.

Yeates, M. 1980. *North American Urban Patterns.* New York: Halsted Press/V. H. Winston.

CHAPTER

9

CITIES AS RETAIL AND SERVICE CENTERS

OBJECTIVES

- To explain the concepts of marketing threshold, range, and hierarchy in the world economy

- To introduce central-place theory and the mercantile model of settlement

- To help you appreciate empirical regularities of the central-place concept

- To explore the market arrangements of different cultures of the world

- To acquaint you with some practical applications of the central-place theory

- To introduce you to computerized marketing geography

Main Street, Schenectady, New York, in the 1940s.
(*Source: Library of Congress.*)

In Chapter 8 we concentrated on individual cities and their patterns of urban land use. However, urban society reveals itself not as one city but as many cities linked in an integrated *hierarchy of centers* of different functions and sizes. Why should there be urban hierarchies? What mechanisms control the size and spacing of cities? This chapter answers these questions by developing the concept of an urban hierarchy and by exploring patterns of service centers that have emerged to satisfy economic demands at local, regional, and international levels.

Although many factors determine locational patterns of cities, one classical location theory, *central-place theory*, provides insights into the urban hierarchy. Central-place theory considers the locational pattern of market-oriented retail and service firms and the hierarchy of urban places insofar as they are market centers. It deals with relationships between market centers and consumers *within* regions. Other types of relationships also link regions to one another. For example, wholesale trade is conducted primarily *between* large regional centers; consequently, the locational pattern of these metropolises is determined by external trade linkages.

The metropolis-and-region network of retail and wholesale centers is a fairly accurate reflection of a domestic urban hierarchy. However, industrial restructuring throughout the world has led to the emergence of a global urban hierarchy. Today, a few international cities serve as centers of business decision making and corporate strategy formulation. To understand the urban hierarchy, these new business and corporate functions must also be considered.

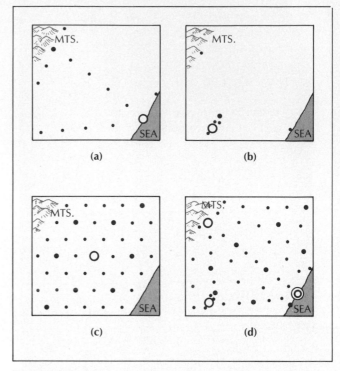

FIGURE 9.1

Different patterns of urban location: (a) transportation centers, aligned along railroads or at the coast; (b) specialized-function centers; (c) theoretical distribution of central places; (d) a theoretical composite grouping of different types of centers.
(Source: Harris and Ullman, 1945, pp. 7–17.)

CENTRAL PLACES AND THEIR HINTERLANDS

Locational Patterns of Cities

The concentration of large populations in cities is essentially the result of the spatial organization of secondary and tertiary activities. These activities can be conducted more profitably when they are clustered rather than dispersed. Locational patterns of cities typically consists of three elements, which often work in concert (Harris and Ullman, 1945) (Figure 9.1):

1. A lined pattern of *transportation centers* that perform break-of-bulk and related services orga-

nized in relation to communication routes. These centers grow along transportation routes and at the junctions of different types of transportation, such as at road and railway junctions and at the head of sea, lake, or river navigation. Most of the largest U.S. cities originated along the seacoast, major rivers, and the Great Lakes, where there was a necessary break in transportation.

2. A pattern of *specialized-function centers*, which develop, either singly or in clusters, around a localized physical resource. Each center or cluster of centers is usually dominated by one activity, such as mining, manufacturing, or recreation. Examples are steel-making and metal-finishing cities in Pennsylvania, in proximity to the coal resources of the Allegheny Plateau, and resort towns along the California and Florida coasts.

3. A uniform pattern of centers that exchange goods and services with their hinterlands. Centers for the local exchange of goods and services are referred to as *central places*. Every settlement—large or small—is a central place, even though most cities do not depend exclusively on central-place functions. Central places provide retailing and wholesaling services; banking, insurance, and real-estate services; governmental and administrative services; and recreational, medical, educational, religious, and cultural facilities.

Cities and Trade

No single locational theory applies to all three components of a settlement pattern, but the arrangement and distribution of central places have been the topics of much research. The central-place theory emphasizes that cities perform extensive services for their hinterlands. Business conducted totally within the hinterland is called *settlement-forming trade*. A true central place is based exclusively on these activities and can never support a population that transcends its hinterland. The number of jobs and, therefore, population size is a direct function of the demand generated in the hinterland. However, most settlements also have other functions that do not depend on hinterland size. For example, a manufacturing plant that sells to a national or an international market does not depend directly on the local retail and service hinterland. Such activity is called *settlement-building trade*. Each settlement also does some internal business—sales of goods and services to the residents of the center. This business is called *settlement-serving trade*.

Hinterlands

Central places serve areas larger than themselves. These areas are called *hinterlands, tributary areas, trade* or *market areas,* or *urban fields*. A trade area may be theoretically continuous. For instance, consider the circulation of a city's newspaper. Most papers are purchased by people who live in or near the city, but some may be purchased by people living thousands of kilometers away. In a graph describing this theoretical relationship, the curve approaches the distance axis infinitely

closely but never reaches zero (Figure 9.2). For practical purposes, however, a city's trade area ends much closer to the origin. Geographers have often used a *median,* or *line-of-indifference,* boundary to delimit trade areas. For example, the median boundary in newspaper circulation is the line between two cities along which 50% of the purchased newspapers are from one city. To further illustrate the concept, we shall consider the line-of-indifference boundary for six goods and services provided by Mobile, Alabama (Figure 9.3). The outermost lines—the isopleths for business in wholesale meat, wholesale produce, and wholesale drugs—mark the approximate boundary of Mobile's influence. From this map, we could delimit the territory over which the city exerts more or less total dominance.

The map of areas influenced by Mobile is the result of fieldwork. To adopt the same method for a number of cities would be tedious. Alternatively, a shortcut means of determining a city's trade area is to measure one activity that is particularly expressive of the trade area. In the United States, for example, metropolitan trade areas can be determined by the extent and intensity of long-distance telephone calls, the length of the journey to work, or newspaper circulation. Newspaper circulation and commuting are conceptually good indicators of the social, economic, and cultural ties between a city and its tributary region. This is especially evident in metropolitan areas. People in the tributary area look to the regional newspaper for information on sales and social events, or to the city as an employment location. Areas of dominant influence are called *daily urban systems* (Figure 9.4).

Areas that focus on central places through circulation networks are known as *functional* or *nodal regions*.

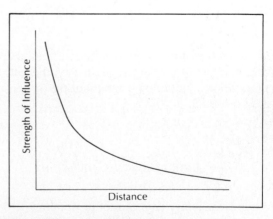

FIGURE 9.2
Cross section of an idealized trade area.

Miami Beach, Florida, is a specialized-function center. Its warm, sunny climate and miles of sandy beach are primary localizing factors.
(Source: U.S. Army Corps of Engineers.)

Every city has a nodal region. The size and shape of this region depends on the size of the city, the influence or competition of dominant neighboring centers, and the ease of travel.

The Law of Retail Gravitation

When satisfactory data cannot be obtained to determine urban trade areas, a modification of W. J. Reilly's (1931) *law of retail gravitation* can be used to provide

estimates. This model, analogous to Newton's law of physics, is designed to identify the exact point between competing centers at which consumers will choose to travel to one center rather than the other. Typically, the law of retail gravitation takes the following form:

$$D_j = \frac{d_{ij}}{1 + \sqrt{P_i/P_J}}$$

where: D_j = the distance from city j to the breaking point

d_{ij} = the distance between cities i and j

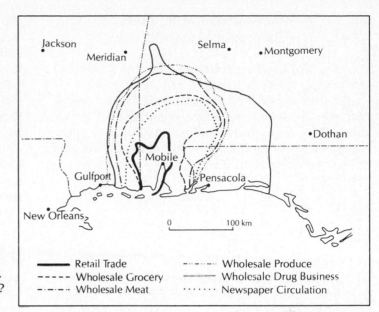

FIGURE 9.3
Areas served and influenced by Mobile, Alabama.
Where would you draw the hinterland of Mobile?
(Source: Ullman, 1943, p. 58.)

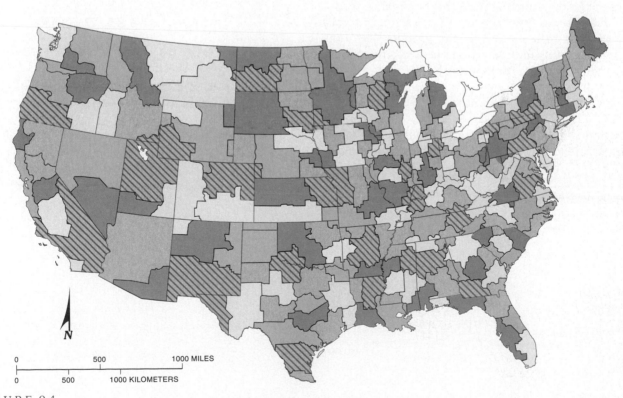

FIGURE 9.4
Daily urban systems. The metropolitan trade areas of the United States, based on commuting to the central city, on newspaper circulation, and on a number of other patronization/marketing entices, are shown in this map. Dividing the country into such regions shows that all households have access, even if distant access, as in the case of Helena, Montana, to jobs, schools, shops, and cultural activities. How many daily urban systems can you name? *(See color insert 2, page 2.6, top)*.

P_i = the population of the ith city
P_j = the population of the jth city

The identified breaking point is assumed to apply to all services located in each center.

Let us illustrate the *break-point model* with a simple example. City *A* and City *B* have populations of 20,000 and 80,000, respectively, and are 60 kilometers apart. According to the formula, the limit of the trading area of *A* in the direction of *B* is this:

$$\frac{60}{1 + \sqrt{\dfrac{80,000}{20,000}}} = \frac{60}{1 + 2} = 20 \text{ km}$$

Therefore, according to the formula, the trading area of *A* would extend 20 kilometers toward *B*. This same analysis can be made in every direction from a particular city; the result is a highly generalized trade area (Figure 9.5).

Although the break-point model provides a shortcut technique for determining trade-area boundaries, it has some deficiencies. City populations are assumed to be homogeneous masses; that is, the formula does not take into account cultural, economic, and other differences among people. Multipurpose trips and ease-of-transportation variables are not considered. The model also ignores the fact that each service has its own threshold and range characteristics.

The break-point model is therefore too rigid, a difficulty partially overcome in the probability model sug-gested by geographer David Huff (1963). This model still uses gravitation-model principles, but assuming that consumers have several centers from which to choose, it specifies that probability of choosing each center. The results can be mapped to produce probability surfaces for consumers choosing to shop in each center. Probability models have been used by applied economic geographers to assess the likely effect of adding to ex-isting shopping centers or, more important, the conse-quences of introducing a new center into an existing system of centers (Batty and Saether, 1972; Clarke and Bolwell, 1968).

Gravitation models are not as useful for understand-ing the processes underlying retail and social behavior as they are for providing descriptions of the behavior of large populations. Moreover, they do not help us to understand the process underlying the formation of trade areas. Central-place theory does, however, pro-vide a good basis for understanding the formation of trade areas.

THE QUESTIONS OF CENTRAL-PLACE THEORY

◈

Central-place theory attempts to answer four ques-tions about cities in a regional economy:

1. How many cities (or central places) will de-velop?

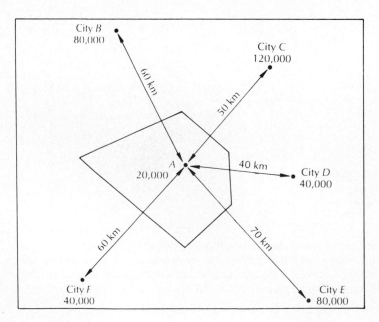

FIGURE 9.5
Hypothetical trade area based on the breakpoint model.

2. Why are some cities larger than others?

3. Where will the cities locate?

4. What will be the size of each city's trade area?

AN ELEMENTARY CENTRAL-PLACE MODEL

◈

To create a general theory of central places, geographers commonly begin with a normative model that assumes the following:

1. An *isotropic surface* (uniform transportation costs in all directions).

2. A given level and uniform distribution per capita of demand and population.

3. Equal ease of transportation in all directions.

4. Settlements depending totally on hinterland trade.

5. Optimizing producers and consumers.

6. A steady-state economy free of government or social classes.

7. Ubiquitous (available at every place) production inputs at the same price.

8. No shopping externalities. Shopping externalities exist with complimentary goods (one-stop shopping) and imperfect substitutes (comparison shopping).

The model also assumes a *linear market*, with consumers evenly spaced along a road that extends across the isolated plain (Figure 9.6). Given these nine constraints, we next investigate the number of central places required to meet consumer demand, the size of trade areas, and the most efficient spacing of central places.

Threshold and Range

Threshold and range are key concepts in central-place theory. For a firm to offer a good—a *central function*—at a point along the road, it must sell enough to meet operating costs. The minimum level of effective demand that will allow a firm to stay in business is called the *threshold of a good,* or its scale economy. But given the assumption of an evenly distributed popula-

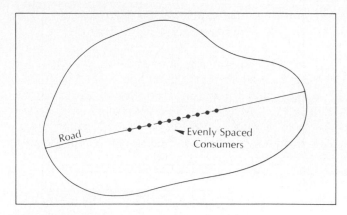

FIGURE 9.6
A linear market.

tion and purchasing power, we can also speak of the minimum number of people necessary to support a central function.

The *range of a good* is the maximum distance that people are willing to travel to obtain the good at market price. A consumer who lives next door to the shop pays the store price ($0.50) for a loaf of bread. However, a consumer who lives at some distance from the shop must pay the store price plus the cost of travel to the central place. If the travel cost is $0.20 per kilometer, a consumer who lives 5 kilometers from the shop pays $1.50 for the bread (Figure 9.7a). Clearly, the price that

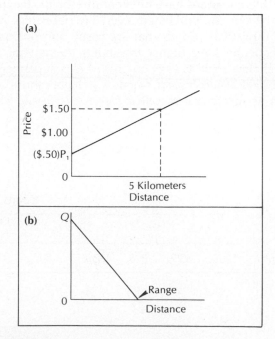

FIGURE 9.7
(a) Price and (b) range of a good.

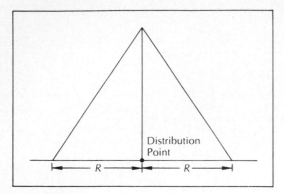

FIGURE 9.8
Range as distance.

a consumer pays is a direct function of distance. If price increases with distance from a central place or distribution point, demand should decline with distance. We can find a distance from the central place at which demand is zero. That point is the range of a good (Figure 9.7b). The range of a good is the distance, R, in both directions from a distribution point in a linear market (Figure 9.8).

Order of a Good and a Center

Different goods have different thresholds. Inexpensive, frequently purchased, everyday necessities have low thresholds. Goods that are costly and purchased infrequently have higher thresholds. Items with low thresholds, such as eggs purchased at a supermarket, are called *low-order goods*. Goods with higher thresholds, such as furniture, are called *higher-order goods*. Thus,

central functions can be ordered on the basis of their threshold size. The highest-order good has the highest threshold, and the lowest-order good has the lowest threshold.

Just as we can order goods, we can order centers. The order of a center is determined by the highest-order good offered by the center. Low-order centers offer only low-order goods; high-order centers offer high-order goods and low-order goods.

Emergence of a Central-Place Hierarchy

We are now in a position to derive a *hierarchy* of central places. Assume that highest-order places, or *A*-level places, offer all goods from 1000 to 1 (Table 9.1). The market area of each *A*-level place must include at least 1000 people. If 10,000 consumers live along our imaginary linear market, 10 *A*-level centers can be established. Two *A*-level centers and their market areas are shown in Figure 9.9. We assume a population density of 10 people per kilometer, so the minimum market area of each *A*-level center is 100 kilometers, or 50 kilometers on either side of each *A*-level center. We also assume that competition forces market areas to be as small as possible—that is, 100 kilometers equals 1000 consumers. This minimizes the travel cost that the most distant consumer must pay. A consumer on the dividing line between two *A*-level centers will purchase goods from both centers in equal measure.

The good that defines the *A* level of the hierarchy has a threshold of 1000, but there is also a good with a threshold of *A* divided by two, or 500. The threshold market area for that good is 50 kilometers long, or 25 kilometers on either side of a distribution point. A mar-

▣

Table 9.1
Goods and Threshold Size

Centers	1000,	999,	998,	. . . ,	502,	501,	500,	. . . ,	252,	251,	250,	. . . ,	3,	2,	1
							Goods								
A	X	X	X	X	X	X	X	X	X	X	X	X	X	X	X
B							X	X	X	X	X	X	X	X	X
C									X	X	X	X	X	X	X

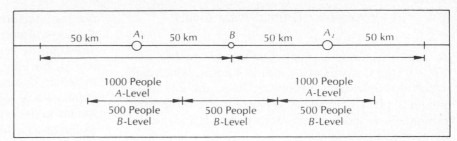

FIGURE 9.9
A *K* = 2 hierarchy.

ket area of 500 centered on A_1 and A_2 allows an additional 500-person market area centered on the midpoint between the two *A*-level centers. A central place locating there is at the *B* level; it can offer all goods with a threshold of 500 or less. The good that defines the *B* level has a threshold of 500 and is called a *hierarchical marginal good*. A hierarchical marginal good is the highest-order good offered by a given level of the central-place hierarchy. What threshold size will define *C*-level centers? Their threshold size is *B* divided by two, or 250. They locate midway between higher-order centers; thus, they occur every 25 kilometers along our imaginary road.

Our linear hierarchy follows the "rule of twos": Each successive level is defined by a function with a threshold one-half the size of the next-highest hierarchical marginal good. The rule of twos also applies to market-area sizes and the spacing of centers. In *central-place theory*, this type of hierarchy is known as a *K*-

equals-two hierarchy because two is the constant parameter of the system. The letter *K* stands for the German word, *Konstant*.

So far in our discussion, we have constructed a hierarchy of central places based on the concepts of threshold and range. We have seen that the number of required centers is minimized, the number of consumers served is maximized, and the distance that consumers must travel for a given set of central functions is minimized. We have seen that higher-order centers, which offer more functions and, therefore, employ more people, have larger populations than lower-order centers. Higher-order centers are also more widely spaced, serve larger market areas, and occur less frequently. In summary, our central-place hierarchy can be regarded as a multiple system of nested centers and market areas. Lower-order centers and their market areas nest under the market areas of higher-order centers. Next, let us look at the more interesting two-dimensional hierarchy.

Madison, Indiana, from across the Ohio River, a low-order central place.
(Source: Piet van Lier, Impact Visuals.)

A Rectangular Central-Place Model

Let us examine a small region of the midwestern United States, Jay Hawk County, Kansas, which has 100,000 people and an economy based on only three products: pizza, CDs, and PCs (Figure 9.10). These three products have different per capita demands and thresholds (or scale economies):

1. *PCs:* Thresholds are high, relative to demand, and each PC store requires a population of 100,000, so only one store is possible. It will serve the whole region by locating in the center of Jay Hawk County.

2. *CDs:* The threshold is medium, compared with PCs and per capita demand. Each CD store requires 25,000 people to support it. Because no excess profits are allowed, four CD stores emerge.

3. *Pizza:* Because pizza is demanded more often than PCs and CDs are, because it is cheaper, and because it has a small scale economy, thresholds are low compared with PCs, CDs, and per capita demand. Each pizza parlor requires a population of 6250 people, so 16 pizza parlors emerge.

Remember that the central-place model is concerned only with retailing and service firms, and their markets, not manufacturing. Therefore, stores locate according to access to customers. This is why the PC store will locate in the center of Jay Hawk County, where the cost of traveling to the store is minimized. The raw materials, or inputs, cost the same everywhere, and the population is initially spread evenly. As the PC store locates in the center of Jay Hawk County, other stores of different factors and thresholds also locate there, and a higher population emerges than in the rural parts of the county. Some of these people in the city are employees of the PC store and the other stores because they want to minimize their commuting costs.

The demand for CDs is greater than the demand for PCs. Likewise, the threshold for a CD store is one-quarter that of a PC store. Consequently, two CD stores will locate in the city, and two additional CD stores will locate outside the city, equidistant to the edge of Jay Hawk County. These locations will minimize the customers' travel costs. Employees of the CD stores, and others, will locate near the stores. As a result, these areas will also have higher densities than the rural areas of the county. The region can support only four CD stores: two in the city and one in each new smaller city, or town.

Next, the pizza parlors enter the Jay Hawk County economy. Because the thresholds of a pizza parlor is one-sixteenth that of a PC store, and one-fourth that of a CD store, four pizza parlors can locate in the city, two additional ones in each of the towns, and eight

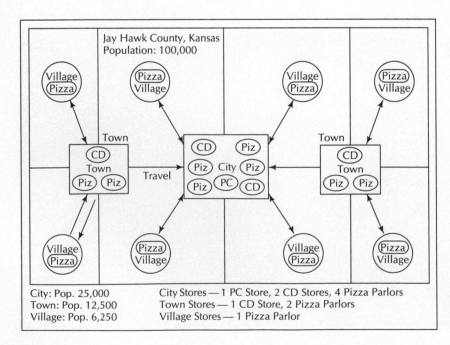

City: Pop. 25,000
Town: Pop. 12,500
Village: Pop. 6,250

City Stores — 1 PC Store, 2 CD Stores, 4 Pizza Parlors
Town Stores — 1 CD Store, 2 Pizza Parlors
Village Stores — 1 Pizza Parlor

FIGURE 9.10
Jay Hawk County, Kansas: a rectangular central-place system.

more elsewhere in Jay Hawk County. As a result, the rural area is divided into eight equal trade areas. Again, these latter eight places are more densely populated than the rural parts of the county, and they develop as small towns, or villages.

Jay Hawk County has a total of 11 central places. Everyone in the county travels to the city to buy a PC. The city is in the center of the county and has a population of 25,000. This means that it is large enough to support two CD stores and four pizza parlors. (It will have other functions or types of stores as well, but for simplicity's sake we chose to use a three-function economy.)

Each of the two towns has a population of 12,500 and a market large enough to support one CD store and two pizza parlors. People who live in villages and want to purchase CDs will come to these towns—if the towns are closer than the city. The four villages on the outskirts of the county are closer to the two towns, so these people will shop for CDs at the towns. The four center villages are as close to the city as to the towns, so these people will shop for CDs at the city. Each village has a population of 6250 and can support only one pizza parlor.

Figure 9.11 shows the frequency distribution of central places in Jay Hawk County by size and by range,

from large (rank = 1) to small (rank = 4–11). There is only one city, and it has high thresholds for its goods (PCs). It can support many goods and services. The small central places have low populations and can support only low-threshold goods (pizza). Goods and services flow down the hierarchy from large places to smaller places. PCs are purchased in the city and flow down to the towns and villages. CDs are puchased in the towns and flow down to the villages as people come to the towns to shop. Two central places of the same order, or size, do not trade with each other because neither has anything that the other needs.

This example includes three levels of central places, each with a distinct trade-area size and city spacing. Each has a set population. Because the city requires many people to support its high-order functions, in this case a PC store, there can be few big cities.

A Hexagonal Central-Place Model

In the early 1930s, the German geographer Walter Christaller (1966) established the foundations of central-place theory. On the basis of the simplifying assumptions that we introduced earlier and the concept

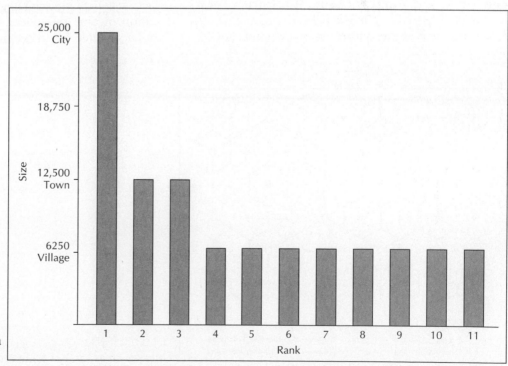

FIGURE 9.11
Rank-size urban hierarchy in Jay Hawk County, Kansas.

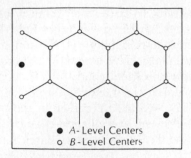

FIGURE 9.12
Location of centers: a $K = 3$ hierarchy.

of a range of a good, Christaller constructed a deductive theory to explain the size, number, and distribution of clusters of urban trade and institutions. To demonstrate hierarchical interrelations between places in a competitive market society, he built three geometric models. His central places are arranged according to marketing, transportation, and administrative principles. According to Christaller, these three principles underlie the most efficient system of central places.

THE MARKETING PRINCIPLE

The *marketing principle* assumes the largest provision of central-place goods and services from the minimum number of central places (Figure 9.12). Each *B*-level central place is midway between three neighboring centers of the next-highest order. Midway points are cor-

ners of hexagonal market areas of the next-highest order. Each higher-order place is surrounded by six places of the next-lowest order.

Figure 9.13 illustrates the progression of central places and market areas for a three-level hierarchy. The market area of each *A*-level center passes through six lower-order *B*-level central places. *A*-level market areas are three times larger than *B*-level market areas: Each *A*-level market area includes the *B*-level market area centered on the *A*-level area, plus one-third of the six surrounding *B*-level market areas [$1 + (^1/_3)(6) = 1 + 2 = 3$ *B*-level areas]. Distances separating places at the same level of the hierarchy are the same. If lower-order places are 1 unit apart, rival higher-order places, dominating three times the area and three times the population are $\sqrt{3}$, or 1.732, units apart. This arrangement of central places is a *K*-equals-three network in which the number of trade areas with successively less specialized levels progresses by a "rule of threes"; that is, the number of central places increases geometrically—1, 3, 9, 27. For example, one *A*-level area contains the equivalent of three *B*-level areas or nine *C*-level areas.

Christaller argued that the system of central places developed on the basis of the range of a good is rational and efficient from an economic viewpoint. However, he did note that real-world conditions produce deviations from this system. Actual conditions include historical circumstance, government interference, social stratification, income differences, and topographical variations not accounted for in the normative model.

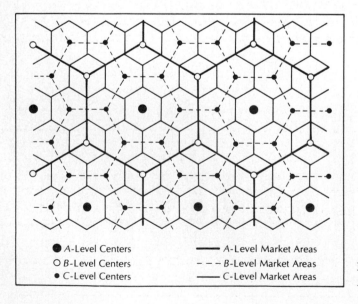

FIGURE 9.13
Market areas: a $K = 3$ hierarchy.

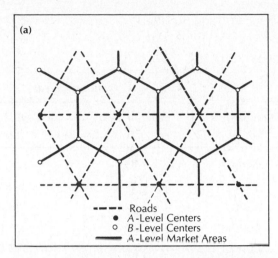

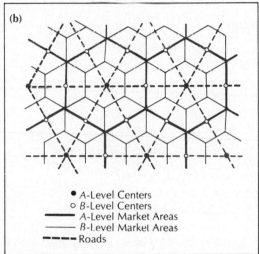

FIGURE 9.14
The traffic principle: (a) optimum transportation network: maximum connectivity for A-level centers ($K = 3$); (b) a $K = 4$ hierarchy.

THE TRAFFIC PRINCIPLE

If an optimum road network is superimposed on a marketing hierarchy, B-level centers do not lie on the A-level road network (Figure 9.14a). More roads must be constructed if B-level centers are to be connected. Christaller rejected traffic routes in the marketing system and asked this: How can connectivity between places be maximized and network length minimized? By shifting B-level centers to a point midway between each pair of A-level centers, he found the answer (Figure 9.14b). The pattern of centers arranged according to the *traffic principle* results in a K-equals-four hierarchy. The B-

level market areas are one-fourth the size of the A-level market areas. Each A-level market area dominates the B-level area centered on it, plus one-half the surrounding six (equals three), for a total of four. The number of market areas at successively less specialized levels of the hierarchy progresses by the "rule of fours"; that is, the number of central places increases geometrically—1, 4, 16, 64. Compared with the marketing principle, the traffic principle requires more centers at each level of the hierarchy if the entire hexagonal landscape is to be adequately provided with central places for the distribution of goods and services. The advantage of a more efficient transportation system for moving goods cheaply is counterbalanced by the additional distance that consumers must travel to reach a center at a given level of the hierarchy.

The Administrative Principle

The *administrative principle* requires sociopolitical separation of market areas. This is achieved when each central place controls six dependent centers (Figure 9.15). Hinterlands nest according to the "rule of sevens" (K-equals-seven). They are larger than those in either K-equals-three or K-equals-four systems, which means that consumers must travel farther to reach a center of a given level in the system.

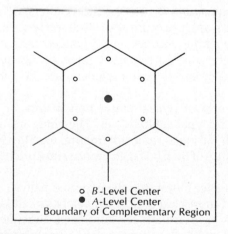

FIGURE 9.15
Two-level hierarchy of central places under the administrative principle.

◈

T a b l e 9.2
The Urban Hierarchy in Southern Germany

Central Place (1)	Towns		Tributary Areas	
	Distance Apart (2)	Population (3)	Size (Sq Km) (4)	Population (5)
Market hamlet (Marktort)	7	800	45	2700
Township center (Amtsort)	12	1500	135	8100
County seat (Kreisstadt)	21	3500	400	24,000
District city (Bezirksstadt)	36	9000	1200	75,000
Small state capital (Gaustadt)	62	27,000	3600	225,000
Provincial head city (Provinzhauptstadt)	108	90,000	10,800	675,000
Regional capital city (Landeshauptstadt)	186	300,000	32,400	2,025,000

Source: Ullman, 1940–1941, p. 857.

Southern Germany

Christaller tested his central-place model in southern Germany and bordering areas of France, Switzerland, and Austria (Table 9.2). He recognized a seven-level hierarchy ranging from market hamlets to regional capital cities in which centers at each level dominate approximately three times the area (Column 4) and three times the population (Column 5). The distance between similar centers increases by three over the preceding smaller category (Column 2). The smallest centers are about 7 kilometers apart because 4 or 5 kilometers, roughly a 1-hour walking distance, corresponded to the market area for the smallest centers. Centers of the next order of specialization, township centers, are 12 kilometers apart.

Networks of central places nest within the market areas of regional capital cities. The cities are Munich, Frankfurt, Stuttgart, and Nuremburg, together with the border cities of Strasbourg in France and Zurich in Switzerland.

Christaller found that the expected pattern was approached most closely in poor, thinly settled farm districts that were virtually self-contained. Thus, deviations from the rational pattern were uncommon in many parts of southern Germany. On the other hand, the theoretical ideal was not evident in the highly industrialized Rhine-Ruhr region.

WHOLESALING AND THE MERCANTILE MODEL OF SETTLEMENT

◈

Geographer James Vance (1970) introduced the argument that central-place theory is too parochial, sufficing as an explanation only for the trading-settlement structure of an area. Central-place theory deals with relationships between customers and sellers of goods *within* regions. It does not account for the wholesale trade that links regions. Wholesaling, which involves the sale of goods from one entrepreneur to another, is conducted primarily *between* higher-order centers, and these external linkages influence their locational patterns. In addition, local settlement hierarchies are influenced by long-distance external ties.

Wholesalers subject regions to external change and stimulate growth of wholesaling centers. Vance thought of these centers as "unraveling points" in the geography of trade. They link production areas, mediate trade flows, and determine the metropolitan centers from which central-place patterns develop to meet the consumers' demands.

Vance doubted whether any region in North America was economically isolated enough to have begun in a closed local region. He preferred to view the

In Walter Christaller's system of central places, Munich represents a regional capital city.
(Source: German Information Center.)

history of settlement patterns not only in terms of local trading patterns (central-place model) but also in terms of long-distance trading connections. He argued that broad-scale settlement of North America must be considered in the context of long-distance trade. Colonial towns—Boston, New York, Philadelphia, Baltimore, and Charleston—were traders' towns. Created before their hinterlands expanded, they were unraveling points for the distribution and collection of goods. Subsequently, interior mercantile cities developed to serve as primary collecting points for resources shipped back to the East Coast. Cities such as Chicago, Cincinnati, Memphis, Minneapolis, St. Louis, Kansas City, and Omaha owe much of their early growth to their wholesaling function. Although Vance regarded only cities of more than 50,000 people as true distribution centers, many small towns also developed on the basis of long-

distance trading connections. Eau Claire, Wisconsin, for example, was a workplace town of about 10,000 people in the 1880s; however, the products of its many lumber companies were shipped to places as far away as St. Louis.

Vance described the development of distant trade between Europe and North America and the subsequent evolution of the American urban hierarchy (Figure 9.16). After ascertaining that an area had sufficient economic potential, Europeans established mercantile centers within it. These centers linked European countries and their sources of raw materials, and the centers grew as the size of the trading system increased. Eventually, the central-place model began to characterize American settlement, with a subsequent parallel growth of settlement in accordance with both central-place and mercantile models.

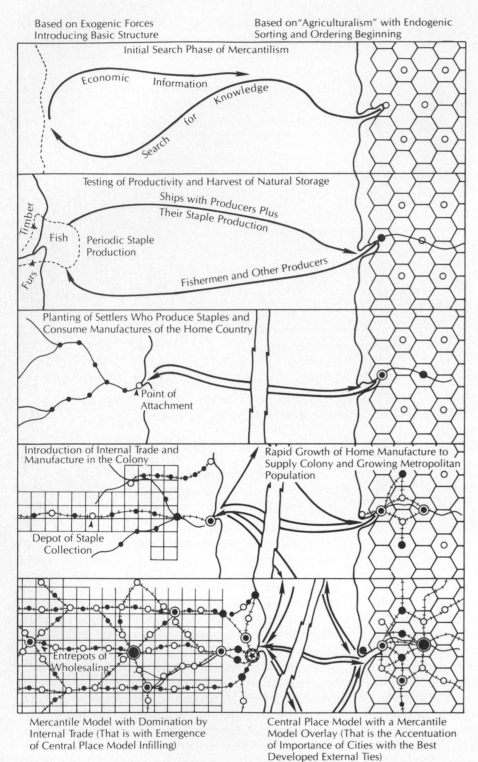

Based on Exogenic Forces
Introducing Basic Structure

Based on "Agriculturalism" with Endogenic
Sorting and Ordering Beginning

Initial Search Phase of Mercantilism

Economic Information Knowledge
Search for

Testing of Productivity and Harvest of Natural Storage

Ships with Producers Plus
Their Staple Production

Timber
Fish
Periodic Staple
Production
Furs

Fishermen and Other Producers

Planting of Settlers Who Produce Staples and
Consume Manufactures of the Home Country

Point of
Attachment

Introduction of Internal Trade and
Manufacture in the Colony

Rapid Growth of Home Manufacture to
Supply Colony and Growing Metropolitan
Population

Depot of Staple
Collection

Entrepots of
Wholesaling

Mercantile Model with Domination by
Internal Trade (That is with Emergence
of Central Place Model Infilling)

Central Place Model with a Mercantile
Model Overlay (That is the Accentuation
of Importance of Cities with the Best
Developed External Ties)

FIGURE 9.16
Urban evolution in the mercantile
and central-place models.
(Source: Vance, 1970, p. 151.)

Vance suggested that central-place dynamics may have sketched the European settlement pattern (Figure 9.16). For example, in areas such as Christaller's southern Germany, economies were fairly isolated from one another in the feudal Middle Ages. However, by the early modern period the feudal economy was giving way to mercantilism, and central places with developing external ties grew rapidly. Long-distance trade accentuated the importance of Bristol, St.-Malo, Seville, Cádiz, and Lübeck, to name only a few merchant cities.

EVIDENCE IN SUPPORT OF CENTRAL-PLACE THEORY

◈

Upper Midwest Trade Centers

We begin our examination by looking at the trade centers of America's northern heartland (Borchert, 1987), or the Upper Midwest. The region coincides with the Ninth Federal Reserve District, which extends 2500 kilometers along the Canadian border, from Montana in the West to the Upper Peninsula of Michigan in the East. In this rather homogeneous region, we might anticipate the regular pattern of hexagonal market areas suggested by Christaller. But the underlying density of the farm population varies considerably. Rural population densities are greatest in the southern and eastern regions of Minnesota, which represent the northern and western margins of the Midwest agricultural heartland. Densities decline toward the west and the north. In the west, aridity reduces the carrying capacity of the land. In the north, infertile soils and short growing seasons produce lower yields per unit of farmland. Compared with southern parts of the region, the amount of land in farms is small. More than 90% of the land in southern Minnesota is in farms, but this figure falls to less than 10% in northern Minnesota, where forests dominate. A hexagonal lattice that conforms to the distribution of the farm population supports Isard's (1956) theory—cells are smaller in areas that are more densely populated and larger in areas of sparse settlement.

Hierarchy of Business Centers

John Borchert (1963), a geographer at the University of Minnesota, demonstrated that a hierarchy of central-place functions exists in the Upper Midwest. He selected 46 functions and determined those that were typical of various orders in the hierarchy of business types. He grouped central functions into convenience, specialty, and wholesale categories for eight types of trade centers (Figure 9.17).

Hamlets, the lowest-order central place recognized by Borchert, have only gasoline service stations and eating and drinking establishments. The next two levels, *minimum-convenience* and *full-convenience centers*, provide everyday necessities. Minimum-convenience centers have hamlet-level functions plus a hardware store, a drugstore, a bank, a grocery store, and two other convenience functions, such as a variety store. Full-convenience centers have all hamlet-level and minimum-convenience functions, as well as stores dealing in laundry or dry cleaning, jewelry, appliances or furniture, clothing, lumber, building materials, shoes, and garden supplies. In addition to shops, most full-convenience centers have a hotel or a motel. Still higher in the hierarchy of business types are *partial-shopping* and *complete-shopping centers*, offering specialty goods and services. *Secondary wholesale-retail*, *primary wholesale-retail*, and *metropolitan retail centers* are the highest-order places. With regard to the frequency of trade-center types, as the hierarchical level increases, the number of trade centers decreases. There is also a strong relationship between trade-center types and population size (Table 9.3).

Minneapolis-St. Paul is the largest and only metropolitan wholesale-retail center in the Upper Midwest. Besides convenience, specialty, and wholesale functions, the Twin Cities provides other services for its massive trade area, such as regional head offices of insurance companies, and specialized medical, educational, and administrative facilities. People living as far as 1600 kilometers away may never visit the Twin Cities. Instead, they obtain goods and services from lower-order trade centers. The highest-level centers that many people living beyond the Twin Cities need to reach are primary and secondary wholesale-retail centers such as Eau Claire, Fargo-Moorhead, and Duluth. Nonetheless, the Twin Cities is the controlling center of the Upper Midwest economy. Trade-area residents feel the influence of the metropolis through communications, banking, agricultural marketing, and retail-wholesale relationships.

CENTRAL-PLACE PATTERN

The geographic distribution of trade centers in the Upper Midwest conforms roughly to central-place theory (Figure 9.18). Wholesale-retail centers are widely spaced, and hamlets are the most numerous centers. Wider spacing of all classes of trade centers to the north and west is a striking feature on the map.

It is generally agreed that there are too many trade centers in the Upper Midwest. Most of the 2500 settlements that dot the Upper Midwest map were established under conditions quite different from those of today. After the railroads opened up the region in the late nineteenth century, immigrants established small farms. To meet the needs of farm families, low-order central places developed. These places were closely spaced in

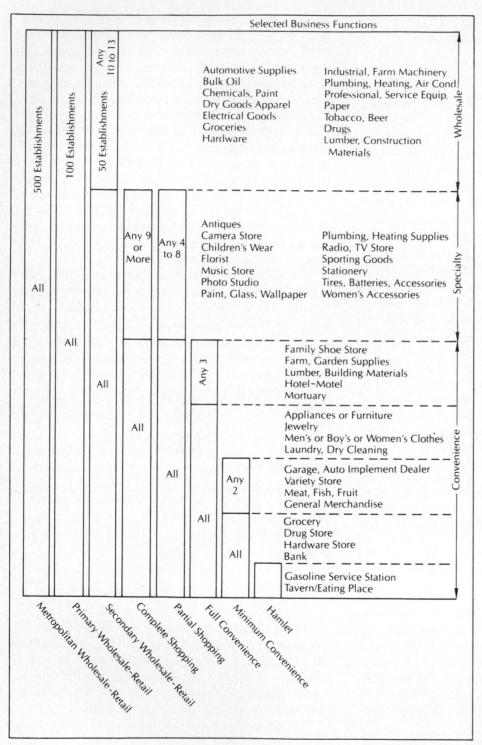

FIGURE 9.17
Trade-center types in the Upper
Midwest.
(Source: Borchert, 1963, p. 12.)

response to slow, difficult travel conditions. In recent decades, two changes have produced stress within the original framework of settlements: migration and transportation.

Migration has had the most influence on the structure of trade centers. In the past 60 years, the farm population has declined sharply as farms increased in size and farmland was abandoned. In addition to a declining farm population, the region has experienced net out-migration. Within the region itself, the population

Table 9.3
Frequency and Median Size of Trade-Center Types in the Upper Midwest

Type of Center	Number of Centers	Median Population (Thousands)
Wholesale-Retail Centers		
Metropolitan	1	1440.0
Primary	7	55.4
Secondary	10	32.2
Shopping Centers		
Complete	78	9.5
Partial	127	2.5
Convenience Centers		
Full	111	1.5
Minimum	379	0.8
Hamlets	1539	0.2

Source: Borchert, 1963, p. 11.

has shifted progressively from farms and small trade centers into larger urban areas, and from central cities into the suburbs and the countryside. Examples of trade centers that have grown rapidly are the Twin Cities, Rochester, and Fargo-Moorhead.

Modern highways crisscrossing the region illustrate a second influence on the structure of trade centers. Improvements in transportation after 1914, such as paved roads and the widespread use of automobiles, enabled consumers to bypass smaller centers and to patronize larger ones. Increased consumer mobility meant that small trade centers could not compete with larger towns that offered a wider variety of services in larger quantities.

DISPERSED CITIES

In the years to come, most of the Upper Midwest population will be concentrated in Minneapolis-St. Paul (metro cluster) and other low-density metropolises (urban clusters). These urban clusters, or dispersed cities, are products of modern transportation and communication networks and are formed by linkages of complete and wholesale-retail centers (Figure 9.19). They all share the following features:

1. The length of any link or corridor can be traveled in less than 60 minutes or 30 minutes, respectively.

2. Each cluster has multiple shopping and service centers, which are more complementary than competitive.

3. Each cluster has many low-order retail and service centers.

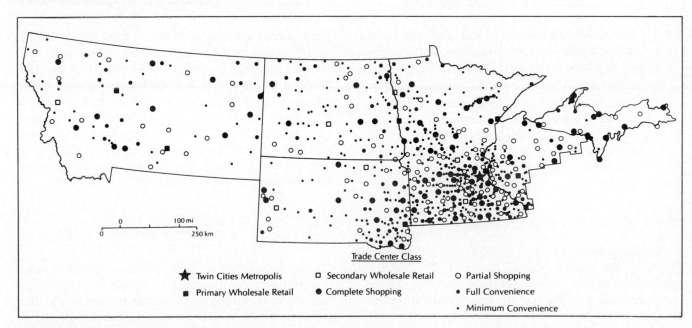

FIGURE 9.18
Distribution of trade centers in the Upper Midwest.
(Source: Borchert, 1963, pp. 13–14.)

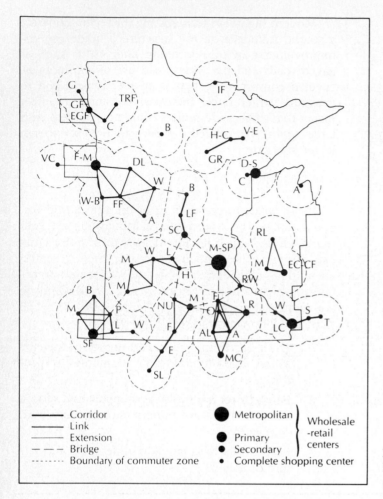

Corridor
Link
Extension
- - - Bridge
·········· Boundary of commuter zone

● Metropolitan
● Primary   } Wholesale
              -retail
● Secondary   centers
· Complete shopping center

FIGURE 9.19
Dispersed cities.
(Source: Borchert and Carroll, 1971, p. 14.)

4. Each cluster has industrial and wholesale zones, public higher-education facilities, public hospital facilities, and newspapers and broadcasting stations.

5. Each city within a cluster functions independently to a large extent. However, there is also considerable interdependence—travel in every direction for business, shopping, education, health care, and social and recreational purposes.

HIGH-ORDER CENTRAL PLACES

Minneapolis-St. Paul is one of 24 high-order central places in the United States (Figure 9.20). Borchert (1967) divided these important trade centers into three orders according to their size and functional complexity. The first-order center is New York City, the national metropolis providing the widest range of specialized activities. There are 6 second-order centers in addition to New York City (which is also a second-order center).

These cities are Chicago, Boston, Philadelphia, Detroit, San Francisco, and Los Angeles. The second-order centers are regional metropolises for much of the U.S. market. Added to the 7 second-order centers are 17 metropolitan centers, for a total of 24 high-order central places. These cities are Baltimore; Washington, DC; Atlanta; Miami; Buffalo; Cleveland; Cincinnati; Pittsburgh; New Orleans; St. Louis; Kansas City; Minneapolis-St. Paul; Dallas-Fort Worth; Houston; Denver; Seattle; and Portland.

Rank-Size Rule

In his study of the Upper Midwest, Borchert noted that the hierarchical structure of trade centers is reflected not only in their functional complexity, but also in their relative size. We can obtain an urban-size hierarchy by ranking centers according to their population sizes. The most well-known representation of this hierarchy is the *rank-size rule,* an empirical finding popularized by G. K.

The downtown Minneapolis skyline. Minneapolis-St. Paul represents the highest-order central place in the hierarchy of Upper Midwest trade centers.
(Source: Greater Minneapolis Convention and Visitors Association.)

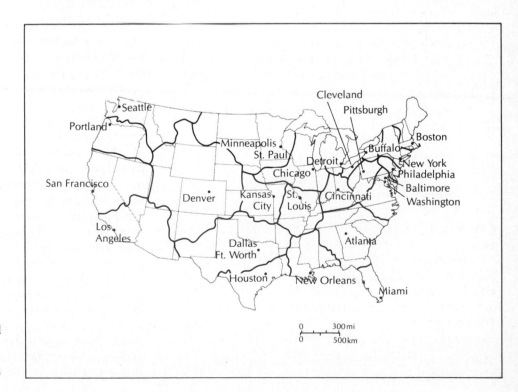

FIGURE 9.20
Higher-order trade centers and trade areas in the United States.
(Source: Based on Borchert, 1967.)

Zipf (1949). The rank-size rule states that if all settlements in an area are ranked in descending order of population size, the population of the rth city is $1/r$ the size of the largest city's population. When plotted on double logarithmic graph paper, the relationship produces a straight, downward-sloping line with a gradient of 45 degrees (Figure 9.21). The hypothetical rank-size distribution describes an urban system containing a few large metropolises, a large number of medium-sized cities, and a still larger number of smaller towns.

The urban-size hierarchy of the United States conforms closely to the rank-size rule (Figure 9.22). For example, New York, the first-ranking city, is nearly twice as large as Los Angeles, the second-ranking city, and nearly three times larger than Chicago, the third-ranking city. However, in many countries the population of the first or largest city is much greater than would be expected from the rank-size distribution, so a condition of *primacy* exists.

Brian Berry (1961), an urban geographer, interpreted city-size distributions through a comparative study of 37 countries (Table 9.4). Berry said that as countries become politically, economically, and socially more complex, they tend to develop straight-line rank-size distributions (Figure 9.23). In the early stages of

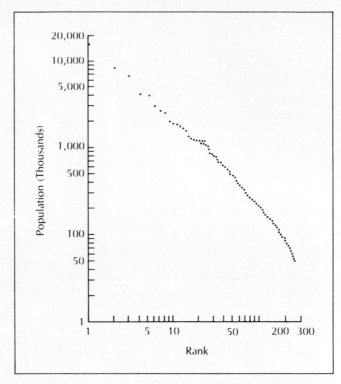

FIGURE 9.22
Rank-size distribution of urbanized areas in the United States, 1980.
(Source: U.S. Bureau of the Census Statistical Abstract of the United States, 1980.)

national development, a simple pattern of primacy prevails. This pattern gradually transforms into a rank-size distribution, which is the steady state of an urban-growth process.

To what extent is there a correspondence between central-place theory and the rank-size rule? The central-place hierarchy is based on the *functional size* of centers. Functional size is determined by the number and order of central functions offered by a place and is tied to the role of settlement-forming functions. The total population of a place is a function of both settlement-forming and settlement-building functions. Two centers at the same level of the hierarchy (that is, equivalent in functional size) may differ somewhat with respect to population. The rank-size rule is based on the population of centers—not their functional size. Population size is reflected by a smooth rank-size curve; functional size produces a stepped hierarchy. The discrepancy between the stepped and continuous curves may also be a function of scale. Rank-size distributions apply to large economic areas, such as the United States, and the central-place model to their smaller subsystems, such as the Upper Midwest.

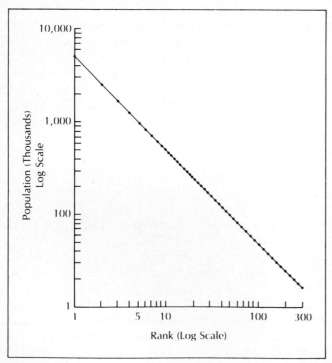

FIGURE 9.21
Rank-size rule: hypothetical sizes of the populations of cities in relation to their ranks.

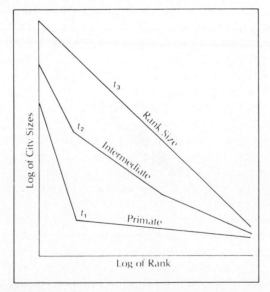

Structural Elements of the Central-Place Hierarchy

Much empirical research has focused on the structural elements of the central-place hierarchy (Berry, 1967). All the elements of central-place theory are structured or tied together logically and proportionately. To illustrate, let us graphically summarize four relationships: (1) the relationship between population size and functional units, (2) the relationship between population size and central functions, (3) the relationship between establishments and population size, and (4) the relationship between trade-area size and population density.

POPULATION SIZE AND FUNCTIONAL UNITS

The term *functional unit* refers to the provision of a central function each time it is offered. A graph of the relationship between population and functional units in southwestern Iowa shows that most centers fall close to the regression line, which is the straight line fitting the data (Figure 9.24). Two centers, Red Oak and Glenwood, however, have larger populations than one would expect, given the number of functional units in each. These discrepancies can be explained by the relatively large settlement-building functions of the centers. When the population of each town that is supported by these noncentral functions is subtracted from the centers' total populations, the number of people supported by settlement-forming functions can be estimated. These estimates fit the regression line well.

POPULATION SIZE AND CENTRAL FUNCTIONS

The term *central function* describes a good or a service offered by a central place. There is a curvilinear or log-linear relationship between population size and the number of central functions performed by centers. This relationship indicates that the population of a central place is a function of the total number of business types offered. Again, there are deviations from the norm. Some settlements that have more central functions than expected may be tourist centers, such as Las Vegas or Reno, Nevada, where excess central functions are supported by transient populations. Other settlements have larger populations than expected, which is usually in-

Table 9.4

City-size Distributions in 37 Countries

Countries with Rank-Size Pattern	Countries with Pattern of Primacy	Countries with Intermediate Patterns
Belgium	Austria	Australia
Brazil	Sri Lanka	Canada
China	Denmark	Ecuador
El Salvador	Dominican	England and Wales
Finland	Republic	Malaya
India	Greece	New Zealand
Italy	Guatemala	Nicaragua
Korea	Japan	Norway
Poland	Mexico	Pakistan
South Africa	Netherlands	
Switzerland	Peru	
United States	Portugal	
West Germany	Spain	
	Sweden	
	Thailand	
	Uruguay	

Source: Based on Berry, 1961.

FIGURE 9.23
Idealized evolution of the city: distributions under increasing size through three time periods.

Copenhagen, Denmark. A primate city in Northern Europe. *(Source: S. Cordier, Photo Researchers, Inc.)*

dicative of the settlement-building functions of the centers.

ESTABLISHMENTS AND POPULATION SIZE

The term *establishment* connotes ownership and control. Increases in the number of establishments are not proportional to increases in center sizes (Figure 9.25). The population/functional-unit and population/central-

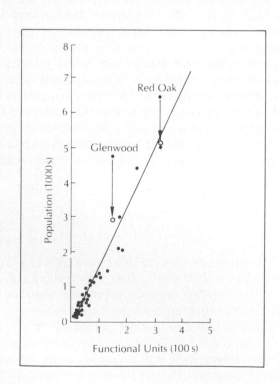

FIGURE 9.24
Relationship between population and functional units in southwestern Iowa.
(Source: Based on Berry and Meyer, 1962.)

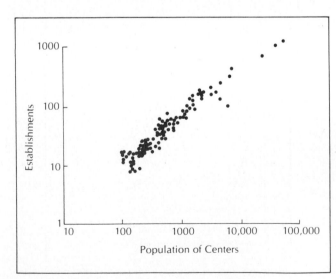

FIGURE 9.25
Relationship between establishments and population of centers.

One of the most common central functions is that of a grocery store. Items are in high demand and are relatively inexpensive. As one climbs the urban hierarchy, increases in the number of establishments are less than proportional to city size because large companies absorb the smaller retailer and offer scale economies to the shopper.
(Source: Frederick P. Stutz.)

function relationships are not proportional—an observation that raises the question of how centers meet increases in demand brought about by population changes. Existing establishments may expand, new establishments of the same functional type may be added, or a combination of the two responses may occur. Empirical evidence as revealed in the graph indicates that increasing the number of establishments tends to occur more often—particularly in the case of lower-order functions and centers.

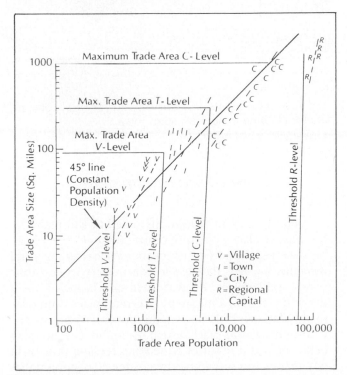

FIGURE 9.26
Density adjustment (southwestern Iowa).
(Source: Based on Berry and Meyer, 1962.)

TRADE-AREA SIZE AND POPULATION DENSITY

There is a strong tendency for trade-area size to adjust to variations in population density (Berry and Meyer, 1962) (Figure 9.26). The 45-degree line in the figure indicates constant population density. Each level of center is arrayed along a line with a slope of more than 45 degrees. Thus, variations in trade-area size are greater than variations in total population influenced by central places. This difference suggests density adjustment.

The central-place hierarchy is sensitive to local variations in population density, but even more so to regional variations. If we examine the relationship between trade-area sizes and total population serviced by central places along a traverse from the densely settled area of Chicago, through the corn and dairy lands of Illinois, Wisconsin, Iowa, and Minnesota, on to the wheat lands of the Dakotas, and into the rangelands of Montana, we discover remarkable regularities. Instead of what appears as a random scattering of settlements on the map, we find a highly regular set of relationships (Figure 9.27). In the urban areas near Chicago, population densities are high, trade areas are small, and numbers of people served, large. As we move through the suburban areas and across the Corn Belt to the wheat lands and rangelands, population densities decline, but the regular relationship between the trade area and the population served is maintained.

Consumer Travel as a Mirror of the Hierarchy

A central-place system depends on consistent consumer behavior. Christaller's theory of central places postulates that consumers behave predictably in that

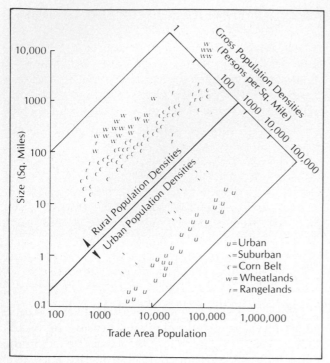

FIGURE 9.27
Density adjustment: large regional variations in population density.
(Source: Berry and Meyer, 1962.)

they will always obtain goods and services from the nearest possible center. However, in reality, this may not be the case.

Figure 9.28 shows the primary purchase movements of rural and urban consumers for clothing in southwestern Iowa. Clothing is the highest-level good (city level) followed by dry cleaning (town level). Groceries are the lowest-level function (village level). Consumers must consider the order of a good because it limits the number of possible purchase points. Within the framework of where goods are actually offered, however, consumers have some flexibility as to where they make their purchases. They will generally go to the nearest place to obtain *convenience goods*. For *shopping goods*, however, they will often travel to higher-level centers, even if these goods can be obtained locally.

The maps of travel patterns in southwestern Iowa do not replicate the geometrical precision of the central-place model. This is because the normative constraints of the model do not actually exist. Central-place theory can help us better understand and predict spatial patterns of consumer behavior. But we must bear in mind that people are not economic optimizers, although they do adhere to the principle of distance minimization to a limited extent.

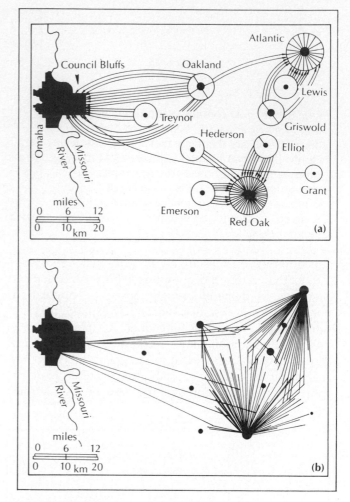

FIGURE 9.28
Purchase movements of (a) urban and (b) rural consumers for clothing in southwestern Iowa.
(Source: Berry and Meyer, 1962.)

Space-Preference Structures

Gerard Rushton (1969) attempted to add reality to the central-place system of central Iowa. In the 1970s, he observed hundreds of locational choices by rural residents as they traveled to the market to consume goods and services. He was interested in how closely the trade areas of a hierarchy of central places and relatively flat, rural Iowa would be described by the Christaller central-place system. He found that shopping behavior was a result of a mental screening process in which travelers sometimes bypass the closest town that offers the good or service that they need. Many times they travel to a farther destination if it offers a better variety of goods and services from which to choose.

Rural residents often minimize their travel time and costs by purchasing needed goods and services at the next-larger central place. The supplies for which they bypass the lower-order center, or the closest central place, are usually low-order convenience goods and services that a larger place can provide as well (e.g., groceries, gasoline, and basic agricultural services for their farms). This type of shopping behavior is sometimes called *multipurpose travel*. Because multipurpose travel is the norm in Iowa and other modern semirural regions, Rushton noticed that the smallest towns have a significantly smaller number of places than is normally predicted by the central-place theory.

Rushton developed an approach called *space-preference structures*, which measures the trade-off between the journey's distance to shop for goods and services, and the town size. In other words, the larger town size is a positive mental stimulus, and the increased distance to the town is a negative mental stimulus. When a town offered a good or a service that the rural resident needed, and the town was within the range of the good but was not patronized, Rushton assumed that the consumer consciously decided not to shop there, but at the next larger place. Rushton found that rural residents receive a certain payoff to go a certain distance, and the payoff can be measured by town size as a surrogate for the *market basket* of shopping possibilities that exist there.

All else being equal, including distance, rural residents prefer to shop in a town with a population of 5000 rather than one with a population of 500 because the town of 5000 offers more opportunities. These findings differed somewhat from the original central-place theory, which included only distance as an important variable.

Rushton also found that as rural residents shop for increasingly high-threshold and high scale economy goods, they are more willing to forgo closer places for a larger place that has a better selection. Rushton found that the space-preference structures of rural Iowans were relatively stable for different townships as well as for various ages. However, the pattern of trading off extra distance to get to a larger town with more choices existed only to a point. Rural Iowans actually preferred somewhat smaller places over very large towns, say those with populations of 200,000, perhaps because of a lack of public parking, increased traffic congestion, and resentment of large, high-density cities.

Rushton represented his space-preference structure findings as a series of curves on a graph shown in Figure 9.29. He called these curves *indifference curves*. Any place along an indifference curve is equally acceptable to the

FIGURE 9.29
Consumer space-preference structure. *(Source: Adapted from Rushton, 1969, pp. 391–400.)* Greater distances to visit towns of larger size in the Midwest. Larger towns have more shopping and entertainment opportunities and therefore appear to be worth the extra travel distance to the traveler. How are recreational travel distances related to duration of recreational activity and expected rewards at the destination. How is the distance from your home to the college you attend related to your expected quality of education or your expected utility from the college experience? How far would you be willing to travel to purchase a new car? a used car?

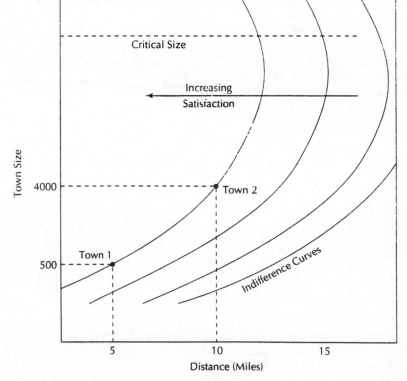

traveler. Because the curve slopes upward to the right, individuals trade extra distance to get to a larger town without being dissatisfied. Individuals along the indifference curves farther to the right must substitute greater differences than individuals along the indifference curves to the left must substitute. The curves farther to the right suggest lower population densities and more widely spaced towns.

If Rushton's space-preference structures are applied, the resulting trade areas of Iowa are shown in Figure 9.30. The *Thiessen polygons* at the left show the trade areas of central places in Iowa, centered on the Des Moines hierarchy. Areas within each trade-area boundary must be closer to the midpoint than to any other point. That is, perpendicular bisectors of lines connecting points are trade-area edges. This is the assumption of central-place theory. Although the trade areas do not result in a perfect hexagonal arrangement in Figure 9.30a, they are relatively close, if we consider that all assumptions of the model are not being met (principally, rural population density spread evenly).

Figure 9.30b shows the assignment of trade-area boundaries on the basis of space-preference struc-

tures. The comparison of the two central-place systems—Thiessen polygons in Figure 9.30a, and the space-preference structure delimitations in Figure 9.30b—shows that many of the small central places in the Thiessen polygon delimitation would yield their trade areas entirely to the next-larger place. In this case, Des Moines and three satellite cities have much larger trade areas than they had in the original delimitation. Small hamlets and villages that are close to larger central places, and within the range of the good of these large places, are at greatest risk of losing their entire trade areas (retail function) while they maintain their residential function.

On the other hand, small central places farther from the main center retained their small trade areas. Consequently, we are left with central places of the same size in the hierarchy, with radically different levels of centrality or different central-place functions. With the advent of telecommunications and improved highway access, many hamlets and villages around large cities, throughout not only Iowa, but also the rest of the world, function as important bedroom communities, where the noise and problems associated with cities are far less.

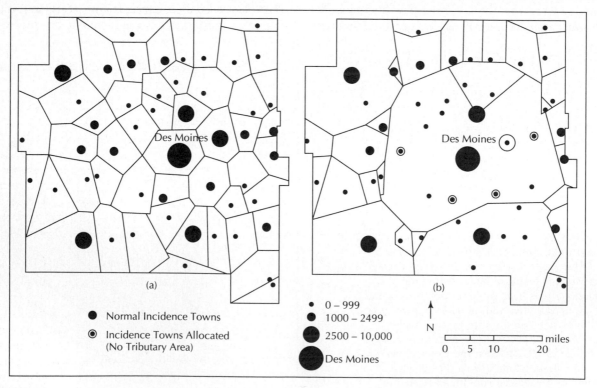

FIGURE 9.30
Alternate trade-area delimitations for grocery stores in Iowa: (a) Thiessen polygon delimitation and (b) space-preference structure delimitation.
(Source: Adapted from Bell, 1973, p. 293.)

Their more distant rural counterparts function as true rural settlement sites with a variety of central-place functions. Each has its importance in the economic landscape.

URBAN EXAMPLES OF SPACE-PREFERENCE STRUCTURES

A central-place hierarchy of goods and services also exists inside the city. This hierarchy is the *retail hierarchy*. At the lowest level are convenience centers, such as gas stations, minimarkets, and perhaps restaurants. This retail mix is comparable to the central functions of a hamlet. At the next level is a neighborhood center, which has more central functions at a somewhat higher threshold level. The rural counterpart of the neighborhood center is the village, which has the same central functions.

The hierarchy continues upward with community centers, regional shopping centers, and even the downtown central business district (CBD), with its wide variety of goods, services, and establishments. CBDs have been compared with the central functions and centrality of a town, a city, and a regional metropolis, respectively.

As in the rural area, when city travelers shop for convenience items with low threshold and scale economies, the closest places are frequently patronized—the convenience centers or the neighborhood centers. But for higher-order shopping, for goods and services that have high thresholds and high scale economies, the closest center offering the goods is frequently bypassed. When several locations can satisfy the demand, comparison shopping is the rule, and the potential locations are selected and sequentially reviewed. While a shopper is on one of these higher-order shopping trips, he or she can purchase lower-order products as well.

Frequently, urban travelers pass the closest place that offers a good or a service and choose instead a new center, with higher reward levels because of variety, price, or shopping comfort and convenience. Thus, in the urban case, shoppers evaluate not only distance and the size of the center, as in Rushton's rural Iowa case, but also a variety of other mental stimuli, including newness of the center, the store mix, parking availability, and design characteristics, such as whether the shopping center is enclosed or open or has a variety of entertainment and restaurants associated with it (e.g., the newer shopping centers in America).

The space-preference structures originally designed by Rushton were also identified in urban travel to various churches in the San Diego region. One would expect that a parishioner would travel to the closest church of his or her denomination. However, this was far from the case in the San Diego Church of Christ study by Stutz and Hinshaw (1976). The closest church was frequently bypassed in favor of a church that was larger and offered more social and personal services. The existence of Sunday schools, counseling programs, Bible classes, Girl Scout troops, a gymnasium, and a day school— although these services were not offered on Sunday morning—were enough of an attraction to draw urban residents from far across town (Figure 9.31).

CROSS-CULTURAL PATTERNS

◈

So far, our discussion has focused on cities as service centers in specialized societies; however, we have not yet considered how cultural differences affect local trade. And what of the situation in societies where specialization is less advanced? How do peasant societies organize their market activities? In seeking answers to these questions, we come to appreciate the rich variety of marketing and distribution systems throughout the world.

Cultural Differences in Consumer Travel

A study by Robert Murdie (1965) of an area in Ontario inhabited by both Old Order Mennonites and non-Mennonite Canadians provides an example of how cultural factors affect the geography of retailing and services in a dominantly specialized society. Mennonites use modern methods to manage their farms' businesses. But in dress, domestic consumption, and travel, they cling to a life-style that existed 200 years ago. Homemade clothes and the horse and buggy for transportation prevail. Few goods are demanded.

When Mennonites have needs similar to those of non-Mennonite Canadians, both groups use the central places in the area in much the same way; for example, Mennonites and non-Mennonite Canadians exhibit similar consumer behavior in their banking transactions. However, when the traditional beliefs of the Mennonites come into play, two distinct types of behavior with regard to central places become evident. Consider for example clothing purchased by non-Mennonite Canadians and yard goods purchased by Mennonites. The difference in mode of transportation is one factor crucial to the two types of consumer behavior. Non-Mennonite

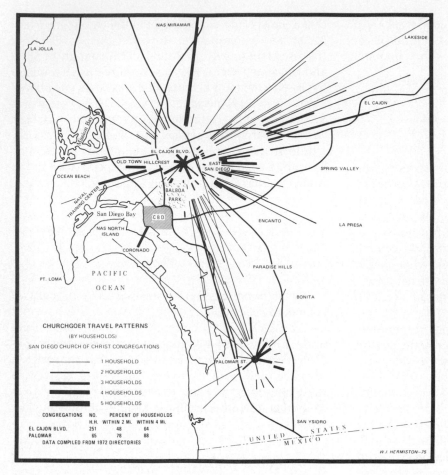

FIGURE 9.31
Churchgoer travel patterns. Revealed space preference is the number one explanatory model of both rural and urban traveler behavior. Here, travel to two San Diego Church of Christ congregations of the 40 studied are shown by graduated line segments. Distance is a constraining factor, but there is some overlap for these two congregations. Forty-two percent did not attend the nearest church. People substituted longer travel distances for greater participation opportunities at the church. Larger churches had more activities than the smaller churches and could pull from a larger catchmant area. *(Source: Stutz, 1977.)*

Canadians demand variety and go for it; hence, the maximum distance that they travel to purchase clothing is related to center size. On the other hand, the Mennonites purchase only a limited variety of yard goods and are restricted by the use of the horse and buggy; hence, the maximum distance that they travel does not vary with center size.

Periodic Markets

The majority of people in underdeveloped countries do not participate fully in the network of enterprises enjoined in the modern urban hierarchy. Rather than being involved in the production of goods for world markets, for the most part they subsist on what they can grow—and trade. Their local transactions often take place at small rural markets, which often operate on a periodic rather than a permanent basis. The market is likely to be open only every few days on a regular basis because its size is limited by the level of transportation technology, and the aggregate demand for goods is insufficient to support permanent shops. In this system, several places in a region profit from a day's trade, and each benefits from its participation in the wider network of interaction. People come to these periodic markets on foot, on bicycles, on the backs of their animals, or by whatever other means are available. Periodic markets are a feature of Southeast Asia, China, India, Middle and South America, and large parts of Africa.

G. William Skinner described the periodic marketing systems of traditional rural China. In one system based on the lunar month (*hsün*), merchants moved between the central market and a pair of standard markets in a 10-day cycle divided into units of three: the central market (day 1), first standard market (day 2), second standard market (day 3), central (day 4), first standard (day 5), second standard (day 6), central (day 7), first standard (day 8), second standard (day 9), and central on day 10, when no business was transacted. The three-per-*hsün* cycle illustrates the periodicities of many market centers of different levels, and it resembles a Christaller-type *K*-equals-four hierarchy.

Fresh fruit and vegetable market, Guadalajara, Mexico.
(*Source: Joel Gordon.*)

Elsewhere in the world, other cycles predominate: two-per-*hsün* cycles are common in Korea. Seven-day cycles occur in Andean Colombia (Symanski, 1971). In Africa, the market week varies from a 3-day to a 7-day week. The 3-day, 4-day, 5-day, and 6-day weeks stem from ethnic differeces, and the 7-day week is a consequence of calendar changes introduced by Islam into Africa.

Periodic markets, then, form an interlocking network of exchange places. As each market in the network takes its turn, it is close enough to one part of the area so that people in the vicinity can walk to it, carrying what they want to sell or trade. The staggered pattern of local markets permits a small volume of produce to move through the market chain to larger, regional wholesaling markets where shipments are collected for interregional or perhaps even international trade. What is traded depends on the market's location. For example, in West Africa's savanna zone, sorghum, millet, and shea butter predominate. Further south, in the forest zone, yams, cassava, corn, and palm oil change hands. In the south, too, there are some imported manufactured goods, especially in markets near the relatively prosperous cocoa, coffee, rubber, and palm oil areas. But wherever the market, the quantities traded are

small—a bowl of rice, a bundle of firewood—and their value is low.

The total amount of goods traded through the periodic marketplace, however, is tremendous; nobody knows the volume or the value of goods that are actually distributed (Bohannan and Curtin, 1971). The task of examining indigenous marketing systems has been largely neglected, primarily in the belief that marketing systems to serve cultivators, distributors, and consumers are economically inefficient and exploitative. According to *The Marketing Challenge* (USDA, 1970), this belief is erroneous, an opinion shared by Earl Scott (1972), whose research in Nigeria indicated that indigenous marketing systems can promote development. In contrast, Linda Greenow and Vicky Muiz (1988) argued that stimulating market trade as it is currently organized is unlikely to encourage development. In their Peruvian study, they showed that market selling for most traders

At Po in southern Burkina Faso, the periodic market occurs on a 4-day cycle.
(*Source: James Pickerell for IDA.*)

is a means of survival. According to Greenow and Muiz, "Traders, most of whom are women, rarely develop stable or growing businesses that support them and their families over a long run" (p. 416).

In general, periodic markets mainly serve people who live near the subsistence level. Market cycles are determined either by *natural* events, using the motions of the heavenly bodies, or they are *artificial*, without reference to natural cycles. Artificial cycles dominate today, with the periodicity of the markets influenced by population density. The more people in an area, the greater the aggregate demand, and the greater the frequency with which a market can operate. Eventually, the demand may be sufficient for a market to become continuous and permanent. Periodic markets are, therefore, logically related to the patterns of market centers observed in complex economies.

Just as the periodicity and types of commodity traded vary culturally, so do the locations of indigenous markets. In West Africa, rural populations live away from market sites, and the hierarchy of rural settlements is unrelated to the hierarchy of markets. In other regions, settlements and periodic markets may coincide. An understanding of periodic market sites requires an appreciation of local culture.

PLANNING USES OF CENTRAL-PLACE THEORY

◼

Central-place concepts, confirmed by the empirical evidence, have been used for planning purposes. They were used to establish a hierarchy of market centers on the Dutch polders and to design a new system of settlements on the Lakhish plain in Israel. They were also used to guide the development of the planned suburban community of Park Forest, Illinois. Residential areas were organized into neighborhoods, each served by a local business center, and one large shopping center was established for the whole community with adjacent land set aside for a village hall and police and fire departments. In England, analysis of the distribution of shopping centers and their service areas was an important component of the administrative reorganization of Greater London. These examples, cited by Berry (1967), are "symbolic of the practical uses of the central-place idea by regional and city planners for locating retail business, business centers, and market towns, or regionalizing an area" (p. 132).

Since the widespread adoption of the spatial organization theme in the 1960s, geographers have devoted much attention to the practical uses of the central-place concept. Making use of the complex variable, accessibility, they have analyzed and planned public and private service facilities. Geographers have also been called upon to give advice on questions of planning spatial patterns and structures in developed and underdeveloped countries.

New Central Places in the Netherlands

The Dutch are a classic example of a hard-working people who have reclaimed portions of their country from the North Sea by building dikes across inlets and pumping water off the land. In the *Zuider Zee reclamation scheme,* no settlement pattern existed, only marshy land and high points that swelled above the marshy level. Settlements and transportation systems were planned for this region. By 1930, the water was drained, which freed the polder of Wieringermeer. Four other polders were pumped and ready for development by 1968. Land was primarily pasture and agriculture, with the towns providing rural services and basic consumer goods.

Central-place theory was used to establish the original towns, but after World War II, transportation accessibility improved substantially. It became clear that too many small towns were too closely spaced for each to prosper economically. In later years, larger farm units and better town spacing, such as the case in East Flevoland and in South Flevoland, became common.

In the case of Lelystad, in the polder of East Flevoland, the rural setting became a destination for residents moving out of impacted Amsterdam. By 1992, Lelystad had a population of 70,000, and more than half the workers commuted to Amsterdam daily. The same became true of Almere in South Flevoland. About 70% of its residents were relocatees from Amsterdam, and the population in 1992 was approximately 60,000.

To conclude, central-place theory has been used not only in Israel, but also in the Netherlands, to plan new, undeveloped land. Because of improved transportation and the history of commuting in the Netherlands, town spacing is much wider than it was before World War II. Large settlements also exist within commuting distance of Amsterdam. These towns are not only bedroom communities to Randstad, the urban circular complex including Utrecht and Rotterdam, but also higher-order central places to the small, planned towns and market areas of the Zuider Zee reclamation project.

Market Area Analysis

Under the title "Being Close to Things and People," Peter Gould (1985) emphasized that often in geographic planning and consulting, questions of accessibility are close to the surface. He illustrated the idea of accessibility with the practical application of where to locate a new service facility. Suppose that you are on a team of geographic consultants working in a poor country where there are only enough resources to build a new school to serve a rather large rural area. (You can substitute a clinic, family-planning center, or any other service because the nature of the problem remains the same.) Obviously, you need to know where the villages are and how many schoolchildren (or people to be served) are in each village. Villages A and D are close to one another, but E, with 52 school-age children, is more remote. Where will you build the school? What is the most accessible location for the new school?

To find out, you can build a simple analog computer, the *Varignon frame* (Figure 9.32). Glue a map of the area to a sheet of plywood. Then, at each village, drill a hole and thread a smooth string through it. Next, tie the strings together on top of the map, and underneath attach weights proportional to the number of children in each village. If the knot represents the school, we can think of each village tugging the school toward it with a force equal to the number of children that it will serve. Where the knot locates is the best location; that is, the one that minimizes the aggregate distance that children must travel to school and back. If the children

Most facility location studies from the local scale to the world scale now take advantage of high-speed computers and very large data sets. (See Internet, p. 256, and MicroVision, p. 344.) *(Source: Frederick P. Stutz.)*

travel to school by bus, this location could save the school district a large amount of money in fuel costs.

The most efficient location for a new facility, however, is unlikely to be the most fair location from the standpoint of social justice. In our school example, the children in villages A to D would have nothing to complain about. But what about those living at E? They would have a long journey to school. Should we sacrifice efficiency for equity and build the school a bit closer to E? The question of equity, which arises whenever we deal with solutions to problems involving people, derives from the ideas of social justice (Harvey, 1973). Viewed in its geographic context, social justice is equated with territorial justice, which expresses a concern for a fair allocation of resources.

The simple analog computer can solve the problem of the best location for a *single* facility, but when you

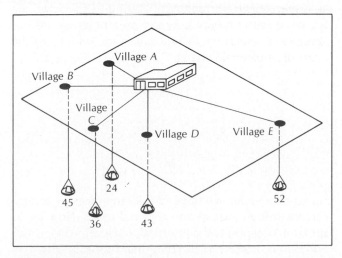

FIGURE 9.32
The best location for a school.
(Source: Based on Gould, 1985, p. 80.)

are searching for and evaluating all the possibilities in locating *multiple* facilities, high-speed computers are necessary. Geographers used computers as early as 1960 to find, for example, the best locations for hospitals in Sweden (Godlund, 1961) and administrative centers in southern Ontario (Goodchild and Massam, 1969). Literally hundreds of geographic applications for computer programs were produced in the 1970s and 1980s since these early studies. More recently, computer algorithms were used in a GIS in San Diego, California, to locate fire stations and areas for new development (Parrot and Stutz, 1992). Several recent examples are presented in Figures 9.33 to 9.39.

Accessibility is a key to measuring the welfare function of a consumer service. If there are variations in the degree to which a service is available to consumers, the welfare function of the service is not being fully used. In this view, the quality of life for consumers is affected to a degree by access to a basket of social goods—a doctor, a dentist, a public library (Smith, 1977).

No matter how hard geographers try, exact territorial equality in the provision of services can never occur. One reason is that there will always be a lag between demand and supply. There is considerable geographic and historical inertia in the locational distribution of services that leads to overprovision in some places and underprovision in other places.

Streamlining Central-Place Systems in Underdeveloped Countries

In many underdeveloped countries, investment is concentrated in large cities with good transportation links and other infrastructural facilities. Is this concentration fair? Should policies be introduced to bring about a Christaller-type pattern of central places to ensure a more equitable distribution of economic development?

Most conservative geographers argue that no intervention is required in the process of spatial organization. Policies intended to reduce the spatial concentration of investment would lead to a less-efficient location pattern for economic activities. Many activities must locate in the city in order to compete with foreign producers. Decentralization policies might deter foreign investments and result in lost jobs. Moreover, decentralization for the sake of interregional equity is costly. Building roads and railroads, as well as the provision and maintenance of other infrastructural facilities, would cost more than the majority of underdeveloped countries could afford. First and foremost in the development process, conservatives advocate attracting firms and jobs. At least in the early stages, the disadvantage of regional disparities is of secondary importance.

Liberals disagree with this view. They believe that urban and regional planning must ensure more even development. They cite increasing regional and rural-urban disparities to emphasize that change must be fostered through the role of urban centers as focal points in the diffusion of innovations. Identification of an urban hierarchy makes possible the evaluation of the system within which change is to take place. The development of a proper hierarchy of centers enables rational planning of facilities to proceed, without waste, and at the correct scales. Liberals believe that upgrading old centers or establishing new ones in peripheral areas can be a powerful stimulus to the development of surrounding areas and can set the pace for their progress.

Radicals have a different spatial image of development patterns in underdeveloped countries. Considering the position of underdeveloped countries in the international economic system, they question conservative and liberal arguments about the nature of economic and social change. Central-place systems in underdeveloped countries form part of the world network of cities. As such, villages, towns, and cities are centers of domination. In the service of international capitalism, regional and national hinterlands are subjected to economic "satellitization" and exploitation. Given that the structure of the capitalist urban system is conditioned by international influence and manipulation, radicals call for revolutionary institutional reform as a prerequisite to regional planning. Otherwise, we are faced with "a very real and present danger of our theories of spatial organization becoming tools for the frustration of social change" (Harvey, 1972, p. 2).

WORLD CITIES

◾

To this point, we have considered cities as service centers at the national and regional levels. Now let us shift our attention to the international level, where cities function as centers of international business. The new international division of labor is forging the cities of the world into a composite system.

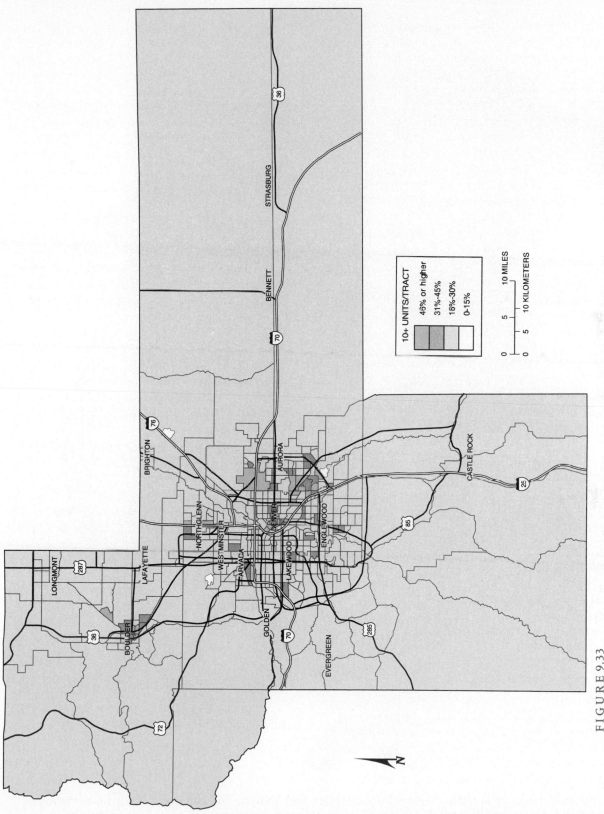

FIGURE 9.33
Beer and Suds in Denver and Boulder, Colorado. Beer and Suds, a laundromat chain serving beer and snacks, gravitates to apartment districts. This company was interested in finding census tracts with high proportions of apartments and, therefore, households without built-in laundry facilities. The census tracts, with high proportions of apartment units, are identified and are clustered in the new residential suburbs of Aurora in East Denver, in central Denver, and in the Colorado University college area of Boulder. (*Source: Stutz, 1994.*)

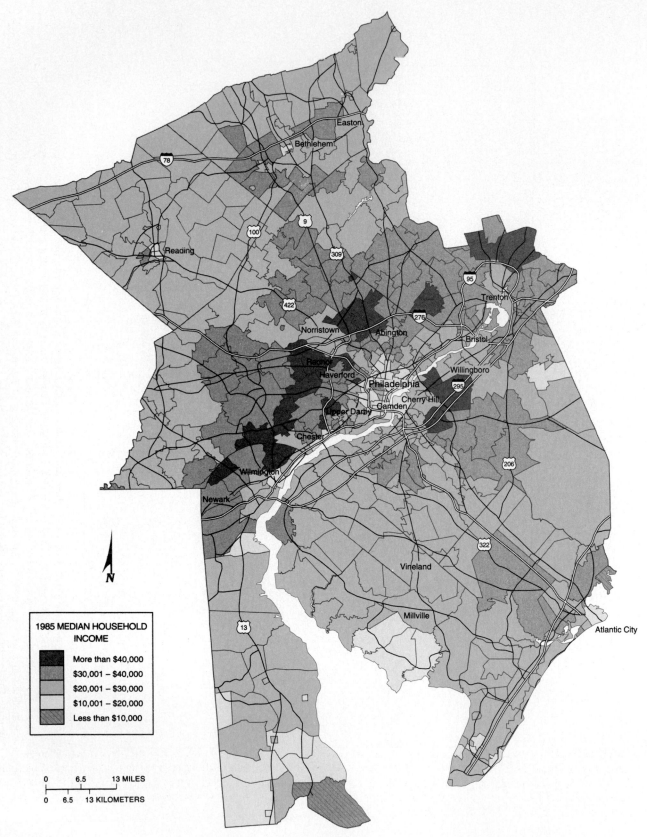

1985 MEDIAN HOUSEHOLD INCOME

- More than $40,000
- $30,001 – $40,000
- $20,001 – $30,000
- $10,001 – $20,000
- Less than $10,000

| 0 | 6.5 | 13 MILES |
| 0 | 6.5 | 13 KILOMETERS |

FIGURE 9.34

Location for Upscale Gyms in Philadelphia, Pennsylvania. Market-area analysts and planners for firms nationwide frequently want to know the median household income of census tracts in a metropolitan area, such as Philadelphia, shown here. High-rent, medium-rent, and low-rent neighborhoods can be targeted for various products. In this case, an upscale and expensive fitness club chain, called Fitness Advantages, selected the census tracts where median household income was more than $40,000, shown in dark grey. These locations were optimum locations for their service clubs. *(Stutz, 1994.)*

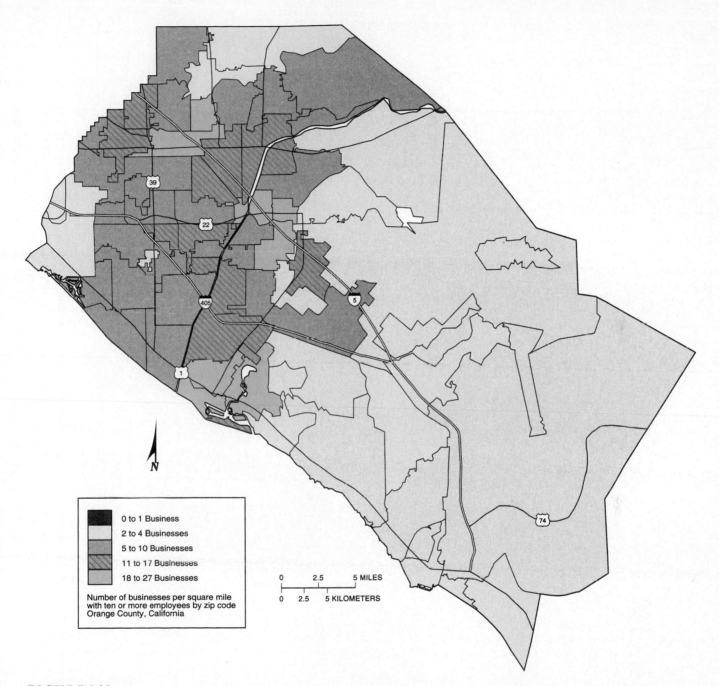

FIGURE 9.35
Xerox Potential Sales Areas in Orange County. Potential sales areas for Xerox machines and equipment are shown here. The problem was to identify census tracts that had numerous businesses and, therefore, clients for Xerox Corporation. The blue areas in the center of the map are clustered on Newport Beach. The top two blue shaded areas are in the Irvine Ranch Industrial Park. The more businesses per square mile with 10 or more employees, the larger the potential sales area for Xerox Corporation. *(Stutz, 1994.)*

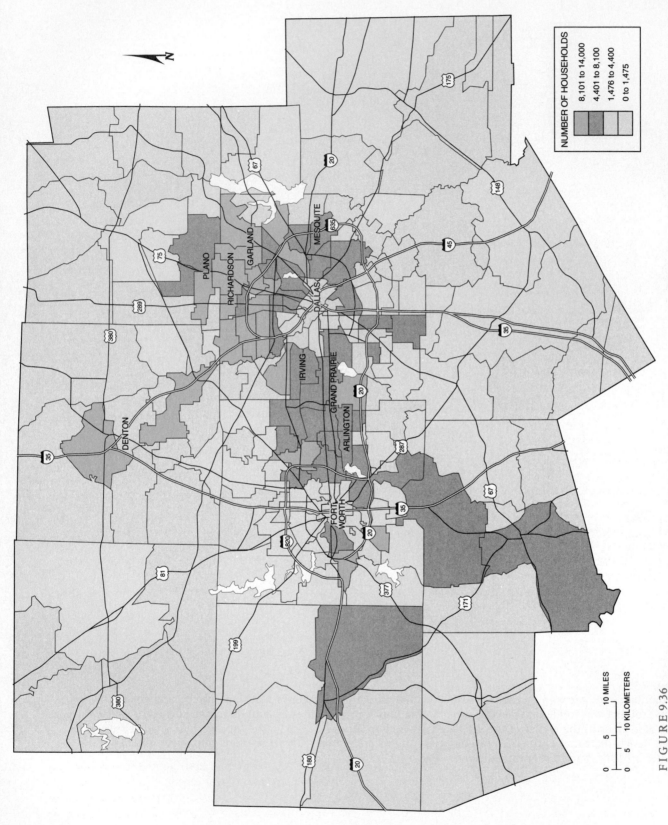

FIGURE 9.36

Direct-Mail Advertising in Dallas, Texas. A direct-mail advertising firm wanted to identify the high-rent districts of the Dallas-Ft. Worth-Denton area. They planned to advertise and mail out to every household a time-share and vacation sales promotion, centered in Vail, Colorado. Census tract groups shown here have average income of $55,000 or more. Dark readings show, for example, census tract groups where at least 8000 to 14,000 households earn more than $55,000. (*Stutz, 1994.*)

NUMBER OF HOUSEHOLDS

8,101 to 14,000
4,401 to 8,100
1,476 to 4,400
0 to 1,475

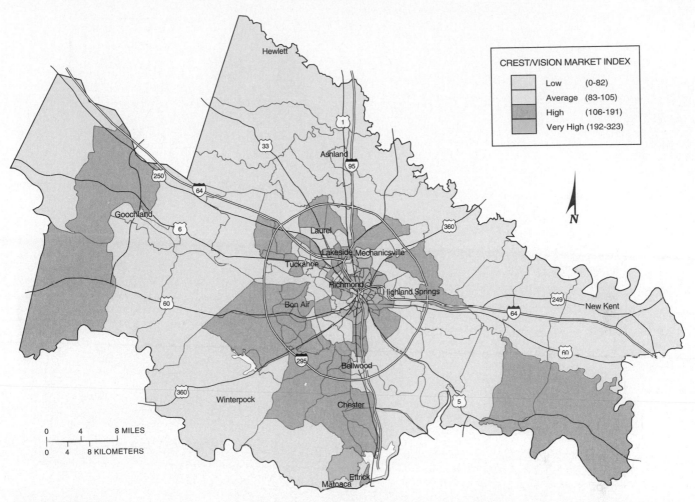

CREST/VISION MARKET INDEX

	Low	(0–82)
	Average	(83–105)
	High	(106–191)
	Very High	(192–323)

FIGURE 9.37

Fried-Chicken Fast-Food Locations in Richmond, Virginia. This map shows the potential sales locations in the greater Richmond, Virginia, area, for a fried-chicken restaurant chain, The Silver Skillet. An eating-habit scale was used, along with a market-segmentation index. Areas shaded in dark red are the most likely to patronize a Silver Skillet fast-food chicken restaurant. Downtown Richmond and nearby neighborhoods rank the highest, whereas suburbs farther away rank somewhat high. The eating-habit scale and the market-segmentation index are based on 70 U.S. census sociode-mographic and economic variables that are keyed to each census tract. *(Source: Stutz, 1994.)*

Industrial Restructuring and the Urban Hierarchy

The *industrial restructuring* that started to take place in the 1960s is changing the global urban hierarchy. The process of restructuring involves the movement of industrial plants from developed to underdeveloped areas within or between countries; the closure of plants in older, industrialized centers, as in the American Rust Belt; and the technological improvement of industry to increase productivity. Forces behind restructuring include the need for multinationals to develop strategies to locate new markets and to organize world-scale production more profitably, the national policies of developed countries to improve their future international competitive position, and the national policies of underdeveloped countries to attract subsidiaries of multinationals. These multinational strategies and governmental policies have contributed to major shifts in employment and trade. The greatest effects have been felt in the urban centers of developed countries and in the larger cities of underdeveloped countries.

FIGURE 9.38

New York City Hardware-Store Sales Penetration. A hardware-store chain, Build-Right, in New York City, wanted to know the percentage of households, by census tract, that were patronizing their stores. This is called *sales penetration* in the marketing literature. From the sales penetration map shown here, a marketing strategy for opening new stores was prepared. The darkest regions show areas of highest sales penetration. Why is sales penetration so low in Harlem? *(Source: Stutz, 1994.)*

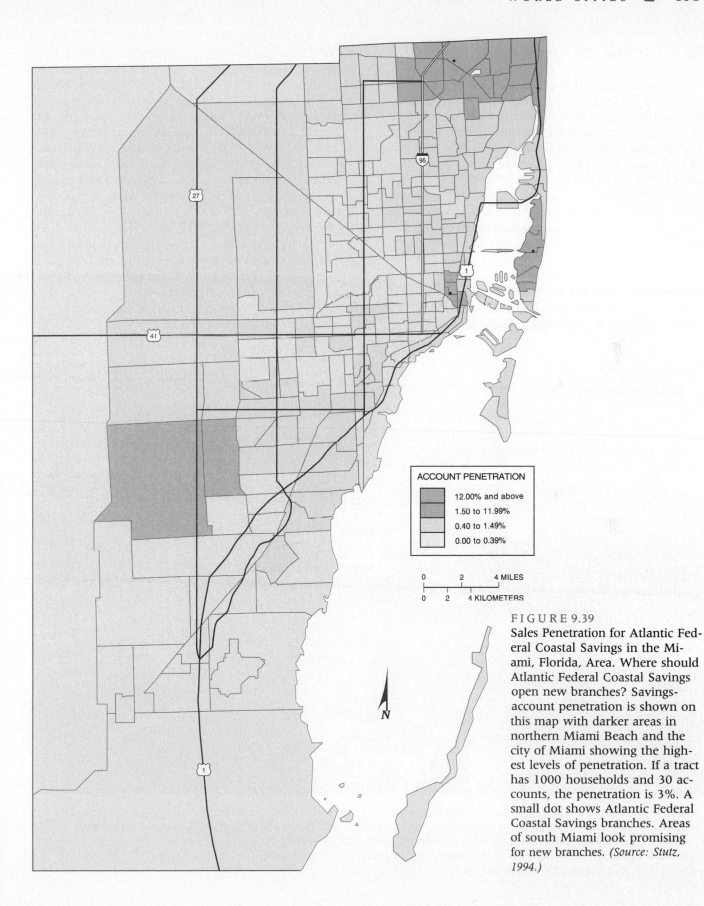

FIGURE 9.39
Sales Penetration for Atlantic Federal Coastal Savings in the Miami, Florida, Area. Where should Atlantic Federal Coastal Savings open new branches? Savings-account penetration is shown on this map with darker areas in northern Miami Beach and the city of Miami showing the highest levels of penetration. If a tract has 1000 households and 30 accounts, the penetration is 3%. A small dot shows Atlantic Federal Coastal Savings branches. Areas of south Miami look promising for new branches. (Source: Stutz, 1994.)

ACCOUNT PENETRATION

12.00% and above

1.50 to 11.99%

0.40 to 1.49%

0.00 to 0.39%

The U.S. Urban Hierarchy

Before industrial restructuring affected the organization of the labor process and the location of industry, the metropolis-and-region pattern of the United States was a fairly accurate reflection of the urban hierarchy. Each regional center—a Minneapolis-St. Paul, a Miami, or a Cleveland—was an important center of corporate services. For example, a large number of corporate law firms in Cleveland complemented that city's corporations. Major accounting firms were based in New York City and Chicago. Important regional banks were a feature of nearly all centers of corporate head offices (Figure 9.40).

By the 1970s, the metropolis-and-region network of corporate head offices and corporate services had expanded, but international business activity had become much more important. International decision making by major firms was concentrated in two cities, New York and San Francisco (Cohen, 1981). Cities that were important in the earlier, national-oriented phase of the economy began to lose ground to these *global cities*. Jobs connected with international operations did not develop as extensively in places such as St. Louis and Boston as they did in New York City and San Francisco.

Along with the growth of international operations, advanced corporate services—banks, law firms, accounting firms, and management firms—expanded their international presence in the 1970s. Similarly, these service activities developed strongly only in a handful of centers. Few banks with international expertise could be found in places other than New York City, San Francisco, and Chicago. Firms with international legal expertise were mostly confined to New York City, Los Angeles, and Washington, DC (Cohen, 1981).

In the 1980s, international activities remained con-

At the southern tip of Manhattan soar the skyscrapers of the financial district, symbolic of New York City's role as a global city. New York is the nation's preeminent international center for business decision making and corporate services. Firms headquartered in New York account for about 40% of foreign sales of Fortune 500 companies. More than 50% of foreign bank deposits in the United States are in New York banks.
(Source: N.Y. Convention and Visitors Bureau.)

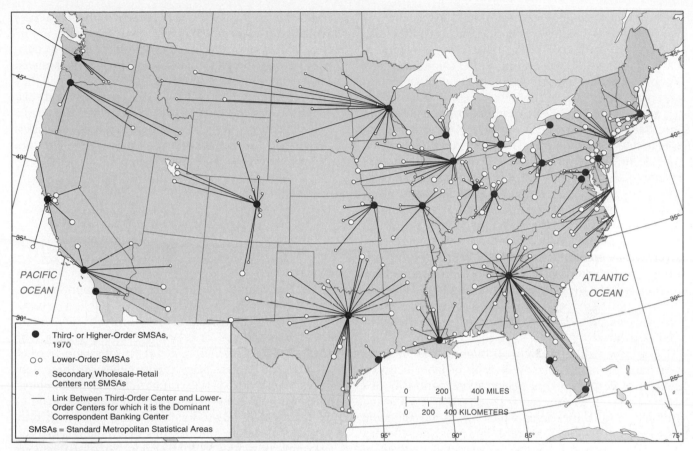

FIGURE 9.40
Banking linkages of third-order centers, 1970.
(Source: Borchert, 1972, p. 253.)

centrated. Los Angeles and Chicago joined New York City and San Francisco as top-level international business and banking centers. International activities of firms headquartered outside these cities became increasingly tied to financial institutions and corporate services located within them. In the next few years, it is expected that only a few additional cities will achieve international status and that New York City and Los Angeles will remain the predominant American global cities.

The rise of Los Angeles from a regional metropolis in the 1960s to a global center of corporate headquarters, financial management, and trade in the 1980s has been remarkable. The Pacific Rim city has become an epicenter of global capital. The transformation of Los Angeles was accompanied by selective deindustrialization and reindustrialization. A growing cluster of technologically skilled and specialized occupations has been complemented by a rapid expansion of low-skill workers fed from the recycling of labor out of declining heavy industry and by a massive influence of Third World immigrants and part-time workers (Soja, Morales, and Wolff,

1987). Sprawling, low-density Los Angeles symbolizes the process of urban restructuring: It combines elements of Sunbelt expansion, Detroit-like decline, and free-trade zone exploitation. In sharp contrast to Los Angeles, arguably one of the world's most successful cities of reconstituted capitalism, Cleveland, which lost many blue-collar jobs because of plant closures, layoffs, and capital mobility, has been unable to attract many international business operations to cushion its economic decline. Although Cleveland may never become a global city, it may boom like Buffalo and experience an economic revival in the next few years because of the 1988 free-trade agreement between the United States and Canada.

The International Urban Hierarchy

The new hierarchy of world cities has elements in common with the changing hierarchy of U.S. cities. In the 1950s and 1960s, we could use the cities identified by British geographer Peter Hall (1971) to examine the world hierarchy. Hall's world cities included the traditional large national and political centers—London, Paris, Randstad Holland, Rhine-Ruhr, Tokyo, and New York City. These places were centers of finance and corporate services.

Starting in the 1970s, multinational business and international finance began to play a more important role in the world economy. This trend was accompanied by a decline of traditional national and regional centers where a high proportion of jobs were tied to old basic industries (e.g., coal mining, iron and steel, and shipbuilding) and where concentrations of international corporations were lacking. Examples include the British cities of Glasgow, Manchester, and Liverpool. Meanwhile, cities predominant as world centers of corporations and finance became still more important. They include some of the centers identified by Hall—London, Tokyo, and New York City—but also others, such as Los Angeles, San Francisco, Chicago, Osaka, Frankfurt, and Zurich.

The new world hierarchy of international business and banking reflects a new division of labor between centers of corporate control and more nationally oriented cities. In Europe, such cities as Paris, Randstad Holland, and Rhine-Ruhr, which are more nationally oriented than London or Frankfurt, consequently play a less significant role in the international network of corporate and financial activities.

Beyond the developed world there are no world centers of corporate decision making and control. Singapore and Hong Kong are major international financial centers, but they are more involved in moving and mobilizing financial resources than in decision-making activities.

As previously mentioned, the new international urban hierarchy has had its strongest effect on the national and regional centers of developed countries and on the larger cities of underdeveloped countries. In the developed world, the concentration of corporate decision making in the global cities has been draining decision-making activities from the traditional national and regional centers—a trend that is fostering uneven urban and regional development. For example, in Great Britain there is a widening gulf between the prosperous "Sunbelt," a swath southeast of a line between Bristol and Cambridge—the outer-outer London metropolitan area—and the "rest." In the underdeveloped world, multinationals, aided by international banks, are establishing more and more subsidiaries in the large cities. Rapid industrialization of parts of the Third World has resulted in a massive flow of migrants to the main cities where, at best, they find menial jobs in low-wage industries. Will cities in developed and underdeveloped countries become centers of social and political turmoil in response to industrial restructuring efforts? Or will they recover from the current capitalist crisis? We will discover the answers in the years to come, and the results will depend on decisions that are made in the office towers of the predominant world cities—London, Tokyo, New York, and Los Angeles.

Summary

◈

In this chapter, we examine the assumptions, content, limitations, and extensions of classical central-place theory, concentrating first on cities as service centers at the national or regional level and ending with examples of urban hierarchies at the international level.

Classical central-place theory relies on three concepts to explain spatial equilibrium: *threshold, range,* and *hierarchy.* Central-place activities are arranged in a hierarchy according to the functions that they perform. High-order places bind regions of a national market-exchange economy. Within each metropolitan trade region we find a chain of low-order centers—smaller cities, towns, villages, and hamlets. These centers function as markets for the distribution of goods and services.

The assumptions on which classical central-place theory is based are unrealistic. Nowhere do we find an even *population distribution*. Resources are never the same everywhere. And landscapes are always in a state of disequilibrium. We discussed how actual conditions distort and transform theoretical networks of central places. Nonetheless, one of the strengths of a good scientific theory is that it can be modified to more closely fit reality by relaxing its assumptions. For example, we pointed to several empirical studies conducted by geographers in different areas that reveal systematic relationships between the sizes of towns, their distances from one another, the trade areas that they serve, and the densities of their surrounding populations. These empirical regularities make the central-place concept valuable for planning purposes. It has proven useful in deciding where to locate educational and medical facilities, as well as shopping centers. It has been used to recommend change in the spatial pattern of settlements.

To some geographers, however, the application of

central-place theory, as well as other theories of spatial organization, is troublesome. British geographer David Harvey (1972) feared that our theories of spatial organization may well be tools for the frustration of social change. Edward Relph (1976) pointed out that much physical and social planning is divorced from places as we know and experience them in our daily lives. He argued that when we reduce places to points or areas, with their most important quality being (profitable) development potential, we are taking an approach that rationalizes draining wetlands for the construction of new regional shopping centers or displacing single-family residences with high-rise office buildings.

A major attribute of central-place theory is that it helps us understand the emergence of an *integrated hierarchy of cities* of different functions and sizes. A weakness is that it fails to explain the underlying forces that control the development of such hierarchies. The urban hierarchy is an important concept that geographers are trying to understand better, particularly because it is instrumental in the development of international capitalism. The consequences of the emergence of a few *global cities*—London, Tokyo, New York, Los Angeles—for decision making and corporate strategy formulation are far-reaching for people in developed and underdeveloped countries.

◼

KEY TERMS

administrative principle
break-point model
central function
central place
central-place theory
complete shopping center
convenience good
daily urban system
establishment
full convenience center
functional size
functional unit
global city
gravity model
hamlet
hierarchical marginal good
hierarchy
hierarchy of central places
higher order goods
hinterland
industrial restructuring
isotrophic surface
law of retail gravitation
linear market
lower order goods
market basket

market segments
marketing principle
mercantile model
Microvision
minimum convenience centers
multipurpose travel
order of good and center
partial shopping centers
periodic market
polder
primacy
range of a good
rank-size rule
settlement-building function
settlement-forming function
settlement-serving function
shopping good
space-preference structure
Thiessen polygon
threshold of a good
trade area
traffic principle
tributary area
Varignon frame
Zuider Zee reclamation

◼

SUGGESTED READINGS

Benevelo, L. 1991. *The History of the City*, 2nd ed. Cambridge, MA: MIT Press.

Berry, B. J. L. 1967. *Geography of Market Centers and Retail Distribution*. Englewood Cliffs, NJ: Prentice Hall.

Christaller, W. 1966. *The Central Places of Southern Germany*. Translated by C. W. Baskin. Englewood Cliffs, NJ: Prentice Hall.

Daniels, P. W. 1985. *Service Industries: A Geographical Appraisal*. New York: Methuen.

Dickinson, R. E. 1964. *City and Region*. London: Routledge and Kegan Paul.

Ford, L. R. 1992. Reading the skylines of American cities. *Geographical Review*, 82:180–200.

Friedan, B. J., and Sagalyn, L. B. 1989. *Downtown Inc.: How America Rebuilds Cities*. Cambridge, MA: MIT Press.

Garreau, J. 1991. *Edge City: Life on the New Frontier*. New York: Doubleday.

Golany, G., ed. 1978. *International Urban Growth Policies: New-Town Contributions*. New York: Wiley.

Gore, C. 1984. *Regions in Question: Space, Development Theory and Regional Policy*. New York: Methuen.

Gos, J. 1993. The "magic of the mall": An analysis of form, function, and meaning in the contemporary retail built environment. *Annals of the Association of American Geographers*, 83:18–47.

Hart, J. F., ed. 1991. *Our Changing Cities*. Baltimore: Johns Hopkins University Press.

Isard, W. 1956. *Location and Space-Economy*. New York: John Wiley.

Johnson, E. A. J. 1970. *The Organization of Space in Developing Countries*. Cambridge, MA: Harvard University Press.

Jones, K. G., and Simmons, J. W. 1990. *The Retail Environment*. London and New York: Routledge.

Knox, P. L. 1991. The restless urban landscape: Economic and sociocultural change and the transformation of metropolitan Washington, DC. *Annals of the Association of American Geographers*, 81:181–209.

Knox, P. L. 1994. *Urbanization: An Introduction to Urban Geography*. Englewood Cliffs, NJ: Prentice Hall.

Lawrence, H. W. 1993. The greening of the squares of London: Transformation of urban landscapes and ideals. *Annals of the Association of American Geographers*, 83:90–118.

Longley, P. A.; Batty, M.; and Shepherd, J. The size, shape, and dimensions of urban settlements. *Transactions of the Institute of British Geographers*, 16:75–94.

Lösch, A. 1954. *The Economics of Location*. Translated by W. W. Woglom and W. F. Stolper. New Haven, CT: Yale University Press.

Lowder, S. 1988. *Inside Third World Cities*. London: Routledge.

O hUallachain, B., and Reid, N. 1991. The location and growth of business and professional services in American metropolitan areas, 1976–1986. *Annals of the Association of American Geographers*, 81:254–270.

Stutz, F. P. 1992. Urban and regional planning. In *Interpreting the City*, edited by T. Hartshorn. New York: John Wiley.

Stutz, F. P., and Parrott, R. 1992. Urban GIS applications. In *GIS: Principles and Procedures*, edited by D. Maguire, M. Goodchild, and D. Rhind, pp. 247–260. London: Longman.

United States National Advisory Commission on Civil Disorders. (Otto Kerner, chairman). 1968. *Report*. New York: Dutton.

Vance, J. E. 1970. *The Merchant's World: The Geography of Wholesaling*. Englewood Cliffs, NJ: Prentice Hall.

Whyte, W. H. 1988. *City: Rediscovering the Center*. New York: Doubleday.

Zipf, G. K. 1949. *Human Behavior and the Principle of Least Effort*. Reading, MA: Addison-Wesley.

INDUSTRIAL LOCATION: FIRMS

◈

OBJECTIVES

- To consider industrial location in terms of business and management decision making
- To present the basic elements of industrial location theory
- To trace the rise of multinational corporations
- To show the relationship between large and small firms
- To explain why and how firms grow
- To describe the industry life cycle and Kondratiev long-wave models of industrial evolution

◈

A General Motors' robotic welding line.
(Source: General Motors Corporation.)

This chapter and the next deal with a crucial activity—manufacturing. To manufacture is to make things—to transform raw materials, under humanly created conditions and in controlled environments, into goods that satisfy our needs and wants. Manufacturing considerations include (1) what will be produced, (2) how it will be produced, (3) where it will be produced, and (4) for whom it will be produced. Manufacturing is important because not only does it produce goods that sustain human life, but it also improves our standard of living, provides employment, and generates economic growth. It has played this developmental role since the industrial revolution in England in the late eighteenth century.

Geographers approach the study of manufacturing from a viewpoint that emphasizes either firms or places. When firms are of primary significance, interest focuses on the locational choices that firms make. When areas are emphasized, attention centers on the nature of industries in a city, a region, or a country. In this chapter, we concentrate on firms; in Chapter 11, we examine the changing geography of industrial areas.

Whether they are considering firms or areas, geographers can adopt a variety of theoretical frameworks for interpreting industrial location. These framworks include normative industrial location theory; the behavioral approach; and the Marxist, or structural, perspective. Normative industrial location theory derives from and shares the conservative ideology of classical economics. This theory uses abstract models to search for best, or optimal, locations. The behavioral approach focuses on the decision-making process. Rather than considering how decisions *should* be made, it examines how decisions *are* made. This liberal and more practical approach recognizes the possibility of suboptimal behavior. The Marxist, or structural, perspective is an all-encompassing radical approach that "permits industrial location to be analyzed as an integral part of the totality of economic, social, and political processes" (Smith, 1981, p. 142). It challenges the ideology of the normative and behavioral industrial theories, which approach the question of location from a strictly managerial perspective. The structural approach calls for "a greater awareness of the social implications of shifts in industrial activity . . . and [of] how inequalities are perpetuated by the functioning of the labor market and managerial hiring practices" (Marshall, 1979, pp. 675–676).

The three frameworks not only reflect the views of the geographers who use them, but also reflect changes in the nature of manufacturing itself. Normative industrial location theory, which prevailed until the 1960s, was formulated in the early twentieth century, when most manufacturing businesses were single-plant firms and when basic heavy industry was in the vanguard of industrial progress. The behavioral approach came to the fore in the 1960s, when rapid economic growth in developed countries provoked an increased academic and political interest in the decision-making process. At first, attention centered on the decision-making behavior of single-plant firms; however, this focus became too narrow with the rise of large enterprises. The late 1960s and 1970s witnessed an upsurge of interest in the geography of large corporations, which geographer Robert McNee (1960) had earlier called the "geography of enterprise." Meanwhile, the world economic crisis, affecting the location of industry, could no longer be ignored. Geographers devoted attention to the role of manufacturing in regional development theory and planning (Pred, 1977) and to radical interpretations of industrial location change (Massey, 1984; Massey and Meegan, 1978). By the late 1980s, few geographers were involved in the development of normative industrial location theory, but many were involved in Marxist analyses of industrial restructuring—selective deindustrialization and reindustrialization in developed countries and industrial revolution in parts of the Third World.

This chapter, which emphasizes normative and behavioral approaches, begins with an extended discussion of the general circumstances that influence industrial locations of single-plant firms. Although most locational factors apply whether or not a firm is a single plant, today individual plants are more often part of larger enterprises. In fact, one of the fundamental revolutions in the global structure of manufacturing is the role played by multiproduct, multiplant, multinational operations. Accordingly, a section of the chapter is devoted to the spatial behavior of large industrial enterprises. Just as companies evolve, so do industries. Thus, the final section considers the evolution of industries.

THE NATURE OF MANUFACTURING

◉

Manufacturing involves four distinct phases: deciding what is to be produced (what?) gathering together the raw materials at a plant (where?), reworking and combining the raw materials to produce a finished product (how?), and marketing the finished product (for whom?). These phases are called *selection, assembly, production*, and *distribution*. The assembly and distribution phases require transportation of raw materials and finished products, respectively. Normative industrial location theory attempts to identify the plant locations that will minimize these transportation costs. The production phase—changing the form of a raw material—involves land, labor, capital, and management, factors that vary widely in cost from place to place. Thus, each of the three steps of the manufacturing process has a spatial or a locational dimension.

Changing the form of a raw material increases its use or value. Flour milled from wheat is more valuable than raw grain. Bread, in turn, is worth more than flour. This increase in labor power is termed *value added by manufacturing*. The value added by manufacturing as a percentage of the total value of a shipment is quite low in an industry engaged in the initial processing of a raw material. For example, turning sugar beets into sugar yields an added value of about 30%. In contrast, changing a few ounces of steel and glass into a watch yields a high value added—more than 60%. The cost of labor, or the availability of skills, plays an important role in high-value-added manufacturing; the cost of raw materials is the key variable in other industries. The relative importance of production factors is called *orientation*. Geographers frequently use a term such as *raw-material-oriented* or *market-oriented* to specify the key variable for a given industry. The orientations of industries affect their patterns of geographic locations and concentrations.

UNEVEN DISTRIBUTION OF RAW MATERIALS

◈

Von Thünen's model of agricultural prodution assumed an even distribution of resources. Points of manufacturing (cities) would develop even if all resources were ubiquitous. Manufacturing would operate at selected points and incur only two kinds of costs: *production costs*, which would arise from interrelationships among other factors of production and demand, and *distribution costs* that would result from transporting the finished product to dispersed markets.

However, in reality, resources are not evenly distributed—especially the raw materials required for basic heavy manufacturing. Even the industries that use manufactured goods as their raw materials face an uneven distribution of inputs. Therefore, manufacturing involves a third kind of cost: *assembly costs*—the price that must be paid to bring raw materials from diverse locations to one plant. Assembly costs are the main concern of classical industrial location theory.

THE SIMPLE WEBERIAN MODEL: ASSEMBLY COSTS

◙

Classical industrial location theory is founded on the work of Alfred Weber (1929), a German economist. Weber was, of course, influenced by the period in which he wrote. Therefore, when we evaluate his model, we must take into account the considerable changes in the manufacturing industry since the early twentieth century. Nonetheless, Weber taught geographers to think about the distinction between material- and market-oriented industries.

Weber attempted to determine the manufacturing patterns that would develop in a world of numerous, competitive, single-plant firms, given a set of normative constraints. He began by assuming that transportation costs are a linear function of distance. He required that producers, who face neither risk nor uncertainty, choose optimal locations. He also implied that the demand for a product is infinite at a given price. Producers could sell as many units as they produced at a fixed price. They could sell none at a higher price, and charging a lower price would not affect the total demand for the product. The producer's strategy was therefore to assemble the product at the lowest possible cost in order to maximize revenue. Weber's system is often called a *least-cost approach* because he assumed that such locations are optimal.

Transportation sets the general regional pattern of manufacturing. This pattern is in turn distorted by spatial variations in the cost of labor. The final determinant is the local factors. In Weber's approach, as each set of forces is considered in sequence, the complexity of analysis increases.

Raw-Material Classes

The first cost faced in the manufacturing process is that of assembling raw materials. In Weber's simple classification system (Table 10.1), raw materials are first classified by their frequency of occurrence. *Ubiquitous raw materials*, such as air, are universally distributed;

◈

Table 10.1
Solutions to Weber's Locational Problems

Raw-Material Classes	Plant Location
Ubiquities Only	Market
Localized and Pure	
One pure	Anywhere between source of raw material and market
One pure and ubiquities	Market
More than one pure	Market
More than one pure and ubiquities	Market
Localized and Weight-Losing (Gross)	
One weight-losing	Source
One weight-losing and ubiquities	Source or market, depending on relative size of input
More than one weight-losing	Indeterminate (mathematical solution)
More than one weight-losing and ubiquities	Indeterminate (mathematical solution)

they always have a transportation cost of zero. *Localized raw materials*, such as coal, are found only at specific locations; their transportation costs are a function of the distance that they must be moved. Second, Weber classified raw materials on the basis of how much weight they lose during processing. *Pure raw materials*, such as an automobile transmission, lose no weight in processing, whereas *gross raw materials*, such as fuels, do lose weight in processing. A weight-losing raw material is assigned a *material index*, which indicates the ratio of raw-material weight to finished-product weight. Pure raw materials have a material index of one. Weight-losing raw materials have material indexes of more than one. Fuels have the highest material indexes because none of their weight affects the weight of the finished product.

We are now ready to discuss transportation costs as they relate to different kinds of raw materials. For each case we must consider (1) the costs of assembling raw materials (*RM*), (2) the costs of distributing the finished product (*FP*), and (3) the total transportation costs (*TTC*). In all cases, we assume the existence of a single market point. The best location for a manufacturing plant is the point at which the total transportation costs are minimized.

Ubiquities/Localized Raw Materials

Only localized raw materials attract production. Ubiquities merely add to the pull of the market. Ubiquitous raw materials occur everywhere, so their assembly costs are always zero. Only finished-product costs are important, and they are reduced to zero when the plant location is at the market point, as illustrated by the graph in Figure 10.1. Raw-material costs (*RM*) are the line *O-O'*. Finished-product costs rise steadily with increasing distance (in either direction) from the market. The cost line *FP* also marks the total transportation costs, which are minimized at the market.

ONE LOCALIZED PURE RAW MATERIAL

Figure 10.2 indicates the costs of a product that requires one localized pure raw material. The raw material is localized at Point *RM*, and the market is at *M*. The line *RM* represents the assembly costs, which increase as a function of distance from the source of the raw mate-

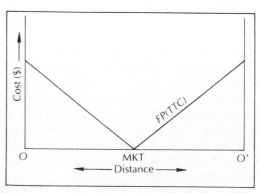

FIGURE 10.1
Weber's model: ubiquities only. Because ubiquities are found everywhere, including at the market, finished product (FP) and total transportation cost (TTC) are lowest at the market.

The Hull Rust iron-ore pit near Hibbing, Minnesota, in 1941. From the late nineteenth century to shortly after World War II, high-grade ore from Minnesota's iron ranges was shipped via the Great Lakes to iron and steel plants. When much of the accessible high-grade ore was exhausted, attention shifted to the exploitation of low-grade ore, known as taconite. Before shipment, taconite is beneficiated and pelletized in plants near the mines. Thus, it falls into the category of a localized weight-losing raw material.
(*Source: Library of Congress.*)

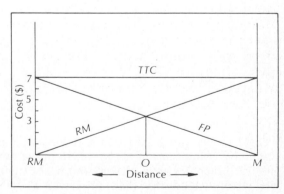

FIGURE 10.2
Weber's model: one localized pure raw material, located at RM. The line RM represents assembly costs, while the line FP represents finished product distribution costs, which are lowest at the market (M). Since the raw material does not lose weight, total transportation costs (TTC) are the same everywhere along a straight line between the raw material and the market.

rial. Similarly, the line *FP* represents the distribution costs for the finished product. Total transportation costs (*TTC*) are the sum of *RM* and *FP*. At *RM*, *TTC* equal $7.00 (*RM* = $0, *FP* = $7.00, *TTC* = $7.00). At *O*, *RM* = $3.50 and *FP* = $3.50, so *TTC* = $7.00. Because the total transportation costs are exactly $7.00 everywhere along a straight line between the source and the market, a manufacturing plant located anywhere along this line can minimize costs.

ONE LOCALIZED PURE RAW MATERIAL PLUS UBIQUITIES

Figure 10.3 shows the costs of a product requiring one localized pure raw material plus ubiquities. The assembly costs for the localized raw material (*RM*) are minimized at Point *RM*. Ubiquitous assembly costs are zero everywhere, and finished-product distribution costs are minimized at *M*. Ubiquitous raw materials, once processed, add to the weight of the finished product, so the total transportation costs (*TTC*) are minimized at the market (*M*). In other words, a plant located at the market eliminates the need to move the ubiquitous material in its processed form.

Bottled and canned soft-drink manufacturing exemplifies the use of one pure raw material (syrup concentrate) and water (in Weberian analysis, a ubiquitous raw material). The strong association between soft-drink manufacturing and population indicates that the industry is market-oriented. If the plant locates at the market, the ubiquitous raw material (water), which

makes the largest contribution to the weight of the finished product, does not need to be moved (Figure 10.4).

SEVERAL LOCALIZED PURE RAW MATERIALS

Figure 10.5 indicates costs for two localized pure raw materials, but the outcome would be the same for more than two. Once again, the single market is at *M*; one pure raw material is localized at Point *RM*₁, and the other is localized at Point *RM*₂. The transportation costs for each raw material are given by the lines *RM*₁ and *RM*₂. We assume that the raw materials are used in equal amounts (1 ton each) and that transportation costs are $1 per ton-kilometer. At Point *RM*₁, the cost of *RM*₁ is zero, and the cost of *RM*₂ is $6, for a total of $6. But the finished product weighs 2 tons; hence, an additional $6 in transportation costs is required to ship the finished product back to *M* (2 tons shipped 3 kilometers at $1 per ton-kilometer equals $6). Total transportation costs (*TTC*) at Point *RM*₁ are therefore $12, and they are the same at Point *RM*₂. At *M*, however, total transportation costs equal only $6. Locating the plant at the market eliminates the need to backhaul a raw material, so total transportation costs are minimized.

SEVERAL LOCALIZED PURE RAW MATERIALS PLUS UBIQUITIES

Remember that ubiquities always add to the pull of the market. In the graph in Figure 10.6, we assume that 1 ton each of *RM*₁, *RM*₂, and the ubiquitous raw material are used; thus, the finished product weighs 3 tons. Finished-product distribution costs at Points *RM*₁ and *RM*₂ are $9 (3 tons shipped 3 kilometers at $1 per ton-kilometer). Localized raw-material costs, *RM*₂, equal $6, and finished-product distribution costs, *FP*₂, equal $9. Total transportation costs equal $15 at Points *RM*₁ and *RM*₂, but equal only $6 at *M*. The pull of the market is considerably strengthened by the addition of ubiquitous raw materials.

Ready-mixed concrete production is a good example of an industry that uses more than one pure raw material plus ubiquities. The industry uses portland cement (pure), aggregate (pure and often ubiquitous), and water (considered to be ubiquitous). Weberian theory indicates that costs are minimized at the market. In the United States, the high correlation between industry distribution and population indicates a market orientation.

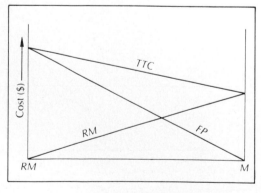

FIGURE 10.3
Weber's model: one localized pure raw material plus ubiquities. Ubiquities add to the weight of the finished product. Ubiquities are available everywhere, therefore, total transportation costs (TTC) are lowest at the market.

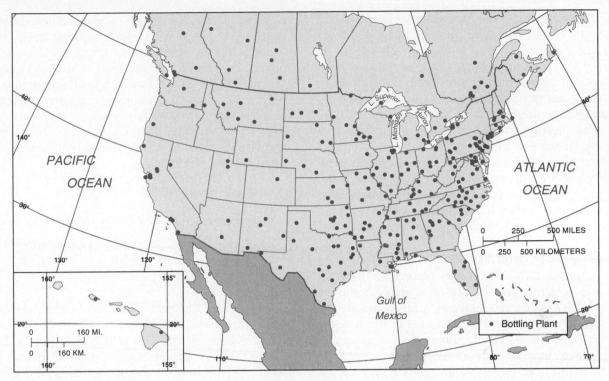

FIGURE 10.4
Bottled and canned soft drink manufacturing exemplifies the use of one pure raw material, syrup concentrate, and one ubiquity, water. Bottling plants must be located near the market because of the relatively high cost of transportation in this bulk-gaining industry. Consequently, there are several hundred bottling plants throughout North America, each located near a large urban center.

PERISHABLE GOODS

Perishable or time-urgent goods and industries are also an example of weight- or bulk-gaining raw materials. Examples of perishable goods include fresh-baked

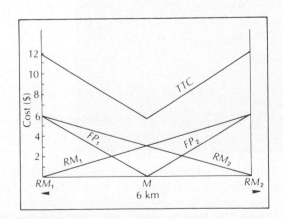

FIGURE 10.5
Weber's model: two localized pure raw materials.

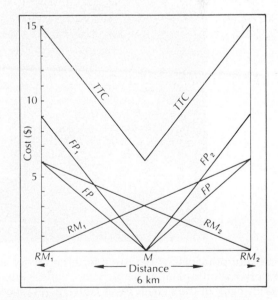

FIGURE 10.6
Weber's model: several localized pure raw materials plus ubiquities.

foods, fresh milk, and other types of manufactured food that require rapid delivery to preserve them. Although butter and milk, which have longer shelf lives, can be produced near the source of the raw materials—at rural dairies—milk and cream production is fixed closer to the markets to minimize the time and cost of delivery to places where these products are consumed.

Communications media, especially the printed medium, are an example of a perishable industry. Newspapers must be printed near the location where they are consumed to minimize the distance that these bulky items must be transported. Consequently, producing a nationwide newspaper is a difficult logistic problem. *The New York Times*, the *Wall Street Journal,* and *U.S.A. Today* are not printed and published in New York City or Washington, DC, and distributed to the entire United States. Instead, these newspaper companies transmit news and columns via satellite to scattered locations such as Atlanta, Chicago, and Los Angeles, where the papers are printed and then distributed to the nation.

Other specialized manufacturers, such as designer-clothing manufacturers, are attracted to large markets as well. Being near accessible locations where buyers can view the merchandise is important. High-fashion

clothing distribution is also a perishable industry because of the speed with which clothing styles change. As a result of the decisions by national and international buyers, merchandising, production, and sales occur at the market. New York City's garment and manufacturing district is a good example of this type of specialized manufacturer. In addition, cloth manufacturers and suppliers of shoulder pads, clasps, pins, zippers, elastic, and thread cluster near the principal garment manufacturers in New York City.

Weight- or Bulk-Losing Raw Materials

ONE LOCALIZED WEIGHT-LOSING RAW MATERIAL

Figure 10.7 illustrates the costs of a product requiring one localized weight-losing raw material. Assume that the raw material, which is localized at Point *RM*, loses half its weight in processing. The material index is therefore 2. The transportation costs for each point between the source and the market are indicated by the line *RM*.

The classical principals of industrial location theory are evidenced in the river valley and railroad site of Bethlehem Steel Corporation's plant at Bethlehem, Pennsylvania. This huge plant, which extends for nearly eight kilometers along the south bank of the Lehigh River converts raw materials—Appalachian coking coal and Minnesota iron ore—into structural shapes, large open-die and closed-die forgings, forged steel rolls, cast steel and iron rolls, ingot moulds, and steel, iron, and brass castings. The main market for the steel products is the American Manufacturing Belt with its abundance of metal-using industries.
(Source: Bethlehem Steel Corporation.)

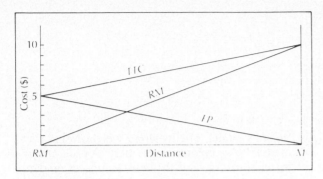

FIGURE 10.7
Weber's model: one localized weight-losing material. Because the raw material loses weight, the total transportation costs (TTC) are minimized at the raw material source (RM) because locating the processing plant at the market (M) would incur transportation costs to partially move leftover waste.

Each unit of the raw material shipped to the market at *M* costs $10. Each unit of the finished product shipped from the source, however, costs only $5. Total transportation costs (*TTC*) are minimized at the raw-material source. The distribution of the copper industry illustrates this situation. Copper ore has a high material index (99), and manufacturing is concentrated near copper mines. A raw-material orientation eliminates the transportation costs of moving waste (Figure 10.8).

ONE LOCALIZED WEIGHT-LOSING RAW MATERIAL PLUS UBIQUITIES

Of importance when a product requires one localized weight-losing raw material plus ubiquities is the ratio of the weight lost through processing to the weight

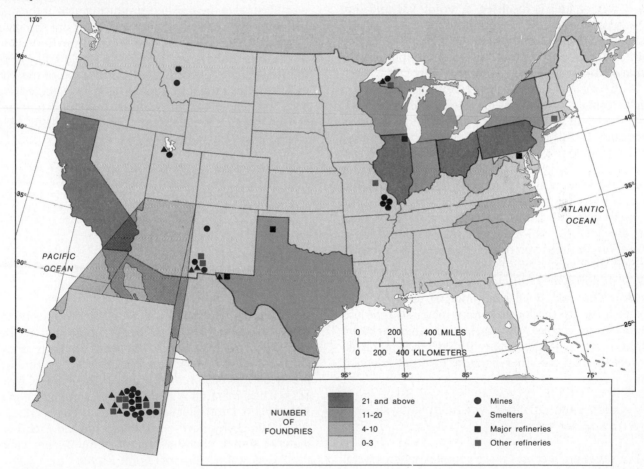

FIGURE 10.8
An example of a weight-losing, or bulk-reducing, raw material is copper ore. Copper has a high material index, meaning that 99% of the ore is wasted, and only 1% can be reduced to pure copper. Manufacturing is concentrated near the copper mines. This orientation to the source of the raw material eliminates moving wasted ore tailings. Refining smelters are also located near the mines. In the case of the United States, Arizona, and New Mexico are most important. (See Color Insert 2, page 2.6, bottom, for more illustrative map.)

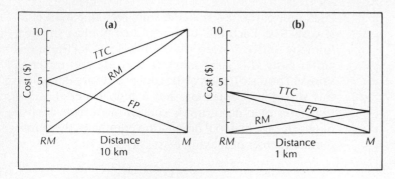

FIGURE 10.9
Weber's model: one localized weight-losing raw
material plus ubiquities. (a) Best location at raw-
material source, and (b) best location at market.

of the ubiquitous material. Two extreme cases are illustrated in Figure 10.9. In the first case (Figure 10.9a), the weight-losing raw material is a fuel, and all of its weight is lost in the manufacturing process. Assume that 1 ton of fuel is localized at Point *RM* and that 1000 kilograms of the ubiquitous pure raw material are required to produce 1000 kilograms of the finished product. Total transportation costs are minimized at the source of the weight-losing raw material.

In the second case (Figure 10.9b), assume that a weight-losing raw material has a material index of 2. Half the weight of the localized raw material is lost in processing. In this case, however, we assume a 3-to-1 ratio of the ubiquitous raw material to the localized raw material. Two tons of the localized raw material plus 3 tons of the ubiquitous raw material are processed into a finished product weighing 4 tons. At Point *RM*, total transportation costs are \$4, but at *M* total transportation costs are only \$2, which is the transportation cost for the amount of the localized weight-losing raw material required for 1 unit of the finished product. Therefore, total transportation costs are minimized at the market (*M*). This case typifies commercial brewing. Barley and hops are the localized raw materials that lose weight in processing, but the major ingredient by weight—water—is ubiquitous in Weberian analysis. Brewers are market- rather than raw-material-oriented.

SEVERAL LOCALIZED WEIGHT-LOSING
RAW MATERIALS

The situation becomes more complex when several weight-losing raw materials are necessary. The Varignon frame, mentioned in Chapter 9, simplifies the problem. The localized raw-material sites are located on a map that is glued onto a board (Figure 10.10). Holes are drilled in the board at each site. A pulley, which

reduces friction, is located at each hole. A raw material is simulated by a weight proportional to the total weight required to produce 1 unit of the finished product. Finished-product distribution costs are simulated by a weight equal to the finished-product weight at the market point (*M*). Ubiquitous raw materials are simulated by adding to this weight. Cords are run from the weights through the pulleys and tied into a single knot. When the weights are released, the final location of the knot indicates the optimal location. This type of analysis has been applied to the steel industry, in which several weight-losing materials are processed (Kennelly, 1954, 1955).

EXTENSIONS OF WEBER'S MODEL

Space-Cost Curves

Weber's basic system can be extended by using the space-cost curves developed by British geographer David Smith (1966). Assume that equal amounts of two localized weight-losing raw materials are required to produce 1 unit of a finished product. The material index of each raw material is 2, so 1 ton of RM_1 and 1 ton of RM_2 yield a 1-ton finished product. In Figure 10.11a, concentric circles have been drawn around each raw-material source and the market point. Weber called these isocost lines for each point *isotims*.

Total transportation costs are the sum of all costs to all three points. At Point *X* (Figure 10.11b), for example, RM_1 costs \$3, RM_2 \$2, and the finished product \$2 to be transported. We can find total transportation costs for as many points as we want and connect points of

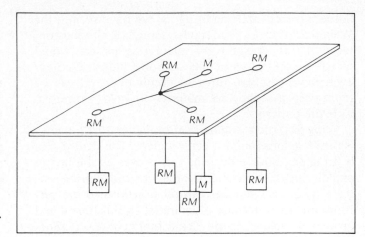

FIGURE 10.10
The Varignon frame, a mechanical device of weights, strings, and pulleys formerly used to find the best location for a plant requiring several localized weight-losing materials. Today, high-speed computers can juggle numerous materials, markets, and other factors (e.g., labor, capital, tax structure) to find the best location.

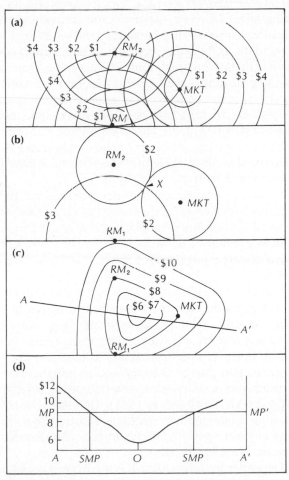

FIGURE 10.11
The development of a space-cost curve: (a) isotims, (b) total cost to Point X, (c) isodapanes, (d) space cost along the line A-A'.

equal value to produce total-cost isopleths, which Weber called *isodapanes* (Figure 10.11c). If we visualize Figure 10.11c in three dimensions, we map a depression (Figure 10.11d). Smith assumed that the market price for the finished product is a spatial constant, the line MP-MP'. The intersections of the space-cost curve and the market-price line delimit the *spatial margins to profitability*. The best location (O) is at the lowest point on the space-cost curve.

Smith's extension of Weber's ideas brings us a step closer to reality. It acknowledges that a least-cost location is not essential for economic survival. Profits can be realized by entrepreneurs who locate farther from the optimal location at Point O.

Distortions of the Isotropic Surface

Weber's assumption of a completely isotropic surface is modified when we account for the effects of localized resources. Thus, we begin a transition from a normative model to a descriptive model. The regular patterns implied by central-place theory are distorted to minimize the pull of nonubiquitous resources. The role of the natural environment (localized resources) distorts the ideal patterns of an isotropic surface.

It becomes apparent, then, that the forces controlling the location of manufacturing may be quite different from those that control the location of central places. The tertiary sector (i.e., retail and services) is market-oriented, but the orientation of the secondary sector (i.e., manufacturing) varies from industry to industry.

Some types of manufacturing, as we have seen in the Weberian model, are market-oriented. If all industries were of this type, the manufacturing pattern would match the central-place pattern. Some industries, however, have cost structures so dominated by localized input costs that they are material-oriented, which distorts the pattern.

This distortion is illustrated in Figure 10.12. Point I is the ideal location for a central place. The shaded area is a major resource deposit. City A was established to exploit this resource and became a manufacturing center. City A also supplies central functions to the surrounding area. Because of its initial establishment and growth, it superseded the establishment of service functions as the theoretical ideal location (I). The purely spatial pattern was distorted by the uneven distribution of resources.

Real-world patterns are evolutionary; they are not the result of decisions made by optimizers. Most real-world decisions do not result in best (most profitable) locations. As we discussed in Chapter 5 on decision making, locational decisions, once made, lead to inertia, in this case, *industrial inertia*. This tendency to continue investing in a nonoptimal site may be strong enough to perpetuate the distorted pattern, even if more optimal locations are discovered in the future. For example, we now have the analytic skills to locate state capitals at the centroids of state or national populations, but the investment that we already have in most state or national capitals precludes us from doing so. Tension develops between ideal spatial patterns and the patterns produced by localized resources. As technology (especially transportation) improves, ideal spatial patterns (from the entrepreneur's viewpoint) become more feasible, but the inertia resulting from past actions exerts a constant deterrent on actualizing these patterns.

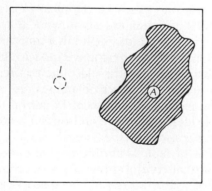

FIGURE 10.12
Distortion produced by localized resources.

We inherited one aspect of inertia from the nineteenth century. Locational patterns were then dominated by coal, which was used as a source of carbon in the iron and steel industry, as a source of fuel for steam engines, and as a source of heating for homes and businesses. As a result, businesses and populations gravitated to the coalfields in the mid- and late nineteenth century. Although other forms of energy gradually replaced coal, the population distribution has changed more slowly. Many of the depressed industrial regions in developed countries are found on coalfields.

Weber in Today's World

Let us conclude this discussion of Weber's basic system and its extensions with a brief appraisal. His model distinguishes between material- and market-oriented industries. Gross localized materials encourage material orientation, so bulk-reducing industries—mineral processing, metal smelting, timber processing, fruit and vegetable packing—are frequently found near material sources. But manufacturing is more complex than it was in the early twentieth century. Many plants begin with semifinished items and components rather than with raw materials. Producers' goods seldom lose large amounts of weight; therefore, there is not much tendency toward material orientation.

Ubiquities encourage material orientation. However, few materials can be classified as ubiquities without qualification. For example, water is scarce in many areas. Water may be ubiquitous for firms that use a little (e.g., a bakery), but not for firms that use a lot (e.g., a steel mill).

Weber's model has been criticized for its unrealistic view of transportation costs as a linear function of distance. Because of fixed costs, especially terminal costs, long hauls cost less per unit of weight than short hauls do. Plants tend to locate at material or market points rather than at intermediate points, unless there is an enforced change in the transportation mode, such as at a port (Hoyle and Pinder, 1981). However, with the expansion of the modern trucking industry and its flexibility in short hauls, the disadvantages of intermediate locations have been reduced.

Two other transportation developments have a bearing on industrial location in the late twentieth century. First, freight rates have risen more sharply on finished items than on raw materials. As a result, raw materials are often shipped nearer to the market to reduce the distance that finished goods must be shipped. Second, transportation costs have been declining. This decline increases the importance of other locational factors. Labor now is the most important industrial location determinant (Rees and Stafford, 1986). This is most obvious in firms producing high-value and high-tech products. For these firms, transportation costs are relatively unimportant (Norcliffe, 1975). Yet, for firms that distribute consumer goods (e.g., soft drinks) to dispersed markets, transportation costs remain a significant factor (Osleeb and Cromley, 1978).

PRODUCTION COSTS AT THE SITE

◈

So far, we have not considered the costs of the actual manufacturing process. After materials are assembled at a point, they must be reworked and combined to produce a finished product. Production costs include land, labor, capital, and managerial and technical skills. All these are necessary for production, and all exhibit spatial variations in both quantity and quality.

The Cost of Land

Since World War II, to minimize distribution costs, industry has been moving closer to the market. Within the urban area, however, there has been a *centrifugal drift* to suburban industrial properties since the 1970s. A large contemporary factory needs a large amount of land, preferably in a one-story building. Large parcels of industrialized land are more likely to be available in the suburbs than in central-city locations. Land in the suburbs is also much less costly than it is in the center of the city, as we learned in Chapter 8. The cost might be a million dollars per acre in the city, but only a few thousand dollars in a distant suburb near a beltway.

More reasons why industrial properties have expanded into the suburbs include locations that are easily accessible to motor freight by interstate highway and beltway, and serviced properties, which have ample sewer, water, parking, and electricity. Industries may also be attracted to the suburbs because of nearness to amenities and residential neighborhoods. Suburban locations minimize the laborers' journey to work. In addition, the U.S. regions of the South and the West

have been attractive recently because of the demand for recreational resources, a mild climate, and opportunities for enjoying the outdoors. Some firms might base their decisions partially on other land factors, including accessibility to educational facilities, cultural facilities, or even major-league sports franchises.

Truman Hartshorn, in his book *Interpreting the City* (1992), identifies eight factors that have accelerated the development of suburban industrial parks:

1. the expansion and dispersion of light assembly and the distribution of its facilities
2. lack of suitable industrially zoned land in older central cities
3. blight, traffic congestion, and cramped conditions of older industrial areas
4. a change in plant design from multistory, mill-type buildings to single-story plants permitting horizontal line production, which requires larger sites
5. more dependence on the automobile for commuting
6. increased transportation of industrialized products by trucks, which requires unloading space
7. a preference by institutional investors for financing construction and planned districts where investor security is more certain
8. the convenience and economy of not having to take care of the details that development and management organizations now handle

The Cost of Labor

Labor inputs are required for all forms of economic production, but the relative contribution of labor to the value added by manufacturing varies considerably among industries. For example, the contribution of labor costs is high in the automobile industry but low in the petroleum-products industry. The supply and demand for labor vary, but those industries in which labor costs play a major role are much more sensitive to local variations in the cost of this input. Under capitalism, the real cost of labor is determined by the relative productivity of labor rather than the dollar cost of wages and fringe benefits. The hypothetical data in Table 10.2 illustrate this point. The labor cost per unit produced is

◈

Table 10.2

Variations in Labor Productivity

Plant	Total Hourly Wages and Fringe Benefits (per Worker)	Output per Hour in Units (per Worker)	True Labor Cost per Unit Productivity
A	$5.50	100	5.5¢
B	$7.80	200	3.9¢
C	$14.20	400	3.5¢

lowest in Plant *B* even though the hourly total of wages and fringe benefits is highest.

Weber considered the cost of labor to be a regional factor controlling manufacturing patterns. The initial manufacturing pattern is set by transportation costs and then distorted by variations in the cost of labor. Weber's model assumed an infinite amount of available labor at different points, but the cost of labor varies from point to point.

Weber's analysis of this problem is illustrated in Figure 10.13. A product requires two localized raw materials and is distributed to a single market at *M*. Isodapanes, which are isopleths of total transportation costs, are indicated in the diagram. These costs are minimized at Point *T*, $4. As we move away from *T*, total transportation costs increase. At Point *L*, labor costs are $2 per unit less than at *T*. This unit labor savings is used to determine the value of a *critical isodapane*. No savings

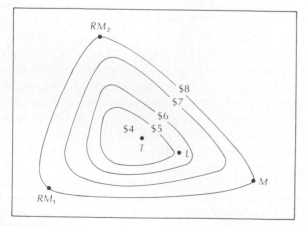

FIGURE 10.13
Critical isodapane for labor.

in total unit cost will result if the plant is moved to another point where the increased transportation costs exceed the labor savings at that point. In other words, the cost of the move must not exceed $2 per unit. Transportation costs at *T* ($4) plus labor savings at *L* ($2) determine the amount that cannot be exceeded ($6). Point *L* lies inside this critical isodapane and is clearly an economic move. Moving to a point on the critical isodapane would result in zero savings; moving to a point outside the line would result in higher total costs. Thus, within the limits established by critical isodapanes, variations in labor costs distort the pattern established by general transportation costs.

In theory, equilibrium conditions should balance regional differences in the supply and demand for labor, which is a mobile production factor. A high demand for labor in one place and an excess supply in another should be brought into equilibrium by labor migration. Such migration has certainly occurred. Examples are the nineteenth-century migration of people from rural areas to the city in countries such as Great Britain, and the twentieth-century movement of labor from the Third World and other peripheral countries to the core of industrial Europe: from the Caribbean and South Asia to Great Britain, from North Africa to France, and from Turkey to Germany.

As in the case of all production factors, the response of labor is not instantaneous. Skilled labor, in particular, has a relatively high degree of inertia, especially in the short run. People are reluctant to leave familiar places, even if jobs are plentiful in other areas. They will sit out short periods of unemployment or accept a smaller net income than could be earned elsewhere. Liberal welfare policies, such as unemployment payments and workers' compensation, have reduced the plight of the unemployed and underemployed in advanced industrial countries in this century.

Cotton textile manufacturing in the United States was in New England, but is now located in the lower labor cost Middle Atlantic states of Virginia, North Carolina, South Carolina, Georgia, Alabama, and Tennessee. No particular agglomeration exists, but many medium-sized and small towns have textile plants. For example, Mt. Vernon Mills and Regal Textile each have 25 plants in this belt. However, the wool industry remains in the Northeast because of larger numbers of skilled laborers and because of inertia. Workers must use complex equipment to accomplish precise cutting and weaving. Another example in the United States of high-skill worker demand is the semiconductor- and computer-manufacturing industry concentrated in California and the Northeast, especially Massachusetts and New York City.

The lack of instantaneous adjustment in labor demand and supply has resulted in variations in the cost of labor within and among countries. In the United States, wages are often higher in the more industrial states, in densely settled areas, and in highly urbanized environments.

At the world scale, developed countries have higher wage rates than newly industrializing countries. One factor responsible for differential wage rates is the level of worker organization. Higher rates of unionization are associated with higher wages. Unionization is generally more prevalent in the older, established industrial countries than in the newly industrializing countries. Thus, considerable advantages can be gained by companies that relocate to, or purchase from, newly industrializing countries, especially if these countries are characterized by low levels of capital-labor conflict. The capital-labor conflict, manifested in industrial disputes, is a powerful force propelling the drift of industrial production outward from the center to the periphery of the world system.

The Cost of Capital

Capital, another necessary production factor, takes two forms: *fixed capital* and *liquid,* or *variable, capital.* Fixed capital includes equipment and plant buildings. Liquid capital is used to pay wages and meet other operating costs. Liquid capital is theoretically the most mobile production factor. The cost of transporting liquid capital is almost zero, and it can be transmitted almost instantaneously in our "wired world." About $9 trillion in electronic funds transfers are completed annually over international communications lines, an amount equal to two-thirds of the global gross national product (GNP). Fixed capital is much less mobile than liquid capital; for example, capital invested in buildings and equipment is obviously immobile and is a primary reason for industrial inertia.

Any type of manufacturing that is profitable has an assured supply of liquid capital from revenues or borrowing. Most types of manufacturing, however, initially require large amounts of fixed capital to establish the operation—or, periodically, to expand, retool, or replace outdated equipment or to branch out into new products. The cost of this capital, which is interest, must be paid from future revenues. Investment capital is not uniformly distributed and does not display great mobility.

Investment capital has a variety of sources: personal funds; family and friends; lending institutions, such as banks and savings and loan associations; and the sale of stocks and bonds. Most capital in advanced industrial countries is raised from the last two sources. The total supply of investment capital is a function of total national wealth and the proportion of total income that is saved. Savings become the investment capital for future expansion.

Whether a particular type of manufacturing, or a given entrepreneur, can secure an adequate amount of capital depends on several factors. One factor is the supply of and demand for capital, which varies from place to place and from time to time. Of course, capital can always be obtained if users are willing to pay high enough interest rates. Beyond supply-and-demand considerations, investor confidence is the prime determinant of whether capital can be obtained at an acceptable rate. Investor confidence in a particular industry may exist in one area but be lacking in another. For example, Henry Ford, of Ford Motor Company, failed to raise investment capital in one area of the United States but was able to secure it in his hometown of Detroit.

Managerial and Technical Skills

Managerial and technical skills are also required for any type of production operation. Corporations are the primary agents responsible for specific industrial patterns. The general pattern is, of course, determined by the localization of other production factors, subsequent transportation costs, and spatial margins to profitability. Ford Motor Company can again be used as an example. The company was established in Detroit, primarily because Henry Ford was able to obtain risk capital there—but any town in the Midwest accessible to raw materials, especially steel, could have supported automobile manufacturing. On the other hand, had Ford attempted to manufacture automobiles on a large scale in Butte, Montana, he would have surely failed. A study by H. Hunker and A. J. Wright (1963) found that the majority of the manufacturing plants in Ohio were in the hometowns of their founders. Historically, the Midwest, and the rest of the American Manufacturing Belt, established the regional pattern of successful locations for

The Ford Motor Company steel mill and auto assembly plant at River Rouge near Detroit, Michigan, is a vertically integrated system. Basic raw materials are used to produce steel, which is incorporated into the engines, frames, bodies, and parts of finished automobiles. It is a transnational corporation with 360,000 employees located in 30 countries.
(Source: Ford Motor Company.)

most types of manufacturing—but the specific locations chosen within these margins were determined by the individual decisions of capitalists.

Theoretically, management should be much more mobile than labor because fewer people are involved, and the higher income of managers should make moving less of a financial burden. But managerial skills, like labor skills, are often highly concentrated. Where are the organizational headquarters of the 500 largest American corporations? Most are in the largest urbanized areas of the country (Figure 10.14). The top 10 metropolitan headquarter areas are New York City (157 head offices), Chicago (41), Los Angeles (28), San Francisco (25), Philadelphia (18), Minneapolis-St. Paul (15), Detroit (13), Boston (12), Pittsburgh (12), and Houston (11) (Rand McNally, 1988).

Technical skills are the skills necessary for the con-

tinued innovation of new products and processes. These skills are generally categorized as research and development (R&D). In the early phases of industrialization in developed countries, product development was usually carried out in tandem with production by small firms, many of which, together with their innovations, failed to survive. Today, the R&D required for new products is a large and expensive process, involving long lead times between invention and production; therefore it is beyond the scope of small firms. The cutting edge of advanced industrial economies, R&D is concentrated in a few major research-university clusters and established areas of innovation (Figure 10.15). Three of these in the United States are Silicon Valley, the region south of San Francisco Bay in the vicinity of Stanford University; Boston and Route 128; and the Research Triangle of North Carolina, so called because of three universities

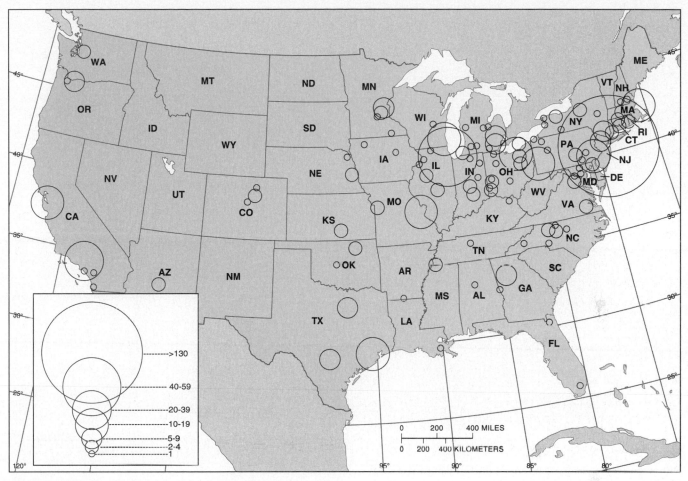

FIGURE 10.14
Corporate headquarters: 500 largest corporations.
(Source: Rand McNally, 1988.)

located there—the University of North Carolina at Chapel Hill, Duke University in Durham, and North Carolina State University at Raleigh. Roughly equidistant from the three main cities, Research Triangle Park is home to the laboratories of IBM, Burroughs Wellcome, Northern Telecom, and other major companies conducting R&D.

For most of the twentieth century, the United States has been the world's leader in technological innovation. In the 1970s, however, the number of new inventions and granted patents declined. Factors that slowed U.S. innovation included a decline in federal support for basic research, an increase in government red tape, an increased managerial interest in improving existing products to yield quick returns, and difficulties in obtaining risk capital. Basically, the United States was not spending enough on R&D. Although outlays for R&D

began to rise in the 1980s as foreign competition forced firms to automate in order to reduce costs and increase productivity, U.S. expenditures for R&D represented only 2.7% of the GNP (United Nations, 1985). This figure compares favorably, however, with the expenditures of other developed countries—Japan (2.6%), Germany (2.5%), Great Britain (2.4%)—which, as a group, dominate the world in the number of R&D scientists and engineers and in the amount of R&D expenditures.

TECHNOLOGICAL CHANGE

As we learned in Chapter 6, the time involved in and the cost of transporting materials, products, and information have decreased substantially in the last 50 years as a result of technological innovations and trans-

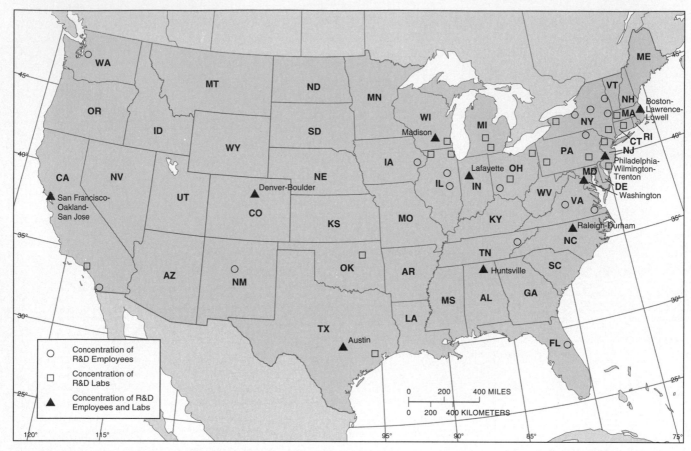

FIGURE 10.15
Major concentrations of research and development activity.
(Source: Based on personal communication with Malecki, 1993.)

portation engineering breakthroughs. The ability to transmit information at faster and faster speeds led to the growth of transnational corporations. In terms of transportation and communications technology, New York City and Tokyo are much closer today than Philadelphia and New York City were during World War I.

As Henderson and Castells (1987) state, "The new telecommunications technologies are the electronic highways of the information age, equivalent to the role played by the railway systems in the process of industrialization" (p. 6). Communications technology is valuable to all types of economic activity, but especially to industries associated with development processing and information transmission—business services, including finance, insurance, and real estate (FIRE).

Satellites, transoceanic cables, and facsimiles (faxes) have revolutionized world communications and inter-

national business (see Figure 10.16, which shows the tremendous change in information technology during the last 40 years). The number of communication satellites alone grew astronomically in the mid- to late 1960s after the Early Bird (Intelsat 1) satellite was launched. In 1980, satellites could carry 150,000 bidirectional circuits for international communications and by the year 2000, they could carry a million circuits each.

As Peter Dicken states in his book *Global Shift: The Internationalization of Economic Activity* (1992), "Satellite technology, together with a whole host of other communication technologies is making possible quite remarkable levels of global communication of conventional messages and also the transmission of data. In this respect, the key element is the linking together of computer technologies with informational transmission technologies over vast distances. It has become possible

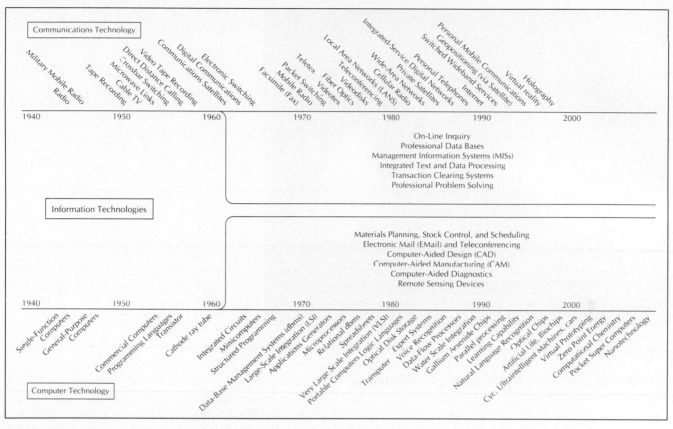

FIGURE 10.16
The convergence of computer technology and communications technology yields information technologies. Two initially distinct technologies have now combined to impact the world economy. Communications technology is concerned with the transmission of information, while computer technology is concerned with the processing of information. The two technologies started to merge in the 1960s. Without information technologies, today's complex world economic system could not exist and develop.
(Source: Based on Freeman, C. 1987. The Challenge of New Technologies NOECD, Interdependence and Cooperation in Tomorrow's World, OECD, Paris, pp. 123–156 and Dicken, Global Shift, 1992.)

for a message to be transmitted from one location and received on the other side of the world virtually simultaneously" (p. 106).

Fiber-optic cable, a new technology in telecommunications, allows a high carrying capacity and signal strength at extremely high speeds across continents and oceans alike. There has been an increase in satellite and cable capacity during the last 20 years. Fiber-optic links are under construction in the Pacific Rim to produce the global digital highway around the world. More than 100,000 simultaneous messages can be carried among North America, Western Europe, and Japan through

the new fiber-optic cables that allow people or facsimile machines to converse with one another.

Texas Instruments, the large transnational American computer and electronics company, operates more than 50 plants in 19 countries, and each plant is linked by satellite communications. Through satellite communications and fiber-optic cables, production planning, cost accounting, financial planning, marketing, customer service, and personnel management are conducted from more than 300 remote planning terminals, 8000 inquiry terminals, and 140 distributed computers around the world (Dicken, 1992). A similar computer network was

R & D firm drafting maps.
(Source: Hewlett Packard.)

presented for I. P. Sharp Canadian Financial Planning Company in Chapter 6.

FLEXIBLE MANUFACTURING

According to Dicken's book (1992), management has attempted to recognize and control the nature, speed, and quality of work through four developmental stages of the labor and production process:

1. *manufacture:* assembling labor workshops and dividing labor into specific jobs and tasks
2. *machinofacture:* further dividing labor by the use of mechanical power through machines in factories
3. *scientific management (Taylorism):* enhancing the degree of the division of labor after scientific study, together with increased supervision and control of the manufacturing process
4. *Fordism:* managing assembly-line work units to control and improve the pace and quality of production

The question now is what will replace Fordism in the future. Fordism in the past, most notable in the automobile industry, produced assembly-line products at rapid speeds using standardized techniques for a mass-consumption market. For example, Womack, Jones, and Roos (1990) suggest that the mass production in the Fordist approach is being replaced by a lean production, which is necessary in competitive world markets today. The most important aspect of this new, or lean, system is flexibility of the production process itself, including the organization and management within the factory, and the flexibility of relationships among customers, supplier firms, and the assembly plant. According to Womack, Jones, and Roos (1990)

The key to production flexibility lies in the use of information technologies in machines and operations. These permit more sophisticated control over the process. With the increasing sophistication of automated processes and, especially, the new flexibility of the new electronically controlled technology, far reaching changes in the process of production need not be associated with increased scales of production. Indeed, one of the major results of the new electronic computer aided production technology is that it permitted rapid switching from one process to another and allows the tailoring of production to the requirements of individual customers. Traditional automation is geared to high volume standardized production; the newer flexible manufacturing systems are quite different.

Flexible manufacturing allows goods to be manufactured cheaply, but in small volumes as well as large volumes. A flexible automation system can turn out a small batch, or even a single item, of a product as efficiently as a production-line, mass-assembled product.

The minimum-change approach to industrial mass production is not necessarily the most cost effective since the advent of flexible manufacturing. Rapid technological change of new products becomes much less costly and risky. The new approach achieves profitability through targeting segmented markets (discussed in Chapter 9) and being able to adapt production systems to local conditions, needs, and demands.

LOCATIONAL COSTS

◈

Now that we discussed the various production costs, we can examine their influence on location in more detail. Smith (1966) pointed out that the establishment of any manufacturing plant in a market economy involves three interdependent decision-making criteria: (1) *scale*—the size of the operation that will determine the volume of total output, (2) *technique*—the particular combination of inputs that are used to produce an output, and (3) *location*. In this section, we concern ourselves with location as a function of input costs and consider technique and scale in subsequent sections.

Let us assume that technique and scale are constant and that variations in demand, if they exist, are solely a function of price. These assumptions allow us to portray three general industrial location cases (Figure 10.17). In Case (a), market price (revenue) is a spatial constant, and costs vary across space. The optimum location is then the lowest point on the space-cost curve, and the spatial margins are where costs equal revenue. Total revenue (demand) exhibits spatial change in Case (b), and costs are a spatial constant. The optimum location is the highest point on the revenue curve, and the spatial margins to profitability are, again, where costs equal revenue. Variations in both cost and revenue across space are shown in Case (c). The optimum location (*O*) is the place where revenue exceeds costs by the greatest amount. For all three cases we can show that *both* curves determine the spatial margins to profitability, that the variable with the *steepest* gradient determines the best location, and that the *slope* of the curve indicates the relative importance of locational costs.

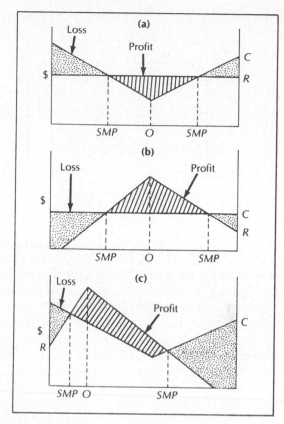

FIGURE 10.17
Spatial margins to profitability: (a) cost variable, revenue constant; (b) revenue variable, cost constant; (c) revenue and cost variable.
(Source: Based on Smith, 1981, p. 113.)

The concept of spatial margins to profitability is noteworthy because it incorporates *suboptimal* behavior. Profits are possible anywhere within the defined limits. The graphs in Figure 10.19 represent the most general statement that can be made about locational viability. Defining these margins in reality and determining specific locations to be occupied within them, however, is a much more difficult problem. We can still make one generalization about real-world patterns within spatial margins to profitability—industries that are clustered must face limited spatial margins to profitability and high location costs. This situation is illustrated in Figure 10.18. Remember that any kind of cost and/or revenue may be a critical factor in determining the spatial margins to profitability.

Weber's theory is preoccupied both with transportation costs and with finding least-cost locations. A more general theory should consider total cost and the possi-

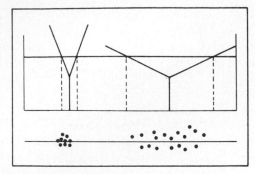

FIGURE 10.18
Spatial margins to profitability and clustering.

bility of suboptimal decisions. Walter Isard (1956) suggested that locational factors can be divided into three general classes on the basis of their geographic occurrence: (1) *transfer charges*—costs that can be portrayed as a regular function of distance; (2) *spatially variable costs*—costs that vary across space (labor, power, capital, managerial skills) but do not vary systematically with distance; and (3) *aspatial costs*—factors that can influence costs but that are independent of location, such as scale changes.

Smith (1966) extended Weber's analysis to all types of costs. He assumed that each input has a least-cost point. Least-cost points for materials may be mines or the factories of parts producers. There is a least-cost point for the particular kind of labor required, and there is a point at which finished-product distribution costs are minimized. Each of these points exerts a certain pull on location (recall the Varignon frame). The relative weight of all these pulls determines the least-cost location.

Smith also acknowledged the distinction between *basic* and *locational costs*. Basic costs are the minimum costs that must be paid regardless of location; they represent the lowest point on the cost surface of a particular input. For example, the basic labor cost is the minimum wage. Locational costs are all costs exceeding the basic cost. They vary with location and may rise as a function of the distance from the least-cost location. Figure 10.19 illustrates the two kinds of costs. We assume that some workers will accept the minimum wage. Their location represents the lowest point on the labor-cost surface, or the basic cost. Away from this point, workers demand more than the minimum wage, but the additional amount takes the form of locational costs.

We see then that the total cost of any input is the sum of locational and basic costs. The relative pull of a given input therefore depends on the slope of the

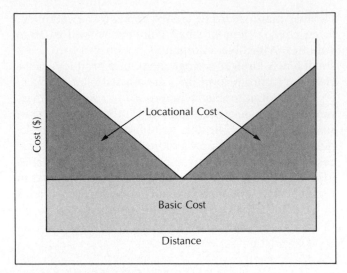

FIGURE 10.19
Basic and locational costs.

(locational) space-cost curve and the percentage contribution of an input to the total cost of output. An input accounting for a large proportion of the total basic cost or varying widely in locational costs should have the most influence on plant location.

Smith (1981) examined this proposition with variable-cost models. He demonstrated that locational costs can occur either because transportation costs per unit of a particular input are high, or because a large quantity (basic cost) of the input is required, even though the unit cost may be low. The latter point can be illustrated by coal, which had a profound effect on past industrial locational patterns for heavy industry. Coal can be moved relatively cheaply on a per ton basis, but the large quantity required in some types of manufacturing has resulted in high locational costs and a pull on industries to locate near coal deposits. This example illustrates the difference between transportation costs per unit and locational costs.

THE LOCATIONAL EFFECTS OF TECHNIQUE

◙

Technique, or the particular combination of inputs used to produce a given finished product, can have an important effect on a firm's locational decision. A certain amount of land (resources), labor, and capital is needed to produce any finished product, but, within limits, capital may be substituted for labor, resources may be substituted for labor, and so forth.

The most evident trend in modern manufacturing has been substitution of capital in the form of machinery and robotics for labor (Sanderson and Berry, 1986). More and more autonomous manufacturing systems, which apply sophisticated technology to improve the quality and efficiency of production, are replacing certain kinds of labor. Whether or not substitution between production factors occurs depends on the relative cost of the two inputs and the scale and locational decisions already made by the firm. If, for example, labor costs rise at a given location, the firm may choose to substitute capital for labor at that location, or it may opt to change locations to take advantage of lower labor costs and thus maintain the same labor-to-capital ratio.

The limits set on substitution vary considerably from industry to industry. Petroleum refining, for example, can be readily automated, whereas garment manufacture cannot. The textile industry, therefore, is much more sensitive to changes in labor costs than the refining industry is. In the late nineteenth and early twentieth centuries, the U.S. textile industry shifted from old multistoried New England mills to new mills in the Southern Piedmont as labor costs rose in the Northeast. This is an example of the influence that options in technique exert to determine the locational decision. The increased labor costs outweighed the costs of moving the industry. Of course, the wage advantage of the South did not persist; as new industry moved south, wages there rose.

This has forced textile industries to move into other areas of the United States where pools of cheap labor are available (e.g., the depressed coal-mining towns of eastern Pennsylvania) or to migrate farther afield—to Mexico, Brazil, South Korea, and Singapore. If capital substitution had been a viable option, the textile industry might not have moved.

Many times a firm may want to change its scale to increase output and to earn extra profits. A change in scale may also require a change in location and/or technique.

SCALE CONSIDERATIONS IN INDUSTRIAL LOCATION

Scale, along with location and technique, is important because it is one of the three interdependent production criteria that drive decision making (Figure 10.20). Smith (1981) states

The choice of location cannot be considered in isolation from scale and technique. Different scales of operation may require different locations to give access to markets of different sizes. . . . Different techniques will favor different locations, as firms tend to gravitate toward cheap sources of the inputs required in the largest quan-

Handcarts, delivery trucks, and agile pedestrians mingle on the teeming steets of New York City's garment district. This is Seventh Avenue, where out-of-town buyers come to place their bets on tomorrow's fashions.
(Source: Van Bucher, Photo Researchers, Inc.)

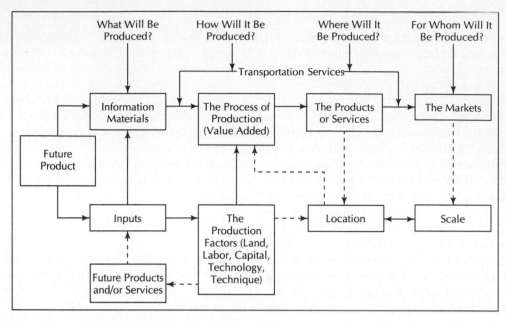

FIGURE 10.20
The four questions of the world economy and the industrial production process.

tities, and location itself can influence the combination of inputs and hence, the technique adopted. (pp. 23–24)

But scale is also important because producers are concerned with the unit cost of production—and adjustments in scale can produce considerable variations in unit cost. Scale is the means by which production is "tuned" to meet demand. In some economies, this tuning may be done by the state; in others, by private entrepreneurs.

Principles of Scale Economies

DIVISION OF LAND AND CAPITAL

Along with standardization of parts, *division of labor* is a primary component of mass production. Workers who perform one simple operation in the production process are much more efficient than those who are responsible for all phases. Division of labor not only speeds up production, but also facilitates the use of relatively unskilled labor. A worker can learn one simple task in a short time, whereas the skills required to master the entire operation may take years to learn. Division of labor, however, requires a relatively large scale be-

cause a large pool of workers is generally necessary. A common way to measure the size of a firm is by the number of employees. Capital, once invested in machinery and buildings, becomes fixed capital and produces income only when in operation. A three-shift firm makes much more efficient use of its fixed capital than a single-shift firm does. The three-shift firm is three times larger in scale, measured by employment, yet its fixed capital investment may be no more than that of the single-shift firm.

MASSING OF RESERVES

Large operations can maintain proportionally smaller inventories than smaller firms can, and therefore reduce unit costs. This principle is called the *massing of reserves*. Assume that a particular type of production requires a large, expensive, complicated piece of machinery. The entire production line is forced to stop if the machine is inoperable. A plant shutdown, even for an hour, is an expensive proposition in that idle workers must be paid while waiting and other operational costs continue to accrue. A firm in this industry must maintain a reserve, or inventory, of spare machine parts to prevent long shutdowns. Firm A has only 1 machine but must maintain an inventory of almost one whole machine in equivalent spare parts. Firm B has 10 machines in operation, but because it is highly unlikely that the same part will fail in all 10 machines at the same time, its reserve of parts needs to be only slightly larger than Firm *A*'s.

IMPERFECTLY DIVISIBLE MULTIPLES

Scale economies also operate when inputs do not allow one-to-one increases in scale. Let's say that we are manufacturing hammers. The machine that produces the hammerheads can output 300 per hour, whereas the hourly output of the handle machine is 400. If we run both machines for an hour, we produce 300 complete hammers and 100 extra handles. Hammer production involves *imperfectly divisible multiples*. The scale of operation can be increased, however, until we find a unitary combination of head and handle machines. Suppose that we increase the number of head machines to four and the number of handle machines to three. Now we produce 1200 complete hammers per hour. It is easy to envision the kinds of savings that result from this principle in an industry such as automobile manufacturing, in which perfectly divisible multiples may be reached only in very large operations.

VOLUME PURCHASES

Large firms generally pay much less for material inputs than small firms do. For example, Ford Motor Company can obtain tires for a much lower unit price than an individual dealing with the same tire company can, because Ford buys millions of tires a year. Increasing scale, in other words, generally lowers the unit cost of inputs.

Possible Scale Economies

Economists portray scale economies as a curve of long-run average costs (LRACs), which graphs the unit costs as a function of scale. Several possible LRAC curves are indicated in Figure 10.21. Notice that unit costs decrease, reach an optimum point, and then began to increase. The rise in the curve is termed *diseconomies of scale* (diminishing marginal returns to scale) and occurs when a firm becomes too large to manage and operate efficiently. The optimum scale of operation is very small in Industry *A*, very large in industry *C*, and fairly wide-ranging in industry *B*. Firms in Industry *A* should be

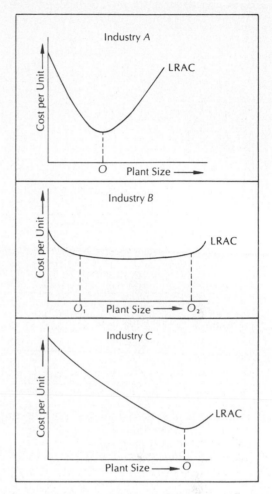

FIGURE 10.21
Variations in long-run average cost (LRAC).

small, they should be large in Industry *C*, and they can range from small to large in Industry *B*.

Possible scale economies also indicate how firms in an industry can expand production. A firm in Industry *A*, for example, can build a branch plant; increasing the size of operations on the original site would produce diseconomies of scale. Firms in Industry *B*, however, can increase production either by expanding existing plants or by building new ones.

Implications of Scale Economies

To explore the implications of scale economies, let us consider a company that operates two small breweries, each in a different town. The entire output of the firm

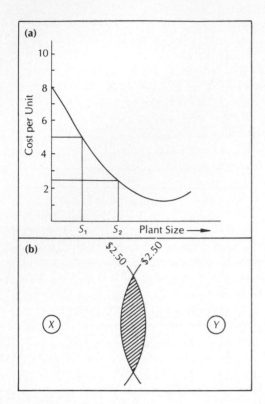

FIGURE 10.22
Spatial implications of scale economies: (a) long-run average costs and (b) transportation cost isolines for break-even total cost with plant size S_2.

Integration and Diversification

Scale refers to anything that changes the volume of a firm's total output. Besides simply increasing plant size, two other means are commonly employed for effecting scale changes. Some firms purchase raw-material sources or distribution facilities. This is called *vertical integration* (or vertical merger) in that the firm controls more "up and down" in the total production process. Some large automobile manufacturing firms, for example, own iron and coal mines and produce their own steel ("down" in the process). They may also own dealerships and do their own transporting and marketing ("up" in the process). Large oil companies are also often vertically integrated; they control exploration, drilling, refining, and retailing. In contrast, *horizontal integration* (or horizontal merger) occurs when a firm gains an increasing market share of a given niche of a particular industry.

Vertical and horizontal integration generally refer to a single finished product. The vertical integration of Ford Motor Company, for example, focuses on controlling the inputs and marketing required for automobile production. However, the trend among corporations in the United States, Japan, and Western Europe has been a strategy of *diversification.* Many large corporations, through *conglomerate merger,* control the production and marketing of diverse products. A company may produce many unrelated products, each with elements of horizontal and vertical integration. Diversification spreads risk and increases profits. Diminishing demand for the products of one division may be offset by rising sales in another.

Most industrial location theory is based on the firm, which implies a small, single-plant operation producing a single product. Large corporations are much more complex, but they deal with all the variables of location theory and must still make locational decisions. Although large enterprises may seem to be more concerned with technique and scale decisions, each locational decision has an effect on scale and technique. We should consider two points: First, large firms may be able to operate in less than optimal locations and still have a significant effect on the market through the control that they exert over government policies and the prices and sources of raw materials. Conversely, large firms may be able to make optimal locational choices through their employment of the scientists and technical personnel who help top management make more profitable decisions.

is sold in the two towns. The LRACs (per barrel) for the firm are illustrated in Figure 10.22a. The firm operates the breweries at scale, S_1, and costs are $5 per barrel. The firm can reduce its cost per barrel by consolidating its operations into a single plant at S_2 ($2.50 per barrel). One plant can be closed and the remaining plant doubled in size, or both plants closed and a new, larger brewery built. However, the firm minimizes its finished-product distribution costs by manufacturing beer in each town. Additional distribution costs will be incurred if a single brewery is used. The question is whether the savings from scale economies outweigh the increased transportation costs. These two items balance at a transportation cost of $2.50 per barrel. Figure 10.22b shows the isocost line of $2.50 per barrel for each town. Notice that the two lines intersect. This intersection indicates that the scale savings outweigh the increased transportation costs, so the larger plant can operate in either city or at an intermediate point with a lower cost per barrel than is possible with the two small-scale plants.

Interfirm Scale Economies: Agglomeration

To this point, we have been concerned with intrafirm scale economies. However, scale economies also apply to clusters of firms in the same or related industries—for example, the computer firms localized in California's Silicon Valley and the metal trades concentrated in the West Midlands of England. By clustering and increasing the spatial scale, unit costs can be lowered for all firms. These economies, often called *externalities, agglomeration economies,* or *linkages,* take several forms. *Production linkages* accrue to firms locating near other producers that manufacture their basic raw materials. By clustering, distribution and assembly costs are reduced. Close physical links between related businesses were more common a century ago than they are now (Muller and Groves, 1979; Wise, 1949). Today, component supplies are often far apart. The Boeing 767 is a case in point. Boeing manufactures its airplane frame in Seattle with parts from Japan and Italy. The engine is assembled in Ohio with parts from Sweden, France, Germany, and Italy. Advances in technology, communications, and transportation have given momentum to the economies of globalization.

Service linkages occur when enough small firms locate in one area to support specialized services. The garment industry in New York City provides an example of service linkages. Firms in the garment district are small, but they require specialized service and maintenance activities, such as the repair of sewing and cutting machines. The clustering of the garment industry in Manhattan has also provided the impetus for increased numbers of investment specialists who deal almost exclusively with loans to the garment industry. They understand the special needs of the industry and are much more likely to advance risk capital than other investors are.

In addition to production and service linkages, there are *marketing linkages,* for which the garment industry again is an example. These linkages occur when a cluster is large enough to attract specialized distribution services. The small firms of the garment industry in New York City have collectively attracted advertising agencies, showrooms, buyer listings, and other aspects of finished product distribution that deal exclusively with the garment trade. Firms within the cluster have a cost advantage over isolated firms that must provide these specialized services for themselves or that must deal with New York firms at a considerable distance and cost.

Some economies are not the result of interfirm linkages, per se, but occur from locating in large cities or industrial complexes. Firms in these locations have an advantage, within limits, over similar firms in more rural areas. Cities provide markets, specialized labor forces and services, utilities, and transportation connections required by manufacturing. *Urbanization* or *industrial-complex economies,* therefore, are a combination of production, service, and marketing linkages concentrated at a particular location.

IBM designed the Yamato Laboratory with the aim of making it the focal point of development of high-technology products for IBM Japan. The laboratory integrates all development groups at a single location and uses IBM's systems to create products suited to local customer needs. The Yamato Laboratory is 1 of more than 30 IBM basic research institutes and product-development laboratories around the world. *(Source: IBM.)*

DEMAND AND INDUSTRIAL LOCATION

◈

Our discussion thus far has focused almost exclusively on the supply side of the industrial problem, in that we examined ways in which firms can reduce unit costs. The other side of the problem is demand. Demand determines the scale of output and, in turn, the technique and location of the firm. Concentrations of high demand certainly attract market-oriented industries and, therefore, influence locational patterns. Demand is essentially a function of income and tastes, both of which change with time. Different industries must deal with different kinds of demand. The locational problems of firms producing goods sold to the general public are different from the problems of firms producing specialized products sold only to other manufacturers or to very select groups of consumers. For example, the demand pattern in the United States that a root-beer producer must deal with is considerably different from that for a manufacturer of snowmobile parts.

A Demand-Potential Surface

Geographers have explored the demand aspect of the industrial problem by employing the concept of a *potential surface* (Harris, 1954). Market-potential models can simulate the accessibility of a place to a given population, measured by such data as numbers of people, income, or retail sales. The basic formula is as follows:

$$D_i = \sum_{j=1}^{n} \frac{P_j}{d_{ij}}$$

where:

D_i = demand potential at i
P_j = population of j (may be income-weighted)
d_{ij} = distance between i and j

The symbol $\sum_{j=1}^{n}$ means that we sum the demand for all points j from the first point ($j = 1$) to the last point (n). Demand potential is computed for many points. Isolines are then drawn to connect points of equal value. Figure 10.23a illustrates the potential surface of the United States resulting from weighting the population by retail sales per county. The actual numbers obtained from this calculation have only relative meaning, so each contour is expressed as a percentage below the highest point. Demand potential is highest at New York City and declines away from the city. This is logical because of the population and purchasing power concentrated in the Northeast. The inset (Figure 10.23b) is a cross section through the demand-potential surface, running from New York City to Los Angeles. We might assume that demand is maximized at the highest point of the surface—and potential sales would be highest there.

The problem of demand can also be viewed in another way. If all demand is concentrated at a single point, as in Weber's model, access to the market is maximized and transportation costs are minimized at this point. If, however, demand is spread among a number of places, then moving to one point increases transportation costs to other points. Moving from Point *B* to Point *C* raises transportation costs to other points. A New York City location maximizes the distance to much of the United States.

A Transportation-Cost Surface

We can conceptualize a transportation-cost surface in much the same way as we did the demand-potential surface:

$$TC_i = \sum_{j=1}^{n} P_j d_{ij}$$

where:

TC_i = total transportation costs at i
P_j = population of j (weighted)
d_{ij} = distance between i and j

This formula increases the importance of distant points rather than diminishing their importance, as in the potential model. Figure 10.24a shows a transportation-cost surface based on the same sample of points used for the potential model. The isolines indicate the percentages above Fort Wayne, Indiana, by land transportation. The uneven population distribution minimizes total cost at Fort Wayne, and total cost rises in all directions as shown in the New York-Los Angeles cross section in the inset (Figure 10.24b). The problem then is to determine the most profitable location: Is it the highest point on the demand-potential surface or the lowest point on the transportation-cost surface? Chauncy Harris (1954) summed up the problem with an example. The West Coast comprised 11% of the U.S. population in 1950 but accounted for only 5% of the sales from

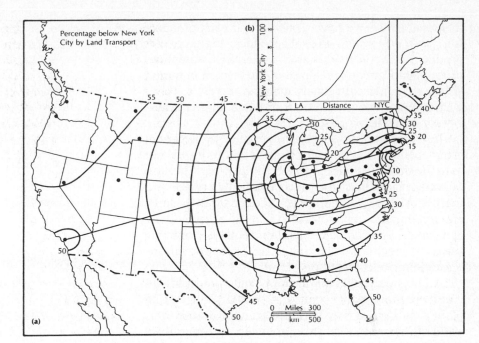

FIGURE 10.23
(a) Market potential; (b) cross section from New York City to Los Angeles in 1954. Now, years after this diagram was first sketched, how do you think the U.S. market potential and cross section have changed? *(Source: Harris, 1954.)*

Chicago firms; yet the West Coast accounted for 22% of the total transportation costs incurred by Chicago firms. The potential model is useful because it allows us to visualize variations in demand. The more localized the market, the more nearly the optimum points on both surfaces coincide, but only for the distribution of the finished product.

LOCATIONAL INTERDEPENDENCE

◈

We turn now to the concept of *locational interdependence*, a concept that implies that competition from rival producers can lower potential revenues at a given point

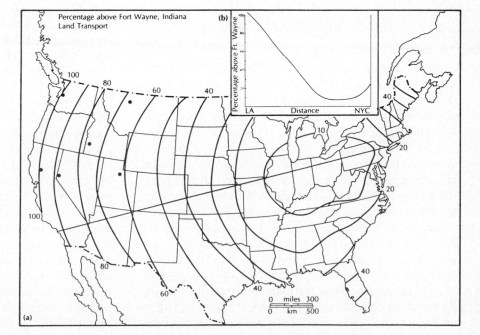

FIGURE 10.24
(a) Transportation cost to the national market; (b) cross section from New York City to Los Angeles in 1954. Since this diagram was sketched 40 years ago, the center of the U.S. population has shifted from Indiana to De Soto, Missouri, 50 miles west of St. Louis. Try drawing what you think is the new transportation-cost cross section from New York to Los Angeles.

in space. So far, we have assumed that each producer is a *spatial monopolist*—the sole producer of a particular product within the market area. Under this assumption, profit maximization is realized at the level of output at which marginal cost equals marginal revenue. However, nonmonopoly conditions dictate a different strategy for maximizing profits.

In the nonmonopoly situation implied by locational interdependence, economic competition occurs, but not as in the classical model of perfect competition. The kind of market faced by spatial rivals is called an *oligopoly:* a market with more than one producer, but a small enough number of producers so that the actions of one can have a considerable effect on another. Economic (price) competition is lacking in an oligopoly, but intense nonprice competition occurs.

An oligopoly takes on meaning when producers are considered in a spatial context. A small manufacturing plant is concerned only with the actions of other firms within the same market area. Producers of ready-mixed concrete in Chicago, for example, are not interested in the actions of similar firms in Los Angeles. Even if the Los Angeles firms lowered their plant price to zero, they could not capture the Chicago market because of the transportation costs involved. The individual Chicago producer is, however, interested in the actions of other ready-mixed concrete firms in the Chicago area. Their actions could exert a considerable effect on profits. Locational interdependence, therefore, is a term that applies to spatial oligopolies.

The Ice-Cream Vendor Analogy

Let us consider a simple oligopoly model first developed by H. Hotelling (1929). Imagine a stretch of beach over which people are evenly distributed. On this beach are two ice-cream vendors, each of whom sells an identical product at the same price. People on the beach, therefore, minimize the cost of their ice-cream purchases by buying from the closer vendor. Initially the two vendors are located at the quartile points of the beach (Figure 10.25a). Each person buys from the closer vendor, so the total market area is equally divided between the two. Vendor *A* could temporarily increase his or her market share by shifting the stand to a site immediately adjacent to Vendor *B* (Figure 10.25b). Vendor *B* would then countermove as shown in Figure 10.25c. In the Hotelling solution, the final location of the stands once again splits the market evenly between the two vendors (Figure 10.25d). Because neither ven-

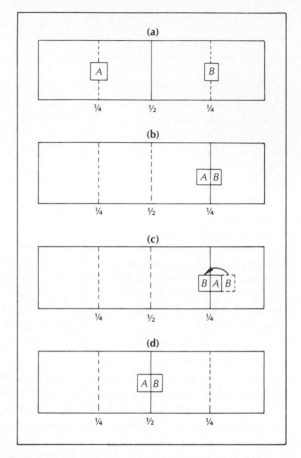

FIGURE 10.25
The ice cream vendor analogy. The kind of market faced by spatial rivals is called oligopoly. Here, *locational interdependence*—intense nonprice competition—occurs. Initially, the two vendors are located at quartile points of the beach. Each person buys from the closest vendor. After several moves, the final location of stands once again splits the market evenly.
(Source: Based on Hotelling, 1929.)

dor can gain an advantage by moving, each must turn to other forms of competition, such as advertising or product differentiation.

The Hotelling solution determines the equilibrium quantity sold by each producer and the equilibrium prices, but we must assume that demand is completely inelastic at any price. If both producers charge the same price (plus the same transportation costs), total demand is shared equally in the equilibrium situation. In other words, Hotelling assumed that the demand of consumers at the edge of the market (who must pay a higher price) is the same as the demand of those near the common selling point. Both producers share the same production costs, so the common market price is that at which marginal costs equal zero. The distance to the most distant consumer is the same from both producers and neither can affect transportation costs. A producer who raises the market price will immediately lose the entire market, and neither producer can lower prices to a point where costs exceed the price per unit; thus, the equilibrium is uniquely determined. The Hotelling solution is an optimum one for each producer, but not for consumers because a vendor location at each quartile point minimizes the consumers' aggregate transportation costs.

The most important form of competition in the initial phase of a spatial oligopoly (before equilibrium) is price competition based on transportation costs. Producers can capture parts of market areas in which their delivered prices are lowest. This outcome holds only if we assume that transportation costs are charged to each consumer as a function of distance and until equilibrium conditions are reached.

Price differentials are the only form of competition allowed in technical economic analysis, but we popularly recognize several other types. Advertising, which adds to the cost of products, is the most important type of nonprice competition. A second strategy is to create perceived quality differentials in products; for example, in the wide range of automobile types (and prices) that all bear a given producer's name. Quality differentiation divides a broad market into a group of submarkets and meets the demand for a wide range of consumers. A third technique of nonprice competition is to introduce design differences into the product line. Tennis racket companies, for example, continually introduce new models that are purported to be superior to the previous year's design and to all competition.

Nonprice competition should be the prevailing form of competition if locational equilibrium prevails. The fact that this form of competition is the most common in the United States may imply a short-run equilibrium, at least in certain industries.

Both long- and short-run locational equilibriums assume that producers can adjust instantaneously to changes in competitors' locations and to other marginal changes in costs and revenues. Locational inertia, however, prevents instantaneous adjustments from occurring, and transportation costs prevent all production factors from being as mobile as assumed in the classical models. Equilibrium adjustment also assumes economic rationality and perfect knowledge, which are not real-world conditions. Producers are reluctant to make major moves—even those of potential economic advantage—because of risk and uncertainty. Spatial equilibrium, if it exists in the short run, is the result of a trial-and-error process that has often resulted in great social costs.

OBSTACLES TO OPTIMAL LOCATION

◙

The final location chosen by an industry is not always determined by the cost of raw-material assembly and distribution, as was Weber's principal question, nor by production costs at the site, including land, labor, capital, and managerial and technical skills. James Rubenstein (1992) lists six factors that complicate locational decisions:

1. A firm may have more than one critical site or situation factor, each of which suggests a different location.

2. Even if a firm clearly identifies its critical factor, more than one critical location may emerge.

3. A firm cannot always precisely calculate costs of situation and site factors within the company or at various locations because of unknown information.

4. A firm may select its location on the basis of inertia and company history. Once a firm is located in a particular community, expansion in the same place is likely to be cheaper than moving operations to a new location.

5. The calculations of an optimal location can be altered by a government grant, loans, or tax breaks.

6. Individual choice and whim play important factors in *foot-loose industries* that have gravitated to coastal areas in the Sunbelt of the United States because of recreational opportunities, availability of amenities, and life-style factors.

EVALUATION OF INDUSTRIAL LOCATION THEORY

◙

Industrial location theory helps us gain insight into how individual manufacturing establishments are located with reference to the production factors and the distribution of customers, suppliers, and competitors. It

Small firms most often use adaptive behavior. This small-scale print and copy center has chosen a location near a very large, West Coast university. But because land rents are expensive next to the school, this firm is located 10 blocks away.
(Source: Frederick P. Stutz.)

also helps us to appreciate plant-location decisions. Are industrial location patterns rational? Do firms search for optimal locations? These questions were partially addressed in Chapter 5. Here, we distinguished between two types of decision making leading to locational patterns: *adoptive* and *adaptive behavior.*

During the nineteenth and early twentieth centuries, when capitalism came into its own in Europe and North America, decision making was of the adoptive kind. Decisions were made arbitrarily and left behind a pattern of survivors lucky enough to have selected good locations for their plants—potteries, textile factories, and ironworks and steelworks. In the competitive economic environment, location mattered. Weber's theory therefore helps us understand the success stories of economic history. It is a framework for understanding *what is.*

In contrast, adaptive behavior focuses on rational decision making. It involves a systematic analysis of alternative locations that leads to the development of rational industrial landscapes. This type of decision making is expected of multinationals in the emerging one-world economy of the late twentieth century. Location theory can guide these enterprises in selecting optimal locations for their manufacturing plants, development centers, and research laboratories. It is a normative framework suggesting *what should be.*

From the perspective of the behavioral geographer, the main defect of normative industrial location theory, based on recognition of spatial limits to profitability, is that it fails to say what decision makers actually do

(Greenhut, 1956; Pred, 1967). How do enterprises actually select profitable sites for branch plants? John Rees (1972, 1974), a British geographer, provided an answer to this question. In his studies of the investment location decisions of large British and American firms, he reported interviews with executives confirming the validity of a framework of locational search, learning, and choice evaluation, as illustrated in Figure 10.26. The first phase of the decision-making process is the recognition that a growth problem (stress threshold) exists with respect to demand satisfaction. (Rees pointed out that the question of demand—whether or not there exists a potential market area of sufficient size to consume the output of a plant—is the prime variable in the locational choice of a large, modern manufacturing firm.) The alternative responses to in situ expansion are relocation, acquisition, or a new plant. A new plant involves a three-stage search procedure, the outcome of which leads to a decision and, finally, to the allocation of resources. It also generates feedback into learning behavior and into the decision-making environment. A major virtue of Rees's model is the distinction between short- and long-term responses of the organization. Classical industrial location theory tends to ignore the time frame within which profit maximization is sought. The behavioral approach is much more realistic in recognizing that the environment in which the enterprise operates is in a constant state of flux.

Industrial location theory has been criticized by radicals, primarily because it focuses on firms as abstract entities, without effective structural relationships to the

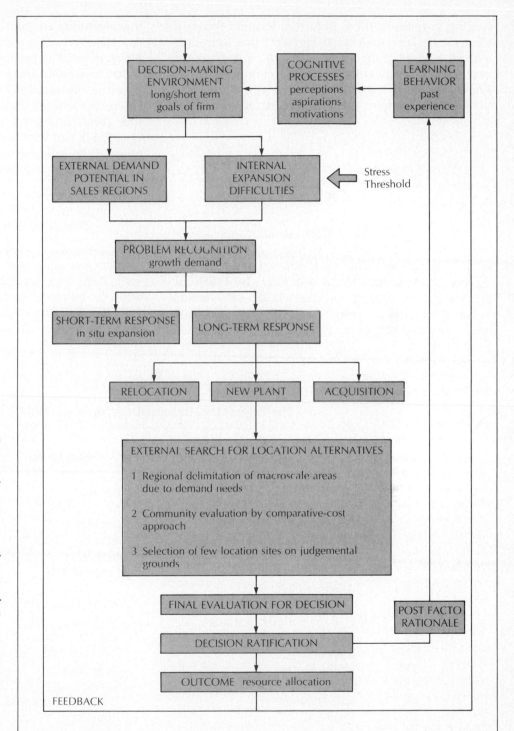

FIGURE 10.26
Weber's model of industrial location is an optimizing approach. Not all economic behavior is normative or optimizing in industrial location. How enterprises actually go about the task of selecting a profitable site is shown. Study of investment location decisions of large British and American firms, including interviews with executives, confirm the framework of locational search, learning, and choice evaluation. The new plant location involves a three-stage search procedure, the outcome of which leads to a location decision and finally to the allocation of resources. The behavioral approach shown is more realistic in recognizing that the environment in which the enterprise operates is in a constant state of change.
(Source: Based on Rees, 1972, p. 203; 1974, p. 191.)

rest of the economy. In the radical view, locational analysis must begin from the top, with the world's capitalist system, not from the bottom, with individual firms (Massey, 1973, 1979). The actual behavior of the individual firm takes on its meaning in the broader economic context that the structural approach seeks to reveal. Working up from the bottom can explain neither the individual elements nor the system as a whole. According to radicals, then, industrial location theory is idealistic because it abstracts elements that form only a small part of reality. This criticism extends to the new approaches in which the simple conception of the single-plant firm has been replaced with a model of the firm as a complex organizational structure.

THE LARGE INDUSTRIAL ENTERPRISE

◈

Although small, single-plant operations remain the most common type of firm, we live in an era in which giant corporations with transnational bases control a large share of the world economy. In 1988, the 600 largest companies in the world—the "billion dollar club" (their annual sales exceed $1 billion each)—created 20% of the world's total value added in manufacturing and agriculture (*The Economist*, 1988a). And the effect of big companies on the global economy, which is out of all proportion to their numerical significance, is steadily increasing. What are the trends in industrial organization? What is the relationship of large enterprises to small firms? Why do firms grow? How do they grow? How are corporate systems geographically organized? Answers to these questions help us to appreciate the role played by multiplant, multiproduct, multinational enterprises in the world economy.

Trends in Industrial Organization

One accessible measure of business size is annual sales. Table 10.3 lists the rank order of 20 of the largest 500 U.S. industrial corporations in terms of this measure. The majority of these enterprises also appear in the combined top-20 ranking of the largest U.S. and

◈

Table 10.3
The Largest U.S. Industrial Corporations, 1987

Rank	Company	Headquarters	Sales ($000)
1	General Motors	Detroit	102,813,700
2	Exxon	New York	69,888,000
3	Ford Motor	Dearborn, MI	62,715,800
4	International Business Machines	Armonk, NY	51,250,000
5	Mobil	New York	44,866,000
6	General Electric	Fairfield, CT	35,211,000
7	American Tel. & Tel.	New York	34,087,000
8	Texaco	White Plains, NY	31,613,000
9	E. I. du Pont de Nemours	Wilmington, DE	27,148,000
10	Chevron	San Francisco	24,351,000
11	Chrysler	Highland Park, MI	22,513,500
12	Philip Morris	New York	20,681,000
13	Amoco	Chicago	18,281,000
14	RJR Nabisco	Winston-Salem, NC	16,998,000
15	Shell Oil	Houston	16,833,000
16	Boeing	Seattle	16,341,000
17	United Technologies	Hartford	15,669,157
18	Procter & Gamble	Cincinnati	15,439,000
19	Occidental Petroleum	Los Angeles	15,344,100
20	Atlantic Richfield	Los Angeles	14,585,802

Source: Rand McNally, 1988.

non-U.S. corporations. These huge companies have annual sales that exceed the GNPs of many countries.

Industry concentration and *aggregate concentration ratios* are frequently used to measure the economic power of large companies. The industry concentration ratio indicates the percentage of total sales accounted for by the largest enterprises (typically between three and eight) in a particular market. However, a business that exerts little influence in a sector can have a great influence on the economy as a whole. This situation can be represented by calculating an aggregate concentration ratio, which indicates the percentage share of national manufacturing sales accounted for by the largest (typically the top 100) companies.

Table 10.4 illustrates industry concentration ratios for the United States. The ratios differ markedly from industry to industry, reflecting the ease or difficulty with which a new firm can enter a particular industry. This, in turn, is related to the technology of the industry. For example, the amount of capital required to establish a modern low-cost iron and steel mill is enormous compared with that required to establish a sawmill. Note, however, that Table 10.4 fails to reveal changes in industry concentration. In advanced industrial countries,

industry concentration increased in the 1950s and 1960s but stabilized in the 1970s and 1980s.

Most large corporations owe their growth and size to diversification. An example of a *multiproduct diversified enterprise* is Tenneco (Table 10.5). For multiproduct enterprises, aggregate concentration is a better measure of corporate power than industry concentration is. As with industry concentration, aggregate concentration in manufacturing increased in the 1950s and 1960s and stabilized or even declined in the 1970s. Does the reversal signify a change in the scale of economic organization? No, it does not. Many of the largest manufacturing companies have expanded into nonmanufacturing activities (Hughes and Kumar, 1984).

Large multiproduct companies are usually *multiplant enterprises*. Their geographic bases are as broad as their product ranges. With factories and offices in other countries, these area-organizing institutions are also *multinational enterprises*.

The emergence of a global production system, having at its heart the multinational corporation, is a recent phenomenon. As late as 1950, most large corporations were barely multinational. But by 1970, the situation had changed dramatically. Large corporations, which for years had exported goods to foreign markets, had set up foreign subsidiaries in numerous countries.

In the 1960s and 1970s, both American and worldwide perceptions of multinational corporations were generally negative. They were widely labeled as exploitative giants—and they still are by radical scholars who view their actions as socially disruptive and likely to promote a general tendency toward world economic stagnation. In contrast, traditional scholars and policymakers in the market-conscious 1980s and 1990s view multinationals as sources of employment and revenue rather than as inherent exploiters.

Multinationals increase employment in their host countries. It is estimated that direct employment of multinationals is 65 million, or 3%, of the world's labor force. Add indirect employment, and these companies may generate 6% of the world's employment. In 1984, American multinationals employed about 6.5 million people abroad, 32% of these in underdeveloped countries, 42% in Europe, 5% in Japan, and 14% in Canada.

Multinationals also increase a host country's output and exports. This is especially important for Third World countries in need of fast growth and foreign exchange to service bank debt. Foreign-owned companies accounted for 35% of Singapore's employment in the manufacturing industry in 1990, 63% of its manufacturing output, and 90% of its exports of manufactured

◉

Table 10.4

Concentration by Industry in the United States, 1977

Industry	Percentage Value of Total Shipments	
	Four Largest Enterprises	Eight Largest Enterprises
Motor vehicles	93	99
Iron and steel	45	65
Bread, biscuits, cake	33	40
Oil refining	30	53
Agricultural machinery	46	61
Soft drinks	15	22
Pharmaceuticals	24	43
Printing and publishing	14	19
Sawmilling and wood planing	17	23

Source: U.S. Bureau of the Census, 1984.

◈

Table 10.5

Companies and Products Controlled by Tenneco

Division	Products
Tenneco Oil	Crude oil, natural gas, refining, service stations
Tennessee Gas Transmission	Natural gas pipelines
J. I. Case	Two- and four-wheel-drive agricultural tractors and implements, loader/ backhoes, crawler and wheel loaders, excavators, trenchers, industrial and materials handling cranes, skid steer loaders, forklift and compaction equipment
Tenneco Automotive	Automotive exhaust systems, shock absorbers and ride-control products, jacks and lifting equipment, filters, wheel oil seals, fans, pulleys, manifolds
Tenneco Chemicals	Fine, intermediate, and hydrocarbon chemicals; plastic resins, stabilizers, plasticizers; paint colorants and dispersions; chemical foam products and fabricated plastic materials; synthetic and organic chemicals; paper and specialty chemicals
Newport News Shipbuilding	Naval and merchant ship construction and repair, nuclear vessel refueling, components and services for the nuclear power industry, heavy castings and sheet-metal products for industrial use
Packaging Corporation of America	Corrugated containers, paperboard, folding cartons, molded pulp products
Tenneco West	Agricultural products (fresh fruits, vegetables, almonds, pistachios, dates, raisins); commercial, recreational, and residential real estate

goods. They produced 71% of Zimbabwe's industrial output. In 1990, nearly 30% of Argentina's manufacturing output and exports came from multinationals.

American, West European, and Japanese enterprises own most of the world's multinational assets, but new sources of capital are emerging. Some Third World countries—Argentina, Brazil, Hong Kong, India, Mexico, Singapore, and Taiwan—have firms that have been establishing foreign direct investment (Kumar and Kim, 1984).

As multinationals have spread across the world, there has been an increasing interpenetration of capital. For example, much Japanese private foreign investment ($33.4 billion at the end of 1987) goes to the United States. Japanese direct U.S. investment, however, lags far behind that of the Europeans (McConnell, 1980). At the end of 1987, the Dutch invested $47 billion and the British $74.9 billion. Most of the new capital from abroad favors the traditional Manufacturing Belt of the Northeast and Great Lakes and the newer Sunbelt areas of the West and the South (McConnell, 1983). The interpenetration of flexible multinational capital means that countries virtually everywhere are facing increased competition from foreign suppliers. It is estimated, for example, that approximately 74% of all U.S. goods produced by domestic corporations face stiff competition inside the United States from foreign suppliers. This level of competition has had a significant effect on the dynamics of U.S. manufacturing and has registered dramatically as a loss of jobs in Rust Belt industries.

In addition to foreign direct investment, which increased fivefold between the mid-1970s and 1990, other forms of international business are open to multinationals. For example, international industrial firms engage in *turnkey projects*, arrangements in which the contractor not only plans and builds the project, but also trains the buyer's personnel and initiates operation of the project before "turning the key" over to the buyer. Corporations also engage in *licensing ventures* such as *franchising*. For example, Pepsi-Cola licenses the use of its name and the right to manufacture and sell its drink abroad. Part of the contract, however, requires that the foreign

Japanese cars are lined up on a pier at Boston's waterfront ready for import. Japanese automobiles have made major penetration into U.S. markets, led by Toyota, Nissan and Honda. The sales have dropped off recently because of the expensive yen on world markets, raising the price of Japanese cars. *(Source: Spencer Grant, Photo Researchers, Inc.)*

licensee buy the syrup from Pepsi; thus, the company enjoys royalty and export advantages.

Another form of international business engaged in by multinationals is the *joint venture*. In this situation, a subsidiary is owned jointly by two or more parties. The joint-venture partners may be either from the private sector of the investing company's home country, from a third country, or from the host country. Corporations also engage in *international subcontracting*, sometimes called *offshore assembly* or *foreign sourcing*. An important form of international subcontracting, especially in textiles, is an arrangement whereby firms based in the advanced industrial countries provide design specifications to producers in underdeveloped countries, purchase the finished products, then sell them at home and abroad.

The Dual Economy

The dominant position of large enterprises in the modern world economy owes much to their relationships with smaller firms. Robert Averitt's (1968) notion of a *dual economy* captures the essence of these relationships and puts them in perspective. According to Averitt, there are two distinct types of business enterprises. On the one hand, there are a few *core* or *center firms*—large, complex organizations that represent the nucleus of the economy and that account for a high proportion of its production and profit-making potential. On the other

hand, there are numerous *satellite* or *periphery firms*—small, straightforward organizations that manage to survive in the market by minimizing labor costs and maximizing labor exploitation. There is no precise boundary between center and periphery firms, but the leading 200 or so industrial corporations form the heart of the U.S. center economy. And at the world level, the international center economy consists of around 500 to 700 firms.

For Averitt, small is not so beautiful from the perspective of industrial relations. The relationship between center and periphery firms is one of dominance and dependence, as reflected in purchasing policies, franchising agreements, and advisory and management contracts. The terms of these arrangements are dictated by the core firms. For example, IBM purchases components for its computers from many smaller firms. However, IBM can, through its purchasing policies, make or break its business partners and dictate their location within a specified distance of IBM's manufacturing facilities (Susman and Schutz, 1983). This relationship emphasizes that the power of core enterprises is often much greater than that implied by industry and aggregate concentration ratios, which fail to take account of unequal relationships between business organizations.

What are the prospects for the survival of small firms in the advanced economies? This question is the subject of considerable debate (Curran and Stanworth, 1986; Storey, 1986). One argument is that small firms will continue to flourish because of their competitiveness, flexibility, dynamism, and innovativeness. The counterargument is that small firms can play only a restricted role in a world in which the terms of production and competition are set by large firms. Indeed, the survival of the small firm is not related to internal advantages so much as to protection from market forces arising from ties with large firms. Moreover, the characteristics of competitiveness, flexibility, dynamism, and innovativeness may be just as applicable to large firms as to small ones.

Why Firms Grow

The notion of the dual economy conflicts with traditional economic thinking about absolute limits on firm size imposed by diseconomies of scale. Most large companies operate at a scale far beyond the initial point on the LRAC curve. In fact, evidence of increasing returns to scale has led to a reappraisal of the theory of the firm.

To explain why firms increase their scales of operation, economists make two distinctions. First, they separate *economies of size* (scale) from *economies of growth*. Edith Penrose (1959) emphasized this distinction when she argued that economies of growth may exist independently of economies of size. For the "enterprising firm," she pointed to unused productive services as "a challenge to innovate, an incentive to expand, and a source of competitive advantage. They facilitate the introduction of new combinations of resources—innovation—within the firm" (p. 85). Second, economists separate *actual* from *perceived* scale economies. As W. H. Starbuck (1965) noted, the actual relationship between unit cost and size is irrelevant. The relationship that is relevant is that which executives believe holds true.

The tendency toward increasing scales of operation is therefore based on the motivating force of growth (Cyert and March, 1963). John Kenneth Galbraith (1967) elaborated on this point. He said that firms expand for two reasons: survival and growth. Both goals are promoted by horizontal and vertical expansion and by diversification.

The view that corporate growth is part of a natural progression is deterministic, however. It flies in the face of reality. The majority of firms in an economy remain small and peripheral. As Michael Taylor and Nigel Thrift (1982) emphasized, only some firms, especially those that manufacture capital goods, have the potential to develop into large corporations. Financial barriers prevent most firms from making successive transitions from a small regional base to larger national organizations and then to multinational operations. Access to finance—banking capital, venture capital, and international bond and currency markets—has become increasingly uneven, favoring some firms and not others. Because these finance gaps have become wider, a small firm has a much less chance of evolving into a corporate giant today than it did a hundred years ago.

How Firms Grow

How a firm grows depends on the *strategy* that it follows and the *methods* that it selects to implement its strategy (Figure 10.27). As we discussed earlier in the chapter, growth strategies are *integration* or *diversification*. In the United States, horizontal integration predominated from the 1890s to the early 1900s, vertical integration came to the fore in the 1920s, and diversification has been the principal goal since the 1950s. This three-stage sequence provides a framework for understanding the interrelationship of the various strategies (Bannock, 1971). The early growth of large enterprises involves the removal of competition by absorption leading to oligopoly. This is followed by a period in which the oligopoly protects its sources of supply and markets by vertical integration. Once a dominant position is achieved, rapid corporate growth can proceed only with diversification.

Methods for achieving growth are *internal* or *external* to the firm. Growth can be financed internally by the retention of funds or new share issues. Or, it can be generated externally by acquiring the assets of other firms through mergers. Most large firms employ both means, but external growth is particularly important for the largest and fastest-growing enterprises.

Whatever strategy and method are adopted, corporate growth typically involves the addition of new factories and, thus, a change in geography. Initially, much of the employment and productive capacity of a firm concentrates in the area in which it was founded. An example is Ford Motor Company. For a long time, most of its operating plants were in the Midwest. As enterprises grow, they become more widely dispersed multiplant operations, which is sometimes accompanied by decreasing dominance of the home region. Exceptions tend to be companies confined to one broad product area and based in a region where there is a historical specialization within that product area. Thus, in Great Britain, the huge glass company of Pilkington

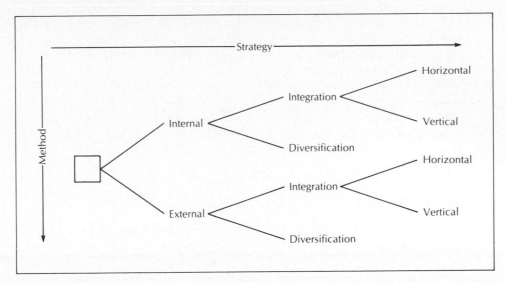

FIGURE 10.27

Strategies and methods of corporate growth. Horizontal integration involves following a similar pattern by expanding the firm's market share in its existing product lines. Often, a company wants to strengthen their position in a particular market. Vertical integration involves a change from present ways of doing business toward diversification by entering new products and new markets. This leads ultimately to backward integration and forward integration.
(Source: Chapman and Walker, 1987, p. 86.)

Bros. remains concentrated in St. Helens. The importance of a home region at the national scale is paralleled by the importance of a home country at the international scale, although the extent of this dominance may also diminish with time.

The choice of growth strategy affects corporate geography. Horizontal integration frequently involves setting up plants over a wider and wider area. The geographic consequences of vertical integration vary according to whether the move is backward ("down" in the production process) or forward ("up" in the production process). *Backward integration*, in which a firm takes over operations previously the responsibility of its suppliers, can lead a firm into resource-frontier areas. An example is the development of iron-ore deposits by American and Japanese companies in Venezuela and Australia. Conversely, *forward integration*, in which a firm begins to control the outlets for its products, can lead a resource-based organization to set up plants in market locations. Diversification does not have such predictable consequences for the geography of large enterprises.

The method of growth also affects the geography of multiplant firms. When growth is achieved internally, enterprises can carefully plan the location of new branch plants. When growth is achieved externally, enterprises inherit facilities from acquired firms; hence, there is less control over their locations. Moreover, the attrac-

tiveness of new facilities often lies in their economic, financial, and technical characteristics. Nonetheless, geography does play a role in the decision process. Firms typically confront the uncertainty and risk of expansion by investing first in geographically adjacent or culturally similar environments. For example, geographer D. Michael Ray (1971) identified a distance-decay relationship between the location of U.S.-owned manufacturing plants in Canada and the head offices to which they report. Most plants were close to the U.S. border, and the proportion of headquarters in Chicago, Detroit, and New York City was much larger than for more distant centers of internationalized American capital, such as Los Angeles.

Geographers have developed models of how firms grow. Most of these models postulate a single development path beginning with a small, single-plant operation and culminating with the multinational enterprise (Håkanson, 1979; McNee, 1974; Taylor, 1975). L. Håkanson, for example, proposed a five-stage model that incorporates the transition from home country to overseas operations. The top, left diagram of Figure 10.28 illustrates the firm's action space, divided into a core area where it was founded, the remainder of the home country, and an outer circle representing the rest of the world. In Stage 1, a single-plant firm is tied to the immediate environment. In Stage 2, the firm pene-

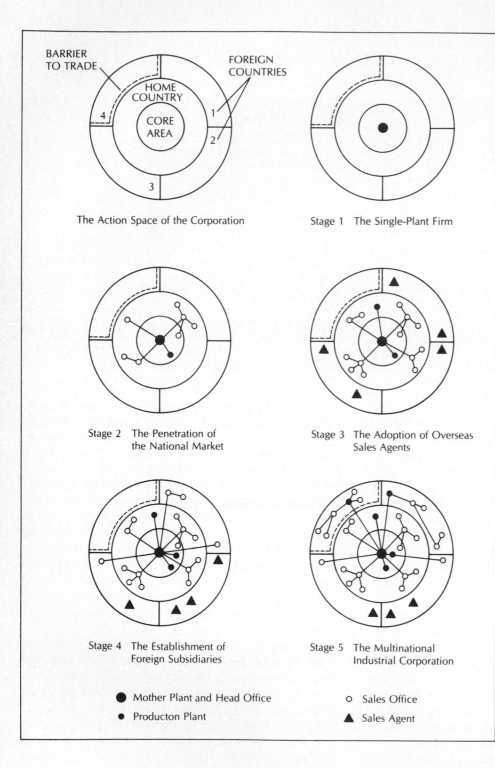

The Action Space of the Corporation

Stage 1 The Single-Plant Firm

Stage 2 The Penetration of the National Market

Stage 3 The Adoption of Overseas Sales Agents

Stage 4 The Establishment of Foreign Subsidiaries

Stage 5 The Multinational Industrial Corporation

● Mother Plant and Head Office
• Producton Plant
○ Sales Office
▲ Sales Agent

FIGURE 10.28
A model of stages of growth and geographic expansion of the industrial corporation. Stage 1 is the single plant firm. A major step is taken in stage 2, as a second plant is located within the same agglomeration as the initial plant. The firm sets up sales offices and expands to the regional scale. Stage 3 represents the penetration of overseas markets, which are developed via a network of sales agents and sales offices. Stage 4 is characterized by company-owned offices established in overseas markets, followed by manufacturing plants. Because of trade barriers and long distances, multinationals extend their geographic range by opening up plants in foreign countries to save on transportation costs, labor costs, and high tariffs.
(Source: Based on Håkanson, 1979, pp. 131–135.)

trates the home market through sales offices, the expansion of central management, and new production capacity away from the original plant. Stage 3 sees the first incursions into foreign markets through a network of sales agents; at home, production capacity may be ex-

panded outside the original core area. In Stage 4, sales offices replace some of the overseas agents. Finally, production plants appear in foreign markets as acquisitions or subsidiaries. Stage 5, then, marks the fully fledged multinational.

This kind of evolution along a path from a local to a national and then to an international company is exceptional. Unequal access to finance makes it difficult, if not impossible, for many firms to expand beyond the subnational scale. In the late twentieth century, the size distribution of firms resembles a broad-based pyramid in which fewer and fewer firms can move from one level to another. Rather than the single development sequence that may have existed in the nineteenth century, today multinationals follow a distinctive path through a series of discrete development sequences.

Geographic Organization of Corporate Systems

Multifacility corporate systems, which include manufacturing plants, research laboratories, education centers, offices, warehouses, and distribution terminals, have their own distinctive geographies. To appreciate the internal geography of these systems, four issues must be considered: (1) the ways in which corporations are organized to maximize efficiency, (2) the influence of hierarchical management structures on the location of employment, (3) the effect of technology-based hierarchies on corporate spatial organization, and (4) the implications of locational shifts in the productive base of large companies.

ORGANIZATIONAL STRUCTURE

Companies organize themselves hierarchically in a variety of ways to administer and coordinate their activities. The basic formats are (1) functional orientation, (2) product orientation, (3) geographic orientation, and (4) customer orientation. A fifth format, which is a combination of at least two of the basic formats, is called a *matrix structure*. Different companies may select different formats, but all formats are always subject to review and modification.

The organizational format that is based on various corporate functions—manufacturing, marketing, finance, and research and development—is illustrated in Figure 10.29a. With this framework, all the company's functional operations are concentrated in one sector of the enterprise. An example of a company with this type of organizational structure is Ford Motor Company. This form of organization works well for companies with relatively confined product bases.

Figure 10.29b illustrates the product-orientation or-

ganizational structure. Product groups can be cars, trucks, buses, and farm equipment for a major motor vehicle manufacturer. Although a corporate central staff is needed to provide companywide expertise and to provide some degree of assistance to each product group, each group also has its own functional staff. Thus, a fairly high degree of managerial decentralization is required. The product-orientation format works well for companies with diverse product lines. Pan American Airways and Westinghouse are examples of companies organized in accordance with this format.

A third organizational format is based on geographic orientation—either the geographic location of customers or of the company's productive facilities. As shown in Figure 10.29c, the company is organized around regions rather than functions or products. Under this form of organization, most or all the corporation's activities relating to any good or service that is bought, sold, or produced within a region are under the control of the regional group head. Each geographic region is under a separate profit center. This organizational format is best suited for companies with a narrow range of products, markets, and distribution channels. It is popular among oil companies and major money-center banks.

Some companies organize according to the types of customers that they want to serve rather than the locations of customers (Figure 10.29d). For example, commercial banks are commonly organized around groups such as the personal, corporate, mortgage, and trust departments. Alternatively, manufacturing corporations might be structured around industrial, commercial, and governmental divisions according to the prevalent type of customer for each group.

The various organizational structures all have advantages, but none is ideal for all companies. Indeed, it is safe to say that these formats have drawbacks for most or all the companies that have adopted them. Nonetheless, a company usually chooses one basic format as the most satisfactory structure for its needs at a particular time in its evolution—or it creates a combination of two or more types.

H. A. Simon's (1960) analysis of these organizational structures identifies three tiers of activities. At the bottom are manufacturing and routine administrative activities. In the middle are coordinating functions that bind the various elements of the enterprise. And at the top are strategic decision-making functions, which control the relationships of economic ownership (i.e., control the overall investment and accumulation process) and the relationships of possession (i.e., the means of production and labor power).

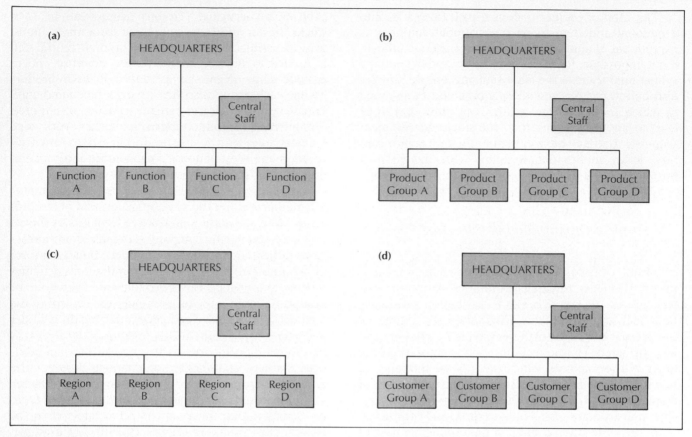

FIGURE 10.29

Organizational structures: (a) functional organization, such as the Ford Motor Company; (b) product orientation, such as Westinghouse; (c) geographic orientation, such as Exxon; and (d) customer orientation, such as Citibank.

Simon's conceptualization has geographic implications. For the small, single-plant firm, strategy and production functions are not geographically separated; hence, there is no need for an intermediate tier of coordinating activities. As firms grow to become multilocational companies, more complex functional and spatial divisions of labor develop. One of the best-known forms of spatial organizations draws on the characteristics of large electronics companies. Strategy functions are performed at the headquarters. Coordinating functions are dispersed to regional offices that control a number of interdependent production facilities. For simplicity, suppose that two production facilities exist: one branch plant manufactures complex components, the other assembles finished products. This organizational structure represents different degrees of removal of job control. It also represents a clear-cut distinction between the functions of conception on the one hand and execution on the other hand, with the parallel distinction between nonproduction and production employment.

ADMINISTRATIVE HIERARCHIES

A major proportion of the employees of large corporations, even those primarily in manufacturing, are involved in nonproduction activities. And the proportion is increasing because of the substitution of capital for labor and because of the growth of R&D activities. The ratio of nonproduction to production employment is less important from a geographic perspective than is the relative location of these activities.

Strategic head-office functions tend to cluster in a relatively few large metropolitan areas, especially in the case of huge manufacturing firms with a financial orientation rather than a production orientation. The concentration of corporate white-collar jobs in or around major metropolitan centers is further reinforced by the distribution of a company's R&D facilities. Corporate R&D establishments often locate close to headquarters. To be sure, there are exceptions. The labor factor has pulled R&D establishments to other locations—in France to the Côte d'Azur on the strength of its glorious climate, and in the United States to Lincoln, Nebraska, and to Austin, Texas, on the strength of their university-research environments.

The contribution of head-office and R&D establishments to nonproduction employment within corporations has more strategic significance than numerical significance. Important administrative jobs are concentrated at the corporate core. But the majority of nonproduction jobs are dispersed among regional offices, branch plants, and depots. Similarly, a high proportion of R&D staff are not involved in basic research, but in the development of existing products and processes. These jobs are often dispersed to industrial manufacturing sites.

TECHNOLOGICAL HIERARCHIES

In addition to administrative hierarchies, there are technology-based hierarchies. Product cycles and production systems help us to appreciate the importance of technological considerations in corporate spatial organization. The *product life cycle*, which begins with a product's development and ends when it is replaced with something better, is important geographically because products at different stages of production tend to be manufactured at different places within corporate systems. Moreover, at any given stage of the cycle, the various operations involved in the manufacture of a product such as a camera are not necessarily concentrated at a single factory. Production of a camera's complex components occurs at a different place from where the final product is assembled.

Economist Simon Kuznets (1930) developed the concept of the three-stage product cycle (Figure 10.30). In Stage 1, innovators discover, develop, and commercially launch a product. They also benefit from a temporary monopoly and all the special privileges—high profits—that result from it. In Stage 2, competitors buy or steal the new idea, which forces an emphasis on low-cost, standardized, mass-production technologies. Sales of the product increase for a while but the initial high returns diminish. By Stage 3, the product begins to be superseded. Markets are lost to new products and manufacturing capacity is reduced.

The implications of the product-cycle model for industrial location at the international scale were recognized by Raymond Vernon (1966) and a group of associates at the Harvard Business School. Innovation begins in an advanced industrial country. These countries have the science, the technology, and the internal market to justify R&D. As a result, they also have an international advantage, and they export their product around the world. But as the technology becomes routinized, other producers appear on the scene, first in the other advanced countries, then on the periphery. Meanwhile, back in the rich country, investment in the newest generation of sophisticated technology is the cutting edge of the economy.

There is no doubt that developed countries are the innovators of the world economy and that Third World countries increasingly specialize in the laborious task of transforming raw materials into commodities. But developed countries are also engaged in activities associated with the second and third stages of the product cycle. Indeed, Great Britain and Canada have expressed concern about their recipient status. This concern has also been voiced in the United States. Consider, for example, who makes what for Mazda. The Japanese multinational manufactures the compact MX-6 in Flat Rock, Michigan, as well as the mechanically and structurally identical Ford Probe. The costly high-tech subassemblies—engine, transaxle, suspension, brakes—are Japanese-made, and the less expensive, lower-tech subassemblies—carpets, glass, tires—tend to be U.S.-made. The upshot of this trend is that American auto-parts companies are often excluded from critical R&D programs associated with the design and engineering of new Japanese cars.

The product life cycle is not the only way that production technology affects corporate spatial organization. Corporations frequently establish fragmented production systems or part-process structures in which the division-of-labor principle is taken a step further. As described by Chapman and Walker (1987), "The various tasks are geographically separated so that the motorway networks and shipping routes which link them effectively become integral parts of the assembly line" (p. 114). This type of system, established for a long time on a regional scale, now operates on a world scale. Consider the Mercury Tracer, an automobile designed by Mazda, which is 25% owned by Ford. The auto's engine is built in Japan. Its glass, trim, and seats are Mexican-made. With other parts from the United States, the Tracer is assembled in Mexico for U.S. sale under the Mercury insignia.

Not all manufacturing operations are fragmented. Corporate branch plants are often *clones*, supplying identical products to their market areas. Examples abound. Medium-sized firms in the clothing industry often have this structure, as do many multiplant compa-

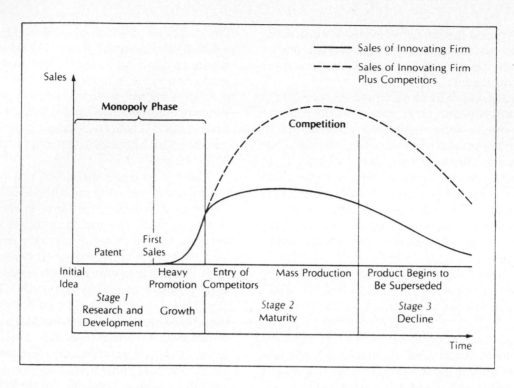

FIGURE 10.30

A typical product life cycle. Stage 1 is the monopolistic phase in which initial discovery and development is followed by the commercial launching of the product. Rapid sales ensue. The company may enjoy a monopoly during this period, at which time they attempt to improve the products. Stage 2 is characterized by the entry of competition. Emphasis is now on mass produced, inexpensive items that are standardized and directed toward expansions of the market. Competition begins to erode a large share of the innovating firm's sales. In stage 3, a large share of the market has been lost to new products and other companies. Overall sales of the product declines as alternative products and manufacturing processes are introduced.

(Source: Chapman and Walker, 1990, p. 28.)

nies manufacturing final consumer products. Part-process structures tend to be associated with certain industrial sectors, such as electronics and motor vehicles, characterized by complex finished products comprising many individual components.

Labor is an important variable in the location of facilities making components. Manufacturers seek locations where the level of worker organization, the degree of conflict, and the power of labor to affect the actions of capital are more limited than in long-established production centers such as Detroit, Coventry, and Turin. Starting in the early 1970s, Fiat began to decentralize part of the company's production away from its traditional base in Turin to the south of Italy. Compared with the workers of Turin, who were relatively strong and well organized, the workers of the south were new to modern industry and had little experience of union organization. At the international level, Ford adopted a similar tactic when it invested in Spain and Portugal

in the 1970s. Ford management perceived that it could operate trouble-free plants in a region of low labor costs. The labor factor is further emphasized by the practice of *dual sourcing*. To avoid total dependence on a single work force that could disrupt an interdependent production system, companies such as Ford and Fiat are willing to sacrifice economies of scale for the security afforded by duplicate facilities in different locations.

LOCATIONAL ADJUSTMENT

Corporate production systems undergo continuous locational adjustment. Shifts may be inspired by technical and organizational developments internal to an industry or by changes in the external environment in which they operate, such as the oil-price hikes of 1973. Particularly significant from a geographic viewpoint are adjustments in response to major shocks or stresses placed on an enterprise. For example, when faced with the challenge of competition from lower-cost regions and with a falling rate of expansion of global markets, an enterprise can adopt a number of strategies—rationalization, capital substitution, outright closure, reorganization of productive capacity associated with the closure of older plants—which all in one way or another result in losses of employment. The recent industrial experience of Great Britain provides many illustrations of painful corporate restructuring programs. The 10 largest manufacturing employers in the West Midlands reduced their British employment by 25% between 1978 and 1981 while increasing their overseas workforce by 9% (Gaffikin and Nickson, 1984). This shift in the productive base of these companies abroad undermined the economic well-being of this area. Such employment withdrawals are an aspect of the growing international integration of production and mobility of capital.

One of capital's crucial advantages over labor is geographic mobility; it can make positive use of distance and differentiation in a way that labor cannot. Corporations take advantage of such flexibility by shifting production to low-wage regions, setting up plants in areas with low levels of worker organization, or establishing plants in areas that offer incentive policies. Many Third World countries offer tax relief and capital subsidies for new industries. These policies have been subject to much debate in the United States and Great Britain, where enterprise zones have been suggested as a way to compete with Third World incentives.

INDUSTRIAL EVOLUTION

◈

Just as firms evolve, so do industries—groupings of firms that have common elements. Industries evolve according to a sequence of developmental stages analogous to youth, maturity, and old age. Models that capture this evolutionary process are industry and Kondratieff cycles.

The Industry Life-Cycle Model

The *industry life-cycle model,* based on a study of historical trends in various U.S. industries between 1885 and 1930 (Burns, 1934), is similar to the product-cycle model (Kuznets, 1930). Industries tend to experience "a period of experimentation, a period of rapid growth, a period of diminished growth, and a period of stability or decline" (Alderfer and Michl, 1942, p. 14). Each period may be related to the technology of an industry. Raymond Vernon (1966) argued that, because of the link between the technology of an industry and its locational requirements, these similarities find geographic expression in characteristic distributions associated with industries in their youth, maturity, and old age.

YOUTH

During this stage of development, an industry is preoccupied with the design and commercialization of a new product. The industry consists of a number of firms, mainly new start-ups, which pursue the adaption of an innovation. The preoccupation with product design and commercialization leads to the geographic concentration of the industry in relatively limited areas. For example, the electronics and computer-related industry began to concentrate in an area to the south of San Francisco in the 1950s. Many of the most significant advances in the electronics industry resulted from the work of scientist-entrepreneurs operating in converted garages and workshops in the area (Saxenian, 1985).

MATURITY

During this phase, growth rates in output rise and then slacken as the industry shifts toward mass production and market penetration. Firm size increases, and the number of firms decreases. Geographically, this phase is associated with production decentralization at interregional and international levels. Cheaper labor costs, better business climates, and proximity to markets pull the more routinized parts of the production process away from the innovating centers of the industry.

OLD AGE

The final stage of the industry life cycle is characterized by market saturation and rationalization. A good example of market saturation is the iron and steel industry in developed countries. Major steel-using industries are relatively less important in developed countries now than they were in the nineteenth century. Consequently, their steel output has stabilized or even declined. In the United States and the United Kingdom, iron and steel plants have closed down—a process called *rationalization*. And the industry has tended to reconcentrate production in a few places, especially at coastal lower-cost production sites.

Kondratiev Cycles

A common criticism of the life-cycle model, which treats industrial history as a natural rather than a social process, is that it neglects relationships between industries. These relationships, of significance to scholars, are interpreted in terms of innovation cycles in the process of economic growth. The cycles are called *Kondratiev cycles*, after the Soviet economist Nikolai Kondratiev (1935) who first identified them in the 1920s.

Kondratiev hypothesized that industrial countries of the world have experienced successive waves of growth and decline since the beginning of the industrial revolution with a periodicity of 50 to 60 years' duration. But it was left to Joseph Schumpeter (1939), a German economist, to explain Kondratiev's observation in terms of technical and organizational innovation. Schumpeter suggested that long waves of economic development are based on the diffusion of major technologies, such as railways and electric power. More recently, another German economist, Gerhard Mensch (1979), argued that throughout capitalist history, innovations have significantly bunched at certain points in time—around 1764, 1825, 1881, and 1935—just when the model of long waves would demand. According to Mensch, innovations come in clusters in response to social needs; they coincide with periods of depression that accompany world economic crises.

Kuznets (1954) described the Kondratiev cycles in terms of successive periods of recovery, prosperity, re-

◈

Table 10.6
Long Waves of Economic Growth

Phase of Growth*	Kondratiev Long Wave				
	I	II	III	IV	V
Recovery	1770–1786	1828–1842	1886–1897	1940–1954	?
Prosperity	1787–1800	1843–1857	1898–1911	1955–1969	
Recession	1801–1813	1858–1869	1912–1924	1970–1980	
Depression (and new innovation)	1814–1827	1870–1885	1925–1939	1981–	

* Macroeconomic characteristics of long-wave phases are as follows:

Characteristic	Recovery	Prosperity	Recession	Depression
Gross national product	Increasing growth rates	Strong growth	Decreasing growth rates	Little or no growth
Investment demand	Increase in replacement investment	Strong expansion of capital stock	Scale-increasing investment	Excess capacity rationalization
Consumer demand	Purchasing power seeks new outlets	Expansion of demand in all sectors	Continued growth of new sectors	For a while continued growth at the expense of savings

Source: Berry, Conkling, and Ray, 1987, p. 280.

cession, and depression (Table 10.6). The upswing of the first cycle was inspired by the technologies of water transportation and the use of wind and captive water power; the second by the use of coal for steam power in water and railroad transportation, and in factory industry; the third by the development of the internal combustion engine, the application of electricity, and advances in organic chemistry; and the fourth by the rise of chemical, plastic, and electronics industries. In the present period of world economic crisis, with higher energy costs, lower profit margins, and growth of the old basic industries exhausted, scholars are asking whether a fifth wave is emerging. A new technoeconomic paradigm does seem to be emerging based on the extraordinarily low costs of storing, processing, and communicating information. In this perspective, the structural crisis of the 1980s and 1990s is a prolonged period of social adaptation to the growth of this new technological system, which is affecting virtually every part of the economy, not only in terms of its present and future employment and skill requirements, but also in terms of its future market prospects.

INFORMATION TECHNOLOGY: THE FIFTH WAVE?

◈

Some scholars, especially Charles Freeman (1988), argue that a fifth Kondratiev cycle appears to have begun in the 1990s, and it is associated with *information technology*. Information technology production in the future is based on microelectronic technologies, including microprocessors, computers, robotics, satellites, fiber-optic cables, and information-handling and -production equipment, including office machinery and facsimile machines. Information technology, production, and use has a strong production pattern in Japan, in Far Eastern newly developing countries, in the United States and Canada, and in Western Europe, notably Germany, Sweden, and France. Freeman (1988) argues that the importance of information technology results from the convergence of communications technology and computer technology (Figure 10.31). Communications technology involves the transmission of data and

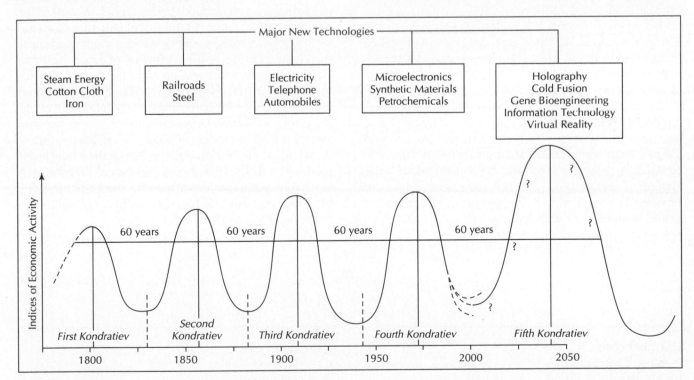

FIGURE 10.31

Kondratiev long waves of economic activity. Kondratiev, or K-waves, last approximately 50 years each and have four phases of activity, including boom, recession, depression, and recovery. Each period of economic activity has its associated major technological breakthroughs that power economic growth and employment. The world economy is presently in a recession as it creeps closer to the year 2000. On the horizon, there appears to be a new boom cycle based on information technology, biotechnology, space technology, energy technology, and materials technology.
(Source: Expanded from Peter Dicken, 1992, The Global Shift, p. 99.)

information, whereas computer technology is concerned primarily with the processing, analysis, and reporting of information.

SUMMARY

◈

In this chapter, we discussed manufacturing from the standpoint of firms rather than areas, with emphasis on normative and behavioral approaches to industrial location theory. Classical location theory stresses that manufacturing patterns are caused by geographic characteristics—*locational factors*—rather than by underlying social relations. According to least-cost location theory, assembly costs are incurred because the raw materials required for a particular kind of manufacturing are not evenly distributed. Production costs vary because of the areal differences in the costs of labor, capital, and technical skills. Finished-product distribution costs are incurred when producers must sell to dispersed or widely scattered markets. All these costs are collectively called *locational costs*. Classical location theory provides a rationale to help find the points of production at which locational costs are minimized.

Once a point of minimum locational costs is determined, however, other decisions must be made. These pertain to the *scale* at which the firm will operate and the particular combination of inputs (*technique*) that will be used. A producer must also be concerned with the actions of competitors. We can see that the location problem is complex, but by applying the concept of *spatial margins to profitability*, we can reduce the complexity. Locational costs, scale, technique, and locational interdependence together determine spatial margins to profitability. By definition, all viable manufacturing must take place within these margins. How these limits are empirically determined and how locations within them are chosen, however, are usually discussed by geographers in a behavioral or decision-making context.

Classical location theory provides many important conceptualizations, but it came under attack in the 1960s and 1970s. Behavioral geographers criticized industrial location theory for its failure to examine what managerial decision makers actually do. Radical geographers argued that dramatic changes in the geography of manufacturing activity were not a result of area characteristics (locational factors) but of social processes and capital-labor conflict. From this standpoint, the analysis of production, and thus of location, must be set in the context of broad social processes, both inside and outside the firm itself.

Most geographers now question the empirical usefulness of industrial location theory in light of the revolutionary role played by *multiproduct, multiplant, multinational operations* in the global structure of manufacturing. Accordingly, we devoted a major portion of the chapter to the spatial behavior of large industrial enterprises. Attention was given to trends in industrial organization, the relationship of large firms to small ones, the reasons for corporate growth, and the internal geography of corporate systems. In the last section, we looked briefly at models of *industrial evolution*—the industry life-cycle model and the Kondratiev long-wave model. The Kondratiev model reminds us that the present world economic crisis may be the beginning of a fifth upswing, this one based on a cluster of microelectronics and information technologies.

▣

KEY TERMS

assembly costs	distribution costs
backward integration	diversification
basic cost	dual economy
centrifical drift	dual sourcing
cloning spatial structure	economies of growth
conglomerate merger	economies of scale
demand-potential surface	externalities
diseconomies of scale	fiber-optic cable

fifth wave
foreign sourcing
forward integration
franchising
horizontal integration
industrial complex economies
industrial inertia
industry concentration
industrial park
industry life cycle
information technology
integration
international subcontracting
isodapane
joint venture
Kondratiev cycles
least cost approach
licensing venture
localized raw material
locational costs
locational interdependence
machinofacture
marketing linkage
market-oriented
massing of reserves
material index
multinational corporation
multiplant enterprises
offshore assembly

oligopoly
orientation
part-process spatial structure
perishable goods
potential surface
product life cycle
production linkages
pure raw material
rationalization
raw-material–oriented
satellite firms
scale
service linkages
space-cost curve
spatial margins to profitability
spatial monopoly
spatial oligopoly
Taylorism
technique
transportation-cost surface
turnkey project
ubiquitous raw material
urbanization economies
value added by manufacturing
vertical integration
Varignon frame
vertical integration
weight-gaining raw material
weight-losing raw material

SUGGESTED READINGS

Amin, A., and Robins, K. 1990. The re-emergence of regional economies? The mythical geography of flexible accumulation. *Environment and Planning D: Society and Space,* 8:7–34.

Bagchi-Sen, S., and Pigozzi, B. M. 1993. Occupational and industrial diversification in the metropolitan space economy in the United States, 1985–1990. *Professional Geographer,* 45:44–54.

Bluestone, B., and Harrison, B. 1982. *The Deindustrialization of America: Plant Closings, Community Abandonment, and the Dismantling of Basic Industry.* New York: Basic Books.

Brotchie, J. F.; Hall, P.; and Newton, P. W., eds. 1987. *The Spatial Impact of Technological Change.* London: Croom Helm.

Bylinsky, G. 1983. The race to the automatic factory. *Fortune,* 21 February, pp. 52–64.

Casetti, E., and Jones, J. P., III. 1987. Spatial aspects of the productivity slowdown: An analysis of U.S. manufacturing data. *Annals of the Association of American Geographers,* 77:76–88.

Chapman, K., and Walker, D. 1993. *Industrial Location.* New York: Basil Blackwell.

Cohen, B. J. 1990. The political economy of international trade. *International Organisation,* 44:261–281.

Dicken, P. 1991. *Global Shift: Industrial Change in a Turbulent World,* 2nd ed. London: Harper & Row.

Drakakis-Smith, D., ed. 1990. *Economic Growth and Urbanization in Developing Areas.* London: Routledge.

Duncan, S. 1991. The geography of gender divisions of labour in Britain. *Transactions of British Geographers,* New Series 16:420–429.

Earney, F. C. F. 1981. The geopolitics of minerals. *Focus,* 31:1–16.

Elson, D. 1990. Marketing factors affecting the globalization of textiles. *Textiles Outlook International,* March, pp. 51–61.

Erickson, R. A., and Hayward, D. J. 1991. The international flows of industrial exports from U.S. regions. *Annals of the Association of American Geographers,* 81:371–390.

Ettlinger, N. 1991. The roots of competitive advantage in California and Japan. *Annals of the Association of American Geographers,* 81:391–407.

Fransman, M. 1990. *The Market and Beyond: Co-operation and Competition in Information Technology in the Japanese System.* Cambridge: University Press.

Glasmeier, A. K. 1991. *The High-Tech Potential: Economic Development in Rural America.* New Brunswick, NJ: Center for Urban Policy Research.

Greenhut, M. L. 1956. *Plant Location in Theory and Practice.* Chapel Hill: University of North Carolina Press.

Grunwald, J., and Flamm, K. 1985. *The Global Factory.* Washington, DC: Brookings Institution.

Hamilton, F. E. I., ed. 1974. *Spatial Perspectives on Industrial Organization and Decision Making.* New York: John Wiley.

Henderson, J. 1989. *The Globalization of High Technology Production.* London: Routledge.

Hoare, A. G. 1993. *The Location of Industry in Britain.* New York: Cambridge University Press.

Hogan, W. T. 1991. *Global Steel in the 1990s: Growth or Decline.* New York: Lexington Books.

Holmes, J. 1991. The continental integration of the North American automobile industry: From the Auto Pact to the FTA. *Environment and Planning A,* 23:122–140.

Howells, J. R. L. 1990. The internationalization of R&D and the development of global research networks. *Regional Studies,* 24:13–29.

Isard, W. 1956. *Location and Space Economy.* Cambridge, MA: The MIT Press.

Law, C. M., ed. 1991. *Restructuring the Global Automobile Industry.* London: Routledge.

McDermott, M. C. 1989. *Multinationals: Foreign Divestment and Disclosure.* London: McGraw-Hill.

Massey, D. 1984. *Spatial Divisions of Labor: Social Structures and the Geography of Production.* New York: Methuen.

Pacione, M., ed. 1985. *Progress in Industrial Geography.* London: Croom Helm.

Paltie, C. J., and Johnson, R. J. 1990. One nation or two? The changing geography of unemployment in Great Britain, 1983–1988. *Professional Geographer,* 42:288–298.

Peet, R. 1991. *Global Capitalism: Theories of Social Development.* London: Routledge.

Pitelis, C., and Suugden, R., eds. 1991. *The Nature of the Transnational Firm.* London: Routledge.

Porter, M. E. 1990. *The Competitive Advantage of Nations.* New York: The Free Press.

Radice, H. 1991. Capital, labour and the state in the world economy. *Society and Space,* 9:102–119.

Rees, J., ed. 1986. *Technology, Regions, and Policy.* Totowa, NJ: Rowman and Littlefield.

Reid, N. 1990. Spatial patterns of Japanese investment in the U.S. automobile industry. *Industrial Relations Journal,* 21:49–59.

Rich, D. C., and Linge, G. J. R., eds. 1991. The State and the Spatial Management of Industrial Change. New York: Routledge, Chapman, and Hall.

Rubenstein, J. M. 1992. The Changing U.S. Auto Industry. London: Routledge.

Sayer, A., and Walker, R. 1992. *The New Social Economy*. Cambridge, MA: Blackwell.

Schmenner, R. 1992. *Making Business Location Decisions*. Englewood Cliffs, NJ: Prentice Hall.

Scott-Quinn, B. 1990. U.S. investment banks as multinationals. In *Banks as Multinationals,* edited by G. Jones, pp. 44–59. London: Routledge.

Sklair, L. 1989. *Assembling for Development: The Maquila Industry in Mexico and the United States*. London: Unwin Hyman.

———. 1991. *Sociology of the Global System, Social Change in Global Perspective*. Hemel Hempstead, England: Harvester Wheatsheaf.

Smith, D. M. 1981. *Industrial Location: An Economic Geographical Analysis*. 2d ed. New York: John Wiley.

South, R. B. 1990. Transnational "Maquiladora" location. *Annals of the Association of American Geographers,* 80:529–570.

Spero, J. E. 1990. *The Politics of International Economic Relations*. 3d ed. London: Allen and Unwin.

Storper, M., and Walker, R. 1989. *The Capitalist Imperative: Territory, Technology and Economic Growth*. Oxford, England: Blackwell.

Stutz, F. P. 1992. Maquiladoras branch plants: Transportation—labor cost, substitution along the U.S./Mexican border. In 27 Congress of the International Geographical Union (Ed.), *Snapshots of North America*. Washington, DC: I.G.U.

Taylor, P. J. 1990. *Political Geography: World Economy, Nation State and Locality*. 2d ed. London: Longman.

Thrift, N. J. 1990. The perils of the international financial system. *Environment and Planning A,* 22:1135–6.23.

Watts, H. D. 1980. *The Large Industrial Enterprise*. London: Croom Helm.

Weber, A. 1929. *Alfred Weber's Theory of the Location of Industries*. Translated by C. J. Friedrich. Chicago: University of Chicago Press.

11

INDUSTRIAL LOCATION: WORLD REGIONS

OBJECTIVES

- To help you appreciate the relationship between social relations and the internationalization of production

- To acquaint you with the major manufacturing regions of North America and the world

- To describe recent global shifts in the internationalization of world manufacturing

- To examine the relocation of the American manufacturing industry

- To explain how Japan became a tower of industrial strength

- To present the problems of industrialization in developed and underdeveloped countries

Toyota manufacturing plant, Georgetown, Kentucky. *(Source: Toyota Motor Manufacture USA, Inc.)*

Having examined the locational choices of firms, let us now consider the effects of these choices on areas. This chapter explores the implications of industrial location for communities, regions, and countries. It seeks answers to the following questions: How do industrial areas develop and change? Why is there industrial growth in some areas, while others exhibit industrial decline? What are the major manufacturing trends in world regions? What is the recent history of the geography of manufacturing in advanced industrial countries and in newly industrializing countries? Geographers are intensely interested in these questions in this period of economic crisis. It is a period marked by the internationalization of production. Rationalization of this program of industrial restructuring has involved fragmentation of the labor process; closures, openings, and new production technology; and the increasing penetration and control of markets by giant corporations.

The focus of this chapter is on recent changes in the industrial geography of regions. Through the years, manufacturing has been a successful activity because it provides the means for its own advancement—it furnishes the tools, machines, and computers that improve productivity. Aided by mechanization and automation, the average rate of manufacturing output in the last two centuries has increased by 2.8% per year—"not a terribly impressive figure until one realizes that it has multiplied more than seventeen hundred fold during that period" (Heilbronner, 1989, p. 100). Moreover, machines and computers have released people from labor drudgery. On the other hand, new technologies have been applied in ways that have displaced millions of workers. Release from drudgery has, to some extent, resulted in the collapse of work.

What are the forces that drive this situation? From the traditional viewpoint, technology develops according to its own imperative, with techniques applied to achieve increased productivity with fewer employees. The alternative view sees technologies and techniques as social products, which are developed according to social relations. The alternative perspective alleges that the framework for analysis is society, not the technologies that it produces. The investigative problem lies not with technology, which has the potential for doing social good; rather, it lies with society, which has the power to misuse this potential.

A similar argument applies to the changing geography of industry and employment. Industrial restructuring can improve human welfare. What is wrong with the selective deindustrialization and reindustrialization of the polluted environments of the old manufacturing areas? What is wrong with industrial revolution in the Third World? Nothing is wrong with industrial restructuring, so long as it does not result in social inefficiency.

Unfortunately, however, industrial restructuring has been a painful process. The movement of British capital to the Third World has had serious effects at home—high levels of unemployment, the destruction of communities, and the loss of valuable skills, plants, and equipment. And in Third World countries, the new manufacturing regions have attracted only selected industries or parts of industries, which makes them vulnerable to outside control by multinationals. In addition, the new industries rarely meet the urgent consumption needs of poor people; yet, they can pollute environments, affect local cultures, and exploit labor—especially female labor. What drives such corporate behavior? Corporations relocate their operations in order to survive in a highly competitive world. In their never-ending quest for profits, they must seek new production frontiers.

To appreciate how the industrial geography of a region changes, we must first learn about the economic structure of society. Thus, the opening section of this chapter provides an introduction to a theory of society, its economy, and the relations that influence locational decision making. Following this section, we look briefly at changes in the geography of world manufacturing, and then take a detailed look at industrial decline and growth in advanced industrial countries and at export-oriented industrialization in parts of the Third World.

The central message of this chapter is that industrial change in a region does not proceed along an evolutionary path involving youth, maturity, and old age. Evolutionary history is mostly irrelevant to an understanding of regional economic history (Peet, 1985). Industrial change in a region is a social, not a physical, process. Old industrial landscapes need not die; they can be rebuilt to fit new technologies. Whether or not rebuilding occurs does not depend on the physical age of the industrial region, "[it depends] on its social conditions, especially those relevant to profit making, and in particular the social relations between capital and labor" (Peet, 1987c, p. 36). Social conditions exert a powerful influence on the geography of manufacturing.

FORCES OF PRODUCTION AND SOCIAL RELATIONS

◈

People must produce objects to satisfy their physical needs. The production of material goods is, therefore, central to an analysis of society. According to this viewpoint, the basic elements of society are the *forces of production* and the *social relations of production*. Together these elements are known as the *mode of production*, and they constitute the *economic structure of society*.

The forces of production include (1) laborers, (2) appropriated natural resources, and (3) capital equipment inherited from past generations of workers. In the early stages of economic development, labor is the chief productive force. The ability to transform nature is limited, and the lives of people revolve around natural forces beyond their control. As the number of workers increases, and as the legacy of capital equipment grows, more and more of nature is harnessed. With more control over nature, people are better able to raise their living standards.

The crucial social relation of production is between owners of the means of production and the workers employed to operate these means. Under capitalism, the means of production are privately owned. Owners of capital control the labor process and the course of economic and social development. Private ownership has two dimensions: on the one hand, competitive relations exist among owners; on the other, cooperative and antagonistic relations emerge between owners (capital) and workers (labor).

The Ruhr industrial district is Europe's largest. This district in northwestern Germany, located on the Rhine River, has more than 20 million inhabitants and consists of a cluster of cities, including Dortman, Dusseldorf, Essen, and Duisburg.
(Source: Paolo Koch, Photo Researchers, Inc.)

Relations Among Owners

Capitalists make independent production decisions under competitive conditions. A raw competitive struggle for survival is fundamental to an appreciation of capitalist development. Competition in the market focuses on price, price depends on cost, and cost hinges on the productive forces used. Competition requires producers to apply a minimum of resources to achieve the highest output. It forces companies to minimize labor costs, which means extreme labor specialization and subordination of workers to machine automation. It demands large-scale production to lower costs and, if possible, to control a segment of the market. It also entails the acquisition of linked or competing companies and the investment of capital in new technology and in research and development (R&D).

Competition is the source of capitalism's immense success as a mode of production. But the tension between opposing elements cannot be solved without fundamental change. Consider, for example, the environmental crises generated by the contradiction between capitalism and the natural environment. For productive

forces to continue to expand without a reduction in living standards, new values must be built into the production system. These values are already evidenced by the use of renewable energy sources and the imposition of pollution controls.

Relations Between Capital and Labor

Capital-labor relations are both cooperative and confrontational. Without a cooperative work force, production is impossible. However, cooperative relations are often subordinate to antagonistic relations.

Because producers make decisions according to their desire to make profits, they try in every way possible to pay workers only part of the value produced by their labor. Value produced by workers in excess of their wages—called *surplus value*—is the basis for profit. On the other hand, workers try to increase their wages in order to enjoy a higher standard of living. They sometimes organize into unions and, if necessary, strike to demand higher wages. If management agrees to meet labor demands, cooperative relations may exist for a time before antagonistic relations resume.

Competition forces management to invest as much as possible in technology and research to increase productivity. As production increases, the struggle between employers and employees puts higher wages into the workers' hands. Increasing purchasing power means expanding markets that absorb a growing supply of commodities, and production development continues in a process of cumulative causation.

Machines and/or low-wage labor can replace high-wage labor. Low-wage peripheral regions can sell products to high-wage center regions. Industrial migration to the periphery removes jobs in the center, which disciplines organized labor. Pressures to increase wages slacken, and mass demand decreases. A crisis of underconsumption develops. Thus, in capitalism, the solution to one crisis may be the breeding ground for new problems.

Competition and Survival in Space

Relations among owners and between capital and labor are sources of change in the geography of production. Competition among owners may cause a company to relocate all or parts of its operation to a place where it can secure low-wage labor. From the company's perspective, this strategy is mandatory for survival; if other companies lower their costs and it does not, it will inevitably lose in the competitive struggle. Capitalists must expand to survive, and the struggle for existence leads to the survival of the biggest. In their search for profits, giant corporations have extended their reach so that few places in the world remain untouched.

The incessant struggle of companies to compete successfully is especially evident in the entrepreneurial response to differential levels of capital-labor conflict. Old industrial regions of the capitalist core—Europe-North America—have high conflict levels. In contrast, peripheral regions have various combinations of lower conflict levels and/or lower wages. Organized labor in the old industrial areas induced the owners of capital to switch production and investment to countries that were not yet industrialized or to newly industrializing countries. The reason that mobile capital could avoid the demands

of organized labor was the development of productive forces—an increased ability to traverse space and conquer the technical problems of production—and the emergence of a huge alternative labor force in the Third World following the colonial revolution in Asia, Africa, and the Caribbean.

These dramatic changes in the 1960s and 1970s ended the original international division of labor that was formalized in the nineteenth century. Under the old imperial system, the advanced powers were the industrialists, and the colonies were the agriculturalists and producers of raw materials. After decolonization, light industry and even some heavy industry began to emerge in the former colonies. The advanced economies assisted this process. The increasing internationalization of production was accompanied by a new international division of labor. The world became a "global factory," in which the developed countries produced the sophisticated technology, and the underdeveloped countries were left with the bulk of the low-skill manufacturing jobs (Froebel, Heinrich, and Kreye, 1977). The emergence of this new international division of labor, mainly a consequence of the activities of the footloose multinational corporations, resulted in deindustrialization in the old industrial regions of advanced economies and a precarious export-led industrial revolution in parts of the Third World.

WHERE INDUSTRY IS LOCATED

◼

Four major areas account for approximately 80% of the world's industrial production (Figure 11.1). These areas are northeastern North America, northwestern Europe, western Russia and the Ukraine, and Japan. In this section, we examine each of the first three regions as well as several nearby subregions. Japan is discussed in detail later in this chapter.

North America

North American manufacturing is still centered in the northeastern United States and southeastern Canada (Figure 11.2). This region is called the North American Manufacturing Belt. James Rubenstein (1994) states that this area encompasses only 5% of the land in North America, but accounts for one-third of the North American population and nearly two-thirds of North American manufacturing.

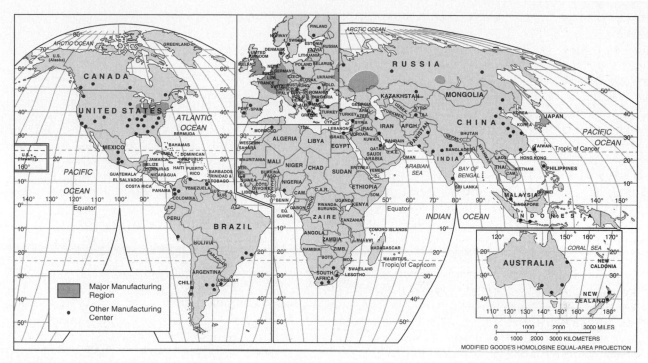

FIGURE 11.1
Worldwide distribution of manufacturing. The four main manufacturing regions include the northeastern United States and southern Great Lakes region, the northwestern European region, the eastern Soviet Union and Ukraine region, and the Japan/South Korea region. See the text for a detailed elaboration of districts within each of these regions, as well as other manufacturing regions shown as dots.

This area was the first region settled by Europeans in the seventeenth and eighteenth centuries. It was tied to the European markets and possessed the raw materials, iron ore, coal, and limestone necessary to produce the heavy machinery and manufactured items on which the industrialization of America was based. In addition, this region had many markets and a large labor pool.

The transportation system included the St. Lawrence River and the Great Lakes, which were connected to the East Coast and the Atlantic Ocean by the Mohawk and Hudson rivers. This transportation system allowed the easy movement of bulky and heavy materials. Later, the river and lake system was supplemented by canals and railroads.

NEW ENGLAND DISTRICT

Within the North American Manufacturing Belt, there are several districts. The oldest is southern New England, centered on Massachusetts and the greater Boston metropolitan area. Historically, this area was the textile and clothing manufacturing center of the early nineteenth century. Cotton was brought from the southern states to be manufactured into garments, many of which were consumed locally and some of which were exported to Europe. As the low-wage European immigrant laborers settled and achieved a higher standard of living and unionization, wages became higher, and the textile industry moved to the South. Today, although it still produces some high-value-added textiles and clothing, the New England district manufactures electrical machinery, fabricated metals, and electronic products. The region is noted for highly skilled labor and ingenuity, with nearby universities—including Boston College, Boston University, Massachusetts Institute of Technology, and Harvard University—providing the chief supply of both. Boston is now called *Silicon Valley Northeast* (or Silicon Strip) (see Figure 11.2).

NEW YORK AND THE MIDDLE ATLANTIC DISTRICT

New York and the Middle Atlantic district (areas 2 and 4 in Figure 11.2) are centered on New York City and include the metropolitan area of Baltimore, Maryland; Philadelphia, Pennsylvania; and Wilmington, Dela-

Anglo-American Manufacturing Region
1   New England district
    Electrical machinery
    Machinery
    Fabricated metals
    Textiles
    Electronic products
    Apparel
2   Greater New York district
    Apparel
    Printing and publishing
    Machinery
    Food processing
    Fabricated metals
    Chemicals
3   Central New York district
    Electrical machinery
    Chemicals
    Optical machinery
    Iron and steel
4   Mid-Atlantic district
    Apparel
    Iron and steel
    Chemicals
    Food processing
    Machinery
5   Pittsburgh-Cleveland district
    Iron and steel
    Machinery
    Electrical equipment
    Rubber
    Machine tools

6   Southeast Michigan district
    Automobiles
    Iron and steel
7   Lake Michigan district
    Iron and steel
    Fabricated metals
    Machinery
    Printing and publishing
    Electrical machinery
8   Southwest Ohio-Eastern Indiana district
    Iron and steel
    Fabricated metals
    Machinery
    Electrical machinery
    Paper manufacturing
9   Great Kanawha and Middle Ohio Valley district
    Chemicals
    Primary metals
    Glass
10 St. Louis district
    Transportation equipment
    Iron and steel
    Fabricated metals
    Food processing
11 Ontario Peninsula district (Canada)
    Iron and steel
    Machinery
    Chemicals
    Food processing
12 St. Lawrence Valley district (Canada)
    Pulp and paper
    Primary metals (aluminum)

Southeastern Manufacturing Region
    Textiles
    Apparel
    Transportation equipment
    Furniture
    Food processing
    Lumber
    Primary metals

Gulf Coast Manufacturing Region
    Petroleum refining
    Chemicals
    Primary metals (aluminum)
    Electrical machinery
    Electronic products

Central Florida Manufacturing Region
    Food processing
    Electrical machinery
    Electronic products

West Coast Manufacturing Region
A   Los Angeles-San Diego district
    Aircraft
    Electrical equipment
    Automobile assembly
    Apparel
    Petroleum refining
B   San Francisco district
    Electronic products
    Food processing
    Shipbuilding
    Machinery

C   Pacific Northwest district (Portland-Seattle)
    Aircraft
    Lumber products
    Food processing

● Other Centers of Manufacturing
I   Kansas City
     Food processing
     Automobile assembly
II   Minneapolis-St. Paul
     Food processing
     Machinery
     Fabricated metals
III Dallas-Ft. Worth
     Transportation equipment
     Food processing
IV   Denver-Pueblo
     Food processing
     Chemicals
     Iron and steel
V   Phoenix
     Electrical machinery
     Electronic products

FIGURE 11.2

Manufacturing regions and districts throughout the United States and Canada.
(Source: Fisher, 1992, p. 155.)

New England became the first and foremost textile-manufacturing region in the United States in the late eighteenth century. The mills pictured here are in Lawrence, Massachusetts. By the 1940s, the textile region of southern New England had been in decline for more than 20 years. Firms left the region in search of more profitable operating conditions, and workers were forced to seek other employment. Recently, the region has experienced a revival as new industries, notably electrical engineering, have replaced the older, declining ones.
(Source: Library of Congress.)

ware. The Great Lakes industrial traffic terminates in New York City via the Mohawk and Hudson rivers. From New York City, foreign markets and sources of raw materials can be reached. New York City is the largest market and has the largest labor pool. Because of its central location among other large cities on the Eastern Seaboard, as well as its ports, many of the Fortune 500 firm headquarters are located in this district. The New York district is in proximity not only to trade with the rest of the world, but also to the population centers and manufacturing hubs of America (Figure 11.2). It is also near financial, communications, and news and media industries, which are important for advertising and distribution. This region produces apparel, iron and steel, chemicals, machinery, fabricated

metals, and a variety of processed foods. In addition, it is the headquarters of the North American publishing industry. Many major book-publishing companies are located in this region.

CENTRAL NEW YORK AND THE MOHAWK RIVER VALLEY DISTRICT

Another major industrial district within the North American manufacturing region is the central New York and Mohawk River valley district. In this region, electrical machinery, chemicals, optical machinery, and iron and steel are produced. These industries agglomerate along the Erie Canal and the Hudson River, which is the only waterway connecting the Great Lakes to the U.S. East Coast. Abundant electrical power produced by the kinetic energy of Niagara Falls provides inexpensive electricity to this district and explains the attraction of the aluminum industry, which requires above average amounts of electricity. The New York industrial cities of Buffalo, Rochester, Syracuse, Utica, Schenectady, and Albany are situated in this district.

PITTSBURGH-CLEVELAND-LAKE ERIE DISTRICT

The Pittsburgh-Cleveland-Lake Erie district, centered in western Pennsylvania and eastern Ohio, is the oldest steel-producing region in North America. Pittsburgh was the original steel-producing center because of the iron ore and coal available in the nearby Appalachian Mountains. When the iron ore became depleted, new supplies were discovered in northern Minnesota and transported in via the Great Lakes system. Besides iron and steel, electrical equipment, machinery, rubber, and machine tools are produced in this region.

WESTERN GREAT LAKES DISTRICT

The western Great Lakes industrial region is centered on Detroit in the east and Chicago in the west (areas 6 and 7 in Figure 11.2). In addition, Toledo, Ohio, in the east and Milwaukee in the west have a dominant position in the North American Manufacturing Belt for the production of transportation equipment, iron and steel, automobiles, fabricated metals, machinery, and printing and publishing. Detroit and surrounding cities, of course, have the preeminent position of automobile manufacture, and Chicago has produced more railroad cars, farm tractors and implements, and food products than any other city in the United States. The convergence of railroad and highway transportation routes in this area makes it readily accessible to the rest of the country, and a good distribution point to a national market.

ST. LAWRENCE VALLEY/ ONTARIO DISTRICT

Canada's most important industrial region by far stretches along the St. Lawrence River Valley, on the north shore of the eastern Great Lakes (areas 11 and 12 in Figure 11.2). This area has access to the St. Lawrence

River/Great Lakes transportation system, is near the largest Canadian markets, has skilled and plentiful labor, and is supplied with inexpensive electricity from Niagara Falls. Iron and steel, machinery, chemicals, processed foods, pulp and paper, and primary metals, especially aluminum, are produced in this district. For example, Toronto is a leading automobile-assembly location in Canada, whereas Hamilton is Canada's leading iron and steel producer.

OTHER DISTRICTS WITHIN THE NORTH AMERICAN MANUFACTURING BELT

Three other districts are important. One is located in southwest Ohio and in eastern Indiana and is centered on the cities of Columbus, Dayton, and Cincinnati, Ohio, and Indianapolis, Indiana (area 8). This district is noted for iron and steel, fabricated metals, machinery, electrical machinery, and paper manufacture. A second is Great Kanawha and middle Ohio Valley district, which specializes in chemicals, metals, and glass (area 9). The last district centers on the greater St. Louis metropolitan area (area 10). In this region, automobiles, transportation equipment, iron and steel, fabricated metals, and processed foods are produced. Brewing and beverage manufacture are also popular.

SOUTHEASTERN MANUFACTURING REGION

The *southeastern manufacturing region* of the United States, sometimes called the *Piedmont region*, stretches south from central Virginia through North Carolina, western South Carolina, northern Georgia, northeastern Alabama, and northeastern Tennessee (Figure 11.2). It centers on the towns of Greensboro and Charlotte, North Carolina; Greenville and Columbia, South Carolina; Atlanta, Georgia; Birmingham, Alabama; and Chattanooga and Knoxville, Tennessee. The district stretches around the southern flank of the Appalachian Mountains because of poor transportation connections across the mountains. Textiles are the main product, the industry having moved from the Northeast to the South to take advantage of less expensive, nonunion labor. Transportation equipment, furniture, processed foods, and lumber are also produced. Aluminum manufacturers moved to this region because of the inexpensive electricity produced by the more than 20 dams built by the Tennessee Valley Authority, and Birmingham has long been the iron and steel center of the southeastern

United States because of the plentiful iron-ore and coal supplies nearby.

Figure 11.3 shows the distribution of hosiery and knit outerwear manufacturers. The hosiery industry is centered on areas from North Carolina southward, which have traditionally supplied low-cost labor. Knit outerwear requires more skill to manufacture and has not decentralized from the Northeast. The New York City region and New England still have the most knit outerwear manufacturers.

GULF COAST MANUFACTURING REGION

The *Gulf Coast manufacturing region* stretches from southeastern Texas through southern Louisiana, Missis- sippi, and Alabama, to the tip of the Florida panhandle. Principal cities include Houston, Texas; Baton Rouge and New Orleans, Louisiana; Mobile, Alabama; and Pensacola, Florida. Because of nearby oil and gas fields, petroleum refining and chemical production are important. The region also produces primary metals, including aluminum, and electrical machinery and electronic products.

CENTRAL FLORIDA REGION

The *central Florida manufacturing region* includes the cities of Jacksonville, Tampa, St. Petersburg, Orlando, and Miami. Processed foods are the most important product, but electrical machinery and electronic parts are also produced.

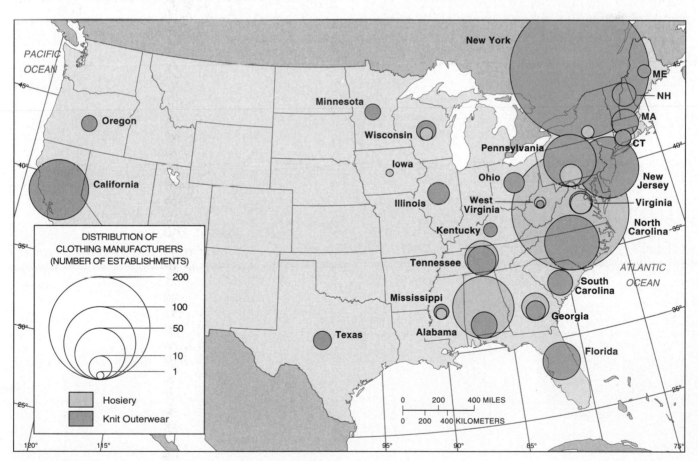

FIGURE 11.3

The distribution of hosiery and knit outerwear manufacturing establishments. Hosiery manufacture is a labor-intensive industry, and it has moved into the southeastern United States where it can obtain cheap labor. Knit outerwear manufacturers have remained primarily in New England and the Northeast because of industrial inertia and because of the availability of more skilled workers, especially in the New York City region. (See Color Insert 2 page 2.7, top, for more illustrative map.)

WEST COAST MANUFACTURING REGIONS

The Los Angeles and San Diego district in southern California specializes in aircraft and aerospace manufacture and electrical equipment (Figure 11.2). In the 1930s, the airline industry chose this location because favorable weather 330 days of the year meant unimpeded test flights and savings on heating and cooling the large aircraft plants. Because of the myriad electronic parts and equipment and the associated high-tech sensing and navigational devices required in aircraft manufacture, the electronics industry was also attracted to this region and was anchored there 30 years later (Figure 11.4). Today, apparel manufacture and petroleum refining are important in Los Angeles, whereas San Diego also specializes in pharmaceutical production and in national defense manufacturing industries.

The San Francisco district is the second most important *West Coast manufacturing region*. Electronic products, processed foods, ships, and machinery are produced in the district. *Silicon Valley*, the world's largest manufacturing area for semiconductors, microprocessors, and computer equipment, is located just south of San Francisco in the Santa Clara Valley (Figure 11.2).

The Pacific Northwest district includes the cities of Seattle, Washington, and Portland, Oregon. Boeing Aircraft is the single largest employer, followed closely by the paper, lumber, and food-processing industries.

OTHER U.S. MANUFACTURING REGIONS

Other manufacturing centers include Kansas City, Missouri, with its food-processing and automobile-assembly industries; Minneapolis and St. Paul, Minne-

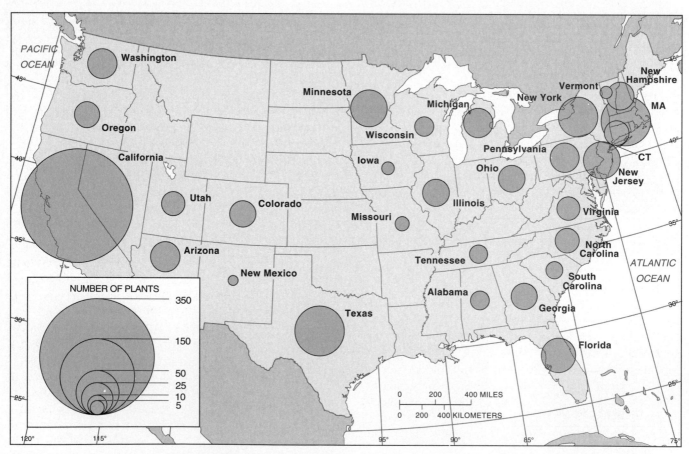

FIGURE 11.4
The U.S. distribution of computer equipment manufacturers. California has the largest number of plants, followed by a cluster in the Northeast. Electronics manufacturing plants gravitate to highly skilled labor. The finished products are more valuable than are items of clothing, and higher wages can be paid. There is a concentration of these manufacturers in California because early electronics production as a part of the aircraft manufacturing industry was centered on the West Coast. (See Color Insert 2 page 2.7, bottom, for more illustrative map.)

San Jose, California. A $1 billion downtown renaissance has helped establish San Jose, capital of Silicon Valley, as California's third and the United States' eleventh largest city. *(Source: San Jose Convention and Visitors Bureau.)*

sota, which produce wheat, processed foods, machinery, and fabricated metals; and Dallas–Fort Worth, Texas, which produce transportation equipment and processed foods. In addition, Denver and Pueblo, Colorado, have food-processing, chemical, and steel-manufacturing industries, and the Phoenix metropolitan region manufactures electrical machinery and electronic products (Figure 11.2).

The electronics and computer industries require high-skilled workers, so, unlike clothing manufacturers, who have gravitated to low-wage districts, manufacturers of electronic and computer equipment have located in relatively high-wage districts to attract skilled workers. The largest high-tech clusters include New England, centered on Boston, and California, centered on Silicon Valley.

Europe

Europe has developed some of the world's most important industrial regions (Figure 11.5). They are located in a north-south linear pattern, starting from Scotland and extending through southern England, continuing from the mouth of the Rhine River valley in the Netherlands, through Germany and France, to northern Italy. Good supplies of iron ore and coal provide fuel to the countries in these industrial regions. In addition, competition among countries has resulted in several subareas within Europe, each near large markets of consumers.

THE UNITED KINGDOM

The industrial revolution started in the United Kingdom in 1750. It had its basis in iron and steel production and textile and woolen manufacture. Because many dependent nations have since learned to produce their own iron, steel, and textiles, the world currently has an oversupply of these items, and the market for British goods has decreased substantially.

Great Britain's outmoded factories and deteriorating infrastructures have also reduced its overall global competitiveness for products. In contrast, Germany and Japan, with U.S. assistance, rebuilt after World War II, modernizing their plants and industrial processes at the same time. As a result, Germany and Japan are industrial successes in the world today, whereas Great Britain, more so than any other modern industrialized country, has suffered an industrial depression.

RHINE-RUHR RIVER VALLEY REGION

The most important European production region today is the northern European lowland countries of Belgium, and the Netherlands, including northwestern Germany and northeastern France. In this region, the Rhine River and the Ruhr River meet. Although no single city dominates the region in Germany, Dortmund, Düsseldorf, Essen, and Duisburg are the centers of this district.

This region's backbone has been the iron and steel industry because of its proximity to coal and iron-ore fields. Production of transportation equipment, machinery, and chemicals helped lead Western Europe into the industrial age long before the rest of the world.

The Rhine River, which is the main waterway of European commerce, empties into the North Sea in the Netherlands at Rotterdam. Consequently, because of its excellent location, Rotterdam has become the world's largest port.

While exports of iron and steel are down from what

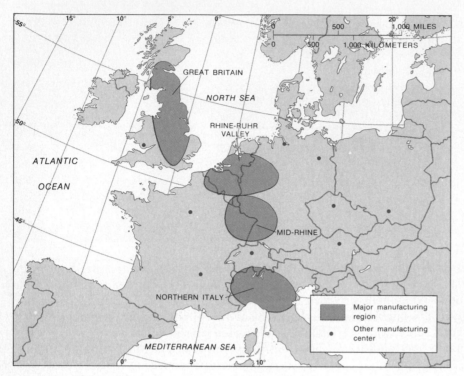

FIGURE 11.5
European manufacturing regions. Much European manufacturing exists in a linear belt from Scotland to the Midlands of Great Britain, to the South, including the London area. This belt continues onward from the low countries of Belgium, Luxembourg, and the Netherlands, south along the Rhine River, including portions of France and Germany, and into Northern Italy. These areas became major manufacturing regions not only because of the concentration of skilled laborers, but also due to the availability of raw materials, principally coal and iron ore. In addition, good river transportation was available, as well as large consuming markets for finished products.

they were 30 years ago, the region has been better able to avoid the depression of the U.K. because of its greater internal conversion of steel into high-quality finished products, which are in demand worldwide.

UPPER RHINE–ALSACE-LORRAINE REGION

Straddling the chief transportation artery for Western Europe, the Upper *Rhine–Alsace-Lorraine Region* (called Mid-Rhine in Figure 11.5) is located in southwestern Germany and eastern France. It is the second most important European industrial district, after the Rhine-Ruhr River valley.

Because of its central location, this area is well situated for distribution to population centers throughout Western Europe. The main cities on the German side include Frankfurt, Stuttgart, and Mannheim. Frankfurt is almost perfectly centrally located in what was West Germany and hence became the financial and commercial center of its railway, air, and road networks. Stuttgart, on the other hand, is a center for precision goods and high-value, volume, manufactured goods, including the Mercedes Benz, Porsche, and Audi automobiles. Mannheim, located along the Rhine River, is noted for its chemicals, pharmaceuticals, and inland port facilities.

The western side of this district, in France, is domi-

nated by the industrial cities of Metz, Nancy, Strasbourg, and Mulhouse. This area, known as Alsace-Lorraine, produces a large portion of the district's iron and steel. Germany and France have fought numerous wars over the occupation of this district, because of its ethnic French- and German-speaking peoples, as well as the rich iron-ore fields that extend northward into Luxembourg. Consequently, this region has changed hands many times. The present political arrangement is a result of World War II. The French were part of the victorious Allies, so they extended the borders of their country to the western bank of the Rhine River.

PO VALLEY OF NORTHERN ITALY

The remaining large industrial district of Western Europe is the *Po River valley* in northern Italy. The principal industrial cities in this area include Torino (Turin), Milan, and Genoa, but other cities of industrial importance include Cremona, Verona, and mainland Venice (Mestre). This area includes only one-fourth of Italy's land, but more than 70% of its industries and 50% of its population (Rubenstein, 1994).

This region specializes in iron and steel, transportation equipment (especially high-value automobiles), textile manufacture, and food processing. The district is bordered on the north by the Swiss Alps, Italy's breadbasket as well as its industrial backbone. The Alps, a barrier to the German and British industrial regions, give the Italian district a large share of the southern European markets. The mountains also provide Italian industries with cheap hydroelectricity and therefore reduced operating costs. Compared with workers in the American Manufacturing Belt, Italian laborers are willing to work for less because of their lower cost of living, thus this region attracts labor-intensive industries, such as textiles, from Northern Europe.

Russia and the Ukraine

Five major industrial regions exist within the former Soviet Union. Four are primarily within Russia, and one is centered on the southern Ukraine (Figure 11.6). Since the demise of the Soviet Union in 1991, production statistics and information on the livelihoods of these regions are not as readily available as in the past. Nonetheless, these industrial regions are the most significant in northern Asia.

MOSCOW, OR CENTRAL, REGION

The *Moscow,* or *central industrial region* is located near the population center of Russia and takes advantage of a large, skilled labor pool as well as a large market, even though natural resources are not plentiful. This region produces more than a quarter of the total industrial output of the former Soviet Union.

The largest single item produced is textiles: linen, cotton, wool, and silk fabrics. This manufacturing complex is set around the city of Ivanovo. Moscow industry also specializes in iron and steel, transportation equipment, chemicals, and automobiles and trucks. Novgorod, the automobile-producing Soviet Detroit, lies 100 miles north of Moscow.

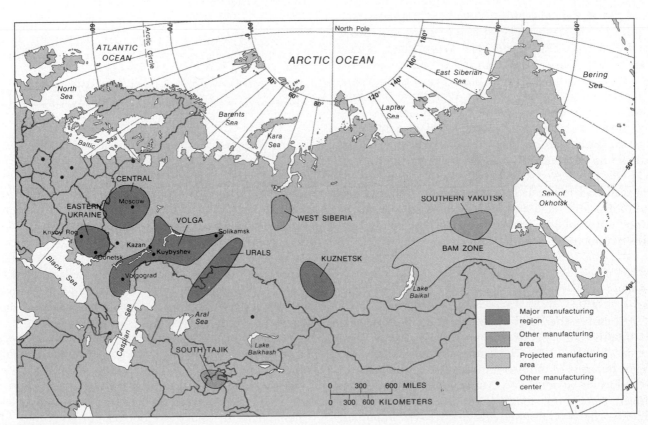

FIGURE 11.6
Manufacturing regions of Russia, Eastern Europe, and Central Asia.

UKRAINE REGION

The *Eastern Ukraine Industrial region* relies on the rich coalfield deposits of the *Donets Basin*. The iron and steel industry base is the city of Krivoy Rog, with nearby Odessa as the principal Black Sea all-weather port. The area is collectively known as *Donbass*. Like the German Ruhr area, the Ukraine's industrial district is located near iron-ore and coal mines, a dense population, and a large agricultural region, and is served by good transportation facilities.

The Ukraine industrial district is now a part of the former Soviet Union. It is severely hampering the Russian industrial effort that formerly controlled this district. Ukrainian leaders have decided to market their goods on an international scale instead of supplying Russia's needs, even though these needs are more urgent than ever.

VOLGA REGION

East of the Moscow industrial region is the linear *Volga region*, extending from Volgograd (formerly Stalingrad) in the south, to Perm in the north, and astride the Volga and Kama rivers. The Volga River, a chief waterway of Russia, has been linked via canal to the Don River and thereby to the Black Sea. This industrial region developed during and after World War II because it was just out of reach of the invading German army that struck not only the Ukraine, but also Moscow. It is the principal location of substantial oil and gas production and refining. Recently, a larger oil and gas field was discovered in West Siberia. Nonetheless, the Volga district is Russia's chief supplier of oil and gas, chemicals, and related products. Recently, one of the largest automobile plants in the world opened in Toglaitti, producing Fiat automobiles.

URALS REGION

Just east of the Volga region are the low-lying Ural Mountains that separate European Russia from Asian Russia (Figure 11.6). The Ural Mountains have the largest deposits of industrial minerals found anywhere in the former Soviet Union. Mineral types include iron, copper, potassium, magnesium, salt, tungsten, and bauxite. The central-lying Ural district was important during World War II because it also was beyond the reach of the German army. Although coal must be imported from the nearby Volga district, the Urals district provides Russia with iron and steel, chemicals, machinery, and fabricated metal.

KUZNETSK BASIN REGION

The Kuznetsk Basin—also called *Kuzbass* and centered on the towns of Novosibirsk, located along the trans-Siberian railroad, and Novokuznetsk—is the chief industrial region of Russia east of the Urals. It is also known as *Russian Asia*. Again, as in the case of the Ukraine and the Urals districts, the Kuznetsk industrial district relies on an abundant supply of iron ore and the largest supply of coal in the country. The Kuznetsk Basin is a result of the grand design of former Soviet city planners. These planners poured heavy investments into this region, hoping that it would become self-perpetuating and eventually the industrial supply region for Soviet Central Asia and the Soviet Far East. It has become the industrial supply region envisioned by the planners, but the planners probably did not foresee the iron and steel industry smokestacks and air pollution that are visible for hundreds of miles.

INTERNATIONALIZATION OF WORLD MANUFACTURING

◈

As the new international division of labor asserted itself, the rate of world economic growth declined. Lower growth rates coincided with the end of the long boom of the quarter-century period after World War II and the beginning of a prolonged period of economic crisis. The world economic crisis started with a deep recession in 1974/1975 following the first oil shock in 1973. One of its most visible effects in the advanced economies was deindustrialization—reflected by the loss of manufacturing jobs. As firms restructured or went out of business in a climate of intense competition, workers were laid off.

Change in the geography of manufacturing began in the postwar period of rapid growth, but accelerated in the crisis of the 1970s and 1980s. Although the advanced countries maintained a huge share in world manufacturing output, their output grew less quickly than that of the underdeveloped countries (Tables 11.1 and 11.2). Nonetheless, manufacturing output in the advanced countries increased in the 1960s, with most economies coasting along with annual growth rates of

■

Table 11.1

Share in Manufacturing Production
by Country Group

	Share in Production		
Country Group	*1965*	*1973*	*1985*
Industrial market economies	85.4	83.9	81.6
Underdeveloped countries	14.5	16.0	18.1
Low-income	7.5	7.0	6.9
Middle-income	7.0	9.0	11.2
High-income oil exporters	0.1	0.1	0.3

Source: World Bank, 1987, p. 47.

between 5% and 8%. Only Great Britain, with a growth rate of 3.3%, hinted at future trouble. The manufacturing output of the advanced economies slowed dramatically in the 1970s, and production actually declined in Great Britain. The number of workers in manufacturing in the advanced countries, which grew in the early 1970s, stabilized in the mid-1970s, and fell in the late 1970s and in the 1980s. Job losses were most numerous in Great Britain and Belgium; each country lost 28% of its manufacturing workers between 1974 and 1983. During the same period, West Germany recorded a loss of 16%; France, 14%; and the United States, 8%. The

■

Table 11.2

Growth in Manufacturing Production by
Country Group

	Growth in Production		
Country Group	*1965–1973*	*1973–1985*	*1965–1985*
Industrial market economies	5.3	3.0	3.8
Underdeveloped countries	9.0	6.0	7.2
Low-income	8.9	7.9	7.5
Middle-income	9.1	5.0	6.6
High-income oil exporters	10.6	7.5	8.4

Source: World Bank, 1987, p. 47.

highest rate of manufacturing job loss in the United States was in the Midwest—more than 11% between 1975 and 1982. However, manufacturing employment increased in new industrial areas—parts of the Southwest, the Mountain states, the Dakotas, and Florida. It also increased in areas successful in restructuring their industrial bases, such as southern New England. With few exceptions, U.S. regions that registered a rapid growth in manufacturing output in the late 1970s and 1980s were low-conflict and/or low-wage states.

Since 1960, manufacturing output has increased sharply in lower-wage industrializing periphery countries. The output of manufactures in Southern Europe and Latin America grew at annual rates of between 5% and 11% in the 1960s (except Argentina). Although this performance was achieved during a period of unprecedented real growth in world output, these regions sustained their progress in the 1970s and 1980s. Their high production rates were usually sufficient to secure increases in industrial employment.

The most rapid growth of manufacturing output occurred in East and South Asia. Japan, with quite high wages but relatively low labor militancy, recorded spectacular annual increases in manufacturing output in the 1960s. Its manufacturing output also expanded impressively in the 1970s, but with a smaller labor force. Several newly industrializing countries equaled or exceeded Japan's annual growth rate in manufacturing output from 1960 to 1993. They also registered prodigious increases in manufacturing employment: 47% in South Korea between 1974 and 1993, 93% in Taiwan, 83% in Hong Kong, and 135% in Malaysia.

In Africa and South Asia, the growth of manufacturing has been slower. One or two countries, such as Bangladesh and the Ivory Coast, have achieved vigorous growth rates on small manufacturing bases. On the other hand, several countries, such as Tanzania and Zaire, have registered reduction in their manufacturing output.

What conclusions can be drawn from this review of changes in the distribution of manufacturing output and employment? Much depends on your perspective. The traditional view is that deindustrialization in some places and industrialization in others are mirror images of each other. Industrial growth and decline are offsetting tendencies, representing a zero-sum, or even a positive, global game. The shift of production processes from the industrial heartland to the underdeveloped periphery releases a skilled labor force for more sophisticated forms of production in developed countries and allows labor in the Third World to move from relatively unproductive employment to more highly productive employment in industry. The shift may lead to some transitional unemployment, but job losses in the industrial heartland are of little significance compared with the enormous rewards attached to a global reallocation of production.

Between 1974 and 1993, the advanced industrial countries lost 18 million jobs, whereas the newly industrializing countries gained 16 million jobs. Jobs lost in the advanced industrial countries paid from $5 to $15 an hour, but those gained in the newly industrializing countries paid only $2.50 per hour or less. The gains from expansion in the newly industrializing countries were more than offset by the losses in the advanced industrial countries. Indeed, the shift led to lower global wage shares that may contribute to stagnation. Nomadic capital, although it may serve individual company interests, can be socially inefficient. Those who hire labor control the work process, and distribution is always in favor of those who control the production location. Corporate allocation of production and investment is guided primarily by profitability concerns, where profitability is determined by the price of labor and the amount of work that can be extracted at this price. Nomadic capital can also be socially inefficient because

giant corporations are rarely faced with the full social costs of their locational decisions. Shifting production from country to country means that the advanced industrial countries must absorb not only most of the social costs of communities that are now abandoned because they can no longer be industrially competitive, but also the costs of the social infrastructure required by the newly industrializing countries. Some geographers view locational change as socially inefficient in a world dominated by giant firms with the power to set the terms under which they operate.

International Shifts in the Textile and Clothing Industries

TEXTILE MANUFACTURE

Textile employment in the United States in 1987 was 831,000 workers, and in Japan, 670,000 workers. Since the 1960s, however, the pattern of textile employment and production has shifted dramatically from the developed nations to the developing nations of Eastern Europe and Asia (Figure 11.7). Employment in textile

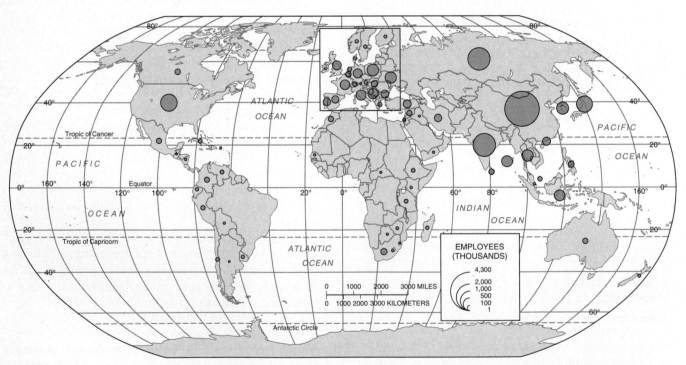

FIGURE 11.7
World distribution of textile manufacturing employment. China, the Soviet Union, and India, followed by the United States, have the largest employment in textile manufacturing. Textile employment in 1990 in the United States totaled 831,000 workers. Japan and Europe comprise the remaining centers of textile employment. *(Source: United Nations (1992) Industrial Statistics Yearbook, 1990, New York: U.N.)*

manufacture is strongest in East Asia. China has the most employees, followed by Russia and India.

Peter Dicken (1992), in his book *Global Shift: The Internationalization of Economic Activity*, documents the broad production changes in textile manufacturing between 1972 and 1987. Textile production between 1980 and 1987 rose by 6% worldwide and even increased by 12% in North America. However, Europe's production decreased, overall, with the notable exception of Italy, which increased its yearly productivity and exports in textiles 2.5% between 1978 and 1987. France, Germany, and the Netherlands all experienced reduced productivity, as did the United Kingdom and Japan. In the developing nations, especially in Asia, however, production during the same period increased 18%. Asia, India, South Korea, the Philippines, and Indonesia dramatically increased their production, and Latin America, Chile, Colombia, Peru, and Venezuela did likewise. Among the Eastern European nations that improved textile production were Bulgaria, Czechoslovakia, and Romania (Figure 11.7).

CLOTHING MANUFACTURE

Textile manufacture is the creation of cloth and fabric, whereas clothing manufacture uses textiles to produce wearing apparel. In 1987, the largest concentration of employment in clothing manufacturing was in the Soviet Union, and the next largest was in the United States. A third cluster, led by Japan, existed in East Asia. Clothing manufacture is still an important industry in Western Europe, especially in Germany, France, the United Kingdom, Italy, and Poland, which each have between 150,000 and 250,000 employees in the industry. For developing countries in 1987, Hong Kong and the Far East was the leading employment center of clothing manufacturers, with 282,000 employees in the industry. South Korea, the Philippines, Malaysia, and Singapore were also significant contributors to worldwide clothing manufacture.

Table 11.3 shows the changes in production in clothing manufacture between 1972 and 1987. During this period, the developed market economies fared rather poorly, while the developing market economies showed a much stronger increase, substantially stronger than the global shift in textile manufacture. For example, Germany's production fell to 77% of its 1980 production level, the Netherlands' production fell to 75%, and France's to 90%. North America, Canada, and the United Kingdom were somewhat more productive. However, the developing market economies—es-

pecially of India, South Korea, Singapore, Malaysia, the Philippines, Venezuela, and the Dominican Republic, Cyprus, Israel, and the formerly centrally planned economies of Eastern Europe—fared extremely well. The most rapid increase in clothing manufacture included Romania, Poland, and the Soviet Union, overall averaging 115% of the 1980 production figures.

World Shifts in the Automobile Industry

Peter Dicken (1992) states that more than 4 million workers are directly employed in car and motor truck manufacture throughout the world, and that twice as many are producing the materials and components that are used in the final assembly of automobiles and trucks. Although many people believe that the semiconductor and computer-chip industry has supplanted the automobile industry as the world's most important type of production, the automobile industry is more important to the world economy than it appears. "Twice in this century it has changed the most fundamental idea of how we make things. And how we make things dictates not only how we work, but what we buy and how we think and the way we live" (Womack, Jones, and Roos, 1990, p. 11). If we add the number of employees engaged in the direct manufacture of automobiles and components to those involved in sales and service, we find a total world employment of 25 million in 1994, not far short of the entire population of Canada.

The automobile industry, more than any other, comprises giant transnational corporations. In no other industry in the world can so few companies dominate the world scene as can the automobile industry. For example, the world's 10 leading automobile manufacturers produce nearly 80% of the world's automobiles (Table 11.4). Each of these, from General Motors and Ford to the smallest automobile producer, has foreign assembly plants in other countries. Many have full-blown vertically integrated manufacturing operations, where all parts in the final assembly are foreign-supplied. For example, the Ford Motor Company, the second largest automobile producer in the world, with an output of more than 4,500,000 cars in 1993, produces almost 60% of its cars outside the United States.

AUTOMOBILE MANUFACTURE

Worldwide automobile production has been rapidly increasing. Between 1960 and 1991, there was a world-

⊕

Table 11.3

Internationalization of Clothing Manufacture,
1972–1992

	1972	(1980 = 100) 1978	1983	1987	1992
Developed Market Economies	101	104	94	94	92
North America	92	105	91	94	88
European community	112	105	96	94	73
Japan	—	102	99	98	97
Developing Market Economies	68	92	106	124	152
Asia	57	96	126	155	145
India	—	104	126	123	162
South Korea	—	102	139	206	225
Singapore	—	77	96	139	165
Malaysia	—	98	—	170	213
Philippines	—	54	—	367	380
Latin America					
Venezuela	—	87	—	214	210
Dominican Republic	—	70	—	156	160
Mediterranean					
Cyprus	—	89	—	136	140
Israel	—	96	—	129	131
Centrally Planned Economies	67	92	105	115	99
World	83	98	99	105	92.5

— No data available.

Source: United Nations, Industrial Statistics Yearbook, 1990, 1991, 1992.

wide increase of 358%, and 43,238,000 cars were produced in 1991. Figure 11.8 shows the 1991 world distribution of automobile production and assembly.

Three major nodes of automobile production exist—Japan, the United States, and Western Europe—with smaller production centers in Brazil, the former Soviet Union, and Australia. In 1991, Europe accounted for 32% of the world's automobiles; Japan, 23%; and the United States, 19%. Collectively, the other regions accounted for 21%. Table 11.5 shows the growth of automobile output by major producing countries between 1960 and 1991. In sum, the three developed regions of the world, East Asia, North America, and Europe, accounted for 86% of the automobiles produced. Unlike the trend in the textile and clothing industries, the developed countries clearly cornered the mar-

ket in automobile manufacture. Only a few developing economies have shown a significant increase in automobile assembly, but not in their full-scale production.

The most dramatic shift in the automobile industry was the tremendous increase in Japan's productivity between 1960 and 1991. In 1960, Japan produced 165,000 cars; by 1991, this figure had increased to over 13 million, more than one-quarter of the world's total output, completely surpassing U.S. output. In 1960, the United States produced more than half the world's automobiles, but by 1991, only 18%. Great Britain produced more than 10% of the world's output in 1960 but less that 3.3% in 1991. Germany and France, however, continued to do well in automobile productivity, although their world share, 9.5% for France and 13% for Germany, declined 2% each during the 30-year span.

◈

Table 11.4
World Auto Production–1991

Rank	1991			World Share %	% Produced Outside Home Country
	Passenger Cars	Commercial Vehicles	Total		
1. General Motors—U.S.........	4,968,659	1,666,076	6,634,735	14.4	44
2. Ford—U.S......................	3,452,039	1,686,321	5,138,360	11.3	46
3. Toyota—Japan	3,597,179	914,040	4,511,219	9.8	11
4. Volkswagen—W. Germany ..	2,921,481	166,952	3,088,433	6.5	30
5. Nissan—Japan.................	2,333,276	692,483	3,025,759	6.3	20
6. PSA—France	2,257,454	209,773	2,467,227	4.6	20
7. Renault—France	1,705,821	298,416	2,004,237	4.3	21
8. Honda—Japan.................	1,765,403	143,361	1,908,764	4.1	23
9. Fiat—Italy.....................	1,636,838	261,717	1,898,555	4.1	7.2
10. Chrysler—U.S................	660,200	1,014,089	1,674,289	3.7	33
11. Mitsubishi—Japan	1,103,606	491,469	1,595,075	3.5	12
12. Mazda—Japan	1,250,714	300,541	1,551,255	3.3	7
13. Suzuki—Japan	542,128	370,650	912,778	2.0	7
14. Daimler-Benz—W. Germany	575,547	285,651	861,198	1.9	12
15. Hyundai—S. Korea	669,551	125,740	795,291	1.8	4
16. VAZ—C.I.S...................	675,000	12,000	687,000	1.5	0
17. Daihatsu—Japan..............	420,313	250,168	670,481	1.5	0
18. Fuji—Japan...................	388,052	256,578	644,630	1.4	18
19. BMW—W. Germany	536,003	0	536,003	1.2	0
20. Isuzu—Japan.................	130,447	340,503	470,950	1.1	0
TOTAL 20 MANUFACTURERS...	31,589,711	9,486,528	41,076,239		
OTHERS...........................	698,879	1,462,882	2,161,761		
TOTAL PRODUCTION.............	32,288,590	10,949,410	43,238,000		

Data compiled by AAMA from various sources. Information was obtained
from published reports issued by various vehicle associations outside the U.S.
and from a number of other sources considered reliable. Because of the
numerous complex factors involved in determining this worldwide ranking,
AAMA does not assume responsibility for the above classification. *World Motor
Vehicle Data*, American Automobile Manufacturing Association, Detroit, 1993

Internationalization of Microelectronics

Microelectronic technology is the dominant technology of the latter 20th century, transforming all branches
of the economy and many aspects of society.

The radio was invented and produced as early as
1901, giving the first indications of an electronics industry, but the modern electronics industry was not born
until the transistor was built in the United States in
1948 by Bell Telephone Laboratories. The transistor

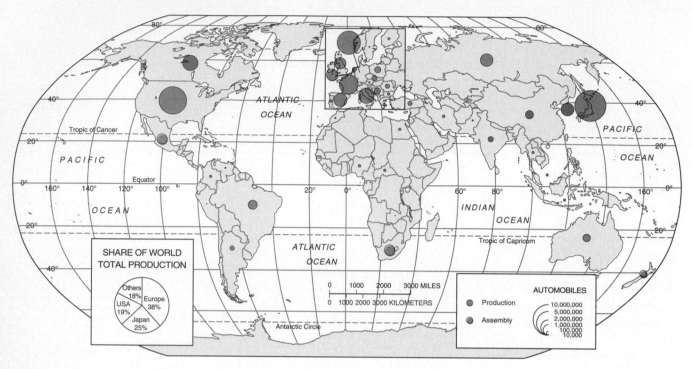

FIGURE 11.8

World distribution of automobile production and assembly. In 1991, Japan produced 13 million automobiles, which was 28% of the world's total output. In 1960, the United States produced half of the world's total automobiles, but by 1991, that proportion had dropped to 19%. The United Kingdom fell in production of automobiles during the same period, from 10.5% to 3.3% of the world total. In Europe, Germany and France comprise the two largest producers, followed by Italy.

(*Source: World Motor Vehicle Data, American Automobile Manufacturing Association, Detroit, Michigan, 1993.*)

supplanted the vacuum tube, which was used in most radios, televisions, and other electronic instruments. The microelectronic transistor was a solid-state device made from silicon and acted as a semiconductor of electric current. By 1960, the *integrated circuit* was produced, which was a quantum improvement because transistors could be connected on a single small silicon chip. By the early 1970s, a computer so tiny that it could fit on a silicon chip the size of a fingernail came into production. Thus, the *microprocessor*, which could do the work of a roomful of vacuum tubes, was born. Increasing power and miniaturization progressed and, at the same time, new applications for the electronics industry were discovered, including calculators, electronic typewriters, computers, industrial robots, aircraft-guidance systems, and combat systems. New discoveries were applied to automobile construction for guidance, safety, speed, and fuel regulation. An entire new range of consumer electronics also became available for home and business use.

Dicken (1992, p. 310) states, "The electronics industry, like textiles, steel and automobiles before it, has come to be regarded as the touchstone of industrial success. Hence all governments in the developed market economies, as well as those in the more industrialized developing countries operate substantial support programs for the electronics industry, particularly microprocessors and computers."

SEMI-CONDUCTOR MANUFACTURE

For nearly two decades, from the 1960s through the 1970s, the United States dominated the field of semiconductor manufacture. However, by 1990, Japan had taken over this role. World production of active electronic components, which includes semiconductors, integrated circuits, and microprocessors, is shown in Figure 11.9. The field is dominated by Japan and the United States, with other significant production in Western Europe and Southeast Asia. In 1992, Japan accounted for 42% of the world production of semiconductors; the United States, 25%; and Europe, 13%. Of the European

Table 11.5

Growth of Automobile Output by Major Producing Countries, 1960–1991

Country	1960 Production (000 Units)	1960 World Share (%)	1991 Production (000 Units)	1991 World Share (%)	Average Annual % Change 1960–1991
Europe					
Belgium	194	1.5	337	0.7	+2.5
France	1175	9.0	3610	7.8	+7.2
West Germany	1817	14.0	5015	10.9	+6.1
Italy	596	4.6	1878	4.1	+7.5
United Kingdom	1353	10.4	1454	3.3	−0.3
Spain	43	0.3	2081	4.3	+160
Sweden	108	0.8	345	0.9	+8.4
North America					
United States	6675	51.4	8810	19.0	+1.1
Canada	323	2.5	1873	3.9	+16.5
Asia					
Japan	165	1.3	13,245	28	+273
South Korea	—	—	1497	3.2	—
Latin America					
Argentina	30	1.0	138	0.4	+12.6
Brazil	38	0.3	960	2.2	+83
Mexico	28	0.2	989	2.3	+118
Australia	—		293	1.0	—
USSR/CIS	139	1.1	2012	4.3	+46
Czechoslovakia	—		206	0.5	—
Poland	—		193	0.7	—
World	12,999	100.0	46,496	100.0	+8.9

— Data unavailable.

Source: World Motor Vehicle Data, American Automobile Manufacturing Association, Detroit, 1993.

share, Germany produced 31%; France, 19%; and the United Kingdom, 16%. In Southeast Asia, South Korea, the Philippines, Malaysia, Taiwan, Thailand, and Hong Kong were significant manufacturers.

The most important component of the semiconductor industry is computer memory, *RAM* (random access memory), production. Although the United States produced 100% of the world's total output in 1974, by 1988 it produced only approximately 20%, and Japan had claimed 75%. Similar to the shift in the automobile industry, there has been a tremendous global shift in the direction of East Asia, primarily to Japan, in RAM production.

CONSUMER ELECTRONICS MANUFACTURE

The world manufacture of consumer electronics is much more widely spread than that of the semiconductor industry. Although in the semiconductor industry, the United States, Japan, and Western Europe account for 80% of the total world production, in the consumer electronics industry, these three regions account for only 44% of television manufacture, for example. Third World countries, especially East Asian and Southeast Asian countries, are more involved in the consumer electronics industries. China emerges as the largest sin-

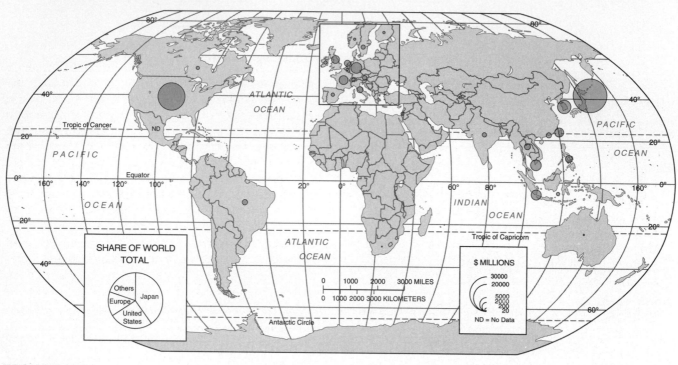

FIGURE 11.9

World production of electronic components; including semiconductors, integrated circuits, and microprocessors. In 1992, Japan produced 42% of the world's total electronic components, followed by the United States with 25%. Europe produced 13% of the world's total; other leading producers included West Germany, France, and the United Kingdom, with 31%, 19%, and 16% of the European total, respectively. Global shifts in the electronics industry have been to the Pacific Rim with recent major centers of production developing in South Korea, Malaysia, Taiwan, Philippines, Thailand, and Hong Kong. *(Source: Yearbook of World Electronics Data, 1994.)*

gle television receiver manufacturer and produces 24% of the world's total output. In addition, South Korea and Japan each produce 14% of the world's televisions. Singapore and Malaysia are also significant producers. The United States' share of the world total was 11% in 1990, having fallen from 15% just 9 years earlier. As in the case of automobile and semiconductor manufacture, there has been a global shift from the developed nations to the Far East. Much of the television production that formerly occurred in the United States, Germany, and the United Kingdom now takes place in Japan. Outside Asia and North America, Brazil produces the most television receivers and manufactures 75% of the units used in Latin America.

This global shift is shown in Table 11.6. Between 1978 and 1990, world production increased by 108%, with a U.S increase of 40.0%, a European increase of 8.8%, and an Asian increase of 253%. Although Japan increased production only 12.6%, China, between 1978 and 1990, increased production a whopping 5900%. Malaysia's output increased 833%, South Korea's, 263%, and Singapore's, 313%.

THE DEINDUSTRIALIZATION OF GREAT BRITAIN

◙

Deindustrialization, an expression of the growing integration of national economies, hit Great Britain earlier and harder than elsewhere. It began with a decline of a range of male-employing basic industries and continued with a loss of employment in virtually all industries. In the 1960s, manufacturing employment began to decline in terms of the total number of jobs it provided. It has since continued to decline, with only occasional stirrings of growth. Moreover, the distribution of job losses has not been even throughout the country. Between 1981 and 1987, northern areas lost 20% of their manufacturing employment, whereas the south lost only 10% (Watts, 1988).

These numbers illustrate the existence of a north-south divide. It separates the prosperous south, especially the Home Counties around London, from the rest of the country. The south—Britain's Sunbelt—is part

The city-state of Singapore, which lacks space, minerals, materials, food, and energy, depends on global demand conditions and trade for its economic growth. Its major trading partners are Japan, the United States, and the European Economic Community. Since the mid-1980s, the dampened international economic environment adversely affected Singapore's manufacturing sector and trade. For the 1990s and beyond, the Singaporean government is depending on the growth of "brain industries"—on the ability of its 2.7 million people to sell their skills and services to the rest of their region and the world.
(Source: Singapore Tourist Promotion Board.)

of Europe's *Golden Triangle*, the corners of which are Birmingham (England), Dortmund (Germany), and Milan (Italy). The *Rest*—much of northern England, most of Wales, and all of Scotland and Northern Ireland—is a major problem area on Western Europe's periphery. This economic border, despite a boom rippling north in the late 1980s, is expected to persist into the twenty-first century (Gribben, 1989).

The International Orientation of British Capital

Great Britain's deindustrialization problem owes much to the international posture of its banking and industrial capital. To a particularly large extent, British capital was shaped by the growth of the empire and of a wider world role. These historical opportunities encouraged the British to invest capital overseas rather than at home, which slowed the development of a strong domestic industrial base. The effect of relatively low levels of domestic investment was a decrease in domestic productivity relative to domestic productivity in other advanced economies without such strong international connections. The result was lower levels of investment in new technologies and products and therefore a relative decline in internal and external demand for British goods. From the late nineteenth century onward, a process of downward cumulative causation has occurred.

After the mid-1960s, the long-term weakness of the British economy became clear. A telling legacy of the high degree of internationalization of British capital was the collapse of the weak, small-firm sector. Many small firms, with their outdated technologies and old physical plants, were unable to compete against the multinationals that dominated their product markets.

Meanwhile, Great Britain experienced a net manufacturing foreign direct investment deficit. From 1965 to 1981, the gap between outward and inward manufacturing investment increased. According to Ash Amin and Ian Smith (1986), the gap is a result of the high level of industrial concentration in the economy, which is a disincentive for inward investment and an incentive for outward investment. The gap also occurred because Great Britain is increasingly a low-buying-power market, which discourages market-oriented inward investment and fosters the need for British-based multinationals to reorganize their capacity internationally in search of new economies. This has been reflected in the rationalization of capacity by the largest British-based multinationals (Gaffikin and Nickson, 1984; Stopford and Dunning, 1983). The growing gap between outward and inward manufacturing investment has contributed to Great Britain's deindustrialization problem.

The deindustrialization problem has also been aggravated by the unwillingness of the state to deal with Great Britain's weak domestic industrial base. For much of this century, the state was more interested in preserving empire and class rule than in intervening directly to modernize British industry. Even if the state had intervened to secure a breakout from the vicious circle

◉

T a b l e   11.6
Global Shift in Television Receiver Production by World Region, 1978–1990

Country/Region	Production (000 Units)		% Change 1978–1990	Share of World Production (%)	
	1978	1990		1978	1990
Asia (excluding former USSR)	21,175	74,802	+253	35.0	60
Japan	13,116	14,730	+12.6	21.7	11.7
South Korea	4826	17,503	+263	8.0	14
China	517	30,123	+5900	0.9	24
Malaysia	150	1421	+833	0.3	1.1
Singapore	725	3001	+313	1.2	2.4
Europe (excluding former USSR)	17,656	19,550	+8.8	29.1	18.9
West Germany	4391	3220	−22.5	7.3	3.3
United Kingdom	2417	2824	+21.0	4.0	2.8
Italy	2172	2321	+2.8	3.6	2.3
France	2101	2011	+3.9	3.5	2.0
United States	9309	13,203	+40	15.4	10.6
World total	60,592	125,161	+108	100.0	100.0

Source: United Nations, 1993, *Industrial Statistics Yearbook, 1990,* New York: United Nations.

of relative decline, success would have been difficult to achieve given the resistance of the well-organized working class to change.

The Geography of Decline

The failure to put the economy on a sound footing during the postwar boom became apparent in the mid-1960s. National employment in manufacturing declined in 1966. Great Britain was the first country to industrialize and the first to deindustrialize. Large cities and inner cities, with their preponderance of old and small plants, suffered the most from the decline in manufacturing employment. London lost 51% of its manufacturing employment between 1960 and 1981. Inner cities lost manufacturing jobs faster than outer cities did in the 1960s, but the rate of job loss became more even in the 1970s because fewer and fewer inner-city firms remained. Like the collapse of traditional industries in the 1930s, this newer loss of employment in manufacturing was widely dispersed throughout the country. Even the southeast could not withstand the onslaught; there,

manufacturing employment increased by 16.6% between 1952 and 1966 but decreased by almost 20% between 1966 and 1975. The decline in manufacturing employment continued in the late 1970s and 1980s. Thus, after 1966, many of the industries associated with the postwar boom—food, drink, and tobacco; mechanical engineering and construction; gas, electricity, and water; and the distributive trades—also began to employ fewer people. By the end of the 1970s, only tertiary activities registered a net increase in employment. Unemployment soared with the reduced capacity of the economy to provide jobs. It rose from 1.5% in 1965 to 10.4% in 1980, and to 13.5% in 1985, a year that saw three million people out of work (U.K. Department of Employment, 1985). Reminiscent of the 1930s, the north suffered higher unemployment rates than the south did.

Although much less smoky, the north of today looks much the same as it did during the Great Depression. True, there are new shopping centers, high-rise office and apartment buildings, greenfield industrial estates, and large tracts of inner-city derelict land awaiting redevelopment. But many of the grimy old factories, warehouses, and row houses remain. In the heart of working-class Britain, factories stand idle, high cranes hang useless over closed shipyards,and people are on welfare, losing their self-respect. For too many people, life has become too hard. Since 1979, their hardship has been exacerbated by cuts in social services, health care, and housing, which have lowered living standards, especially for low-paid workers, single parents, the elderly, and the infirm. These cuts reflect the policies of a ruling Conservative party that believes in the free-enterprise capitalism and self-reliance popular with Great Britain's new, rising, hard-working, low-middle-class majority. With this rising lower middle class in mind, the government has accepted high unemployment and the transfer of capital abroad to allow real wages to continue to increase and to enable Great Britain to play a major role in international oil, business, and finance. Unlike the United States, real wages in Great Britain are increasing, by 3.4% in 1986; as a result, domestic industries are finding that they can no longer compete, and they are closing. The burden of this policy has been borne by the unemployed, concentrated in the north and its cities.

The Shape of the New Great Britain

For some of the people who live there, modern Great Britain seems like a rich and booming society. But in this Great Britain, it is better to be highly trained than untrained, white than black, male than female, and young than old. It is also better to live in the south than in the north.

THE SOUTH

Southern England is booming, with few of the benefits spreading into the north. Its rapid economic growth in recent years has been built around control and conception functions. The City of London has a thriving banking and business sector, which is absorbing many of Great Britain's most able people. After the oil-price rise in the 1970s, the famous Square Mile—Great Britain's Wall Street—became the center of the Eurodollar market and the world headquarters for the oil companies. Spreading out over the poor lands of the East End and onto the old dock lands, once the heart of British imperial sea trade, it is the core of a new empire, now based on invisible transactions, electronic impulses, video display terminals, and facsimile machines. The city is now the world capital of foreign investment, with the most foreign banks, a tradition of free entry, plus markets in shipping, insurance, commodities, and banking all closely located.

The south is the location of choice for multinational corporations and company head offices. More than 75% of the head offices of the largest manufacturing companies are in the south (Watts, 1988). This statistic is even more revealing in light of the fact that Great Britain is also home to most of Europe's giant firms. No fewer than 25 of the top 60 corporations in Europe are based in Great Britain.

The concentration of head offices in the south attracts research and business services. In fact, 80% of the entire British employment in business services is in the south, rendering it fertile ground for the formation of new companies specializing in such activities as electronics and biotechnology. Outside London, the largest concentration of microelectronics industries in England is along the M4 motorway (freeway) from Slough to Swindon and the M11 to Cambridge. Small, high-tech companies are scattered throughout the region, however, especially in such areas of considerable environmental advantage as Plymouth and Bournemouth.

The south also benefits from its location close to the international core of Europe. Since joining the European Economic Community (EEC) in 1973, trade with its new partners has increased. The EEC now accounts for nearly one-half the country's exports and imports. Great Britain's largest container port, Felixstowe, and its two largest airports, London Heathrow and Gatwick, are in this region. Investment in a third London airport at Stansted to the north of London and the Channel Tunnel further strengthens the European and international accessibility to this region.

The booming south, however, is a weight on the rest of the country. Imports are escalating at an enormous rate to satisfy middle-class consumer demand. Increasing subsidies are pouring into the region to finance a new infrastructure to cope with transportation congestion and mounting mortgage tax relief as housing prices soar. Housing prices are more than twice as high in the south as they are in the north (Table 11.7). The high cost of houses in the south is a major obstacle to job recruitment.

THE NORTH

The area north of the Trent River and west of the Bristol Avon River is not all in decline. Great Britain's Rust Belt is being restructured. In contrast to the south's

◍

Table 11.7
The House Price Divide

Region	Average Price (U.S. $)
Greater London	175,328
Southeast	159,240
East Anglia	146,190
Southwest	129,738
East Midlands	97,462
West Midlands	105,607
Yorkshire and Humberside	73,082
Northwest	74,832
Northern	63,541
Scotland	77,012
Wales	77,884
Northern Ireland	60,518

Source: Financial Times, 1989, p. 35.

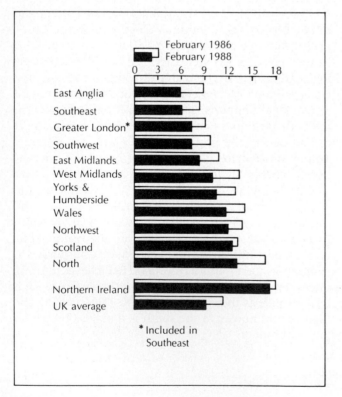

FIGURE 11.10
Regional unemployment as a percentage of working population in February 1986 and February 1988.
(Source: The Economist, 1988b, p. 45.)

control and conception functions, the north is increasingly home to new production functions. It is becoming a branch-plant economy.

The Shape of Things to Come

Although the gulf between the north and the south is wide and may become wider, an economic recovery in the late 1980s slowed the deepening of Great Britain's center-periphery structure. Unemployment, which in 1988 was 8.8%, had declined in all regions (Figure 11.10). Regions adjacent to the southeast did particularly well.

The 1990s may also be the decade that reveals whether Great Britain is on its way to becoming a semiperipheral economy within the international capitalist hierarchy. Already, Great Britain is dependent on imported technology and on imported manufactured goods. Whereas in 1979, Great Britain was a net exporter of manufactured goods, by 1988 it was a net importer of manufactured goods.

THE RELOCATION OF THE AMERICAN MANUFACTURING INDUSTRY

◈

The United States also experienced industrial devolution in the 1970s and 1980s, a period during which its share of world manufacturing output decreased. This points to a more rapid growth of manufacturing output in other countries, especially Japan. Can the relative decline of the American manufacturing economy be attributed to Japanese expansionism? Certainly, Japan has increased its share of world industrial production and exports, but a different picture emerges if changes in world sales are classified by the nationality of the parent company. Although Japanese industrial capital made gains at the expense of U.S. capital in the 1960s, almost no further advances were achieved in the 1970s and 1980s. Thus, deindustrialization within the United States was occurring at a time when American capital was either increasing or maintaining its share of the world economy—at a time when American corporations were reacting to the prolonged economic crisis. Inside the United States, corporate profit rates were declining. The advantages that promoted rapid capital accumulation in the old manufacturing areas were giving way to contradictions to high profits—rising real wages and obsolete infrastructure. As profit rates declined, corporations switched capital in space. The effect of locational change has been most severe in the American Manufacturing Belt.

The American Manufacturing Belt

North America has numerous manufacturing regions (Figure 11.2). By far the largest is the North American Manufacturing Belt, which accounts for about 53% of the manufacturing capacity of the United States and Canada. The U.S. portion of this region is called the *American Manufacturing Belt*, the historic heartland of the nation. The belt extends from Boston westward through upstate New York, southern Michigan, and southeastern Wisconsin. At Milwaukee it turns south

to St. Louis, then extends eastward along the Ohio River valley to Washington, DC. This great rectangle encompasses more than 10 districts, each with its own specialties that reflect the influences of markets, materials, labor, power, and historical forces.

The first major factories in the belt—the textile mills of the 1830s and 1840s—clustered along the rivers of southern New England. When coal replaced water as a power source between 1850 and 1870, and when railroads integrated the belt, factories were freed from the riverbanks. Industrialists began to pursue their profits in towns and cities.

Between 1850 and 1870, many urban areas of all sizes enjoyed rapidly expanding industrial production. But after 1870, manufacturing concentrated in a few large cities. Manufacturing employment in New York City, Philadelphia, and Chicago soared more than 200% between 1870 and 1900. The 10 largest industrial cities increased their share of national value added in manufacturing from less than 25% to almost 40% between

Unloading automobile seats. Chrysler's just-in-time system supplies procurement in Detroit, Michigan. Just-in-time systems are more than simply a quick, efficient delivery of needed parts and supplies. They are part of a broader system of organization and production adopted by firms. Work is done only when needed and in the necessary quantity at a given time. Little waste occurs and little stock is kept on hand, which keeps prices low. Proximity among suppliers and manufacturers is essential since orders and deliveries may be made several times a day. Just-in-time operation systems tend toward localized agglomeration economies. A manufacturer can choose a single sourcing agent and, thus, buy supplies and products in large quantity, achieving scale economies. Other plants might chose multiple sourcing and spread the subcontracting network more widely, reducing the risk of procurement interruptions. *(Source: Michael L. Abramson, Woodfin Camp & Associates.)*

1860 and 1900 (Pred, 1966). Why did metropolitan complexes draw such a great proportion of manufacturing activity?

The orthodox view is that factories concentrated in cities such as Baltimore, Chicago, Cleveland, Cincinnati, Philadelphia, and Pittsburgh for a combination of the following reasons: (1) They could be near large labor pools; (2) they could secure easy railroad and waterway access to major resource deposits, such as the Appalachian coalfields and the Lake Superior-area iron mines; (3) they could be near industrial suppliers of machines and other intermediate products; and (4) they could be near major markets for finished goods. In other words, *agglomeration economies* accounted for the concentration of industrial activity in the belt.

The highly concentrated pattern of industrial production in the belt served the nation well for almost 100 years—roughly the century between 1870 and 1970. *Inertia*, the immobility of the investment forces and social relations, ensured considerable locational stability. Inertia was particularly pronounced in the capital-intensive steel industry.

However, cracks in the accumulation regime appeared as early as the late nineteenth century. Contradictions erupted. Labor unrest intensified. After 1885, the number of workers involved in strikes increased rapidly, with many of the most bitter strikes occurring in the largest manufacturing complexes. Gradually, owners lost power to labor—a power that enabled labor to negotiate higher wages than were paid previously or elsewhere, to organize high levels of unionization and extract good working conditions, and to command progressive welfare policies. By the early twentieth century, the dense centralization of industrial workers in inner-city areas backfired on factory owners.

As labor control subsided, manufacturing started to move out of central cities to the suburbs. Between 1899 and 1909, central-city manufacturing employment increased by 40%, whereas outer-city manufacturing employment increased by nearly 100%. After the late 1920s, the use of the truck for freight transportation accelerated the movement of manufacturing to the suburbs. But as transportation costs equalized across the nation, even the suburbs of the older manufacturing belt cities were unable to compete with more agreeable labor environments in the South and the West. The 1960s marked the start of the steady gain of manufacturing employment in the South, parts of the Southwest, the Mountain states, and the Dakotas. Since the recession of the early 1980s, however, there has been evidence that these areas where class conflict is low are being bypassed in favor of even cheaper labor regions in Mexico and East Asia.

U.S Domestic Movement of Manufacturing

The locational change of manufacturing in the United States was particularly strong in the 1970s and 1980s. Virtually all states in the American Manufacturing Belt experienced manufacturing job loss, and virtually all states in the South and the West registered manufacturing job gains (Figure 11.11). The migration of employment from areas of high labor costs to areas where the labor costs were less saved U.S.-controlled companies billions of dollars. From 1960 to 1980, roughly 1.7 million jobs shifted from states with high labor costs to states with low labor costs.

The expansion of manufacturing in the West is not immediately explained by labor costs. California is characterized as a state of high labor costs, yet it has registered substantial increases in manufacturing employment. In California, class struggle loses its primary determining effect to physical and environmental factors, the role of the state (defense spending), and the dimension of consciousness (the "California image").

FIGURE 11.11

Employment shifts in manufacturing in the United States between 1967 and 1987. The top map shows employment change in thousands for the 20-year period, while the bottom map shows employment change as a percent for the 20-year period. The American manufacturing belt uniformly had received substantial declines in employment, while the South and the West have increased substantially. The recent increase in employment in these regions is a continuation of the process of population disbursal, followed by industrial disbursal, from the Northeast to the rest of the nation. The process continues today. The largest losses occurred in New York and Pennsylvania, followed by Illinois and Ohio. The largest gaining state was California, followed by Texas and Florida. The first major manufacturing activity to move south from the Northeast was the textile industry. World War II created a defense industry on the West Coast with aircraft manufacture and shipbuilding. This early boom has been followed by electronics industries, petrol chemical industries, and apparel manufacture.
(Source: Fisher, 1992, p. 156.)

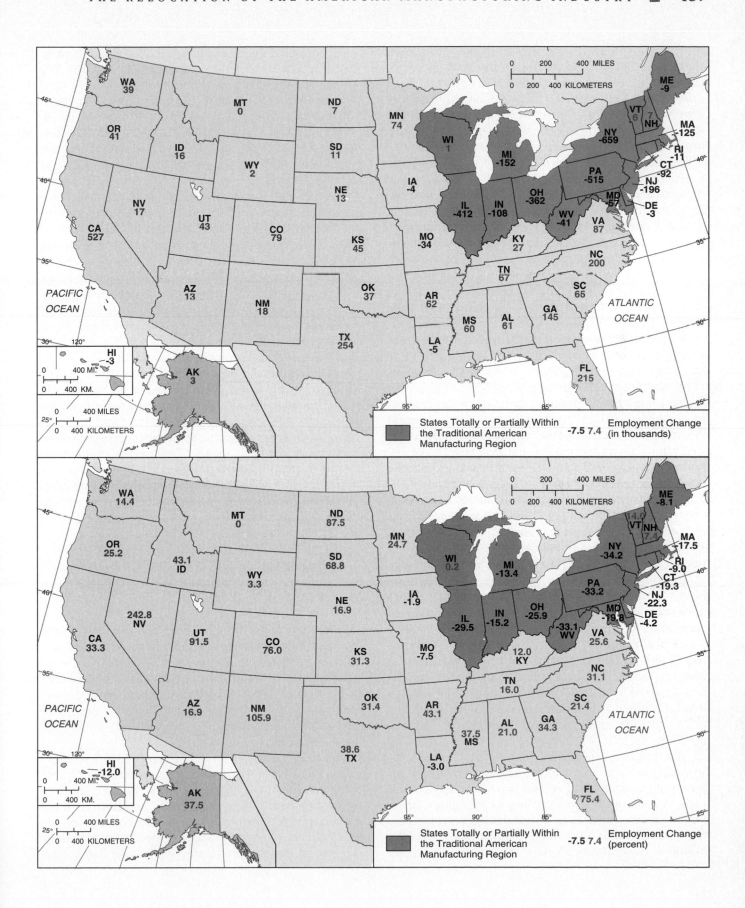

The West Coast manufacturing district does, however, represent an outstanding example of industrial restructuring in response to economic crisis and labor unrest. The Los Angeles-San Diego district has been extremely successful. Since the 1960s, the district has shed much of its traditional, highly unionized heavy industry, such as steel and rubber. At the same time, it has attracted a cluster of high-tech industries and associated services, centered around electronics and aerospace and tied strongly to the now depressed defense and military contracts from the U.S. government. Added to the combination of Frostbelt-like deindustrialization and Sunbelt industrialization has been the vigorous growth of "peripheralized" manufacturing, which resembles the industrialization of Hong Kong and Singapore and depends on a highly controllable supply of cheap, typically immigrant, and/or female labor from Mexico and the Far East.

Meanwhile, industrial restructuring continues to be a painful process throughout much of the American Manufacturing Belt. The region contends with problems of obsolescence and reduced productivity, especially in such leading industries as steel, automobile manufacturing, and shipbuilding. It contends with inner-city areas littered with closed factories, bankrupt businesses, and struggling blue-collar neighborhoods. The effect of disinvestment on workers and their communities has been devastating.

Victims of plant closings sometimes lose not only their current incomes, but their total accumulated assets as well. And when savings run out, people lose their ability to respond to life crises. Although job loss respects neither educational attainment nor occupational status, some groups are more vulnerable than others. Because blacks are concentrated in areas where plant closings have been most pronounced, this group has been especially hard hit.

Plant closings can be extremely costly to a community. J. Wiss & Son was a large cutlery manufacturer in Newark, New Jersey, for 75 years. In 1978, the company was acquired by a Texas conglomerate and relocated to North Carolina. This shutdown resulted in a direct loss of 760 manufacturing jobs and an additional 468 jobs in stores, banks, and other local businesses. According to Bluestone and Harrison (1987, p. 88), "more than $14 million in purchasing power was removed from the local economy, half of which had resided in local bank deposits used for loans to finance mortgages, home improvements, purchases of automobiles, televisions, refrigerators, and other major appliances." Literally hundreds of communities have experienced the agony of unregulated deindustrialization. And these communities are not restricted to the manufacturing belt. Perhaps the most dramatic example is the case of Anaconda, Montana, a classic "company town." In 1978, Anaconda Copper & Mining Co. was acquired by the Los Angles-based Atlantic Richfield Co. (ARCO). Two years later, ARCO closed the town's copper smelter and eliminated 80% of the payroll in the community of 12,000 people.

Although the widespread manufacturing decline has produced a lasting effect on people and communities in the manufacturing belt, all is not lost in the region. Already there are attempts to respond to the economic crisis. Old industrial cities such as Pittsburgh are building new bases for employment, and so too are the major urban complexes of Megalopolis. Southern New England stands out as a good example. This region, which suffered higher-than-average unemployment rates throughout much of the post-World War II period, now has the lowest unemployment rate in the belt. A new round of industrial expansion is taking place with a disciplined pool of highly skilled and unskilled workers. The industrial revival of southern New England emphasizes high-value products—electronic equipment, electrical machinery, firearms, and tools. A current worry, however, is the permanence of the revival. In the early 1990s, high-tech firms in Silicon Valley East were affected by the sluggish national economy and were forced to lay off workers, so doubt was cast on the "Massachusetts miracle."

Movement of the North American Automobile-Manufacturing Industry

In recent years, there has been a marked shift in the locations of automobile assembly in the United States. The most important reason for this shift has been to minimize the transportation cost of the finished product to the market. Another reason is the change in consumer preference, in that more models of each car type, such as Ford, are in demand, thus fewer plants are needed for each model.

In 1955, General Motors assembled identical Chevrolets at 10 cities to supply local consumers with cars (Rubenstein, 1994) (Figure 11.12). Because the cars were fairly perishable and expensive to transport, distribution cities were located across the country, evenly proportional to the population. Ford had a similar arrangement for its production of standardized, low-

An emerging

postindustrial economy

The economic restructuring of the United States since 1970 is regarded by sociologist Daniel Bell (1973) as evidence of the emergence of a *postindustrial society*. The term postindustrial refers to a fundamental change in the character of technology use—from fabricating to processing—in which telecommunications and computers are vital for the exchange of knowledge. Information becomes the basic product, the key to wealth and power, and is generated and manipulated by an intellectual rather than a machine technology. Yet, postindustrial society does not displace industrial society, just as manufacturing did not cast aside agriculture. Instead, the new developments simply overlie the previous layers.

Economic activities involving the collection, processing, and manipulation of information are called *quaternary economic activities*. These activities are increasingly dominating the work force: They employed 30% of U.S. workers in 1950, 46% by 1980, 60% in the late 1980s, and employ more than 70% by the mid-1990s. There is a fear that the new service economy will eliminate more jobs than it creates. With growing automation, high-tech companies will increasingly employ more highly trained scientists and fewer less-skilled workers. As a result, thousands of production and clerical workers may soon lose their jobs. Is education the key to solving this problem? Will the U.S. educational system create a broad, educated work force with flexible, high-tech skills in order to better match people with jobs? Or will postindustrial society remain a long way off for millions of Americans? How will NAFTA affect America's postindustrial society?

Source: Based on de Blij and Muller, 1992, p. 217.

---

priced models. Top-of-the-line luxury cars, such as Lincoln and Cadillac, were still assembled in Detroit.

Beginning, however, in the 1960s, a variety of models of each particular automobile began to appear, ranging from subcompacts of 150 inches long to full-size vehicles of more than 220 inches long. Part of this diversity offered by U.S. manufacturers was a result of Japanese and European imports. Each time a successful import penetrated the market, the Detroit automobile manufacturers attempted to challenge the competition with another model in the same product line.

Soon consumers expected a wide choice in automobiles. With this increased demand for more models, major automobile producers began to build only one or two plants for each model, and to distribute the vehicles from these points to the rest of the country and Canada. Because fewer assembly plants were needed for each model, new assembly plants were located near the center of the country, again to minimize the distribution costs (Figure 11.13). Consequently, from 1970 to 1990, many coastal automobile-assembly plants were closed.

James Rubenstein (1994) identifies two types of automobile plants in existence today. Approximately 70 *automobile- and truck-assembly plants* exist in North America, as well as several thousand *component plants*. The component plants manufacture parts required in the assembly of the vehicle. Because of the increasing importance of *just-in-time inventory* and delivery, component plants locate close to assembly operations.

Just-in-time systems reduce not only labor and machine inefficiency, but also the amount of capital tied up in large inventories. Just-in-time systems deliver parts to the manufacturing plant only hours or days before they are used in the manufacturing process. Computerized automatic order and billing operate in real time and on line between suppliers and final assembly plants so that parts needs can be filled immediately. Clustering of parts suppliers around automobile- and truck-assembly plants suggests a strong move to just-in-time delivery

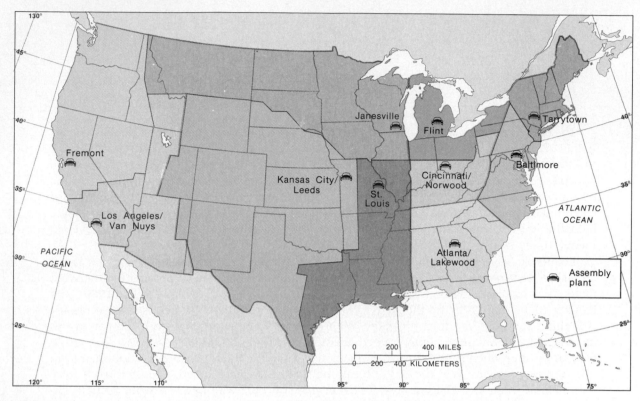

FIGURE 11.12
General Motors, Chevrolet assembly plants in 1955. The distribution of 10 assembly plants across the United States helped Chevrolet minimize the cost of distributing the bulky products to consumers in each region. (See Color Insert 2 page 2.8, top, for more illustrative map.)

systems. In contrast, Japanese companies have located along interstates 65 and 75 from Tennessee, Kentucky, Indiana, and Ohio, to Michigan (Figure 11.14). Rubenstein (1994) determined that Japanese companies avoid large cities and those traditionally associated with automobile assembly because of the strong unions and high fixed operation costs in these areas.

JUST-IN-TIME MANUFACTURING

The Japanese developed *just-in-time manufacturing* systems shortly after World War II to adapt U.S. practices to car manufacturing. Just-in-time refers to a method of organizing immediate manufacturing and supply relationships among companies to reduce inefficiency and increase time economy. Stages of the manufacturing process are completed exactly when needed, according to the market, not before and not later, and parts required in the manufacturing process are supplied with little storage or warehousing time. This system

reduces idle capital and allows minimal investment so that capital can be used elsewhere.

Occasionally machines are idle because they run only fast enough to meet output. If machines run more quickly than the market requires, they must be shut off and manufactured items warehoused. The manufacturing run proceeds only as far as the market demands and no faster, thus suppliers and producers of raw materials must warehouse their inventories. As Andrew Sayer and Richard Walker (1993) describe

Buffer stocks are very small and are only replenished to replace parts removed downstream. Workers at the end of the line are given output instructions on the basis of short term order forecasts, and they instruct the workers immediately upstream to produce the part they will need just-in-time, and those workers in turn instruct workers upstream to produce just-in-time, and so on. . . . In practice this means that buffers between workers are extremely small. In short, it is a pull rather than a push system. (p. 171)

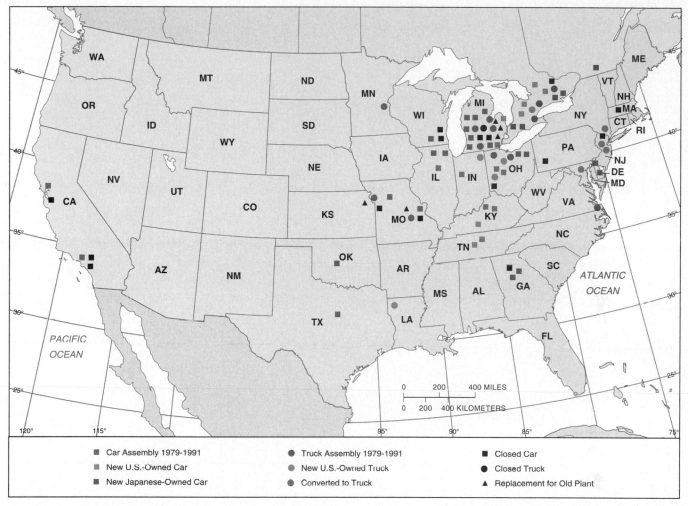

■ Car Assembly 1979-1991	● Truck Assembly 1979-1991	■ Closed Car
■ New U.S.-Owned Car	● New U.S.-Owned Truck	● Closed Truck
■ New Japanese-Owned Car	● Converted to Truck	▲ Replacement for Old Plant

FIGURE 11.13
The distribution of auto and truck assembly plants in the United States, 1991. There has been a marked national shift from a disbursed, coastal pattern during the last 20 years to a concentrated pattern near the original automobile core area in Michigan.

The International Movement of American Manufacturing

The relocation of manufacturing within the United States is only one aspect of a wider dispersal of American manufacturing capital. Foreign direct investment by American enterprises was established as early as the end of the nineteenth century. But only since World War II have American enterprises become major foreign investors. The 1940s saw heavy investment in Canada and Latin America; the 1950s in Western Europe; and the 1960s and 1970s in Western Europe, Japan, the Middle East, and South and East Asia. According to Peet (1987c, p. 59), "[By 1977] some 1,841 United

States manufacturing companies had 15,316 foreign affiliates, the result of an accumulated direct foreign investment of $62,019 million, over $40,000 million of which had been made since 1966." Most of this investment occurred in advanced industrial countries rather than in Third World countries (Figure 11.15).

Between 1945 and 1960, most U.S.-based companies were content to produce in the old industrial districts. But by 1960, the European Common Market and Japan had become competitors. Mounting international competition and falling profit rates at home coerced American companies to decentralize not only within the United States, but also abroad. By 1980, the 500 largest U.S.-based corporations employed an international labor force almost equivalent to the size of its

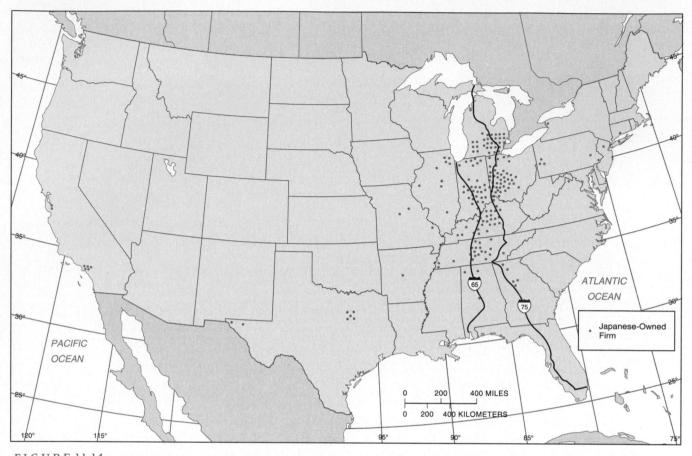

FIGURE 11.14
The distribution of Japanese-owned automobile parts manufacturing plants, 1991. This Midwestern concentration of parts plants facilitates rapid delivery to closeby automobile assembly plants. (See color insert page 2.8.)

national labor force. From 1960 to 1980, manufacturing employment outside the United States directly controlled by U.S. corporations increased from 8.7% to 17.5% of the total, a 169% increase compared with a 20% increase within the United States.

The dispersal of manufacturing investment to foreign lands resulted in a more competitive base and in enormous savings in wages for American firms. In 1980, the annual wage savings from 1.6 million jobs opened by U.S.-based corporations in developed countries between 1960 and 1980 was $8.4 billion, and the annual savings from 1.1 million jobs opened in underdeveloped countries between 1960 and 1980 was $14.5 billion (Peet, 1987c). Even more savings were achieved in the 1980s as U.S.-based companies increasingly established manufacturing operations in low-wage regions of the Third World.

THE INDUSTRIALIZATION OF JAPAN

◈

Japan's record of economic achievement, now tarnished by recession at home in Japan and worldwide, has no equal among advanced industrial countries in the post-World War II period. Between 1970 and 1984, when industrial production declined by 4% in Great Britain and increased by 48% in the United States, Japan's industrial output soared by 162% (World Bank, 1987). Unemployment in 1992, which registered 13.5% in Great Britain and 7.7% in the United States, was a modest 3.5% in Japan. And when, in the 1980s, the U.S. trade deficit mushroomed, Japan's trade surplus mounted. In that decade, Japan took America's place as chief creditor, buying stocks, bonds, and real estate

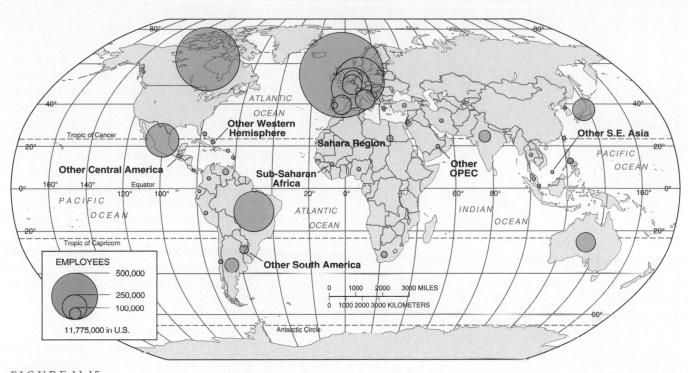

FIGURE 11.15
World employment in manufacturing of U.S.-based multinational corporations in 1992. *(Source: U.S. Department of COMMERCE, Survey of Current Business, 1983.)*

around the world. Although the U.S. economy is still clearly the world's largest—producing 25% of total global output in 1990 compared with Japan's 10%—the economic pendulum is swinging slowly toward Japan. Given Japan's increasingly powerful economy, which seems certain to become more dominant toward the twenty-first century, regardless of the fact that Japan is in its worst depression in 40 years, it is timely to answer the following questions: What is the basis for Japan's astonishing industrial record? What price is Japan paying in its bid to become the world's foremost industrial nation? Is Japan the working model for industrial success?

Physical Resources

What gave Japan, an island nation that is slightly smaller than California, the opportunity to become an industrial juggernaut? What part of the answer lies in its raw-material base? Compared with the United States and Great Britain—countries with the physical resources to sustain an industrial revolution—Japan is much less well off. Except for coal deposits in Kyushu and Hokkaido, which provided a stimulus for nineteenth-century industrial development, Japan is practically devoid of significant raw materials for major industry. It has depended in large measure on imported raw materials for its recent industrial growth.

Human Resources and Culture

Japan may lack physical resources, but human resources for industrial development are not scarce. There are more than 120 million Japanese, mostly crammed into an urban-industrial core that extends from Tokyo on the east to Shimonoseki at the western end of Honshu (Figure 11.16). The Japanese regard the homogeneity that characterizes their population as a major contributor to their nation's industrial success. Within this homogeneity, Confucianism and Buddhism, acquired from China and in place for more than a thousand years, have instilled such traits as self-denial, devotion to one's superiors, and the prevalence of group interests over individual interests. These social attributes lend Japan a high degree of *national consensus*. And when a strong work ethic combines with a high level of collective commitment and incredible government support, it produces a work culture in which everyone, from the top

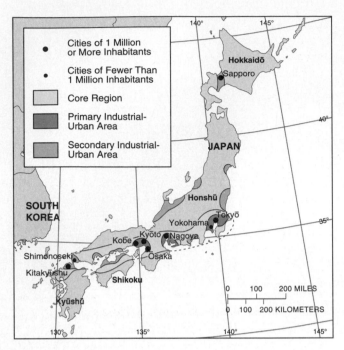

FIGURE 11.16
Japan's core region and selected cities.
(Source: Williams, 1989a, p. 331.)

to the bottom, knows his or her place and can pull in the same direction. A chilling degree of national consensus was apparent after World War II, when the Japanese set about the task of rebuilding their shattered economy.

A high degree of national consensus, however, in no way implies a passive society. The Japanese undoubtedly prefer to conform, but they are also fiercely competitive and assertive. After World War II, this assertiveness was channeled not only into trade and industry, but also into capital-labor conflict. Labor unrest certainly unmasks the image of the docile Japanese worker, unwilling to oppose his or her boss. In concert with workers in Western Europe and North America, the Japanese worker greeted the postwar period with an outburst of dissatisfaction. In 1946, General MacArthur, supreme commander of the Allied powers, warned that mass violence would severely damage Japan's development prospects. Widespread demonstrations and strikes were not contained until the mid-1950s, however, when enterprise unions, lifetime employment, and other measures were introduced to integrate workers into the fabric of Japanese industry. These measures have effectively reduced industrial strikes in Japan to a rare occurrence. In 1987, Japan lost only 256,000 worker-days to disputes compared with the U.S. total of 4,481,000.

Although permanent workers in large firms are well paid, especially when viewed in relation to part-time workers in small and medium-sized firms, the relative share of the product going to labor is lower in Japan than in any other advanced industrial country. Savings and profits are directed by the state toward whatever goals are set forth by a unique collaborative partnership between MITI—Japan's Ministry of International Trade and Industry—and private enterprise. This marriage between government and private enterprise, helping to make Japan the envy of the West, is sometimes called *Japan Incorporated*. The days of the successful relationship between MITI and industry, however, may be numbered. MITI has less controlling power than it once had. Japanese firms no longer need the watchful eye of MITI or much of its money. For example, Hitachi spent about $2.2 billion on R&D in 1988, or about 50% more than MITI's total R&D budget.

Substantial change may also be looming on Japan's labor front. The wealth generated by the Japanese system in the 1960s and 1970s has produced a work force that is gingerly experimenting with traditions and customs. Japan's young people still adhere to the ideal of consensus, but they are unwilling to sacrifice their individuality. They are not satisfied with simply working hard. They prefer to work less and take all the vacations that their bosses offer. In the 1990s, more and more clashes will occur between the young and the old over the commitment of the individual to the ideals that propelled postwar rebuilding.

The Problems of Japan Incorporated

In the postwar period, Japan set about the task of becoming a potent economic force. All other considerations were subordinated to that one overriding good. The drive for economic growth was at the expense of social welfare, the environment, and international relations. Japan is beginning to pay the price for its industrial achievement.

INTERNATIONAL RELATIONS

In the 1980s, the gap between Japan's imports and exports created tensions with its trading partners. As a result, Japan found its markets in key exports restricted. Protectionist tendencies have been sidestepped to some extent by foreign direct investment. Japan has invested heavily in big projects in the advanced industrial countries. It has also established numerous joint ventures that reduce the capital and political risks for Japanese companies. Examples include not only the link between American steel giant USX and Japan's Kobe Steel to manufacture tubular steel for automakers producing vehicles in the United States, but also the link between Boeing and Fuji Heavy Industries, Kawasaki, and Mitsubishi to build commercial aircraft. For critics who espouse the notion of economic nationalism, Japan's foreign investment policies are subject to as much "Japan bashing" as its trading policies.

THE DUAL ECONOMY

The most pressing Japanese problem is its dual economy. At the top are a handful of successful international corporations that thrive and change. Under MITI's guidance, Japan has relocated industries such as steelmaking and shipbuilding "offshore" in the newly industrializing countries (NICs), where labor costs are lower. Now, countries such as South Korea are developing their own higher technologies (e.g., consumer electronics). Meanwhile, Japan is challenging the United States in the newest generation of sophisticated technology. Even if they succeed, the Japanese worry about the transition to postindustrialism with less manufacturing and more stress on services. Manufacturing industry's share of both output and employment is predicted to decline by the turn of the century.

At the low end of the Japanese economy are thousands of tiny workshops. The large corporations job out parts of their production to the small firms with their underpaid and exploited workers. About 70% of Japan's labor force still works in these tiny firms. This mom-and-pop structure prevents Japan from playing its superpower role as the world's buyer of last resort, soaking up foreign goods to maintain international economic order and growth.

ENVIRONMENTAL POLLUTION

The pursuit of economic efficiency was the be-all and end-all of Japanese endeavor until the late 1960s, when the consequences of environmental pollution demanded immediate attention. The most serious aspects were air and water pollution, which killed hundreds of people who lived around the factories (Junkerman, 1987). In the 1970s, the government introduced pollution-control measures and tried to shift polluting industries out of congested areas. Still, Japan remains the most environmentally polluted country in the developed world.

REGIONAL IMBALANCE AND URBAN ILLS

Japan's uncontrolled and rapid industrial development created an unusually sharp economic divide between the core region and the rest of the country. In the late 1970s and 1980s, as efforts to overcome environmental pollution by relocating industry to less developed parts of the country started to take effect, the gap between the rich core region and the poor periphery began to narrow. Yet, the regional contrast will persist throughout the 1990s.

The problems of Japan's large cities are another by-product of rapid economic growth. These problems include traffic congestion, noise, insufficient parking, accidents, air pollution, and, of course, land madness. When the Japanese government put 66 new apartments on the market in Tokyo in 1987, more than 18,000 people rushed to apply for what was considered a bargain: $200,000 for a small two-bedroom apartment. In one of the world's richest countries, most people cannot afford to buy their own homes. Housing is a great social problem, with young couples forced into 2-hour commutes into Tokyo just for the luxury of owning their own "rabbit hutches," as Japan's cramped quarters have come to be known. Although Japan has a higher gross domestic product (GDP) per capita than the United States, Canada, or most Western European countries, because of scarcity and very high costs of living, its standard of living is actually less than the United States, Canada, and some European countries (see Chapter 12).

The Japanese Model

Japan's postwar industrialization, now slowed by world recession and a crashing stock market, has nonetheless been remarkable. It has created a rich country but a poor people. Is Japan really the working model for industrial success? Would Americans embrace a system in which the majority of the work force is controlled in a feudal-like serfdom? Would a job-for-life policy be realistic in contemporary Great Britain? Even if it were

Pusan, South Korea, is a purpose-built city for shipbuilding and the export-import trade. Other towns in South Korea dedicated to specialized industrial functions include Changwan for machine tools and heavy plant, Ulsan for automobiles, and Yosu for petrochemicals.
(Source: World Bank.)

desirable, the Japanese model could not be readily adopted by other countries; it is the product of a unique culture and of a unique regional historical experience.

THIRD WORLD INDUSTRIALIZATION

◈

Deindustrialization in the Western Hemisphere in the 1970s and 1980s did not induce widespread industrialization in the Third World. In 1990, 40 countries accounted for 70% of manufacturing exports from de-

veloping countries; the top 15 alone accounted for about 60% (World Bank, 1992). Even more striking is that about one-third of all exports from the Third World came from four Southeast Asian countries—Hong Kong, South Korea, Singapore, and Tiawan. Industrialization occurred, therefore, only in selected parts of the Third World.

Manufacturing was slowest to take hold in the poorest countries of the periphery, most of which are in Africa. It grew fastest in the NICs. These countries made a transition from an industrial strategy based on import substitution to one based on exports. The exporters can be divided into two groups. First, countries such as Mexico, Brazil, Argentina, and India have a relatively large domestic industrial base and established infrastructure. All four of these countries are primarily exporters of traditional manufactured goods—furniture, textiles, leather, and footwear—exports favored by natural-resource conditions. Second, countries such as Hong Kong, Taiwan, South Korea, and Singapore have few natural resources, small domestic markets, and little infrastructure. But by tailoring their industrial bases to world economic needs, they have become successful exporters to developed countries. These four peripheral countries emphasize exports in clothing, engineering, metal products, and light manufactures. The success of South Korea, for example, has encouraged other Third World countries to adopt a similar program of export-led industrialization.

Why did import-substitution industrialization fail? What are the characteristics of export-led industrialization? What are the consequences of this strategy on economies and people? Can this form of industrialization in the periphery be sustained if the tendency toward slower economic growth in the center of the world economy continues? In the following sections, we attempt to answer these questions.

Import-Substitution Industrialization

In the post-World War II period, newly independent Third World countries sought to break out of their domination by, and dependence on, developed countries. Their goal was to initiate self-expanding capitalist development through a strategy of *import-substitution industrialization*. This development strategy involved the production of domestic manufactured goods to replace imports. Only the middle classes could support a domestic market; thus, industrialization focused on luxuries and consumer durables. The small plants concentrated in existing cities, which increased regional inequalities. These "infant industries" developed behind tariff walls in order to reduce imports from developed countries, but local entrepreneurs had neither the capital nor the technology to begin their domestic industrialization. Foreign multinational corporations came to the rescue. Although projects were often joint ventures involving local capital, "independent" development soon became *dependent industrialization* under the control of foreign capital. Many countries experienced an initial burst in manufacturing growth and a reduction in imports. But after a while, the need to purchase raw materials and capital goods and the heavy repatriation of profits to the home countries of the multinationals dissipated foreign-exchange savings.

Export-Led Industrialization

By the 1960s, it was apparent to Third World leaders that the import-substitution strategy had failed. Only countries that had made an early transition to *export-led industrialization* were able to sustain their rates of industrial growth. Once again, Third World development became strongly linked to the external market. In the past, export-oriented development had involved the export of primary commodities to developed countries. Now, export-oriented development was to be based on the production and export of manufactures.

The growth of export-led industrialization coincided with the international economic crisis of the 1970s and 1980s. It took place at a time when the demand for imports in the advanced industrial countries was growing despite the onset of a decline in their industrial bases. It was a response to the new international division of labor.

Export-oriented industrialization tends to concentrate in *export-processing zones*, where four conditions are usually met: "First, import provisions are made for goods used in the production of items for duty-free export and export duties are waived. There is no foreign exchange control and there is generally freedom to repatriate profits. Second, infrastructure, utilities, factory space and warehousing are usually provided at subsidized rates. Third, tax holidays, usually of five years, are offered. Finally, abundant, disciplined labor is provided at low wage rates" (Thrift, 1986, p. 52).

The first export-processing zone was not established in the Third World; it was established in 1958 in Shannon, Ireland, with the local international airport at its core. In the late 1960s, a number of countries in East Asia began to develop export-processing zones, the first being Taiwan's Kaohsiung Export-Processing Zone, set up in 1965. By 1975, 31 zones existed in 18 countries. By the early 1980s, at least 68 zones were established in 40 principally Third World countries. Most of them are in the Caribbean, in Central and Latin America, and in Asia (Figure 11.17).

Central to the growth of Third World manufacturing exports to the developed countries are multinational corporations, which establish operating systems between locally owned companies and foreign-owned companies. The arrangement is known as *international*

Maquilladora textile operation in Ciudad Juarez. By January 1994, there were almost 3000 maquilladora plants near the U.S. border in Mexico owned and operated by U.S. companies. Total employees number three-fourths of a million, and value-added approaches $4 billion. What effect will NAFTA have on the growth of American-owned plants in Mexico? *(Source: Cara Lise Metz, Impact Visuals.)*

subcontracting, or offshore assembly and sourcing. Although numerous legal relationships exist between the multinational and the subcontractor, from wholly owned subsidiary to independent producer, the key point is that Third World exports to developed countries are part of a unified production process controlled by firms in the advanced industrial countries. For example, Sears Roebuck Company might contract with an independent firm in Hong Kong or Taiwan to produce shirts; yet, Sears retains control over design specifications, advertising, and marketing. This is similar to the putting-out system in textiles that was developed in preindustrial England. "With modern transport and communications, it is probably no more difficult for today's merchants to organize a putting-out system between New York and Hong Kong, or between Tokyo and Seoul, than it was for the early English merchants to organize their putting-out system between London and the surrounding villages" (World Bank, 1987, p. 46).

Consequences of Export-Led Industrialization on Women

Export-led industrialization moves work to the workers instead of workers to the work, which was the case during the long postwar boom. In some countries this form of industrialization has generated substantial employment. For example, since their establishment, export-processing zones have accounted for at least 60% of manufacturing employment expansion in Malaysia and Singapore. But, in general, the number of workers in the export-processing zones' labor forces is modest. It is unlikely that these zones employ more than a million workers worldwide.

Much of the employment in export-processing zones is in electronics and electrical assembly or in textiles. Young, unmarried women make up the largest part of the work force in these industries—88% of zone employment in Sri Lanka, 85% in Malaysia and Taiwan, and 75% in the Philippines (Morello, 1983). Explanations for this dominance of women in the work force vary; it is often attributed to sexual stereotyping, in which the docility, patience, manual dexterity, and visual acuity of female labor are presupposed. Of more significance is the fact that women are often paid much less than men are for the same job. Cheap labor is essential in the labor-intensive industries of the global assembly line.

According to A. Sivanandan (1987), export-led industrialization gives rise to *disorganic development*—an imposed economic system at odds with the cultural and political institutions of the people that it exploits. People produce things of no use to them. How they produce has no relation to how they formerly produced. Workers are often flung into an alien labor process that violates their customs and codes. For example, female factory

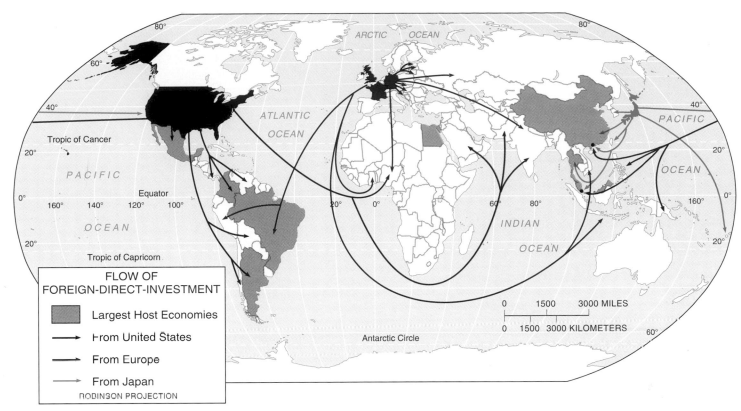

ABOVE: The great majority of the world's transitional corporations are based in the United States, Europe, or Japan. Most transitional corporation investment has been in companies and resources of other relatively developed countries. The U.S. transitionals make most of their investments in European and Japanese companies. Third World investment is channelized, with the United States investing in Latin America, Europe investing in Eastern Europe, and Japan investing in East Asia.

BELOW: Many less developed countries of the world have borrowed heavily from developed countries in order to finance economic development. Some countries, especially in Africa, have larger debts than their total GNP, resulting in little revenue left over to invest in their economies. Some countries are so heavily in debt that they cannot repay loans to banks or governments of developed countries, and must renegotiate or default, adding fuel to the North/South debate.

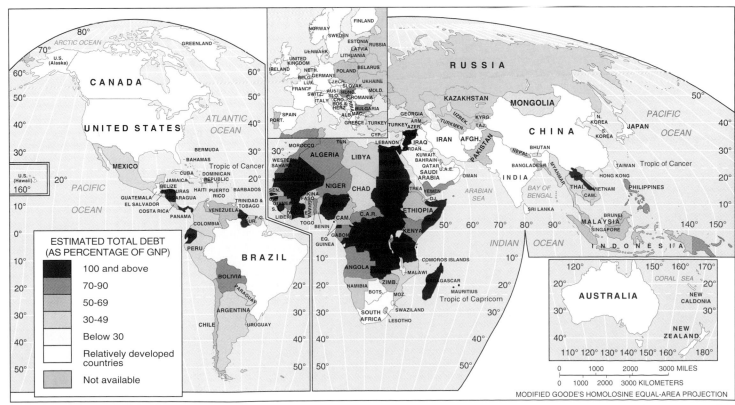

3.1

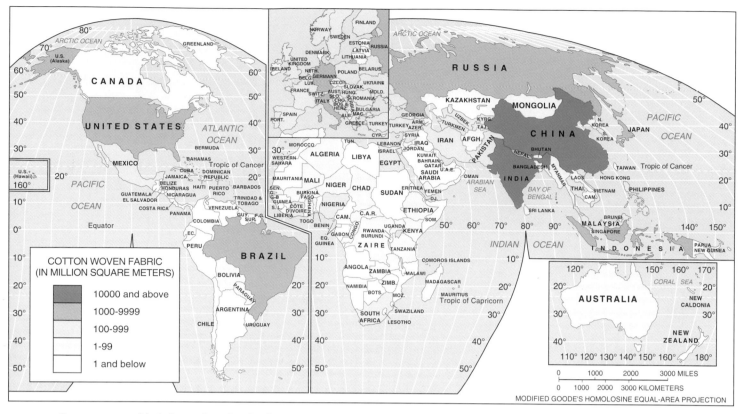

ABOVE: Cotton woven fabric is produced in both countries that have an abundant supply of inexpensive labor, such as China and India, and in countries that have an abundant supply of cotton or where demand is high, such as in the United States and Brazil. In spite of the return to woven cotton fabric as the preferred material worldwide, a depression in world prices throughout the 1980s and 1990s contributed to a crisis in the industry. Attempts are now being made to introduce new marketing policies in the hope that prices will recover as the developed world turns away from synthetic materials, back to the use of more popular natural fibers.

BELOW: Unlike the production of cotton, yarn, and woven cotton fabric, the production of men's and boy's shirts takes place almost exclusively in developed countries. Here, the principal locational factor is proximity to market. Inexpensive labor is still important and is supplied by locations such as the southeastern United States, Southern Europe, the Ukraine, Brazil, and Indonesia.

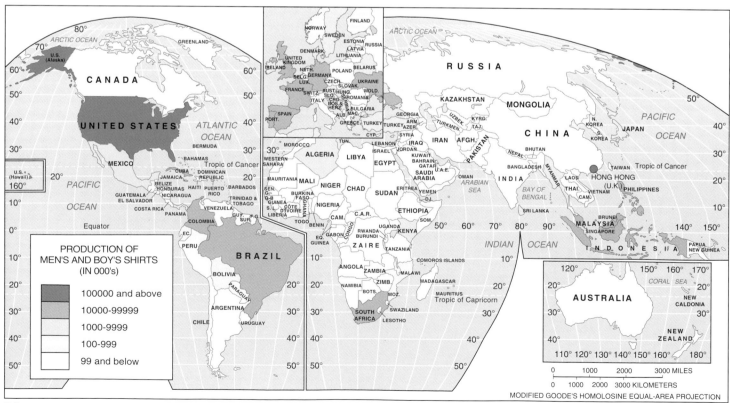

3.2

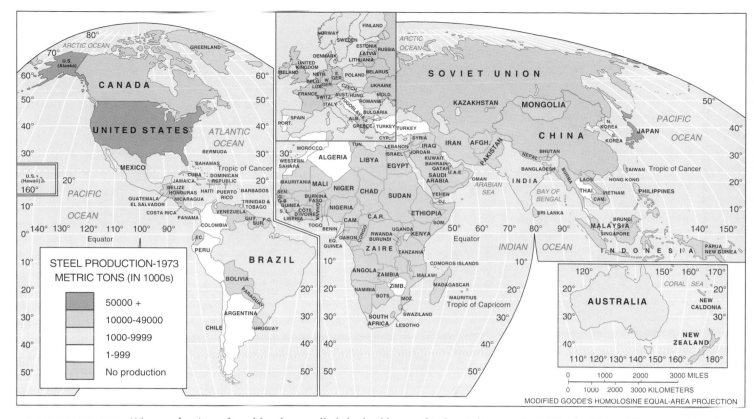

ABOVE AND BELOW: The production of steel has been called the backbone of industrialization. In 1973, the United States was the clear world leader in the production of steel, but developing countries were interested in building their own steel plants to foster their economic development process. By 1991, Brazil, the former Soviet Union countries, and China had become major steel producers, and Mexico, Argentina, South Africa, India, Iran, and several Eastern European nations had become important steel producers. The United States, Western Europe, and Japan actually reduced their production of steel due to dwindling world markets. Furnaces using metal scrap led to plants being located close to markets. New ore refining and metal concentrating techniques that raise the iron content to 95%, make the ore easily transportable, permit a vast increase in blast furnace capacity, and also favor market locations, such as the Great Lakes concentration of steel making in North America, which stretches from Chicago, Illinois, to Hamilton, Ontario. Electric arc furnaces have brought high quality steel making to areas deficient in coal, but with cheap hydroelectricity or gas supplies.

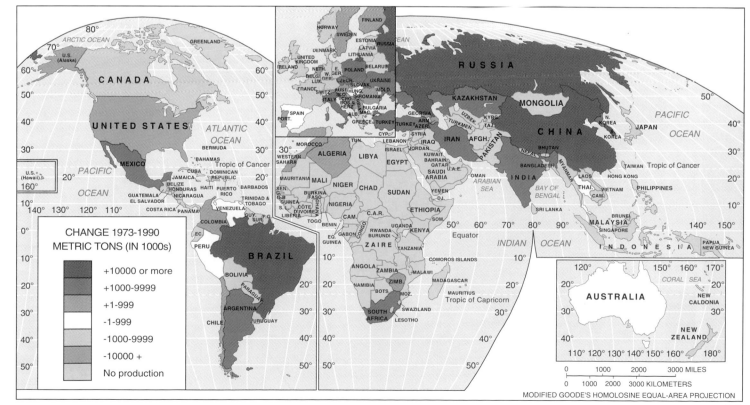

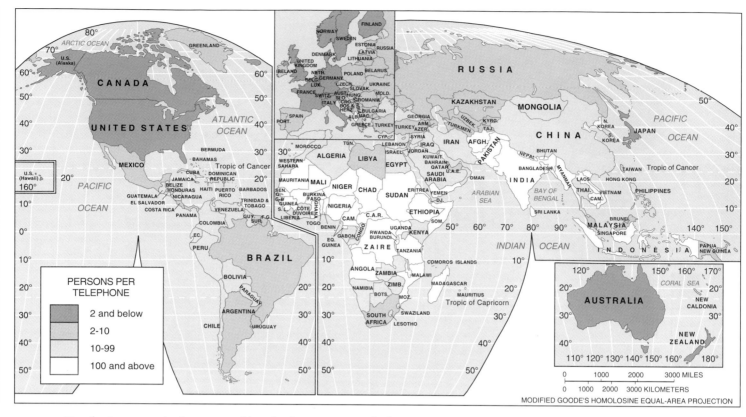

MODIFIED GOODE'S HOMOLOSINE EQUAL-AREA PROJECTION

ABOVE: Developing countries have several hundred persons per telephone, while relatively developed countries have two persons per telephone. The United States is approaching one person per telephone and will soon surpass this ratio with the proliferation of cellular phones. By 1994, there were 1.1 million voice circuits between the United States and Europe. Private global satellite constellations are being created. Large scale, low earth orbit systems such as Motorola's 66 satellite Iridium system provide telephone communications to and from any place on earth.

BELOW: In developing countries, the percentage of women in secondary schools is far below that of men. This fosters lower educational development among women and lowers prospects for economic development and gender equality.

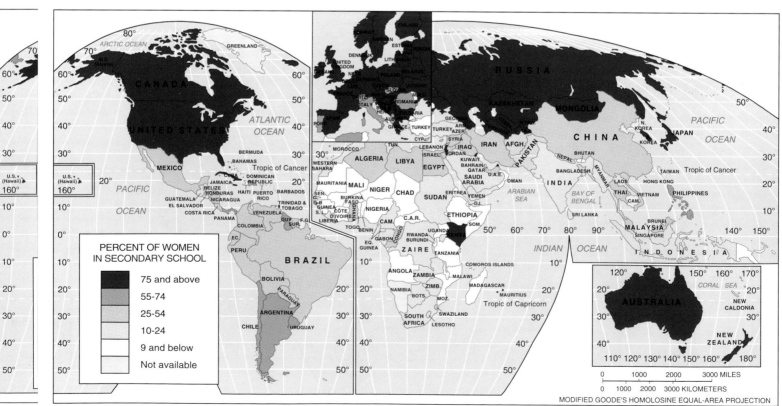

PERCENT OF WOMEN IN SECONDARY SCHOOL

75 and above

55-74

25-54

10-24

9 and below

Not available

MODIFIED GOODE'S HOMOLOSINE EQUAL-AREA PROJECTION

3.4   3.6

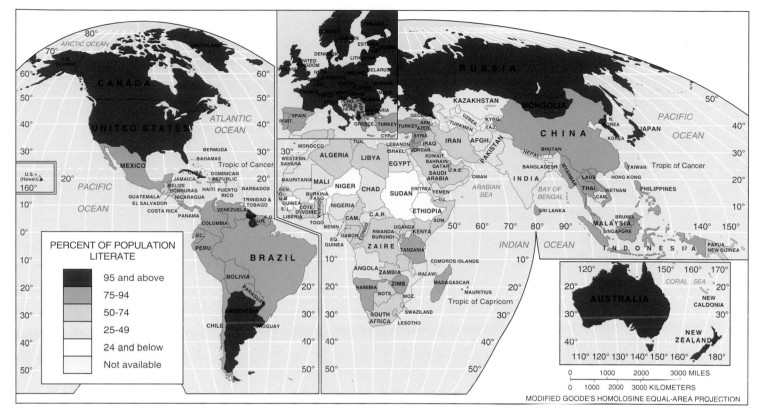

ABOVE: A great disparity in literacy rates exists between inhabitants of developed and less developed countries. In the United States and other highly developed countries, the literacy rate is greater than 98%. Notice the large number of countries in Africa and South Asia that have a literacy rate of less than 50%. As the global information age matures, education becomes even more paramount. In order to compete effectively in world trade, countries must learn how to invest in human capital. Educated workers in other countries are an incentive to transnational corporations. The transnational business and hyperfluidity of information assures that the business community will find the workers that they need at lower costs.

BELOW: The gender gap for literacy is most pronounced in the developing world, especially in Africa, South Asia, and the Middle East. In most developing countries, the female literacy rate is far below the male literacy rate.

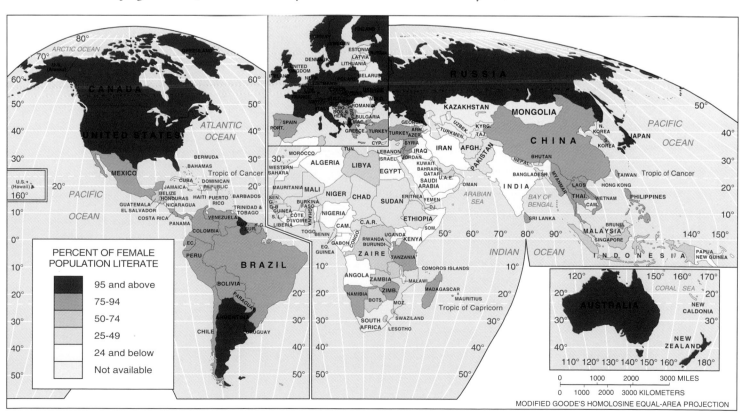

3.7

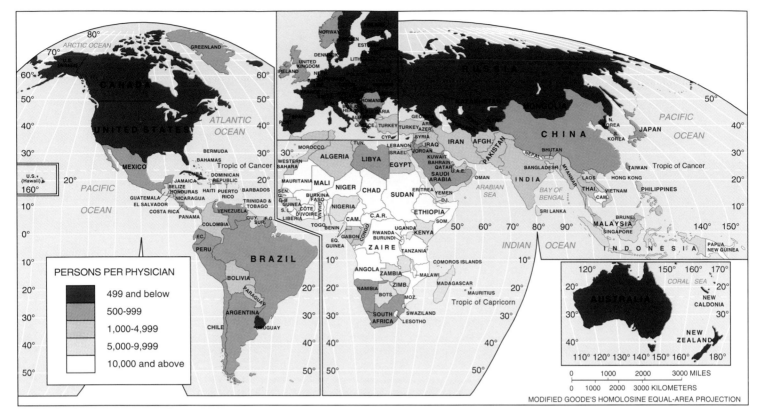

ABOVE: Persons per physician. An important measure of economic development is the number of persons per physician in a country. This measure is a surrogate for health care access, which includes hospital beds, medicine, nurses, and doctors. Most of Africa exhibits 10,000 people per physician or more, while Europe and the United States average approximately one doctor for every 200 people. Advances in medical and biotechnology will significantly lengthen the average life of humans in the near future. New ideas in medicine that revolve around holism are coming into the mainstream of thought, but the global AIDS epidemic will strike 100 million people in the next two decades. Entire countries in Africa and Asia are being ravaged by AIDS, which threatens to destroy the merchant class of some societies.

BELOW: The Human Development Index is perhaps the best overall measure of economic development. It combines three measures, including life expectancy, adjusted GDP per capita, and education (years of schooling literacy).

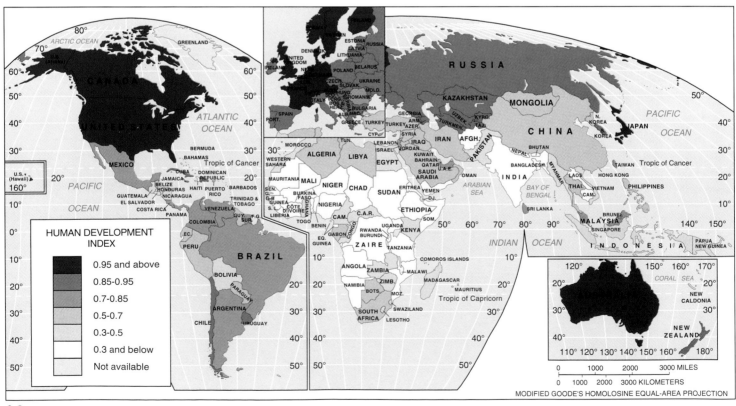

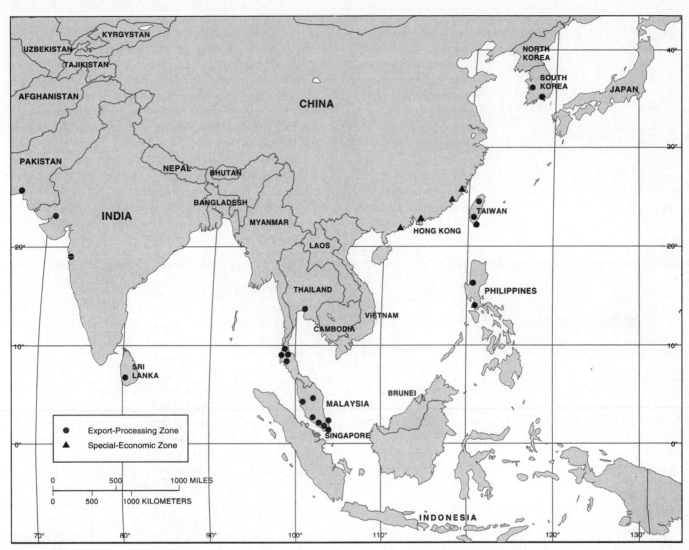

FIGURE 11.17
Export-processing zones in Asia.
(Source: Wong and Chu, 1984, p. 4.)

workers often pay a high price for their escape from family and home production, especially in Asia, where women's family roles have been traditionally emphasized. "Because of their relative independence, westernized dress and changed lifestyles, women may be rejected by their families and find it hard to reassimilate when they can no longer find employment on the assembly line" (Fuentes and Ehrenreich, 1987, p. 209).

Although export-oriented industrialization leads to growth in production and employment, as well as to increases in foreign exchange, Martin Landsberg (1987) argued that "it will not lead to the creation of an indigenous, self-expanding capitalist economy" (p. 235). The

linkages between "export platforms" and local economies are minimal. Scholars who oppose Landsberg's view cite South Korea as a shining example of a country that has completed a successful transition to industrial capitalism. But so far Korean industrial expansion has not taken place because of domestic demand. Rather, it has occurred because the Koreans have sought to increase exports and international competitiveness. This expansion is changing, partly because of the general global tendency to stagnation.

Economic stagnation in developed countries is a major concern of countries that have enjoyed tremendous success with the export-led industrialization strategy.

In this textile factory in Fortaleza, Brazil, women constitute the largest part of the work force. Brazil is a major exporter of textiles to advanced industrial countries. *(Source: World Bank.)*

For developed countries, where production and investment are moving out, purchasing power will be lost. The resultant spiraling down of general economic activity will choke off dependent industrialization and increase poverty and suffering for Third World workers and peasants.

WORLD INDUSTRIAL PROBLEMS

◈

Global industrial problems center on a level, nonincreasing demand for many products that have traditionally increased in demand since the industrial revolution began. Dwindling growth rates of developed nations have reduced the increasing demand for many manufactured items. At the same time, as a result of technological innovation and because many other developing countries desire to generate their own industrial bases, the world is now saturated with excess output capacity, meaning that the supply is greater than the demand for industrial products.

Decreasing Demand for Industrial Products in the Mid-1990s

Since the mid-1970s, the industrial world has approached saturation for many consumer goods. Most of these countries have little population growth, and because of world recession, average personal disposable income, when adjusted for inflation, has not increased, but in most cases has decreased. Thus, the demand for industrial products has also decreased.

In addition, changing technology has, in part, reduced the demand for some products. For example, the global demand for steel is now less than it was in the 1970s. Part of the reason for this is that today's automobiles use one-fourth less steel than they did 20 years ago because they must be lighter weight in order to be energy efficient.

At the same time, the quality of products has improved. In the early stages of manufacturing and demand for household goods, lower-quality products were mass produced. Now, emphasis is on high-quality products that last longer. The automobile industry is a prime example. Twenty years ago, the average American owned a car for 5 years. Today, the original buyer owns the average automobile for 11 years. Thus, again, with longer useful lives, fewer products are required.

Excess World Capacity

Although the worldwide demand is stagnant or decreasing for industrial products, capacity has increased.

The higher industrial output now experienced is a result of three factors:

1. the diffusion from the developed world to the less developed world of the industrial revolution and basic levels of technology for manufacturing commonly demanded items, such as textiles, iron and steel, tools, motors, and clothing

2. increased output capacity by developed nations as a result of technological innovation, robotics, and flexible manufacturing systems

3. the desire by developed, as well as developing, countries to maintain their own industrial bases because of positive effects on their overall economies, despite global overproduction

For much of the nineteenth century, the United Kingdom dominated world industry. From the late nineteenth century onward, the United States, the then Soviet Union, Germany, and Japan, followed by China, Indonesia, and Mexico, all increased world industrial productivity. In addition, because most countries want to establish their own industrial bases as a hedge against world inflation and dependence on foreign imports, Asian countries such as South Korea, Singapore, Taiwan, and Hong Kong have recently contributed to the overproductivity. These countries can produce at cheaper rates than developed countries can, and thus have a place in the global competitive marketplace.

The steel industry is a prime example. Between 1970 and 1990, world steel demand did not increase. However, there was a global shift in this industry from northwestern Europe and North America to less developed regions of the world. During this period, one-fourth of the production in North America and Western Europe evaporated. This shift was partially to Eastern Europe and the Soviet Union. But, output more than doubled in certain developing countries. In this short period of 20 years, the North American and Western European proportion of total global steel production declined from 67% to 50%, whereas developing countries' production levels increased from 10% to more than 20%.

Many steel-manufacturing firms have gone out of business as the global steel-production capacity exceeds global demand. Because of government subsidies, steel mills in some countries, especially in Europe, have remained opened in the face of dwindling quotas. The U.S. government, however, has been less willing to pay unemployment compensation to displaced workers and has allowed the U.S. steel industry to decline. Since the 1970s, U.S. production has decreased 33%, whereas employment in the steel industry has declined 66%.

Industrial Problems in Developed Countries

Developed countries are challenged to find new markets for their industrial output. At the same time, they are faced with reduced demand and increased unemployment levels in older industries. Their goal is to make their local industries competitive in an increasingly globally integrated world economy.

COMPETITION FROM MARKET BLOCS

Competition of markets has led to blocs of countries grouping to reduce trade barriers and to increase integration of supply and demand. One example is the cooperation of Western European countries, called the *EC*, or *European Community*. In North America, the United States and Canada have a North American Trade Agreement, which reduces imports and exports of industrial goods. Cooperation in East Asia between Japan and other countries is also leading to trade liberalization.

Such trade agreements allow individual countries to take advantage of agglomeration economies or natural resources. Currently, the United States has passed the North American Free Trade Agreement (NAFTA) between Canada, the United States, and Mexico. With the addition of Mexico to the North American Free Trade Zone, large markets are becoming available for Canadian and U.S. products. At the same time, it is expected that many North American labor-intensive industries will decentralize to Mexico to take advantage of labor rates that are 20% of American wage rates. American organized labor fears that many manufacturing jobs will be lost, whereas environmentalists fear that firms producing in Mexico, which has more lax environmental regulations, will increase the amount of pollution in an already very polluted environment. NAFTA proponents thus far have been unable to convince America that a free trade agreement that includes Mexico would benefit the American public. Time will tell.

MULTINATIONAL CORPORATIONS

Most giant industries in the highly developed countries are *transnational corporations*, meaning that they operate factories in countries other than their country of origin. America, Japan, Germany, Great Britain, and France each have numerous transnational corporations operating in many countries throughout the world. Because of trade barriers and import limitations in desired foreign markets, transnational corporations operate in other countries to overcome restrictions placed on product imports when the corporation operates in its home country. In addition, it can increase its sales and decrease transportation costs by opening a factory in the country whose market it wants to penetrate. With regard to developing countries, transnational corporations have penetrated countries with extremely low site costs based on production factors. One site factor that varies from country to country for many industries is labor cost.

However, the social problems created by industrial change and worldwide deindustrialization and reindustrialization in the global system have been substantial. Multinational corporations' *nomadic capital* and the switching of production from place to place in the 1970s through the 1990s, because of production innovation and transportation and communications savings, has disrupted some countries that have industrialized upon the transnational corporation's demand. In some cases, factory closures and job losses have been the result of shifting capital to increase profits and pay stockholders. In other cases, they have resulted from changing world demands and political postures. In the United States up to a million manufacturing jobs per year were lost between 1978 and 1990, just by plant closures. Since 1991, the reduction of hostilities and the end of the Cold War has meant the loss of a million jobs in California alone because of reduced demand for aerospace industries, combat aircraft industries, and related electronics manufacturing and defense contracting. In some cases, the transnational corporation has no control over which plants it must close. The International Monetary Fund reported that economies of industrialized countries grew by a mere 1.1% in 1993.

RICH CITY–POOR CITY REGIONS

Within some countries and regions, disparities between relatively well off and relatively depressed economic areas exist. As discussed earlier in this chapter, unemployment in the United Kingdom is 50% higher in the northwest than in the south and in the east, and incomes average 30% higher in the south, near London. French industry is centrally distributed, with Paris being the area of wealth, whereas southern and western France is relatively depressed and nets only two-thirds the per capita income of the Paris region. No regional disparities are greater than those of Italy. Italy has been described as two different countries, the north and the south, with per capita incomes three times higher in

the northern industrial Po River valley compared with the areas south of Rome, in southern Italy, and Sicily. Sweden's regional disparities are likewise immense, with the prosperous southern region centered on Stockholm and Göteborg in sharp contrast with much less populated and poorer northern regions.

Germany presents a particularly interesting problem in its attempt to integrate former East Germany with its depressed level of industry and high unemployment levels with the much more prosperous west. In the United States, although the South has been the most depressed region historically since the 1960s, it has been the region of the most rapid industrial and per capita income gains. The original hearth area of the nation, New England, and the industrial heartland of the American Manufacturing Belt throughout the Midwest are now some of the more depressed areas of North America, but cities rich and poor vary by local region.

Industrial Problems in Developing Countries

Developing countries have a special set of problems in increasing their industrial output. As we discussed, many developing countries foster their own set of basic manufacturing industries, including iron, steel, and textiles, regardless of the glut on the world market for these products. Western countries built their power and wealth on industrialization, which developing countries see as an avenue to growth. Their problems center around accessibility to the distant world markets, lack of real investment capital, and lack of labor training capable of producing a management class. Other problems include an inadequate supporting infrastructure, which is critical for the development of industrial activity, and exploitation by transnational corporations, which aggressively control the developing countries' industrial potential.

Although the developing countries' own demand may be sufficient to warrant new industrialization, distant markets of the developed world compose a much larger source of revenue. But the United States, Western Europe, Japan, Russia, and some of the other former Soviet Union countries can produce enough industrial output to satisfy themselves. Thus, there is no excess demand to help the developing countries get started.

Frequently the education system of NICs cannot produce university-trained managers, accountants, and other white-collar professionals to support industrialization. In addition, capital is needed for basic demands such as clean water, transportation, and food production. Many times a country cannot afford to drain scarce capital from these basic necessities to aid industrialization.

The poor state of the transportation, communications, and service infrastructure in developing nations is often not at the level necessary to produce and support new factories. We have already discussed the consequences of export-led industrialization and import-substitution industrialization. Some African countries take advantage of proximity to raw materials, mineral resources, and the like. Most developing countries, however, have an abundant supply of cheap labor that is useful for certain types of industrialization.

However, transnational corporations involved in many developing countries take advantage of this low-cost labor supply and profit from selling the products produced by the labor. Consequently, often a developing country must compete against transnational corporations who have outside capital and large supplies of trained professionals to help in the industrialized management task.

Because of these reasons, industrialization of developing nations is extremely difficult, and no immediate future solution to the problem is on the horizon.

SUMMARY

◈

Four major regions of the world account for approximately 80% of the world's industrial production—northeastern North America, northwestern Europe, western Russia, and Japan. The textiles, clothing manufacture, and consumer electronics industries have shifted globally from the developed world to the underdeveloped world. Automobile production and semiconductor manufacture have also experienced global shifts, from North America and Europe to Japan and the Far East.

In this chapter, we explored the social relations that lead to industrial change, described worldwide manufacturing trends, and examined the recent history of industrial devolution in advanced industrial countries and of industrial revolution in the Third World. It was argued that the processes of *deindustrialization* and *industrialization* are not offsetting tendencies within the global system; rather, they constitute a negative-sum global game played by multinational nomadic capital. Multinationals switched production from place to place in the 1970s and 1980s because of varying relations between capital and labor and new technological innovations in transportation and communications. With improved air freight, containerization, and telecommunications, multinational corporations can dispatch products faster, cheaper, and with fewer losses.

In the United States, 500,000 manufacturing jobs per year were lost between 1978 and 1992. These losses were hidden to some extent by selective reindustrialization and the migration of manufacturing from the American Manufacturing Belt to the South and the West. However, a worldwide recession and the end of the Cold War military buildup have also doomed many manufacturing companies. Overall, world industrial problems now center on overcapacity and the decreasing demand for industrial products.

In Great Britain, losses occurred in virtually all industries and regions. In underdeveloped countries, *import-substitution industrialization* and *export-led industrialization* produced *dependent development* and *disorganic development*. Workers and peasants have borne the deleterious consequences of these forms of industrialization.

Japan, on the other hand, has been an industrial success story. However, its economic miracle has been achieved at the expense of social welfare, the environment, and international relations. In the future, its economic miracle may be stymied by its aging population (the median age of Japanese workers is already about 41, and it is predicted to rise to nearly 44 by 2020), the rising value of land, and its falling stock market.

◈

KEY TERMS

American Manufacturing Belt	capital-labor relations
assembly plants	Central Florida manufacturing region
Britain's north-south divide	component plants
Britain's sunbelt	deindustrialization

dependent industrialization
disorganic development
Donbass
economic structure of society
export-led industrialization
export-processing zones
forces of production
global shift of manufacture
Gulf Coast manufacturing region
just-in-time inventory
just-in-time manufacturing
import-substitution industrialization
industrial restructuring
industrialization
inertia
integrated circuit
international subcontracting
Japan Incorporated
just-in-time manufacturing
Kuzbass
materialist science
microprocessor
MITI

mode of production
Moscow region
NAFTA
NICS
nomadic capital
Po Valley region
postindustrial society
quaternary economic activities
Rhine–Alsace-Lorraine region
Ruhr region
Russian Asia
Silicon Valley
social relations of production
Southeastern manufacturing region
surplus value
transnational corporations
Ukraine region
Urals region
value added
Volga region
West Coast manufacturing region
Zaibatsu

◎

SUGGESTED READINGS

Amin, A., and Robins, K. 1990. The re-emergence of regional economies? The mythical geography of flexible accumulation. *Environment and Planning D: Society and Space*, 8:7–34.

Bagchi-Sen, S., and Pigozzi, B. M. 1993. Occupational and industrial diversification in the metropolitan space economy in the United States, 1985–1990. *Professional Geographer*, 45:44–54.

Belassa, B. 1981. *The Newly Industrializing Countries in the World Economy*. New York: Pergamon.

Blackaby, F., ed. 1979. *De-industrialization*. London: Heinemann.

Bluestone, B., and Harrison, B. 1982. *The Deindustrialization of America: Plant Closings, Community Abandonment, and the Dismantling of Basic Industry*. New York: Basic Books.

Brotchie, J. F.; Hall, P.; and Newton, P. W., eds. 1987. *The Spatial Impact of Technological Change*. London: Croom Helm.

Bylinksy, G. 1983. The race to the automatic factory. *Fortune*, 21 February, pp. 52–64.

Casetti, E., and Jones, J. P., III. 1987. Spatial aspects of the productivity slowdown: An analysis of U.S. manufacturing data. *Annals of the Association of American Geographers*, 77:76–88.

Cohen, B. J. 1990. The political economy of international trade. *International Organisation*, 44:261–281.

de Blij, H., and Muller, P. 1992. *Geography: Region and Concept*. New York: John Wiley & Sons.

Dicken, P. 1986. *Global Shift: Industrial Change in a Turbulent World*. London: Harper & Row.

Dicken, P. 1991. *Global Shift: Industrial Change in a Turbulent World*, 2nd ed. London: Harper & Row.

Dicken, P. 1992. *Global Shift: The Internalization of Economic Activity.* New York: Guilford.

Drakakis-Smith, D., ed. 1990. *Economic Growth and Urbanization in Developing Areas.* London: Routledge.

Duncan, S. 1991. The geography of gender divisions of labour in Britain. *Transactions of British Geographers,* New Series 16:420–429.

Earney, F. C. F. 1981. The geopolitics of minerals. *Focus,* 31:1–16.

Elson, D. 1990. Marketing factors affecting the globalization of textiles. *Textiles Outlook International,* March, pp. 51–61.

Erickson, R. A., and Hayward, D. J. 1991. The international flows of industrial exports from U.S. regions. *Annals of the Association of American Geographers,* 81:371–390.

Ettlinger, N. 1991. The roots of competitive advantage in California and Japan. *Annals of the Association of American Geographers,* 81:391–407.

Fransman, M. 1990. *The Market and Beyond: Co-operation and Competition in Information Technology in the Japanese System.* Cambridge, England: Cambridge University Press.

Glasmeier, A. K. 1991. *The High-Tech Potential: Economic Development in Rural America.* New Brunswick, NJ: Center for Urban Policy Research.

Henderson, J. 1989. *The Globalization of High Technology Production.* London: Routledge.

Hoare, A. G. 1993. *The Location of Industry in Britain.* New York: Cambridge University Press.

Hogan, W. T. 1991. *Global Steel in the 1990s: Growth or Decline.* New York: Lexington Books.

Holmes, J. 1991. The continental integration of the North American automobile industry: From the Auto Pact to the FTA. *Environment and Planning A,* 23:100–115.

Kirkpatrick, C. H., and Nixson, F. I., eds. 1983. *Trade and Employment in Developing Countries.* Chicago: University of Chicago Press.

Law, C. M., ed. 1991. *Restructuring the Global Automobile Industry.* London: Routledge.

McDermott, M. C. 1989. *Multinationals: Foreign Divestment and Disclosure.* London: McGraw-Hill.

Markusen, A.; Hall, P.; and Glasmeier, A. 1986. *High Tech America.* Winchester, MA: Allen and Unwin.

Massey, D. 1984. *Spatial Divisions of Labor: Social Structures and the Geography of Production.* New York: Methuen.

Morishima, M. 1982. *Why Has Japan Succeeded?* Cambridge: Cambridge University Press.

Nash, J., and Fernandez-Kelly, M. P. 1983. *Women, Men, and the International Divison of Labor.* Albany: State University of New York Press.

Pacione, M., ed. 1985. *Progress in Industrial Geography.* London: Croom Helm.

Paltie, C. J., and Johnson, R. J. 1990. One nation or two? The changing geography of unemployment in Great Britain, 1983-1988. *Professional Geographer,* 42:288–298.

Peet, R., ed. 1987. *International Capitalism and Industrial Restructuring.* Boston: Allen and Unwin.

Pitelis, C., and Suugden, R., eds. 1991. *The Nature of the Transnational Firm.* London: Routledge.

Porter, M. E. 1990. *The Competitive Advantage of Nations.* New York: The Free Press.

Radice, H. 1991. Capital, labour and the state in the world economy. *Society and Space,* 9:51–63.

Reid, N. 1990. Spatial patterns of Japanese investment in the U.S. automobile industry. *Industrial Relations Journal,* 21:49–59.

Scott-Quinn, B. 1990. U.S. investment banks as multinationals. In *Banks as Multinationals,* edited by G. Jones, pp. 315–342. London: Routledge.

Sklair, L. 1989. *Assembling for Development: The Maquila Industry in Mexico and the United States.* London: Unwin Hyman.

———. 1991. *Sociology of the Global System, Social Change in Global Perspective.* Hemel Hempstead, England: Harvester Wheatsheaf.

South, R. B. 1990. *Transnational Maquiladora location. Annals of the Association of American Geographers,* 80:529–570.

Spero, J. E. 1990. *The Politics of International Economic Relations.* 3d ed. London: Allen and Unwin.

Storper, M., and Walker, R. 1989. *The Capitalist Imperative: Territory, Technology and Industrial Growth.* New York: Basil Blackwell.

Taylor, P. J. 1990. *Political Geography: World Economy, Nation State and Locality.* 2d ed. London: Longman.

Thrift, N. J. 1990. The perils of the international financial system. *Environment and Planning A,* 22:1135–6.23.

UNIDO. 1983. *Industry in a Changing World.* New York: United Nations.

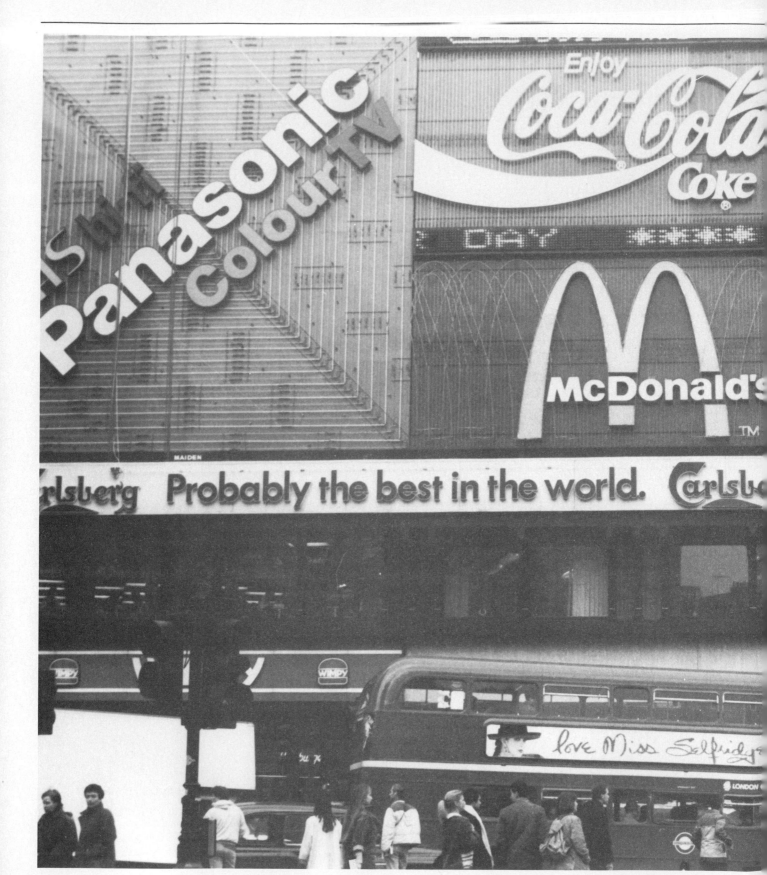

INTERNATIONAL BUSINESS I: DYNAMICS

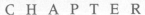

OBJECTIVES

- To consider the nature of international business

- To explain the bases of international trade and factor flows

- To examine the effects of natural and artificial barriers on international business

- To acquaint you with the major international institutions that deal with problems of trade, investment, and development

- To examine the effects of tariffs and quotas on international trade

- To understand the financing of international trade

Multinational corporate advertising, Piccadilly Circus, London, England.
(Source: Photo by A. R. de Souza.)

Since World War II, world economies have become more integrated than ever. *International integration* refers to the concept of international specialization or division of labor. Contributing to this widespread integration have been technological breakthroughs in transportation and communications and massive transformations in business behavior. These innovations and developments have greatly enhanced the role of *international business*, which is any form of business activity that crosses a national border. International business includes the international transmission of merchandise, capital, and services. International trade is expanding, and its composition and patterns are changing. But in many respects, it is now less significant in the global business structure than the international movement of capital and services. More and more companies are investing in foreign countries to acquire raw materials, to penetrate markets, and to exploit cheap labor. The expansion of production overseas has been matched by a parallel, symbiotic expansion of service enterprises, which now account for an increasing share of foreign direct investments (FDIs).

As we saw in Chapter 5, the actors in the international business arena have become more numerous and relationships among them more complex in the postwar years. The immediate postwar decade was primarily a *two-actor era*, the firm and its foreign commercial constituents—customers, suppliers, joint-venture partners, licensees. During these years, the United States spent billions of dollars on the reconstruction of Japan and West European countries. The economic revival of these countries represented huge markets for U.S. capital, equipment, and consumer goods, and few political barriers impeded their flow.

By the mid-1950s, with postwar reconstruction virtually complete, Japan and several West European countries challenged the economic dominance of the United States. The high value of the dollar in relation to other currencies dampened demand for U.S. goods and services and encouraged other countries to aggressively seek export markets. Between 1955 and 1970, the years of the long postwar boom, an increasing volume of trade was associated with multinational corporations, domiciled in the United States, Western Europe, and Japan. These giant companies intensified the sensitivities of host governments, which became a *third actor* in international decision making. Corporate strategists had to contend not only with host-country policies in developed countries, but with policies in the new, self-conscious underdeveloped countries as well.

The early 1970s marked another watershed as the world economy entered a prolonged period of disorder.

Foreign direct investment by U.S. firms in the Pacific.
(Source: Greg Davis, The Stock Market.)

This time of crisis stemmed from four structural changes: First, the industrialized countries experienced a marked slowdown in their economic growth rates. Second, competitive rivalry among industrialized countries increased significantly. This competition was stimulated by the slower and more unstable growth rates and, in turn, contributed to them. The rivalry gave rise to an increase in restrictive policies as each country sought to overcome its national crisis at the expense of other countries. Third, in 1973, the collapse of the Bretton Woods monetary arrangements, involving the replacement of fixed exchange rates and the convertibility of the dollar into gold with a system of more or less freely fluctuating exchange rates, permitted the United States to devalue its currency in an effort to retrieve lost competitiveness with its trading rivals. The new world monetary system, in which exchange rates shift almost daily, fueled inflation and destabilized commodity markets. The fourth structural change, increases in oil prices by

400% in 1973/1974 and 165% between 1979 and 1981, reduced real income in the advanced countries and dealt a particularly harsh blow to the oil-importing Third World countries. The oil crisis induced worldwide recession in the mid-1970s and again in the early 1980s. Recovery from the recessions has been weak in all countries except the western Pacific nations. In fact, Japan and other East Asian nations emerged from the recessions stronger than ever, their industrial growth fed by an expanding market in the Western Hemisphere.

While these events unfolded, the activities of multinational corporations grew substantially. In pursuit of larger profits than could be obtained domestically, multinationals built up industrial capacity in "offshore" production centers. Parent governments recognized that the ability of multinationals to transfer capital, production, and labor across national boundaries was a major cause of instability in the global economy. So began the *four-actor era* as parent governments sought to regulate the activities of multinationals.

In the late 1970s, international business became more and more politicized at home and abroad. An increase in government regulations at both ends occurred in response to mounting public concerns about pollution, natural-resource allocation, income and wealth distribution, consumer protection, energy, and the governance of corporations. These concerns were expressed by a variety of special-interest groups—ethnic, religious, occupational, and political.

Because these special-interest groups are now developing international linkages and loyalties as they strive to create international orders in their own image, we live in the *multiactor era*, in which a variety of actors are relevant to corporate decision making. In the new environment, multinational corporations find it difficult to react swiftly enough to changing opportunities and constraints. As a result, new forms of business entities such as trading companies, financial groups, and service companies are developing, and they have become preeminent features in the international business climate of the 1990s.

The increasingly complex international business environment warrants the attention of geographers. Knowledge of the international sphere of business helps us to understand what is occurring in the world as well as within our own countries. This chapter examines the concepts and patterns that underlie the expanding world of international business. It seeks answers to the following questions: What theories shed light on the processes of international interaction? What are the dynamics of world trade and investment? What are the patterns of international commerce?

INTERNATIONAL TRADE

◈

Why International Trade Occurs

Why are so many countries, large and small, rich and poor, deeply involved in international trade (Figure 12.1)? One answer lies in the unequal distribution of productive resources among countries. Trade offsets disparity with regard to the availability of productive resources. However, whether a country can export successfully depends not only on its resources, but also on the conditions of the economic environment; the opportunity, ability, and effort of producers to trade; and the capacity of local producers to compete abroad.

NATURAL AND HUMAN-MADE RESOURCES

Production factors—labor, capital, technology, entrepreneurship, and land containing raw materials—vary from country to country. One country is rich in iron ore, and another has tremendous oil deposits. Some countries have populations large enough to support industrial complexes; others do not. People are not only a natural resource, but also a precious human-made resource with differential skills. One country is home to an enormous pool of workers adept at running modern machinery; another abounds with scientists and engineers specializing in research-laden products. In some countries, entrepreneurs are more able and knowledgeable than in others. The imbalance in natural and human-made resources accounts for much of the international interchange of production factors and/or the products and services that the factors can be used to produce.

CONDITIONS OF THE ECONOMIC ENVIRONMENT

A country that is well endowed in natural and human-made resources has an advantage over countries that lack these assets. But the assets in and of themselves are insufficient to guarantee success in the export market. American producers, for example, tend to be less successful exporters than their Japanese or European counterparts. Numerous economic environmental factors may reduce the ability of countries to best use their resources and productive advantages. These

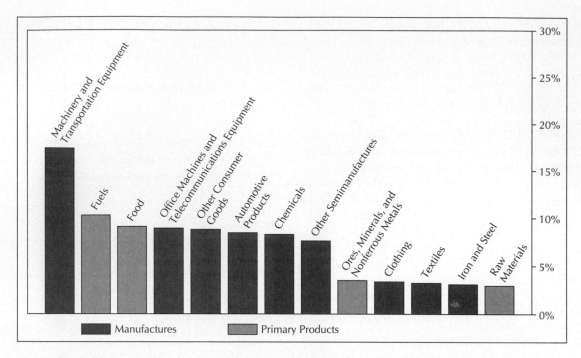

Note: Machinery and transportation equipment excludes automotive products, office machines, and telecommunications equipment.

FIGURE 12.1
Total shares of product groups in world merchandise trade, for all countries combined, 1990.
(Source: United Nations, 1992, p. 35.)

factors include inflation, exchange rates, labor conditions, governmental attitudes, and laws.

Inflation, which is a rise in the general level of the prices of goods and services, can be detrimental to a country's ability to compete domestically or internationally. Exchange rates, the prices of currencies in foreign-exchange markets, can also influence competitiveness. For example, if a currency is overvalued in relation to other currencies, local producers may find it difficult not only to compete with foreign imports, but also to export successfully. In addition, recurring labor disputes that interrupt production can create serious obstacles for exporters, and governments can encourage or discourage their export sectors. Finally, the competitiveness of exporters is affected by laws—labor laws, tax laws, and patent laws.

OPPORTUNITY, ABILITY, AND EFFORT OF THE PRODUCER TO TRADE

Success in the international trade arena hinges on demand for the good or service produced, an awareness of the demand by suppliers, the availability of appropriate foreign distribution channels, and a minimum of governmental controls. But even if all these conditions are met, many producers fail to respond. Some may lack the desire to try, whereas others may have the desire but never make the effort. The importance of desire and effort in determining success in international trade is exemplified by Japan. Although this island nation lacks raw materials, it has successfully imported materials and components for use in manufacturing goods for domestic and foreign markets.

COMPETITIVENESS OF LOCAL PRODUCERS ABROAD

The ability of a country to export is affected by the capacity of foreign producers to compete. A crucial element in the ability of domestic producers to compete is the relative cost of production. Countries with high labor, capital, and energy costs can expect strong competition from abroad. The existence of strong competitors may act as a disincentive to successful and profitable exporting.

Trade by Barter and Money

At one time, trade was simple and was conducted on a barter basis. *Barter,* or *countertrade,* is the direct exchange of goods or services for other goods or services. It still occurs in some traditional markets in underdeveloped countries and is of increasing importance in the modern world economy. Roughly 30% of world commerce is now countertrade. Russia and Eastern European countries use barter to trade among themselves and with underdeveloped countries. Major oil-exporting countries such as Iran and Nigeria barter oil and gas for manufactured goods.

Despite its widespread use, particularly by governments that have turned toward national economic protectionism, barter is a cumbersome way of conducting international exchange. Even within a country, consumers would find it difficult to barter the goods or services that their families produce for goods and services to satisfy their daily needs. In fact, more time would be devoted to exchange than to production. Money provides a means for simplifying the domestic exchange procedure and trade between countries. Money does present some problems, such as those associated with exchange rates, but introducing it as an exchange medium does not alter the theoretical bases for international trade.

Classical Trade Theory

ABSOLUTE ADVANTAGE AND COMPARATIVE ADVANTAGE

The flow of trade arises from an economic advantage that one country has over another in the output of a good or a service. It may occur because of the *absolute advantage* of one country in the production of a good. For example, Country A produces cloth twice as efficiently as Country B does, whereas Country B is 50% more productive than Country A is in the output of wheat; thus, Country A will be inclined to exchange its cloth for Country B's wheat, and vice versa. Each country has an absolute advantage in producing its good.

However, both countries need not have absolute advantages for trade to occur. Indeed, a country can successfully export a good in which it has an absolute cost *disadvantage.* This phenomenon is called the *theory of comparative advantage,* or the *theory of comparative cost.*

Developed by eighteenth- and nineteenth-century English economists, notably David Ricardo (1912), the theory states that all countries have comparative advantages and that countries will export the goods that they can produce at the lowest *relative* cost. For example, Country A specializes in the export of raisins because it can produce them more cheaply, compared with other goods, than Country B can, and Country B exports paper because it can produce paper more cheaply than other goods. Raisins may be cheaper than paper in both countries, but the cost differential between raisins and paper is wider in Country A than in Country B. To explain the foreign-trade structure of a particular country, we must identify its comparative advantage, which involves a study of its productive resources.

A SIMPLE MODEL

To see how a difference in productive resources can lead to international trade, consider a simple labor-cost model, such as the one that David Ricardo used in the nineteenth century. The model excludes economies of scale; neglects transportation costs; and assumes free trade, full employment of productive resources, and the same technological conditions and tastes everywhere. To make things even more simple, assume that only two countries, A and B, exist and that each country produces only two commodities, coal and corn.

Countries A and B are the same in every respect except one. Each country has 120 person-days of labor at its disposal. Each country requires 2 person-days of labor to produce 1 ton of corn and has enough arable land to employ all its workers in corn farming. In Country A, however, coal deposits are much nearer the surface than those in Country B. As a result, Country A requires only 1 person-day of labor to mine 1 ton of coal, whereas Country B needs 4 person-days.

Table 12.1, which is a production possibilities schedule, illustrates that if Country A decided to grow only corn or mine only coal, it could produce either 60 tons of corn or 120 tons of coal. It also shows that Country A could produce both corn and coal by choosing from various production opportunities. Each opportunity point represents a mutually exclusive combination of corn and coal. Thus, if Country A selects one combination, it must reject all other combinations. The opportunity points in Table 12.1 are graphed in Figure 12.2. The output of coal is plotted on the horizontal axis, and the output of corn is plotted on the vertical axis. The sloping line, AE, connecting the various points on the

Table 12.1
Production Possibilities Schedule for Country *A*

Opportunity Points	Corn	Coal
A	60	0
B	45	30
C	30	60
D	15	90
E	0	120

Table 12.2
Production Possibilities Schedule for Country *B*

Opportunity Points	Corn	Coal
A_1	60	0
B_1	45	7.5
C_1	30	15
D_1	15	22.5
E_1	0	30

graph, is called the *production possibilities curve*. Without international trade, Country *A* would have to select one combination of corn and coal along the curve.

Table 12.2 and Figure 12.3 illustrate the production possibilities schedule and curve for Country *B*. The maximum output of corn is the same as in Country *A* because both countries have the same amount of labor and are equally efficient in growing corn. But maximum coal output in Country *B* is smaller than that in Country *A* because its mines are deeper and therefore more expensive to operate. In the absence of international trade, Country *B* would have to select one combination of coal and corn along its production possibilities curve.

Suppose now that Country *A* and Country *B* are no longer isolated, and that trade between them is possible. An opportunity for trade creates a single market, and a common price for coal is established. Let's say that this new price for coal is lower than the previous price in Country *B* but higher than the previous price in Country *A*. Country *B* can now obtain a ton of coal without giving up so much corn as in the past, when it mined coal domestically. It can now specialize in growing corn

and use some of its corn to buy coal from Country *A*. Similarly, Country *A* can now obtain more corn for its coal. It can now specialize in mining coal and use some of its coal to buy corn from Country *B*.

Figure 12.4 illustrates one possible rearrangement of production where the common price for coal is set at 1 ton of corn for 1 ton of coal. The left-hand triangle is the production possibilities curve for Country *A*, and the upside-down triangle is the production possibilities curve for Country *B*. In the absence of trade, when each country was confined to its own production possibilities curve, Country *A* produced 60 tons of coal and 30 tons of corn (Point *P*), whereas Country *B* produced 22.5 tons of coal and 15 tons of corn (Point P_1). The opportunity for trade enables both countries to rearrange production and consumption to mutual advantage. Country *A* can specialize in coal production and mine 120 tons, and Country *B* can specialize in corn production and grow 60 tons. As shown in the graph, Country *A* now consumes 80 tons of coal and exports 40 tons to buy corn, and Country *B* consumes 20 tons of corn and exports 40 tons to buy coal. Country *A*'s consumption

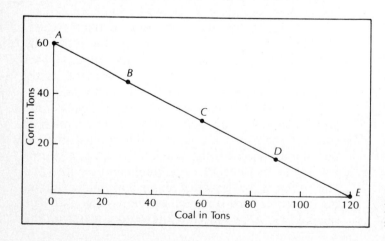

FIGURE 12.2
Production-possibilities curve for Country *A*. (Constructed from data in Table 1.)

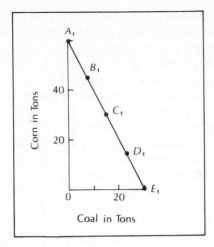

FIGURE 12.3
Production-possibilities curve for Country B. (Constructed from data in Table 2.)

shifts from P to Q, and Country B's consumption shifts from P_1 to Q.

Our simple Ricardian model shows that both countries enjoy a higher level of consumption with trade than without. Moreover, trade enlarges world output of coal and corn by allowing both countries to specialize. Before trade, coal output was 82.5 tons (60 tons for Country A plus 22.5 tons for Country B). With trade, coal output increases to 120 tons. Before trade, corn output was 45 tons (30 tons for Country A plus 15 tons for Country B). With trade, corn output increases to 60

tons. This increase in output points to a fundamental principle in orthodox trade theory: Free trade is best because it allocates economic tasks so as to maximize world output and income.

Modern Trade Theory

Although David Ricardo's two-country, two-product, labor-cost model is simple, it provides the basis for modern trade theory. The Ricardian model can be expanded by taking into account several countries and commodities and by allowing several production factors. The multifactor approach to trade theory derives from work by two Swedish economists, Eli Heckscher (1919) and Bertil Ohlin (1933). In brief, the *Heckscher-Ohlin theory* takes the view that a country should specialize in producing those goods that demand the least from its scarce production factors and that it should export its specialties in order to obtain the goods that it is ill-equipped to make (Olsen, 1971). Thus, if Countries A and B have different endowments of labor and machinery, both can gain from trade. Country A with many laborers and few machines can concentrate on, say, corn production and export its specialty in order to import cloth. Similarly, Country B with few laborers and many machines can specialize in cloth and export some cloth to import corn. Again, free trade is best from a global standpoint. When specialization is fostered, world output is maximized.

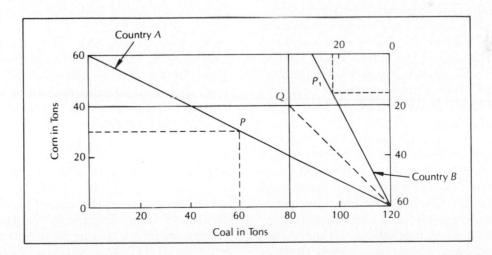

FIGURE 12.4
Trade between country A and country B. Without trade, country A produces 30 tons of corn and 60 tons of coal; country B produces 22.5 tons of coal and 15 tons of corn. After trade, country A consumes 80 tons of coal and exports 40 tons to buy corn. Country B consumes 20 tons of corn and exports 40 tons to buy coal. As a result, both countries are better off. The equilibrium has moved from P for country A, and P_1 for country B to Q.

The Heckscher-Ohlin theory argues not only that trade results in gains, but also that wage rates will tend to equalize as the trade pattern develops. The reasoning behind this *factor-price equalization,* as it came to be called, is as follows: As Country *A* specializes in corn production and diverts production from cloth, its production pattern becomes more labor intensive. As a result, Country *A*'s abundance of labor diminishes, the marginal productivity of labor rises, and wages also increase. Conversely, in Country *B,* as cloth production replaces corn production, labor becomes less scarce, the marginal productivity of labor falls, and wages also fall.

Some economists find the notion that foreign trade evens out the production factors too simplistic. But others cling to the Heckscher-Ohlin theory with considerable tenacity. The theory has ideological importance, and in 1919, when Heckscher first put it forward, it was particularly opportune. After World War I, the United States introduced restrictions on immigration, and there was also a growing interest in protectionism. With the interests of free traders under threat, a strong case for free trade needed to be made. The Heckscher-Ohlin theory showed not only that free trade was desirable, but also that it could compensate for restrictions on labor migration.

Inadequacies of Trade Theories

Trade theories are based on restrictive assumptions that limit their validity. They generally ignore considerations such as scale economies and transportation costs. Scale economies improve the ability of a country to compete even in the face of higher factor costs. The cost of moving a product greatly affects its "tradability." Brick, which has a high transportation cost relative to value and therefore is not extensively traded internationally, is a good example.

Trade theories assume perfect knowledge of international trading opportunities, an active interest in trading, and a rapid response by managers when opportunities arise. However, executives are often ignorant of their trading opportunities. And even if they are aware, they may fear the complexities of international trade.

Other inadequacies of trade theories include the assumptions of homogeneous products, perfect competition, the immobility of production factors, and freedom from governmental interference. Products are not homogeneous. Oligopolies exist in many industries. Production factors such as capital, technology, management, and labor are mobile. Governments interfere with trade; they can raise formidable barriers to the movement of goods and services.

The most important shortcoming of trade theories, however, is their failure to incorporate the role of firms, especially that of multinational corporations. Trading decisions are usually made on the microeconomic level by managers, not by governments in Country *A* or Country *B*. Multinational corporations also operate from a multinational perspective rather than from a national perspective. When international trade occurs between different affiliates of the same company, it is referred to as *intramultinational trade.* Special considerations, such as tax incentives or no competition from other affiliates of the same company, can often play a pivotal role in a company's international decisions.

Despite their limitations, trade theories provide an essential basis for our understanding of international business. They still underlie the thinking of many scholars, managers, labor leaders, and government officials. They offer a background for understanding the barriers to international business. They also frequently explain commodity trade, such as the international movement of wheat.

Fairness of Free Trade

Free trade is best from the standpoint of efficiency, but is it fair given the relationship of *unequal exchange* between developed and underdeveloped countries? This question is raised by radical theorists for whom imperialism is associated with relatively free trade (Amin, 1976; Baran, 1957; Emmanuel, 1972; Frank, 1969; Sunkel, 1982; Wallerstein, 1974). Their argument is that an artificial division of labor has made earning a good income from free trade difficult for most Third World countries.

AN ARTIFICIAL DIVISION OF LABOR

The British were instrumental in creating an unfair division of labor. Implicit in the early nineteenth-century argument for free trade was the notion that what was good for Great Britain was good for the world. But free trade was established within a framework of inequality among countries. Great Britain found free trade and competition agreeable only after becoming established as the world's most technically advanced

A tea-buying center in Kenya. Sixteen percent of Kenya's export earnings come from tea and 34 percent from coffee. Thus, Kenya depends largely on two commodities for export income.
(Photo: World Bank.)

Cash crop production in the third world is primarily a result of European colonization. With so many people in East Africa having insufficient food, the large expanses of land devoted to tea and coffee is difficult to understand. Most of the export will be sent to the United States and Western Europe. As a result of the former colonial status of developing areas of the world, a country may be confined to a one or two cash crop economy. Consequently, economically third world countries are almost doubly dependent on western nations. Yet, every country needs to import some goods in order to manage. Foreign exchange is needed and it is generated from cash crops. A balance needs to be made between the need for exporting of cash crops and the need for food supplies to feed a country's population. The way cash crops are distributed is one of the principal problems. Most plantations are owned by multi-national companies and they have a reputation for paying their workers very low wages.

industrial nation. Having gained an initial advantage over other manufacturers, Great Britain then threw open its markets to the rest of the world in 1849. Other countries were instructed or lured to do the same. The pattern of specialization that resulted was obvious. Great Britain concentrated on producing manufactured goods, such as vehicles, engines, machine tools, paper, and textile yarns and fabrics, and exporting them in exchange for a variety of primary products. Imports included specialized cargoes such as Persian carpets, furs, wines, silks, and bulk imports such as timber, grains, fruit, and meat. Although many countries gained from the application of this artificial division of labor, none gained more than Great Britain did.

The only way other countries could break out of this artificial division of labor was by interfering with free trade. The United States and Germany did so in the 1870s by adopting protectionist policies. France and a few other European countries with embryonic industries did the same. Underdeveloped countries, however, failed to escape, either because of colonialism, or because it was not in the interest of their ruling groups to do so.

The original division of labor changed little until after World War II, when a new structure began to evolve. Some underdeveloped countries were given a limited license to industrialize. As we saw in Chapter 11, the basic trend was export-led industrialization,

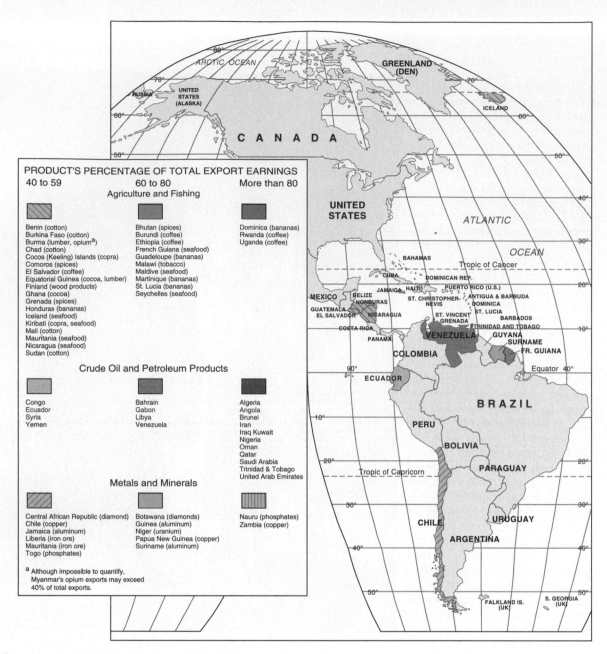

FIGURE 12.5

Vulnerable, single-commodity dependent countries. At least 40% of exports hinge on a single product. Regionally, Africa and the Middle East countries bordering the Persian Gulf are the most vulnerable.
(Source: United Nations, 1992, pp. 170–171.)

concentrated in a few countries. For the best-off poor countries, industrial growth is geared to the needs of the old imperial powers. Thus, the growth of manufacture in the Third World, under multinational corporate auspices, is not a portent of its emancipation from an artificial division of labor.

THE WORSENING TERMS OF TRADE

A deterioration in the *terms of trade*—the prices received for exports relative to the prices paid for im-ports—exemplifies the problem of unequal exchange for Third World countries. By and large, underdeveloped countries export raw and semiprocessed primary goods—agricultural commodities (cocoa, tea, coffee, palm oil, rubber, sisal, spices, bananas, seafood, sugar, jute, and cotton) and minerals (tin, iron ore, bauxite, aluminum, phosphate, diamonds, oil, copper, and uranium). In 1990, primary commodities accounted for 70% and 47% of the total exports of low- and middle-income countries (excluding China and India), respectively. The proceeds from these exports are needed to

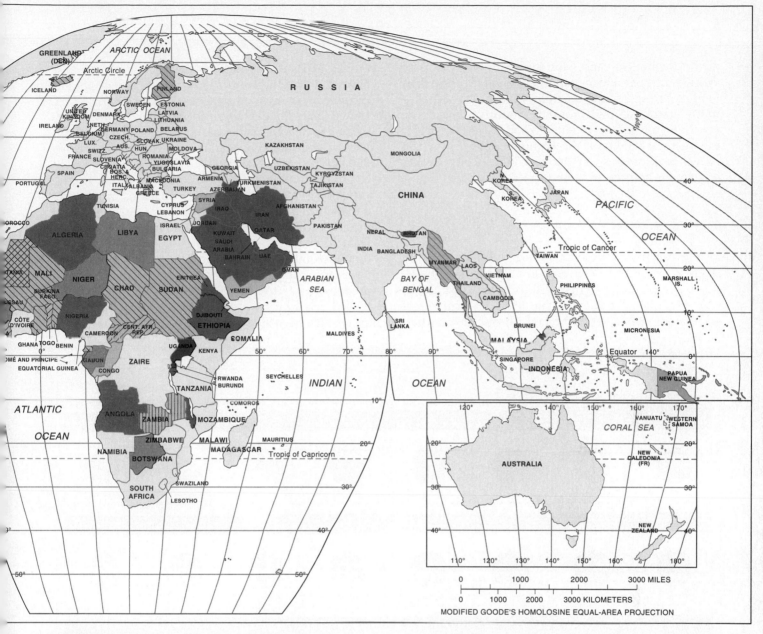

FIGURE 12.5
(*Continued*)

pay for imports of manufactures, which are vital for continuing industrialization and technological progress. Shifts in the relative prices of commodities and manufactures can therefore change the purchasing power of the exports of underdeveloped countries dramatically (World Bank, 1988). The situation is exacerbated because many of these low- and middle-income countries are vulnerable, single-commodity-dependent countries (Figure 12.5).

Between 1970 and 1990, Third World countries experienced a worsening in their terms of trade. This was caused by a decline in the prices of primary commodities and an increase in the prices of manufactures. In some years, the adverse shift was offset by an increased volume of Third World exports. For the period as a whole, however, import volume growth exceeded export volume growth and, given the overall deterioration in the terms of trade, the result was large current account deficits. Maintenance of these deficits was possible only because the Third World had access to external finance sources.

Economist Keith Griffin (1969) provided an account

of the theoretical causes for the decline in the Third World terms of trade for export commodities, especially food crops. According to Griffin, the cause of a decline in the terms of trade for any country depends on (1) the nature of the product exported, (2) the degree of structural rigidity in the economy, and (3) the bias of technical progress. Let us now look at how Engel's law applies to each of these factors.

ENGEL'S LAW

We can use a statistical finding known as *Engel's law* to account for a deterioration in the terms of trade. Nineteenth-century German statistician Ernst Engel, who examined the income and spending patterns of wage-earning families in several European countries,

arrived at the following conclusion: As incomes rise beyond a certain point, the proportion of disposable income spent on food declines (Figure 12.6). In the United States, for example, the percentage of disposable income spent filling supermarket carts is greater for families earning $20,000 a year than it is for families earning $60,000 a year. If we extended the concept of Engel's law to international trade, we could argue that as consumption of manufactured goods increased, agriculture would form a decreasing proportion of total trade, and income elasticity of demand would increase for manufactured goods. Thus, we would have a built-in structural disequilibrium, which would result in worsening terms of trade for exporters of primarily agricultural produce.

The economies of many underdeveloped countries are characterized by structural rigidity. They cannot alter

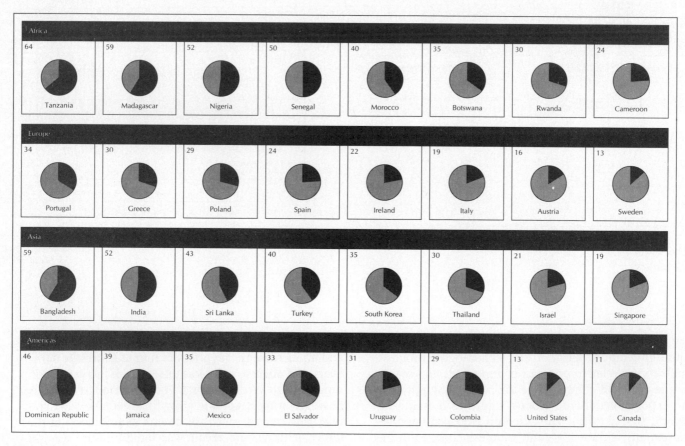

FIGURE 12.6
Food consumption as a percentage of total household expenditure for selected countries, 1981–1986.
(Source: United Nations, 1992, p. 140.)

the composition of exports rapidly in response to changing relative prices. Thus, if their commodity export prices decrease, they have no alternative but to accept declines in their terms of trade (Figure 12.7, Table 12.3). Assume, for example, that the price of coffee is initially P_0, as determined by the intersection of the supply and demand curves—S_0-S and D_0, respectively. Assume further, that demand increases to D_1, caused, say, by the outbreak of war. At first the price of coffee will rise sharply because of the fixed capacity of existing coffee plantations. These extraordinarily high prices will encourage people to invest in this sector; output will eventually increase substantially, and the price will settle at P_1. Increased prices may encourage expansion of output among established producers and may encourage new competitors to enter the market. If, now, demand decreases, say to its original level, it will move along a new supply curve—S_1-S. The price will not return to its initial level; on the contrary, it will fall considerably below that level, to P_2. Once capacity has been installed in new, stable plantations, variable production costs may be low, and, hence, supply may be quite insensitive to price reductions. Once resources become fixed in specific and long-lived capital—in this case, coffee trees—the economy becomes inflexible and cannot

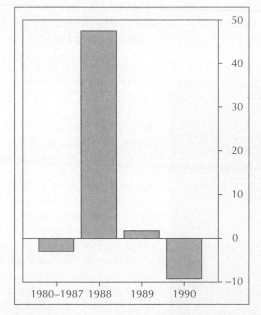

FIGURE 12.7
The worsening terms of trade for ores, minerals, and nonferrous metals, 1980–1990. Many underdeveloped countries cannot alter the composition of exports rapidly in response to changing relative prices.
(Source: Handbook of International Trade Statistics, 1993, C.I.A., p. 170.)

◈

Table 12.3
Prices of Selected Ores, Minerals, and Nonferrous Metals, 1988–1991

	Annual Percentage Change			
	1988	*1989*	*1990*	*1991*
Copper	46	9	−7	−12
Aluminum	63	−23	−16	−14
Iron ore	4	14	12	7
Tin	5	19	−29	−11
Nickel	183	−3	−33	−1
Zinc	55	33	−8	−33
Lead	10	3	20	−32
Phosphate rock	16	13	−1	4
Ores, minerals, and nonferrous metals	48	2	−9	−11
Primary products	18	2	−3	−4

Source: Handbook of International Trade Statistics, 1993, C.I.A., p. 170.

transform resources from declining-price to rising-price sectors.

A third factor that may lead to worsening terms of trade is technological advances in developed countries. Advanced technology (1) enables the industrial economies to reduce the primary content of final products, (2) enables the wealthy nations to produce high-quality finished products from less valuable or lower-quality primary products, and (3) enables the advanced economies to produce entirely new manufactured products, which are substitutes for existing primary products. These three technological developments are irreversible. The demand for many primary products may be inelastic for price decreases, but in the long run it may be very elastic for price increases. A rise in the price of a raw material provides an incentive for industrial research geared to economizing on the commodity, or substituting something else for it, or producing it in the importing country (Figure 12.7). For example, a fall in the world price of copper may result in only a small increase in the quantity demanded, but a rise in the price of copper may result in the use of aluminum and silicon as permanent substitutes. Such an event has dealt a severe blow to Zambia and Zaire, the economies of which are overwhelmingly dependent on exports of copper ore to developed countries (Figure 12.5).

Griffin (1969) concluded that slow technical development is one of the major factors accounting for the inflexibility of economies in underdeveloped countries. The terms-of-trade difficulties of underdeveloped countries are based on their inability to shift resources from declining to expanding sectors. Until underdeveloped countries reduce structural rigidities by transforming their economic, social, and institutional frameworks, they will continue to experience trade difficulties.

INTERNATIONAL FLOWS OF PRODUCTION FACTORS

◈

Production factors include capital, labor, technology, and entrepreneurial skill. This section discusses the flows of these factors among countries worldwide and the implications of these flows.

Why Production-Factor Flows Occur

Besides trade, movement of international production factors can overcome differences in resource availability among countries. Profit and economic efficiency are the basic forces underlying the demand and supply incentives for international flows of production factors.

From the supply side, the search for more profitable employment of production factors is the primary motive for most factor flows. For example, *capital* commonly goes to places where interest, profits, and capital gains promise to be favorable. Labor—unskilled, technical, or managerial—often flows to where opportunity and potential returns are better. And the incentive in international *technology transfer* results from a desire to tap additional markets. From the demand side, international flows of production factors are frequently initiated in a similar way: The company that needs capital, labor, and technology starts the search in response to its need to lower costs, improve its productive efficiency, and introduce new products.

Let us look at capital flows in detail and then look briefly at labor and technology flows. The market for capital flows is far more efficient and integrated than the markets for labor and technology. The labor and technology markets generally suffer from poor information flows. In addition, the labor market is the most politically and socially sensitive of the international markets—and the most heavily regulated.

Forms of Capital Flow

Capital movement takes two major forms. The first type involves lending and borrowing money. Lenders and borrowers may be in either the private or the public

Harvesting coffee in Colombia. Coffee plantations have survived independence movements, having been originally established by European colonization. Coffee plantations are mainly run by multinational corporations. Plantations were established in the most agriculturally rich areas of the tropics and the work force was originally slave labor. The world's largest coffee exporter, Colombia, also exports bananas and flowers, not to mention illegal cocaine. The capital, Bogota, looks very Americanized, but the rest of the country is struggling with important social, economic, and political problems. *(Photo: Diego Goldberg/Sygma.)*

sector. The public sector includes governments or international institutions such as the World Bank and agencies of the United Nations.

The second type of capital movement involves investments in the equity of a company. If a long-term investment does not involve managerial control of a foreign company, it is called *portfolio investment*. If the investment is sufficient to obtain managerial control, it is called *direct investment*. Multinational corporations are the epitome of direct investors.

Sources of Capital Flow

Monetary capital is the result of historical development. Unlike a natural resource like iron ore, it must be accumulated with time as a result of the willingness of a society to defer consumption. Low-income countries have low capacities to generate investment capital; all the capital that they do generate is usually employed domestically. Developed countries have much greater capacities for generating investment capital. They provide most of the world's private-sector capital, although a few fast-growing underdeveloped countries, such as South Korea, are also capital exporters.

Optimally, financial markets should produce an efficient distribution of money and capital throughout the world. However, there are many barriers to optimal distribution. Personal preferences of investors, practices of investment banking houses, and governmental intervention and controls confine money and capital movements to well-worn paths. They flow to some areas and not to others, even though the need in neglected areas may be greater.

International Money and Capital Markets

The global expansion of the financial system has three components: the internationalization of (1) domestic currency, (2) banking, and (3) capital markets. *International currency markets* developed with the establishment of floating exchange rates in 1973 and with the growth in private international liquidity, mostly in the form of Eurocurrencies. The growth of Eurocurrencies was only partly a reflection of the decline of the dollar, because the dollar remains the major trading currency. It was more the result of continued integration of the world economy—with the growing internationalization of productive and financial capital—and the result of increased competition among financial institutions, especially the commercial banks.

What are Eurocurrencies? *Eurocurrencies* are bank deposits that are not subject to domestic banking legislation. With relatively few exceptions, they are held in outside countries, "offshore" from the country in which they serve as legal tender. They have accommodated a large part of the growth of world trade since the late 1960s. The Eurocurrency market is attractive because it provides funds to borrowers with few conditions; it also offers investors higher interest rates than can be found in comparable domestic markets.

EURODOLLARS

At first, Euromarkets involved U.S. dollars deposited in Europe; hence, they were called *Eurodollar* markets. Although the dollar still represents about 80% of all Eurocurrencies, other currencies, such as the deutschemark and yen, are also vehicles of international transactions. Therefore, *Eurocurrencies* is preferred to the less accurate term *Eurodollar*. However, even *Eurocurrencies* is a misnomer. Only 50% of the market is in Europe, the major center of which is London. Other Eurocenters have developed in the Bahamas, Panama, Singapore, and Bahrain.

Eurocurrencies first became significant with the growth in the Eurodollar deposits of the former Soviet Union. In the immediate postwar years, the Soviets doubted the safety of holding dollar reserves in the United States (where they could be confiscated) and transferred them to banks in Paris and London. However, three occurrences added impetus to the market in Eurocurrencies. First, during 1963 and 1964, President Kennedy, worried by the increased flow of dollars abroad, announced a program of capital control that lasted until 1973. As a consequence, international borrowers looked to Europe and the Eurocurrencies market. The main borrowers were U.S. multinational corporations raising loans to continue their expansion abroad. Second, in 1971, the United States began to finance its budget deficit by paying its own currency and flooded the world with dollars that helped to fuel worldwide inflation. Third, the oil crises of the 1970s were a major stimulus to the growth of Euromarkets. *Petrodollars* (OPEC oil surpluses) poured into the major Eurobanks.

The city of London is a major center of Eurocurrencies, international banking, and capital markets.
(Photo: British Tourist Authority.)
Because American banks were not happy with government controls in the post-war period, they began setting up branches overseas. This was called moving "off-shore." These off-shore deposits, whether they came from the United States or Japan, were called "Eurodollars." They were gladly received by most international banks because they were not regulated by national banking controls. London became the center of Eurocurrencies. Because banks were able to make loans on the basis of their Eurodollar accumulations, off-shore banking business expanded rapidly during the 1970s and 1980s, leading to the internationalization of world finance. Eurocurrency deposits increased much more rapidly than official country reserves, allowing international money markets and international banks to take over international finance from their own governments. Major banks, such as Citibank or Chase Manhattan, expanded rapidly in the 1960s and 1970s, returning high rates of profit.

THIRD WORLD DEBT CRISIS

The banks had to find outlets for all the money that they suddenly found in their coffers. One outlet was to send money to Third World countries. Commercial lending to underdeveloped countries—along with official lending and aid—grew rapidly between 1974 and 1982. As a result, the total debt of underdeveloped countries rose fourfold, from about $140 billion at the end of 1974 to about $560 billion in 1982. Third World countries were happy to take advantage of this unaccustomed access to cheap loans with few strings attached. The borrowing enabled them to maintain domestic growth. However, these countries could not pay off the debts that they incurred, so now a widespread *debt crisis* exists among them, especially in Central and South American countries such as Mexico, Brazil, and Argentina (Figure 12.8, Table 12.4).

In 1982, top-level bankers expressed concern about the stability of the international monetary system. The cause of this instability was the overexpansion of credit, particularly through the Eurocurrency market in the 1960s and 1970s, which led to a crisis that had its roots in the overaccumulation of capital and the declining rate of profit. The general crisis of a declining rate of profit was exacerbated by the imbalances caused by the oil-price hikes of the 1970s.

The financial crisis came to a head in 1982. A sharp

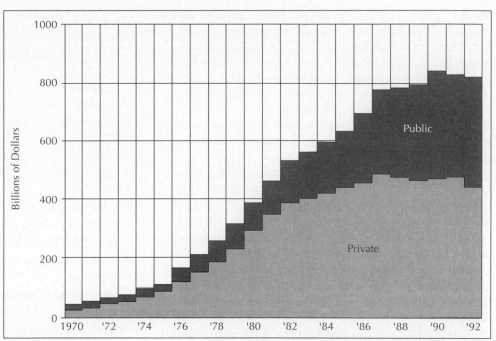

The external debt of developing countries (billion $) grew substantially between 1970 and 1992. It consists of two parts: the public debt, which is owed to foreign governments, and the private debt, which is owed to private banks. *(Source: International Monetary Fund, 1991, p. 24.)* The developed world was shocked in 1982 when Mexico defaulted on its loans. African countries also had a bout with debt rescheduling in the 1970s and 1980s. The Mexican default was followed by defaults in Brazil and Venezuela in 1983 and Peru in 1985, hitting the major banks of the United States the hardest. By the end of 1993, North American and European commercial banks were owed $400 billion by debtor countries. Risky lending practices in the 1970s, on the part of the banks, coupled with mismanagement and squandering on bad projects on the part of the debtor nations, were largely to blame for the international debt crisis. Other contributing factors were the international downturn in the economy in the 1980s, the stranglehold on developing nations by OPEC for importing oil, the doubling of world interest rates, causing debt payment to go up, and the plummeting of commodity prices on the world markets, reducing foreign revenue for third world nations.

rise in bankruptcies involving industrial capital put pressure on the banks and other financial institutions. In May 1982, when the American brokerage Drysdale went bankrupt, the heavy losses sustained by Chase Manhattan Bank forced the Federal Reserve Bank to

◈

T a b l e   12.4

Selected Heavily Indebted Less Developed Countries, 1989

Country	Total External Debt (Billions of Dollars)	External Debt as a Percentage of GNP
Brazil	111	35
Mexico	96	48
Argentina	65	123
India	63	27
Indonesia	53	56
Venezuela	33	75
Nigeria	33	114
Philippines	29	66
Thailand	23	32
Chile	18	72
Colombia	17	44

Source: World Bank, 1991, pp. 244–245, 250–251.

pump approximately $3 billion into the banking system. Worse followed. In August 1982, Mexico ran into difficulties meeting interest and capital payments on its debts. Brazil and Argentina also appeared ready to default. A collapse of the financial system was forestalled by a series of emergency measures designed to prevent large debtor countries from defaulting on their loans. These measures involved banks, the International Monetary Fund (IMF), the Bank for International Settlements, and the governments of lending countries in massive bail-out exercises that accompanied debt reschedulings. The debt overhang persists in the 1990s because debt-service ratios—annual interest and amortization payments as a percentage of total exports—remain at dangerously high levels. In 1990, it was estimated that Third World external debt was equal to 45% of Third World gross national product (GNP) (World Bank, 1992). Consequently, the Third World is extremely vulnerable to changes in the world economy.

INTERNATIONAL BANKING

Paralleling the internationalization of domestic currency is the *internationalization of banking*. International banks have existed for centuries; for example, banking houses such as the Foggers, the Medici, and the Rothschilds helped to finance companies, governments, voyages of discovery, and colonial operations. The banks of the great colonial powers—Great Britain and France—have long been established overseas. American, Japanese, and other European banks went international much later. Major American banks—Bank of America, Citicorp, Chase Manhattan—moved into international banking in the 1960s, and the Japanese banks and their European counterparts in the 1970s. Today, Japanese-based banks, such as Sumitomo Bank, Fuji Bank, and Mitsubishi Bank, surpass the U.S.-based banks in global banking.

Banks were dragged into international banking because of the explosion of foreign investment by industrial corporations in the 1950s and 1960s. The banks of different countries "followed the flag" of their domestic customers abroad. Once established overseas, many of the banks found international banking highly profitable. From their original focus on serving their domestic customers' international activities, banks evolved to service foreign customers as well, including foreign governments.

As we said, a major problem for the banks is that their Third World lending decisions were often imprudent and resulted in excessive indebtedness. They lent too much money. For example, in 1981, the ratio of the banks' capital to total assets was around 4%, whereas in the early nineteenth century it was about 40%. Loans to Mexico from the Bank of America amounted to more than 70% of the bank's capital. Thus, the banks have a collective interest in the debts of other countries. In 1990, Mexico's foreign debt was more than $100 billion. Mexico owed $26 billion to U.S. banks and the rest to multilateral lending institutions, Western Europe, and Japan. If indebted countries such as Mexico were to default, a number of global banks would fail. The result would be dim prospects for further internationalization of banking and capital and for continued growth in the world economy in the 1990s.

CAPITAL MARKETS

Capital markets, or long-term financial markets, form the third component of the international financial system. Stock exchanges, futures exchanges, and tax havens have proliferated. American, European, and Asian multinational corporations take advantage of *tax-haven countries*, countries near their home countries where taxes on foreign-source income and/or capital gains are low or nonexistent (Table 12.5). The internationalization of capital markets has made international finance a round-the-clock business, with trade in currencies, stocks, and bonds transversing the world with the passage of the sun.

◈

Table 12.5
Tax and Banking Havens

No Taxation
  Bermuda, Bahamas, Monaco, Cayman Islands, New Hebrides, Macao, Andorra, Anguilla, Maldive, Brunei

Low Taxation
  Virgin Islands, United Arab Emirates, Hong Kong, Isle of Man

Strict Banking Secrecy
  Switzerland, Costa Rica, Andorra

Tax Benefits for Companies
  Jamaica, Antigua, Barbados, Liberia, Bahrain, Philippines, United Kingdom, Luxembourg, Greece, Liechtenstein, Cyprus

Tax Benefits for Shipping Companies
  Panama, United States, Malta, Cyprus

Tax Benefits for Certain People
  Israel, Liberia, Sri Lanka

Financing International Trade

International trade is not primarily a barter transaction. Money for products is transacted as opposed to products for products. Thus, the buyer country must swap its currency, in proportion to the value of the product, for the currency of the exporting country. If a Silo or Circuit City retail chain in the United States wants to buy televisions, video camcorders, or AM/FM stereo cassettes from Japanese firms, the buyer must, unless otherwise agreed upon, convert U.S. dollars to Japanese yen in order to satisfy the terms of the purchase. As in the case with most international transactions—exports and imports—the seller receives payment in the currency of his or her own country, not in the currency of the purchasing country.

The value of the U.S. dollar, compared with foreign currency, is called the dollar's *exchange rate*. An exchange rate is the number of dollars required to purchase one unit of foreign money. For example, in mid-1993, the price of Japanese yen, as stated in U.S. currency, was 101. That is, 1 American dollar would purchase 101 Japanese yen. A Canadian dollar would be purchased for $0.80 in U.S. currency, or 1 U.S. dollar could purchase 1.22 Canadian dollars. Table 12.6 shows that the value of the U.S. dollar strengthened in Europe

◈

Table 12.6

1993 Foreign Exchange Rates (as of June 29)

Country (Unit)	Per One U.S. $	Year Ago
Africa		
Kenya (shilling)	43.85	20.83
Morocco (dirham)	7.40	8.97
South Africa (rand)	3.05	3.17
The Americas		
Argentina (peso)	.87	10,309
Brazil (formerly cruzeiro)	38,461	3745
Canada (dollar)	1.22	1.20
Jamaica (dollar)	20.5	22.62
Mexico (nuevo peso, formerly peso)	3	3096
Asia-Pacific		
Australia (dollar)	1.40	1.33
Hong Kong (dollar)	7.19	7.73
India (rupee)	24	30.77
Japan (yen)	101.4	127.2
New Zealand (dollar)	1.7	1.85
South Korea (won)	673.4	805.8
Tahiti (franc)	93.8	100.9
Europe		
Austria (schilling)	11.04	11.31
Belgium (franc)	31.16	33.06
Great Britain (pound)	.63	.547
Czech/Slovak Republic (koruna)	No market	31.5
Denmark (krone)	6.01	6.176
Finland (mark)	5.33	4.34
France (franc)	5.39	5.40
Germany (mark)	1.60	1.61
Greece (drachma)	205.3	111.9
Ireland (pound)	.66	.59
Italy (lira)	1429	1190
Netherlands (guilder)	1.80	1.77
Norway (krone)	6.61	6.15
Portugal (escudo)	142.2	131.8
Spain (peseta)	118.3	100.9
Sweden (krona)	7.17	5.69
Switzerland (franc)	1.42	1.42
Middle East		
Israel (new shequilim)	2.10	2.54
Turkey (lira)	8929	7692

From Foreign exchange rates. San Diego Union, July 4, 1993.

during 1992/1993, especially in Great Britain, Greece, Italy, Spain, and the Scandinavian countries, as a result of economic stagnation abroad and currency devaluation by European governments. However, the value of the dollar decreased in Asia and the Pacific during the same period. For American travelers, this meant taking a cruise to the Greek Islands or examining the ruins of Rome but postponing the hiking trip to Mount Fuji.

DETERMINING EXCHANGE RATES

If the value of a currency fluctuates according to changes in supply and demand for the currency on the international market, a *floating exchange rate* is in effect. Figure 12.9 shows the relationship between Mexican pesos and U.S. dollars. The demand curve, D, shows dollars sloping downward to the right. U.S. citizens will demand more Mexican pesos if they can be purchased with fewer dollars. Point p_0 suggests that fewer pesos can be purchased with a dollar, whereas Point p_1 suggests that many more pesos are available per dollar. For example, 1 dollar could purchase 3096 pesos in June 1992.

The demand for Mexican pesos in the United States is based on the amount of goods and services that a U.S. citizen wants to purchase in Mexico. A lower exchange rate for the peso makes Mexican goods less expensive to Americans.

In Figure 12.9, the supply of pesos is upward sloping to the right, which suggests that, as the number of dollars increases per 10,000 pesos, more pesos are offered

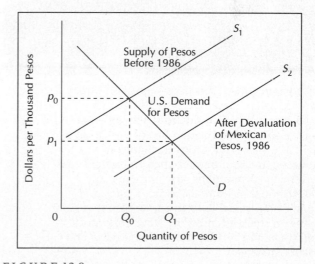

FIGURE 12.9
Determining the exchange rate of the U.S. dollar and the Mexican peso.

in the marketplace. Mexican residents desire more goods from the United States when the dollar exchange rate (price) for the peso is high. The more dollars per 10,000 pesos, the relatively cheaper American products are for Mexicans. Therefore, Mexican residents will demand more dollars with which to purchase American goods and will consequently supply more pesos to foreign-exchange markets when the exchange rate for the peso increases. The equilibrium position is reached when supply and demand conditions for foreign exchange is, therefore, based on supply and demand of international goods produced in Mexico demanded by Americans and American goods demanded by Mexicans.

Line S_2 represents devaluation of the peso because of economic restructuring in Mexico in 1986. This restructuring effectively reduced the number of dollars per 10,000 pesos on the international market. The result was that fewer American products could be purchased for the same amount of pesos because American goods and services became relatively more expensive. Cross-border purchases by Mexican border residents decreased dramatically, as did the international flow of goods and services from America to Mexico. At the same time, the quantity of pesos available to Americans increased from q_0 to q_1. American purchasers poured into border communities and increased their travel to the main tourist destinations within Mexico. The international flow of goods from Mexico to the United States increased because Mexican goods and services were relatively less expensive.

When the dollar appreciates in foreign-exchange markets relative to other currencies, it can buy more foreign currency and, therefore, more goods and services from other countries (Figure 12.10). As a result, American retailers import more goods to the United States. At the same time, the appreciated U.S. dollar means more costly American goods and therefore less demand for them. Exports from America decline under these circumstances. Thus, a so-called strong dollar, which means that the dollar can buy more units of foreign currency, is not always desirable for U.S. trade. Conversely, when the dollar depreciates and is a "weak" dollar, it can buy fewer units of foreign currency and therefore fewer goods and services. Imports usually decline under these circumstances.

Located on Broad Street between Wall Street and Exchange Place, the New York Stock Exchange is a hub of financial activity—not only of the city and nation but of the world as well. The New York Stock Exchange is a domestic financial market open to participation by foreign corporations, governments, and international institutions, as both users and suppliers of funds. Foreign companies also have shares of stock listed on the New York Stock Exchange, just as they do on the London and Tokyo exchanges.
(*Source: New York Convention and Visitors Bureau.*)

WHY EXCHANGE RATES FLUCTUATE

Exchange rates fluctuate for five reasons. First, as a country becomes wealthier and increases its real output and efficiency compared with that of other countries, it imports goods from abroad. The result is that the increased demand for foreign currency raises the exchange rate of the currency and decreases the value of the dollar internationally.

A second factor that influences the exchange rate is the inflation rate of a nation. If the inflation rate of one nation increases faster than that of its trading-partner nations, the currency of the nation with high inflation

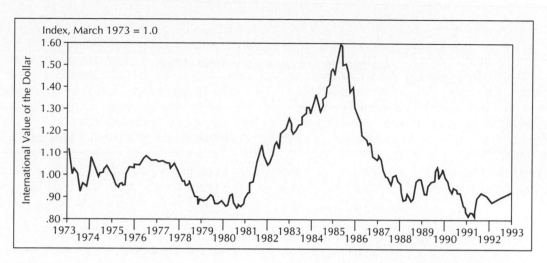

FIGURE 12.10
International value of the dollar, 1973–1993. From 1981 to 1986, the value of the dollar was relatively high compared to other major currencies. Since foreign goods were cheap, the U.S. imports increased, and their exports decreased. The dollar fell abruptly from 1986 to 1988 and has remained relatively weak on international currency exchanges, but the trade deficits continue.
(Source: McConnell and Brue, 1993, p. 425.)

will depreciate compared with the currency of its trading-partner nations. Consequently, the products of the trading-partner nations will be more attractive to consumers in the country with high inflation. For example, when the U.S. inflation rate increases, the demand for Canadian dollars increases. This demand raises the U.S. dollar price of both the Canadian dollar and Canada's goods and services. At the same time, Canadians demand fewer of the comparatively higher-priced U.S. goods. Thus, Canada supplies fewer Canadian dollars to the U.S. foreign-exchange market. As a result, the U.S. dollar depreciates.

Third, domestic demand is a factor in determining exchange rates. Real income growth and the relative price levels between countries affect domestic demand. However, domestic demand also depends on consumer tastes and preferences. Americans will pay higher prices for specialty items and technologically advanced foreign goods than for comparable products at home. Examples of these foreign goods are VCRs and electronic consumer products from Japan, French wines and perfumes, German automobiles, and Italian shoes. A shift in the direction of foreign goods decreases domestic demand and causes the dollar to depreciate.

Fourth, the dollar may appreciate on foreign-exchange markets if interest rates in America increase and, therefore, provide a higher yield to foreign investors who are interested in U.S. assets. Foreign investors

increase their demand for dollars in order to purchase American companies and thus supply more of their foreign currency in exchange for U.S. dollars in the world foreign-exchange markets. In the early 1990s, U.S. interest rates were the lowest in 20 years, so rates on investments were lower than those in foreign nations. Foreign investors, although still drawn to companies, land, and fixed assets, were not drawn to U.S. government securities, and the associated real rates of return were low. Therefore, the dollar continued to depreciate in the early 1990s.

Fifth, currency speculation helps determine exchange rates worldwide. Real events are important in determining exchange rates, just as they are in determining home prices in any U.S. city. However, the expectation of future events is almost as important as actual events. The expectation that economic events will cause the dollar to appreciate or depreciate promotes currency speculation that may, in the not-too-distant future, be a self-fulfilling prophecy. If a major event such as a sudden war or the assassination of a major political figure occurs in a foreign country, it can trigger fear, which encourages individuals to sell the currency of that country to buy dollars. If all people reacted in the same manner to such events, the market would be driven down for that currency against the dollar, and the anticipated depreciation would actually occur.

◈

T a b l e 12.7

Trade in the U.S. Economy, 1960–1991*

	1960		1975		1991	
	Amount†	Percent of GDP	Amount†	Percent of GDP	Amount†	Percent of GDP
Exports of goods and services	$25.3	4.9	$136.3	8.6	$592.5	10.4
Imports of goods and services	22.8	4.4	122.7	7.7	621.9	11.0
Net exports	2.4	0.5	13.6	0.9	−29.4	0.6

* Data are on a national income accounts basis.
† In billions of dollars.
Source: Statistical Abstracts of the United States, 1994, p. 81.

U.S. Trade Deficit

The United States enjoyed a trade surplus throughout most of its history. Starting in 1976, however, the volume of imports began to exceed the volume of exports (Table 12.7). The merchandise *trade deficit* was $25 billion in 1980, but by 1987, it had jumped to $160 billion, then decreased to $74 billion in 1991 (Figure 12.11). What was the cause of the American merchandise trade deficit and the negative trade balance? How has this deficit affected the United States?

CAUSES OF THE U.S. TRADE DEFICIT

Three causes of the U.S. trade deficit are generally cited: the increase in the value of the dollar, the rapid growth of the American economy, and the decrease in the volume of goods exported to less developed countries.

As shown in Figure 12.11, the international value of the dollar increased substantially between 1980 and 1985. This increase meant that American currency and products were expensive to foreign nations, whereas

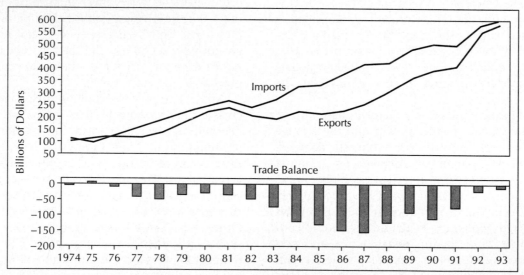

FIGURE 12.11

U.S. merchandise trade, 1974–1993. Until 1970, U.S. export value exceeded the value of imported goods. Since that time, the value of imports have exceeded exports, creating a trade imbalance. The greatest level of trade imbalance occurred betwen 1984 and 1988, mirroring the strong international value of the dollar.
(Source: Statistical Abstracts of the United States. 1994, p. 81.) U.S. Foreign Trade Highlights, 1993, U.S. Department of Commerce, International Trade Admin.)

foreign goods were less expensive to Americans. Consequently, Americans imported a large number of products from other countries—more than they exported. The American government borrowed heavily to finance its deficit. This increased the demand for money locally and boosted interest rates. The high interest rates lured foreign investors to American securities. These investors expected high returns on their investments.

During these Reagan years, the United States shifted to a more stringent policy to control inflation. The money supply was reduced relative to its demand, which kept interest rates high. The low inflation and high interest rates again increased foreign demand for U.S. investments because the real rate of return on investments was high.

By 1985, when the value of the dollar was 60% more than its 1980 average, the deficit was $212 billion. What caused the dollar to decline, and what effect did this have on the trade balance?

As the value of the dollar increased sharply and the volume of foreign imports to America increased, the demand for foreign currency to pay for the expanding volume of imports began to lower the value of the dollar to 1980 levels. In the United States, the demand for yen, marks, francs, pesos, and other currencies increased. At the same time, Great Britain, France, Japan, Germany, and the United States agreed to increase the supply of dollars in foreign-exchange markets to reduce the value of the dollar. The value of the dollar began to shift downward rapidly, but the annual federal deficit persisted through 1994, even though the export-import trade imbalance decreased by 50% from 1987 to 1994.

The second reason for the large trade deficit of the 1980s and 1990s is that the economic growth in America outpaced that of the rest of the world by a large amount. For example, America's growth was three times European growth in 1984, and American growth continued to outpace European growth between 1985 and 1990.

Rapid growth affected domestic consumption, so Americans purchased foreign goods in proportion to their relatively high domestic income. One result was that America, by 1990, had a substantially larger real per capita purchasing power than that of any European country, even though nominal rates in Switzerland, Sweden, and Germany were higher than those in America. This slower European growth meant slower importation of U.S. goods.

The third factor that caused the American trade deficit was the reduction in exports to less developed countries. As the international debt of less developed countries increased in the 1980s, many of those countries, including Mexico, Brazil, and Argentina, restricted the amount of foreign imports and restructured their debts, agreeing to lessen their trade deficits. These austerity programs reduced U.S. exports. With devalued currencies, these countries could not afford U.S. goods. The combined effect was that the United States could export fewer goods to developing countries, while importing a large amount of goods from those countries.

RESULTS OF THE U.S. TRADE DEFICIT

The U.S. deficit had three results: First, a reduction in aggregate demand occurred in the United States. Furthermore, an increase in the volume of imports pushed prices of domestic goods downward as domestic goods competed with imports for consumer demand.

Second, the trade deficit hurt the industries that are highly dependent on international trade. In the 1980s, for example, automobile manufacturers, steel manufacturers, and the American farmer struggled the most because of the trade deficit.

Third, America is now a debtor nation instead of a creditor nation, owing foreign governments more than they owe us. The U.S. foreign debt climbed to $721 billion in 1991, which made the United States the largest debtor nation in the world. In other words, American consumers have been subsidized because more goods and services flowed into the country than flowed out of the country. The reverse is true for Japan and its consumers. America has been living above its means, and consumers have received an economic boost during this period. This boost in domestic living standards is only temporary and not without cost to America. The federal budget deficit and the balance of trade deficit have led to the so-called selling of America to foreign investors. Foreign investors now own 20% of America's total domestic assets.

Classical Capital Theory

In the nineteenth and early twentieth centuries, foreign portfolio investment overshadowed *foreign direct investment* (FDI). Theorists concentrated therefore on foreign portfolio investment, which was directed toward raw-material extraction, agricultural plantations, and trade facilities. The theory of FDI received relatively little attention and remained underdeveloped. Given the massive scale of FDI today, however, an understanding of the rationale for such investment is important. The only help that classical capital theory gives us is that under free-market conditions capital will flow from where it is abundant to where it is in short supply or, in other words, from where the rates of return are low to where they are high.

As with classical trade theory, classical capital theory is macroeconomic. However, in reality international money and capital flows are dependent on managerial decisions. Therefore, it is necessary to examine international capital movements from a microeconomic perspective. Even a brief examination reveals that although foreign investment is a simple process conceptually, a complex of motivations is involved.

Motivation for Foreign Direct Investment

The primary reason for a firm to go international is profit. Three strategic profit motives drive a firm's decision to operate abroad. One motive for many direct investments is to obtain natural or human resources. *Resource seekers* look for raw materials and/or low-cost labor that is also sufficiently productive. A second motive is to penetrate markets, especially when *market seekers* have been prevented from exporting to a particular country. The third goal is to increase operating efficiency. *Efficiency seekers* look for the most economic sources of production to serve a worldwide, standardized market. These three motives are not mutually exclusive. Some segments of a corporation's operation may be aimed at obtaining raw materials, whereas other segments may be aimed at penetrating markets for the products made from the raw materials. These operations may also result in some productive and market efficiencies.

There may be a strong motivation for a firm to internationalize, but there may also be compelling constraints. Prominent among these are the uncertainties of investing or operating in a foreign environment. Consumers' incomes, tastes, and preferences vary from country to country. Japanese consumers, for example, are wary of foreign products, at least those that are not name brands. Cultural differences in business ethics and protocol, attitudes regarding time, and even body language in interpersonal relationships complicate the task of conducting business in two or more languages (McConnell and Erickson, 1986). Added to these barriers are problems relating to currencies, laws, taxation, and governmental restrictions (Stutz, 1992).

Bias in Foreign Direct Investment

Although managers may have the initiative and ability to implement rational investment scenarios, they often take a path of least resistance, which results in a less than ideal allocation of the world's investment capital and of the investors' capital. For example, the direct investment patterns of American companies overseas exhibit considerable bias. In the 1980s, 45% of FDI by American companies was in Europe, 20% in Canada, and 13% in Great Britain, but only 3% was in Japan and less than 2% in Africa (excluding South Africa). These patterns indicate a geographic bias (investing close to home), a cultural bias (investing in countries with similar cultures, especially the same language), and a historical bias (investing in countries to which they are tied historically). Historical bias is often encouraged by the investor's government. This bias maintains a strong national presence in these countries. The trend in the 1990s is for the United States to increase their investment in the Far East, countering past FDI biases.

Origin and Destination of Foreign Direct Investment

The period since World War II has been characterized by a massive flow of FDI associated with the growth of multinational corporations. Capital export was five times more in 1986 than it was in 1970 (United Nations, 1988). The postwar years have seen the development of the international car (Figure 12.12), television set, cassette recorder, and home computer, with different components produced in different countries under the same corporate control. In addition to manufacturing multinationals, the growth of international banks and of service multinationals has been strong. Service multinationals sell services related to business and professional activities—medical, publishing, agrotechnology, warehousing, distribution, computer science, laboratory testing, hotel management, education, entertainment—and personal and social activities. The share of America's outward investment in services increased from 24% in 1975 to 34% in 1990; Great Britain's share, from 29% to 35%; and Japan's share, from 36% to 52%. In the 1990s, a still larger share of outward investment has been devoted to exportable services, particularly those related to improving international markets, such as information. In fact, "the firm may simply be the supplier of information to those essentially national

Foreign direct investment. Ford Motor Company's headquarters in Britain. The Ford Motor Company is a true multi-national corporation with 330,000 employees scattered throughout the world in 30 countries. Although accused of exploiting local labor in developing countries, Ford and other multi-nationals helped to stimulate the economy and, therefore, provide foreign sources of revenue for a struggling economy.
(Source: Ford Motor Company.)

firms responsible for physically moving the goods and services and for investment in fixed industrial assets'' (Robinson, 1981, p. 17).

World Investment by Multinationals

American firms lead the world in FDI, but their share of the total is slipping. Until the early 1970s, U.S.-based multinationals accounted for nearly two-thirds of the world's corporate investment abroad. This figure decreased to 45% in 1977, and it continued to fall throughout the 1980s as corporations headquartered in other countries stepped up their rates of FDI. The rate of increase has been most rapid for companies domiciled in Western Europe and Japan; however, some underdeveloped countries have also increased their outflow of FDI (Figure 12.13). Major bases are Hong Kong, Brazil, Singapore, South Korea, Taiwan, Argentina, Mexico, and Venezuela.

In 1990, the share of stocks held abroad by U.S. companies fell to approximately one-third of the world total. The United Kingdom, a country of only 60 million, ranks in second place, with approximately 15% of world FDI, followed by Japan, a country of 120 million, at 13%. Germany is not far behind with approximately 10%, followed by Switzerland and the Netherlands, each at approximately 6.5%. Other industrialized countries make up 15%, whereas less developed countries make up only 2%.

Significant changes in the destination of FDI are the increased flow to the United States and to the Third World (Figure 12.14). In 1975, the United States accounted for only a small proportion of the stocks held by foreign companies; 10 years later, the United States emerged as a major host country. Investment in the Third World has focused mainly on eight countries—Brazil, Mexico, Singapore, Indonesia, Malaysia, Argentina, Venezuela, and Hong Kong—which accounted for more than one-half the stock for foreign investment in underdeveloped countries in the early 1980s (Figure 12.14). Availability of natural resources, recent strong growth, and political and economic stability were among the factors that attracted foreign investment to these Third World countries.

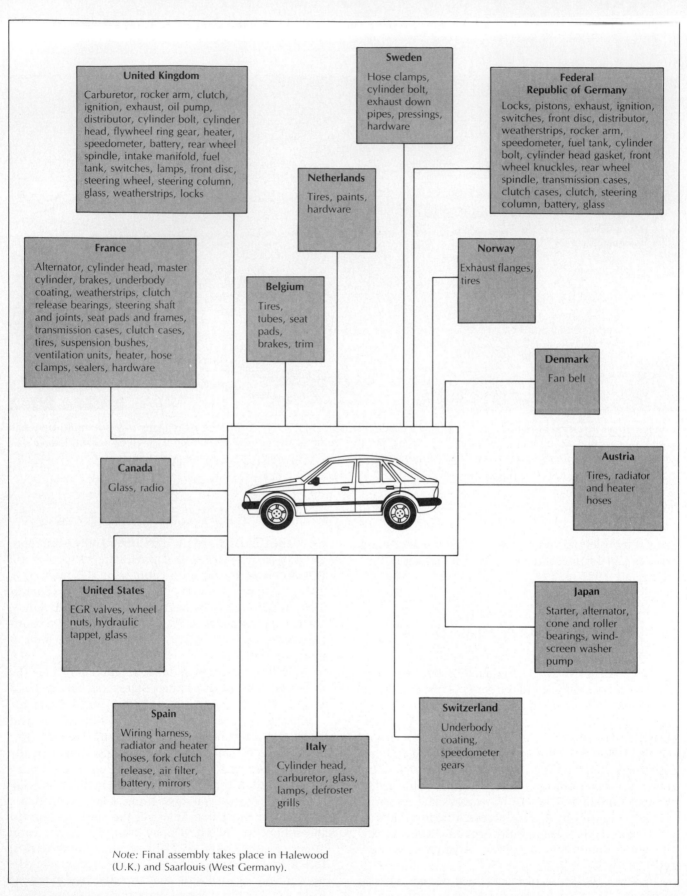

United Kingdom

Carburetor, rocker arm, clutch, ignition, exhaust, oil pump, distributor, cylinder bolt, cylinder head, flywheel ring gear, heater, speedometer, battery, rear wheel spindle, intake manifold, fuel tank, switches, lamps, front disc, steering wheel, steering column, glass, weatherstrips, locks

Sweden

Hose clamps, cylinder bolt, exhaust down pipes, pressings, hardware

Federal Republic of Germany

Locks, pistons, exhaust, ignition, switches, front disc, distributor, weatherstrips, rocker arm, speedometer, fuel tank, cylinder bolt, cylinder head gasket, front wheel knuckles, rear wheel spindle, transmission cases, clutch cases, clutch, steering column, battery, glass

France

Alternator, cylinder head, master cylinder, brakes, underbody coating, weatherstrips, clutch release bearings, steering shaft and joints, seat pads and frames, transmission cases, clutch cases, tires, suspension bushes, ventilation units, heater, hose clamps, sealers, hardware

Netherlands

Tires, paints, hardware

Norway

Exhaust flanges, tires

Belgium

Tires, tubes, seat pads, brakes, trim

Denmark

Fan belt

Canada

Glass, radio

Austria

Tires, radiator and heater hoses

United States

EGR valves, wheel nuts, hydraulic tappet, glass

Japan

Starter, alternator, cone and roller bearings, windscreen washer pump

Spain

Wiring harness, radiator and heater hoses, fork clutch release, air filter, battery, mirrors

Italy

Cylinder head, carburetor, glass, lamps, defroster grills

Switzerland

Underbody coating, speedometer gears

Note: Final assembly takes place in Halewood (U.K.) and Saarlouis (West Germany).

FIGURE 12.12
The international car: the component network for the Ford Escort (Europe).
(Source: Dicken, 1992, p. 301.)

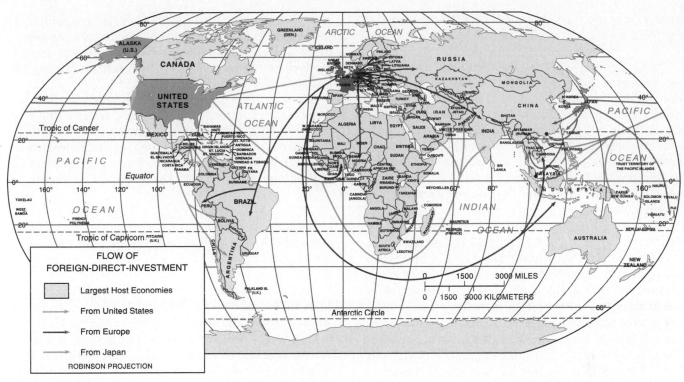

FLOW OF
FOREIGN-DIRECT-INVESTMENT

Largest Host Economies

→ From United States

→ From Europe

→ From Japan

ROBINSON PROJECTION

FIGURE 12.13

Flow of foreign direct investment. Multinational's foreign direct investment originates, for the most part, in the United States, Japan, the United Kingdom, Germany, and France. These transnational corporations have invested most of their resources in other developed countries of the world. In addition, U.S. multinational corporations are more likely than the Japanese or Europeans to invest in Latin America. European multinational corporations are more likely to invest in Eastern Europe and the Middle East, while Japanese transnationals are more likely to invest resources in the Far East. (See color insert 3, page 3.1, top.)

FIGURE 12.14

The stock of foreign investment in underdeveloped countries in percent: (a) where it is (1983); (b) where it came from (1982). *(Source: World Bank, 1987, p. 117.)* The debate rages in the world economy over the value of MNCs to foreign host economies. Local leaders are sometimes skeptical of foreign direct investment because of its local economic influence. Often, domestic companies are damaged by the competition, especially if there is little technological transfer to the host country, and if most all of the high value-added research and design are forthcoming from the investor country. Exploitation of local labor is another burning issue, as well as the fear of national economic dependence on managerial decisions made in a distant foreign investor nation.

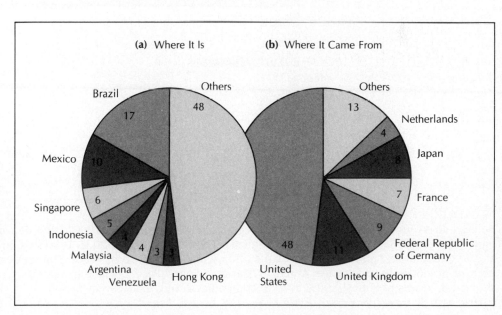

(a) Where It Is

Brazil 17

Others 48

Mexico 10

Singapore 6

Indonesia 5

Malaysia 4

Argentina 4

Venezuela 3

Hong Kong 3

(b) Where It Came From

Others 13

Netherlands 4

Japan 8

France 7

Federal Republic of Germany 9

United Kingdom 11

United States 48

INVESTMENT BY U.S. MULTINATIONALS IN FOREIGN COUNTRIES

The pace of FDI by U.S. multinational corporations has increased since the 1960s. In 1960, almost two-thirds of foreign investment by U.S. companies was in nearby Canadian ventures. Other foreign investment was located in Europe and in Latin America. The Far East saw little investment by U.S. multinationals, partly because of distance, cultural, and political barriers. The pattern changed slightly, and, by 1980, U.S. FDI was positioned chiefly in Europe in principally manufacturing operations.

Figure 12.15 shows that by 1990 Europe still remained the preeminent area for U.S. FDI. In the 1980s, investment in Europe increased by 112%, whereas U.S. investment in Canada increased only 51%. The single greatest proportional increase, however, occurred in the Far East, with nearly a 300% increase in Japan and a 247% increase in Asia and the Pacific, primarily in the Four Tigers of South Korea, Taiwan, Singapore, and Hong Kong, but also in Malaysia and the Philippines. Part of the reason for the increase in investment in the Far East is that the labor-intensive semiconductor assembly plants are located in these cheap-labor countries.

Because of strong Japanese barriers to foreign invest-ment, Japan entertains a relatively small proportion of total FDI by U.S. firms. Another notable and disappointing world region is Africa, which, during the 1980s, received no increase in U.S. FDI, further hurting its opportunities for development.

Until the 1980s, FDI by U.S. firms centered on manufacturing and mining activity; more recently, investment has targeted service activities. By 1990, manufacturing and mining investment by U.S. firms worldwide had decreased to less than 50%, whereas investment in services amounted to 34% and was on the increase.

INVESTMENT BY FOREIGN MULTINATIONALS IN THE UNITED STATES

FDI in the United States grew at an incredible rate from 1970, when it was a skimpy $13 billion, to 1990, when it amounted to $403.7 billion (Table 12.8). In fact, between 1980 and 1989, it increased more rapidly than U.S. foreign investment did (Figure 12.16). The popularity of investing in the United States was a result of the power and stability of the country economically and politically and the relatively inexpensive dollar in world markets. As discussed previously, during the 1970s and 1980s, the United States accumulated an

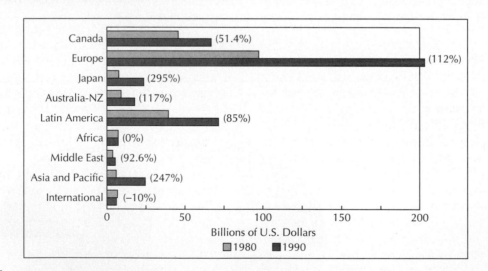

FIGURE 12.15
Foreign direct investment of U.S. firms by region and percent change, 1980–1990. Europe remained the favored destination for U.S.-based multinational investments. The change from 1980 to 1990 was an increase of investment by 112%. Canada and Latin America remained in a virtual tie for second place. The greatest proportional increases, however, came not in Europe or the Americas, but in Asia and Pacific, which increased by 247%, and Japan, which showed increases of almost 300% by U.S. companies during this 10-year-period.
(Source: U.S. Bureau of the Census, 1992b.)

U.S. Ford plant in Europe. General Motors and the Japanese manufacturers of automobiles produce two-thirds to nine-tenths of their products in their home countries. The Ford Motor Company produces two-thirds of its more than 5 million manufactured vehicles abroad.
(Source: Ford Motor Company.)

Ford Motor Company has been one of the most prolific of the American multi-national corporations. The post-war years were the years of most rapid expansion with over 300 new subsidiaries being set up annually between 1960 and 1965 by American companies in foreign countries. American firms saw the advantage of multi-national expansion because post-war markets were developing rapidly for their goods in Europe, Japan and throughout the world. By establishing manufacturing plants in those foreign countries, expensive transportation costs of finished products could be reduced, as well as import duties. A major factor is sometimes overlooked, and that is *transfer pricing*. Japan and European countries have higher rates of corporate tax than does America. Shrewd multi-nationals can invoice their subsidiaries in these foreign countries in such a way to show low profits in high tax countries and vis-versa, and, therefore, shelter their income.

increasing trade deficit. A chain of events created the intense FDI in the United States as a result of this deficit.

The dollar peaked in value internationally in 1985. This peak increased the amount of foreign imports to the United States and decreased the amount of domestic exports. The result was a trade deficit. Between 1985 and 1992, the value of the dollar began to fall. The trade deficit reduced, but a large negative differential still exists. The deficit led to the outflow of American dollars into foreign hands. This money allowed foreign governments and corporations to buy American real estate, as Japan has done, and American factories, as Great Britain has done. Ironically, many foreign firms that sell to U.S. markets found it cheaper to produce products from plants that they own and operate *in* the United States. For instance, foreign multinational corporations such as Honda and Mazda opened plants in America to build automobiles that the U.S. formerly imported from Japan. Land, labor, and capital were cheaper in the United States; therefore, the product was less expensive to produce there.

As a result, foreign investment in the United States increased sharply. The average increase was 33% between 1980 and 1990 (Table 12.8). Almost 1000 new foreign enterprises were founded each year until 1990. However, since 1990, the American trade deficit has been shrinking because the importation of goods to America is being supplanted by the flow of goods from foreign-owned American plants.

As of 1990, because of cultural affinities and the lack of language barriers, the United Kingdom maintained its lead as America's chief foreign investor, boasting 27% (Figure 12.17). Other European nations, especially the Netherlands, Germany, Switzerland, France, and Sweden, in that order, are strong investors in the United States. The Netherlands is especially noteworthy, if we consider its relatively small size. It commands a 16% share of FDI in the United States. Japan, however, had the largest proportional increase in the last 20 years. In 1970, Japan owned only 2% of foreign investment in the United States, but, by 1990, its share had risen more than tenfold to 21%.

Table 12.8

Foreign Direct Investment Position in the United States—Value, by Area and Industry: 1980–1990

Area and Industry	1980	1982	1983	1984†	1985†	1986†	1987†	1988	1989	1990, prel.
All areas‡	83,046	124,677	137,061	164,583	184,615	220,414	263,394	314,754	373,763	403,735
Petroleum	12,200	17,660	18,209	25,400	28,270	29,094	37,815	36,006	37,201	38,004
Manufacturing	32,993	44,065	47,665	51,802	59,584	71,963	93,865	122,582	151,820	159,998
Finance and insurance	12,027	17,933	10,934	24,881	27,429	34,978	39,455	44,010	58,215	58,437
Trade, wholesale and retail	15,210	23,604	26,513	31,219	35,973	42,920	45,399	53,590	55,310	61,996
Canada	12,162	11,708	11,434	15,286	17,131	20,318	24,684	26,583	28,686	27,733
Petroleum	1817	1550	1391	1544	1589	1432	1088	1181	1233	1417
Manufacturing	5227	3500	3313	4115	4607	6108	8085	9730	9934	9327
Finance and insurance	1612	1801	1061	3245	4008	4283	5797	5769	7227	7325
Europe	54,688	83,193	92,936	108,211	121,413	144,181	161,006	208,942	242,961	256,496
Petroleum	10,137	15,071	16,326	23,142	25,636	26,139	35,700	33,499	32,476	31,197
Manufacturing	21,953	33,032	36,866	39,083	45,841	56,016	74,300	95,641	120,132	125,568
Finance and insurance	8673	12,601	8450	15,945	17,022	21,787	26,336	27,121	31,609	30,329
United Kingdom	14,105	28,447	32,152	38,387	43,555	55,935	75,519	95,698	105,511	108,055
Petroleum	− 257	5444	5955	10,991	12,155	11,758	17,950	19,522	16,545	15,310
Manufacturing	6159	8504	9221	9170	11,687	16,500	30,372	41,708	51,798	52,955
Finance an insurance	3350	5661	3777	5485	6483	10,163	9801	11,256	11,859	13,139
Netherlands	19,140	26,191	29,182	33,728	37,956	40,717	46,636	48,128	56,316	64,333
Petroleum	9265	8098	8646	9981	11,481	(D)	(D)	9045	9889	10,527
Manufacturing	4777	9901	11,222	12,497	13,351	13,293	15,615	17,843	23,709	24,446
Switzerland	5070	6378	7464	8146	10,568	12,058	13,772	14,372	18,772	17,512
Manufacturing	3116	3584	4165	4774	6881	7520	6921	7613	10,412	9113
Finance and insurance	1033	1473	1830	(D)	5425	2517	3211	3506	4671	4947
West Germany	7596	9850	10,845	12,330	14,816	17,250	21,905	25,250	29,015	27,770
Manufacturing	3875	4239	4497	4389	6015	7426	10,298	13,980	15,722	15,216
Finance and insurance	1248	1426	1416	1902	(D)	1962	3442	2683	3396	2767
Other Europe§	8777	12,327	13,293	15,620	15,417	18,221	23,174	25,494	33,347	38,826
Petroleum	991	1380	1679	2080	(D)	(D)	(D)	4580	4920	4760
Manufacturing	4026	6804	7771	7704	7907	11,277	11,094	14,497	18,491	23,838
Finance insurance	1193	429	− 900	(D)	(D)	(D)	2189	406	2574	1119
Japan	4723	9677	11,336	16,044	19,313	26,824	34,421	51,126	67,319	83,498
Other Areas	11,472	20,099	21,356	25,043	26,758	29,091	23,283	28,120	34,797	36,008

† D = Withheld to avoid disclosure of data of individual companies.
‡ Area totals include industries not shown separately.
§ Direct investments in 1990 (in millions of dollars): Belgium and Luxembourg, 6061; France, 19,550; Italy, 1552; and Sweden, 5450.
Source: U.S. Bureau of Economic Analysis. 1991, and earlier issues.

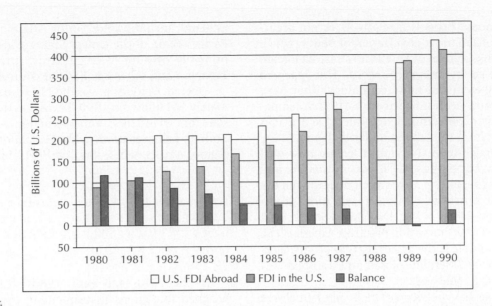

FIGURE 12.16

U.S. foreign direct investment balance, 1980–1990. Until 1980, foreign direct investment in the United States by foreign multinationals was a fraction of the investment abroad by U.S. multinationals. In 1980, $200 million were invested abroad by the U.S. multinationals, while only $100 million was invested in the United States by foreign multinationals. This yielded a positive balance of more than $100 billion. That positive balance has been steadily eroded as the percentage of FDI in the United States has steadily increased at a more rapid rate than U.S. FDI abroad. In 1988, they both stood at approximately $330 billion. After a slight deficit in 1989, U.S. FDI abroad surged past FDI in the United States in 1990.

(Source: U.S. Bureau of the Census, 1992b.)

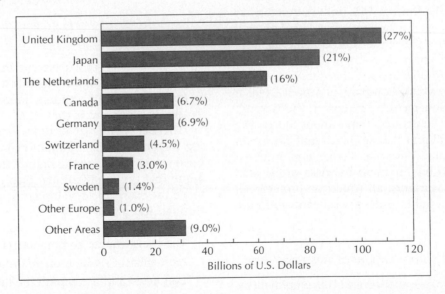

FIGURE 12.17

Foreign direct investment (FDI) in the United States by country, 1990. FDI in the United States is defined by the U.S. Bureau of the Census as all U.S. companies in which foreign interest or ownership is 10% or more. Demonstrating cultural affinity and historical inertia, the United Kingdom remains the largest single country for FDI in the United States. While Europe remains relatively strong, its position is being eroded by Japan and other Far Eastern countries. In 1970, Japan's FDI in the United States amounted to only 2%. By 1990, it was 21%. Canada's position has fallen from 31% in 1970 to only 6.7%. Other areas include primarily the Four Tigers of the Pacific Basin and Middle Eastern oil-exporting countries.

(Source: U.S. Bureau of the Census, 1992b.)

FDI by Japanese firms is a relatively recent occurrence because of Japanese governmental policy, which regulates capital outflows in an effort to restrict foreign exchange claimed by other countries. The Japanese have been slow to invent new technology. They have found it much more economical to invest in U.S. companies and thereby export knowledge-intensive activities and technology from the United States to Japan. Many of these knowledge-intensive industries are now well placed in Japan, but because of import restrictions and the high price of Japanese currency compared with the dollar, Japanese firms have found it even more profitable to sell to their chief buyer, the United States, from Japanese-owned manufacturing plants in America. The most notable example is the accumulation of Japanese-owned automobile-assembly plants and autoparts industries in the U.S. Midwest.

The Japanese have exported their labor-intensive industries to developing countries, where the labor rate is much lower. Notable locations include Australia, the Middle East, Brazil, and East Asia.

FDI in the United States is centered on manufacturing, chemicals, electrical machinery, electronics, pharmaceuticals, and services. Japanese investment also has controlling interests in 60 U.S. steel operations, 25 rubber and tire factories, 10 automobile-assembly plants, and 300 autoparts distributors. U.S. public attention has been heightened by recent Japanese purchases of retail and service industries that have been considered, until now, all-American industries—owned by Americans for Americans. Examples include the purchase of Columbia Records; the Music Company of America, which owns several motion-picture studios in Hollywood; Rockefeller Center; Federated Department Stores; the famous Spyglass Hill and Pebble Beach golf courses in Monterey, California; Yosemite Lodge and National Park Company. When Japanese interests anticipated buying the Seattle Mariners, an American professional baseball franchise, a public outcry was heard across the United States.

Foreign Direct Investment in the United States by Region

Similar to the U.S. population and U.S. employment, FDI in the United States has moved west. The original pattern of investment in the Middle Atlantic and Great Lakes states of the north central United States has been historically strong by British and other European nations, including Canada. Canadian investment has been the strongest, not unexpectedly, along the border states from the western north central region through New England, including the South Atlantic states. But the Pacific region of the United States leads overall in FDI, primarily because of recent heavy investment by the Japanese and other Far Eastern countries.

Overall, California was the FDI leader with approximately $61 billion in 1990. Texas was the second largest state for FDI in 1989, with $48 billion, followed by New York as a distant third, with $32 billion. In the Pacific region, Alaska was second with $19 billion.

BALANCE BETWEEN U.S. FOREIGN DIRECT INVESTMENT AND FOREIGN DIRECT INVESTMENT IN THE UNITED STATES

In the 1970s and early 1980s, U.S. FDI far outweighed foreigners' investment in the United States. However, in 1988 and 1989, U.S. FDI was slightly less than investment by foreign companies in America. Since 1989, however, U.S. foreign investment has surpassed FDI in the United States, so the balance is now a positive $20 billion rather than a deficit as in 1989.

Effects of Foreign Direct Investment

Are the effects of widespread FDI desirable? Should the operations of multinationals be controlled? There is no unanimity of opinion, particularly when Third World development is the issue.

There are two polar attitudes among scholars regarding the presence of multinationals in the underdeveloped world. Those on the right of the political spectrum argue that the multinational firm has a high potential to aid the economic development process. According to Herman Kahn (1973)

The transnational corporation (TNC) is probably the most efficient social, economic and political institution ever devised to accomplish the following tasks for the less developed nations:

(1) Raising, investing, and reallocating capital.

(2) Creating and managing organizations.

(3) Innovating, adopting, perfecting and transferring technology.

(4) Distribution, maintenance, marketing, and sales (including trained personnel and providing financing).

(5) Furnishing local elites with suitable—perhaps ideal—career choices.

(6) Educating and upgrading both blue collar and white collar labour (and elites).

(7) In many areas, and in the not-so-distant future, serving as a major source of local savings and taxes and in furnishing skilled cadres (i.e., graduates) of all kinds to the local economy (including the future local competition of the TNC).

(8) Facilitating the creation of vertical organizations or vertical arrangements which allow for the smooth, reliable, and effective progression of goods from one stage of production to another. In many cases, while such organization is a partial negation of the classical free market, it is still often a very efficient and useful method of stable and growing production and distribution.

(9) Finally, and almost by themselves, providing both a market and a mechanism for satellite services and industries that can stimulate local development much more effectively than most (official) aid programmes.

Of course, the transnational corporation is not doing any of this for altruistic or public interest reasons (though sometimes elements of such motivations are important), nor do TNCs always operate in the best interest of the host country. I am simply saying that under proper conditions the above nine points should, and in fact often do, hold at least to an important degree. (p. 2)

This view is in marked contrast to that of scholars who argue that the multinational corporation is counterproductive to development. In the view of *dependency theorists*, modern capital-intensive industry does not result in rapidly increasing employment. "Its development as an enclave with limited links with the surrounding economy reduces its effectiveness in propagating change . . ." (Livingstone, 1971, p. 244).

Furthermore, multinationals engender balance-of-payments problems because of heavy profit repatriations. Although the balance-of-payments problem could be avoided, in part, if multinational firms reinvested more of their profits in the host country, it is uncertain that the national interest would be served. Reinvestment causes "growing foreign control of the economy and the denationalization of local industry" (Griffin, 1969, p. 148). The multinational firm is an assault on political sovereignty. Moreover, "[the] transnational system internationalizes the tendency to unequal development and to unequal income" (Galbraith, 1973, p. 174).

The contentions of dependency theorists, however, do not always stand up to empirical verification. To illustrate, de Souza, 1985 tested the relationship between multinational corporation (MNC) penetration and average annual percentage growth in per capita GNP. Growth rates in per capita GNP from 1962 to 1982 were regressed on the logarithm of 1967 MNC penetration scores. Data on growth rates were from the World Bank (1984), and information on the extent to which countries are penetrated by multinationals was from Thanh-Huyen Ballmer-Cao and Jürg Scheidegger (1979). Ballmer-Cao and Scheidegger defined MNC penetration as the ratio of capital controlled by multinationals to the geometric mean of domestic capital and population. The 1967 figures were taken by de Souza to represent the initial level of penetration. The correlation between MNC penetration and subsequent economic growth was weak ($r = -0.208$). A separate correlation for First World countries was also weak ($r = -0.317$). A scattergram revealed no systematic relationship between MNC penetration and subsequent economic growth in Third World countries, nor for that matter in First World countries. The results of this bivariate test tempt one to conclude that the dependency paradigm is insufficient to explain differential patterns of economic growth among countries. It seems that endogenous factors, particularly the autonomous role of the state, may have more to do with economic growth than such exogenous influences as the role of the MNC.

To be sure, multinationals are imperfect organs of Third World development, and their potential for the exploitation of poor countries is tremendous. There is, therefore, an inherent tension between the multinational's desire to integrate its activities on a global basis and the host country's desire to integrate an affiliate with its national economy. Maximizing corporate profits does not necessarily maximize national economic objectives. Stephen Krasner (1985) pointed to the many issues over which conflict could develop:

> Host-country governments generally prefer that vertical links be established among operations within their national boundaries; MNCs may prefer to locate upstream and downstream facilities in other countries. The technology possessed by multinationals has usually been developed in industrialized countries. Less developed countries may prefer technology more suited to the local environment. Multinationals have been accused of introducing inappropriate products to developing countries, products that may be tolerable in wealthier countries but involve a misallocation of resources in poorer ones. Similarly, multinationals have been accused of generating tastes and preferences that reflect standards in rich countries but are inappropriate for poor ones. Fundamental decisions about corporate activity are taken by executives in advanced countries whose behavior cannot be directly controlled by host-country officials. Because they can affect economic performance, tastes, and the direction of development, MNCs pose a threat to the functional control a state can exercise within its own territorial boundaries. (pp. 179–180)

Conflicts with host countries are a feature of multinational corporate activity. To deal with multinationals, governments have introduced rules and regulations regarding the establishment of branches, repatriation of profits, debt refinancing, employment of nationals, and tax rates. However, formal rules and regulations are one thing; effective control is another. Aside from nationalization, no government action guarantees total and effective control.

In general, the relative bargaining power of host countries has increased with time because the number of multinationals has grown; thus host countries have a wider range of choice. Larger and wealthier Third World countries have more bargaining leverage. A consumer-products manufacturing corporation will accept more controls to gain access to a country with a large market. Finally, the degree of host-country control varies across industries. Manufacturing industries with advanced and dynamic technologies are more difficult to control than firms in the raw-materials area.

Third World countries have changed the rules of the game for FDI. The new rules, however, have made corporations hesitant to risk large amounts of capital in the raw-materials area and in smaller and poorer Third World countries. Corporations prefer to invest in countries that follow an outward-oriented development strategy, impose few controls, offer incentives, and therefore appreciate the employment, skills, exports, and import substitutes that foreign investment can bring. The newly industrializing countries (NICs) exemplify this posture, and they do not align themselves with Third World countries that want to see multinational activity regulated.

Labor and Technology Flows

Besides capital, labor and technology constitute the other readily movable production factors. International labor flows fall into two categories: unskilled and highly skilled (technological and managerial). Unskilled labor flows occur on large scales in various parts of the world, as we saw in Chapter 3. Aside from political and religious motivations, workers migrate for income reasons and also for learning purposes. A smaller number of migrants may be motivated by a desire to travel or to get away from family or locale. Technological and managerial labor flows occur on a much smaller scale. These flows involve the permanent emigration of highly skilled professionals, managers, and technicians—the so-called brain drain. Flows of highly skilled labor may also result from the temporary assignment of managers and technicians abroad. Increasing immigration and even guestworker controls are being imposed by countries to limit the effect of foreigners. These controls are tighter for the unskilled than for the highly skilled. They are partly responsible for the movement of capital to labor-abundant areas.

Technology is internationally mobile, but its markets are fragmented and inefficient. It may be subject to control by a firm's parent government. On the other hand, it may be encouraged by a host country, which can help to introduce a company's products into a new market. Technology transfer may be the only way that a company can penetrate restricted markets.

BARRIERS TO INTERNATIONAL BUSINESS

Just as trade can, international flows of the production factors can help to reduce imbalances in the distribution of natural resources. Whereas trade *offsets* differences in factor endowments, factor movements *reduce* these differences. International trade and factor flow would occur more commonly if barriers did not exist. The main barriers relate to management, distance, and government.

Management Barriers

A number of managerial characteristics reduce trade and investment expansion. These characteristics include limited ambition, unawareness of opportunity, lack of skills, fear, and inertia.

LIMITED AMBITION

Firms may have the potential to expand but fail to do so because they are *satisficers*—settle for less than the optimal. Until the economic crisis of the 1970s, many U.S. firms paid little attention to foreign markets. They were satisfied with the large domestic market.

UNRECOGNIZED OPPORTUNITY

Firms may have the will to go international but may lack knowledge of potential markets. "Even the largest multinational firms cannot possibly access, much less interpret, all of the potential information about other countries that may be available. Managers' mental maps and images of world order, including such aspects as size, shape, proximity, intensity of activities, or geopolitical affiliations, are relative and reflect considerable amounts of distortion from reality" (McConnell and Erickson, 1986, p. 101). The burden of recognizing export opportunities rarely falls on the managers of individual companies, however. Most national and local governments are actively involved in increasing international awareness and in promoting exports.

LACK OF SKILLS

Firms may have the potential and will to go international *and* an awareness of the opportunities, but they may be thwarted by the complexity of international business and ignorance of foreign cultures. Governments and universities can aid companies by providing education. Knowledge of intermodal rate structures, freight forwarders, shipping conferences, and customshouse brokers (firms that contract to bring other companies' imported goods through local customs) is vital for the conduct of international business. Just as necessary is a knowledge of foreign cultures. According to McConnell and Erickson (1986), "More than a few international business 'blunders' can be attributed to a lack of information or misinterpretation of basic cultural patterns" (p. 101). In the past, for example, U.S. firms

Manufacturing of electronics in Shinjuku, near Tokyo, Japan. Shinjuku is one of the busiest manufacturing locales in Japan. *(Photo: Kuninori Takahashi, Impact Visuals.)* Japan enjoys a $60 billion plus *export surplus*. Its largest trading partner is the United States. The manufacture of electronics and automobiles has been its most important export product. Because Japan is in a severe recession, having lost 50 percent of its equity on the Japanese stock exchange, Japan refuses to lower trade barriers to United States products. It has had a long history of such seemingly unfair trade practices. The stage is set for a new trade war between Japan and the United States, consequently.

could not penetrate the Japanese market, partly because of a failure to appreciate the Japanese culture. This is changing. American entrepreneurs are no longer likely to lose deals by forgetting respectful bows at the beginning of meetings.

FEAR AND INERTIA

Firms may avoid international business activities because of a fear of the unknown or what is foreign—different currencies, laws, documentation requirements, taxation, political systems, languages, and customs. They may also fail to capitalize on opportunities because of inertia.

Distance as a Barrier

Companies that go international confront the geographic distance barrier. Obviously, distance affects international business in that all movement costs money. But the international movement of goods is not restricted to line-haul costs. Shipments of goods to foreign destinations incur bank collection charges, freight forwarders' and customs-house brokers' fees, consular charges, and cartage expenses. These costs entail extra clerical costs for preparing bills of lading (receipts given by carriers to exporters), customs declarations, and other shipping documents. Adding these terminal costs to line-haul costs yields a total outlay called *transfer costs*, which make goods more expensive to importers and less valuable to exporters. As we saw in Chapter 6, total transportation costs vary from commodity to commodity. They are higher on finished goods than on bulk shipments of raw materials requiring less care and less special handling. Small firms must pay what the market will bear. However, multinationals, through intrafirm trade, have the opportunity to practice *transfer pricing*—fixing prices for the movement of goods between affiliates.

Distance also influences trade in ways other than cost. Commercial relations are often smoother and less complicated between neighboring countries, if only because managers are more aware of export opportunities. Propinquity brings with it the possibility of frequent contact. A high level of interaction between neighboring countries enables each to better understand the other's economic and political system and culture.

Government Barriers to Trade

No country permits a free flow of trade across its borders. Governments have erected barriers to achieve objectives regarding trade relationships and indigenous economic development. Trade barriers include *tariffs*—schedules of taxes or duties levied on products as they cross national borders—and *nontariff barriers*—quotas, subsidies, licenses, and other restrictions on imports and exports. These kinds of obstacles (apart from *political bloc prohibitions*) are the most pervasive barriers to trade.

COSTS OF PROTECTION

Free marketeers advocate free trade because it promotes increased economic efficiency and productivity as a result of international specialization. They argue that trade, a substitute for factor movements, benefits each participating nation and that deviation from free trade will inhibit production. It follows, then, that *protectionism* will adversely affect the welfare of the majority. For example, it is estimated that in 1983 every dollar spent to preserve employment in the U.S. steel industry cost consumers $35 and amounted to a net loss of $25 for the economy (World Bank, 1988).

What are some of the major arguments in favor of protectionism? One of the most common is the cheap foreign-labor argument, which suggests that a country such as the United States with its high union wages must protect itself against a country such as Taiwan with its low-paid workers. This argument contradicts the principle of comparative advantage. Other more compelling arguments appeal to national gain. One argument asserts that a country with market power can improve its terms of trade with a tax that forces down the price at which other countries sell to it. Another argument is that tariffs can be used to divert demand from foreign to domestic goods so as to shift a country's employment problem onto foreign nations. Still another argument is that tariffs can be used to protect an infant industry that is less efficient than a well-established industry in another country. The *infant-industry argument* was invoked to justify protectionist policies in nineteenth- and twentieth-century America and nineteenth-century Germany (Figure 12.18). It was also used to justify the protection that developed in the Third World in the 1960s. Although these arguments have some merit, free marketeers recommend other ap-

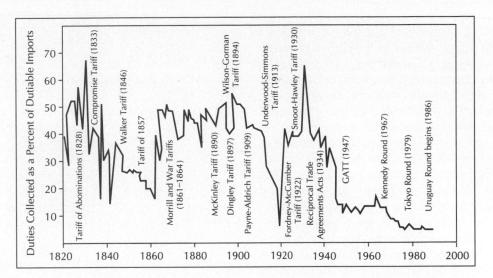

FIGURE 12.18
U.S. tariff fluctuations, 1820–1992. Compared to the inception of General Agreement on Tariffs and Trades (GATT) in 1947, U.S. tariff rates have been historically high. They reached a peak during this century in the mid-1930s, with the Smoot-Hawley tariff, designed to protect U.S. markets for U.S. goods.
(Source: McConnell and Brue, 1993, p. 399.)

proaches to attain desired goals. For example, they suggest that if grounds exist for protecting an infant industry until it has grown large enough to take advantage of scale economies, protection could be given through a subsidy rather than through a protective tariff.

The arguments for free trade and low tariffs have been accumulating over the years, yet one could argue that throughout the history of the United States, tariff rates have been unquestionably high (Figure 12.18). The Compromise Tariff of 1833 and the Smoot-Hawley Tariff of 1930 put rates at almost 70% of dutiable imports; that is, 70% of imports were subject to the tariff. The reasons for tariffs are clear. Special-interest groups who stand to gain economically from tariffs and quotas press the government for protection through the use of high-powered, politically savvy lobbyists and indoctrinators. The public, which must then absorb these tariffs and quotas as a surcharge on all imported products, are politically uninformed and not represented in Washington, DC.

In 1947, however, the United States and 25 other nations signed the *General Agreement on Tariffs and Trade* (GATT). GATT established multinational reductions of tariffs and import quotas and now has more than 110 signatories. It is discussed in more detail later in this chapter. The *Uruguay Round,* which began in 1986 and has now ended, once again reduced tariffs, so U.S. tariff rates are currently appoximately 5% of dutiable imports.

Marxists are also skeptical about protectionist policies. They argue that protectionism in a capitalist state is likely to benefit capital at the expense of labor because within such a state capital generally makes and breaks the rules. They believe that protectionist policies are acceptable only if the policies lead to increased control of production by workers, which is unlikely in a state driven by capitalist interests.

TARIFF AND NONTARIFF BARRIERS

Tariffs are the most visible of all trade barriers, and they can be levied on a product when it is exported, imported, or in transit through a country. The tariff structure established by the developed countries in the post-World War II period works to the detriment of underdeveloped countries. The underdeveloped countries encounter low tariffs on traditional primary commodities, higher tariffs on semimanufactured products, and still higher tariffs on manufactures. These higher rates are, of course, intended to encourage firms in industrial countries to import raw materials and process them at home. They also discourage the development of processing industries in the Third World.

In recent years, the relative importance of tariff barriers has decreased, whereas nontariff barriers have gained significance. The simplest form of nontariff barrier is the *quota*—a quantitative limit in the volume of trade permitted. A prominent example of a product group subject to import quotas in developed countries is textiles and clothing. Since the early 1970s, textiles and clothing have been subject to quotas under successive Multifibre Arrangements (MFAs). These arrangements have created a worldwide system of managed trade in textiles and clothing in which the quotas severely curtail underdeveloped-country exports. Another common nontariff barrier is the *export-restraint agreement*. Governments increasingly coerce other governments to accept "voluntary" export-restraint agreements, through which the government of an exporting country is induced to limit the volume or value of exports to the importing country. The United States has employed this special type of quota—*an export quota*—extensively. It has concluded "bilateral export agreements with . . . the Republic of China with respect to footwear and color television sets, Hong Kong with respect to textiles, Korea with respect to footwear, textiles and color television sets and with Japan as regards color television sets" (International Monetary Fund, 1978, pp. 6–7). Other nontariff barriers include discretionary licensing standards; labeling and certificate-of-origin regulations; health and safety regulations, especially on foodstuffs; calendriers, which allow foodstuffs to be imported only during certain seasons to avoid competing with the peak production of the importers; and packaging requirements. Increasingly, loose, or break-bulk, cargo is unacceptable to developed-country mechanized transportation handlers. Dockers and longshoremen often demand bonuses for handling such items as unpacked skins and hides. Consumers, too, demand agricultural products in packaging that requires more investment on the part of the exporting country. These examples represent only a few of the hundreds of nontariff barriers devised by governments. The evidence indicates that these barriers in developed countries are higher for exports from underdeveloped countries than they are for exports from rich, developed countries (Edwards, 1985).

Effects of Tariffs and Quotas

The economic effect of tariffs and quotas in the host country is the development and expansion of inefficient industries that do not have comparative advantages. At the world level, tariffs and quotas penalize industries that are relatively efficient and that do have comparative advantages. The result is less international trade and penalized consumers.

Figure 12.19 shows the economic effects of a protective tariff and an import quota. Let's first deal with the

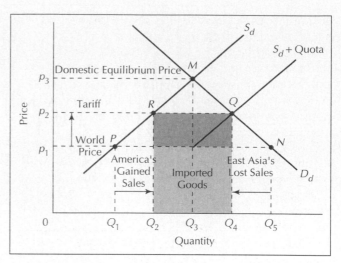

FIGURE 12.19
The economic effects of tariffs and quotas.

case of a protective tariff. Line D_d represents domestic demand in, for example, the United States for AM/FM auto cassette players, whereas line S_d is the domestic supply. (Disregard the S_d + Quota line for now.) The domestic equilibrium position is at price p_3 and quantity q_3. Now assume that the United States market for AM/FM auto cassette players is open to world trade. The world price is lower than the domestic price because, compared with Japan, Malaysia, or Taiwan, the United States has the comparative disadvantage of high labor costs.

The world equilibrium price is p_1. At this price, Americans will consume the quantity Q_5 at Point N. With the low price, the domestic supply is only q_1 at Point P, with the quantity Q_5-Q_1 supplied by foreign imports (Figure 12.19).

Next, let's say that the United States imposes a tariff on the import of AM/FM auto cassette players. This tariff raises the price from p_1 to p_2. The equilibrium price and quantity are now p_2, q_4, respectively, at Point Q. The first reaction will be a decline in quantity demanded by American consumers, from Q_5 to Q_4, as they lock up their demand curve toward the higher price (Figure 12.19).

American consumers are hurt by the tariff because they can buy fewer goods at a much higher price. While the consumers move back up the demand curve to Point Q, domestic producers, with a higher price opportunity, increase their production and move up their supply curve from Point P to Point R. Domestic production has increased from Q_1 to Q_2. Consequently, we can easily understand why domestic producers send lobbyists to

Washington, DC, to invoke tariffs that give the producers a relative advantage in the market.

The increased tariff reduces the number of Far East Asian imports from Q_5-Q_1 to Q_4-Q_2. The U.S. government, not the East Asian supplier, receives the tariff monies, p_2-p_1. At the same time, the market decreases because of reduced demand, and domestic supply increases. The shaded area represents the amount of tariff revenue paid to the U.S. government. This revenue is an economic transfer from the consumers of the country to the government.

The result of levying a tariff is reduced world trade and reduced efficiency of the international economic system, which hurts foreign suppliers, aids domestic producers, and costs the consumer. The indirect effect is that the supplying countries have a smaller market in America and thus earn fewer dollars with which to exchange or invest in American resources. As FDI decreases, trade deficits may increase.

Next, let us consider the effects of levying of an *import quota*. The difference between a tariff and an import quota is that a tariff yields extra revenue to the host government, whereas a quota produces revenue for the foreign suppliers. Imagine that the United States subjects a foreign nation to an import quota, rather than imposing a tariff (Figure 12.19). The import quota in this case is Q_4-Q_2. The quantity Q_4-Q_2 is the number of auto cassette players that foreign producers are allowed to supply. Note that for easy comparison this example limits the quota to the exact amount of imported goods in our tariff example. The quota establishes a new supply curve, S_d + Quota, with an equilibrium position at Point Q. The new supply of auto cassette players is the result of domestic supply, plus a constant amount, Q_4-Q_2, which is supplied by importers.

The chief economic outcomes are the same as with the tariff example. The price is p_2 rather than p_1, and domestic consumption is reduced from q_5 to q_4. The American manufacturers enjoy a higher price for their goods, p_2 rather than p_1, and increased sales, q_2 rather than q_1. But the main difference is that the shaded box, paid by the domestic consumer on imports of Q_4-Q_2, is not paid to the U.S. government. Instead, the extra revenue in the shaded box is paid to the foreign supplier. That is, no tariff exists, and consequently, the foreign supplier keeps all the revenue in the box q_2-q_4-Q-R.

The result is that for local consumers, and their government, a tariff produces a better revenue situation than a quota does. Tariff money can be used to lower the overall tax rate and provide social services and infrastructure for the population as a whole. However, either case is detrimental to international trade and economic efficiency and takes away from the comparative advantages of supplying nations.

STIMULANTS TO TRADE

Not only do governments attempt to control trade, but they also attempt to stimulate trade. Free marketeers believe that government intervention to promote trade is yet another obstacle to free trade. In their view, gains from trade should result from economic efficiencies, not from government support. Examples of governmental assistance to promote exports include market research; provision of information about export opportunities to exporters; international trade shows; trade-promotion offices in foreign countries; and free-trade zones, areas where imported goods can be processed for reexport without payment of duties.

THE REDUCTION OF TRADE BARRIERS

Several efforts have been made to eliminate some of the trade barriers that were erected in the past. GATT and the Uruguay round were two of these efforts. In addition, the United States continues to try to penetrate Japan's closed markets.

General Agreement on Tariffs and Trade

The most notable effort to reduce trade barriers has been a multilateral effort known as GATT. GATT was put into operation in 1947. When 23 developed and underdeveloped countries signed the agreement, they thought that they were putting in place one part of a future International Trade Organization (ITO). The organization would have wide powers to police its trading charter and regulate international competition in such areas as restrictive business practices, investments, commodities, and employment. It was to be the third in the triad of Bretton Woods institutions charged with overseeing the postwar economic order—along with the International Monetary Fund and the World Bank. But the draft charter of the ITO encountered trouble in the U.S. Congress and was never ratified. Only GATT remained—a treaty without an organization.

GATT is now administered on behalf of more than 100 member countries, which make decisions by a process of negotiation and consensus. This process has resulted in a substantial reduction of tariffs. However, GATT's rules have proved inadequate to cope with new forms of nontariff barriers such as export-restraint agreements. Such areas as services, which now account for about 30% of world trade, are not covered by GATT at all. GATT has also been of little help to underdeveloped countries with limited trading muscle. True, underdeveloped countries did gain acceptance of the General System of Preferences (GSP). Under GSP, which developed countries adopted in 1971, tariffs charged on imports of manufactured and semimanufactured products are granted preferential treatment. However, one of the more striking features of GSP schemes is the low proportion of manufactured goods that are eligible for preferential treatment. Because most GSP schemes are restrictive, few underdeveloped countries have benefited.

Since the mid-1970s, and especially since 1980, the liberal trading order that GATT helped to uphold has been steadily eroding. The resurgence of protectionism, especially in the guise of nontariff barriers, is a reflection of the world economic crisis. Between 1981 and 1990, the proportion of imports to North America and the European Economic Community (EEC) that were affected by nontariff barriers increased by more than 20%. Trade between developed and underdeveloped countries is increasingly affected by nontariff barriers; roughly 20% of underdeveloped-country exports were covered by such measures in 1990. In the coming years, pressure on governments in developed countries to protect domestic jobs through trade barriers is likely to mount.

Uruguay Round

In 1986, the eighth round of GATT opened in Montevideo, Uruguay. This Uruguay round of GATT negotiations centered on (1) removing barriers to international trade and services, which now account for 21% of all international trade; (2) ending limits on foreign economic investments; (3) establishing and policing patent, copyright, and trademark rights (*intellectual property rights*) on an international basis; and (4) reducing agricultural trade barriers and domestic subsidies.

The problem in 1990 with the Uruguay round was European opposition to reducing and phasing out agricultural subsidies. The EEC wanted to maintain *export subsidies,* which are government payments that reduce the prices of goods to buyers abroad. Another type, the *domestic farm subsidy,* constitutes direct payments to farmers according to their production levels in order to subsidize their output. The result of these subsidies is increased domestic food output, which provides unfair competition for U.S. and Third World agricultural products on the world market. Both types of subsidies are

artificial barriers that reduce prices on the world market and provide advantages to local farmers. French farmers roadblocked Paris in October 1993 to pressure the government into negotiating a better farm deal with America. The United States had pressed the European economic community (EEC) in early 1993 to phase out all subsidies over a 10-year-period, but settled for a deal that reduced EEC farm subsidies by 21% over 6 years. France reluctantly agreed to that, but the farmers refused to go along.

In 1993, the Uruguay round of negotiations reconvened in an attempt to further resolve trade disagreements. The U.S. effort was an attempt to pry open foreign markets, especially those considered to be unfair traders. Because most of the industrialized world was in the midst of an economic slowdown or an outright recession in 1992, there was much interest in the international trade measures of GATT at Uruguay.

GATT Concludes in Victory

Finally, in Geneva on December 15, 1993, 117 nations agreed to reduce worldwide tarriffs, lower subsidies, and eliminate other barriers to trade. In reducing worldwide protectionism, the GATT nations have chosen to improve resource allocation, which will increase trade and employment and raise wages and standards of living.

The United States obtained most of what they sought: the opening of agriculture markets, cuts in industrial tariffs, intellectual property rights, and the opening of markets in the world's service industries. These were both losers and gainers. America's heavy equipment manufacturers, toy makers, and beer brewers were joyful, but the pharmaceutical industry, Hollywood film makers, and textile manufacturers were not too pleased.

Closed Japanese Markets

The accusation of closed Japanese markets is a contentious issue that is difficult to prove. A number of econometric studies have failed to support unequivocally the conclusion that Japan's imports of American products are less than can be expected given its level of income and resources. In the recent past, Japan increased its imports and was the third largest importer of world merchandise as of 1990 (Table 12.9). It ranked first in importation of commercial services.

President Bush's visit to Japan in 1992 and President

◈

Table 12.9

Leading Exporters and Importers in World Merchandise Trade, 1990

	Exporters					Importers			
Rank	Country	Value*	Share†	Annual Change†	Rank	Country	Value*	Share†	Annual Change†
1	Germany‡	421	12.1	—	1	United States	517	14.3	$4^{1}/_{2}$
2	United States	394	11.3	8	2	Germany‡	356	9.9	—
3	Japan	288	8.3	5	3	Japan	235	6.5	12
4	France	217	6.2	$20^{1}/_{2}$	4	France	234	6.5	$21^{1}/_{2}$
5	United Kingdom	185	5.3	$21^{1}/_{2}$	5	United Kingdom	223	6.2	$12^{1}/_{2}$
6	Italy	170	4.9	21	6	Italy	182	5.0	19
7	Netherlands	132	3.8	22	7	Netherlands	126	3.5	21
8	Canada	132	3.8	$9^{1}/_{2}$	8	Canada	124	3.4	4
9	Belgium-Luxembourg	118	3.4	18	9	USSR§‖	121	3.3	$5^{1}/_{2}$
10	USSR§	104	3.0	−5	10	Belgium-Luxembourg	120	3.3	$21^{1}/_{2}$
11	Hong Kong#	82	2.4	$12^{1}/_{2}$	11	Spain	88	2.4	$22^{1}/_{2}$
12	Taiwan	67	1.9	$1^{1}/_{2}$	12	Hong Kong††	82	2.3	14
13	Korea, Rep.	65	1.9	4	13	Switzerland	70	1.9	$19^{1}/_{2}$
14	Switzerland	64	1.8	24	14	Korea, Rep.	70	1.9	$13^{1}/_{2}$
15	China	61	1.8	$17^{1}/_{2}$	15	Singapore††	61	1.7	$22^{1}/_{2}$
16	Sweden	58	1.7	$11^{1}/_{2}$	16	Taiwan	55	1.5	4
17	Spain	56	1.6	25	17	Sweden	54	1.5	11
18	Singapore**	53	1.5	18	18	China	52	1.5	$-10^{1}/_{2}$
19	Saudi Arabia	44	1.3	$57^{1}/_{2}$	19	Austria	49	1.4	26
20	Austria	41	1.2	$29^{1}/_{2}$	20	Australia	42	1.2	$-6^{1}/_{2}$
21	Mexico††	41	1.2	$15^{1}/_{2}$	21	Mexico††	42	1.2	23
22	Australia	40	1.1	6	22	Thailand	33	0.9	$29^{1}/_{2}$
23	Denmark	35	1.0	25	23	Denmark	32	0.9	19
24	Norway	34	1.0	$25^{1}/_{2}$	24	Malaysia	29	0.8	30
25	Brazil	31	0.9	$-8^{1}/_{2}$	25	Finland	27	0.7	$10^{1}/_{2}$
	Total	2933	84.3	$13^{1}/_{2}$		Total	3024	83.6	$13^{1}/_{2}$
	World	3480	100.0	13		World	3610	100.0	$13^{1}/_{2}$

* Billions of dollars.

† Percent.

‡ Combined trade values for the former Federal Republic of Germany and the former German Democratic Republic.

§ Because of difficulties involved in converting data expressed in the national currency into dollars, the figures are at best rough approximations.

‖ Imports FOB.

Includes reexports. In 1990, they amounted to $53.0 billion compared with $44.3 billion in 1989.

** Includes reexports. In 1990, they amounted to $18.0 billion compared with $16.4 billion in 1989.

†† Includes substantial imports for reexport.

‡‡ Includes trade flows through processing zones.

(Source: Handbook of International Trade Statistics, 1993, Directorate of Intelligence, C.I.A., p. 15, and International Trade, 91–92, GATT, General Agreement on Tariffs and Trade, p. 3.)

Clinton's trip in 1993 were efforts by the United States to pry open Japanese markets. The results were minimal at best, with an agreement by Japanese automakers to import automobile parts worth $10 million and 22,000 Chrysler, Ford, or General Motors vehicles by 1995. Other agreements were made to boost the sales of computers and computer products by American companies in Japan. However, part of Japan's reluctance to open its markets may be because it is experiencing a lingering recession and continuing political turmoil and scandal, and it is not as economically robust as it was 5 years earlier.

Government Barriers to Production-Factor Flows

Although not as complex as trade barriers, obstacles to the free flow of capital, labor, and technology constrain international managerial freedom. Exchange controls and capital controls are the main types of controls that interfere with the movement of money and capital across national borders. *Exchange controls,* which restrict free dealings in foreign exchange, include multiple exchange rates and rationing. In multiple-exchange-rate systems, rates vary for different kinds of transactions. For example, a particular commodity may be granted an unfavorable rate. Foreign exchange may also be rationed on a priority basis or on a first-come, first-served basis. Thus, exchange rates are political tools bearing little relationship to economic reality. *Capital controls* are restrictions on the movement of money or capital across national borders. They are typically designed to discourage the outflow of funds.

All countries regulate migration, but the movement of workers from poorer to richer countries was the dominant pattern during the long postwar boom. When the boom ended, jobs moved to the workers. One reason for this change was tighter immigration laws in the advanced industrial countries. These tighter laws strengthened the position of labor and resulted in a growth in managed trade and a decline in managed migration.

Technology, which is highly mobile, can be transferred in many ways: export of equipment, provision of scientific and managerial training, provision of books and journals, personal visits, and the licensing of patents. Political and military controls regulate the export of technology. Although these controls are not yet terribly onerous, demands for more stringent controls are on the increase. One source of demand for control is labor unions in advanced industrial countries. These unions attribute domestic job loss to the export of high technology.

MULTINATIONAL ECONOMIC ORGANIZATIONS

◈

In the world today, as nations turn inward to concentrate on problems of economic growth and stability, we are witnessing a resurgence of protectionism. But also in evidence is a strong, simultaneous countermovement toward international interdependence. This movement is exemplified by scores of multinational organizations, which for the most part are loosely connected leagues entailing little or no surrender of sovereignty on the part of member nations.

Some of these international organizations are global in scale. The most inclusive is the United Nations (UN), with 159 member nations that account for more than 98% of humankind. Much of the UN's work is accomplished through approximately two dozen specialized agencies such as the World Health Organization (WHO) and the International Labor Organization (ILO). Other international organizations have a regional character; for example, the Association of South-East Asian Nations (ASEAN) and the Asian Development Bank (ADB). Many international organizations are relatively narrow in focus—mostly military, such as the North Atlantic Treaty Organization (NATO), or economic, such as the Organization of Petroleum Exporting Countries (OPEC). Some international organizations are discussion forums with little authority to operate either independently or on behalf of member states; for example, GATT and the Organization of Economic Cooperation and Development (OECD).

Others have independent, multinational authority and power, performing functions that individual states cannot or will not perform on their own; for example, the IMF and the World Bank. Some international organizations integrate a portion of the economic or political activities of member countries; for example, the EEC and the European Free Trade Area (EFTA). International organizations to promote regional integration are the most ambitious of all. Some observers believe that regional federations are necessary to the process of weakening nationalism and developing wider communities of interest. However, if a rigid, inward-looking regionalism is substituted for nationalism, the ultimate form of international integration—world federation—will be difficult to achieve (Schwartzberg, 1987).

This section examines international economic organizations that affect the environment in which firms operate and thus influence the development of underdeveloped countries. We look at international financial institutions, groups that foster regional economic integration, and groups such as commodity cartels, which deliberately manipulate international commodity markets. We also assess the attempt of the United Nations Conference on Trade and Development (UNCTAD), the so-called trade union of the Third World, to establish a New International Economic Order (NIEO).

International Financial Institutions

International financial institutions are a phenomenon of the post-World War II period. The IMF and the International Bank for Reconstruction and Development (IBRD), or World Bank, were established in 1945. Regional development banks—the Inter-American Development Bank (IADB), Asian Development Bank (ADB), and African Development Bank (AFDB)—were established in the 1960s. Various other multilateral facilities, of which the United Nations Development Program (UNDP) is the most important, were also established after 1960. These institutions are significant sources of multilateral capital, especially aid (i.e., capital provided on concessional terms) for underdeveloped countries. Multilateral capital is particularly important for the poorer underdeveloped countries that do not have access to private capital markets.

The IMF is an international central bank that provides short- to medium-term loans to member countries, and the IBRD is an international development bank that provides longer-term loans for particular projects. Both institutions are clusters of governments, each government paying a subscription or quota determined by the size of its economy. Because quotas determine a member's voting power, the banks are dominated by the most powerful economies—particularly, by the United States.

The IMF and the World Bank were established to prevent a recurrence of the crisis of the 1930s. They embody Keynesian principles, which offer a rationale for state intervention in the market. The right of the state to act in the economy is a principle of great importance to many Third World countries, which prefer an authoritative to a market allocation of resources. Despite weighted voting, both institutions give Third World members a degree of formal power in excess of their share of actual financial contributions.

With the passage of time, underdeveloped countries have obtained more resources on better terms, especially as a result of the creation of two subsidiary World Bank organizations: the International Finance Corporation (IFC), founded in 1956, and the International Development Association (IDA), founded in 1960. These organizations provide loans with stipulations less stringent than those of the IBRD. For example, the IDA may provide loans with no interest charges, 10-year grace periods (no repayment of principal for the first 10 years), or 50-year repayment schedules for poorer underdeveloped countries. Because the IDA is much less creditworthy than the IBRD, all its resources must come from member-government contributions.

Although the IMF and the World Bank have become more solicitous of Third World opinions and preferences, these institutions remain firmly wedded to liberal, as opposed to dependency, interpretations of development. The market-oriented position is consistent with the basic orientation of the industrialized world, especially that of the United States. Loans from the IMF and the World Bank, therefore, tend to uphold the basis of U.S. economic and foreign policy.

The Third World has never been satisfied with the IMF and the World Bank, particularly with regard to the level of available resources and the conditions imposed on their use. One counter has been the regional development banks—the IADB, ADB, and AFDB. These banks reflect the desire of underdeveloped countries to enhance their control. Of the three banks, the ADB is most under the control of developed countries, in particular Japan. The AFDB has been the most independent, but it is also the smallest.

Another counter was the creation of the UNDP in 1965. In terms of formal voting structure, the UNDP provides the Third World with dominant influence, even though approximately 90% of the contributions are from advanced industrial countries. The UNDP provides assistance to a wider variety of countries than the World Bank does. It also supports the demands embodied in the call for a New International Economic Order (NIEO). For example, the program has offered assistance to commodity-producer associations, has encouraged regional cooperation among underdeveloped countries, and has made efforts to increase the bargaining power of underdeveloped countries vis-à-vis multinational corporations.

The atrium of the International Monetary Fund (IMF) headquarters in Washington, DC. The IMF attempts to maintain foreign exchange balances and to promote economic modernization and growth in the Third World. Adjustment programs generally include measures to manage demand, improve the incentive system, increase market efficiency, and promote investment.
(Source: International Monetary Fund.)

International financial institutions are important for international business. The IMF, the World Bank, and regional development banks annually finance billions of dollars of the import portion of development projects. This can be valuable business for foreign companies involved in the projects, either occasionally as part owners or, more commonly, as contractors or suppliers.

Although international financial institutions facilitate international business, their project aid may not promote development. Conservative and radical critics agree that development must be primarily an indigenous process. Foreign aid has served many underdeveloped countries as an easy substitute for devising means to generate domestic development. It is also apparent that aid from institutions heavily influenced by developed countries is a palliative designed to ensure the continuity of unequal exchange in the world economy.

Regional Economic Integration

Regional integration is the international grouping of sovereign nations to form a single economic region. It is a form of selective discrimination in which both free-trade and protectionist policies are operative: free trade among members and restrictions on trade with non-members. According to economist Bela Balassa (1961), five degrees of economic integration are possible. At progressively higher levels, members must make more concessions and surrender more sovereignty. The lowest level of economic integration is the *free-trade area*, in which members agree to remove trade barriers among themselves but continue to retain their own trade practices with nonmembers. A *customs union* is the next higher degree of integration. Members agree not only to eliminate trade barriers among themselves, but also to impose a common set of trade barriers on nonmembers. The third type is the *common market*, which, like the customs union, eliminates internal trade barriers and imposes common external trade barriers; this regional grouping, however, permits free production-factor mobility. At a still higher level, an *economic union* has the common-market characteristics plus a common currency and a common international economic policy. The highest form of regional grouping is full *economic integration*, which requires the surrender of most of the international sovereignty of its members.

Regional economic integration is evident within three major trade blocs in Figure 12.20. Western Europe has more than 70% of its imported items originating from within the region, and the percentage reached 75% by 1993. North American trade regionalization has fallen from 45% to 35% between 1970 and 1990, while East Asia's has increased from 35% to 45%.

Table 12.10 lists the different levels of integration of a variety of economic groups. In part B, the main provisions of the groups are described. These groups range from loosely integrated free-trade areas such as the Latin American Free Trade Association (LAFTA) to common markets such as the EEC. There are also links between members of regional blocs. Thus, East-West ties exist between EEC countries and the Eastern countries' Council for Mutual Economic Assistance

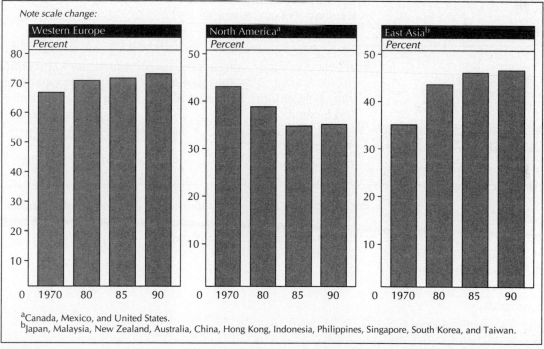

FIGURE 12.20
Regionalization of trade: nonfuel imports originating within the regions of Western Europe, North America, and East Asia. Of the three principal world trade blocs, Western Europe has the greatest regionalization with almost 75% of its trade originating with Western Europe itself. North America has seen its intraregional trade slip from 45% to 35%, while intraregional trade for East Asia has increased from 35% to 45% between 1970 and 1990. What effect will NAFTA have on the percentage of intraregional trade in North America?
(*Source:* Handbook of International Economic Statistics Directorate of Intelligence, C.I.A., 1993).

◈

Table 12.10
Levels and Examples of Regional Integration

A. Levels of Regional Integration

Level	Characteristics	Examples
Free-trade area	Common internal tariffs but differing external tariffs	EFTA, LAFTA
Customs union	Common internal and external tariffs	UDEAC, CEAO
Common market	Common tariffs and few restrictions on production-factor mobility	EEC, COMECON

B. Examples of Regional Integration

Year	Grouping	Main Provisions
1949	Council for Mutual Economic Assistance (COMECON): USSR, Bulgaria, Czechoslovakia, German Democratic Republic, Hungary, Poland, Romania, Mongolia, and Cuba	Trade and development agreements and contracts
1957 (1973: plus U.K., Ireland, Denmark) (1981: plus Greece) (1986: plus Spain and Portugal)	European Economic Community (EEC): France, West Germany, Italy, Belgium, the Netherlands, and Luxembourg	Common market (common internal and external tariffs and common agricultural and industrial policies)
1960 (1961: plus Finland as an associate member) (1970: plus Iceland) (1973: minus U.K. and Denmark)	European Free Trade Association (EFTA): U.K., Switzerland, Austria, Denmark, Norway, and Sweden	Common internal tariffs but not common external tariffs
1960	Latin American Free Trade Association (LAFTA): Mexico and all of South America, except the Guyanas	Free-trade area (no common external tariff) and sectoral agreements

▦

T a b l e 12.10 (Continued)

Year	Grouping	Main Provisions
1966	Union Douanière et Economique de l'Afrique Centrale (UDEAC): Cameroon, Central African Republic, Congo, Gabon	Customs union with common central bank
1967	Association of South-East Asian Nations (ASEAN): Indonesia, Malaysia, Philippines, Singapore, and Thailand	Some regional trade preferences and sectoral agreements
1969 (1973: plus Venezuela) (1976: minus Chile)	Andean Common Market (ACM): Bolivia, Chile, Colombia, Ecuador, and Peru	Common market envisaged, common policy on foreign investment
1979	Southern Africa Development Co-ordination Conference (SADCC): Angola, Botswana, Lesotho, Malawi, Mozambique, Swaziland, Tanzania, Zambia, Zimbabwe	Sectoral integration
1989	United States-Canadian Free Trade Agreement: Canada and the United States	Free trade area
1993	North American Free Trade Agreement (NAFTA): Canada, the United States, Mexico	Free trade area

(COMECON). By 1993, most of the COMECON countries had applied for membership in the EEC. There are North-South ties between the EEC and LAFTA, South-South ties between LAFTA and ASEAN, and some East-South ties between COMECON and various underdeveloped countries. Most of these links are bilateral; that is, agreements between nations within different regions. Fully fledged interregional integration has yet to be achieved. Indeed, regional groups are more concerned with closer economic integration *within* regions than *among* regions.

Barriers to successful regional integration are stronger in underdeveloped countries than in developed countries. The most significant barriers are political—an unwillingness to make concessions. Without concessions to the weaker partners of a regional group, the benefits from cooperation pile up in the economically more prosperous and powerful countries. This problem causes much strain and may lead to the dissolution of a regional integration scheme. The breakup of the East African Community (EAC) in 1978 was caused partly by the inability of Kenya to make concessions with its two weaker partners, Uganda and Tanzania. Another difficulty is that underdeveloped countries have not historically traded extensively among themselves. Still another obstacle to integration is the issue of integrating transportation and power networks. Nonetheless, much potential for integration exists in underdeveloped countries, particularly because many are too small and too underdeveloped to grow rapidly as individual units.

Many underdeveloped countries turned to regional integration schemes in the 1960s and 1970s. Reasons for integration included a need to gain access to larger markets, to obtain more bargaining power with the developed countries than they could if they adopted a "go-it-alone" policy, to create an identity for themselves, to strengthen their base for controlling multinational corporations, and to promote cohesion solidarity. It was for the last reason that the Southern Africa Development Co-ordination Conference (SADCC) was formalized in 1979. The main provision of SADCC is sectoral integration to build regional self-reliance for the front-line countries of Angola, Botswana, Lesotho, Malawi, Mozambique, Swaziland, Tanzania, Zambia, and Zimbabwe. These countries are adjacent to a dominant South Africa.

Regional groupings are rejected by conservatives but viewed with sympathy by most liberals and radicals. For free marketeers, regional integration is unnecessary (Viner, 1950). The "open economies" of Singapore, Hong Kong, Taiwan, and South Korea are a vindication of comparative advantage. In contrast, dependency theorists are pessimistic about the benefits from open-economy policies. They claim that workers in the open economies are "superexploited" (Frank, 1981) and that access to the markets of the developed world will not lead to authentic indigenous development (Landsberg, 1987).

The effect of regional groupings differs from one company to another. Companies that enjoy a secure and highly profitable position behind national tariff walls are unlikely to favor removal of these barriers. Conversely, companies that see the removal of trade barriers as an opportunity to expand their markets see integration as a favorable development. Similarly, companies that traditionally exported to markets absorbed by a regional grouping have a strong interest in integration. They perceive these enlarged markets to be more attractive than they were in the past. But as outsiders, the shipments of these companies will be subject to trade controls, whereas barriers for internal competitors will decrease. Thus, foreign companies may face the prospect of losing their traditional markets because they are outside the integrated group of countries. As a result, there is an incentive to invest inside the regional grouping. This is why many U.S. firms invested directly in the EEC countries in the late 1950s and early 1960s, and again in the late 1980s.

THE COMMON MARKET

The most successful example of economic integration is the European Economic Community, also known as the Common Market or EEC. It was begun with six nations: France, West Germany, Italy, Belgium, the Netherlands, and Luxembourg, in 1957, and since then has added the United Kingdom, Ireland, Denmark, Greece, Spain, and Portugal. This group is known as the EC-12. The EFTA nations—Switzerland, Austria, Norway, Sweden, Finland, and Iceland—have applied for membership and will be admitted to the EEC soon. In addition, most Eastern European nations have applied for membership in the EEC. The population of potential EEC countries numbers almost 350 million. The EEC today is the largest single trade bloc in the world and, along with the EFTA, accounts for 46.5% of international trade, which is three times its fair world share based on its population (Figure 12.21). Western Europe is noted as a region of high world trade as a proportion of a country's GDP (Table 12.11).

The intent of the Common Market was to give its members freer trade advantages while limiting the importation of goods from outside Europe. It called for (1) the establishment of a common system of tariffs applicable to imports from outside nations; (2) the removal of tariffs and import quotas on all products traded among the participating EEC nations; (3) the establishment of common policies with regard to major economic matters such as agriculture, transportation, and so forth; (4) free movement and access of capital, labor, and currency within the market countries; (5) transportation of goods and commodities across borders with no inspection or passport examination; and (6) a common currency.

The EEC has made tremendous progress toward its stated goals. The member nations have been afforded more efficient, large-scale production because of poten-

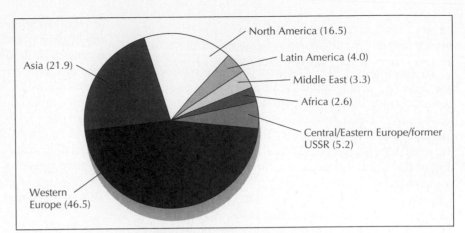

FIGURE 12.21
Regional shares of world merchandise trade, 1990. Based on the value of exports and imports, Western Europe produces 47% of the world trade. This region is followed by Asia with 21.9% and North America with 16.5%.
(Source: U.S. Department of Commerce, 1993.)

tially larger markets within the EEC, permitting them to achieve scale economies and lower costs per manufactured unit, something that pre-Common Market economic conditions had denied them. However, the current stumbling block seems to be the lack of a common economic unit of currency. In addition, certain countries, such as the socialized north, especially Denmark and Germany, have scoffed at opening borders that would allow southern Europeans to immigrate and thereby take advantage of very liberal social welfare programs of economic assistance from cradle to grave.

Americans are concerned about the economic power of the EEC. Present tariffs have been reduced to zero among EEC nations, whereas tariffs for American-made products have been maintained. Consequently, im-

porting goods to EEC nations is relatively more difficult. At the same time, increased prosperity among EEC nations because of increased trade and comparative advantage allows these nations to become potential customers for more American export products.

The pressure placed on the United States by the Common Market has led the United States to promote freer trade through GATT and the U.S.-Canadian Free Trade Agreement. In the fall of 1992, the North American Free Trade Agreement (NAFTA) was signed by the U.S. and Mexican presidents and the Canadian Prime Minister, and in 1994 the U.S. Congress passed it. The United States, Canada, and Mexico have become the largest free-trade zone in the world.

◈

Table 12.11

Exports of Goods and Services as a Percentage of Gross Domestic Product, Selected Countries, 1990

Country	Exports (% of GDP)
The Netherlands	57
Germany	36
New Zealand	27
Canada	25
United Kingdom	24
France	22
Italy	19
Japan	11
United States	10

Source: International Monetary Fund, 1992, p. 31.

U.S.-CANADIAN FREE TRADE AGREEMENT

Even before signing the U.S.-Canadian Free Trade Agreement in 1989, Canada and the United States were each other's largest trading partners. According to the agreement, tariffs, quotas, and nontariff barriers will be totally eliminated by 1999. The agreement helps producers on both sides of the border. For example, for Canadian producers, their potential markets increase by a factor of 10. The population of Canada is about 25 million, but that of the United States is 265 million. At the same time, the Canadian market becomes a large group of consumers for U.S. producers. The reduced Canadian tariffs will help American producers gain access to the Canadian consumer. The estimate is that when the U.S.-Canadian Free Trade Agreement is fully enacted by 1999, 3 billion dollars' worth of annual gains will accrue to each country in 1990 dollars.

NORTH AMERICAN FREE TRADE AGREEMENT

In December 1993, President Clinton signed into law NAFTA, which could create one of the two most powerful trade blocs in the world. (The Mexican population is 90 million and estimated to be 100 million by the year 2000. Consequently, the total population in the trade bloc would be 380 million, slightly more than that of the EEC.) Access to the North American market is coveted by Common Market countries and Japan. Proponents of NAFTA argued that Common Market nations would negotiate a free-trade agreement between the two blocs. Japan would then be left out of the world's wealthiest trading markets. The argument is that Japan would then be forced to reduce its tariffs and barriers to world international trade.

The problem with NAFTA is that it is not well received by all members of North American society. The critics' main argument was that it would rob lower-skilled assembly and manufacturing jobs from America and transplant them to Mexico, where the labor rate is one-fifth to one-eighth as much as it is in America. In addition, companies would flee America's more stringent climate regarding environmental pollution and workplace safety controls. No one is certain how many workers NAFTA will replace in already hard-hit North America. Critics of NAFTA also suggest that Japan, Korea, Taiwan, and other Far East Asian countries would build plants in Mexico and import goods duty free to the American and Canadian markets, which would hurt U.S. firms and workers even further.

The principal argument in favor of NAFTA was that free trade would enhance both American (U.S. and Canadian) and Mexican comparative advantages: raise per capita income in Mexico and increase Mexican demand for goods from the United States and Canada. Another argument suggests that higher living standards in Mexico would help control the flow of undocumented aliens crossing the U.S. border, which is now estimated at 1 million per year. With free trade, wages would rise in Mexico, therefore, undocumented aliens could stay home and work in their native country.

Trade-Restriction Agreements

As a group, Third World countries find the existing market-oriented regime unsatisfactory. The regime exposes underdeveloped countries, which rely heavily on foreign-exchange receipts from a limited range of commodity exports, to shocks from the international environment. Underdeveloped countries find access to markets of the developed countries restricted by a revival of protectionism, experience fluctuating prices for their exports, and suffer unfavorable terms of trade. As mentioned previously, these problems have compelled Third World countries to alter the rules of the game so as to lessen their vulnerability. Through cartels and commodity price agreements, they have attempted to replace the existing regime governed by market-oriented principles with new regimes governed by authoritative principles.

ORGANIZATION OF PETROLEUM EXPORTING COUNTRIES

A *cartel* is an agreement among producers that seeks to artificially increase prices by arbitrarily raising them, by reducing supplies, or by allocating markets. The most successful Third World commodity cartel is the Organization of Petroleum Exporting Countries (*OPEC*). Founded in 1960, OPEC consists of 13 countries—Saudi Arabia, Iran, Venezuela, Kuwait, Libya, Nigeria, Iraq, Indonesia, Algeria, Gabon, Qatar, Ecuador, and the United Arab Emirates. In the 1970s, it forced acceptance of authoritative rather than market-oriented principles. The success of OPEC at raising oil prices encouraged other underdeveloped countries to create new regimes.

The first oil shock occurred in 1973, followed by another in 1978. The price for a barrel of crude petroleum oil peaked in 1981 at $36 (Figure 12.22). Major new exploration by American oil companies commenced, and billions of dollars of infrastructure were erected in territories of North America that were rich in oil, low-grade oil, shales, and tar sands, notably Colorado, Wyoming, Alberta, and Montana. With the decline in world oil prices, these new oil operations and oil explorations likewise declined, which sent shock waves through the oil industry and depreciated home and business values throughout Houston, Texas, and other oil-dependent cities.

By 1986, the price of a barrel of crude petroleum on the world market had declined to $15, but it was pushed up again in 1990 to $21 because of the Persian Gulf War and the closing of wells in Iraq and Kuwait. In 1991 and 1992, however, prices again gyrated downward because of the sluggish world economy and the overproduction of OPEC nations. By 1994, the price was again $16 a barrel. Several years have past since the Persian Gulf War, but the oil industries' return to

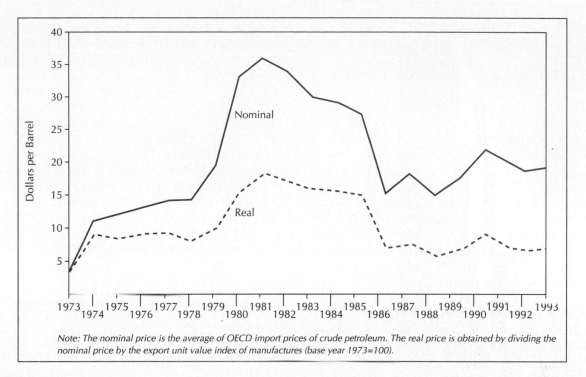

Note: The nominal price is the average of OECD import prices of crude petroleum. The real price is obtained by dividing the nominal price by the export unit value index of manufactures (base year 1973=100).

FIGURE 12.22
Nominal and real prices of crude petroleum, 1973–1993. The nominal price is the average OECD import price of crude petroleum. The real price is obtained by dividing the nominal price by the export unit value index of manufacturers, with a base year of 1973 equals 100.
(Source: U.S. Department of Commerce, 1993. International Trade 91–92, GATT, p. 37)

prewar production levels has not occurred because of the devastation in Iraq and Kuwait. With the lower output by Iraq and Kuwait as of 1994, higher levels of production or refining capacity are required by other OPEC nations.

World oil prices depend on the resumption of economic growth in not only the developed nations, but also the less developed nations, and the demand for crude petroleum. The resumption of production and refining in Russia and the former Soviet Union will also affect world petroleum prices.

The future demand for OPEC oil in the mid- to late 1990s is likely to be substantial and increasing because of the expected recovery of world economic output and OPEC's large reserves offered at relatively low prices. At present, OPEC produces less than 50% of the world's output but controls 80% of the proven reserves. Despite the tremendous oil reserves of several trillion barrels, generating enough money to maintain its production and increased capacity will be a problem for OPEC nations because, surprisingly, most have serious financial debt problems. Much of their petrodollar accumulation

is spent on military equipment to keep the wealthy sheiks in power.

OTHER TRADE-RESTRICTION AGREEMENTS

Since 1974, UNCTAD has been trying to obtain an international agreement for an integrated commodity program through a Common Fund in order to combat price instability and price deterioration. The cornerstone of this multicommodity approach was the proposal to establish international commodity stocks for a number of commodities. Eighteen commodities of special interest to underdeveloped countries were considered suitable for such stocks. In successive meetings, the original 18 commodities became 17, representing about 75% of the Third World's total nonpetroleum mineral and agricultural exports, but priority was afforded to 10 commodities—cocoa, coffee, cotton, copper, jute, rubber, sisal, sugar, tea, and tin. These 10 commodities were alleged to have characteristics suitable for price

The South Korea World Trade Center is symbolic of the rise of East Asia as a locus of international economic activity. A combination of trade tower, exhibition complex, and other supportive facilities, the center provides all services required for the transaction of international business.
(Source: Korean Information Service.)

stabilization through buffer-stock schemes. To date, not much progress has been made. The Common Fund was accepted by the North in 1980, but it was funded at a meager level. Some existing commodity agreements, such as the International Coffee Agreement and the International Tin Agreement, continued. A few new arrangements have been concluded, the most important of which dealt with rubber.

Developed countries, especially the United States, resist commodity control. American private and public actors view commodity agreements as unfortunate departures from the liberal, market-oriented principles governing the movement of most traded goods. Thus, except for oil, which is a special case, commodity cartels are unlikely to be successful. Oil has a high-income elasticity of demand; that is, as individuals prosper, their expenditures on oil increase proportionately. Oil is concentrated in a few countries. And it has no close substitutes.

The most comprehensive and important commodity agreement between the North and the South is the *Lomé Convention*, signed in 1975 by the EEC and states in Africa, the Caribbean, and the Pacific (ACP states). This North-South agreement gives Third World countries who are associate members of the EEC preferential access for their exports of primary products. Thus, the Ivory Coast, an associate member of the EEC, receives preferential access for its coffee exports, whereas Brazil, a nonmember, does not. The Lomé Agreement, therefore, provides a framework for continuing a colonial-type relation and for discriminating against non-ACP states. Like all trade-restriction agreements, it obstructs market forces.

A New International Economic Order

In the late 1960s and early 1970s, there was a growing demand among underdeveloped countries to change the rules and principles that govern most kinds of international transactions, especially in the areas of trade, private capital flows, and FDI. As we discussed in Chapter 1, demands for authoritative resource allocation in the interests of equity and justice were consolidated in 1974 at the Sixth Special Session of the United Nations General Assembly in a call for the establishment of a NIEO. The call for a NIEO, which took developed countries by surprise, was made at a time when many underdeveloped countries perceived a golden opportunity to tip the balance of international power in their favor. Commodity producers thought that they might be able to emulate OPEC in bidding up prices for their primary products. However, it soon became clear in the crisis of the 1970s and 1980s that they had less bargaining power than they thought.

The NIEO was not an exercise in empty rhetoric among underdeveloped countries. The kinds of demands embodied in the call for a NIEO, which included such areas of concern as trade, primary commodities, aid, debt, multinational corporations, and shipping, will not disappear. The structural conditions that prompted them are defining and enduring characteristics of the international system.

The intensity of the North-South conflict could be reduced by three developments, however. First, some underdeveloped countries may generate the national power capabilities needed to cope with the existing international system. Second, developed countries could pay less attention to existing international organizations. If developed countries ceased to concern themselves with UN happenings or ceased to fund its activities, the underdeveloped countries would have a program without an audience. Third, and less likely, the North-South conflict could be reduced if there were more collective self-reliance in the South and consequent widespread delinking from the North.

SUMMARY

◈

This chapter examined aspects of the international sphere of business. *International business* is any form of business activity that crosses a national border. It includes the international movement of almost any type of economic resource—merchandise, capital, or services.

Our discussion of traditional trade theory pointed to *comparative advantage* rather than *absolute advantage* as the underlying explanation for much of the trade that occurs. Beyond predicting that everyone gains something from trade, classical trade theory neglects to consider the distribution of benefits. Free trade was established in the nineteenth century within a framework of inequality among countries. An artificial division of labor was established between developed and underdeveloped countries. Third World countries as primary producers became dependent on foreign demand and, therefore, vulnerable to the business cycle of expansion and contraction in developed countries.

The theoretical basis for international business was extended in a consideration of the basis of *production-factor flows*. Production factors that are most readily movable are capital, technology, and labor. We focused primarily on *capital movements*, enhancing understanding of FDI by using a managerial perspective. In many respects, the international movement of capital, technology, and managerial know-how is now more important than international trade is. In fact, the preeminent international business organizations of the future will be those "devoted to improving international markets in terms of special inputs—services, skills, knowledge, capital. . . . The guts of such firms will be information network and data banks" (Robinson, 1981, pp. 18–19).

Theories of international trade and production-factor movements emphasize the benefits of a liberal, market-oriented business environment. However, a number of obstacles significantly impede the flow of merchandise, capital, technology, and labor. These obstacles include distance barriers, managerial barriers, and governmental barriers. Much progress was made in reducing governmental barriers—*tariffs* and *nontariff barriers*—during the long postwar boom. But the 1970s and 1980s saw a steady erosion in the liberal trading order as governments started to erect new barriers to international business.

International trade is not normally a barter arrangement. Money must be exchanged on international markets for goods and services. Determination of exchange rates allows world trade to function. Explanation of why exchange rates fluctuate is no easy matter but is related to levels of real output, inflation rates, demand factors, and currency speculation in trading-partner countries.

Despite the chillier economic climate since the mid-1970s, countries continue to participate in myriad multinational operations. Major organizations that can be important to international business are *international financial institutions* and groups that promote *regional integration*. Groups that obstruct market forces include *commodity cartels*. Leaders in developed countries view commodity cartels as an unfortunate departure from market-oriented principles. In contrast, most Third World leaders view commodity cartels as a means to reduce their vulnerability in a world of unequal exchange.

The General Agreement on Tariffs and Trade (GATT) has reduced trade barriers worldwide. The most recent Uruguay round of GATT has made progress in a number of difficult issues—farm policy, intellectual property rights, and trade barriers related to a growing international provision of services. The United States' current, most troublesome world trade problems, however, are the sluggish world economy and the closed Japanese markets. The Japanese own a $60 billion trade surplus.

The most widely acclaimed regional integration to date is the EEC of Western Europe. By the year 2000, it is likely that most Eastern and Western European nations will be associated in a powerful trade bloc that manages almost 50% of worldwide trade. The United States and Canada followed suit in 1989, with the U.S.-Canadian Free Trade Agreement. Final approval for the momentous North American Free Trade Agreement (NAFTA), involving Canada, Mexico, and the United States, to challenge the EEC head-on occurred in 1994.

▣

KEY TERMS

absolute advantage
aid
brain drain
capital controls
cartel
common market
comparative advantage
countertrade
customs union
dependency theorists
development bank
direct investment
domestic farm subsidies
economic integration
economic union
efficiency seekers
Engel's law
Eurocurrency
Euromarket
exchange controls
exchange rate
export quota
export subsidies
export-restraint agreement
factors of production

floating exchange rates
foreign direct investment (FDI)
free trade
free-trade area
General Agreement on Tariffs and Trade (GATT)
Heckscher-Ohlin theory
import quota
infant industry
intellectual property rights
international business
international currency markets
International Monetary Fund (IMF)
intramultinational trade
Lomé Convention
market seekers
multinational corporation (MNC)
NAFTA
New International Economic Order (NIEO)
nontariff barrier
Organization of Petroleum Exporting Countries (OPEC)
production factors
petrodollars
portfolio investment
production-possibilities curve

protectionism
regional integration
specialization
tariff
tax-haven country
terms of trade
trade deficit

transfer costs
transfer pricing
unequal exchange
United Nations Conference on Trade and
  Development (UNCTAD)
Uruguay round
World Bank

◈

SUGGESTED READINGS

Bagchi-Sen, S., and Pigozzi, B. M. 1993. Occupational and industrial diversification in the metropolitan space economy in the United States, 1985–1990. *Professional Geographer*, 45:44–54.

Behrman, J. N. 1984. *International Policies: International Restructuring and Transnationals*. Lexington, MA: D. C. Heath.

Bluestone, B., and Harrison, B. 1982. *The Deindustrialization of America: Plant Closings, Community Abandonment, and the Dismantling of Basic Industry*. New York: Basic Books.

Brotchie, J. F.; Hall, P.; and Newton, P. W., eds. 1987. *The Spatial Impact of Technological Change*. London: Croom Helm.

Casetti, E., and Jones, J. P., III. 1987. Spatial aspects of the productivity slowdown: An analysis of U.S. manufacturing data. *Annals of the Association of American Geographers*, 77:76–88.

Cline, W. R. 1983. *International Debt and the Stability of the World Economy*. Washington, DC: Institute for International Economics.

Daniels, J. D.; Ogram, Jr., E. W.; and Radebaugh, L. H. 1982. *International Business: Environment and Operations*. 3d ed. Reading, MA: Addison-Wesley.

Dicken, P. 1991. *Global Shift: Industrial Change in a Turbulent World*, 2nd ed. London: Harper & Row.

Duncan, S. 1991. The geography of gender divisions of labour in Britain. *Transactions of British Geographers*, New Series 16:420–429.

Dunning, J. H., ed. 1985. *Multinational Enterprises, Economic Structure and International Competitiveness*. New York: John Wiley.

Earncy, F. C. F. 1981. The geopolitics of minerals. *Focus*, 31:1–16.

Economic Report of the President, 1994.

Edwards, C. 1985. *The Fragmented World: Competing Perspectives on Trade, Money and Crisis*. New York: Methuen.

Erickson, R. A., and Hayward, D. J. 1991. The international flows of industrial exports from U.S. regions. *Annals of the Association of American Geographers*, 81:371–390.

Ettlinger, N. 1991. The roots of competitive advantage in California and Japan. *Annals of the Association of American Geographers*, 81:391–407.

Glasmeier, A. K. 1991. *The High-Tech Potential: Economic Development in Rural America*. New Brunswick, NJ: Center for Urban Policy Research.

Helleiner, G. K. 1981. *Intra-Firm Trade and the Developing Countries*. London: Macmillan.

Hoare, A. G. 1993. *The Location of Industry in Britain*. New York: Cambridge University Press.

Hogan, W. T. 1991. *Global Steel in the 1990s: Growth or Decline*. New York: Lexington Books.

Korth, C. M. 1985. *International Business: Environment and Management.* 2d ed. Englewood Cliffs, NJ: Prentice Hall.

Krause, L., and Sekiguchi, S., eds. 1980. *Economic Interaction in the Pacific Basin.* Washington, DC: The Brookings Institution.

Law, C. M., ed. 1991. *Restructuring the Global Automobile Industry.* London: Routledge.

Linder, S. B. 1986. *The Pacific Century: Economic and Political Consequences of Asian-Pacific Dynamism.* Stanford, CA: Stanford University Press.

Murray, R., ed. 1981. *Multinationals Beyond the Market.* Brighton, England: Harvester Press.

Paltie, C. J., and Johnson, R. J. 1990. One nation or two? The changing geography of unemployment in Great Britain, 1983–1988. *Professional Geographer,* 42:288–298.

Pauls, B. D. 1990. U.S. exchange rate policy: Bretton Woods to present. *Federal Reserve Bulletin,* 76(11).

Porter, M. E. 1990. *The Competitive Advantage of Nations.* New York: The Free Press.

Robock, S. H., and Simmonds, K. 1983. *International Business and Multinational Enterprises.* 3d ed. Homewood, IL: Richard D. Irwin.

Ronen, S. 1986. *Comparative and Multinational Management.* New York: John Wiley.

Root, F. R. 1990. *International Trade and Investment.* 6th ed. Cincinnati, OH: South-Western Publishing.

Salvatore, D. 1990. *International Economics.* 3rd ed. New York: Macmillan.

South, R. B. 1990. Transnational Maquiladora location. *Annals of the Association of American Geographers,* 80:529–570.

Taoka, G., and Beeman, D. R. 1991. *International Business: Environments, Institutions, and Operations.* New York: Harper Collins.

Terpstra, V., and David, K. 1985. *The Cultural Environment of International Business.* 2d ed. Cincinnati: South-Western Publishing.

United Nations. 1983. *Transnational Corporations in World Development, Third Survey.* New York: United Nations.

———. 1988. *Transnational Corporations in World Development: Trends and Prospects.* New York: United Nations.

United Nations. *Monthly Bulletin of Statistics,* 1994.

United Nations, *World Economic Survey,* 1992.

United States Department of Commerce, *Survey of Current Business,* Bureau of Economic Analysis, 1994.

INTERNATIONAL BUSINESS II: WORLD PATTERNS

OBJECTIVES

- To describe the evolving pattern of international commerce

- To understand the important position of North America within the pattern of international trade

- To assess the effect of East Asia as an economic powerhouse on the industrial democracies of North America and Western Europe

- To examine global trade flows of six commodities and goods: microelectronics, automobiles, steel, nonoil commodities, grains and feed, textiles and clothing

The G-7 economic summit leaders in Tokyo, July 7, 1993. From the left is Cimpi (Italy), Kohl (Germany), Mitterand (France), Clinton (U.S.), Miyazawa (Japan), Campbell (Canada), Major (Britain), and the EC president and vice-president. *(Source: Larry Rubenstein/Reuters/Bettmann.)*

In Chapter 12, we considered the nature of international business—the forces that foster international commerce and the forces that interfere with it or modify it. In this chapter, we turn to a historical and geographic account of actual flows. What factors influence the strength of trade flows? What major changes have occurred in the volume and structure of international commerce? What are the consequences of the global crisis on world trade and foreign investment? And to what extent has the rise of Asia altered patterns of international commerce?

MODELING COMMODITY FLOWS

◈

Several scholars have attempted to predict commodity flows between pairs of countries by using interaction or gravity models (see Chapter 6). According to the gravity model, the intensity of trade flows between two countries is directly proportional to their trading capacities and inversely proportional to the barriers separating them. A significant study by Dutch economist Hans Linneman (1966) provides a generalized explanation for the existence of trade flows. According to Linneman, three groups of influences determine the size of trade flows: potential total demand of the importing country, potential total supply of the exporting country, and the physical and artificial barriers impeding the flow of goods between pairs of countries. Linneman developed a model based on these influences, using the following variables for each of 80 countries: (1) gross domestic product (GDP), (2) population size, (3) distance, (4) preferential trading relations, and (5) commodity composition of flows. All five variables proved to be important bases for trade. The most influential were gross national product (GNP)—a measure of potential demand—and distance. Also significant was preferential trading relations, particularly between colonial powers and their dependencies.

World trade is dominated by rich, densely populated industrial countries. In particular, it is dominated by the member countries of the European Economic Community (EEC). These countries are so busy trading with one another that they account for more than one-third of all world commerce. Some observers would argue that trade between EEC neighbors is domestic in character rather than international, similar to U.S. interstate commerce. But the EEC is only a qualified international association, not a country with states. In any event, the immense trading power of the members of the EEC owes much to their physical proximity and the absence of internal trade barriers, as well as to such factors as high demand and supply potential.

Major changes in the relative shares of world trade enjoyed by particular countries have occurred. Between 1971 and 1991, declines were registered in Europe, North America, and parts of the Third World. At the same time, sharp increases took place in oil-exporting countries, Japan, and the Four Tigers of Singapore, Hong Kong, Taiwan, and South Korea. Why did these changes occur? The concept of *competitive advantage of a nation* can help explain.

COMPETITIVE ADVANTAGE OF A NATION

◈

Michael Porter (1990), in his seminal study, *The Comparative Advantage of Nations*, examined the 10 most important trading nations in the world for a period of 5 years. Porter, from the Harvard University School of Business, concluded that four attributes of a nation combine to increase or decrease its global competitive advantage and world trade: (1) factor conditions; (2) demand conditions; (3) supporting industries; and (4) firm strategy, structure, and competition.

Factor Conditions

To Porter, *factor conditions* include what we call in this text the *production factors*—land, labor, capital, technology, and entrepreneurial skill. Porter structures them slightly differently and elaborates on them as follows:

1. *Human resources:* Human resources include the quantity of labor, the skill and cost of labor, the cultural factors that determine the motivation for the work ethic, and so forth.
2. *Physical resources:* Physical resources include (a) raw materials and their costs and (b) site and situation factors of the land and location itself, including physical geography, international time distance, and space conveyance.
3. *Capital resources:* Capital resources include all aspects of money supply and availability to finance the industry and trade from a particular country. Capital resources include the amount

of capital available; the savings rate of the population; the health of capital, money markets, and banking in the host country; government policies that affect interest rates, savings rates, and the money supply; levels of indebtedness; trade deficits; public and international debt; and so forth.

4. *Knowledge-based resources:* Knowledge-based resources are research, development, the scientific and technical community within the country, its achievements and levels of understanding, and the likelihood for future technological support and innovation.

5. *Infrastructure:* Infrastructure includes all aspects of public services available to develop the conditions necessary for producing the goods and services that provide a country with a competitive advantage. Included are transportation systems; communications and information systems; housing; cultural and social institutions; education; welfare; retirement; pensions; and national policies on health care and child care.

These five factors are identified in current international and economic circles as the keys to the competitive advantage of a nation in the 1990s.

Porter also groups the five factors into *basic factors,* which are fixed and have an availability limit, such as natural resources, location, distance from markets, and so forth, and *advanced factors,* which have no upper limits and can change dramatically. Examples of advanced factors are knowledge-based resources, capital resources, and human resources.

Demand Conditions

Porter defines *demand conditions* as the market conditions in a host country that aid the production processes in achieving better products, cheaper products, scale economies, and higher standards in terms of quality, service, and durability. Demand conditions cause firms to become innovative and therefore produce products that will sell not only in the local market, but also in the world market. For example, in the United States, consumers are well read and have a sophistication and demand that require producers to make products that are high value, durable, compact, and attractive. The result is a series of technologically advanced products that sell not only locally, but also internationally. Japan provides another example. Because of Japan's demand

conditions—the compact nature of the country and its high population density—the Japanese have honed their techniques to produce high-value, attractive items that are smaller than many products found in America.

Different portions of a national market are in different stages of a life cycle. For example, mass-produced, identical items are no longer in high demand in the United States. Instead, individualistic applications of technology to produce goods for small market segments have led to flexible manufacturing and, consequently, because of demanding domestic buyers, high-quality, upscale items.

Supporting Industries

Related and supporting industries supply the parts and semifinished goods needed to complete and market a high-quality product. Supporting industries are vital to the overall global competitive advantage of industries in the domestic market.

Fiber-optic cables, for example, have aided the space-shrinking technologies of a global communications industry. Without them, today's complex global economic system could not function as it does, nor could it expand. Likewise, various means of propulsion, including the steam engine, revolutionized transportation technology. The use of the internal combustion engine and different parts of the automobile transformed the way that we live, move, and settle. In addition, the semiconductor and microprocessor industry allowed the extremely successful American computer-manufacturing industry to be born and to grow. For example, in 1965, the memory capacity of a computer chip was 1024 bytes of information (1K). By 1970, the capacity had increased to 10K; by 1977, 16K; and by 1980, 64K. Since 1970, a new high-capacity memory chip has appeared approximately every 3 years, each with quadruple the capacity of the last one. The chip that appeared in 1983 had a capacity of 256K, and through the years 1989, 1992, and 1996? chip capacity increased from 4 to 16 to 64? megabytes (MB).

Firm Strategy, Structure, and Competition

Firm strategy, structure, and competition relates to the conditions under which firms originate, grow, and mature. For example, because stockholders demand

U.S. companies to show short-term profits, U.S. corporate performance may be less successful in the long run than it would be if it were judged for a much longer time, as Japanese and German corporate performance is.

State support of corporate strategy and performance is important. For example, a country can regulate taxes and incentives so that investment by a firm is high or low. In addition, competition within a country can impose demands on company performance; new business formations often pressure existing firms to improve products and lower prices and thus increase competitiveness. In Japan, for example, no fewer than 200 firms produce portable cassette player earphones. The market is extremely competitive, so quality is high and price is low. U.S. industries have adopted the so-called developmentalist stance of the Japanese government; doing so has fostered competitiveness in Japan but halted U.S. penetration into its markets.

Porter's Stages of Economic Development

Given the levels of global competitive advantage determined by human resources, physical resources, knowledge-based resources, capital resources, and infrastructure, Porter identifies four stages of economic development through which countries progress:

1. factor driven
2. investment driven
3. innovation driven
4. wealth driven

The four stages of economic development differentiate countries on the basis of technology, consumption, and successively higher levels of productivity. Each nation is on a continuum within one of these four stages, and as it moves forward, it takes on a new series of competitive tasks and leaves less sophisticated activities to countries at lower levels of development.

The *factor-driven stage* of economic development includes countries that generate most of their GDPs from processing and exporting natural resources and primary products. In addition, cheap, manual-skilled labor in these countries may host a variety of mass-production assembly plants. Nations such as OPEC, in which most of their GDPs are generated from fuel exports, fall into the factor-driven category.

In the second stage, the *investment-driven stage*, countries are further advanced along the technological ladder than countries in the factor-driven stage. Domestic investments and investments from abroad are funneled into plants taking advantage of scale economies, using transferred technology from more advanced countries, and producing standardized products with mass labor inputs provided by the local population. Examples of

The Suez Canal remains a vital link for distribution of oil from the Persian Gulf to Europe.
(Photo: Frederic Neema/Reuters/Bettmann.)

Despite the fact that the Middle East was one of the early hearths of civilization and city development, it did not share in the capitalist expansion and prosperity of the last 300 years that was centered on Europe and North America. It was only with the discovery of vast oil deposits by United States' companies in the Persian Gulf area in the second half of the 20th century that the focus of world attention returned to the Middle East. Today, the Middle East contains the greatest extremes of wealth, versus poverty, to be found anywhere in the world, all based on have and have-not oil supplies.

investment-driven economies include Taiwan, Mexico, Hong Kong, and South Korea, which use imported technologies and capital to mass-produce clothing and electronics.

The third stage of economic development identified by Porter is the *innovation-driven stage*. In this stage, firms are driven by increased levels of world competition to innovate new product designs, which are no longer based on factor costs or inexpensive labor but are derived from high levels of technology and skill. The multinational corporation (MNC) originates during this stage. It looks toward avenues of international marketing and overseas firm locations. Agglomeration economies exist, which cluster suppliers near production plants and generate a growth pole. This growth pole fosters not only expansion of productivity, but also the possibility of innovation and of cloning new firms that produce similar goods at even higher levels of quality and acceptability.

The service industries in the investment-driven and factor-driven stages are relatively undeveloped. However, in the innovation-driven stage, these industries rapidly increase in importance and surpass 50% of total employment.

Educational levels are the key to development in the innovation-driven stage, and, because of the need for more efficiency, primary production and mass-produced, labor-intensive activity are exported to regions that are on a lower plain of economic development. Many Southern European and Far East Asian countries are in this stage.

The last stage of economic development is the *wealth-driven stage*. This stage is described by a population that has a high overall standard of living and is most concerned with high levels of mass consumption and technological virtuosity. Priorities are centered on accumulating wealth and protecting one's material position in society, both as a nation and as an individual.

At this stage, however, a nation looks beyond its productive capabilities to political and social causes and thus allows growth to take second priority. The result is, perhaps, a slowdown of growth, an increased trade deficit, inflation, and long-term unemployment. The European nations certainly have allowed their dominant position to erode because of burdensome taxation and a huge welfare state economy. The United Kingdom, Sweden, and the Netherlands are cases in point. Germany and the United States also fall into this fourth category of wealth-driven economic development. In this stage, global competitive advantage starts to wane. With many First World countries in the wealth-driven

stage currently losing economic ground to countries in the other stages, we can clearly see that the world economy is in transition.

THE WORLD ECONOMY IN TRANSITION

International commerce has evolved far beyond the original pattern in which industrial countries exported manufactured goods to underdeveloped countries in exchange for primary commodities. Today, a few underdeveloped countries are among the world's most successful exporters of manufactures. In advanced industrial countries, intraindustry trade has reached a high level of specialization. Production of a single good now spans several countries, with each country on the global assembly line performing tasks in which it has a cost advantage. Immense changes have taken place in international specialization and trade during the last 200 years.

The first major change occurred with the technological advances spawned by the industrial revolution. Innovations in cotton textiles, the steam engine, iron and steel, railways, and steamships took place in a relatively free-enterprise environment, increasing output and international trade, particularly between 1820 and 1870 (Figure 13.1). Between 1870 and 1913, additional technological advances reinforced the trend toward further international integration. For example, by the 1880s because of refrigeration, frozen meat could be shipped from Australia to Great Britain. However, despite technological advances and increased international integration, output in the major industrial countries was not much greater than it was between 1820 and 1870, and the growth rate of exports fell (see Figure 13.1). A major reason for this decrease was the onset of protectionism in the 1870s.

Economic liberalism, which waned between 1870 and 1913, collapsed with either stagnation or depression in the world market between 1913 and 1950. Although the period inherited past technological innovations and contributed many of its own, their spread was impeded by political and economic turmoil. Growth of output plummeted, and the growth of trade decreased even more (see Figure 13.1).

Between 1950 and 1973, the world enjoyed unprecedented prosperity. The General Agreement on Tariffs

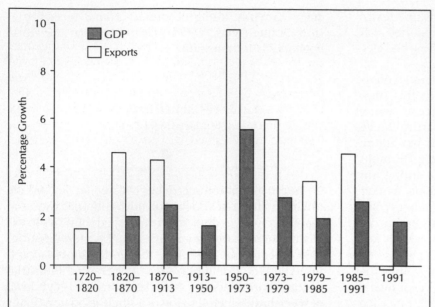

FIGURE 13.1
Historical trends in the growth of gross domestic product (GDP) and exports in selected countries, 1720–1991.
(Data: World Bank, 1993, p. 132.)

Post-World War II years showed the greatest growth in exports and gross domestic product, while post-World War I and depression years showed the lowest levels of exports and GDP. While GDP and exports were down substantially in 1991, prospects of world trade block solidarity in Europe and North America should increase export growth by the mid-1990's. Unprecedented prosperity is still in the future for some of the world's nations, including Japan, United States and Germany, for example. Income gaps, with less developed nations, are widening and the threat of increased debt and political unrest threatened global prosperity. Most of the people in Africa will be left out of the improving world economy because of underdevelopment. What can the developed nations do on behalf of these poor people. Socialism no longer seems to be the answer. How can rich nations transfer part of their wealth to poorer nations? How can continued growth of the world economy be tempered with protection of the environment? How should international business and monetary policy be altered to answer these above questions?

Note: Accurate historical data for world exports and GDP are difficult to obtain, so the chart shows average growth rates for six major industrial countries: France, Germany, Italy, Japan, the United Kingdom, and the United States. For exports, the growth rate for 1720–1820 includes only France and the United Kingdom; the average for 1820–1870 includes France, Germany, the United Kingdom, and the United States. The GDP growth rates have the same coverage, except the first period is 1700–1820 instead of 1720–1820, and the United States is excluded from both the first and second periods.

and Trade (GATT) liberalized trade. Decolonization swept Africa, Asia, and the Caribbean. MNCs rose to prominence. World output and trade expanded (see Figure 13.1), with manufacturing leading the way in both output and export growth (Figure 13.2). The growing trade in manufactures reflected the ever-increasing integration of world markets. This integration was fostered by transportation innovations that decreased travel time, telecommunications that allowed MNCs to coordinate the activities of their subsidiaries more easily, and electronics media that helped to shape a world market with increasingly similar consumer tastes.

The era of unprecedented growth ended abruptly in the early 1970s, when a series of world economic crises occurred. The first crisis was the collapse of the Bretton Woods agreement. A second development was a dramatic rise in the prices of industrial raw materials that ended the commodity price stability of the postwar period. This increase occurred at a time of high demand from developed countries and of rising nationalism among underdeveloped countries supplying these commodities. These conditions ignited world inflation, which soared after the 1973 oil-price increases. The oil shock brought on a deep worldwide recession reminiscent of the 1930s. After a weak recovery, another economic downturn followed in the early 1980s.

The recessions, which led to immediate cutbacks in import demand by the industrialized world, hit Third World countries particularly hard. Many have yet to recover. Recovery has also been slow in the older industrial countries. Only the western Pacific nations, whose cheaply produced goods swamped world markets, emerged from the recessions stronger than ever.

Underlying the crises of the 1970s and 1980s, and contributing independently to global instability, has been a fundamental reordering of world economic relationships. The original international capitalist division of labor gave way in the face of increased rivalry and competition among advanced industrial countries to a new international division of labor based on the internationalization of production. As we saw in Chapter 11, this development resulted in deindustrialization in Western Europe and North America, where countries are now competing with one another in developing still more sophisticated technology and attaining a leadership position in supplying the world with capital and services.

Composition of World Trade

The turbulent decades of the 1970s and 1980s saw major changes in the volume and composition of trade. World trade grew throughout the period, reaching

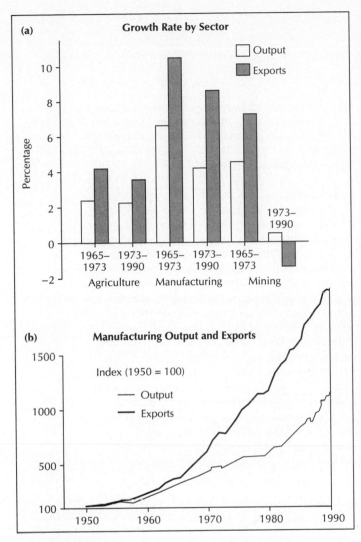

FIGURE 13.2
Postwar growth in world output and exports.
(Source: World Bank, 1992, p. 134.)

about $2 trillion in 1986. Rates of trade growth, however, declined after 1973. Manufacturing exports, with the exception of a dip in the mid-1970s, continued their rapid growth (see Figure 13.2b). They now account for about 60% of world exports by value. Fuel exports doubled their value share in the 1970s from less than 10% to more than 20%, but they declined with an oversupply of oil and weakening demand in the 1980s. The export value share of other primary commodities—food, beverages, and crude materials—decreased from nearly 30% in the mid-1960s to less than 15% in the mid-1980s.

The changing structure of trade has affected different types of countries differently. OPEC countries recorded a meteoric rise in the value of their exports in the 1970s

and a precipitous decline after 1980. The industrial countries of North America, Western Europe, and East Asia experienced a drop in their export earnings after the oil crisis. But as a group they recovered and now account for 80% of the value of world trade. With the exception of the major oil exporters, Third World countries that depend heavily on the export of a few primary commodities fared badly. For them, the growth in volume of primary commodity exports has been negative since 1980.

Increased diversification of trade ties represents one of the most significant developments in the contemporary world economy. Advanced industrial countries still trade primarily among themselves, but the proportion has declined from more than 75% in 1970 to around 66% today. They have increased their share of exports to underdeveloped countries and, despite a resurgence of protectionism, their imports from underdeveloped countries have increased still more. Another major development has been the growth of manufacturing exports from Third World countries to developed countries and, to a lesser extent, to other Third World countries. Manufacturing exports now account for about 40% of total nonfuel exports of these countries compared with 20% in 1963, and Third World countries now supply 13% of the imports of manufactures by developed countries compared with only 7% in 1973. Yet, only a handful of Asian and Western Hemisphere countries are involved in this development.

The State of the World Economy

The growth rates of global gross domestic product and the total output of goods and services actually dipped below zero for the first time in 1991 (Figure 13.1, Table 13.1). It dipped only −0.4%, but a negative world output is a rare occurrence. The main reasons for this decline were a world recession and a major economic interruption in Eastern Europe and the former Soviet Union.

World output per capita fell more than 2% below zero in 1991, after an almost complete stagnation in 1989 and 1990. East Asia remained the fastest-growing area despite a slowdown in total world trade. Major military activity in the Persian Gulf disrupted financial markets and ruined the oil exports of Kuwait and Iraq. The Uruguay round of GATT negotiating was postponed, and controversy among the EEC countries over the Maastricht Agreement also derailed European integration temporarily. Democracy in South Africa was at

Japanese woman carries home the "original recipe." American foreign direct investment, culture, and products have saturated much of the world markets.
(Photo: Greg Davis, The Stock Market.)

American cultural and business influences are likely to increase in the future. As United States' television programming becomes ubiquitous and the global information network becomes increasingly mature, American culture, the U.S.'s most powerful export (services) will grow in popularity and power. This will have both good and bad effects, but it will broaden the linkage between America and other countries, especially for the younger generations. At the same time it will threaten and further alienate the U.S. from more conservative cultures in the third world, especially Islamic countries. Multi-national corporations will continue to play an increasing role on the world scale. Many MNCs have grown to be larger in terms of annual sales than the economies of many countries. Additionally, MNCs are more informed and sophisticated than most governments and can act much faster because of less bureaucracy.

■

Table 13.1

Growth of the World Economy, 1988–1993

| | *Annual Percentage Change* | | | | | |
	1988	*1989*	*1990*	*1991**	*1992†*	*1993†*
World output	4.4	3.2	1.8	−0.4	1.0	3.0
Developed market economies	4.4	3.3	2.6	0.9§	1.7	3.2
Economies in transition‡	4.5	2.3	−5.0	−15.9§	−12.0	−4.1
Developing countries	4.4	3.3	3.2	3.4	4.5	5.5
World trade (export volume)	8.5	7.2	4.7	3.4	4.5	6.5
Memo item						
Growth of world output per capita	2.7	1.5	—	−2.1	−0.7	1.3

* Preliminary.
† Forecast, based on Project LINK and DESD estimates.
‡ The former Soviet Union and Eastern Europe.
§ After 1990, the former German Democratic Republic is included in Germany.
Source: U.N. World Economic Survey, 1992/93, p. 1.

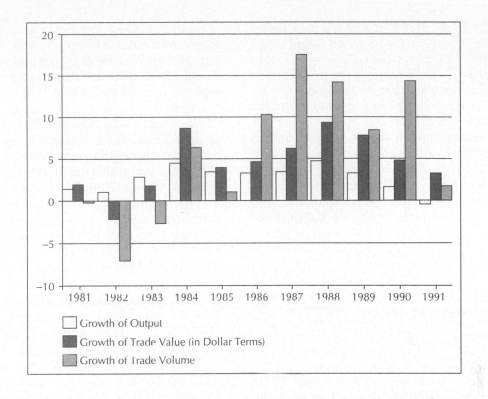

FIGURE 13.3

Until the early 1970s, the United States maintained a trade surplus, and both exports and imports hovered around 4% to 5% of gross domestic product (GDP). With the oil price rise of the 1970s, the United States was forced to increase the expensive imports and to increase the number of exports to keep the trade deficit relatively small. In the mid-1980s, with the international value of the dollar at an all-time high, foreign countries stopped importing U.S. goods, and the trade deficit widened. Oil prices dropped back to lower levels in the early 1980s, allowing imports to adjust downward. The value of the dollar sank in international markets in the late 1980s and early 1990s, thus substantially reducing the trade deficit, which has now climbed to approximately 10% of GDP.

(Source: United Nations, Department of Economic and Social Development, 1993, World Economic Survey, 1992/93, p. 130.)

a standstill, and Moscow announced the dissolution of the Soviet Union. Some of these world events created uncertainties in the international world economy and the world of trade.

Growth of world trade slowed substantially by 1991 to about 3%, the smallest gain since 1985 (Figure 13.3). But even this small gain was welcomed because of the negative growth rate of world output. World merchandise exports actually increased 2% in value in 1991 to a record $3.47 trillion, as prices declined on the average.

By 1993 and 1994, there was high unemployment worldwide, disenchantment and withdrawal from the labor force that had been restructured, widespread frustration, homelessness, drug trafficking, and ethnic tensions and riots in the developed world. All this turbulence caused the electorate to express dissatisfaction,

most notably in the United States with the election of the 1993 Clinton administration. While the entire world waited for recovery from recession and for new growth, heavy indebtedness by households and firms, by governments, notably that of the United States, as well as others continues into 1994. High debts and high real long-term interest rates cooled the supply and demand for credit and international trade.

The world is still in a general recession in 1994, and the economy is in transition. The international financial system is ruled by foreign-exchange markets and markets for short-term international funds. Governments try to keep track of their own funds while competing for short-term and long-term funds. Many people are anxious about the day-to-day fluctuations in money markets, stock markets, exchange rates, and interest rates around the world. However, the widely accepted theory is that recovery from the recession is now under way, but that it is weaker than hoped for and will make a small impression on world unemployment and principal market improvements in the world economy.

The length of the current recession will determine the point and strength of revival of world trade. Pent-up import and export demand, especially in the Eastern European countries and the former Soviet Union, if adequately financed by the West, will increase world imports. Recent efforts by the 110 signatories of GATT toward trade liberalization in the developing countries should also contribute to the revival of international trade.

A NEW FOCUS OF INTERNATIONAL ECONOMIC ACTIVITY

◈

Undoubtedly, the most significant structural development in the world economy in recent years is the shift in focus of international economic activity. At least from the age of colonization to around 1960, the North Atlantic Basin dominated world commerce. As a result of the rise of East Asia, this is no longer true.

Since 1960, the East Asian economies have grown at around 6% a year. During the same period, the United States and the EEC have experienced only a 3% growth rate. East Asia's share of gross world product more than doubled from 1967 to 1987. Its share of manufactured exports increased from 8% to 17%. Equally remarkable has been the growth of East Asia's financial power. Of the world's 10 largest banks by asset value, 7 are Japanese. Since the yen began rising in 1985, Japan's net capital outflows have amounted to a staggering $400 billion, and it provided nearly 15% of the foreign capital imported into the United States in 1987.

What do these figures mean? East Asia's rise has sharply increased the dependence of U.S. and East Asian economies on each other. However, America's trade with Canada is still greater than its trade with Japan—$129 billion with Canada and $116 billion with Japan in 1987. The EEC still imports almost as much from the United States as all the countries of East Asia do—$61 billion for Europe and $62 billion for Asia in 1987. The EEC is also America's biggest foreign direct investor; Japan is a distant second.

The rough parity in the sphere of international business between the blocs of the Atlantic and Pacific basins will change if East Asia's economic growth and trade growth rates continue to outstep those of the United States and Europe. But how will the picture change? Surely the United States' trade with East Asia will grow faster than its trade with Europe, but then again Europe's trade with East Asia will likewise grow faster

T.V. assembly line, Bloomington, Indiana.
(Photo: Photo courtesy of Thomson Consumer Electronics.) Televisions have diffused from North America to the rest of the world. In 1954, the United States had 200 television sets per 1,000 inhabitants, while Argentina, Germany, Italy, Japan, Netherlands, Spain, Sweden and Switzerland all had less than 1. Large corporations in the future will be less international or transnational than they will be "non-national." They will continue to pursue courses of action and economic policies and politics that favor themselves without a particular national flavor.

than its trade with the United States. Since 1967, trade between the EEC and East Asia increased by 240%; trade between the EEC and the United States increased by only 108%. Another likely change will be increased economic ties between Japan and the newly industrializing countries (NICs) of East Asia. Already Japan is superseding the United States as their main source of foreign direct investment (FDI); and the largest increases in manufactured exports to Japan since 1985 have come from Taiwan, Thailand, and South Korea—not from the United States or the EEC.

There is much talk that the economic rise of East Asia will prompt the United States to turn away from Europe. However, despite growing U.S.-East Asian economic links, the attachments and interests of the United States still lie more with Europe than with Asia, at least for now. Project 1992 has the potential to change America's world view, however. By passing the Single European Act, all EEC members committed themselves to creating a frontier-free internal market. If that means putting in place a protectionist Fortress Europe, as it appears, America's allegiance to Europe could be diverted.

The way that the United States views the world may also hinge on events taking place in California,

the nation's most populous state. By the year 2000, Hispanic, black, and Asian Californians will outnumber Europeans. Asian money is also pouring into the state. After Canada, Japan has the largest single stake of foreign capital in California; Japanese companies represent the largest foreign source of employment. The de-Europeanization of California—of its population and of its sources of wealth—is likely to carry over to the rest of the country. As a result of this impending change, will the United States be forced to choose between the Pacific and the Atlantic in the next century?

Table 13.2 shows the merchandise trade of the seven regions of the world, and Table 13.3 shows the network of origins and destinations of world merchandise trade by region for 1990. Line 1 of Table 13.2 shows North American exports of 525 billion dollars' worth of goods, and imports of more than 640 billion dollars' worth of goods. The United States is the world's largest single trading nation. However, because of the proximity of countries, the relatively small size, good transportation and communication, and varying complementary patterns of comparative advantage, Western Europe accounts for more than 1600 billion dollars' worth of exports and imports per year and is the largest world trading region. In contrast, Eastern Europe, the former

Table 13.2

Population and Merchandise Trade of the Seven World Regions, 1990

	Population		Exports		Imports	
	Million	Average Annual Change[†]	Value*	Average Annual Change[†]	Value*	Average Annual Change[†]
	1990	1980–1990	1990	1980–1990	1990	1980–1990
North America	275	1	525	6	641	7
Latin America	451	2	148	3	133	$1/2$
Western Europe	438	$1/2$	1613	7	1685	6
Central/Eastern Europe/USSR[‡]	407	1	182	—	187	—
Africa	645	3	94	$-2^{1/2}$	93	0
Middle East	126	3	132	-5	103	0
Asia	2903	$1^{1/2}$	791	$9^{1/2}$	765	8
World	5245	$1^{1/2}$	3485	$5^{1/2}$	3608	$5^{1/2}$

* Billions of dollars.
[†] Percent.
[‡] Imports FOB.

◈

Table 13.3
Network of World Merchandise Trade by Region, 1990*†

Origin	Destination							
	North America	Latin America	Western Europe	Central/ Eastern Europe/ USSR	Africa	Middle East	Asia	World
North America	178.0	55.8	125.0	5.3	9.0	12.1	133.0	525.3
Latin America	68.6	19.8	33.4	8.5	1.7	1.8	13.7	148.0
Western Europe	127.7	28.8	1164.2	45.4	54.0	44.8	119.8	1612.8
Central/Eastern Europe/USSR	2.9	6.9	62.3	76.9	3.5	2.4	20.6	181.7
Africa	13.2	1.7	50.8	2.9	5.9	2.1	5.7	93.7
Middle East	19.0	7.9	34.2	4.2	3.2	7.0	52.1	132.0
Asia	210.4	15.4	148.4	13.8	13.3	22.3	358.1	791.2
World	619.7	136.3	1618.2	157.1	90.5	92.4	703.0	3485.0

* Billions of dollars.
† World totals include exports to unspecified destinations.
Source: Handbook of International Trade Statistics, 1993, Directorate of Intelligence, C.I.A., p. 4.

Soviet Union, Africa, and the Middle East all show relatively small proportions of world merchandise trade. Asia, with 60% of the world population, shows the most rapid average annual change in the value of exports and imports, with more than 790 billion dollars' worth of exports and more than 760 billion dollars' worth of imports.

Table 13.3 shows the interregional world trade for 1990. Once again, the largest trade volumes of more than $100 billion include trade within North America (primarily between Canada and the United States), trade between North America and Western Europe, trade within Western Europe, trade between Western Europe and Asia, and trade between North America and Asia. Asian trade with North America is more than $200 billion per year, which accounts for the flows of goods and services to and from Japan and North America (mainly the United States) and to and from the NICs of South Korea, Taiwan, Singapore, Hong Kong, Malaysia, Indonesia, the Philippines, and Thailand.

In summary, the North Atlantic Basin has dominated world trade since the days of colonization, but this pattern has shifted in focus. The North Atlantic Basin accounts for a smaller proportion of international trade than in earlier years. Trade in the Pacific Basin is now the new focus of economic activity, as well as trade within Western Europe itself (line 3, Table 13.3). Western Europe's trade with North America is more than

$100 billion per year, but intra-European trade, at $1164 billion, is the single largest trade flow in the world.

MAJOR GLOBAL TRADE FLOWS IN THE 1990S

◼

Although we do not have space in this text to identify every major international trade-flow pattern of most manufactured items and services, six have been selected for examination: microelectronics, automobiles, steel, textiles and clothing, grains and feed, and nonoil commodities. Each of these goods shows major patterns of international trade and has been selected for examination on the basis of its representativeness and importance.

Global Trade Flow of Microelectronics

Microelectronics includes semiconductors, integrated circuits and parts for integrated circuits, and electronic components and parts. Japan and the Far East countries, especially the Four Tigers of South Korea, Taiwan, Hong Kong, and Singapore, but including the 14 Pacific Basin nations, together account for the predominant flow of microelectronics in the world (Figure 13.4). The single largest flow from this group is from the developing countries of the Western Hemisphere, other than the United States and Canada, most notably Mexico, and the countries in South Asia and East Asia, which send more than 7 billion dollars' worth of microelectronics to the United States. Japan sends another 5.69 billion dollars' worth of microelectronics to developing countries and more than 3.2 billion dollars' worth to the United States. The single largest flow of microelectronics in the world is from the United States to developing countries and is worth $7.52 billion.

Although the United States no longer leads the world in the manufacture of semiconductors, it is still a major player in the global trade flow of microelectronics. Canada and the Western European nations of the EEC and the European Free Trade Area (EFTA) account for a much smaller proportion of overseas trade in this category. However, intra-European trade in microelectronics accounts for almost 6 billion dollars' worth.

Global Trade Flow of Automobiles

Global trade within the EEC accounts for the largest single flow of automobiles. More than 61 billion dollars' worth of automobiles were shipped among EEC countries in 1990, and more than another 8 billion dollars' worth were sent to EFTA countries (Figure 13.5). The United States received more than 8 billion dollars' worth

FIGURE 13.4

Global trade flow of microelectronics, 1990, in billions of U.S. dollars. *(Data: United Nations, 1992, p. 173, Handbook of International Economic Statistics, Directorate of Intelligence, C.I.A., 1993.)* There has been a revolution in microelectronics production and use worldwide since the mid-20th century. Each stage of innovation and development has made microelectronics industry more powerful, more sophisticated, faster in processing, lighter in weight, smaller in size, and cheaper in cost. In five decades, computers have reduced in size from a room to the size of a lap top dictaphone. Calculators have reduced to the size of a watch and pocket televisions and cellular phones now clip on one's waist band. (See photo, page 350.) The most important leap forward in the evolution of electronic computers was the invention of the *integrated circuit*, or *silicon chip* in 1958 by an American corporation, Texas Instruments, thus incorporating the functionality of hundreds of electric circuits in one small piece of plastic. The first *microprocessor*, invented by Intel in 1969 of the United States, was the basis of the modern computer industry today. Now, microprocessors are used in not only high tech industries such as aircraft manufacture and computer assembly, but also in household consumer products such as televisions, washing machines, word processors, fax machines and cellular phones. The microelectronics industry today is vitally linked to information and knowledge. We are quickly moving towards the time when anyone can get information to almost anyone else in the world at any location and at any time. Computing power is being reduced in cost precipitously and increasing at the rate of 4,000 times in computing power per decade for a given unit of cost. The production of transistors, the most basic unit in the microprocessor is exploding, and over 1 million are produced each year for every person on earth, and the rate is growing.

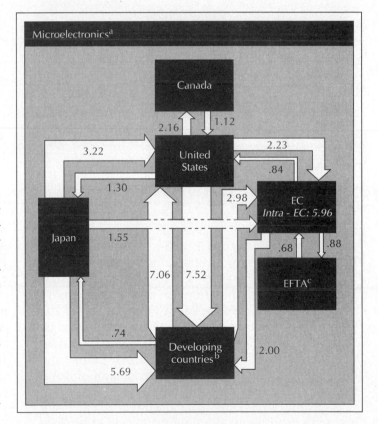

[a] Including integrated circuits and IC parts, semiconductors, and electronic component parts.
[b] Including Western Hemisphere other than the United States and Canada; Africa and the Middle East; South Asia; and East Asia other than Japan, Mongolia, North Korea, Laos, and Cambodia.
[c] Including Austria, Switzerland, Sweden, Norway, Finland, Iceland, and Liechtenstein.

Note: Width of arrows scaled to dollar volume. Trade flows less than $500 million not shown.

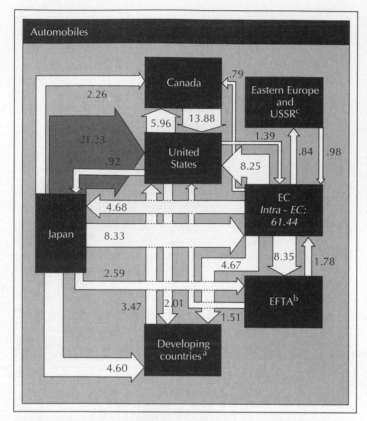

FIGURE 13.5

Global trade flow of automobiles, 1990, in billions of U.S. dollars. *(Data: United Nations, 1992, p. 173 and op. cit. Fig. 14.3.)* General Motors, producing over 5 million cars per year, and Ford Motor Company, producing over 4 million cars per year comprise the largest automobile manufacturers worldwide. The rise of the Japanese automobile manufacturers in the last 40 years have been the most dramatic in change in the industry, however. Japan now leads the world automobile production, with the United States in second place. These countries are followed by Germany, France, Soviet Union, Italy, Canada, Spain and the United Kingdom. In the 1950s, Japanese companies made significant progress, studying the mass production methods from Detroit, the home of vehicle manufacturer in the world. Toyota and Mitsubishi, which had been making military vehicles during World War II, were able to transfer technology required in the building of war time vehicles, including fighter aircraft, to automobile manufacturing. Japan and East Asia were demanding smaller cars than the United States companies were willing to make and, thus, Japanese small car mass production gained ground. The Japanese motorcycle industry had perfected miniaturization of motors, gears and working parts, and this helped foster the light, small, fuel efficient automobile industry. Another major aspect of Japan's phenomenal post-war development was their expanding steel industry, their ability to employ state of the art mass production techniques borrowed from Detroit, cheap raw materials that they assembled from the Pacific Rim nations, and dedicated, almost mesmerized labor, willing to work hard for very low wages.

a Including Western Hemisphere other than the United States and Canada; Africa and the Middle East; South Asia; and East Asia other than Japan, Mongolia, North Korea, Laos, and Cambodia.

b Including Austria, Switzerland, Sweden, Norway, Finland, Iceland, and Liechtenstein.

c Including East Germany, Poland, Hungary, Czechoslovakia, Yugoslavia, Albania, Romania, Bulgaria, and the former USSR.

Note: Width of arrows scaled to dollar volume. Trade flows less than $500 million not shown.

as well, including Mercedes, Audis, Porsches, Volkswagens, Peugeots, Fiats, and Renaults. If we consider the value and production of automobiles in Europe, it is surprising that half way around the world Japan made a major inroad into the European market, shipping 11 billion dollars' worth to Western Europe in 1990. The single largest volume of flow is also accounted for by Japan and its shipment to the United States, more than 21 billion dollars' worth in 1990. Eastern Europe and the USSR accounted for a minuscule amount of global trade flow in automobiles.

Japanese automobile manufacturers made major penetrations in the world automobile market between 1960 and 1990 (Figure 13.6). During the same time, the big three automakers in America scaled down operations substantially. However, General Motors and Ford remained the world's largest automobile manufacturers by 1990 (Table 13.4), even though the Japanese had

captured almost 26% of the American automobile and light truck market. In 1990, the American competitors appeared to be losing out to the high-quality, beautifully engineered subcompacts and luxury models from Japan. But then, slowly, between 1990 and 1994, the market share situation in the United States began to reverse itself.

By 1993, Japan's share was 22%, and by 1994, 20%. The problem for Japan was the increased value of the yen compared with the dollar. As we learned in Chapter 12, the dollar is now weak on world international markets. In contrast, the yen has appreciated more than 16% in each of the last 2 years and now stands at approximately 100 to the dollar. The high value of the yen adversely affects Japanese sales in America because comparable vehicles are now priced $2000 more than American vehicles. Another factor is that American car builders, after years of struggle, are finally turning out

FIGURE 13.6

The rise of Japanese automobile manufacturers, 1960–1989.

(Source: World Motor Vehicle Data, 1993; American Automobile Manufacturers Association, Detroit, Michigan.)

Now, most Japanese automobile manufacturers use *assembly line robots* because, before automation, manufacturers could not keep pace with world demand for Japanese vehicles. Factories have been linked with clusters of hundreds of competing parts producers, which provide specialized flexibility to major manufacturers, as well as economies of scale.

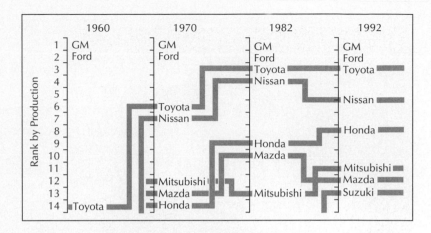

higher-quality competitive products with a flair for style not seen since the 1960s. The Honda Accord has fallen from grace in America because analysts believe that the styling is too bland and conservative. Public taste has changed, too. Porter (1990) described demand conditions and taste as an important factor in global comparative advantage. American consumers are bypassing ordinary passenger cars for light trucks, minivans, four-wheel drives, and sporty utility vehicles. This preference gives American companies a strong edge because Japan is just entering these other product lines. The final reason for the reversal is that some consumers look at the hostile relationship between America and Japan and choose to buy American. Only 2 of the top 10 cars and

◈

Table 13.4

Top Automobile Manufacturers Worldwide, 1989

Rank	Company	Country of Origin	Passenger Car Production*	Share of World Total (%)	Percentage Produced Outside Home Country
1	General Motors	USA	5,523,134	15.6	41.8
2	Ford	USA	4,060,586	11.5	58.7
3	Toyota	Japan	3,330,380	9.4	8.3
4	Volkswagen	Germany	2,713,671	7.7	30.5
5	Peugeot–Citroën	France	2,320,266	6.5	15.4
6	Nissan	Japan	2,289,123	6.5	13.8
7	Fiat	Italy	2,108,622	6.0	7.1
8	Renault	France	1,755,510	5.0	17.6
9	Honda	Japan	1,604,430	4.5	28.0
10	Mazda	Japan	1,184,166	3.3	18.3
11	Chrysler	USA	1,052,537	3.0	13.0
12	VAZ	USSR	724,740†	2.0	—
13	Mitsubishi	Japan	708,418	2.0	—
14	Daimler–Benz	Germany	536,993	1.5	—
15	BMW	Germany	489,742	1.4	—
16	Rover	UK	466,619	1.3	—
17	Volvo	Sweden	423,385	1.2	33.8

* Excludes commercial vehicles.

† 1987.

Source: Calculated from SMMT, 1990, pp. 28–33. World Automotive Statistics: SMMT, in Dicken, 1992.

Forklifts awaiting export to America from Yokohama, Japan. Japan is the world'smost prolific producer of motorized vehicles, automobiles, and commercial vehicles. More spectacular than the sheer volume of automobiles produced is the rate of industrial growth in this area. From 1960 to 1990, Japanese auto production increased by more than 5000%. *(Photo: Pam Hasegawa, Impact Visuals.)* Japan birthed the *just-in-time technique,* which organizes parts deliveries so that materials arrive as they are needed in the production process. Companies, therefore, save the trouble and expense of transporting huge stocks of components unnecessarily.

trucks sold in America were imported from Japan in 1993. Honda's compact-sized Accord was the nation's best-selling import car for several years. However, the Ford Taurus supplanted it in the 1993 list of 10 best-selling cars and light trucks in America (Table 13.5).

The situation for Japanese MNCs, Toyota, Nissan, Mitsubishi, Mazda, and Honda, would be much worse if it had not been for political pressure to build U.S.

◎

Table 13.5

Top Ten United States Vehicle Sellers, Second Half of 1993

Type of Vehicle	Vehicle Sales
Ford F-series pickup	263,574
Chevrolet C/K pickup	258,234
Ford Taurus	173,819
Ford Ranger	165,136
Toyota Camry	149,499
Chevrolet Cavalier	146,612
Dodge Caravan	145,442
Ford Explorer	145,270
Ford Escort	141,816
Honda Accord	133,005

Source: Automotive News Data Center, Detroit, Michigan, 1994.

factories, starting with the Honda plant in 1982 in Marysville, Ohio (Table 13.6). Japanese-made vehicles that are assembled and built in America account for nearly half the Japanese-U.S. car sales. Locally made Japanese cars are cheaper than those imported from Japan because they escape the high-priced parts and labor associated with the yen. Nissan's newest plants are built in low-wage Smyrna, Tennessee, producing Sentras and Ultimas. These American-made Japanese cars are called *Japanese transplants.* Transplant sales are down.

Exports of automobiles from major European producing countries have been extremely heavy. Although France produces innocuously designed cars—the Peugeot, the Renault, and the Citroën—it is second in Western Europe in terms of passenger car exports, with Germany number one at 2,451,251 vehicles in 1989 and Belgium and Spain third and fourth. U.S. companies have diversified, so both Ford and General Motors now have substantial international automobile production (Figure 13.7).

Global Trade Flow of Steel

Whereas America has lost as much as two-thirds of its steelworker employment in the last 20 years and now is a net importer of steel, Western Europe continues

T a b l e 13.6

Final Assembly Foreign Automobile Plants in North America

Company	Plant Location	Date Opened	Current Planned Capacity	Projected Plant Employment
United States				
BMW	Greer, So. Carolina	1996	150,000	1000
Honda	Marysville, Ohio	1982	360,000	2600
	East Liberty, Ohio	1989	150,000	1800
Nissan	Smyrna, Tennessee	1983	480,000	3300
	Decherd, Tennessee	1996	300,000 engines	1000
Toyota/GM (NUMMI)	Fremont, California	1984	340,000	2500
Toyota	Georgetown, Kentucky	1988	400,000	3000
Mazda	Flat Rock, Michigan	1987	240,000	3500
Mercedes Benz	Vance, Alabama	1997	50,000	600
Mitsubishi/Chrysler (Diamond Star)	Normal, Illinois	1988	240,000	2900
Subaru/Isuzu	Lafayette, Indiana	1989	120,000	1700
Canada				
Honda	Alliston, Ontario	1987	100,000	700
Hyundai	Bromont, Quebec	1989	20,000	400
Toyota	Cambridge, Ontario	1988	50,000	1000
Suzuki/GM (CAMI)	Ingersoll, Ontario	1989	200,000	2000
Volvo	Halifax, Nova Scotia	1990	40,000	300

Source: Press and company reports, and Dicken, 1992 p. 294.

to lead the world in steel production and in the steel trade (Figure 13.8). The EEC accounted for more than 33 billion dollars' worth of steel traded internally in 1990, and trade with the EFTA accounted for another 10 billion dollars' worth.

The single largest flow of steel was from Japan to developing countries. In addition, the EEC sent 7.38 billion dollars' worth of steel to developing countries in 1990. Steel requires large and highly efficient plants, which are possible only with tremendous capital invest-

ments and large scale economies. Africa, for example, has only a tiny portion of world steel making, less than 1% of the world's total output.

In the post-World War II period, steel made by traditional producers in Europe and North America became overpriced. New production centers began to emerge in Brazil, South Korea, Taiwan, and Japan. The migration of steel production to the Third World reflected the growing importance of labor costs, government subsidies, and taxes to the delivered cost of steel. In Chapters

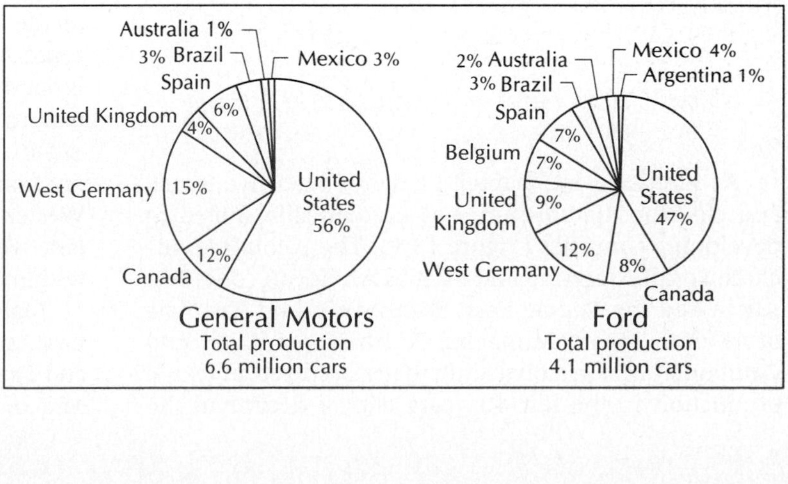

FIGURE 13.7
International automobile production by GM and Ford, 1990. *(Source: World Motor Vehicle Data, 1992.)*

General Motors
Total production
6.6 million cars

Ford
Total production
4.1 million cars

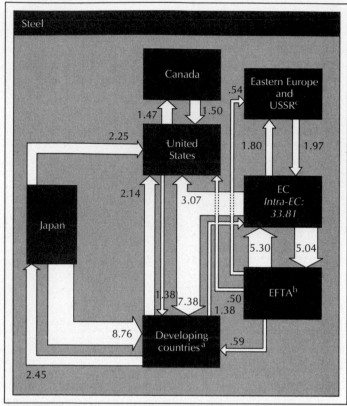

[a]Including Western Hemisphere other than the United States and Canada; Africa and the Middle East; South Asia; and East Asia other than Japan, Mongolia, North Korea, Laos, and Cambodia.
[b]Including Austria, Switzerland, Sweden, Norway, Finland, Iceland, and Liechtenstein.
[c]Including East Germany, Poland, Hungary, Czechoslovakia, Yugoslavia, Albania, Romania, Bulgaria, and the former USSR.
Note: Width of arrows scaled to dollar volume. Trade flows less than $500 million not shown.

FIGURE 13.8
Global trade flows of steel, 1990, in billions of U.S. dollars. *(Data: United Nations, 1992, p. 174.)* op. cit. Fig. 14.3 The *second wave* of the industrial revolution between 1825 and 1880 was based on the invention of steel making. Steel allowed metal parts to be improved to cope with greater heat, friction, and weight of working machinery. The development of railroads and steamships went hand-in-hand with the production of steel, allowing innovations and mechanical engineering, coal mining and steel making. Until the early 20th century, iron and steel furnaces were located in close proximity to coking coal, since transporting fuel was wasteful and expensive. Since that time, steel making has cut fuel costs and reduced the locational attraction of coal fields. Plants have shifted to the market as scrap metal and *electric arc furnaces* have bought high quality steel manufacturing to areas without much coal, but which had cheap hydroelectric power or gas supplies, such as Northern Europe and the Western United States. Japan, the United States and Europe continue to dominate in steel production, but the shift has been in the direction of developing countries. New furnaces use not only coal, but oil, natural gas or liquid propane, or electricity, in steel making. Most steel plants are located at coastal sites because much of the bulky materials have to be transported in. A major invention from the United States allowed direct reduction, using enriched iron ore pellets to make steel using electric hearth furnaces. Third world nations, many of which have their own fuel and iron ore, have now entered the race for world steel making and have absorbed many of the U.S. and European markets.

10 and 11, we discussed at length the British and U.S. steel industries: too many employees, reluctant unions, demoralized management, inefficiency, and lack of government support of an ailing industry.

Competition has made the international steel industry highly mobile. In the past, competition was national; now it is global.

Global Trade Flow of Textiles and Clothing

As discussed in Chapter 11, labor-intensive textile and clothing manufacture has dramatically shifted to developing countries (Figure 13.9). These countries include South American and Central American countries; Africa and the Middle East; South Asia; and East Asia other than Japan, Mongolia, North Korea, Laos, and Cambodia. Major global shifts have occurred in textile production in the last 40 years with a decline in the

United States and Western Europe, which were the dominant producers as late as 1950. New production centers include the Far East, India, and China. International trade in textiles reflects these shifts in production. Developing countries accounted for more than 70 billion dollars' worth of exports in 1990.

Surprisingly, Germany and Italy lead the world in textile export, even though the main manufacturing centers of older industrialized nations have given ground to the Third World in textile and clothing manufacture. Tiny Hong Kong leads the world in clothing export. Some of the top six leading world exporters are from East Asia and the Pacific (Table 13.7). Again, Western Europe accounts for more than 70 billion dollars' worth of textile and clothing trade among nations within Western Europe (EEC and EFTA).

Major gainers during the last 30 years include the East Asian countries of China, Hong Kong, South Korea, and Taiwan. By 1990, European nations accounted for 47% of the world trade flow, whereas East Asian coun-

FIGURE 13.9
Global trade flow of textiles and clothing, 1990, in billions of U.S. dollars.
(Data: United Nations, 1992, p. 174.) op. cit. Fig. 14.3.
One of the greatest shifts in the internationalization of manufacturing has been that of textiles and clothing, shifting from developed countries of Northern Europe and the United States to developing countries. Most textile manufacturing today occurs in the third world, using small scale home-based production, as well as large, modern mills. Cotton is the basis for much of the world textile industry and has grown in vast areas of China, India and Egypt, for example. In developing countries, thread is produced from cotton fiber, using a spinning wheel. The thread then can be woven into cloth and dyed with synthetic dyes produced by the chemical industry. Synthetic fabrics were in great demand in the 1970s and early 1980s, and relied on petrochemical industries for raw materials. Today, the world has discovered the comfort of natural fibers and synthetics are now more likely to be used in blends and as strengthening agents. Throughout East Asia, textiles are a vital constituent of each country's economy. Most textile factories are small family-owned operations that employ only a handful of people and yet sell their garments through a wholesaler who operates on an international market.

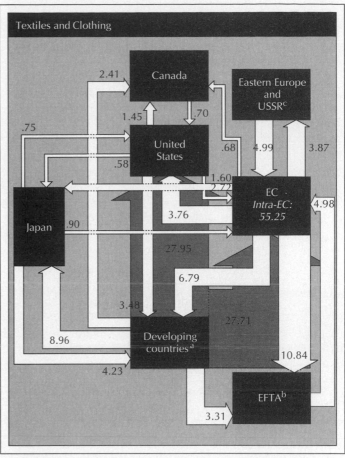

[a]Including Western Hemisphere other than the United States and Canada; Africa and the Middle East; South Asia; and East Asia other than Japan, Mongolia, North Korea, Laos, and Cambodia.
[b]Including Austria, Switzerland, Sweden, Norway, Finland, Iceland, and Liechtenstein.
[c]Including East Germany, Poland, Hungary, Czechoslovakia, Yugoslavia, Albania, Romania, Bulgaria, and the former USSR.
Note: Width of arrows scaled to dollar volume. Trade flows less than $500 million not shown.

tries accounted for another 43%. However, a much larger proportion of textiles and clothing flowed from developing countries to the United States than they did from Western Europe to the United States. Eastern Europe, the former Soviet Union, Japan, and Canada are relatively small players in the world textile and clothing trade.

Global Trade Flow of Grains and Feed

The primary products of wheat, corn, rice, other cereals, feed grains, and soybeans are included in the category of grains and feed. The United States exports more than 20 billion dollars' worth of feed and grains

and thus is a world leader in this category (Figure 13.10). Considering its huge area, Canada is also a major exporter.

Japan, with its small base of agriculture and arable land, is a net importer, as is Eastern Europe and the former Soviet Union. Trade within the EEC is large and was $13.5 billion in 1990. Developing countries such as India, Egypt, and Argentina are some of the largest net exporting developing countries in this category.

World trade in grains, feeds, and food products had been as high as 30% in 1965, but these commodities slipped to only 15% by 1990. Some of this reduction is because Western seeds, grains, and fertilizers are now commonplace in Third World nations, and technology from the grain revolution has taught developing countries to provide for themselves. Another portion of the

▣

Table 13.7
The World's Leading Clothing-Exporting Countries, 1991

Rank	Exporter	Share of World Clothing Exports (%)		Average Annual Growth (%)		
		1980	1991	1980–1988	1988	1989
1	Hong Kong*	12.0	14.5	11.5	10.0	18.5
2	Italy	11.0	9.5	9.0	1.0	4.0
3	South Korea	7.0	9.5	14.5	17.5	4.5
4	China	4.0	6.5	14.0	30.0	26.0
5	West Germany	7.0	5.5	8.0	7.5	5.0
6	Taiwan	6.0	5.0	8.5	−5.5	0.5
7	France	5.5	3.5	4.5	8.0	10.0
8	Turkey	0.5	3.0	43.5	7.0	18.0
9	Portugal	1.5	2.5	17.5	11.5	12.6
10	United Kingdom	4.5	2.5	3.5	7.5	−6.0
11	Thailand	0.5	2.5	27.0	21.5	28.0
12	United States	3.0	2.5	3.5	36.0	34.5
13	India	1.5	2.0	13.0	7.5	24.5
14	Netherlands	2.0	1.5	7.0	9.5	4.0
15	Greece	1.0	1.5	15.0	−16.5	22.5
Above 15 countries		67.0	72.0			

* Includes substantial reexports.
Source: GATT, 1992, p. 21.

Combined grain is off-loaded on a farm near Wataga, Illinois. The United States is a world supplier of primary products, including grains, timber, and other agricultural products. *(Photo: Martha Tabor, Impact Visuals.)* Most every country in the world grows grain and approximately a quarter of the 600 million tons of wheat produced each year enters world trade. By 1960, overpopulation in the third world had begun to outstrip its own food production and Europe had long been a grain importer by then. The United States and Canada became the only large grain exporters, providing 80 percent of the world's exports. No doubt, the Richard Nixon grain deals with the Soviet Union countries, in the mid-1970s, helped establish *Detente,* and ease tensions during the Cold War.

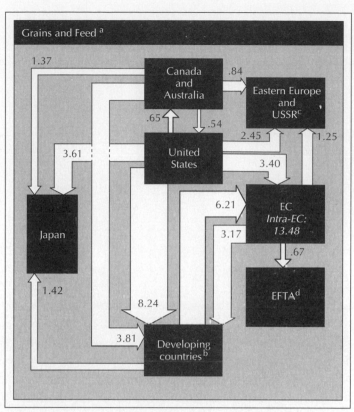

FIGURE 13.10
Global trade flows of grains and feed, 1990, in billions of U.S. dollars. *(Data: United Nations, 1992, p. 175, op. cit Fig. 13.4.)*
Even though North America is still the leading exporter of grains and feed, the dominance of North America has declined steadily since 1980 as a result of foreign subsidies within the European community, which have increased grain surpluses. A stumbling block to the Uruguay Round of tariff reductions, which have now been completed, were the agricultural subsidies to European farmers which have been left largely in tact. *Green Revolution* hybrid and hearty seed varieties have also helped third world nations, including India, Japan and Southeast Asian countries. India has been able to achieve self-sufficiency in grain production, for example—something that was impossible 30 years ago. Grain remains the most important traded food commodity in the world today, but few countries have large surpluses to export. Attempts to control a political situation or exert influence over another country by withholding grain exports have usually not worked. Food aid is a more humanitarian way of exerting political influence, since receiving countries are too poor to buy the food and the shipping countries usually have enough grain so that much of it will be wasted. While donor countries can be selective about where food aid is sent, increasing food aid by the developed nations of the world, especially North America and Europe, must be forthcoming to the third world nations in order to give *biotechnology* time to ripen.

[a]Including wheat, corn, rice, other cereals, feedgrains, and soybeans.
[b]Including Western Hemisphere other than the United States and Canada; Africa and the Middle East; South Asia; and East Asia other than Japan, Mongolia, North Korea, Laos, and Cambodia.
[c]Including East Germany, Poland, Hungary, Czechoslavakia, Yugoslavia, Albania, Romania, Bulgaria, and the former USSR.
Note: Width of arrows scaled to dollar volume. Trade flows less than $500 million not shown for grains/feed; trade flows less than $2 billion not shown for nonoil commodities.

reduction from 1965 to 1990 reflects the worsening terms of trade (Chapter 12) for primary goods, as prices of manufacturers and energy rose rapidly and gave producers of feed, grains, and agricultural products less leverage in world international commerce. The 1973 and 1978 Middle East oil crises and the sharp increase in oil prices in 1979 signaled the beginning of the falling prices of such energy-intensive products.

Global Trade Flow of Nonoil Commodities

Nonoil commodities include copper, aluminum, nickel, zinc, tin, iron ore, pig iron, uranium ore, and alloys. Crude rubber, wood and pulp, hides, cotton fiber, and animal and vegetable minerals and oils are included in this category. Although the United States, for a highly

developed country, shows an amazing export potential, sending more than 7 billion dollars' worth to Japan, 9.5 billion dollars' worth to developing countries, and another 5 billion dollars' worth to EEC countries, the developing countries of the world lead in the export of nonoil commodities (Figure 13.11). The largest single flow of nonoil commodities outside the more than 30 billion dollars' worth exchanged within the EEC is from developing countries to Japan (15.7 billion dollars' worth) and from developing countries to Western Europe, approximately 22 billion dollars' worth.

Since the early days of Europe, the international division of labor was based on international trade. Under this unfair program, less developed countries traded their nonoil commodities—grains, feed, food stocks, and energy sources—for industrialized goods from primarily Europe and other developed nations. This pattern still existed in 1990 but had weakened somewhat with the internationalization of manufacturers.

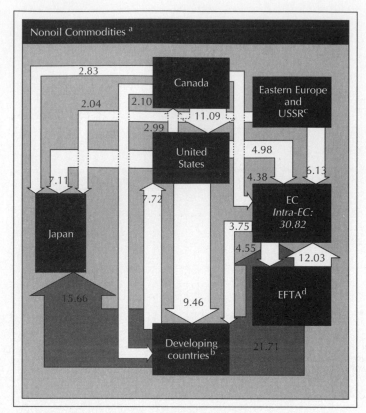

^aIncluding unwrought copper, aluminum, nickel, zinc, and tin, and ores thereof; iron ore and pig iron; uranium ore and alloys; other nonferrous ores, unwrought metals, and crude minerals; crude rubber, wood and pulp; hides; cotton fiber and other textile fibers; crude animal and vegetable materials.
^bIncluding Western Hemisphere other than the United States and Canada; Africa and the Middle East; South Asia; and East Asia other than Japan, Mongolia, North Korea, Laos, and Cambodia.
^cIncluding East Germany, Poland, Hungary, Czechoslovakia, Yugoslavia, Albania, Romania, Bulgaria, and the former USSR.
^dIncluding Austria, Switzerland, Sweden, Norway, Finland, Iceland, and Liechtenstein.
Note: Width of arrows scaled to dollar volume. Trade flows less than $500 million not shown for grains/feed; trade flows less than $2 billion not shown for nonoil commodities.

FIGURE 13.11
Global trade flows of nonoil commodities, 1990, in billions of U.S. dollars. *(Data: United Nations, 1992, p. 175; op. cit. Fig. 14.3.)* Developing countries dominant global trade flows and non-oil commodities. For example, South Africa is the world's leading producer of chromium, gold and platinum, while the former Soviet Union countries lead in iron ore, nickel, lead, zinc, manganese, mercury and cobalt. China is a world leader in the production of tungsten, tin, iron ore and lead. India produces chrome, manganese, bauxite, iron ore. Brazil is the world's leading producer in bauxite, tin, manganese, and iron ore. Nonmetallic minerals, such as phosphates, potash, sulfur, salt, diamonds, gypsum and graphite are also in large supply from developing countries, as is timber and related products. Metals and non-metallic minerals are the key resources in modern manufacturing today. Combined with *energy resources* and *flow resources,* such as rubber, pulp, hides, cotton fiber, crude animal and vegetable minerals, air and water, they form a still greater pool of resources on which industries and services are based.

REGIONAL PATTERNS OF WORLD TRADE

❖

North America

UNITED STATES

The United States is the world's largest trading nation, accounting for more than 1.1 trillion dollars' worth of exports and imports in 1990 (Tables 13.8 and 13.9). During the 1950s, the United States accounted for 25% of total world trade but now accounts for only approximately 10%. From 1960 to 1970, the United States enjoyed a net trade surplus as a result of OPEC price rises and the weak value of the dollar. However, this surplus turned into a deficit by 1985. Throughout much of the 1970s, the United States sold only 4% of its goods overseas but raised the overall level to approximately 7% during the late 1970s and the 1980s.

Exports and imports as a proportion of GDP are shown in Figure 13.12. Because of the heightened value of the dollar, which peaked in 1985, the trade gap in 1986 was its all-time widest. Imports exceeded exports by 90%.

The deficit problem began to ease itself in the late 1980s because of an agreement by the five major trading countries—France, Germany, Great Britain, Japan, and the United States—to lower the value of the dollar on world markets and to revive the exporting business for the United States (Figure 13.13). By 1992, the trade

Table 13.8
Leading Exporters and Importers in World Merchandise Trade, 1990

Rank			1990		Rank			1990	
1980	1990	Exporters	Value*	Share†	1980	1990	Importers	Value*	Share†
2	1	Germany‡	398.4	11.4	1	1	United States	517.0	14.3
1	2	United States	393.6	11.3	2	2	Germany‡	342.6	9.5
3	3	Japan	287.6	8.3	3	3	Japan	235.4	6.5
4	4	France	216.6	6.2	4	4	France	234.4	6.5
5	5	United Kingdom	185.2	5.3	5	5	United Kingdom	222.8	6.2
7	6	Italy	170.3	4.9	6	6	Italy	182.0	5.0
9	7	Netherlands	131.8	3.8	7	7	Netherlands	126.1	3.5
10	8	Canada	131.7	3.8	10	8	Canada	124.4	3.4
11	9	Belgium-Luxembourg	117.7	3.4	9	9	USSR§‖	120.9	3.4
8	10	USSR§	103.8	3.0	8	10	Belgium-Luxembourg	119.7	3.3
24	11	Hong Kong#	82.2	2.4	12	11	Spain	87.7	2.4
23	12	Taiwan	67.2	1.9	18	12	Hong Kong#	82.5	2.3
32	13	Korea, Rep.	65.0	1.9	11	13	Switzerland	69.7	1.9
13	14	Switzerland	63.8	1.8	20	14	Korea, Rep.	69.6	1.9
31	15	China	60.9	1.7	17	15	Singapore#	60.9	1.7
12	16	Sweden	57.6	1.7	23	16	Taiwan	54.7	1.5
21	17	Spain	55.6	1.6	13	17	Sweden	54.4	1.5
26	18	Singapore#	52.8	1.5	22	18	China	52.3	1.4
6	19	Saudi Arabia	43.7	1.3	16	19	Austria	49.1	1.4
33	20	Austria	41.3	1.2	19	20	Australia	42.0	1.2
30	21	Mexico**	41.1	1.2	21	21	Mexico**	41.6	1.2
18	22	Australia	39.8	1.1	47	22	Thailand	33.4	0.9
35	23	Denmark	35.1	1.0	24	23	Denmark	31.8	0.9
29	24	Norway	34.0	1.0	40	24	Malaysia	29.3	0.8
22	25	Brazil	31.4	0.9	30	25	Finland	27.0	0.7
40	26	Malaysia	29.4	0.8	28	26	Norway	26.9	0.7
37	27	Finland	26.6	0.8	46	27	Portugal	25.3	0.7
19	28	Indonesia	25.7	0.7	14	28	Saudi Arabia	24.8	0.7
46	29	Ireland	23.7	0.7	33	29	India	23.6	0.7
16	30	South Africa	23.6	0.7	15	30	Brazil	22.5	0.6
48	31	Thailand	23.1	0.7	51	31	Turkey	22.3	0.6
28	32	German Dem. Rep.§	22.7	0.7	39	32	Indonesia	21.8	0.6
17	33	United Arab Emirates	22.0	0.6	38	33	Ireland	20.7	0.6
39	34	Iran, Islamic Rep.	18.8	0.5	42	34	Greece	19.8	0.5
45	35	India	18.0	0.5	32	35	Yugoslavia	18.9	0.5
27	36	Venezuela	17.5	0.5	36	36	Iran, Islamic Rep.	17.5	0.5
58	37	Portugal	16.4	0.5	25	37	South Africa	17.5	0.5
34	38	Poland§	14.3	0.4	44	38	Israel	16.5	0.5
43	39	Yugoslavia	14.3	0.4	31	39	Czech and Slovak Fed. Rep.§‖	13.3	0.4

(continued)

■

T a b l e 13.8 (Continued)

38	40	Algeria	13.9	0.4	27	40	German Dem. Rep.§‖	13.1	0.4
		Total	3218.1	92.3			Total	3315.5	91.9
		World	3485	100.0			World	3608	100.0

* Billions of dollars.
† Percent.
‡ Unless otherwise indicated, the German figures throughout this volume refer to the former Republic of Germany.
§ The figures are affected by marked difficulties in converting data expressed in national currencies into dollars.
‖ Imports FOB.
Includes significant reexports and imports for reexport.
** Includes trade flows through processing zones.
Source: Handbook of International Trade Statistics,1993, Directorate of Intelligence, C.I.A., p. 5, and International Trade, 91–92, GATT, General Agreement on Tariffs and Trade, p. 3)

■

T a b l e 13.9

Leading Exporters and Importers in World Trade in Commercial Services, 1990

Rank			1990		Rank			1990	
1980	1990	Exporters	Value*	Share†	1980	1990	Importers	Value*	Share†
2	1	United States	119.1	14.7	3	1	Japan	88.6	11.2
1	2	France	81.9	10.1	4	2	United States	87.6	11.1
3	3	United Kingdom	55.3	6.8	1	3	Germany	82.1	10.4
4	4	Germany	51.8	6.4	2	4	France	65.4	8.3
6	5	Japan	41.6	5.1	5	5	United Kingdom	44.1	5.6
5	6	Italy	40.8	5.0	7	6	Italy	38.6	4.9
7	7	Netherlands	30.2	3.7	6	7	Netherlands	28.7	3.6
9	8	Spain	29.2	3.6	9	8	Belgium-Luxembourg‡	26.5	3.4
8	9	Belgium-Luxembourg‡	27.7	3.4	10	9	Canada	22.7	2.9
10	10	Austria	22.6	2.8	12	10	Sweden	17.0	2.2
12	11	Switzerland‡	17.3	2.1	17	11	Spain	16.4	2.1
14	12	Canada	15.1	1.9	13	12	Switzerland‡	15.5	2.0
15	13	Singapore	14.9	1.8	19	13	Taiwan	15.0	1.9
21	14	Hong Kong‡	14.4	1.8	29	14	Yugoslavia	15.0	1.9
13	15	Sweden	13.7	1.7	14	15	Australia	14.1	1.8
17	16	Denmark	12.9	1.6	8	16	Saudi Arabia	12.7	1.6
11	17	Norway	12.4	1.5	11	17	Norway	12.5	1.6
18	18	Mexico	11.3	1.4	16	18	Austria	11.4	1.4
20	19	Korea, Rep.	10.9	1.3	25	19	Korea, Rep.	11.1	1.4
23	20	Australia	10.5	1.3	21	20	Denmark	10.3	1.3
33	21	Thailand	7.5	0.9	15	21	Mexico	9.9	1.2
30	22	Taiwan	7.4	0.9	31	22	Hong Kong‡	9.4	1.2
57	23	Turkey	7.1	0.9	32	23	Singapore	7.9	1.0
22	24	Greece	6.6	0.8	35	24	Finland	7.8	1.0

(continued)

29	25	Egypt	6.6	0.8	41	25	Thailand	6.3	0.8
19	26	Yugoslavia	6.4	0.8	28	26	Malaysia	5.9	0.7
28	27	China	5.7	0.7	27	27	Indonesia	5.8	0.7
31	28	Portugal	5.2	0.6	36	28	Israel	5.5	0.7
27	29	Finland	4.9	0.6	30	29	India§	5.3	0.7
25	30	Israel	4.6	0.6	22	30	Brazil‖	5.1	0.6
41	31	Malaysia	4.1	0.5	20	31	South Africa	5.0	0.6
35	32	Philippines	4.1	0.5	37	32	Egypt	4.3	0.5
26	33	India§	3.7	0.5	40	33	China	4.1	0.5
24	34	South Africa	3.5	0.4	47	34	Portugal	3.7	0.5
32	35	Poland	3.2	0.4	33	35	Kuwait§	3.6	0.5
34	36	Brazil‖	3.1	0.4	44	36	New Zealand	3.6	0.5
39	37	Ireland	3.0	0.4	42	37	Ireland	3.4	0.4
16	38	Saudi Arabia	2.9	0.4	26	38	Argentina	2.9	0.4
37	39	Czech and Slovak Fed. Rep.	2.6	0.3	46	39	Greece	2.9	0.4
50	40	New Zealand	2.4	0.3	38	40	Poland	2.8	0.4
		Total	728.2	89.8			Total	740.5	93.9
		World	811	100.0			World	789	100.0

* Billions of dollars. † Percent. ‡ Estimates. § 1988 rather than 1990. ‖ 1989 rather than 1990.
(Source: Handbook of International Trade Statistics, 1993, Directorate of Intelligence, C.I.A., p. 6, and International Trade, 91–92, GATT, p. 4.) (op. cit. (p. 580) p. 6) of this text.

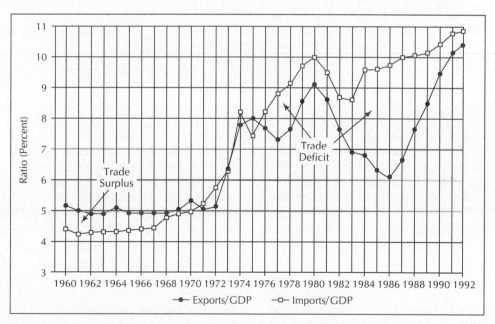

FIGURE 13.12
U.S. ratio of exports to gross domestic products (GDP), ratio of imports to GDP, trade surplus, and trade deficit, 1960–1992.
(Source: U.S. Bureau of the Census, Statistical Abstracts of the United States, 1993.)
Since the 1970s, the United States has more than doubled its international trade, even though it developed a trade deficit in the 1970s and 1980s. It remains the world's most powerful economy founded on a) natural resources, b) shear size, c) entrepreneurial and enterprise ability and d) large assistance from federal and state governments and taxpayers. Since 1970, economic growth has been at a much slower rate and America now is pulling out of a disastrous economic downturn that has lasted since 1989. While per capita GNP is over $23,000, income is unequally divided between rich and poor. While a national health care plan is a major topic of discussion, the welfare system seems to be breaking down and certain ethnic minorities have become downwardly mobile, rather than upwardly mobile.

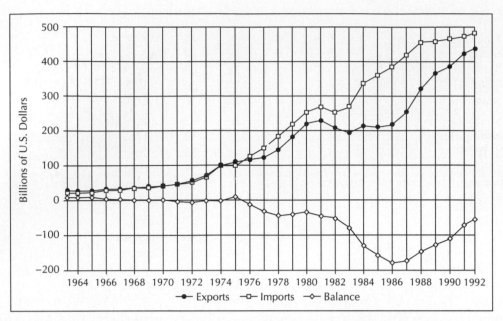

FIGURE 13.13
Trade balance is shown in billions of U.S. dollars. Exports and imports were approximately equivalent until the oil price hikes of the mid-1970s. The increased price of OPEC oil and the increasing value of the dollar, which peaked in 1986, widened the trade imbalance. Reduced savings rates by Americans and enlarged public debt added to the woes. American products became too expensive for foreign consumers, while at the same time, Americans increased their purchasing of foreign goods because they were relatively cheaper. It took an international agreement to stabilize and then reduce the value of the dollar in the mid-1980s, and this has led to a substantial decrease in the trade imbalance as exports and imports are becoming more equivalent. The restructuring the U.S. industry into highly efficient production units helped to make American goods more competitive on the world market, raising U.S. exports.
(Source: United Nations, Yearbook of International Trade Statistics, 1993, p. 437.)

gap had narrowed substantially because the decreasing value of the dollar made U.S. goods more attractive abroad. From a ratio of approximately 6% of exports to GDP in 1973 and 1986, the United States raised its proportion to approximately 10% by 1992 (see Figure 13.12).

Another factor that helped narrow the U.S. trade gap is the so-called invisible exports. These exports involve international financial and consumer services, such as transportation, tourism, entertainment, finance, and banking.

Figure 13.14 shows the composition of U.S. merchandise trade with the world in 1992. As you can see in Figure 13.14a, machinery accounted for the largest single proportion of exports, 31%, whereas transportation equipment added another 17%. Chemicals and other manufactures added another 34%, whereas agricultural products amounted to 9%. More than 80% of U.S. exports are manufactured items. The United

States, with its varying productivity and physical conditions, as well as its competitive edge in technology, is the chief world manufacturer today.

Figure 13.14b shows that manufacturing goods also accounts for approximately 80% of the traded goods flowing to America from foreign companies. America has essentially farmed out much of its labor-intensive manufacturing to developing countries. At the same time, it has acquired an expensive taste for foreign-made luxury items such as automobiles from Germany and Japan, shoes from Italy and Brazil, electronic items from the Far East, and perfume and wine from France. Other imports include fuels for which the United States is not self-sufficient. Principal commodity exports and imports of the United States are shown in Table 13.10.

The direction of U.S. merchandise trade with the world is shown in Figure 13.14c. Canada, with its 26 million people, located on the northern border of the United States, represents the single largest trading part-

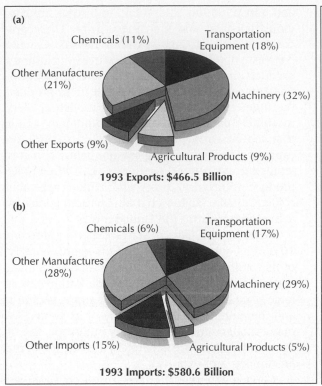

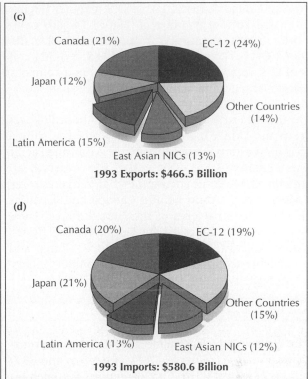

FIGURE 13.14

Composition of U.S. world merchandise trade, 1992. The United States is the largest trading nation in the world, but has a huge trade deficit of more than $100 billion. Despite the restructuring of U.S. industry, manufactured goods accounted for more than 80% of all exports and total exports grew from 1990 to 1992 by more than $54 billion. Exports were almost equally divided among Canada, Japan, and the EEC countries. These same countries accounted for 55% of all U.S. exports.

(Source: U.S. Department of Commerce, 1994.)

▣

Table 13.10

Principal Commodity Exports and Imports of the United States, 1990

Exports	Amount*	Imports	Amount*
Chemicals	28.4	Petroleum	62.1
Computers	25.9	Automobiles	45.9
Consumer durables	21.0	Clothing	23.9
Aircraft	18.4	Computers	23.0
Grains	14.9	Household appliances	18.7
Semiconductors	13.3	Chemicals	14.3
Generating equipment	12.7	Semiconductors	12.2
Automobiles	10.9	Iron and steel	11.3
Nonferrous metals	10.9	Toys and sporting goods	9.7
Telecommunications	9.6	Telecommunications	9.4

* Billions of dollars.

Source: U.S. Department of Commerce.

ner of the United States. 21% of U.S. exports (Figure 13.14a) and 20% of its imports (Figure 13.14d) go to and come from that country. As an economic bloc, the EEC or EC-12, accounts for 24% of U.S. exports and 18% of U.S. imports. The United States has a competitive disadvantage and trade deficit with Japan, however.

During the last 30 years, the pattern of trade linkages between the United States and the world has shifted away from Western Europe toward the Asian and Pacific regions (Figure 13.15). Ties with Latin America, although they have contracted somewhat, remain strong, and Mexico ranks third behind Canada and Japan as the leading trade partners of the United States (Table 13.11). Mexico is followed by Germany, the United Kingdom, Taiwan, South Korea, France, China, and Italy, which each had more than 20 billion dollars' worth of trade with the United States in 1991.

CANADA

The United States is Canada's most significant trading partner and accounts for 75% of exports and 65% of imports (Figure 13.16). Canada exports automobiles and transportation equipment, industrial supplies, and industrial plant and machinery parts. These products compose 60% of Canada's total exports. Canada also has vast supplies of natural resources, including forest products, iron ores, metals, oil, natural gas, and coal. The United States is in need of all these products. On the other hand, Canada imports industrial plant and machinery parts, transportation equipment, and industrial supplies from the United States. In addition, because of a longer growing season, balmy climates, and temperate agricultural territories, the United States can produce subtropical fruits and winter vegetables for colder Canada. High-tech manufactured goods are also a chief import from the United States.

Whereas the United States exports approximately 10% of its output, Canada exports approximately 20% of its total output. Because of its small population of approximately 26 million, Canada cannot attain the large scale economy necessary for superefficient plants and therefore must import many of its goods. As with many small countries, especially in Europe, the smaller the country, the more dependent it is on foreign markets for imports and exports.

Canada can export energy resources because of its

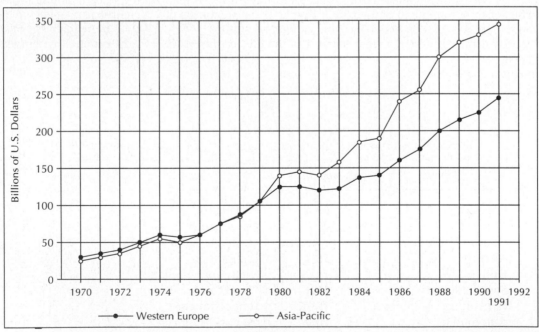

FIGURE 13.15
American trade, with both Western Europe, Asia and the Pacific, was approximately equal until 1980. Because of the growth of newly industrialized countries (NICs) in Asia and the Pacific, including Japan, the Four Tigers, and the Five Dragons (see text for descriptions), Asia and the Pacific have taken over the lead from the age-old North Pacific ties between North America and Europe, *(Source: U.S. Foreign Trade Highlights, 1993. U.S. Department of Commerce, International Trade Administration.)*

◈

Table 13.11
Top 50 Partners in Total U.S. Trade in 1991*

Country	1985	1986	1987	1988	1989	1990	1991
Canada	122,293	123,764	130,899	153,020	166,762	175,054	176,244
Japan	91,414	108,793	112,824	127,244	138,046	138,264	139,729
Mexico	32,767	29,693	34,853	43,888	52,144	58,436	64,470
Germany	29,453	35,839	38,956	40,929	41,927	46,922	47,546
United Kingdom	26,210	26,814	31,455	36,341	39,156	43,679	40,583
Taiwan	21,096	25,315	32,034	36,843	35,647	34,157	36,227
Korea, South	15,969	19,084	25,086	31,337	33,195	32,889	32,543
France	15,578	17,344	18,673	22,478	24,593	26,818	28,738
China	7717	7877	9791	13,532	17,745	20,044	25,263
Italy	14,299	15,446	16,569	18,351	19,148	20,743	20,366
Singapore	7735	8105	10,254	13,741	16,347	17,823	18,784
Netherlands	11,350	11,913	12,180	14,675	16,174	17,974	18,355
Saudi Arabia	6381	7061	7806	9396	10,731	14,070	17,550
Hong Kong	11,182	11,921	13,837	15,925	16,014	16,438	17,427
Belgium-Luxembourg	8305	9405	10,360	11,904	13,077	15,036	14,929
Venezuela	9936	8238	9165	9769	9796	12,588	12,897
Brazil	10,666	10,698	11,905	13,561	13,214	12,946	12,881
Australia	8277	8179	8500	10,514	12,204	12,984	12,426
Switzerland	5764	8229	7400	8808	9626	10,530	11,142
Malaysia	3839	4150	4818	5833	7614	8697	10,004
Thailand	2277	2684	3764	5172	6668	8284	9883
Spain	5039	5317	5987	7419	8113	8524	8336
Sweden	6049	6290	6652	7684	8030	8342	7790
Israel (including Gaza)	4702	4657	5770	6216	6067	6517	7353
Nigeria	3678	2939	3869	3635	5774	6535	6193
Philippines	3524	3336	3863	4545	5270	5855	5741
India	3937	3820	3992	5440	5772	5683	5200
Indonesia	5364	4257	4161	4209	4775	5238	5130
Colombia	2798	3193	3644	3915	4479	5197	4681
Ireland	2243	2437	2922	3558	4048	4295	4639
Former Soviet Union	2831	1806	1904	3355	4993	4146	4390
South Africa	3276	3523	2627	3200	3190	3429	3847
Dominican Republic	1724	2006	2305	2769	3291	3407	3760
Turkey	1896	1793	2304	2829	3375	3426	3433
Argentina	1791	1799	2170	2490	2430	2690	3340
Denmark	2370	2515	2671	2633	2586	2989	3239
Chile	1428	1644	1777	2247	2707	2977	3143
Norway	1830	2016	2246	2375	3028	3111	3115
Egypt	2402	2093	2675	2553	2838	2647	2927
Algeria	2763	2284	2425	2544	2585	3577	2827
Austria	1275	1328	1478	1821	2008	2193	2329
Ecuador	2428	2065	1887	1909	2117	2054	2275

(continued)

◙

T a b l e 13.11 *(Continued)*

New Zealand	1584	1856	1864	2101	2326	2332	2221
Costa Rica	923	1124	1251	1470	1844	1991	2188
United Arab Emirates	1267	849	1283	1284	1922	1893	2170
Finland	1333	1288	1514	1964	2339	2388	2040
Angola	1191	764	1388	1317	2025	2056	1974
Guatemala	814	1001	976	1023	1270	1558	1851
Netherlands Antilles	1235	869	1028	939	923	1176	1620

Source: Handbook of International Trade Statistics, 1993, Directorate of Intelligence, C.I.A., p. 7. U.S. Foreign Trade Highlights, 1992, U.S. Department of Commerce, International Trade Administration.

vast amounts of hydroelectric power and its ability to manufacture hydraulic turbines and electric generators. It also produces high-tech communications equipment, including fiber-optic cables. Transportation and telecommunications equipment are required because of the vast territories that must be overcome to interconnect with the second largest country in the world. For Canada, automobiles and automobile parts represent the largest category of exports to the United States. This is a result of the U.S.-Canadian Free Trade Agreement,

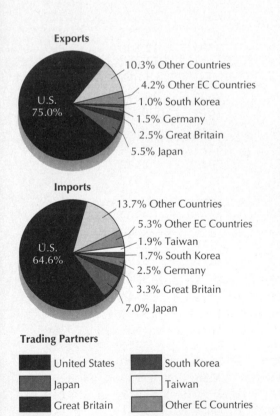

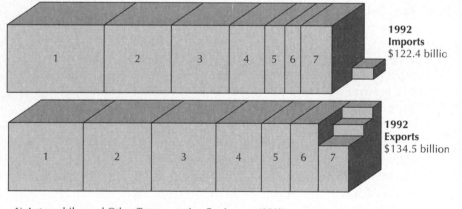

1) Industrial Plant and Machinery Parts (29%)
2) Automobiles and Other Transportation Equipment (22%)
3) Industrial Supplies (17%)
4) Consumer Goods (11%)
5) Agricultural Produce and Food (6%)
6) Energy Products (4%)
7) Other (11%)

1) Automobiles and Other Transportation Equipment (23%)
2) Industrial Supplies (20%)
3) Industrial Plant and Machinery Parts (17%)
4) Forest Products (15%)
5) Energy Products (8%)
6) Agricultural Products and Foods (8%)
7) Other (9%)

FIGURE 13.16

Composition of Canada's world merchandise trade, 1992. The United States is by far Canada's biggest trading partner, accounting for 75% of Canadian exports and almost 65% of Canadian imports. Canada exports primary products, including natural resources of oil, natural gas, coal, hydroelectricity, processed metals, and timber products, including paper pulp and paper. Imports, however, are primarily manufactured goods and industrial equipment.
(Source: United States Department of Commerce, National Trade Data Bank, C.D. ROM, Bureau of the Census, 1994.)

which favored the export of automotive industrial goods from Canada to the United States.

Canada's second most important regional partner, according to Figure 13.16, is Western Europe, followed by Japan. Japan actually ranks second as an individual country, ahead of Great Britain, Germany, and other EEC countries, which as a bloc constitute approximately 8% of Canadian exports and imports.

Latin America

Latin America comprises the South American countries of Colombia, Ecuador, Bolivia, Chile, Venezuela, Brazil, Argentina, Uruguay, and Paraguay, as well as the Central American countries, which are dominated by Mexico. All these countries are considered developing countries, and their traditional role since the time of exploration and colonization has been to provide primary materials, namely agricultural exports and mineral resources, to the developed world of Europe and more recently to North America.

Latin America has economically advanced countries, including gigantic Brazil, with a population of 160 million, as well as some of the poorest countries in the world (e.g., Bolivia and Paraguay in South America and Haiti and Guatemala in Central America). Latin American countries are diverse not only with regard to population and size, but also with respect to development and natural resources. Some countries, such as those in the Caribbean and Central America (Costa Rica, Dominican Republic), have agricultural plantation surpluses. Others, as in Argentina, have midlatitude grain surpluses, whereas still others, such as Venezuela and Mexico, are rich in iron ore and oil. Brazil has a wealth of minerals and is a strong producer of manufactured goods.

The balance of merchandise trade and trading partners of Brazil and Mexico are shown in Figures 13.17 and 13.18. Once again, the chief trading partner is the United States. Mexico's proximity and 2000 miles of common border suggest that the United States is a much stronger trading partner with Mexico than with Brazil. Brazil continues to export primary products, such as soybeans, iron ore, and coffee, but also exports transportation equipment and metallurgical products. Imports include industrial plant and machinery parts, fuel and lubricants, chemicals, and iron and steel.

Mexico's balance of merchandise trade is centered on labor-intensive manufactured products (52%), many of which flow from plants along the border that are owned by American MNCs (*maquiladoras*) back to America (South, 1992; Stutz, 1992a) (Figure 13.19). Petroleum and by-products, as well as agricultural products, account for 45% of Mexico's exports. Mexico is one of the world's largest exporters of energy, and oil provided more than 35% of its export revenue in 1991. Semifinished industrial supplies that act as input materials for final production compose 60% of Mexican imports, and manufacturing and plant equipment another 23%. These types of imports are necessary for Mexico to maintain its level as a rapidly industrializing Third World nation.

In 1990, for Latin America as a whole, 85% of the region's exports, mainly food, minerals, and fuels, went to the United States. This pattern was typical for Third World nations. For a long time, Latin America had an import-substitution policy for industrialized products. In 1990, Latin American imports from the United States consisted of 85% manufactured goods and only 15% consumer goods. However, today, Latin America's new hope to achieve wealth and a prominent place in the world economy is centered on export-led industrialization, and a growing variety of manufactures are exported, led by Brazil, Argentina, and Mexico.

The southern countries of Argentina, Uruguay, Chile, and Bolivia, farther from the United States, have had stronger ties to Western Europe. The East Asian NICs are currently strengthening their economic ties with Latin America. Unfortunately, Latin American trade within the region is not nearly so strong as that for North America, Western Europe, or the Pacific Basin. Each country seems to be tied more politically and economically to Europe, the United States, and the Far East than to one another.

One problem in Latin America has been negative growth rates. During the 1980s, only Colombia, Chile, and Paraguay increased their per capita incomes, whereas the remaining countries experienced a decline. Between 1981 and 1991, per capita GDP actually fell 30% in Peru, 29% in Guyana, 23% in Argentina, 23% in Bolivia, and 20% in Venezuela. Inflation was out of control in Latin America as well, running at 11,000% in Bolivia, 5000% in Argentina, and 8000% in Peru from 1981 to 1991. Under such circumstances, export producers were discovering that it was not profitable to concentrate on world markets because exchange rates and government taxes were putting them out of business.

At the present time, few Latin American countries can keep up with debt service on their international

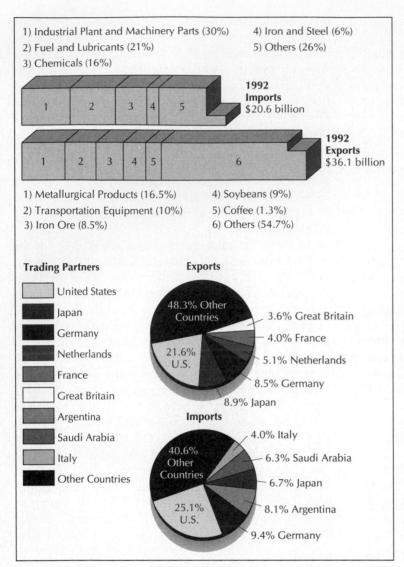

1) Industrial Plant and Machinery Parts (30%)   4) Iron and Steel (6%)
2) Fuel and Lubricants (21%)   5) Others (26%)
3) Chemicals (16%)

1992 Imports $20.6 billion

1992 Exports $36.1 billion

1) Metallurgical Products (16.5%)   4) Soybeans (9%)
2) Transportation Equipment (10%)   5) Coffee (1.3%)
3) Iron Ore (8.5%)   6) Others (54.7%)

Trading Partners

United States
Japan
Germany
Netherlands
France
Great Britain
Argentina
Saudi Arabia
Italy
Other Countries

Exports

48.3% Other Countries
3.6% Great Britain
4.0% France
5.1% Netherlands
8.5% Germany
8.9% Japan
21.6% U.S.

Imports

40.6% Other Countries
4.0% Italy
6.3% Saudi Arabia
6.7% Japan
8.1% Argentina
9.4% Germany
25.1% U.S.

FIGURE 13.17
Composition of Brazil's world merchandise trade, 1992. Although Brazil is two-thirds the size of the United States in population, its imports are only 5% of the United States and its exports are only 7%. Because it is a highly indebted nation, exports outnumber imports three to two. The United States accounts for 21% of its exports and almost 26% of its imports. Brazil has been waiting for *take-off* into a new era of prosperity based on manufacturing and international export. Take-off has not come. Additionally, there is a great uneven distribution of wealth within the developing world, Latin America in particular, and notably in Brazil. On the average, Brazil is one of the wealthiest of South American countries, but the richest 20 percent of the population owns 95 percent of the wealth. Thousands of young orphans wander the streets of Rio and São Paulo. Brazilians lack access to education, health care and good paying jobs. Government mismanagement of vast resources has contributed to the problem, as well as graft and corruption of public officials.
(*Source: op. cit. Fig. 13.16.*)

loans. As previously discussed, Mexico, Brazil, and Argentina owe $100 billion to the developed world, and several other Latin American countries are following closely behind. Most of the loan money was put into urban infrastructures, but high world interest rates and international recessions have minimized exports. Brazil is a case in point. Exports are a little more than one-tenth those of the United States, but the population is approximately two-thirds that of the United States. In general, now is a disadvantageous time for Latin America because Latin American governments have been asked by the International Monetary Fund (IMF) to devalue their currencies once again and to invoke austerity programs by restructuring their economies, raising taxes, decreasing public expenditures, and selling unprofitable government-owned business enter-

prises, such as state banks, power companies, metal refineries, and transportation and airline companies.

Western Europe

Western Europe's trade, as a proportion of total world trade, is disproportionately large compared with its population, a mere one-third of a billion. Although it possesses only one-fifteenth of the world population, it accounts for between 40% and 50% of world trade because of the strength of the EEC; short distances; and good river, canal, and motorway transportation that connects relatively small countries who need complementary trade flows with one another in order to exist

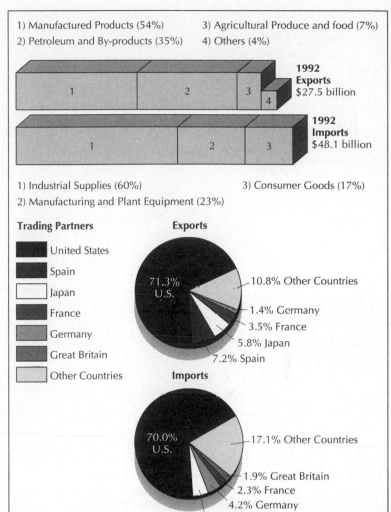

1) Manufactured Products (54%)   3) Agricultural Produce and food (7%)

2) Petroleum and By-products (35%)   4) Others (4%)

1992 Exports $27.5 billion

1992 Imports $48.1 billion

1) Industrial Supplies (60%)   3) Consumer Goods (17%)

2) Manufacturing and Plant Equipment (23%)

Trading Partners

■ United States
■ Spain
□ Japan
■ France
▨ Germany
■ Great Britain
▨ Other Countries

Exports

71.3% U.S.

10.8% Other Countries
1.4% Germany
3.5% France
5.8% Japan
7.2% Spain

Imports

70.0% U.S.

17.1% Other Countries
1.9% Great Britain
2.3% France
4.2% Germany
4.5% Japan

FIGURE 13.18
Composition of Mexico's world merchandise trade, 1992. Mexico's proximity and the fact that it is a large supplier of energy are reasons why the United States dominates its exports. In addition, Mexico imports 68% of its products from the United States. NAFTA should increase both exports and imports with the United States. Two rather shocking predictions can be made about Mexican trade, now that NAFTA has been passed. The U.S. and other foreign companies will probably dominate the management of Mexico's high value-added and high volume manufacturing, as well as its agriculture and services. Already there is tremendous increase of imports of unfinished products into Mexico, which threatens to wipe out its own domestic industries. Mexico's population by the year 2000 will be approximately 40 percent of the United States' population, but its economy will remain less than 5 percent of the United States' economy in total size. Its trading portion with America amounts to probably only twice San Diego's regional GNP. One could argue that Mexico has an almost total lack of *world class management* know-how, and an efficient manufacturing and service base. Mexico's private sector wealth is great, but, as in other third world countries, it is limited to a few families and was created in an environment of an *authoritarian political system*. That system continues to nurture crony and *concession capitalism*, which requires an entirely different set of management skills from those required in the market capitalism of the United States and Canada. Other problems include a lack of critical mass of human capital investment, a lack of research universities, and a lack of a culture friendly to modernization and economic development. If NAFTA is going to be a success, the United States must consider what it can do to speed Mexico's development along, while Mexico must recognize the need to cooperate in this effort. *(Source: op. cit. Fig. 14.16.)*

and flourish. Western Europe is barely half the size of the United States; some countries are comparable in population and size to individual U.S. states. Italy, France, the United Kingdom, and former West Germany have a population of almost 60 million each (with the addition of East Germany, Germany is now pushing toward 80 million). Other countries are much smaller. Some have food resources, such as Denmark and France; some have energy resources, such as Norway, the Netherlands, and the United Kingdom; some produce iron, steel, and heavy equipment, such as Italy, Germany, France, and Spain; and others produce high-value consumer goods.

The proximities, geographies, and areal complementarities of Europe have made intraregional trade ideal. This type of trade has increased from 55% of all Western European exports to 73% in 1992. That is, 73% of all

exports from Western European nations go to other Western European nations. If the EEC grows from its present 12 countries to include the 6 EFTA countries as well as associate members from Eastern Europe and the Mediterranean, the clout and intraregional flow of European trade will continue to increase. The balances of trade for Germany, Great Britain, France, and Italy are shown in Figures 13.20, 13.21, 13.22, and 13.23.

GERMANY

Germany is the third leading country in the world in terms of international trade; it is also the third most important trading partner of the United States. It exports a large percentage of its GDP and is the world's leading exporter of merchandise and second leading exporter

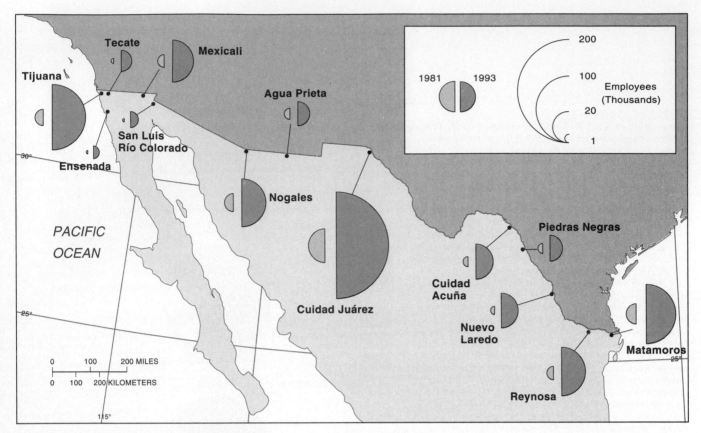

FIGURE 13.19
Maquilladora employment in the major border cities of Mexico, 1981 and 1988. Because of America's need for inexpensive labor, it signed the Border Industrialization Program with Mexico in the 1960s. Raw materials and semifinished goods may be transported from the United States to Mexico for fabrication and back to the United States with a much reduced tariff. Wage rates for comparable work in Mexico are from one-fifth to one-tenth of what would be paid for labor in America. The Mexican maquilladora program is a tremendous growth industry, with most plants hovering near the border to minimize transportation costs. By 1994, Tijuana, Mexico, for example, had 550 plants, with 75,000 employees. Critics of NAFTA fear that the total removal of tariffs will escalate the maquilladora program even faster and displace hand-assembly workers from Los Angeles to Detroit because of the new agreement.
(Source: Stutz, 1992b; and San Diego Economic Development Corporation, 1993.)

of merchandise and services after the United States. In addition, it has a trade surplus of more than $55 billion but has a heavy dependency on imported energy. Motor vehicles and mechanical engineering products are its chief exports, but it also exports a notable amount of chemicals and electrical engineering products (Figure 13.20). It imports many of the same items that it exports—motor vehicles, chemicals, and electrical engineering products—and is unable at the present time to provide the necessary amount of agricultural produce, which is its largest single import, 12.5%. Most of its trading partners are other EEC countries.

Germany's exports are worth approximately $6600 per capita per year, whereas those of the United States

are worth approximately $1500 per capita per year. Germany exports as many goods as the United States does but has only a quarter of the population.

Germany also enjoys a remarkably healthy balance of trade, exporting almost 22% more than it imports. Its industrial sector has been paramount in the manufacture of high-value products, including automobiles, chemicals, and machinery. Recently, however, its economy and trade have shifted from that of manufactured goods to the service sector. Frankfurt is now Europe's second largest banking center, after Switzerland and prosperous Liechtenstein. Both of the latter two are important investment and banking centers not only because of Liechtenstein's tax-free status and Switzer-

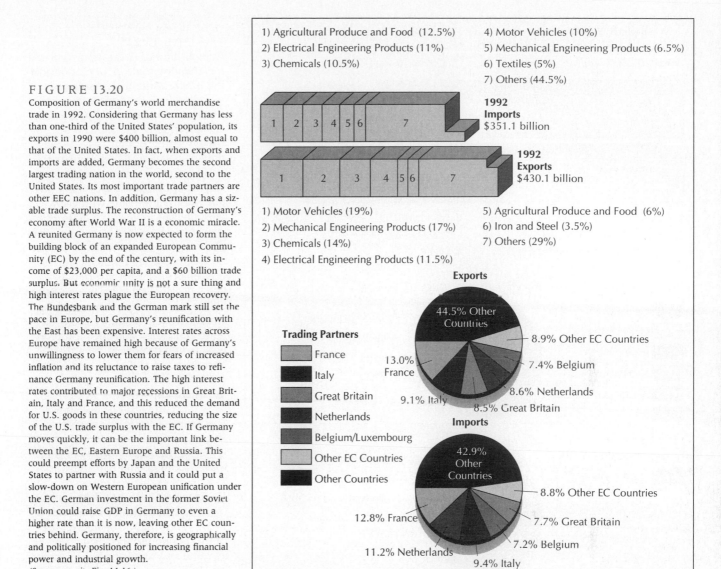

1) Agricultural Produce and Food (12.5%)
2) Electrical Engineering Products (11%)
3) Chemicals (10.5%)
4) Motor Vehicles (10%)
5) Mechanical Engineering Products (6.5%)
6) Textiles (5%)
7) Others (44.5%)

1992 Imports $351.1 billion

1) Motor Vehicles (19%)
2) Mechanical Engineering Products (17%)
3) Chemicals (14%)
4) Electrical Engineering Products (11.5%)
5) Agricultural Produce and Food (6%)
6) Iron and Steel (3.5%)
7) Others (29%)

1992 Exports $430.1 billion

Exports
44.5% Other Countries
8.9% Other EC Countries
7.4% Belgium
8.6% Netherlands
8.5% Great Britain
9.1% Italy
13.0% France

Imports
42.9% Other Countries
8.8% Other EC Countries
7.7% Great Britain
7.2% Belgium
9.4% Italy
11.2% Netherlands
12.8% France

Trading Partners
France
Italy
Great Britain
Netherlands
Belgium/Luxembourg
Other EC Countries
Other Countries

FIGURE 13.20
Composition of Germany's world merchandise trade in 1992. Considering that Germany has less than one-third of the United States' population, its exports in 1990 were $400 billion, almost equal to that of the United States. In fact, when exports and imports are added, Germany becomes the second largest trading nation in the world, second to the United States. Its most important trade partners are other EEC nations. In addition, Germany has a sizable trade surplus. The reconstruction of Germany's economy after World War II is a economic miracle. A reunited Germany is now expected to form the building block of an expanded European Community (EC) by the end of the century, with its income of $23,000 per capita, and a $60 billion trade surplus. But economic unity is not a sure thing and high interest rates plague the European recovery. The Bundesbank and the German mark still set the pace in Europe, but Germany's reunification with the East has been expensive. Interest rates across Europe have remained high because of Germany's unwillingness to lower them for fears of increased inflation and its reluctance to raise taxes to refinance Germany reunification. The high interest rates contributed to major recessions in Great Britain, Italy and France, and this reduced the demand for U.S. goods in these countries, reducing the size of the U.S. trade surplus with the EC. If Germany moves quickly, it can be the important link between the EC, Eastern Europe and Russia. This could preempt efforts by Japan and the United States to partner with Russia and it could put a slow-down on Western European unification under the EC. German investment in the former Soviet Union could raise GDP in Germany to even a higher rate than it is now, leaving other EC countries behind. Germany, therefore, is geographically and politically positioned for increasing financial power and industrial growth.
(Source: op. cit. Fig. 14.16.)

land's extreme secrecy about foreign bank deposits, but also because of the keen political stability of the two countries.

The problem now facing former West Germany is the integration of former East Germany into its prosperous borders. During the first 2 years of unification, GDP in what was formerly East Germany decreased by more than 40%. Only now, in 1994, is recovery and growth beginning to occur. Unification has meant a drop in economic activity for Germany as a whole and has necessitated extreme financial support for the social programs of the east. But former East Germany has had the luxury of shock therapy with a safety cushion. Neither Russia, the former republics of the Soviet Union, nor

any other Eastern European nation has had such an easy transformation.

FRANCE AND ITALY

France exports approximately $3000 per capita per year and suffers from a slight trade imbalance, with more imports than exports. Nonetheless, it is the fourth largest trader in the world. Exports include industrial plant and machinery parts and other manufactured goods such as chemicals, automobiles, iron, and steel (Figure 13.22). But unlike other European nations, it exports a much higher proportion of agricultural prod-

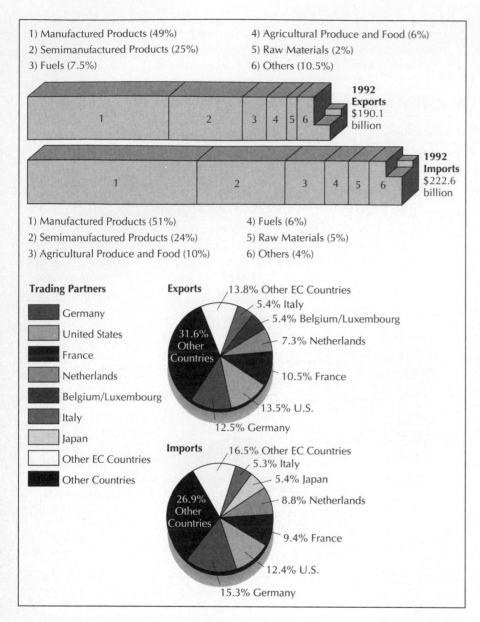

1) Manufactured Products (49%)
2) Semimanufactured Products (25%)
3) Fuels (7.5%)
4) Agricultural Produce and Food (6%)
5) Raw Materials (2%)
6) Others (10.5%)

1992 Exports $190.1 billion

1992 Imports $222.6 billion

1) Manufactured Products (51%)
2) Semimanufactured Products (24%)
3) Agricultural Produce and Food (10%)
4) Fuels (6%)
5) Raw Materials (5%)
6) Others (4%)

Trading Partners

- Germany
- United States
- France
- Netherlands
- Belgium/Luxembourg
- Italy
- Japan
- Other EC Countries
- Other Countries

Exports

13.8% Other EC Countries
5.4% Italy
5.4% Belgium/Luxembourg
7.3% Netherlands
10.5% France
13.5% U.S.
12.5% Germany
31.6% Other Countries

Imports

16.5% Other EC Countries
5.3% Italy
5.4% Japan
8.8% Netherlands
9.4% France
12.4% U.S.
15.3% Germany
26.9% Other Countries

FIGURE 13.21

Composition of Great Britain's world merchandise trade in 1992. Considering its size, Britain is a leader in world trade, in fifth place nationally. Its most important trade partners include Germany, France, and the United States. Britain's role as the dominant financial and industrial power of the world in the 19th century, controlling a vast overseas empire, has had to come with grips with the shocking reality of its 20th century decline. Manufacturing, especially steel making and textile production, has declined markedly and its per capita GNP rests at $16,000. It has a negative trade balance of $40 billion, even though it is one of the world's leaders in luxury goods, defense equipment and chemical products. A bright spot has been the production of North Sea oil, and it has especially affected East Anglia and the Midlands, the latter which has been hit hard with unemployment. The financial sector remains strong and, as noted above, London retains its position as a primate city of Northwestern Europe and the British Isles. A series of exchange rate crisis in the 1990s forced Britain to delink their currencies from the German mark in 1993. Following the delinkage, the British pound dropped 20 percent of its value and sent confidence plunging, and layoffs increased across Great Britain and Northern Europe. *(Source: op. cit. Fig. 14.16.)*

ucts and consumer goods. In fact, France produces more food than any other European nation does. As most other technologically advanced nations do, France also imports industrial plant and machinery parts, consumer goods, and chemicals. Agricultural products and transportation equipment account for another 21% of imports.

Whereas the United States exports 10% of its GDP, France exported almost 30% of its GDP in 1990. During the last 20 years, France's trade with Western Europe increased while trade with French colonial markets in Africa and East Asia declined substantially. Trade with less developed countries amounts to only 15% of

France's international flow, whereas trade with the EEC amounts to 60%. Energy imports have been a particular stumbling block because France is not endowed with coal, as Germany is, or North Sea oil, as the Netherlands, Norway, and the United Kingdom are. More than 50% of France's electricity is generated from nuclear power.

Similar to Great Britain and the United States, France has been forced to restructure industrial jobs, which have decreased by 2 million during the last 15 years. France has also experienced economic difficulty in its balance of trade and suffered from a $7.5 million deficit in 1990. This deficit has impeded its overall trade and economic development.

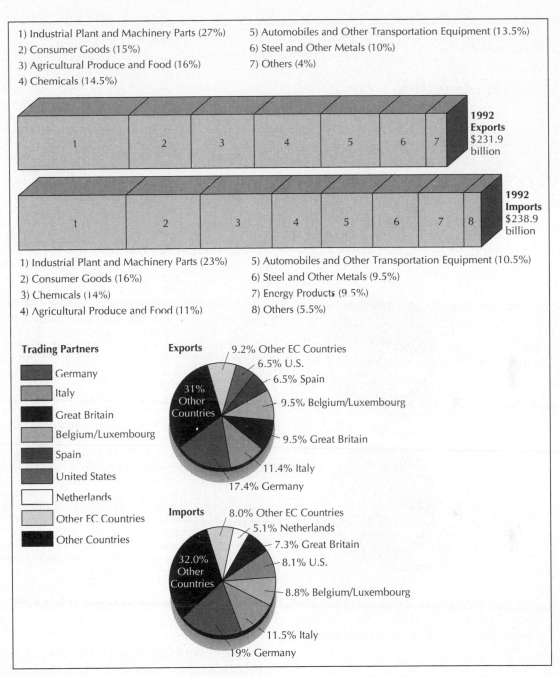

1) Industrial Plant and Machinery Parts (27%)   5) Automobiles and Other Transportation Equipment (13.5%)
2) Consumer Goods (15%)   6) Steel and Other Metals (10%)
3) Agricultural Produce and Food (16%)   7) Others (4%)
4) Chemicals (14.5%)

1992 Exports $231.9 billion

1992 Imports $238.9 billion

1) Industrial Plant and Machinery Parts (23%)   5) Automobiles and Other Transportation Equipment (10.5%)
2) Consumer Goods (16%)   6) Steel and Other Metals (9.5%)
3) Chemicals (14%)   7) Energy Products (9.5%)
4) Agricultural Produce and Food (11%)   8) Others (5.5%)

Trading Partners
- Germany
- Italy
- Great Britain
- Belgium/Luxembourg
- Spain
- United States
- Netherlands
- Other EC Countries
- Other Countries

Exports
- 9.2% Other EC Countries
- 6.5% U.S.
- 6.5% Spain
- 9.5% Belgium/Luxembourg
- 9.5% Great Britain
- 11.4% Italy
- 17.4% Germany
- 31% Other Countries

Imports
- 8.0% Other EC Countries
- 5.1% Netherlands
- 7.3% Great Britain
- 8.1% U.S.
- 8.8% Belgium/Luxembourg
- 11.5% Italy
- 19% Germany
- 32.0% Other Countries

FIGURE 13.22
Composition of France's world merchandise trade in 1992. France is the world's fourth largest trading nation. Considering its size of approximately 60 million, less than a quarter of the population of the United States, it is surprising that its exports and imports are almost one-half as great as the latter. France is energy poor and, therefore, imports fuels, while exporting high-value industrial products, including automobiles and aircraft. (op. cit. Fig. 14.16.)

France, as with other Organization of Economic Cooperation and Development (OECD) countries, has shifted more of its work force toward the services. Employment in restaurants, retailing, publishing, banking, personal services, finance, and government-run social services is on the increase.

The Italian government heavily subsidizes Italian manufaturing (15 billion in 1990, twice the EEC aver-

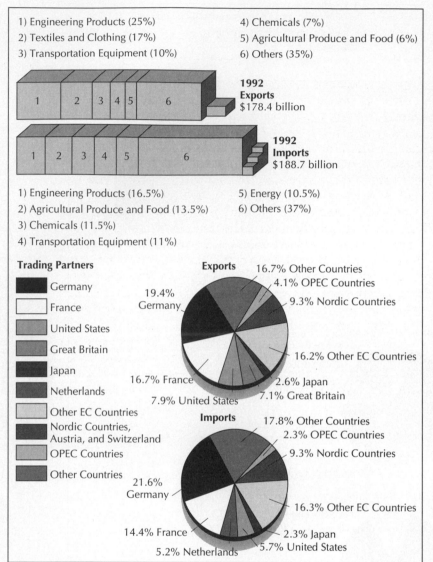

1) Engineering Products (25%)
2) Textiles and Clothing (17%)
3) Transportation Equipment (10%)
4) Chemicals (7%)
5) Agricultural Produce and Food (6%)
6) Others (35%)

1992 Exports $178.4 billion

1992 Imports $188.7 billion

1) Engineering Products (16.5%)
2) Agricultural Produce and Food (13.5%)
3) Chemicals (11.5%)
4) Transportation Equipment (11%)
5) Energy (10.5%)
6) Others (37%)

Trading Partners
- Germany
- France
- United States
- Great Britain
- Japan
- Netherlands
- Other EC Countries
- Nordic Countries, Austria, and Switzerland
- OPEC Countries
- Other Countries

Exports
16.7% Other Countries
4.1% OPEC Countries
9.3% Nordic Countries
16.2% Other EC Countries
19.4% Germany
16.7% France
7.9% United States
2.6% Japan
7.1% Great Britain

Imports
17.8% Other Countries
2.3% OPEC Countries
9.3% Nordic Countries
16.3% Other EC Countries
21.6% Germany
14.4% France
5.2% Netherlands
2.3% Japan
5.7% United States

FIGURE 13.23
Composition of Italy's world merchandise trade in 1992. In 1990, Italy accounted for $193 billion worth of imports and $182 billion worth of exports, making it one of the world's trading leaders. Italy exports industrialized products, chemicals, machinery, textiles, and automobiles. Two thousand years ago, Rome had conquered the then known world. The period in between saw Italy fall far behind industrializing countries due to political mismanagement, a lack of natural resources, protectionist policies, all which acted to restrict economic growth. However, today Italy is the fifth largest economy in the world and distributes consumer goods to international markets around the world. Italy's per capita GNP is $17,000, although the northern regions, centered on Genoa, Milan, Turin and Venice, throughout the Po River Valley, are well over $20,000, while that of areas south of Rome are well below $10,000. Italy, largely without fossil fuels, fell on hard times with the oil crisis of the 1970s and 1980s, creating labor unrest and political instability. Larger companies suffered the most and were also plagued with underfunding and limited access to loans from the government-dominated banking system. By 1990, large private sector multinational corporations had reestablished themselves and their efficiency, especially in engineering products, textiles, clothing and transportation equipment. Widespread exploitation of cheap labor from the south and tax evasion on a large scale, made smaller firms competitive in foreign markets against newly industrializing countries. *(op. cit. Fig. 14.16.)*

age). Thus, manufactured goods including machinery and metal-engineered goods, textiles and clothing, shoes, and automobiles are Italy's most important export products (Figure 13.23).

UNITED KINGDOM

Great Britain's balance of merchandise trade was slightly negative in 1990. Similar to France, its export profile suggested a per capita level of $3000 per person per year, approximately 20% of its GDP. Fifty percent of both imports and exports were manufactured products, and another 25% of both exports and imports were semimanufactured products (Figure 13.21). Great Britain is a net exporter of fuels because of its North Sea

oil bonanza but a net importer of agricultural products and foodstuffs. It has a trading-partner profile similar to that of France and Germany.

Birthplace of the industrial revolution, Great Britain became a net importer of manufactured goods by 1990. The restructuring of the British economy, away from manufacturing, caused the country to depend on North Sea oil profits and overseas investments and services. The U.K. firms invested heavily outside the United Kingdom, especially in the United States. Relative to its population and economy, the United Kingdom owns more foreign assets than any other OECD nation does, including Japan and the United States. In addition, FDI by Japan in the United Kingdom has been greater than in any other Western European nation.

PURCHASING POWER PARITY

The usual measure of a country's economy and strength is its GDP—that is, the value of all goods and services produced. When one divides the GDP by the population, the result is GDP per person. The following figure, however, shows GDP per person adjusted for the cost of living by the United Nations—in other words, GDP per person with *purchasing power parity*.

Some experts argue that European nations, notably Germany, Switzerland, and Sweden, have higher GDPs per capita than the U.S. GDP per capita. However, countries such as Norway, Sweden, Germany, Switzerland, and Great Britain have some of the highest costs of living in the world, with Japan topping the list. A Burger King Whopper, now $0.99 in the United States, costs from $6 to $9 in the capitals of these countries. The figure below shows that in 1990, at least, the United States had a clear superiority over other nations with regard to GDP per person, which averaged just about $20,000. Switzerland ranked below the United States at seven-eighths the U.S. level, whereas Kuwait, West Germany, and Singapore were rated at approximately three-quarters the U.S. level. Japan ranked at only seven-tenths the U.S. level, and the United Kingdom and France at two-thirds. Southern European countries fared even more poorly; Spain ranked at less than 50% of the U.S. level, and Eastern European countries, the most prosperous of which is Hungary, ranked at less than one-third the U.S. level.

South Africa, Mexico, and Korea showed only about one-quarter the U.S. GDP per capita, whereas Pakistan, the Philippines, and China averaged only one-tenth. India and the most prosperous African nations averaged only one-twentieth the U.S. level. The poorer African nations ranged from 1% to 2% of the U.S. level.

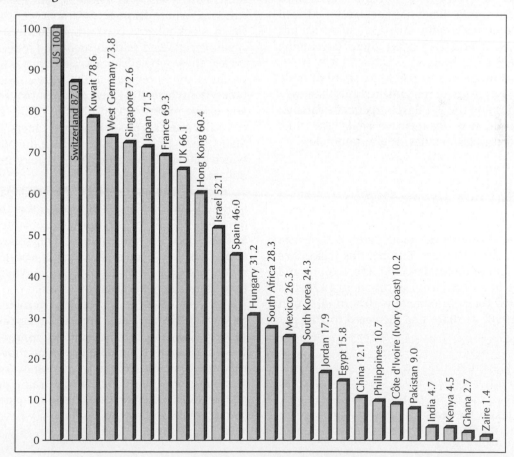

As with the United States and France, a current problem in Great Britain is the overcapitalized defense research, development, and manufacturing industry. Attempts to find commercial applications of defense plants and weapons are currently being pursued.

Recently, Great Britain has suffered balance-of-payment problems and a declining standard of living. Referring to the box, we can see the United Kingdom's purchasing power parity, which shows its true standard of living as compared with those of other countries.

SHIFTS IN WESTERN EUROPEAN WORLD TRADE

During the last 20 years, Western European world trade has shifted substantially. The OPEC oil prices of 1973 and 1978 meant that the long-distance, worldwide distribution of goods to former colonies in Africa, Asia, and South America were more costly. Western Europe's economic prosperity peaked in 1973 when oil was cheap. After 1980, exports began to become more localized. The shift to closer markets within Western Europe has persisted, even though oil has dropped in price to less than $20 per barrel. The long-standing relationships with the former colonies have not been resumed, and consequently trade with Latin America and Africa has dwindled to just a trickle, hurting these developing countries more than Europe.

In contrast, Europe has increased its share of trade with Japan and East Asia for the same reasons that trade between America and the Far East burgeoned—quality products produced with inexpensive labor. The chief products are electronics, textiles, and automobiles.

East Asia and the Pacific

The fastest-growing world trade region is East Asia and the Pacific. After Western Europe, this region has the largest amount of internal world trade. Exports and imports in 1990 amounted to $1.6 trillion. In 1970, this region accounted for approximately 10% of all world trade, but by 1990, its share had increased to 25%.

JAPAN, THE FOUR TIGERS, AND THE FIVE LITTLE DRAGONS

Japan has taken the lead role in the development of East Asia and the Pacific. The growth of its flattened economy, which occurred after World War II, is nothing short of an economic miracle and parallels that of Germany. It has been joined by the *Four Tigers* of Taiwan, South Korea, Singapore, and Hong Kong. However, five new emerging *"little dragons"* have followed suit with rapidly growing economies: the Philippines, Thailand, Malaysia, Indonesia, and the People's Republic of China.

While the rest of the world reeled from two major oil-price hikes and experienced a major recession, lower productivity, high unemployment, economic restructuring of manufacturing jobs, and a shift toward the service sector of the economy, East Asia and the Pacific forged ahead with unprecedented growth. It is difficult to identify the factors that account for this growth. However, diligence and hard work, a culture dedicated to succeeding competitively, and the work ethic that weds the laborer to the firm and to the government are part of the answer. In addition, Japan and other countries have protected home markets with extremely high import duties, while continuing to encourage rivalry among domestic companies to prepare them for international export wars.

Two other factors contributed to the prosperity of these East Asian and Pacific countries. First, unlike America, where short-term profits were important to satisfy stockholders, banks, and financial institutions, Japan encouraged reinvestment and long-term growth cycles. These long cycles allowed firms time to develop products and to reinvest in the highest-quality production systems before the owners or employees could reap any of the profits. Second, many of the Asian/Pacific countries acted as resource supply centers for the United States from 1965 to 1975, during the Vietnam War, which allowed them to collect a heavy inflow of U.S. dollars.

All these factors combined allowed Japan to develop the world's second largest economy, after the U.S. economy, by 1980. Japan's economy supplanted that of the Soviet Union, which has almost three times the population of Japan. Japan's economy is also tremendously more prosperous than that of China, which has nearly nine times the population of Japan.

Between 1960 and 1990, the combined domestic product of East Asia and the Pacific increased 20 times over, which changed the economy from one of developing nations to NICs. The economy moved toward a new emphasis on electronics, automobiles, steel, textiles, and consumer goods. At the same time, internal policies required these countries to manage their population growth and natural resources, whereas other developing countries in Latin America, Africa, and South

At a Samsung VCR assembly line in Seoul, South Korea.
(Photo: T. Matsumoto/Sygma.)
Foreign national corporations, like Samsung, have raised foreign exchange and have helped pay off Korea's massive debts, a total of $45 billion by 1990, making Korea one of the most indebted nations of the world for its size. Because of competitive exports, inexpensive labor and a booming economy, its debt service ratio is now only 13 percent of its GNP. By contrast, some African nations are at 100 percent debt payment of their GNP per year. The debt services ratio for South American nations is 37 percent by comparison. Recent downturns in the global economy have slowed South Korea's journey out of heavy debt. New problems now exist with North Korea's nuclear capability and sullen response to trade.

Asia did not have such policies. From 1970 to 1990, foreign investment in the region, especially in Japan and the Four Tigers, grew tenfold. This investment was led not only by U.S., British, German, Canadian, and Australian firms, but also by the Japanese.

The United States has taken the lead in trade with Pacific Rim nations, even though it is separated from them by 10,000 miles or more of ocean. Former U.S. trade ties were with the North Atlantic, but the focus has changed to the Pacific. Figure 13.15 shows North American (U.S. and Canadian) trade ties with East Asia and the Pacific versus ties to Western Europe. Until 1970, Western Europe was North America's chief trading partner. From 1970 to 1980, however, Asia and the Pacific had caught up with Western Europe in terms of total trade with North America, and since 1979, North American trade with Asia and the Pacific increased more rapidly than trade with Western Europe. The trade gap continued to increase until 1990, when North American trade with Asia and the Pacific outpaced trade with Western Europe by 50%, nearly hitting the $350 billion mark.

Japan is the second leading international trading nation. Figure 13.24 shows the Japanese balance of merchandise trade. Unlike most of Western Europe and North America, Japan shows a huge export trade surplus. Although the United States is its principal trading partner, both for exports and for imports, Japan has a tremendously diversified trading base, with almost 50% of exports and imports going to countries each composing less than 4% individually. Second-, third-, fourth-, and fifth-place countries relying on Japanese exports are Germany, Taiwan, Hong Kong, and Great Britain— an interesting mix of Asian/Pacific and EEC nations. The other 50% of Japanese world trade is with Pacific Rim nations.

The United States provides fewer imports to Japan than the exports that it receives from Japan. However, U.S. products still account for the largest single proportion of goods imported by Japan. Indonesia, Australia, China, South Korea, and Germany follow. The United States and Indonesia fill a large need for energy that Japan cannot meet domestically. In addition, because of Japan's mountainous terrain, agricultural and food products compose 16% of total imports. Chemicals, textiles, and metals are also imported.

The world dominance of Japan in the manufacture of motor vehicles is truly phenomenal (Figure 13.25). Fully 22% of its exports are motor vehicles, followed by high-tech office machinery, chemicals, electronic tubes, iron and steel products, and scientific and optical equipment (Figure 13.24). Diversification is a key word used to describe the breadth of Japanese exports. Fifty-two percent are products that do not individually account for more than 4% in any one industrial category. Per capita exports amount to $2500 in Japan, comparable to those of many of the EEC nations, which are much smaller.

Similar to America's exportation of manufacturing jobs to Mexico and East Asia, Japan has done the same

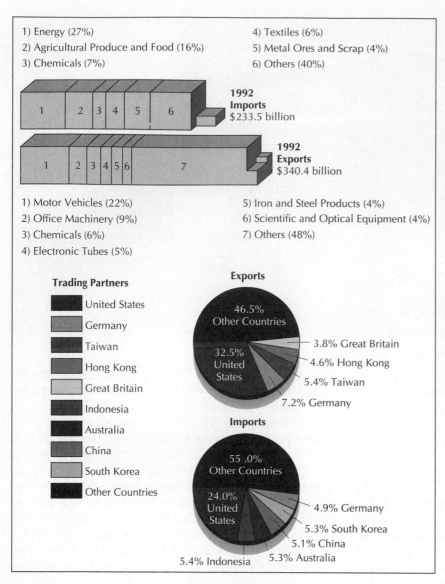

1) Energy (27%)
2) Agricultural Produce and Food (16%)
3) Chemicals (7%)
4) Textiles (6%)
5) Metal Ores and Scrap (4%)
6) Others (40%)

1992 Imports $233.5 billion

1) Motor Vehicles (22%)
2) Office Machinery (9%)
3) Chemicals (6%)
4) Electronic Tubes (5%)
5) Iron and Steel Products (4%)
6) Scientific and Optical Equipment (4%)
7) Others (48%)

1992 Exports $340.4 billion

Trading Partners

- United States
- Germany
- Taiwan
- Hong Kong
- Great Britain
- Indonesia
- Australia
- China
- South Korea
- Other Countries

Exports

46.5% Other Countries
32.5% United States
3.8% Great Britain
4.6% Hong Kong
5.4% Taiwan
7.2% Germany

Imports

55.0% Other Countries
24.0% United States
4.9% Germany
5.3% South Korea
5.1% China
5.3% Australia
5.4% Indonesia

FIGURE 13.24

Composition of Japan's world merchandise trade in 1992. Japan has shown prodigious growth in manufacturing and trade and now stands as the world's second largest economy, after that of the United States. Most important, Japan has a huge trade surplus, exporting $64 billion more than imports in 1990. Japan's leading trade partner for both exports and imports is the United States. Leading products include automobiles and microelectronics. (op. cit. Fig. 14.16.) Powerful Japanese companies, with dedicated work forces and ample capitalization, plan many decades into the future for their economic growth, unlike American companies, which are planning for stockholder dividends in the short-run. Powerful Japanese economic institutions formed alliances of firms well connected with the government that are known as *zaibatsus*. Unlike America's government, which stood to enforce anti-trust violations and regulate banking and unfair sales tactics, Japan's business leaders, aligned with government leaders, forged ahead to create, through pain and pleasure of hard work, the most stunning economic miracle of the world economy to date. Because Japanese banks have based their leverage on paper gains from their holdings of real estate equities, they have seen fallen equity by 1995, of up to 50 percent of their banking and stockmarket assets. As banks have come under scrutiny, imprudent lending, shocking practices and corruption on an alarming scale, have been exposed. Japan continues to slide to economic chaos and, even now, after the United States has begun its economic recovery, Japan still surprisingly has not encouraged imports from the United States. In fact, the reverse is true! Japan now finds itself with a labor surplus rather than a shortage, and for the first time, major companies are doing the unheard of, laying off employees!

with automobile-assembly plants and autoparts firms in the United States, which now number near 400. In addition, with regards to grains, feed, and nonoil commodities, the United States ships these primary products to Japan as a chief way of accounting for its reception of high-tech manufactured items—microelectronics and automobiles, primarily. There is a reverse flow of high-tech goods from North America to Japan, most notably Boeing aircraft.

Japan, by 1980, had become the world's leading creditor nation and a dominant player in the world financial scene. Currently, Japanese banks account for all but 2 of the 10 largest in the world and dominate the 500 largest banks in the world. Tokyo became one of the main financial centers, alongside London and New York. Brokerage firms and banks from Japan occupy cities not only on the West Coast of America, but throughout the world as well. Japan has managed all this with almost a total lack of food, mineral, and energy resources. It has shown the way for other East Asian and Pacific countries to follow suit. Singapore and Hong Kong are also major players in the world banking scene and have important money markets.

From 1980 to 1994, Japan attained a trade surplus of $700 billion, by far the largest in the world. It enjoyed a $60 billion bilateral trade surplus with the United States, $35 billion with Western Europe, and $25 billion with Asia and the Pacific. Both the EEC, which received 20% of Japanese exports, and the United States, which received 33%, contributed to this trade surplus. As a

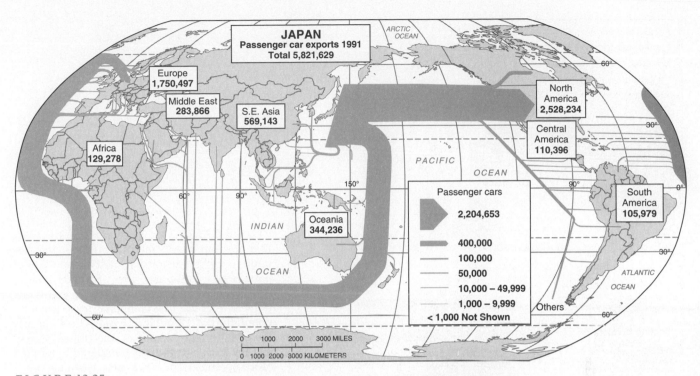

FIGURE 13.25
The global distribution of Japanese automobile exports, 1987.
(*Source: World Motor Vehicle Data, 1993, American Automobile Manufacturing Association, Detroit, Michigan.*)

result, protectionist voices in Europe and in America can be heard periodically accusing Japan of establishing new markets for itself by temporarily undercutting prices of foreign competitors. This monopolistic approach to competition is illegal in North America. The Japanese have also been accused of selling goods by dumping them on local markets to weaken rivals and force them to sell their market shares to Japanese firms. At the same time, it is argued, the Japanese have restricted foreign firms from selling in Japan by a huge amalgam of import duties, tariffs, and regulations.

As mentioned earlier, in 1985, the United States, Japan, Great Britain, France, and Germany began selling dollars on the world market to try to drive down the currency's value. The result was a big success, and the dollar is now quite weak on world markets and is creating a trade surplus for America. The surplus has not eliminated the U.S. trade deficit yet, but movement is in that direction. At the same time, the yen soared, which caused the prices of Japanese goods in Europe and America to skyrocket. Japanese sales dropped, and the deficit narrowed even more. However, although the American and Japanese deficits have been narrowing from 1988 to 1994, they still represent a huge surplus for the Japanese.

The Japanese response to the decreased demand for

their goods was to establish manufacturing plants in America and in Europe to reduce the prices of their marketed items. They also established manufacturing locations in Southeast Asia, where costs were lower. Both approaches—in North America and in Southeast Asia—allowed the Japanese to continue trading competitively with cheaper products. Thus, Japan has relegated Southeast Asia and the United States to Third World status by using its vast amounts of inexpensive labor to produce its manufactured products.

The selling of America to Japan certainly is no more true than on the U.S. West Coast, where, from San Diego to Vancouver, Japanese banks are more numerous than American banks and own 30% of the major buildings and real estate downtown. Americans cannot help but wonder: Will Augusta National Golf Course or Yellowstone National Park be next?

AUSTRALIA

Australia's balance of merchandise trade is shown in Figure 13.26. Australia's main trading partners are the United States, the EEC, and Japan. Exports go primarily to Japan, which accounts for 27%. The next largest share, 16%, goes to China, Hong Kong, Taiwan,

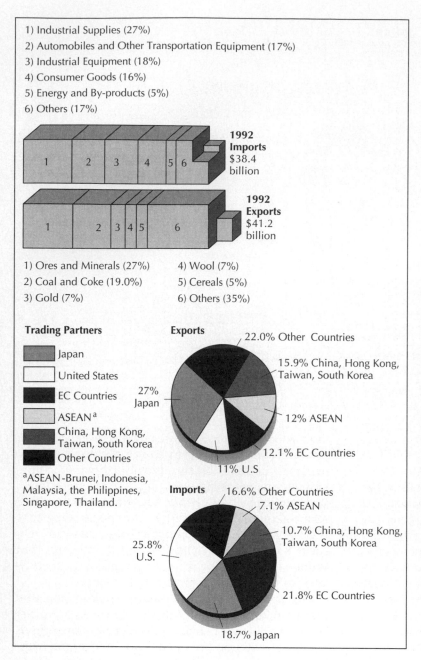

1) Industrial Supplies (27%)
2) Automobiles and Other Transportation Equipment (17%)
3) Industrial Equipment (18%)
4) Consumer Goods (16%)
5) Energy and By-products (5%)
6) Others (17%)

1992 Imports $38.4 billion

1992 Exports $41.2 billion

1) Ores and Minerals (27%)   4) Wool (7%)
2) Coal and Coke (19.0%)   5) Cereals (5%)
3) Gold (7%)   6) Others (35%)

Trading Partners

Japan
United States
EC Countries
ASEAN[a]
China, Hong Kong, Taiwan, South Korea
Other Countries

[a]ASEAN - Brunei, Indonesia, Malaysia, the Philippines, Singapore, Thailand.

Exports

22.0% Other Countries
15.9% China, Hong Kong, Taiwan, South Korea
27% Japan
12% ASEAN
12.1% EC Countries
11% U.S

Imports

16.6% Other Countries
7.1% ASEAN
10.7% China, Hong Kong, Taiwan, South Korea
25.8% U.S.
21.8% EC Countries
18.7% Japan

FIGURE 13.26
Composition of Australia's world merchandise trade in 1992. Australia's small economy exports primary products: ores, minerals, coal, gold, wool, and cereals. Its territory and natural resources are vast compared to its small population of 17 million. Exports and imports are divided between Japan, the United States, and the EEC. Australia is hampered by physical remoteness. For 200 years, Australia and New Zealand were used by Europe as exporting economies, based on minerals and agricultural produce. Because Europe is turning inward with moves toward the formation of the European Community (EC), Australia has looked to the Pacific Rim nations for trading partners, especially Japan and United States. Australia needs to develop new industries and to establish more value added products, as well as a commercial banking plan. The EC's common agricultural policy, which propped up farm prices in Europe, reduced Australia's trade with member nations. New prohibitive tariffs also were enacted, pushed by the French farming lobby. Because of these measures, Australia slipped from having the highest GNP per capita in the world to 20th by the end of 1993, standing at $17,000 per person. (op. cit. Fig. 14.16.)

and South Korea. The Association of South-East Asian Nations (ASEAN)—Indonesia, Malaysia, the Philippines, Singapore, and Thailand—account for an additional 12%, whereas the United States and the EEC account for approximately 11% each.

The United States leads the list of importers, providing 25.8%, while EEC countries supply 21.8%. Japan follows with 19%.

Australia is a nation that exports primary products—mainly ores and minerals, coal and coke, gold,

wool, and cereals. Almost all of its exports are from the vast wealth of land and resources that it enjoys. Because of its small population, 16 million, industrial supplies, automobiles, and industrial equipment account for more than 60% of imports. Japan has made its greatest market penetration into Australia and accounts for 50% of all vehicles purchased.

Australia is one of the leading raw-material suppliers in the world. It is the largest exporter of iron ore and aluminum and the second or third largest exporter of

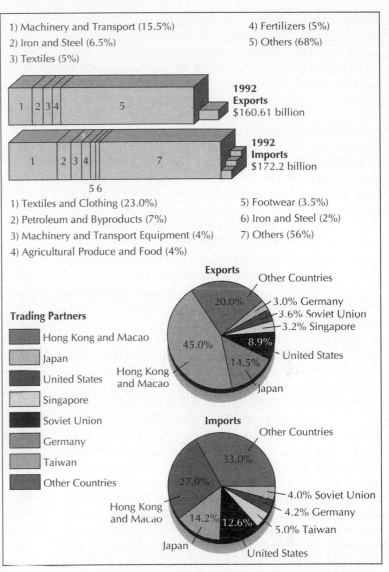

FIGURE 13.27

Composition of China's world merchandise trade in 1992. World trade is tiny compared to its population size or more than 1.2 billion people, yet it enjoys a trade surplus, exporting more than it imports, including textiles, clothing, petroleum, and by-products. (op. cit. Fig. 14.16.) The fact that the Chinese people have never really been free to exercise their own economic initiative, which is vast, has undermined their economy and trade. First, the emperors who ruled China kept the populous under their thumb. Civil war and WWII ensued between 1911, when the emperors were overthrown, and 1949 when the communists finally won out over the nationalists. Socialist reforms then finally allowed China's economy to grow at an unprecedented rate of 10 percent per year. Per capita incomes, however, are only $350 per year. With such a low base, a rapid GDP growth per year seems like a sure thing. However, the Chinese must overcome a) an inefficient socialist system, b) a leadership vacuum in Beijing, and c) a huge population. If China can overcome these problems, it may become the most significant new economic force in the next century. At its present rate of growth, China will be the third largest economy by the year 2000. It could surpass that of the United States as early as 2020. The Chinese government plans for growth rates to average above 10 percent through the end of the decade. The Chinese people maintain the second highest savings rate in the world, close behind the leader, Liechtenstein. The Chinese version of capitalism is flourishing but still has a long ways to go. China's main job on the part of its energetic and entrepreneurial people is to draw capital and high technology from the United States and Japan to itself. It will soon become the biggest market in the world for consumer products! Establishment of the Shenzen economic zone has created a vital free market in the coastal area surrounding Hong Kong. It offers to multi-national corporations lower taxes, and investment consessions to attract numerous joint ventures, particularly textiles, oil, and telecommunications manufacturing. Hong Kong will serve as the main conduit for Chinese exports. Direct foreign investment in China, via Hong Kong and Taiwan, which was $15 billion in 1992, is expected to be $100 billion by the year 2000.

nickel, coal, zinc, lead, gold, tin, tungsten, and uranium. Consequently, Australia's current problem is to withstand the declining world prices of raw materials. To cushion against fluctuations in these prices, Australia needs to industrialize itself so that it can transform its raw materials into finished products and become an exporter of higher-value items. However, doing so is nearly impossible with a small industrial base that demands consumer products before industrial products.

CHINA

Where does China stand in world trade? China enjoys a favorable trade balance, but its exports amount to only $60 per capita, one-hundredth of the German level of $6000 per capita. China's primary trading partners are Hong Kong and Macao, which uses Hong Kong as a port of entry and export for its goods (Figure 13.27). Exports and imports are further connected to countries beyond the tiny borders of Hong Kong and Macao. Japan is China's second leading trade nation, followed by the United States.

China suffers from the communist ideology of *autarky*, which suggests that countries should be self-sufficient economically. This view was part of Mao Tsetung's utopian vision of the nation. China opened its door of trade quite late, after the death of Mao in 1976. Shortly after President Nixon visited China, the first American president to do so, he granted them Most

Favored Nation status as a trading partner. During the early 1980s, China finally allowed foreign companies to set up joint ventures there. Special economic zones were created near Hong Kong to produce goods for world markets. These economic zones received tax incentives but were subject to a host of legal red tape that was typical of the Communist government.

China, the largest nation in the world, with 1.2 billion people, has the potential to become a major actor in world trade. It has a large worker base, low wages, and, because of the East Asian work ethic, relatively high levels of worker productivity. In addition, some Chinese who fled during the Maoist cultural revolution of 1966 to 1976, and who settled in the capitalistically successful countries of the Four Tigers or the Five Little Dragons, have now returned to China with new entrepreneurial skills and some investment capital. The result has been a dramatic increase in foreign trade. For example, exports increased from only 5 billion in 1976 to almost 62 billion in 1990.

By all measures, however, China is a poor country. It still struggles to provide its many people with sufficient food and housing. Almost no capital is available for start-up programs, and, therefore, China has open doors to foreign companies, especially in the industrial sector. Foreign investment has flooded in to establish factories, to mass-produce items in the areas of oil exploration, to manufacture motor vehicles, and to construct commercial buildings and hotels in the major cities. State-owned manufacturing plants account for approximately 50% of manufacturing exports. The other 50%, and an increasing proportion, are small-scale industrial plants that are owned by rural townships but leased to private individuals for profit. Textiles, clothing, and industrial products accounted for 70% of exports in 1990.

In the early 1990s, the United States took issue with China's Most Favored Nation trade status. China has a very poor record of human rights violations, most notably the Tiananmen Square Massacre of hundreds of students in the summer of 1989. For this reason, U.S. protectionist sympathies in Congress have asked for China to be stripped of its Most Favored Nation status. Although China seems to have weathered this storm and is moving ahead under the leadership of quite aged Deng Xiaoping, he has been reluctant to allow Chinese manufacturing to privatize as he has, in part, allowed the agricultural sector to do. Until privatization occurs, China's vast human resources will not be used efficiently to produce items for world trade.

China is currently watching Russia and former East Germany. High levels of unemployment that would initially be caused by privatization of state-owned industry in China may cause major social unrest, it is feared, and thus lead to a revolt that could topple the Communist Party. The safe approach is to allow state-owned industry to be heavily subsidized for the near term.

INDIA

In South Asia, India, with its 860 million people, is like a human flood of population in a land smaller than that of the United States. Its world trade is minuscule but growing, at about $15 per capita. India is, at long last, self-sufficient in food production and is an exporter of primary products, including gems and jewelry, textiles, clothing, and engineering products (Figure 13.28). In order for its factories to operate, it must import industrial equipment and machinery and crude oil and by-products, as well as chemicals, iron, and steel. Twelve percent of its imports include uncut gems for its expanding jewelry trade.

In terms of trading partners, India is no longer dominated by its formerly colonial overseer, Great Britain. Its leading countries of export include the United States (16%) and the former Soviet Union (16%), although the latter figure, for 1990, must have surely decreased by now. Great Britain and other EEC countries account for 19% of total exports and 25% of total imports. Because India represents such a large pool of demand, most manufactured goods and consumer goods are consumed locally, not exported. Since 1990, India has also become an exporter of cereals and grains, and textiles and clothing are now the chief exports.

Eastern Europe and the Former Soviet Union

The most momentous occurrence in our lifetimes is certainly the breakup of the former Soviet Union and the return of Eastern European nations to market economies. If gigantic China and tiny Vietnam followed suit, this would be one memorable decade, or even century. As of 1994, the former Soviet Union's 15 republics—Russia and the 14 republics—and the Eastern European nations were still in transition. The old central-planning systems had clearly broken up, but new systems that would replace them were not yet fully in place.

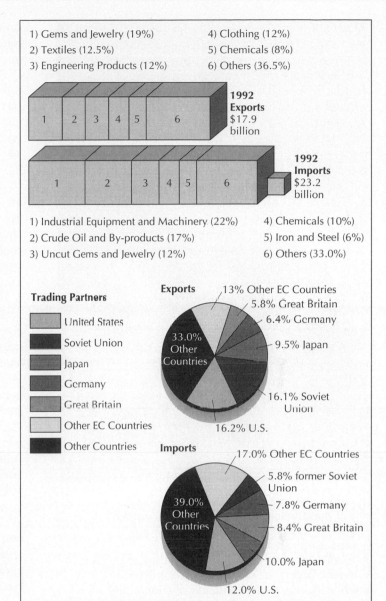

1) Gems and Jewelry (19%)   4) Clothing (12%)
2) Textiles (12.5%)   5) Chemicals (8%)
3) Engineering Products (12%)   6) Others (36.5%)

1992 Exports $17.9 billion

1992 Imports $23.2 billion

1) Industrial Equipment and Machinery (22%)   4) Chemicals (10%)
2) Crude Oil and By-products (17%)   5) Iron and Steel (6%)
3) Uncut Gems and Jewelry (12%)   6) Others (33.0%)

Trading Partners
- United States
- Soviet Union
- Japan
- Germany
- Great Britain
- Other EC Countries
- Other Countries

Exports
13% Other EC Countries
5.8% Great Britain
6.4% Germany
9.5% Japan
33.0% Other Countries
16.1% Soviet Union
16.2% U.S.

Imports
17.0% Other EC Countries
5.8% former Soviet Union
7.8% Germany
8.4% Great Britain
39.0% Other Countries
10.0% Japan
12.0% U.S.

FIGURE 13.28
Composition of India's world merchandise trade in 1992. India exports gems, jewelry, and textiles. The country imports badly needed industrial equipment and machinery, as well as crude oil for fuel. Its total trade is tiny compared to its 900 million population. Most of the India subcontinent is very poor, although per capita incomes range from $250 to $500 in Western India, to less than $150 in Central and Eastern India. For the first time, India now manufactures most of its equipment used to make consumer goods, but trade deficits and repayment of interest on international debt, as well as internal political conflicts amongst Hindus and Muslims, and class conflicts, strain economic development. The a) increases in oil prices in the 1970s, b) rapid population increases, c) the continuing conflict with Pakistan and d) unresolved border issues in Kashmir all have slowed economic progress. Infant mortality remains at 92 per 1,000 live births, over ten times that of the United States, but government welfare programs have improved life expectancy, literacy and general health care in many areas with aid from the International Monetary Fund, World Bank and United States Aid to International Development programs.
(op. cit. Fig. 14.16.)

Before the breakup of the Soviet Union in 1991 and the return to market economies by the Eastern European nations, beginning in 1989, this communistic, centrally planned region accounted for only 8% of world trade. The Communist ideology was based on autarky, or self-sufficiency, which meant that these nations kept their distance from the rest of the world in terms of trade. This policy was disadvantageous because Western Europe produced many items that Eastern European nations and the Soviet Union needed. At the same time, Western Europe had a great demand for energy resources and raw materials from the Soviet Union. Only near the end of the empire did a major pipeline provide natural gas from the Ural Mountains to Germany and other Western European nations.

It is impossible to gauge what the future will hold for world trade from this region. In 1992, the national income was 20% less in the former Soviet Union than it was in the previous year. In 1993, output decreased 16% in the region as a whole because the economies were in major transition. However, not all countries were suffering equally (Figure 13.29), as shown by the credit ratings of Eastern Europe and the republics of the former Soviet Union (Table 13.12). These credit ratings

The production of handicrafts is an important tool in the development of the world's poorer nations. In many areas, the meager income derived from craftworking can mean the difference between starvation and subsistence. In rural villages, such as this one in India, handicrafts help form the matrix of community life and providing incentives to remain and not to migrate. Globally, trade involving handicrafts is one of the few sources of income for some of the poorest countries.
(Source: John Isaac/UN Photo.)

were based on a United Nations/Department of Economic and Social Development (UN/DESD) survey of 100 banks, and credit was rated according to analysis of economic conditions, and the chance of default within the countries. With 100 being good, repressive Albania, closed for most of its history, rated 41, whereas Bulgaria, Poland, and Romania hovered around the 50s to 60s. The former Soviet Union, which had a credit

rating of 168 in 1988, could barely register 79 in 1992, whereas Hungary and Czechoslovakia were rated 111 and 126, respectively.

Comparable ratings for the republics of the former Soviet Union were much, much worse than those of Eastern Europe. Armenia rated 39; Estonia, 69; Georgia, 36; Kazakhstan, 47; the Kirghiz Republic, 34; Latvia, 64; Lithuania, 63; Moldavia, 38; the Tajik Republic, 34; the Turkmen Republic, 34; and the Uzbek Republic, 37.

The output of this region, country by country, was less than it was 10 years earlier, and investment fell to pre-1970 levels. It was clear that the former Soviet Union and Eastern Europe were in the throes of a savage economic restructuring and contraction. With the collapse of trade under the Council for Mutual Economic Assistance (COMECON), orders from nearby COMECON countries decreased by more than 50%, seriously hurting internal production and trade. There is a slowdown in the production of necessary raw materials, equipment, and replacement parts, and a massive shortage of food, pharmaceuticals, textiles, garments, footwear, and machinery. Bulgaria, formerly a food exporter, was forced to import large quantities of food to feed its population during the winter of 1992 and 1993. In the former Soviet Union itself, agricultural production decreased 25% since 1991, and the area under cultivation decreased by 5 million hectares. The former Soviet Union is wrecked by inflation, which increased 400% between 1990 and 1994.

The 14 republics of the former Soviet Union lag most in the transition to a market economy, and Russia is not far ahead. Eastern European nations vary, but the central ones, Czechoslovakia and Hungary, are farther ahead than Poland in the north and the southern republics of Romania, Albania, and Bulgaria.

What does the future hold for this region with regard to international trade? There is a certain complementarity in Euro-Asia. Western Europe needs the minerals, oil, natural gas, and other raw materials that are in vast supply in Russia and the republics of the former Soviet Union. At the same time, the Eastern bloc nations need foodstuffs and industrial equipment and machinery to resume their powerhouse of economic production.

Multinationals from every OECD country are investigating the potential for investment in the Soviet Union. For example, Pizza Hut, a Chicago-based company, has unveiled plans to open 1000 new restaurants within Russia and the 14 republics of the former Soviet Union. Automobile manufacturers from Western Europe, Japan, and the United States are also investigating

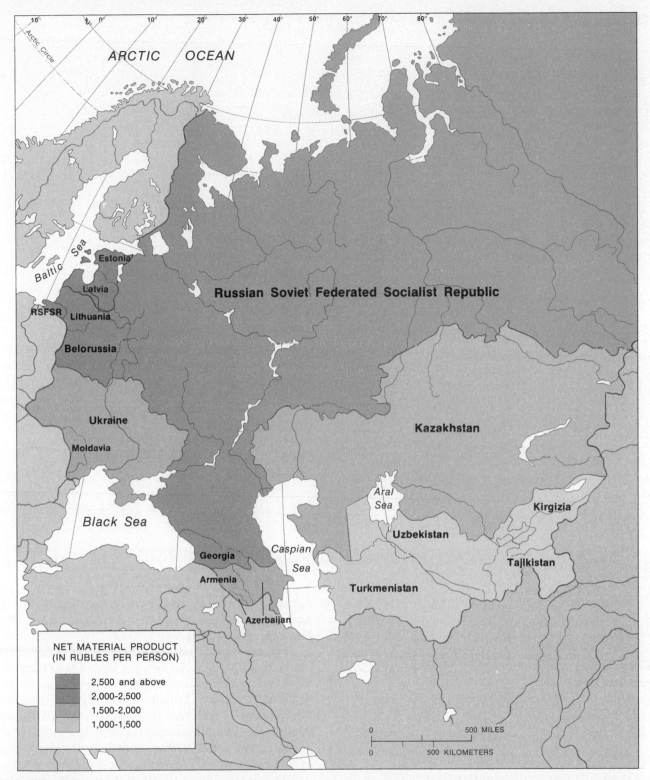

FIGURE 13.29
Per capita gross national product (GNP) varies widely among the republics of the former Soviet Union. Levels are much higher in the European portion of the region. Republics of the former Soviet Union vary widely in per capita GNPs. Levels are higher in Russia and the European regions. Credit ratings, provided by the World Bank, are shown for Eastern Europe and the former Soviet Union, from 1988 to 1992, in Table 13.12. The worst credit risks are the Uzbek Republic, Turkmen Republic, Tajik Republic, Kirghiz Republic, Georgia, and Armenia.

617

⬙

Table 13.12

Credit Ratings of Eastern Europe and the Former
Soviet Union, 1988–1992

Country	1988	1989	1990	1991	1992
Albania	—	—	—	—	41
Bulgaria	123	120	111	73	56
Czechoslovakia	140	141	112	132	126
Hungary	120	115	112	108	111
Poland	46	47	49	57	68
Romania	86	84	85	73	68
Former Soviet Union	168	168	159	117	79
Armenia					39
Azerbaijan					40
Belorussia					51
Estonia					69
Georgia					36
Kazakhstan					47
Kirghiz Republic					34
Latvia					64
Lithuania					63
Moldavia					38
The Russian Federation					66
Tajik Republic					34
Turkmen Republic					34
Ukraine					60
Uzbek Republic					37

Source: United Nations, World Economic Survey, 1992/93, Student Edition, p. 67.

their opportunities, as are consumer electronics producers. However, uncertainties still exist, and these multinationals must be cautious because of the gigantic economic uncertainties in the political and economic transformation of the former Soviet Union and its former member states.

The Middle East

The Middle East contains approximately 60% of the world's oil reserves, with Saudi Arabia containing 200 billion barrels, more than one-third of the world's total. Other oil producers and exporters are Bahrain, Kuwait, the United Arab Emirates, Oman, and Qatar. Five other countries also produce oil but have either interrupted supplies or very small amounts of oil—Libya, Iraq, Iran,

Egypt, and Syria. Countries in the region without oil supplies include Afghanistan, Israel, Jordan, Lebanon, Turkey, Yemen, Morocco, and Tunisia.

Inexpensive oil from the Middle East has fueled the world for a long time. In fact, the United States and the Western European nations have enjoyed a large supply. At $4 to $5 a barrel, Middle Eastern oil helped rebuild Europe after World War II. However, the 1970s and 1980s were tumultuous with regard to international oil prices. In 1973 and 1979, oil supplies were interrupted by Arab boycotts of Western political maneuvering, by Israel's Western bloc support in the Yom Kippur War, and by the overthrow of the Shah of Iran. Prices increased dramatically to $25 a barrel. In 1980, the Iraq-Iran War reduced world flow further and prices continued to climb toward $30 a barrel. OPEC's revenues reached $300 billion, and a worldwide recession was triggered. However, because of squabbling among OPEC members and because U.S.-backed Saudi Arabia decided to undercut the market to provide Western stability, oil prices decreased to less than $10 a barrel in 1986. Revenues plummeted (Figure 13.30). In January of 1994, prices were again at $16 a barrel, and OPEC nations had lost much of their stranglehold on the world market, dropping to approximately equal to OPEC's pre-1973 levels.

While all the fluctuations were occurring, other sources of oil; synthetic fuels; and solar, geothermal, and nuclear power sources had been explored and embraced. The United States reduced its import of oil from 33% of total consumption to 15%, thus, OPEC now has less power over America. OPEC's largest stranglehold was on Western Europe, which traditionally had poor supplies of fossil fuels. Even before the oil crisis, the Middle Eastern nations fulfilled 45% of Western Europe's energy needs. By 1994, however, that proportion had dropped to 20% as a result of not only the exploitation of the North Sea oil fields, but also increased coal production in Central Europe.

The Persian Gulf War between Kuwait and Iraq further suggested to the world that Middle Eastern oil supplies would be erratic. Nonetheless, because the former Soviet Union ceased its oil production while changing over to a market economy, the demand for international trade in oil is still significant.

The region's second most important activity after oil is agriculture, but water is scarce and the few sources that do exist are heavily tapped. The Tigris and Euphrates rivers, for example, as well as the Jordan River, are argued over by countries such as Turkey, Lebanon, Syria, Israel, and Iraq. In any case, wheat, barley, vegetables, cotton, and citrus fruits can be grown and supplied to Europe, which is a short distance away. Agriculture is also the basis of Turkey's export economy. Turkey is a large exporter of wheat and mineral resources, including iron, copper, and zinc.

Egypt is now one of the world's leading exporters of cotton, yarns, textiles, and denim. Egypt has been criticized because much of its agricultural base is devoted to cotton at the expense of food crops needed to

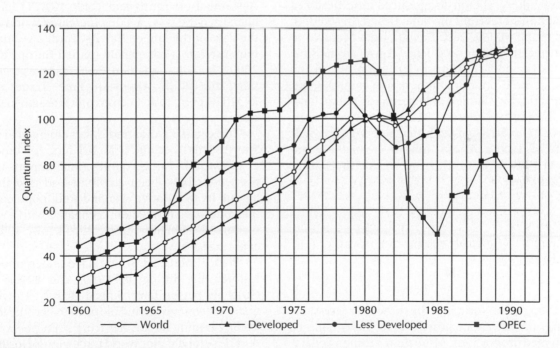

FIGURE 13.30
Export growth for the world economy, for developed country economies, for less developed country economies, and for OPEC countries: Quantum Entices, 1960 to 1990 (1980 equals 100). All four categories showed substantial growth when measured against actual quantity, rather than price, thereby cutting the distorting effects of price variations. Once again, the oil price hike by OPEC triggered a high export growth from 1970 to 1979, when the price dropped substantially. Because of the oil price hikes, the world suffered a recession, which reduced the value of exports during the 1980s. Recovery was almost complete by 1988, whereupon world recession once again set in.
(Source: United Nations, 1992, p. 61.)

Iranian oil field and peasant herder. Iran remains an important source of world oil supplies, but squabbles among OPEC members have kept world prices low—$16 for a 50-gallon barrel in January 1994.
(Source: Paolo Koch/Photo Researchers, Inc.)

feed its people. Israel exports cut and polished diamonds, machinery, chemicals produced from Dead Sea salts, and phosphates from the Sinai Desert. In addition, countries of the Middle East, ranging from Morocco to Jordan, especially Egypt and Israel, have an invisible trade in tourist dollars. Tourism has been one of the mainstays of the economies of these two countries, but recent uprisings by Islamic fundamentalists in Iran have shocked the tourist industry. Recently, several tourist buses have been attacked with machine-gun fire near the town of Luxor. These attacks created a scare throughout Western countries and was detrimental to foreign exchange.

SUMMARY

◈

Even though the world is in the throes of a recession, it is feeling the effects of growth and world trade of unprecedented proportions. More than 3 trillion dollars' worth of goods and services changed hands by 1994, and even more trade is projected in the not-too-distant future. Economic indicators suggest that world domestic products are improving and that the world recession is gradually diminishing. In addition, Eastern Europe and the former Soviet Union countries are coming on line, having opened to the world through their economic restructuring and political realignments. The General Agreement on Tariffs and Trade (GATT) has certainly liberalized the way, making increased world trade since the days of the Smoot-Hawley Tariff a reality. German reunification, a completely unified Europe by the year 2000, the U.S.-Canadian Free Trade Agreement, and now the North American Free Trade Agreement (NAFTA) point to an even greater strength in total world trade.

Three major world trade blocs emerged in the 1990s. The EEC has become a model bloc for other regions of the world. Tariffs, quotas, and import and export restrictions have been eliminated so that this region, despite its diminutive size and total population of less than one-third of a billion, compared with a world population of 5.5 billion, now controls fully 40% of world exports and imports.

France and Great Britain have undergone economic restructuring during the 1980s and 1990s, and their GDPs per person have slipped slightly. However, Germany's seemingly invincible push to become the world's leading trading nation has truly been phenomenal.

The second major world trade bloc is North America. Canada and the United States have always been political and economic allies, and Mexico is now approved for 1994 admission into the bloc. With Mexico added, this block will certainly be one of the largest and most powerful in the world.

The third leading trade bloc, which is actually a staged growth rally, unprecedented in world history, is

East Asia and the Pacific. Japan, of course, leads the rise of this bloc. Because of dedication, hard work, and the East Asian work ethic, which harnesses government administrators and firm vice presidents into a cartel of cooperation, Japan, the Four Tigers, and the Five Little Dragons have moved to new levels of export, shifting their labor-intensive clothing and textile technologies of the 1950s and 1960s to new, higher levels of more expensive and sophisticated export products, including automobiles and microelectronics.

Will the competition among these three emerging super trade blocs damage the freedom and trade liberal-ization that has been enjoyed since 1945? How will the former Communist world involve itself in the shifting world economy by the year 2000? Will the nations of South Asia, Latin America, and Africa, which are now almost completely left out of world trade, be included? What will happen in the Middle East, which attained a meteoric rise in the 1980s to 15% of total international trade but by 1984 had slumped back and remains in 1994 at its former 1973 levels of only 4% of international trade? Will Islamic fundamentalism rob this region of its fair share of international cooperation and trade?

◈

KEY TERMS

capital resources
demand conditions
factor conditions
factor-driven stage
five little dragons
Four Tigers
General Agreement on Tariffs and Trade (GATT)
human resources
infrastructure
innovation-driven stage
investment-driven stage

Japanese transplants
knowledge-based resources
little dragons
microelectronics
physical resources
purchasing power parity
Organization of Economic Cooperation and
    Development (OECD)
supporting industries
wealth-driven stage

◈

SUGGESTED READINGS

Bater, J. H. 1989. *The Soviet Scene: A Geographical Perspective.* New York: Routledge.

Behrman, J. N. 1984. *International Policies: International Restructuring and Transnationals.* Lexington, MA: D. C. Heath.

Berry, B. J. L., Conkling, E. C., and Ray, D. M. 1993. *Economic Geography.* Englewood Cliffs, NJ: Prentice Hall.

Brett, E. A. 1985. *The World Economy Since the War.* London: Macmillan.

Cline, W. R. 1983. *International Debt and the Stability of the World Economy.* Washington, DC: Institute for International Economics.

Corbridge, S. 1993. *Debt and Development.* Oxford: Blackwell.

Daniels, J. D.; Ogram, Jr., E. W.; and Radebaugh, L. H. 1982. *International Business: Environment and Operations.* 3d ed. Reading, MA: Addison-Wesley.

Dunning, J. H., ed. 1985. *Multinational Enterprises, Economic Structure and International Competitiveness.* New York: John Wiley.

Edwards, C. 1985. *The Fragmented World: Competing Perspectives on Trade, Money and Crisis.* New York: Methuen.

Forbes, D. K. 1984. *The Geography of Underdevelopment: A Critical Survey.* Baltimore: The Johns Hopkins University Press.

Helleiner, G. K. 1981. *Intra-Firm Trade and the Developing Countries.* London: Macmillan.

Hoffman, G. W., ed. 1989. *Europe in the 1990s: A Geographical Analysis.* 6th ed. New York: Wiley.

Holloway, S. R., and Pandit, K. 1992. The disparity between the level of economic development and human welfare. *Professional Geographer,* 44:57–71.

Janelle, D. G., ed. 1992. *Geographical Snapshots of North America.* New York: Guilford.

Korth, C. M. 1985. *International Business: Environment and Management.* 2d ed. Englewood Cliffs, NJ: Prentice Hall.

Krause, L., and Sekiguchi, S., eds. 1980. *Economic Interaction in the Pacific Basin.* Washington, DC: The Brookings Institution.

Krugman, P. 1992. *The Age of Diminished Expectations.* Cambridge, MA: MIT Press.

Linder, S. B. 1986. *The Pacific Century: Economic and Political Consequences of Asian-Pacific Dynamism.* Stanford, CA: Standford University Press.

Momsen, J. H. 1991. *Women and Development in the Third World.* London: Routledge.

Momsen, J. H., and Townsend, J. 1987. *Geography of Gender in the Third World.* Albany: State University of New York Press.

Murphy, A. B. 1992. Western investment in East-Central Europe: Emerging patterns and implications for state stability. *Professional Geographer,* 44:249–259.

Murray, R., ed. 1981. *Multinationals Beyond the Market.* Brighton, England: Harvester Press.

O hUallachain, B., and Reid, N. 1992. Source country differences in the spatial distribution of foreign direct investment in the United States. *Professional Geographer,* 44:272–285.

Porter, D., Allen, B., and Thompson, G. 1991. *Development in Practice: Paved with Good Intentions.* London and New York: Routledge.

Porter, M. E. 1990. *The Competitive Advantage of Nations.* New York: The Free Press.

Robock, S. H., and Simmonds, K. 1983. *International Business and Multinational Enterprises.* 3d ed. Homewood, IL: Richard D. Irwin.

Ronen, S. 1986. *Comparative and Multinational Management.* New York: John Wiley.

Root, F. R. 1990. *International Trade and Investment.* 6th ed. Cincinnati, OH: South-Western Publishing.

Rostow, W. W. 1960. *The Stages of Economic Growth.* Cambridge: Cambridge University Press.

Terpstra, V., and David, K. 1985. *The Cultural Environment of International Business.* 2d ed. Cincinnati, OH: South-Western Publishing.

Thurow, L. 1992. *Head to Head: The Coming Economic Battle Among Japan, Europe, and America.* New York: William Morrow.

United Nations. 1983. *Transnational Corporations in World Development. Third Survey.* New York: United Nations.

———. 1988. *Transnational Corporations in World Development: Trends and Prospects.* New York: United Nations.

Wallace, I. 1990. *The Global Economic System.* London: Unwin Hyman.

Wallerstein, I. 1979. *The Capitalist World-Economy.* Cambridge: Cambridge University Press.

Wallerstein, I. 1991. *Geopolitics and Geoculture: Essays on the Changing World-System.* Cambridge: Cambridge University Press.

Wilbanks, T. J. 1980. *Location and Well-Being: An Introduction to Economic Geography.* San Francisco: Harper & Row.

DEVELOPMENT AND UNDER-DEVELOPMENT

❖

OBJECTIVES

- To outline the goals of development

- To acquaint you with the attributes of less developed nations

- To examine major theories and perspectives on development

- To examine the causes of Soviet collapse and the formidable transition process

- To describe the urban peasantry as an example of a marginal social formation

◈

Collecting water from a well in Ethiopia.
(Source: World Bank.)

The modern world has its origin in the European societies of the late fifteenth and early sixteenth centuries. One of its most striking characteristics is the division between rich and poor countries. Early on, this division was achieved through an international system in which the wealthy minority industrialized, using primary products produced by the impoverished majority. More recently, as we have seen in Chapters 11 through 13, this original division of labor gave way to a new division of labor. Now, the wealthy minority are increasingly engaged in office work and the masses in hands-on manufacturing jobs on the global assembly line as well as in agriculture and raw-material production. The creation of today's world with a rich core and a poor periphery was not the result of conspiracy among developed countries, but of an "invisible hand." It was the outcome of a systemic process—that process by which the world's political economy functions.

This chapter deals with how this world of unequal development came about, how present structures are the result of the past. It also outlines a positive, idealistic proposal for enhancing Third World development. We begin with a discussion of the characteristics of underdevelopment and of some frequently propounded views on the nature of development and underdevelopment. Goals for development are introduced, and development objectives that most people would subscribe to are listed. This list provides a basis of comparison for arguments developed later in the chapter.

WHAT'S IN A WORD? "DEVELOPING"

◙

From Primitive to Underdeveloped

If America, with its high level of material consumption, is described as a developed country, then what adjective should we use to describe Third World countries? Certainly, there are many from which to choose. In the past half-century, each of the following terms has flourished in succession: primitive, backward, undeveloped, underdeveloped, less developed, emerging, developing, and rapidly developing. Today, Western social scientists use the word *developing* and, increasingly, the phrase *less developed countries* (LDCs), but social scientists in the Marxist tradition favor the term *underdeveloped*.

Underdeveloped was formerly used by Western social scientists to describe situations in which resources were not yet developed. People and resources were seen as existing, respectively, in a traditional and natural state. Scholars in the Marxist tradition now use *underdeveloped* to describe not an initial state, but rather a condition arrived at through the agency of imperialism, which set up the inequality of political and economic dependence of poor countries on rich countries. Thus, instead of viewing underdevelopment as an initial or *passive state*, Marxists view it as an *active process* (Rodney, 1972).

THE GOALS OF DEVELOPMENT

◙

In his plea for a definition of development based on human well-being, Dudley Seers (1972) asked, "Why do we confuse development with economic growth? . . . Development means the condition for the realization of the human personality. Its evaluation must therefore take into account three linked economic criteria: Whether there has been a reduction in (i) poverty; (ii) unemployment; (iii) inequality" (p. 21). He pointed out that some countries have experienced not only rapid growth of per capita income, but also increases in poverty, unemployment, and inequality. He urged for measures of development at the family level based on nutrition, health, infant mortality, access to education, and political participation.

Seers (1972) cited works indicating that during the United Nations Development Decade of the 1960s "the growth of economic inequality and unemployment may actually have accelerated" (p. 34). For example, in India, the much heralded Green Revolution, which depends on fertilizer and water inputs, has benefited mainly the farmers in the Punjab who were already wealthy and who owned large tracts of land (Wharton, 1969). Seers (1972) also urged the use of measures that indicate a degree of national independence. Among them, "the proportion of capital inflows in exchange receipts, the proportion of the supply of capital goods (or intermediates) which is imported, the proportion of assets, especially subsoil assets owned by foreigners, and the extent to which one trading partner dominates the pattern of aid and trade" (p. 30).

A related view of development goals was expressed by Denis Goulet (1971), who echoed Seers' concern: "There may be considerable merit . . . in asking whether higher living standards, self-sustained growth and modern institutions are good in themselves or necessarily constitute the highest priorities" (p. 85). Goulet

African children watching television. Although literacy levels increased between 1970 and 1990 in all but one country, literacy rates for women are still below 50% in 45 of the countries for which data are available. Literacy rates for men are below 50% in only 17 countries.
(*Source: UN/UNESCO/RACCAH Studio.*)

argued for three general development goals: life sustenance, esteem, and freedom.

LIFE SUSTENANCE

There can be no dispute that food, health, adequate shelter, and protection are essential to human well-being. When they are sufficient to meet human needs, a state of development exists; when they are insufficient, a degree of underdevelopment prevails.

ESTEEM

All people value respect. The feeling that "one is being treated as an individual who has worth, rather than as a tool for the satisfaction of other individuals'

purposes, is . . . the basic source of human contentment" (Hagen, 1968, pp. 411–412). Esteem or recognition is closely associated with material prosperity. Consequently, it is often difficult for those who are materially deprived or "underdeveloped" to experience a sense of pride or self-worth. Mass poverty prevents people and societies from receiving due recognition or esteem. These people may even reject development. For example, if people are humiliated or disillusioned through their contacts with the "progress" introduced by foreigners, they may return to their traditional ways in order to regain a sense of self-respect.

FREEDOM

Freedom can be defined as "the capacity, the opportunity to develop and express one's potentialities" (Warwick, 1968, p. 498). As with life sustenance and esteem, the degree to which freedom exists in a society can be used to assess development.

Donald Warwick (1968) asked students of development to "devote explicit attention to the values used in gauging progress [of individuals or societies]" (p. 498). Moreover, he remarked that it is not useful to define development in terms of urbanization, commercialization, industrialization, or modernization. Instead, he advised that development be viewed as a coordinated series of changes from a phase of life perceived by a population as being less human to a phase perceived as being more human.

Freedom of expression and achievement of a humane life-style are ultimate, essentially unresolvable issues. More down-to-earth development goals include the following: (1) a balanced, healthful diet; (2) adequate medical care; (3) environmental sanitation and disease control; (4) labor opportunities commensurate with individual talents; (5) sufficient educational opportunities; (6) individual freedom of conscience and freedom from fear; (7) decent housing; (8) economic activities in harmony with the natural environment; and (9) social and political milieus promoting equality.

In conventional usage, *development* is a synonym for economic growth. But growth is not development, except insofar as it enables a country to achieve the nine goals. If these goals are not the objectives of development, if modernization is merely a process of technological diffusion, and if spatial integration of world power and world economy is devoid of human referents, then *development* should be redefined. The realities of the contemporary world, however, do not offer much hope for achieving these humane objectives any time soon.

CHARACTERISTICS OF LESS DEVELOPED COUNTRIES

◈

Rapid Population Growth

Can we ascribe underdevelopment to rapid population growth? Yes, to a degree. After all, the present rapid increase of population is most apparent in underdeveloped countries, many of which have average annual population growth rates of at least 2.5%. It seems there are just too many millions of people in underdeveloped countries who must be fed, housed, clothed, educated, employed, cared for in illness, and, finally, looked after in old age. Most people would argue that these populations should be controlled if development is to take place.

Table 14.1 shows population statistics for various countries. The most striking dimension is the *annual population increase*. Keep in mind that a steady 2% annual population increase will double the population in 35 years. A 3% annual population increase means that the population will double in about 17 years. Population *densities* are also high in LDCs. These statistics show why such a large income gap exists between LDCs and industrially advanced countries (IACs) (see Table 14.2).

In many LDCs, the rapid population growth rates tax the food supplies. Becuse more mouths must be fed, less food is available per person, and some LDCs approach levels of subsistence and starvation. Perhaps the standard of living could be raised by producing more consumer goods and food in particular. But any increase in consumer goods and food production is likely to increase the population first, before it increases the standard of living. One reason for this is that the death rate, or mortality rate, declines with increased production. Higher per capita food consumption leads to better chances of survival and longer life spans. In addition, medical and sanitation improvements usually accompany the early stages of increased productivity and reduce the infant mortality rate. Kenya is a prime example of this phenomenon. Consequently, the relationship between a population increase and an increase in goods and food is a complex one. In the long run, a population increase will accompany an increase in the standard of living and will probably stop only when the standard of living again plunges to the bare subsistence level.

Rapid population growth also reduces the ability of households to save; therefore, the economy cannot accumulate investment capital. In addition, with rapid population growth, more investment is required by the government to maintain a level of real capital per person. If government investment fails to keep pace with the population growth, each worker will be less productive, having fewer tools and equipment with which to produce goods. This declining productivity results in reduced per capita incomes and economic stagnation. (See the section later in this chapter entitled Vicious Cycle of Poverty.)

Rapid population growth in agriculturally dependent countries, such as China and India, means that the land must be further subdivided and used more heavily than ever. Smaller plots from subdivision inevitably lead to overgrazing, overplanting, and the pressing need to increase food production for a growing population from a limited amount of space.

Many LDCs are rapidly urbanizing. Rapid population growth means large flows of rural farmers to urban areas and more urban problems. Housing, congestion, pollution, crime, and lack of medical attention are all seriously worsened by the rapid urban population growth.

Assuredly, a rapid increase in population—especially the number and proportion of young dependents—creates serious problems in terms of food supply, public education, and health and social services; it also intensifies the employment problem. However, a high rate of population growth was once a characteristic of present-day developed countries, and it did not prevent their development. This observation makes it difficult

◈

Table 14.1

Population Density and Increase, 1980–1990

	Population per Square Mile, 1990	Annual Rate of Population Increase, 1980–1990
United States	69	0.8
Bangladesh	2130	3.0
Venezuela	56	2.7
Haiti	573	1.2
Kenya	110	3.9
Pakistan	369	3.0
Philippines	570	2.6
India	669	2.1
World	101	1.7

◈

Table 14.2
GNP Per Capita, Population, and Growth Rates

	GNP Per Capita		Population	
	Dollars, 1989	Annual Growth Rate (%), 1965–1989	Millions, 1989	Annual Growth Rate (%), 1980–1989
Industrially advanced countries IACs (19 nations)	18,330	2.4	830	0.7
Less developed countries LDCs (97 nations)				
Middle income LDCs (56 nations)	2040	3.3	1105	2.1
Low income LDCs (41 nations)	330	2.9	2948	2.0

Source: World Bank, World Development Report, 1992.

to argue that population growth necessarily leads to underdevelopment or that population control necessarily aids development.

Unemployment and Underemployment

Is underdevelopment a product of unemployment and underemployment? Unemployment and underemployment are major problems in LDCs. *Unemployment* is a condition in which people who want to work cannot find jobs. *Underemployment* means that those people who are working are not able to work as many hours as they would like, usually much less than 8 hours per day. Reliable statistics on unemployment and underemployment in LDCs are difficult to obtain, but many scientists suggest that unemployment in these countries is approximately 20%.

Many of the cities in LDCs have recently experienced rapid flows of migrants from rural areas as a result of poor agricultural output and lack of land reform. This large number of migrants is created by the expectation of jobs and higher salaries in the cities. However, the cities usually have much higher unemployment rates than their rural counterparts. Once in the cities, many of the migrants cannot find work and contribute to the unemployment situation. Other migrants find limited amounts of work as shop clerks, handicraft peddlers, or street vendors. If you visit an LDC, such as Mexico, you can easily see that idleness in the shop or on the

street occupies a larger amount of time than work does. Although these people are not without jobs, they are without jobs that require substantial work and, therefore, they are underemployed.

Certainly, unemployment and underemployment do not lend themselves to development. However, they are not the sole reasons for underdevelopment.

Low Labor Productivity

Is underdevelopment a result of low labor productivity? It is true that a day's toil in an underdeveloped country produces very little compared with a day's work in a developed country. This is particularly evident in agriculture. American farmers spread their labor over 30 to 60 hectares; African or Asian farmers pour their energies into a hectare or so. As a consequence, human productivity in an underdeveloped country may be as little as one-fiftieth of that in a developed country. Why is this?

The populations of LDCs are not equipped for high productivity for several reasons. One reason is the small scale of operations. Another is that physical capital investment is extremely low. Rapid population growth has reduced the amount of investment available to maintain productivity. Most underdeveloped countries lack the machines, engines, power lines, and factories that enable people and resources to produce more than is possible with bare hands and simple tools. In addition,

LDCs are less able to invest in *human capital* (Table 14.3). Investments in human capital—such as education, health, and other social services, including provision of food—prepare a population to be productive workers. When an LDC lacks human capital, productivity is low.

Low labor productivity in LDCs is exacerbated by a lack of organizational skills and the absence of a management class, both of which are necessary for increased productivity. Workers have low skill levels, and few are able to handle supervisory jobs. Many of the most intelligent workers immigrate to IACs, where they are more highly paid for their labor. The United States and Europe, for example, are replete with some of the best-trained labor from LDCs, including doctors, engineers, mathematicians, and scientists who have come looking for more challenging work and better support services from companies or the government. This immigration has contributed to a so-called *brain drain*, whereby LDCs lose talented people to IACs. The U.S. immigration policy has encouraged the brain drain as well.

Although it must be acknowledged that low labor productivity is a universal attribute of underdevelopment, it is not a *causative* factor. The important question to consider is this: What prevents labor productivity from improving in underdeveloped countries?

Adverse Climate and Lack of Natural Resources

Can underdevelopment be traced to an adverse climate, insufficient rainfall, poor soils, and a lack of mineral resources? Yes, to a degree. Obviously, the uneven allocation of the gifts of nature makes development more difficult in some areas than in others. East Africa is a case in point. Large areas of East Africa have poor soils and little, unpredictable rainfall. The dry, wooded steppe in the rain shadow of Mount Meru, Tanzania, is on the arid margins of agriculture, and supports Masai pastoralists at low population densities. In contrast, large numbers of East African farmers live in better-watered areas—along the coast, near the lakes, and in the highlands. For example, in the Kigezi district of southwest Uganda, fertile volcanic soils and ample rainfall make agriculture highly productive on carefully terraced hillsides. In many densely populated areas of East Africa, the main problems are not environmental but economic and political.

Some LDCs have sizable natural-resource endowments of minerals such as bauxite, copper, tin, tungsten, nitrates, and petroleum. The Organization of Petroleum Exporting Countries (OPEC) is an example of LDCs that have used their resource endowments for rapid economic growth. In other cases, natural resources in

Table 14.3

Selected Socioeconomic Indicators of Development

Country	Per Capita GNP ($), 1989	Life Expectancy at Birth in Years, 1989	Infant Mortality per 1000 Live Births, 1989	Adult Literacy Rate (%), 1985	Daily per Capita Calorie Supply, 1988	Per Capita Energy Consumption, 1989*
Japan	23,810	79	4	99	2848	3484
United States	20,910	76	10	99	3666	7794
Brazil	2,540	66	59	78	2709	897
Mauritania	500	46	123	17	2528	114
Haiti	360	55	94	5	1911	51
India	340	59	95	43	2104	226
Bangladesh	180	51	106	33	1925	51
Ethiopia	120	48	133	5	1658	20
Mozambique	80	49	137	28	1632	84

* Kilograms of oil equivalent.
Source: World Bank, World Development Report, 1992, and U.S. Bureau of the Census, 1991.

This market near Toussiana in Burkina Faso exemplifies the so-called traditional sector of a Third World country. *(Source: UNESCO/Labordiére.)*

LDCs are controlled by multinational corporations (MNCs), who divert their profits abroad to their home countries. Still other LDCs just lack mineral and petroleum deposits and have little arable land.

Limited natural resources can pose a serious developmental problem for LDCs. An LDC may be able to receive grants from more prosperous nations and to train workers to increase output, but increasing the supply of natural resources is impossible in most cases. With few natural resources, certain LDCs may be unwise if they expect to achieve development levels such as those of Germany and Japan. On the other hand, we must be careful not to entirely rule out the potential for high levels of development just because an LDC lacks natural resources. For example, Japan, Israel, Switzerland, Ireland, Norway, and Singapore achieved high levels of development despite a dearth of natural resources. Likewise, the Netherlands has, for centuries, obtained its necessary resources through various long-distance trading connections.

It is untenable to attribute underdevelopment solely to a lack of resources or a poor climate. Vagaries of weather, exposure to natural disasters such as flood or drought, and danger of soil erosion are not exclusive to the underdeveloped world. Despite technological advances in North America, Europe, and the former Soviet Union, climate still poses recurring problems for farmers in these countries. Furthermore, as we said, some developed countries have unfavorable natural-resource endowments, yet they were able to develop.

Lack of Capital and Investment

Is underdevelopment attributable to a lack of capital and investment? Most LDCs suffer from a lack of capital accumulation in the form of machinery, equipment, factories, public utilities, and infrastructure in general. The more capital, the more tools available for each worker, thus a close relationship exists between output per worker and per capita income. If a nation expects to increase its output, it must find ways to increase per capita income. Furthermore, an increase in the investment of an individual country will increase its gross domestic product (GDP).

In most cases, increasing the amount of arable land for an LDC is no longer a possibility. Most cultivable land is already in use, as we learned in Chapter 4. Therefore, capital accumulation for an LDC must come from savings and investment. If an LDC can save, rather than spend all its income, and invest some of its earnings, resources will be released from the production of consumer goods and be available for the production of capital goods, as we saw with the production-possibilities curve analysis in Chapter 2. But barriers to saving and investing are high in LDCs. The United States has had notable problems in the recent past with savings and investing. An LDC has even less margin for savings and investing, particularly when domestic output is so low that all of it must be used to support the many needs of the country. Ethiopia, Bangladesh, Uganda, Haiti, and Madagascar save between 2% and 3% of their domestic outputs. In 1989, India and China managed to save an average of 27% of their domestic outputs compared with 33% for Japan, 25% for West Germany, and 10% for the United States.

Many LDCs have suffered from *capital flight*, which means that individuals in these countries have invested and deposited their monies in overseas ventures and in banks in IACs for safekeeping. They have done so for fear of expropriation by politically unstable governments, future unfavorable exchange rates brought on by hyperinflation in the LDCs, high levels of taxation, and the possibility of business and bank failure. World Bank statistics for 1992 suggest that inflows of foreign aid and bank loans to LDCs were almost completely offset by capital flight. By 1990, for example, Mexicans were estimated to have held about $100 billion in assets abroad. This amount is roughly equal to their international debt. Venezuela, Argentina, and Brazil also have foreign holdings between $30 and $60 billion each.

Finally, investment obstacles in LDCs have impeded capital accumulation. The two main problems with investment in LDCs are (1) lack of investment opportunities comparable to those available in IACs and (2) lack of incentives to invest locally. We just discussed investment abroad, but what deters local investment? Usually LDCs have lower levels of domestic spending per person, so their markets are weak compared with those of advanced nations. Factors that keep the markets weak are a lack of demand, a lack of trained personnel to manage and sell products at the local level, and a lack of government support to ensure stability. There is also a lack of infrastructure to provide transportation, management, energy production, and community services—housing, education, public health—which are needed to improve the environment for investment activity.

Again, a shortage of capital and low investment are not causative factors of underdevelopment. But the important point is to understand what prevents capital from accumulating in LDCs.

Lack of Technology

Can underdevelopment be attributed to the absence of technology? Yes, to a degree. LDCs lack the basic technological advances necessary for creating capital and for applying methods to increase productivity and accumulate wealth. The IACs already have a large body of research and high-level technology from which the LDCs could draw. In the past, technological borrowing from advanced nations occurred in the Pacific Rim countries of Hong Kong, Singapore, South Korea, and Taiwan. In addition, OPEC nations benefited from the IACs' advanced technology in oil exploration, drilling, and refining. Today, the former Soviet Union countries desire technology from North America to aid their fledgling economies. Unfortunately, for LDCs to put this available technology to use, they must have a certain level of capital goods (machinery, factories, etc.), which they by and large do not possess. The need is to channel the flow of technologically superior capital goods that have high levels of reliability to the developing nations so that they can improve their output.

In IACs, technology has been developed primarily to save labor and to increase output. This technology has been capital intensive. However, in LDCs the reverse is needed. The large pool of unskilled labor must not be supplanted by new technology. LDCs need capital-saving technology that is labor intensive. Therefore, much of the mid-latitude technology of the IACs is unsuited for low-latitude agricultural systems. The same is true for advanced technologies in the manufacturing and service sectors.

In LDCs, there is a strong inertia to maintain traditional production methods, in agriculture and in industry, so that a basic level of food can be maintained and starvation can be avoided. If a new technological application fails, even only temporarily, malnutrition and starvation will not hesitate to overcome these coun-

Information is the capital commodity of the 1990s. Individual access will increase, and information will be used as a means to gain wealth and power. Most of the peoples of the world will not participate in this revolution. The implications will be profound.
(Source: Frederick P. Stutz.)

tries. Consequently, LDCs must be very traditional and conservative when they borrow technology.

Cultural Factors

Can cultural factors account for underdevelopment? Perhaps in part. Economic factors and forces of nature are not sufficient in themselves to explain the poverty cycle and attributes of LDCs. Economic development frequently involves a new world view and a willingness to accept changes in resource utilization, changes in customs and traditions that frequently hamper the developmental process. Whether we like it or not, we must acknowledge that economic development is a change of the person—the way he or she thinks, does business, operates, and maintains relationships with other members of society. If the will to change is strong, economic development is more likely to take place. If there is little will to develop and a particular group within society is unwilling to change its ways of doing things, economic development is less likely to occur.

Tribal allegiances in Africa, for example, are stronger than national allegiances are. Warring tribes dilute economic efficiency and hamper economic development because of the political and economic disorganization associated with defending territories and ways of livelihood. Yugoslavia has likewise disintegrated because of ethnic clashes.

Religious beliefs in some nations hamper economic development because of a built-in resistance to change. For example, in India, a highly religious nation, it has been estimated that 8% of the per capita income is spent on religious ceremonial activities, to the economic detriment of most families who are desperately struggling to provide for themselves. Another impediment to economic development is *fatalism*, which dominates the populations of some LDCs. Fatalism is the religious or philosophical belief that future life conditions will not improve, regardless of the amount of work or effort involved. Fatalism is widespread in India. In Africa, a similar condition could be called the "capricious cosmos." The individual sees no correlation between personal actions and the experiences or outcome in the future. Both attitudes impinge on all aspects of life, including family planning, work, savings, investment, effort, and relationships with other individuals.

Finally, the existence of a strong social stratification system or a caste system works against peoples in developing countries. If better jobs, education, and positions in society are allocated according to one's class, a certain feeling of futility develops. People are less likely to work hard or to attempt to improve their status with so little incentive.

Political Factors

Do institutional and political factors play a certain role in underdevelopment? Yes. Petty politics and inept social service administration create certain problems for LDCs. In Nigeria, for example, 20% of the oil profits are stolen every year. The institutional situation in other LDCs such as Somalia is totally out of control. Political corruption and bribery are commonplace in Latin America, for example, and are actually expected as a way of life. Political decisions and even laws are interpreted according to individual whim and personal gain. Throughout much of the developing world, land reform, which is vitally important to increased agricultural output, is lacking because the government is too inept to redistribute the land owned by a few wealthy families. For some nations, such as the Philippines, land reform is the single most pressing problem deterring them from economic development. In contrast, strong action taken by the South Korean government after the Korean War allowed for increased productivity and the development of an industrial and commercial middle class that made South Korea one of the true success stories of the Pacific Rim.

Vicious Cycle of Poverty

Is underdevelopment the consequence of a catalog of causally related internal factors? The idea of causal links between attributes of underdevelopment is sum-

marized in the often-used expression *vicious cycle of poverty*. Vicious-cycle explanations emphasize the multicausality of underdevelopment. These explanations suggest that it is not "just" a lack of ambition, or "just" an absence of specialization, or "just" a low output per capita, or "just" a population problem, or even "just" a political problem that holds back underdeveloped countries. Rather, a combination of interwoven limiting factors thwarts development. An example of a vicious cycle is shown in Figure 1.5. According to Hungarian economist Tamás Szentes (1971), "the main weakness of the vicious cycle theories is that they reveal neither the historical circumstances out of which the assumed 'magic' circle originated, nor the underlying socioeconomic relations and the fundamental, determinant causes" (p. 54).

The specification of *limiting factors* illustrates the gravity of the problem of underdevelopment. But some scholars go further and use limiting factors as a starting point for certain theories of underdevelopment. For example, internal factors hindering development often serve the view that underdevelopment is an original

A

B

Consumers in relatively developed countries of the world obtain their food in supermarkets, such as the one shown (a). Abundance, availability, and great variety are the norm at grocery stores throughout the United States. However, three-fourths of the population of the world have food that is much less available. If developing countries produce a food surplus, it may be sold at a market such as this one (b) near Bangkok, Thailand.
(Source: Richard Hayman, Photo Researchers, Inc., and Susan McCartney, Photo Researchers, Inc.)

state or a lagging behind in the development of productive forces.

THE LESS DEVELOPED COUNTRIES' DEBT CRISIS

◈

The foreign debt of LDCs has grown significantly during the last two decades. The debt is owed to foreign governments and to private banks. The total debt of nations in trouble as of 1993 exceeded $900 billion, and most LDCs that are heavily in debt are experiencing difficulties in repaying their debts. All LDCs, including those who are not experiencing debt-payback difficulties, owe IAC governments and banks more than $1.5 trillion. According to the World Bank, this represents approximately 30% of the combined GNPs of the LDCs. Table 12.4 lists some of the more heavily indebted LDCs as of 1990. This table lists the absolute amount of each country's debt as well as the proportion of debt compared with annual GNP. Some nations, notably Argentina and Nigeria, have debts in excess of 100% of their annual GNPs.

Causes of the Debt Crisis

In the 1970s and 1980s, LDCs took out large loans from IACs. These loans were granted with the expectation of future growth of the LDC economies. But a series of major economic changes in the world scene meant that many of these loans could not be repaid.

The Arab oil embargoes of 1973 and 1978 sent the price of crude oil from $8 a barrel to $35 a barrel. It has since dropped significantly and currently hovers at $20 a barrel on the world markets. However, the phenomenal oil prices created a cash-flow crisis for oil-importing LDCs. Oil-importing LDCs, as well as some of the oil-producing LDCs, based their expectations of future development on inexpensive oil. From 1973 onward, these nations faced increased foreign deficits because they had to continue to borrow money so that oil could flow into their nations. These borrowed funds increased their debt crisis. Furthermore, monies spent for oil could have been used for economic development, such as for increased infrastructure, improved education, and needed agricultural reforms. The debt of oil-

importing LDCs grew from $150 billion in 1973 to $800 billion by 1985. Even oil-exporting nations such as Mexico, Libya, and Nigeria overborrowed to build economic strength based on their expectations of rapidly inflated oil prices, and, therefore, profits. When oil prices fell from $35 a barrel to $15 a barrel in the mid-1980s, these nations found themselves with debts that they could not afford.

Another blow to LDCs occurred between 1980 and 1985, when the U.S. dollar appreciated in value on world markets. Because many of the goods imported by LDCs were based on dollar value, the prices of these goods increased and foreign exchange decreased. This meant that the LDCs had to produce more domestic goods in order to import the same level of foreign goods. They also needed to export more goods to compensate for each dollar's worth of debt—and interest on the debt—because most LDC loans were denominated in U.S. dollars.

Finally, some of the LDCs, notably Mexico, Brazil, and Argentina, have been on the verge of bankruptcy. These countries required the IACs to rewrite their loans and cancel or *write-down* a portion of the principal and interest. Creditor banks in the United States were required to rewrite loans and even to increase loans. The result was a loss of confidence in the future ability of many LDCs to repay. The stocks of the creditor banks fell, and some CEOs were replaced. At the same time, in the early to mid-1980s, the United States experienced a large budget deficit that continues into 1994. To finance the payback of this deficit, the U.S. government issued bonds. The issuance of bonds on the world market absorbed a large portion of investor revenue that would have been absorbed by LDCs as loans and private capital flows, thus they were further deprived of the ability to grow and pay off their debts.

Higher oil prices, a decreased ability to produce goods and sell them on the world market, higher world interest rates, a valuation of the U.S. dollar, and a decline in public and private lending to LDCs because of loss of confidence all contributed to the enormous LDC debt crisis that prevails today. As mentioned, these difficulties triggered banking problems in the IACs, particularly in America. For example, in the mid-1980s, Citicorp and Chase Manhattan Bank determined that a large portion of the LDC debt would never be repaid. This threatened Citicorp's banking and financial system because a large portion of the LDC debt had to be written off as uncollectible. The International Monetary Fund (IMF) chose to attack this problem and to deal with each nation on an individual basis in an attempt to solve the debt problems. Many nations were able to rewrite their debts and schedule them for longer periods as long as their governments agreed to implement austerity programs. In order to invoke domestic austerity programs, these nations had to reduce imports and expand exports, which further reduced their living standards. Even so, from 1980 to 1990, the GDP for LDCs as a whole increased 3.8% per year, partly as a result of the agreements with the IMF. In comparison, the rate for IACs was only 2%. This enormous growth amidst economic difficulty is proof that, in certain cases, LDCs can improve their plight and, in time, join the ranks of the advanced nations.

HOW ECONOMIC DEVELOPMENT IS MEASURED

◙

Geographers measure economic development through a number of social, economic, and demographic indexes.

Per Capita Income

Per capita income is a statistic that is seldom readily available to economic geographers. However, the GNP and the population of a country are more easily acquired. Consequently, by dividing GNP by the number of people in a country, the economic geographer can determine GNP per capita. GNP per capita is more than $15,000 in most highly developed nations. At the same time, the United Nations estimates that 1 billion people live on less than $1 a day, or $365 per capita per year. Japan, North America, Western Europe, Australia, and New Zealand have the highest per capita incomes in the world. The Middle East, Latin America, South Asia, East Asia, Southeast Asia, and sub-Saharan Africa have the lowest. Income and GNP figures for former Soviet Union countries, portions of Eastern Europe, Iraq, Iran, Afghanistan, and portions of Southeast Asia were unavailable in 1990.

Per capita purchasing power is a more meaningful measure of actual income per person (Figure 14.1). The relative purchasing power in developed nations is more than $10,000 per capita per year, whereas in Africa it

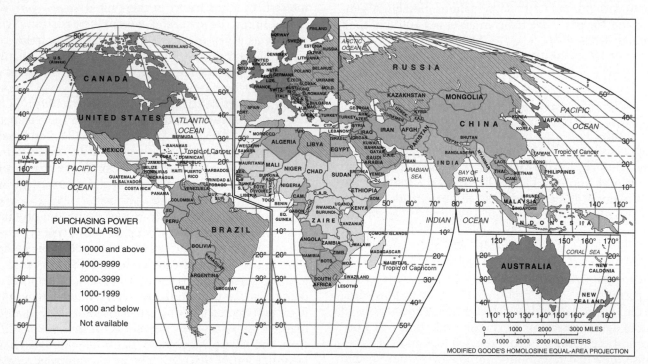

FIGURE 14.1
Per capita purchasing power. Per capita purchasing power is a better measure of a country's relative wealth than is GNP per capita because it includes the relative prices of products. For example, Switzerland, Sweden, and Japan have higher per capita GNPs than the United States. However, the United States has the world's highest per capita purchasing power because of relatively low prices for food, housing, fuel, general merchandise, and services (see "Purchasing Power Parity" box in Chapter 13).

is much less than $1000 per capita per year. Per capita purchasing power includes not only income, but the price of goods in a country. The United States is surpassed by Japan, Switzerland, and Germany in per capita income. However, it surpasses all countries in per capita purchasing power because goods and services are relatively inexpensive in America compared with those in other IACs. Although a Big Mac at McDonald's may cost as little as 99¢ in America, it costs as much as $6 in Europe and $10 in Japan. Prices in IACs, especially for food, are generally higher outside the United States. (See "Purchasing Power Parity" box in Chapter 13.)

Economic Structure of the Labor Force

The economic structure of a country also bespeaks its economic development. Economic geographers divide employment into four categories:

1. The *primary sector* mainly involves the extraction of materials from the earth—mining, lumbering, agriculture, and fishing.

2. The *secondary sector* includes assembling raw materials and manufacturing.

3. The *tertiary sector* is devoted to the provision of services—most notably wholesaling, retailing, and professional and personal services, including medical, legal, and entertainment.

4. The *quaternary sector* of the economy includes information processing, such as finance, insurance, real estate, education, and computer-related fields.

We learned in Chapter 7 that fewer than 2% of the workers in America and Western Europe are engaged in agriculture, whereas in certain African nations, India, and China, more than 70% of the laborers are in the primary, or agricultural, sector. More than 75% of U.S. laborers are in the tertiary and quaternary sectors.

Consumer Goods Produced

The quantity and quality of consumer goods purchased and distributed in a society is also a good measure of the level of economic development in that society. A large amount of consumer goods means that a country's economic resources have fulfilled the basic human needs of shelter, clothing, and food, and more resources are left over to provide nonessential household goods and services. Televisions, automobiles, home electronics, jewelry, watches, refrigerators, and washing machines are some of the major consumer goods produced worldwide on varying scales. Figure 14.2 shows persons per telephones and Figure 14.3 shows the number of televisions per 1000 people worldwide for 1970 and 1991. In IACs, more than one television, telephone, or automobile exists for every two people. In developing nations, only a few of these products exist for a thousand people. For instance, the ratio of persons to television sets in developing countries is 150 to 1, and population to automobiles is 400 to 1. In California, the ratio for these consumer items is almost 1 to 1. The number of consumer goods such as telephones and televisions per capita is a good indicator of a country's level of economic development.

Education and Literacy of a Population

The more men and women who attend school, usually the higher the level of economic development in a country. Unfortunately, in the world today, only 75 women attend school for every 100 men who attend. Some areas of the world are particularly disadvantageous to women's education (Figure 14.4). The regions that have low percentages of women attending secondary school also generally have poor social and economic conditions for women.

The *literacy rate* of a country is the proportion of people in the society who can read and write. Figure 14.5 shows the literacy rates of men and women worldwide, and Figure 14.6 shows the literacy rates of women only. Comparing these two figures, one can clearly see that in some countries the percentage of women who can read and write is much lower than that of men. In many nations, the literacy rate of women is less than 25%, whereas the literacy rate of men is between 25% and 75%. The Middle East and South Asia, where the role of women is clearly subservience to men, show the greatest disparities. However, in the highly developed world of the IACs, the literacy rates of men and women are almost identical. In addition, because more people can read and write, a proliferation of newspapers, magazines, and scholarly journals improve and foster communication and exchange, which leads to further development.

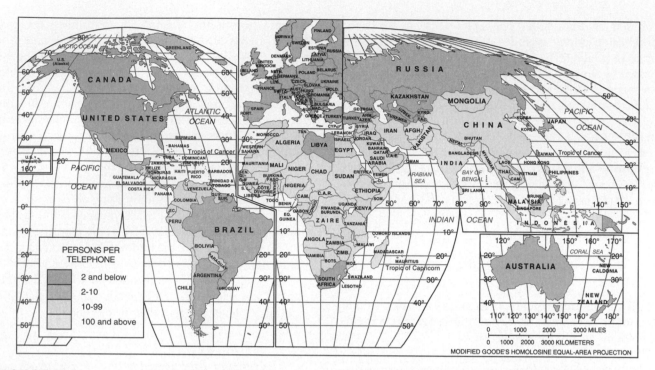

FIGURE 14.2
Persons per telephone. Developing countries have several hundred persons per telephone, while relatively developed countries have two persons per telephone. The United States is approaching one person per telephone and will soon surpass this ratio with the proliferation of cellular phones. (See color insert, page 3.6, top.)

Health and Welfare of a Population

Measures of health and welfare, in general, are much higher in developed nations than in LDCs. One measure of health and welfare is diet. Most people in Africa do not receive the U.N. daily recommended allowance. However, in developed nations, the population consumes approximately one-third more than the minimum daily requirement and are therefore able to maintain a higher level of health. In all cases, the figures represent averages. Naturally, in some areas of each country calories and food supplies are insufficient, even in the United States.

People in developed nations also have better access to doctors, hospitals, and medical specialists. Figure 14.7 shows worldwide access to physicians and health care.

For relatively developed nations, there is one doctor for 1000 people, but in developing countries, each person shares a doctor with many thousands of others. Africa by far has the worst access to health care, followed by Southeast Asia and the East Indies. Portions of the Middle East are also lacking in medical care.

Demographic Characteristics

IACs have much lower infant mortality rates than those of LDCs. In developed nations, on the average, fewer than 10 babies in 1000 die within the first 100 days. In many less developed nations, more than 100 babies die per 1000 live births. Paradoxically, as noted

FIGURE 14.3
Televisions per 1000 population 1970 (top) and 1991 (bottom). Televisions have diffused from North America to the rest of the world. The diffusion is not completed, however, as some countries in Africa and South Asia have less than 10 televisions per 1000 population. In 1954, the United States had almost 200 television sets per 1000 inhabitants, while Argentina, Germany, Italy, Japan, the Netherlands, Spain, Sweden, and Switzerland had less than one. (See color insert, page 3.5.)

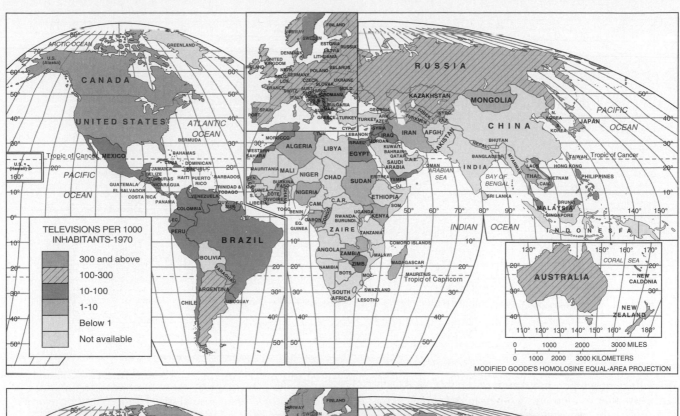

TELEVISIONS PER 1000
INHABITANTS-1970

300 and above

100-300

10-100

1-10

Below 1

Not available

MODIFIED GOODE'S HOMOLOSINE EQUAL-AREA PROJECTION

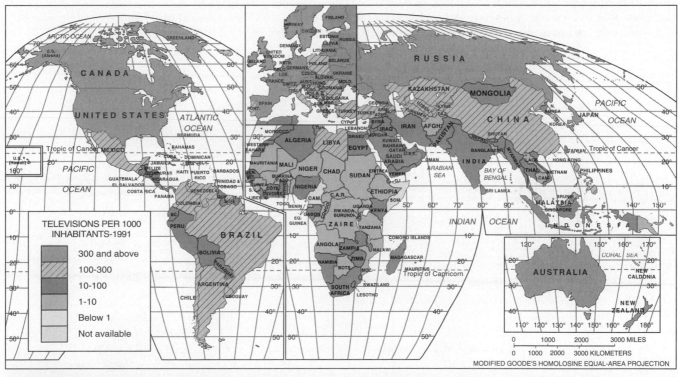

TELEVISIONS PER 1000
INHABITANTS-1991

300 and above

100-300

10-100

1-10

Below 1

Not available

MODIFIED GOODE'S HOMOLOSINE EQUAL-AREA PROJECTION

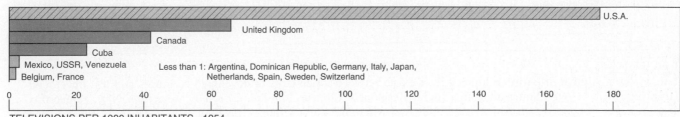

U.S.A.

United Kingdom

Canada

Cuba

Mexico, USSR, Venezuela

Belgium, France

Less than 1: Argentina, Dominican Republic, Germany, Italy, Japan,
Netherlands, Spain, Sweden, Switzerland

0   20   40   60   80   100   120   140   160   180

TELEVISIONS PER 1000 INHABITANTS - 1954

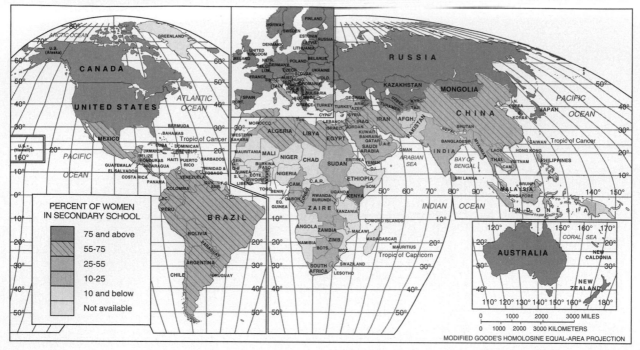

FIGURE 14.4

Percentage of women in secondary schools. In developing countries, the percentage of women in secondary schools is far below that of men and women in developed countries. This fosters lower educational development among women and lowers the prospects for economic development and gender equality. (See color insert, page 3.6, bottom.)

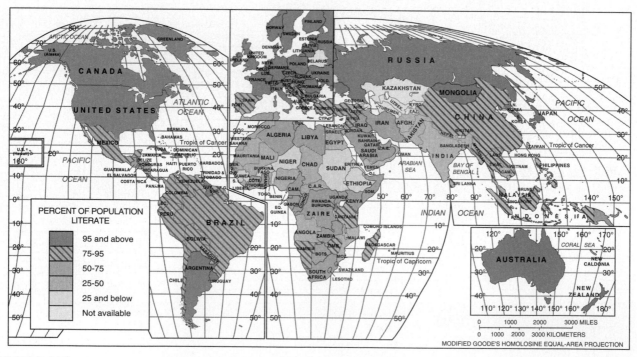

FIGURE 14.5

Literacy rate. A great disparity in literacy rates exists between inhabitants of developed countries and less developed countries. In the United States and other highly developed countries, the literacy rate is more than 98%. Notice the large number of countries in Africa and South Asia where the literacy rate is less than 50%. (See color insert 3, page 3.7, top.)

640

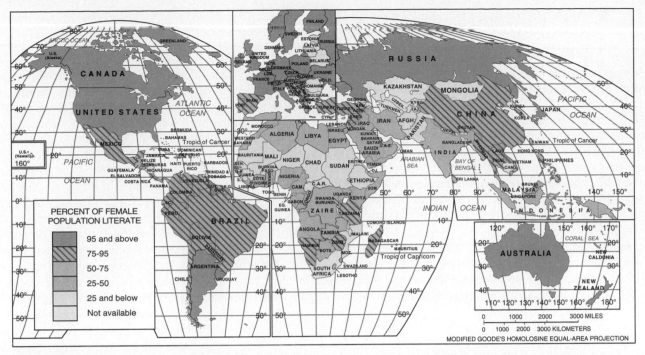

FIGURE 14.6

Literacy rate of women. The gender gap for literacy is most pronounced in the developing world, especially Africa, South Asia, and the Middle East. In most developing countries, the female literacy rate is much below the rate for men. (See color insert 3, page 3.7, bottom.)

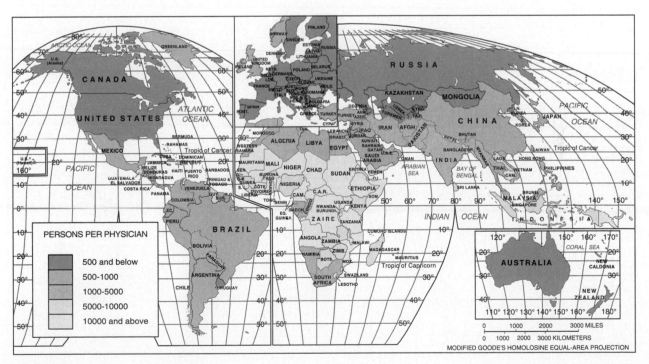

FIGURE 14.7

Persons per physician. An important measure of economic development is the number of persons per physician in a country. This measure is a surrogate for health care access, which includes hospital beds, medicine, and nurses and doctors. Most of Africa exhibits 10,000 people per physician or more, while Europe and the United States average approximately one doctor for every 200 people. (See color insert, page 3.8, top.)

in Chapter 3, even though the infant mortality rate is higher in developing nations, the natural rate of increase and the crude birth rate are higher as well. Some developing nations show a 3% per annum growth, which means that the population doubles in 17 years, although the average for LDCs is closer to 2%, with a doubling time of 35 years. In contrast, most developed nations have a less than 0.8% relative increase per year, and a few nations are at zero population growth (ZPG). LDCs average 40 live births per 1000 population, while IACs average 10.

Age structures also differ substantially. In developing nations, as many as 50% of the people are younger than age 15. In IACs, however, median ages range from 30 to 40, and life expectancy is longer (Figure 14.8).

Total Human Development

Figure 2.2 shows the six developing regions of the world—Latin America, the Middle East, East Asia, Southeast Asia, South Asia, and sub-Saharan Africa. It also shows the six developed regions of the world—Japan, Western Europe, the South Pacific, Anglo-America, Eastern Europe/former Soviet Union, and South Africa. The boundaries of each of these so-called *world cultural realms* follow continental outlines and major political boundaries or climatic zones. Each region has more highly and less highly developed regions within it. For example, Latin America varies dramatically, from the more advanced nations of Argentina and Venezuela to the less advanced nations of Bolivia, Paraguay, and Guyana. Within each cultural realm, similarities of language, religion, race, population characteristics, and economic development characteristics exist. But with all the differences among nations and realms, how can their development levels be compared?

The United Nations devised a way to measure total human development, a *Human Development Index* (HDI), which combines three development factors: life expectancy (a demographic factor), literacy rate (a social factor), and per capita purchasing power (an economic factor). Because it includes all three factors—social, demographic, and economic—it is a useful index, even though the variables selected are somewhat arbitrary (Figure 14.9). The index is a standardized scale, where the highest possible value is 1.0 and the lowest is zero.

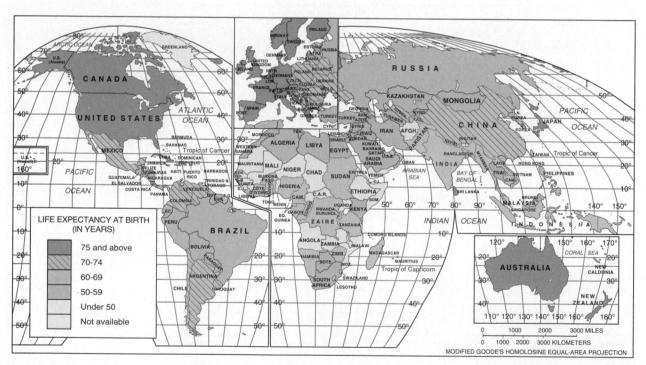

FIGURE 14.8
Life expectancy at birth. Life expectancy at birth reflects access to health care and food. For the world as a whole, babies born this year will live to their mid-60s. Life expectancy at birth actually ranges from the high 70s in Canada, the United States, Europe, and Japan, to the mid-60s in most Latin American and Middle Eastern countries, Russia, and China, to the mid-40s in most African nations. (See color insert, page 1.4, top.)

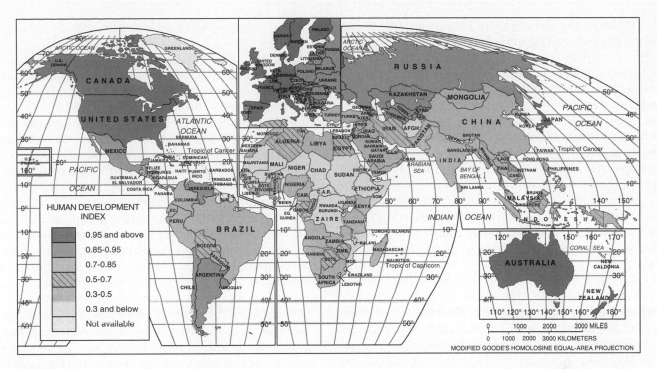

FIGURE 14.9
The Human Development Index is perhaps the best overall measure of economic development. The United Nations constructs a single index measuring life expectancy at birth, per capita purchasing power, years of schooling, and literacy rates (see Table 14.4 for actual values by cultural realm). Northwestern Europe is clearly distinguished from the remainder of Europe. Central America and Bolivia have the lowest scores for Latin America. Sub-Saharan Africa, South Asia, and Southeast Asia have the lowest scores overall. (See color insert 3, page 3.8, bottom.)

The minimum for each index was set as the lowest level actually observed; for example, the minimum index for literacy was 12%, which was Somalia's rate. Overall, Anglo-America and Japan had the highest human development score, 0.98, followed by Australia and New Zealand with 0.97, and Western Europe with 0.95. The lowest scores were in sub-Saharan Africa, which averaged 0.23. Nigeria, for example, had a literacy rate of 14%, a per capita purchasing power of $450, and a life expectancy of 45 years (Table 14.4).

MAJOR PERSPECTIVES ON DEVELOPMENT

◎

Development is usually equated with economic growth (Partant, 1982). The following definition of A. Eugene Havens and William Flinn (1975) is characteristic:

Development . . . involves three interrelated societal activities: (1) the establishment of increased wealth and income as a perceived, attainable goal for the broader masses of society; (2) the creation and/or selection of adequate means to attain this goal; and (3) the restructuring of society so that there is persistent economic growth. (p. 469)

◎

Table 14.4
Human Development Index, 1993

Less Developed Regions		Industrially Advanced Regions	
Latin America	.76	Japan	.98
East Asia	.61	Anglo-America	.98
Southeast Asia	.52	Australia/New Zealand	.97
Middle East	.51	Western Europe	.95
South Asia	.29	Eastern Europe	.87
Sub-Saharan Africa	.23	South Africa	.67

"Theories" of development have existed for many years. The earliest of them can be traced to the classical economists. But discussion of the term *development* in the social sciences is fairly recent. It was not required before the collapse of the colonial system or before the onset of the Cold War between the United States and the USSR for power and influence in the world. Since the late 1940s, however, the problem of how to accelerate the pace of development in roughly 100 ex-colonial countries has generated intense interest among planners and in the academic world.

Three groups of perspectives on development can be identified in terms of the scale upon which they concentrate (national, global) and whether or not development is defined exclusively in terms of economic growth. The first and most widely accepted theories of development are *modernization theories*. These concentrate on the national scale and define development in terms of economic growth and Westernization. Their underlying assumption is that modernization influences are projected to peripheral regions from Western Europe and North America; hence, the path to progress from traditional to modern is unidirectional. In this view, rich industrial countries, without rival in social, economic, and political development, are modern, whereas poor countries must undergo the modernization process to acquire these traits (Pletsch, 1981; Tipps, 1973).

The second group of theories are *world political economy theories*. They focus on the structure of political and economic relationships between dominant and dominated countries. They pay special attention to the global history of economic growth that brought poor countries to their present position (Agnew, 1982). Their underlying assumption is that the poverty of the Third World is the outcome of a worldwide network of intrusion by the rich countries into the poor.

Theories that make up a third group come from scholars who wonder whether certain kinds of development are desirable, and if, indeed, development will ever materialize for people in underdeveloped countries. These *ecopolitical economy theories* concentrate on the ecological and cultural consequences of economic growth. Their proponents are disenchanted with research that (1) neglects the diverse value systems and world views of societies engaged in the process of development, (2) equates development with economic growth, (3) advocates the trickle-down theory of benefits to the poor instead of the channeling of resources directly into basic human needs, and (4) ascribes no merit whatsoever to the contributions of indigenous systems to the development process (Yapa, 1980).

Modernization Theories

The best-known modernization theories are *growth-stage theories,* and the one most often cited was advanced by economic historian Walt W. Rostow (1960). He identified in European history five stages of growth: (1) the traditional society, (2) the transition or preconditioning stage, (3) takeoff, (4) the drive to maturity, and (5) the stage of high mass consumption (Figure 14.10). According to Rostow, this sequence can be used as a framework for the national development of underdeveloped countries. The problem is to get poor countries, which must pass through these stages in order to develop, into that crucial third stage, after which sufficient surplus is generated to sustain economic growth. It is necessary in the takeoff stage to reallocate a punishing amount of annual production for reinvestment—the equivalent of 10% of national income each year. The underdeveloped country is treated as a self-contained unit that generates its own transformation. Agriculture is the most important sector in the transformation from traditional to modern society, and technology plays a decisive role in development by transforming subsistence agriculture into commercial agriculture. According to some modernization theorists, commercialization of agriculture is the central feature of development (Mellor, 1962; Wharton, 1963).

The most widely accepted economic theory of underdevelopment is that of the *dual economy*—one sector modern and tied through export, organization, capital support, and use of technology to the developed countries of Europe and North America; the other sector traditional and engaged in subsistence activities (Higgins, 1956; Lewis, 1954). These sectors, according to the theory, exist independently, yet side by side, in the underdeveloped country. An additional assumption of the theory is that the traditional sector is at one end of a continuum of development. The concern of dual-economy theorists is to generate interaction between the two sectors. For example, W. Arthur Lewis (1954) observed that increases in agricultural productivity are central to the modernization process because they permit the movement of surplus labor from the traditional agricultural sector to the modern industrial sector.

Modernization and *institutional reform theories* are the domain of sociologists, psychologists, and political scientists (Cochran, 1966; Hagen, 1962; McClelland, 1961; Said, 1981; Tipps, 1973). Development is viewed as dependent on transforming a stagnant, traditional society that lacks the qualities, propensities, motivations, and incentives of advanced capitalist society. It

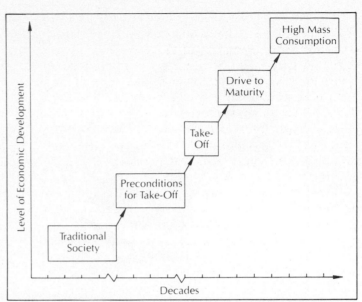

FIGURE 14.10
Rostow's five stages of economic growth. This sequence is a framework for the national economic development of underdeveloped countries. Each country must pass through these stages in order to develop. The crucial stage is the take-off stage, after which surplus production and capital is generated by a country to facilitate economic growth in the last two stages.

requires the spread of a strong achievement orientation, a profit incentive, a willingness to take entrepreneurial risks, and the institutionalization of efficiency and productivity.

Geographic studies of modernization have drawn on the ideas of economists, sociologists, historians, and political scientists, and have relied strongly on two concepts to explain how the nation and its space economy develop. These concepts are (1) unilinear evolution of societies, epitomized by Rostow's stages of economic growth and (2) growth of and diffusion within a world hierarchy of urban centers.

Peter Gould (1964) spearheaded the study of modernization as a spatial diffusion process. The modernization theme exemplified by geographers who followed the lead of Gould dealt explicitly at the macroscale with the evolving structure of urban places, the interconnections of these places through transportation and communication, and the penetration of indigenous social systems by Western elements of modernization (Gould, 1970; Riddell, 1970; Soja, 1968). Gould (1970) argued that the diffusion of Western elements of modernization would promote the downfall of traditional societies. In his study of the spatial impress of the modernization process in Tanzania, he interpreted modernization, as defined by a host of infrastructural variables such as roads, railways, telephones, postal stations, hospitals, schools, and administrative offices, as diffusion outward from foreign enclaves. His modernization surface maps (Figure 14.11) and accompanying descriptions indicate that beyond towns, and in some cases their rich agricul-

tural hinterlands, levels of modernization decrease sharply. Peripheral areas are illustrated in the sequence of maps as shrinking areas of "no modernization." Gould (1970) noted that in the 1920s a few islands of development were focused on Dar es Salaam and the lower order centers of Tanga, Mwanza, and Tabora that "float in the still mill-pond of traditionalism" (p. 156). By the 1960s, the spatial pattern of modernization was more widespread and intense, but the larger towns remained the major centers of change.

World Political Economy Theories

World-system theory provides a framework for understanding the development of the capitalist system and its three components—the core, the semiperiphery, and the periphery—from the start of the sixteenth century (Wallerstein, 1974). The *development-of-underdevelopment theory* owes much to the work of André Gunder Frank (1969). He drew on the Latin American experience to argue that the development of the West depended on the impoverishment of the periphery. The development-of-underdevelopment theory pays special attention to a complement of the theory of imperialism, a theory of dependence that relates the effects of imperialism on underdeveloped countries.

An attractive theory for geographers is Johan Galtung's (1971) *structural theory of imperialism* based on *center-periphery relations* (Figure 14.12). The Center is

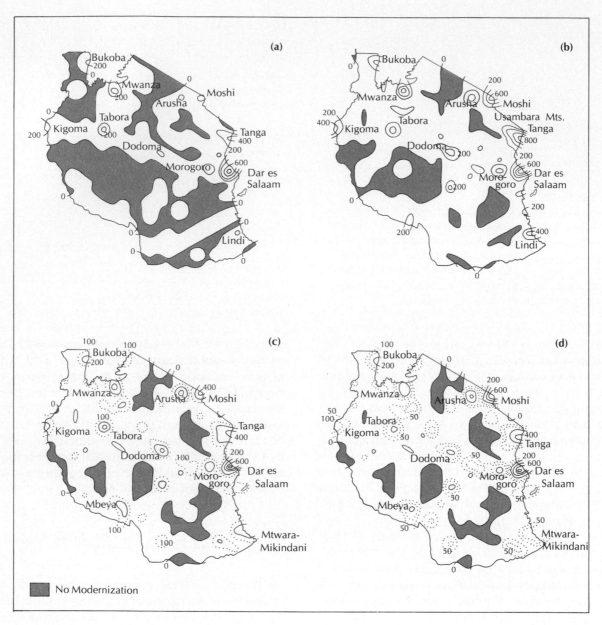

FIGURE 14.11
The diffusion of modernization in Tanzania: (a) early 1920s; (b) late 1920s and early 1930s; (c) late 1940s and early 1950s; (d) late 1950s and early 1960s.
(Source: Gould, 1970, p. 168.)

represented by wealthy industrial nations, the Periphery by underdeveloped nations. Both the Center and the Periphery have centers of their own, mainly urban elites and some rural elites, and peripheries, essentially the rural poor and also the urban powerless. The dominant economic and political power lies with the center in the Center (i.e., the elites in the industrialized countries);

the dominant strength in numbers lies with the periphery in the Periphery (i.e., the majority of Third World people). For Galtung, the center-periphery theory of imperialism provides a fruitful basis for empirical research within liberal and radical schools of thought.

Another way to examine imperialistic relations is to focus on the *role of the MNC* as a source of political

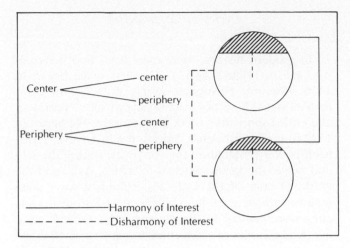

FIGURE 14.12
The structure of imperialism.
(*Source: Galtung, 1971, p. 84.*)

and economic control (Barnet and Müller, 1975). The buildup of crises in the capitalist core, frequently expressed as conflicts between capital and labor, has forced firms to emphasize multinational production and to channel capital in the direction of peripheral regions, where hourly wage rates and fringe benefits are low (Table 14.5). The theory emphasizes that the global corporation is the linchpin of a precarious dependent

⊕

Table 14.5

Hourly Wage and Fringe Benefits in the
Apparel Industry

Country or City	U.S. $
Sweden	7.22
Netherlands	5.68
Belgium	5.49
New York (legal)*	4.58
United States	4.35
Puerto Rico	2.57
New York (sweatshops)*	1.75
Singapore*	1.10
Hong Kong	0.96
Brazil	0.86
Taiwan	0.56
South Korea	0.41

* No fringe benefits.
Source: Ross and Trachte, 1983, p. 417.

development. Despite the economic benefits derived from the transfer of capital, the foreign enclaves of multinationals, their "export platforms," create few jobs relative to the size of the massive industrial reserve army now encamped in the Third World. Moreover, the relocation of industry to the periphery is a prime cause of the crisis now afflicting the major metropolitan areas and threatening the social harmony that has prevailed in the core.

Ecopolitical Economy Theories

Ecopolitical economy theories stem from concern over the meaning of development and the costs and benefits of economic growth and cultural change. These theories are reflected in the work of anthropologists on the cultural ecology of development (Geertz, 1963) and in the work of economists who question why we make a fetish of growth (Mishan, 1977; Schumacher, 1973).

Geographer Lakshman Yapa (1980), who coined the term *ecopolitical economy*, pointed to insights derived from world political economy theory in criticizing the conventional wisdom of striving for higher and higher rates of economic growth in underdeveloped countries in the hope that benefits will diffuse to the poor. The benefits of economic growth fail to reach the poor because the economic surplus is diverted to national and foreign elites, in effect preempting the basic-goods fund. The only way that economic development can improve the living conditions of the poor is by using resources directly in the production and distribution of basic goods.

Bring Culture Back In

With the possible exception of the ecopolitical approach, all major perspectives on development emphasize the economic aspect and downplay the cultural dimension. To promote a fuller understanding of the process, John Agnew (1987) entreated geographers to bring culture back into their development studies. Agnew stressed that every part of the world has had its own particular and peculiar relationship with the evolution of the world economy. The success of Japan in the world economy, the dependence of South African economic growth on apartheid, the religiously inspired backlash against American-style development in Iran, and even the rise of the modern world economy in Europe cannot be explained solely in economic terms. In Europe, the *cultural system* of exchange and value dating back to medieval times paved the way for the modern world economy.

COLONIALISM AND GLOBAL CORE-PERIPHERY RELATIONS

◈

Thus far, we have dealt with attributes of underdevelopment and ideas about development that find expression in the social sciences. The balance of the chapter examines the themes of inequality and unequal development in more detail. We begin with the development of the capitalist world economy, viewed in terms of waves of colonialism and core-periphery relations.

Cycles of Colonialism

In modern history, there have been two waves of colonialism (Figure 14.13). The first wave began in 1415, when the Portuguese seized control of the commercial naval base of Ceuta on the Strait of Gibraltar, and ended soon after 1800. The second wave began in 1825 and ended in 1969. During the first wave, European power centered on the Americas; during the second wave, the focus switched to Africa, Asia, and the Pacific (Figure 14.14). Colonies of the first wave were mainly settlement colonies where quasi-European societies were created by immigrants. The second wave involved colonies of occupation, in which a small number of Europeans exercised political control. Exceptions to the latter included nineteenth-century settler colonies in Australasia and in southern and eastern Africa.

In each wave, a few colonial powers overshadowed the rest (Figure 14.15). During the first wave, Spain

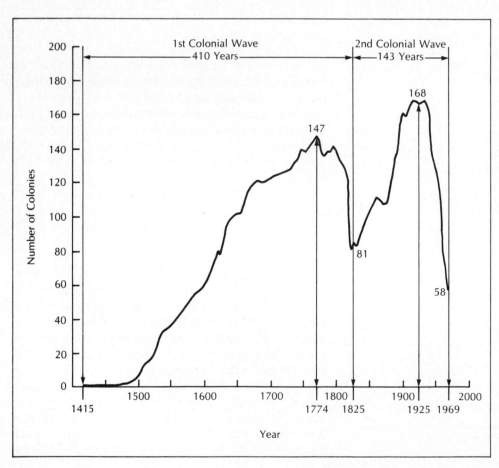

FIGURE 14.13
Waves of colonialism. The first wave of colonialism peaked in the mid-eighteenth century, and it involved conquest, plunder, slavery, and annihilation of indigenous peoples, such as the Spanish and Portuguese in Latin America. The second colonial wave peaked in the early twentieth century, in which there was less destruction and disruption of local societies.
(Source: de Souza, 1986, p. 15. Based on data in Henige, 1970.)
By the late 1800s, Europe's drive for colonial expansion reached a high point and its ability to control the economies of new colonies was realized. Europe was the most important supplier of manufactured goods to the colonies while usurping most raw materials. Europe moved quickly to secure distant territories as sources of labor and raw materials, as well as outlets for products that were emanating from European mills and factories.

FIGURE 14.14
The colonized periphery.
(Source: de Souza, 1986, p. 16. Based on data in Henige, 1970.)
By the end of the 18th century, European powers had moved quickly to establish former trading "partners" as colonies. By exploiting the resources of the colonies, they were able to show substantial profits back home, with sugar, spices, tobacco, and slave trade as the most profitable commodities. South America, including the Caribbean Islands, Africa, India and Southeast Asia became the most valuable sources of revenue. The last great surge in overseas colonization was centered on Africa, the dark continent. Up to this point, poor harbors and mooring facilities on the west coast, inhospitable climates, steep cataracts near the coasts, disallowing continental penetration and unfriendly tribes, kept exploration and colonization to a minimum.

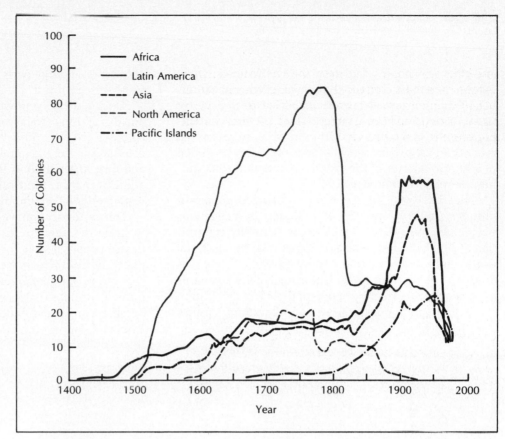

FIGURE 14.15
Major colonial powers.
(Source: de Souza, 1986, p. 16. Based on data in Henige, 1970.)
By the end of the 18th century, the rest of the world had been usurped. Therefore, Africa was up for grabs. Although there was some missionary zeal to convert the natives, African penetration was primarily economic, based on inexpensive food, cheap labor, abundant raw materials and a huge supply of minerals for European mills and markets. In South Africa, for example, wealthy Europeans set up mining operations to extract gold, platinum and diamonds. Thousands of Black Africans came to the mines to do the work, which allowed the white settlers and prospectors to make a fortune.

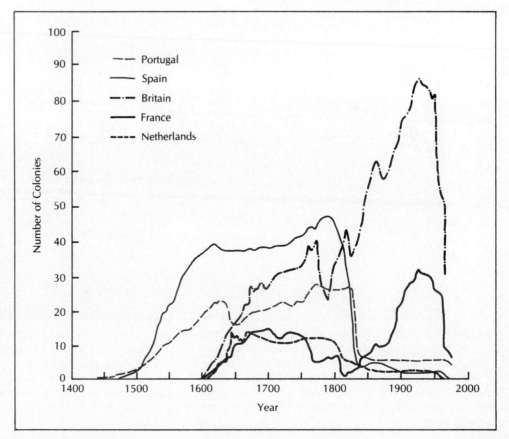

and Portugal stood apart from the Netherlands, Great Britain, and France. In the second wave, when the number of major colonial powers increased from 5 to 10, Great Britain and France were far ahead of their contemporaries. At its peak in 1933, the British Empire covered more than 24% of the world's land surface and included nearly one-quarter of the world's population (502 million people) (Fieldhouse, 1967).

The first wave of colonialism involved conquest, plunder, slavery, and the annihilation of indigenous people. The Spaniards, for example, virtually exterminated the Carib population of Hispaniola; in 1492, the Caribs numbered 300,000, but by 1548 the figure was down to 500 (Griffin, 1969). The arrival of the Spaniards in Mexico led to the destruction of the Aztec civilization and a population decline from 13 to 2 million (Griffin, 1969). In Africa, the slave trade greatly reduced the population in large parts of the Congo Basin and in the West African forest.

During the second wave, there was less destruction and disruption of local societies. Conditions varied from colony to colony, however. For example, the effects of colonialism were generally stronger in southern Africa and East Africa than in West Africa. In southern Africa and East Africa, the British alienated land to build an export-oriented economy.

During the second wave of colonialism, the imperialist countries saw the underdeveloped regions as immense supply depots for the cheap production of raw materials from which their economies could profit. The economies of underdeveloped countries were often deformed into subsidiaries of the colonial powers: Jamaica became a sugar plantation, Sri Lanka a tea plantation, Zambia a copper mine, and Arabia an oil field.

Nairobi, capital of Kenya, is a city created by Europeans out of the African "wilderness." Home to more than 2 million people, Nairobi originated in 1899 as a railway camp during the building of the Mombasa-Lake Victoria railway line. To the north and west of the city, the fertile "White Highlands" were alienated to European farmers who specialized in wheat, corn, pyrethrum, sheep, and cattle. Land was also alienated along the coast for European use—often as a vacation spot on the Indian Ocean. Since independence, colonial land ownership and use has been modified. Land in the "White Highlands," for example, has been acquired by Africans and divided into small holdings. *(Source: World Bank.)*

Core Structure and Global Center-Periphery Relations

Why did colonialism expand at a particular time and contract at another? World-system theory suggests that the key to understanding waves of colonialism is the changing structure of the core: periods of instability and stability in the core coincide with periods of colonial expansion and contraction in the periphery (Figure 14.16). During periods of instability, when there is competition among rival core countries, colonialism expands. In the presence of a single, hegemonic core country, colonialism contracts. A hegemonic power can control the world without the expensive encumbrances that colonies represent.

Hegemony exists when one core power enjoys supremacy in production, commerce, and finance and occupies a position of political leadership. The hegemonic power owns and controls the largest share of the world's production apparatus. It is the leading trading and investment country, its currency is the universal medium of exchange, and its city of primacy is the financial center of the world. Because of political and military superiority, the dominant core country maintains order in the world system and imposes solutions to international conflicts that serve its self-interests. Consequently, hegemonic situations are characterized by periods of peace as well as by universal ideologies such as freedom to trade and freedom to invest.

During a core power's rise to hegemony, core-periphery relations become more informal. Economic linkages between center and periphery increasingly focus on the hegemonic power. This reorientation results in decolonization. The hegemonic power relies on economic mechanisms to extract the surplus value of the periphery. Lopsided development between the core and the periphery flourishes, and terms of trade deteriorate for the colonized periphery. During a power's fall from hegemony, rival core states, which can focus on capital accumulation without the burden of maintaining the political and military apparatus of supremacy, catch up and challenge the hegemonic power.

Competition exists when power in the center of the world system is dispersed among several countries. With pluralization, competing centers control and own a larger part of the world's production apparatus. They increase their shares of world trade, enclose national economic areas behind tariff and nontariff barriers, and use their national currencies in a growing volume of transactions. Without a hegemonic power dominating the world system, political tensions increase and may develop into armed conflicts.

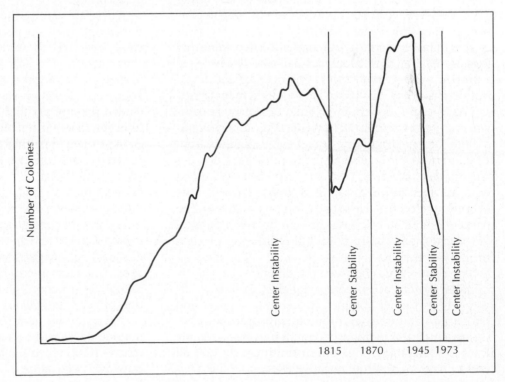

FIGURE 14.16
The relationship between colonialism and center stability.

Competition forces increasingly more formal core-periphery relationships. Competing core countries rely on the mechanism of colonialism to extract the surplus of the periphery. Economic linkages between the colonized and the colonizers become multilateral to a greater extent, and economic transactions with core countries become more frequent.

World-system theory maintains that periodic fluctuations from a single, hegemonic power to a group of competing countries are essential to the survival of the world system. The system would break into separate empires if competition at the center were to persist, or mutate into a world empire if hegemony were to last. Moreover, this cyclic realignment of core-periphery relations is not limited to colonialism; it is manifested in all the ways that the world system binds itself together. Trade, for example, is more formally structured during periods of core instability.

REGIONAL DISPARITIES WITHIN UNDERDEVELOPED COUNTRIES

Inherited colonial structures inhibit Third World development efforts in the postindependence era. Major cities of underdeveloped countries are still "export platforms." They link the rich industrial countries and their sources of raw materials. And, under the new industrial division of labor, they supply a small core of developed countries with manufactures: engineering and metal products, clothing, and miscellaneous light manufacturing. As a result, modern large-scale enterprise remains concentrated in capital and port cities. Injections of capital into urban economics attract new migrants from rural areas and provincial towns to principal cities. Urban primacy increases. Migrants, absorbed by the system, are maintained at minimal levels. There is little incentive to decentralize urban economic activities. The markedly hierarchical, authoritarian nature of political and social organization retards the diffusion of ideas throughout the urban hierarchy.

The relationships between the different parts of the capitalist system accentuate inequality. Polarizing effects within former colonies concentrate services and innovations at the center, promoting the imbalance between center and periphery. Capital movements, trade flows, internal migration, and institutional controls all tend to have an absolute negative effect on the growth rate and development of the periphery. In this section, we survey the persistence of disequilibrium within underdeveloped countries.

The Center-Periphery Concept

The center-periphery concept is one of the most geographic ideas presented by regional analysts. It echoes the Marxist argument that the center appropriates to itself the surplus of the periphery for its own development. The center-periphery phenomenon may be regarded as a multiple system of nested centers and peripheries, like a Chinese puzzle box. At the world level, the global center (rich industrial countries) drains the global periphery (most of the underdeveloped countries). But within any part of the international system, within any national unit, other centers and peripheries exist. Centers at this level, although considerably less powerful, still have sufficient strength to appropriate to themselves a smaller, yet sizable, fraction of remaining surplus value. A center may be a single urban area or a region encompassing several towns that stand in an advantageous relation to the hinterland. Even in remote peripheral areas local, regional imbalances are likely to exist, with some areas growing and others stagnating or declining.

There are reverse flows from the various centers to the peripheries—to peripheral nations, to peripheral rural areas. Yet these flows, themselves, may further accentuate center-periphery differences. In a study of foreign aid to Tanzania for 1971, Giovanni Arrighi and John Saul (1973) observed that agreements were concluded for projects that tended to reflect and buttress its dependence on and integration into the center. World Bank, United States Aid for International Development (USAID), and International Development Association (IDA) loans generally support major infrastructural projects such as roads and power stations, which are proven money earners, and which reinforce the centrality and drawing power of the cities and the modern export sector of agriculture. AID strongly supports projects dealing with agriculture (so long as they do not upset U.S. farm interests), health and family planning, school construction, and road building; industrialization projects are seldom financed.

Yet many Western social scientists see core regions in underdeveloped countries as " 'beachheads' . . . the centres from which the benefits of modernization flow outwards to revitalize the stagnating agricultural sector"

The periphery in the Center is illustrated by these shacks occupied by North African migrant workers in Paris.
(Source: ILO, I-France-Migration: 26.)

(McGee, 1971, p. 13). Such a vision could cast social scientists in the role of augmenting national, regional, and individual inequalities in underdeveloped countries. Let us see why by describing and analyzing some of the major center-dominant models of regional development.

Center-Dominant Models of Regional Development

One view of regional development stems from the studies of neoclassical theorists. They hypothesize that differences between center and periphery are only temporary within a free-market system. Regional development inequalities that occur at first will be corrected by the mobility of factors under pure competition. For example, if wages are higher in Region *A* than in Region *B*, labor will move from the lower-paid area to the

higher, thereby leading to an adjustment in relative wage rates. Because the mechanism in a free-market economy is self-regulating, no government intervention is necessary: Regional differences in wage rates and income will occur automatically. Unfortunately, little evidence exists to support such a view—especially in underdeveloped countries, where perfectly mobile production factors are hardly characteristic features.

Two models offering an alternative explanation of regional differentials emerged in the late 1950s. Both models suggest that, with time, interaction *increases* rather than *decreases* inequalities between rich and poor regions. The models of Swedish economist Gunnar Myrdal (1957) and American economist Albert Hirschman (1958) indicated that in an underdeveloped country operating under a capitalist system, *deviation-amplifying forces*, rather than *deviation-counteracting forces*, increase and rigidify the differences between center and periphery. *Deviation-amplification* (as opposed to *deviation-reduction*) refers to any process that amplifies an initial "kick" and increases divergence from an initial condition.

MYRDAL'S CIRCULAR AND CUMULATIVE CAUSATION MODEL

Myrdal (1957) argued that during early stages of development, economic inequalities are increased through the operation of *circular and cumulative causation*. He reasoned that "change does not call forth contradicting forces [as equalization models suggest] but, instead, supporting changes, which move the system in the same direction as the first change but much further [*sic*]" (p. 13). According to Myrdal, once growth has been initiated in favored locations in a free economy, inflows of labor, skills, capital, and commodities develop spontaneously to support these locations. The flows, however, induce *backwash effects* that amplify inequalities between expanding and other regions. Myrdal argued that if events follow an uncontrolled course, backwash effects perpetuate growth in expanding regions and retard growth elsewhere. For development to occur throughout a country, *spread effects* must, on the average, be stronger than backwash effects.

In underdeveloped countries, spread effects often refer to the benefits that trickle down from a major city to surrounding areas. These *trickle-down effects* may include increased demand for primary commodities, increased investment, and the diffusion of modern technology. Conversely, backwash effects are the demands by the city on surrounding areas. These effects can include an inward flow of commodities, capital, and skilled workers. Even a new transportation route can initiate backwash. It can permit industrial plants in the growing city to supply stagnating areas with goods formerly supplied by the poor region's own craft industries.

HIRSCHMAN'S CIRCULAR MODEL

Hirschman (1958) advanced a similar model of polarized development. His model shows that after an initial decision is made to locate a particular industry at a specific point, it has an initial multiplier effect, as shown in Figure 14.17. New local demands are generated by the factory and by the purchasing power of its labor force. The labor force creates a demand for housing and for a set of services. The new factory attracts industries producing complementary goods. Linked industries either provide needed inputs or purchase semifinished products from the initial factory. The entire process has a cumulative self-generating momentum; after the first cycle of growth is completed, a new spiral of growth is initiated at a higher threshold. The diagram of circular and accelerative growth illustrates that cycles of growth can be carried through *any* number of times—at least until the process is arrested by diseconomies or interrupted by the competitive advantages of other growth points. Figure 14.17 also shows that the initial multiplier stimulates expansion of nonindustrial activities; they, in turn, trigger a second multiplier that induces further growth and still higher thresholds.

Thus, through the operation of unrestrained market forces, the center grows, feeding on more and more resources from the hinterland. The result is unbalanced or polarized growth. According to Hirschman, *polarization effects* are offset eventually by *trickle-down effects*—the equivalent of Myrdal's spread effects. However, Hirschman thought that only governments can provide enough incentives for positive trickle-down effects to outweigh negative polarization effects and ensure sustained peripheral growth.

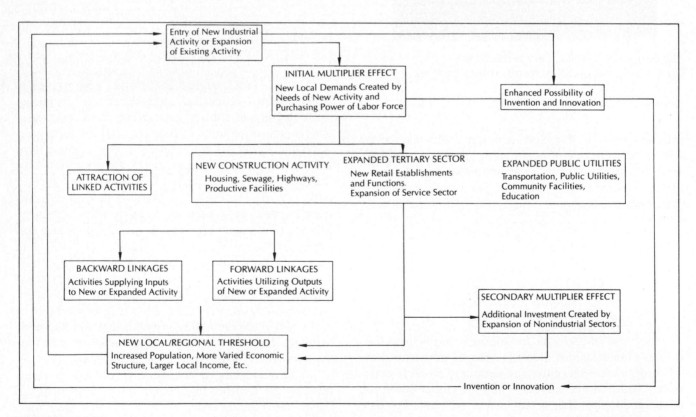

FIGURE 14.17
Initial multiplier effect and the process of cumulative upward causation.
(Source: Pred, 1966, p. 25.)

FRIEDMANN'S EVOLUTIONARY MODEL

Myrdal's model helps us to understand the process of regional-income divergence, but it does not relate the problem to the interaction between cities and their hinterlands. To some extent, John Friedmann (1966) has filled this gap in Western social science. His descriptive four-stage model relates the process leading to regional inequality to the stage of development and to the city system typical of that stage (Figure 14.18). Friedmann recognized the following stages of spatial evolution:

1. A *preindustrial phase*, characterized by a number of small independent urban centers spread throughout a large region. With no urban hierarchy, the possibilities for growth are soon exhausted and the economy tends to stagnate. Friedmann assumed the system to be in balance, each center by and large serving only its local area.

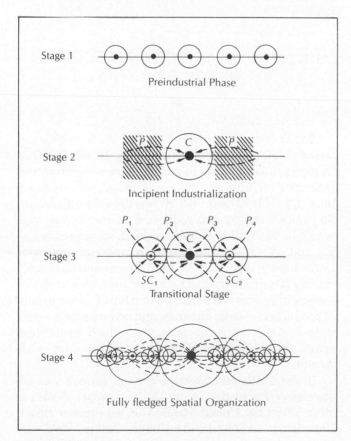

FIGURE 14.18
Friedmann's stages of spatial evolution.
(Source: Friedmann, 1966, p. 36.)

2. A period of *incipient industrialization*, characterized by a city of primacy (C), which dominates a large region and exploits the natural resources of its periphery (P). Local economies in the periphery are undermined in consequence of a mass movement of would-be entrepreneurs, intellectuals, and labor to the city. Friedmann viewed the primacy-dominated organization of space as unstable because the system is generated by exogenous forces.

3. A *transitional stage* toward industrial maturation in which the city of primacy (C) still dominates the large region, but not to the extent that it did previously. The construction of strategically located urban centers or growth centers (SC_1 and SC_2) reduces the influence of the large city. Friedmann regarded the third stage as still unstable because of the persistent backwardness in peripheral areas (P_1, P_2, P_3, P_4).

4. A final stage consisting of a *fully fledged spatial organization* based on the hierarchy principle and encompassing the entire national territory. According to Friedmann, this functionally interdependent system of cities will fulfill essential goals of internal spatial organization such as national integration, efficiency of location, maximum growth potential, and a high degree of interregional balance.

Friedmann's evolutionary model posits ultimate convergence between center and periphery. He emphasized the prolonged nature of the process, convergence occurring only when a society has reached an advanced stage of industrial maturation. Friedmann suggested, however, that continued urban-industrial expansion in major metropolitan areas should lead to catalytic effects on surrounding regions. He offered a number of propositions that reflect the ongoing urban-regional development process in the United States. The propositions, which have an explicit link with central-place theory and innovation-diffusion theory, are as follows:

Economic growth takes place in a matrix of urban regions through which the space economy is organized. . . . Cities organize the space economy. They are centers of activity and of innovation, focal points of the transport network, locations of superior accessibility at which firms can most easily reap scale economies and at which industrial complexes can obtain the economies of localization and urbanization. Agricultural enterprise is more efficient in the vicinity of cities. The more prosperous commercialized agricultures encircle the major cities. . . . There are two major elements in this organization of economic activities in space:

(a) A system of cities, organized in a hierarchy according to the functions performed by each;

(b) Corresponding areas of urban influence or urban fields surrounding each of the cities in the system.

Generally we can argue the following about this system of spatial organization:

(a) The size and function of a central city and the size of the urban field are proportional.

(b) The spatial incidence of economic growth is a function of distance from the central city. Troughs of economic backwardness lie in the most inaccessible areas along the intermetropolitan peripheries.

(c) Impulses of economic change are transmitted in order from higher to lower centers in the urban hierarchy, in a "size-rachet" sequence, so that continued innovation in large cities remains critical for extension of growth over the complete economic system.

(d) The growth potential of an area situated along an axis between two cities is a function of the intensity of interaction between them. (Berry, 1969a, p. 288)

Brian Berry concurred with Friedmann that Western growth theory suggests that cities are gateways for development that transmit economic change to smaller centers. Berry noted, however, that growth impulses do not always trickle down from town to country. "As a consequence, growth and stagnation polarize; the economic system remains unarticulated" (Berry, 1969b, p. 207). To remedy this, Western regional science recommends that planners provide a hierarchy of growth centers to link central cities with interstitial areas. In this hierarchy, "growth impulses and economic advancement should 'trickle down' to smaller places and ultimately infuse dynamism into even the most tradition-bound peripheries" (Berry, 1969a, p. 288). Cities, as centers of influence over regional and national hinterlands, are catalysts to development.

Those who favor the center-dominant thesis argue that "the history of the West from the nineteenth century onward is being reiterated in the underdeveloped countries today" (Reissman, 1964, p. 158). However, according to André Gunder Frank (1969) or Lin Piao (1965), both of whom acidly see cities as capitalist structures, this article of faith is nothing more than colonialism thinly disguised. According to Frank, cities in underdeveloped countries are centers of colonial domination. In the service of international capitalism, they subject regional and national hinterlands to economic "satellitization" and exploitation. Certain forms of international influence and manipulation condition the structure of urban systems in underdeveloped countries; thus, mercantile cities are dependent on overseas metropolitan centers, and they in turn dominate domestic fields of influence. This view calls into question Friedmann's assumption that urbanization is necessarily coupled with development. On the contrary, it asserts that unless external dependency is eliminated, the urbanization process stimulates the underdevelopment of hinterlands.

THE COLLAPSE OF COMMUNISM IN THE SOVIET UNION

Soviet communism was based on the *labor theory of capital*. It viewed capitalism as a way for the few elite in the capitalist system to gather extra value from the laborers. Communism, on the other hand, was to extract the extra value of labor, which was the value of production minus wages, and redirect it to the society as a whole in the form of subsidized food, subsidized housing and education, and subsidized medical attention. Unfortunately, much of this capital went into an unnecessarily large military machine. The primary features of the Soviet system were state ownership of all the means of production—land, factories, and raw materials—and state-directed economic planning, which established prices, set quotas, and directed the distribution of all wealth.

In the 1950s and 1960s, economic growth was an impressive 6% in the Soviet Union, compared with a mere 3% in the United States. This led premier Nikita Khrushchev to state in the United Nations, "We will bury you with the superiority of our economic system through world competition and trade." However, 6% growth rates could not continue; by 1990, the rate was −4%, and by 1991, −14%.

An abortive attempt in 1991 to push President Mikhail Gorbachev into the background failed, but the break in the Soviet Union had already occurred. Boris Yeltsin emerged as the strong leader of the Russian Republic. The former Soviet Union today is loosely called the *Commonwealth of Independent States,* or CIS, but this commonwealth is extremely weak. The position and quality of the economy continues to deteriorate. Production is declining, prices have risen, and shortages are massive. The political situation also continues to be completely unstable, and civil war could break out at any time, reverting the country to the old authoritarian ways. Many members of the Russian Congress would like to see the authoritarian system reinstated because they have everything to gain if it is, but Yeltsin dissolved Congress, stormed the Parliament, and arrested the policymakers.

One of the single largest causes of economic development worldwide today exists in the former Soviet countries (Figure 14.19); the Eastern European nations of Czechoslovakia, Hungary, Poland, Romania, Bulgaria, and Albania; and the fractured republics of former Yugoslavia are also readying themselves for development.

These countries provide major lessons for LDCs that are pursuing or contemplating pursuing the economic development model given by the former Soviet Union's central-planning programs.

What caused the decline of the former Soviet Union in the 1990s? What created the long queues of consumers on the streets of St. Petersburg (Leningrad), Kiev, and Moscow? In this section, we first attempt to answer these questions. Then we discuss how the Soviet Union can embrace a market economy and what the IACs can do to help.

Why Soviet Communism Failed

Soviet-style communism failed in the early 1990s after 70 years of struggle. The factors that led to its downfall were an inability to meet consumer demand, lack of proper motivation and labor incentives in the economic system, central-planning problems and mismanagement, inadequate agriculture, and too much military investment.

FIGURE 14.19

Economic development potential of Russia and the former Soviet Republics, which show large variation in their potential for economic development. The Ukraine has the best potential and has recently been provisionally admitted to the Common Market countries of Western Europe. The Russian Federation and other former Soviet Republics are judged by the West to continue to be a bad investment risk. There is instability and uncertainty about every aspect of Russian life—political, economic, legal, monetary and social systems, are either unknown or poorly established. The U.S. businesses are shying away from substantial investment. The West has won the cold war, but as of mid-1994, is losing the prolonged peace. In the best case scenario, Russia and the former Soviet Republics will evolve into peaceful, democratic, capitalist societies, posing no threat to the world economy and mutually striving with other world countries to contribute to the human and natural resources of the planet. The worse case scenario is that Russia and the other Republics, or some of them, will disintegrate into civil war and chaos on a scale many times beyond that of Yugoslavia today. The threat of nuclear weapons makes the potential for nuclear and ecological holocaust real. The tide now seems to be surging in favor of autocracy and extreme nationalism. The mood of the population is ugly and the political ramifications could be dangerous. The reformist block in the Parliament seems to be waning and the power seems to be shifting towards a statist-nationalist block.

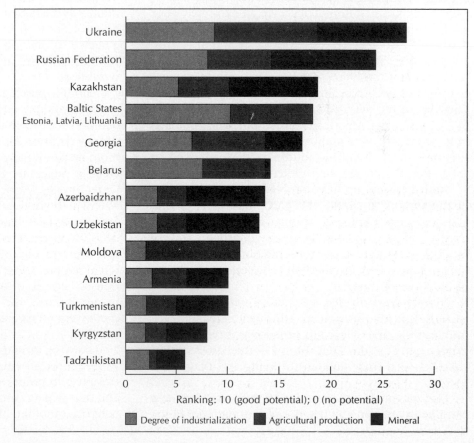

INABILITY TO MEET CONSUMER DEMAND

Before the collapse of communism, the poor quality and shortages of Soviet manufactured goods suggested that failure was imminent. What caused the shortages? Why were the goods substandard?

After World War II, rapid Soviet growth was possible with more labor, more capital, and more land. However, by the 1980s, these resources were being maximized, so no growth occurred, and in the 1990s growth was negative.

The military machine and capital goods were all-important, so attempts were made to increase the production of these goods. However, this emphasis had several costly consequences. First, the percentage of output devoted to consumer products decreased. Store shelves became empty, and the standard of living dwindled.

Second, the World Bank estimated that the manufacturing sectors of the economy were so heavily subsidized and overemphasized by the central economic planning groups that the Soviet Union lagged 12 to 15 years behind the United States and Germany in technological expertise and machinery. Refrigerators, televisions, radios, and automobiles were all extremely poor quality—primitive by German, Japanese, and U.S. standards.

Both these factors had an adverse effect on the citizens. Incentive problems, discussed in more detail next, already existed. According to estimates, the labor productivity of the average Soviet worker was only 35% that of his or her American counterpart. The poor attitude of citizens was aptly expressed by one worker's response to an inquiring journalist: "We pretend to work, and the government pretends to pay us."

Added to the incentive problems was the inability of the system to supply the goods and services that the consumers wanted. Consumer expectations always outstripped supply. Long lines existed for almost every product, and many times stores ran out of goods before the lines dwindled. Empty shelves became the hallmark of the Soviet Union.

Morale was lowered even more when the Soviet citizens quickly discovered—through satellite communications and television broadcasts from Western Europe and Radio-Free Europe—the gross difference between their standard of living and that of the IACs.

Understandably, the result of all these problems was extreme frustration and deteriorating confidence in the system. This unrest finally led to rebellion and the collapse of Soviet communism in 1991.

The poor standard of living in the Soviet Union continues today. Whereas in 1993 the United States produced 600 cars, 800 television sets, and 1000 telephones for every 1000 people, the former Soviet Union had only 40 cars, 50 television sets, and 100 telephones for each of its 1000 citizens. Overall, the total consumption per capita by Soviet citizens was less than 25% that of Americans.

LACK OF INCENTIVES AND MOTIVATION

The Soviet system lacked incentives—the key ingredient of the capitalist system—for workers, for managers, and for competition. In a capitalist system, more work effort, greater creativity, and an improved product mean higher wages and promotions for workers. However, in the Soviet Union, work effort was not necessarily rewarded with higher wages or promotions. For the few workers who did receive promotions, even though their wages were higher, increased purchasing power never materialized because of what is known in economics as the *ruble overhang:* the accumulation of rubles by a society with no real wealth or purchasing power attached to them. If extra rubles are paid but no consumer goods are available for purchase, the ruble is worthless.

Another problem was that the output and mix of products and prices were determined by Soviet central planners. In a capitalist system, if a product is in short supply, its price increases. The incentive is to produce more items to make more profit. When production increases, prices are forced back down because of the larger supply. These self-correcting mechanisms were absent in the Soviet system. Without such price changes, Soviet planners had no way to gauge whether their decisions were correct or incorrect. Thus, many products that were in high demand were in short supply and remained so. Other items remained stored in warehouses because of an overabundance and lack of demand. Because the planners determined the output, there were no incentives for managers to increase their supplies.

Likewise, incentives for competition and innovation were almost absent. New firms could not come into existence to produce better products at cheaper prices and thus win advantages over opponents through competition, another trademark of capitalism. Consequently, the techniques used in the Soviet Union were considered obsolete by world standards. However, there was no incentive for changing them and no *way* to change them.

MISMANAGEMENT AND CENTRAL-PLANNING PROBLEMS

Richard Ericson (1992) points out that the Soviet planning system that worked in the 1930s and 1940s, wherein production goals, quotas, prices, and supplies were set individually and separately from one another, could not work in the 1980s and 1990s because of the increased complexity of the international market. In the later years, there were far more industries for which to plan, and many more components and supplies for each item produced. In 1990, 48,000 industrial enterprises in the Soviet Union produced goods that were demanded at various stages in the economy. The planners had to ensure that all resource demands were met and that final production targets were achieved. Literally billions of supplies and demands had to be met. The outputs of any one industry were inputs to other industries, and these were yet inputs to the final products demanded in stores across the Soviet Union. If a supplier experienced a slowdown in production because of a closed mine or a breakdown in the transportation system, supplies along the way would not be met, and the entire system would break down. Then, no one would be able to fulfill production goals and quotas. The bottleneck or chain reaction would be passed on to the consumer and to the state, which consumed a large portion of its own products. The result would be resource immobilization.

The capitalist economy is a powerfully organizing force that sets millions of laborers, companies, nations, and prices in motion and allocates resources in an efficient manner. Coordination is accomplished according to consumer wants, resource availability, and business efficiency and practices. However, duplicating this coordination with state-operated economic planning units run by individuals making arbitrary decisions on allocations, prices, and resources was impossible.

With time, the inherent inefficiency of the command administrative economic system began to dominate its effectiveness in achieving the priority objectives of the Soviet central authorities. Methods and institutions that were effective at an earlier, simpler stage no longer generated the desired outcomes. The mobilization of resources and effort that produced collectivization, industrialization, and a sizable chemical industry failed to develop modern computer technology and to modernize consumer goods industries. The administrative suprastructure, methods of planning, and plans themselves had become ever less adequate for the needs and flow of economic activity. The natural consequence was dysfunctional behavior of subordinates. This behavior increased the obvious microeconomic waste and inefficiency, slowed or reduced economic growth and productivity, and failed to achieve or claim priorities more frequently. Even with the most recent mainframe computers and industrial organizational techniques, the former Soviet Union has been unable to coordinate its complex economy.

AGRICULTURAL FAILURE

As discussed in Chapter 7, Soviet agricultural programs were essentially disappointing. One-fourth the Soviet Union's annual GNP and 30% of its labor force were engaged in agriculture, yet it became the world's largest importer of food. According to one estimate, the average Soviet agricultural worker was only 10% as efficient as an agricultural worker in the United States. There is no question that the Soviet Union possessed a relatively small amount of good agricultural land, but it had enough land to be more productive.

The main problems discussed so far also apply to agriculture: inadequate administration and planning, insufficient incentives for workers, and an increasing import drain on the foreign currency reserve, which should have been used for investment, technology, and infrastructure.

MILITARY WASTE

Throughout history, Russia and the Soviet Union have been repeatedly invaded from the outside. Most recently were invasions by Napoleon in 1805 and Hitler's army in 1942. Prior to this, a series of other dictators and warring tribes had disrupted the region. Consequently, the Soviet Union became paranoid of its neighbors, especially its most powerful neighbors: In the later stages of the Cold War, fear was focused on the United States. This fear led to the arms escalation of the 1970s and 1980s, with thousands of nuclear warheads stockpiled on each side. The Soviet military expenditure accounted for 15% to 20% of the GNP, while in America it accounted for 3% to 6%. Consequently, much money that could have been used for investment, development, and growth was funneled into the military. At the same time, the most talented people were also channeled into the military as administrators and planners, including research scientists and engineers who created plans and devices for defense and attack military systems. This talent could have been best used in other sectors of the economy.

The Transition to a Market Economy

Most of the 15 former Soviet socialist republics shown in color insert 3.4 top and notably Russia, have committed themselves to forming capitalist-type market economies. The political and economic undertones of maintaining the status quo, however, are still quite powerful. What do these countries require to establish strong market economies? Many factors, most of which Americans take for granted.

PRIVATIZATION

If the former Soviet Union countries are to move toward a market system, private ownership of the means of production is necessary. This means private ownership of land, factories, houses, and machinery. Department stores must also be privatized. Private property must be established and rules for its governance maintained. How this will occur is not altogether clear, but there has been a mad scramble to resurrect titles, deeds, and ownership papers from the period of 1900 to 1917, when most property was expropriated.

INTRODUCTION OF COMPETITION

If a market economy is to develop and flourish, competition must be introduced. Once again, this is a tall order. The 48,000 state-owned enterprises that were the backbone of the Soviet economy must be free to operate as independent agents, competing with one another for improved products and lower prices. Because most of these stable enterprises are operating as monopolies, competition was all but absent in the former Soviet Union. But competition is necessary for products to improve, for efficiency to take hold, and for profits to accrue to the laborers, who now have a vested interest in these enterprises. Competition is already budding as a result of joint ventures between the former Soviet

republics and foreign governments or MNCs. For example, Pizza Hut is opening 1000 restaurants from the Ukraine to the Baltic republics, and many American firms are attempting to establish a foothold in what will be one of the world's largest markets.

A REDUCED ROLE FOR GOVERNMENT

A reduced role for government in the control and operation of enterprise needs to occur. At the same time, the government must establish and maintain law and order in a new economy where privateers and black markets flourish. The government's first order of business is to establish private ownership and some level of equality with regard to opportunities for advancement in order to set the tone and to guarantee competition. At the same time, it must realize that all government-controlled enterprises may fail in the privatization process and that unemployment will flourish. In the old Soviet system, unemployment was quite low, so in order to prevent civil unrest with the higher unemployment levels that capitalism will bring, some measure of unemployment insurance must be provided immediately.

DEREGULATION OF PRICES

In a market economy, prices are not regulated the way they are in a Communist system. Consequently, prices must be deregulated in the former Soviet Union. Because most prices were set artificially low, without regard for market demand and supply, the decontrol of prices will have a serious inflationary effect. With increased prices, workers will demand and receive higher wages. In 1992, Boris Yeltsin decontrolled prices in the former Soviet republic of Russia. Immediately, prices tripled.

PARTICIPATION IN THE WORLD ECONOMY

For most of its 70 years of existence, the Soviet economy was isolated from the rest of the world. So that it can convert to a market system, it will have to join the world economy and take part in international trade, making its currency convertible to world standards, such as the deutsche mark, the yen, and the dollar. Firms that want to do business in the former Soviet Union currently cannot buy and sell because the

1994 RUSSIAN CONSTITUTION HAS

ROOTS IN AMERICA AND FRANCE

Russia's new constitution took effect January 1, 1994. It was the first multiparty election since 1917. The constitution is based on both French and American constitutions.

1. The Parliament is bicamarelm, with the upper house comprised of indirectly elected regional senators.

2. The president appoints the prime minister and other ministers, and has the right to dissolve Parliament.

3. The impeachment process is complex, as is the case in France.

4. The president is limited to two consecutive 4-year terms, as the American presidents.

5. The president has to submit his or her choices for judges, prosecutors, and chairman of the National Bank to the Parliament for approval.

6. The Parliament needs two-thirds majority to override a presidential veto of legislation.

Critics say the 137th Article document grants President Boris Yeltsin dictatorial powers, while supporters say a country the size of Russia needs a strong president. Some of Russia's 89 regions and republics object that the word "sovereign" was removed from the document's definition of their status, but most Russians are thought to want a united Russia with the threat of succession largely removed.

No guide books exist for the passage from communism to democracy and, in Russia, it has been a bumpy process. Economic shock therapy, carried out by Yeltsin's government, to move Russia toward a free market economy, has led to high unemployment, falling production, and high inflation. Although that policy is starting to pay some dividends, short-term economic costs have been high.

---

ruble does not exchange in world monetary markets. Buying and selling can occur only with in-kind types of real-money products. In-kind, or nonfinancial, investment is a means of capital exchange without converting to world monetary standards. However, this method is cumbersome and not attractive to many foreign investors.

DECREASED RESISTANCE BY HARDLINERS

Hardline Soviet economists currently outnumber reform moderates in the Russian congress. Many former Communist Party members who held office in dissolved Congress would like to see the return of Soviet communism to protect their status and position. These older

Communist Party members are most reluctant to admit that Soviet communism has failed. Currently, the economy is lagging and promises made by reform leaders such as Yeltsin have not materialized, so these bureaucrats' position remains strong. Decreased resistance by the hardliners would allow a market economy to take root more easily.

WORKER INCENTIVES

In order for the former Soviet Union to convert to a market system, the workers, the former *proletariat*, will have to be strongly in favor of the move. Currently, workers in the Soviet Union who want change outnumber those who want to return to the old Communist ways. But under the new capitalist system, new chal-

Russian shoppers are at a disadvantage compared to their American counterparts. With ideology diminishing, the Iron Curtain fallen, and the empire collapsed, Russia must now operate in an open, competitive world like other developed nations. Russia's decision to join NATO's Partners for Peace is a sharp contrast to Stalin's decision to keep the Soviet Union from participating in the Marshall Plan in 1948. Nonetheless, Russia's transition from totalitarianism to democracy is a huge undertaking, and there are no guarantees. Russian nationalism is on the rise, and free market economic reforms are on the wane.
(Source: Frederick P. Stutz.)

lenges await these workers. Harder work, longer hours, and increased productivity are needed. Workers in the former Soviet Union are accustomed to little or no responsibility for the quality and quantity of their work. All this will change. In addition, harder work should result in higher wages, which should yield more consumer goods: housing, food, appliances, and even automobiles. If these increases do not result from harder work in the short run, reform may not be given enough time to succeed. The Soviet Union laborers for 70 years have been trained to abhor private property. Now that they suddenly have the opportunity, can 70 years of hardened attitudes be changed overnight? Nobody seems to know the answer to this question.

How to Help the Former Soviet Union Embrace a Capitalist Economy

Assistance for Russia and the former Soviet federated socialist republics in their move toward a market economy can take public and private avenues: *direct foreign aid* and *private investment*.

DIRECT FOREIGN AID

In 1992, the IMF approved $24 billion in emergency aid to Russia. By 1994, about $12 billion has been spent. and another $6 billion went toward writing down the

Russian debt. The remaining $6 billion for currency stabilization has not yet been dispersed because of policy differences between the IMF and Russia. The U.S. share of IMF and World Bank funding is large. In addition, many other IACs claim that they will contribute more toward direct foreign aid than Gorbachev asked for in 1991, but only after the substantial costs of the Soviet military are redirected toward economic development.

So far, in 1994, the Russian economy has deteriorated still more. Hyperinflation, a collapsing ruble, rising unemployment, decreased production, and a huge budget deficit have pointed toward political disaster.

Moscow's total debt, including the debt taken over from the former Soviet Union, is about $100 billion. All that Western creditors can hope for in the short term is for renegotiated debt-restructuring deals, similar to the one negotiated with Mexico and Argentina 3 years ago. The long-term solution requires converting some loans and credit to Russia into direct aid, as America has done with other Third World nations. The money that America gives to Egypt, Israel, Pakistan, and others each year is not repaid. Why is America's investment in Russia any less important?

The situation in Russia is likened to that of post-World War II years, when Western Europe lay prostrate. "The patient is sinking while the doctor deliberates" was the famous statement by Secretary of State George Marshall in 1947. At first, Americans thought that Europe could rebuild itself after the war but were proven wrong. By 1947, America knew that democracy would not spring automatically from the tired soil of continental Europe, particularly with Communist propagators in the region. For democracy to grow, it first had to be planted. Unfortunately, the Eastern European nations were already out of reach.

The Marshall plan was not cheap; it cost America about $60 billion in today's market, in the form of direct foreign-aid grants, not repayable loans. Public money seeded the ground for private investment money, which began flowing heavily into Europe when the Marshall plan was terminated in 1952. What was the payoff?

Today, every nation in Western Europe has a stable democratic government in alliance with the United States. NATO is the most successful alliance in history. The population flourishes by every social and economic measure. Because of NATOs solidarity, the Cold War ended successfully more than 3 years ago. The EEC is America's most significant trading partner and among the few with which the United States has a trade surplus.

Without the Marshall plan, Western Europe, defeated and destitute, could easily have followed Eastern Europe down the Communist path that it is currently trying to retrace. Thanks to America's help, the nations of Western Europe are fully recovered and were able to help in the current endeavor, which is to rebuild Eastern Europe and Russia.

PRIVATE INVESTMENT

The former Soviet Union's 15 republics compose a market comparable to that of the North American Free Trade Association—Canada, the United States, and Mexico. The total EEC market is just 25% larger. The former Soviet Union is such a large market that one would expect it to attract a vast amount of foreign investment and to use this investment to strengthen its economy. The hope is that not only private investment and capital will flow into the former Soviet Union, but also the managerial skills and investment behavior necessary to put the nations back on their feet economically.

Deep problems exist, however. No one is sure exactly who is setting the standards for government and business reform. No one is exactly sure who holds the power. No one is sure how quickly the political and economic climate will change. No one is sure of the eminence of suppliers for products that are needed to produce consumer goods for such a large market in the present Soviet system. Another major problem is lack of convertibility of the ruble. How will American firms be paid? How will IACs receive a profit? Answers to

these questions and others remain ominous and can be sorted out only with time.

THIRD WORLD URBAN PEASANTS: A STUDY IN THE UNEQUAL

◾

Many political and economic theorists in underdeveloped countries argue that center-periphery relationships are features of the world economy that contribute strongly to the poverty of not only peasants in the rural areas, but also their urban counterparts, the *urban peasants,* who often inhabit squatter settlements. In a world viewed as a set of Thünian rings, the peasants and urban peasants exist at its outer fringe—poor and discriminated against with respect to use and control of the world's resources (Figure 14.20). Their access to credit, insurance, manufactured goods, technical knowledge, and infrastructure is virtually nil.

Let us have a closer look at the urban peasants as an example of a marginal social formation, the rapid growth of which is tied to the metropolitan intrusion into underdeveloped countries. Members of the urban peasantry are engaged primarily in the economic activity of the *traditional* as opposed to the *modern* sector—therefore, they are not regular wage earners. In underdeveloped countries, urban and rural areas have a dual economy: one sector traditional, the other an intrusive modern sector. These two sectors do not exist independently side by side; they are interlaced and unequal.

Urban Growth with Dependent Industrialization

Fundamental to the development of the United States was its emphasis on the domestic requirements of the national economy. The first need to be met was food, followed by the establishment of producer-goods and mass-consumption-goods industries. In contrast, the allocation of economic resources in most underdeveloped countries is topsy-turvy. Urban industrial growth takes priority over rural development. Industrial growth is increasingly based on the production and export of manufactures. The chief beneficiaries of this kind of dependent industrialization are the already wealthy people of developed and underdeveloped

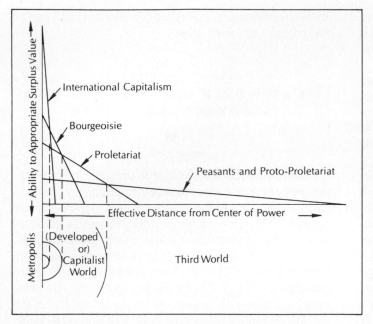

FIGURE 14.20
The world's stratified society. In a world viewed as a
set of von Thünen rings, the peasants exist at its
outer fringe—poor and discriminated against with respect to the use and control of world resources. Their
access to credit, insurance, education, manufactured
goods, technical knowledge, and infrastructure is virtually nonexistent.
(Source: de Souza and Porter, 1974, p. 81.)

countries. Except for a few privileged industrial workers, the broad mass of population is more or less excluded from the export-oriented economy.

Although urban areas have achieved remarkable industrialization since 1945, industrial employment has not kept pace with population growth. The employment situation has been aggravated by the introduction of advanced technology that permits high worker-output ratios. As a consequence, the urban peasants are absorbed by small-scale family enterprises, personal services, and unemployment. Its members are victims of urban growth with dependent industrialization, which itself is a consequence of the internationalization of direct production capital.

A Neglected Occupational Element

Today alarm is voiced about an impoverished and jobless class in Third World cities. But until the late 1960s, most social scientists failed to examine the urban peasantry for at least three reasons. First, there was a lack of data. Most systems of data collection recorded activities of the wage-earning population only. Second, most development models tended to concentrate on the economic growth features of the modern sector, to the exclusion of the traditional sector. Third, the modern-traditional dichotomy—a major evolutionary theory of social and economic change—encouraged social scientists to view development as intrusion of traditional systems by Western elements of modernization.

By the late 1960s, there was a growing awareness of the size and activities of the urban peasantry. Three main factors contributed to this awareness. First, a group of writings drew attention to the emergence of the urban peasantry as a major element in the class structure of urban areas. Frantz Fanon's (1963) *The Wretched of the Earth* and André Gunder Frank's (1969) *Capitalism and Underdevelopment in Latin America* are examples. Second, members of international organizations such as the United Nations drew attention to the grave employment problem in most cities of the underdeveloped world. Finally, some scholars began to examine their own recommendations for development. More specifically, these scholars questioned the validity of equating development with Western economic growth. Some of their disillusionment traced to the ecological and energy crises in developed countries. They began to exhibit less interest in capital-intensive production systems and more interest in labor-intensive production systems that minimize waste and pollution and that do not rely on high-energy consumption of fossil fuels.

Those who now study the urban peasantry of underdeveloped countries can be divided into two main groups. One group sees the process of occupational formation as *evolutionary*. In this view, problems posed by the urban peasantry are temporary. With continued economic growth, the urban peasantry will be absorbed into the bourgeoisie, just as in nineteenth-century Europe. The other group sees the process of occupational formation as *involutionary*. Comparison of the accelerated curve of technological evolution with the population explosion leads this group to fear the permanent establishment of an impoverished and jobless class. High rates of population growth in town and country, together with a large volume of urban migration, pose a constraint on labor absorption in capital-intensive enterprises. The result is mass unemployment and a proliferation of mainly service activities.

Despite the rapid growth of modern-sector activity in the 1970s and 1980s, it seems unlikely that most Third World cities will be able to provide labor-absorptive environments in the 1990s. With slower growth at the center of the world economy, the export-oriented route to industrialization in the periphery may be cut off. Moreover, demographic projections also support the view that the process of occupational formation is involutionary. Trends indicate that cities in the underdeveloped world will absorb more than a billion people between 1980 and the year 2000. Population growth of this magnitude—from 972 million city dwellers in 1980 to 2115 million in 2000—will ensure that unemployment and underemployment will remain acute problems for years, especially in population giants such as India.

Defining the Urban Peasantry

Thus far, we have noted that the urban peasants are a persistent and expanding class of people, but we have not delineated precisely who these people are. We can define the urban peasants in terms of structural, institutional, and income dimensions.

First, members of the urban peasantry conduct their activities within one sector of the dualistic structure of a Third World city (Figure 14.21). American anthropologist Clifford Geertz (1963) divided the structure of a Third World city into two economies: (1) a *firm-centered economy* (modern and capital intensive), where trade and industry occur through a set of impersonally defined social institutions with a variety of specialized occupations organized with respect to some particular or distributive ends, and (2) a *bazaar economy* (traditional and labor intensive), based on the independent activities of a set of highly competitive commodity traders who do business mainly by means of an incredible volume of ad hoc acts of exchange.

Second, the urban peasantry can be defined institutionally. Three systems of production exist: capitalist, socialist, and peasant. Like small farmers in the countryside, the urban peasantry are engaged in a peasant system, but within the urban environment.

Third, the urban peasantry can be defined in terms

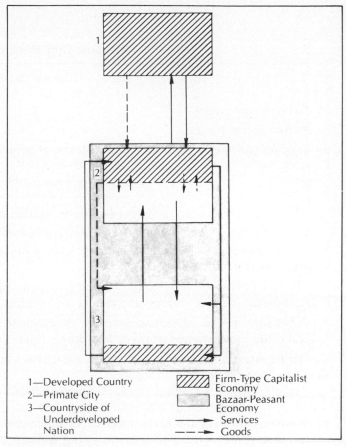

1—Developed Country
2—Primate City
3—Countryside of Underdeveloped Nation

▨▨▨ Firm-Type Capitalist Economy
▢ Bazaar-Peasant Economy
——→ Services
- - -→ Goods

FIGURE 14.21
The economic setting of the Third World primate city. *(Source: McGee, 1971, p. 70.)*

of income opportunities (Table 14.6). *Formal income opportunities* are associated with the legal activities of the *upper circuit. Informal income opportunities,* legal and illegal, are associated with activities of the *lower circuit.* The urban peasantry gain income mainly from informal opportunities.

On the basis of structural, institutional, and income dimensions, it is possible to define the urban peasantry as a substantial group engaged in a peasant system of production in the lower circuit and deriving income mainly from informal opportunities.

Economic, Ecological, and Political Features

ECONOMIC

Some economists, W. Arthur Lewis (1954) for one, have suggested that the economic activities of the urban peasantry are unproductive. Moreover, these econo-

Table 14.6
Income Opportunities in a Third World City

Formal Income Opportunities

- Public sector wages
- Private sector wages
- Transfer payments—pensions, unemployment benefits

Informal Income Opportunities: Legal

- Primary and secondary activities—farming, market gardening, building contractors and associated activities, self-employed artisans, shoemakers, tailors, and manufacturers of beers and spirits
- Tertiary enterprises with relatively large capital inputs—housing, transport, utilities, commodity speculation, and rentier activities
- Small-scale distribution—market operatives, petty traders, street hawkers, caterers in food and drink, bar attendants, carriers, commission agents, and dealers
- Other services—musicians, launderers, shoeshiners, barbers, night-soil removers, photographers, vehicle repair and other maintenance workers; brokerage; ritual services, magic, and medicine
- Private transfer payments—gifts and similar flows of money and goods between persons; borrowing; begging.

Informal Income Opportunities: Illegal

- Services—hustlers and spivs, receivers of stolen goods; usury and pawnbroking (at illegal interest rates); drug-pushing, prostitution, poncing, smuggling, bribery, political corruption (Tammany Hall-style), protection rackets.
- Transfers—petty theft (e.g., pickpockets), larceny (e.g., burglary and armed robbery), embezzlement, confidence tricksters (e.g., money doublers), gambling.

Source: McGee, 1974.

mists believe that the number of occupations can be reduced without decreasing output. In other words, there is "hidden unemployment" or "disguised unemployment" in the traditional sector. Various estimates have been made of the percentage of adult male population that can be withdrawn from a local economy without impairing productivity. The Firestone Plantation Company used a figure of 30% of Liberia's healthy adult male population in the 1950s.

Although no one has any idea how much the economic activities of the urban peasantry contribute to total income generated in the Third World city, it is clear that this group is engaged in an immense range of activities:

1. trade and transportation activities—taxi and truck operators, wholesalers, market vendors, and street traders

2. services—self-employed mechanics, car washers, shoe cleaners, and bicycle-tire pumpers

3. industrial activities—food preparers, furniture makers, carvers, and potters

4. financial activities—money lenders

The relative importance of lower-circuit economic activities compared with the upper-circuit activities varies inversely with city size (Figure 14.22). In absolute terms, however, the volume and degree of specialization of activities varies directly with the importance of cities. Whereas in the small city the economic activities of the urban peasants sometimes replace nonexistent modern services, in the large city the activities of this class serve growing populations that do not have regular access to upper-circuit activities, and also may function as external economies for upper-circuit activities (Santos, 1977).

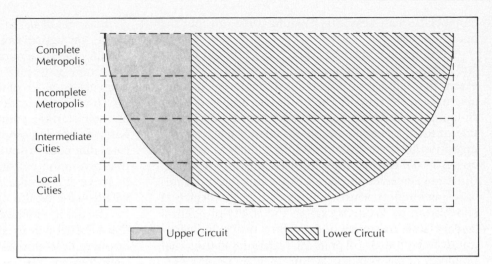

FIGURE 14.22
Relative importance of the two circuits and the systems of Third World cities. The relative importance of lower circuit economic activity compared to upper circuit economic activity varies inversely with city size.
(Source: Santos, 1977, p. 54.)

ECOLOGICAL

Members of the urban peasantry inhabit three main ecological milieus. They live on streets, rivers, canals, or waterfronts; in overcrowded inner-city slums; and in squatter settlements on the outskirts of cities. Squatter homes are built of makeshift materials, and sanitation and water facilities are often inadequate. Squatter settlements are far from ideal, but they do form an integral part of the informal sector, and they embody a number of features that favor the activities of the urban peasantry.

Consider some of the advantages of squatter settlements. They contribute to capital formation in the housing sector and add to social overhead in the form of schools, churches, and halls. They offer urban peasants full-time and part-time work. They support economic pursuits—bars, restaurants, repair shops, grocers, and fruit stores. They stimulate the growth of markets. Their strong social organization lends support to the urban peasantry in times of crises. Squatter settlements enable residents to live close to work; to carry out activities, such as food preparation, that are subject to legal restriction in the modern sector; to employ labor of all ages; and to conceal illegal activities, such as the preparation of drugs. Because they are often illegal, squatter settlements also enable residents, at least in theory, to live tax and rent free.

Although most politicians and planners believe that cities offer the best hope for the future of underdeveloped countries, they tend to condemn squatter settlements. Two solutions to the "squatter problem" are generally advocated. One is to replace "uncontrolled" settlements with housing projects. The other is to tear down the settlements and send the squatters back to the countryside. Now, however, a third solution is being considered: government help for projects undertaken by residents. Through the provision of suitable sites, of water and sanitation services, and of technical assistance for building, governments can accelerate housing improvements.

POLITICAL

Some observers (Fanon, 1963) liken the urban peasantry to a revolutionary force. They argue that the unequal distribution of power and wealth within cities of the underdeveloped world frustrates, angers, and alienates the urban poor. But Terry McGee (1971), in one of the most interesting applications of Clifford Geertz's (1963) involutionary construct, argued that "the dualist economic structure of the Third World city and its relationship with the rural hinterland will prevent the emergence of . . . a revolutionary demand among the urban poor in the short term" (Geertz, 1963, p. 28). He illustrated how available income is spread through a system of reciprocity, which facilitates the absorption of an ever-larger urban peasantry population.

According to McGee, the traditional sector acts as a safety valve and maintains the social and political status quo; but the traditional sector in a Third World city is heavily dependent on the existence of a traditional agricultural resource base and the activities and policies of the modern sector. He argued that "under conditions of penetration of the traditional structure—whether in the city or in the countryside—by capitalist modes of production and/or appropriation, traditional labour absorptive capacity would fall and the polarization between the modern capital-intensive sector [and the unemployed urban peasantry] would come out into the open" (p. 85).

It "came out into the open" in Cuba during the late 1950s. Western imperialism penetrated to such an extent that indigenous urban-rural involution was unable to develop further. The result was a revolutionary situation. A similar situation was averted in Jamaica and Puerto Rico, where an additional safety valve, external migration to Great Britain and the United States, was operative. Of course, other "Cubas" are not inevitable. Underdeveloped countries are at various stages of capitalist penetration. Much will depend on the degree of penetration by Western capital, the ability of political leaders to set the terms under which the capital penetrates, and the ability of political leaders to solve internal problems of development within their own societies.

Policy Issues

The urban peasantry are a direct result of the export-led economic model pursued in many underdeveloped countries. This model prescribes that the mass of people of the underdeveloped world work for others, not for themselves. It ensures a continuing process of underdevelopment that encourages population growth in most Third World cities. Planning strategies are necessary to cope with exacerbating unemployment and poverty. If the traditional pejorative view of the urban peasantry prevails, policies will be devised to eliminate their activities. Conversely, if more positive views prevail, policies may be designed to increase income and growth of the traditional sector. Policies should be directed toward improving rural life and reversing, or at least slowing, the trend toward urban development at the expense of the rural areas. They should also be directed toward solving the unprecedented crisis in basic-needs satisfaction.

THE BASIC-NEEDS CRISIS

◉

The United Nations Development Decades of the 1960s, 1970s, and 1980s held out promise of freeing the people of the Third World from poverty, ignorance, and disease. Experts generated hundreds of development plans in the interest of achieving this ambitious goal. Despite all the years of effort, however, the Third World still faces a basic-needs crisis in the 1990s.

In *Stranglehold on Africa*, René Dumont, a French expert on agricultural economics, and Marie-France Mottin (1983) demonstrated that the basic-needs crisis is far more acute now than it was during colonial times. They placed much of the blame for the worsening crisis on Third World leaders who took the Western model as their starting point for development. This model, based on the philosophy of Walt Rostow (1960), indicates that poor countries have only to replay the industrial revolution essentially as it happened in the West to arrive at a position where all their people will enjoy wealth—the wealth of a mass-consumer society.

The model emphasizes economic growth in the hope that benefits will trickle down to the poor. But in the incoherent economies of the Third World, growth in GNP does not filter down to the masses. Moreover, the composition and distribution of GNP—not its absolute size or growth rate—are critical for the social welfare of poor people.

Faced by failure of the income-oriented approach to development, some scholars began to hammer out a basic-needs approach in the late 1970s (Streeten, 1981). This approach is based on the assumption that the essential needs of all—food, clothing, shelter, water, and sanitation—should be satisfied before the less essential needs of a few are met. Although there is almost universal agreement on this objective, there is little agreement on the most effective way of achieving it.

One method of implementation—the count, cost, and deliver approach—consists of counting the number of the deprived, determining the cost of the goods and services needed to eradicate deprivation, and delivering them to target groups. Another approach focuses on providing economic opportunities for the poor, raising their productivity, and improving their access to both inputs and markets. A third approach involves seeking out processes by which the system that perpetuates poverty can be destroyed or reformed.

American geographer Lakshman Yapa (1980) favors the last approach. He argues that the allocation of resources to basic needs cannot be divorced from the circumstances of the means of production. Therefore, the direct eradication of poverty must proceed from a study of the institutions that maintain poverty.

The Development of Underdevelopment

Contrary to what is commonly believed, underdevelopment is not a state caused by physical and cultural factors, subject to the corrective influence of moderniza-

Water is vital for human life. No one could survive without it for more than a few days. Although the earth's fresh water reserves are plentiful, more than 98% of the supply is locked into polar ice caps and glaciers, or underground aquifers. These women fill their jugs at a communal well in Kairouan, Tunisia, then begin the long trek home.
(Source: UN Photo 156286/John Isaac.)

The most basic need in the world today is for safe water, improved sanitation and immunization programs. There is a *basic needs crisis* in the third world today. Infections, parasitic disease, respiratory illness and injury from warfare continue to threaten life, so health care is oriented primarily to disease prevention rather than cure. The minimal welfare resources and public infrastructure in developing countries are often supplemented by charitable organizations throughout the world. The question is, how should high mass consumption countries aid the traditional societies. America, Japan and Europe have followed the *entitlement theory*, suggesting that each person earns a standard of living according to his value and contribution to the world's economy. *Social contract theory* of justice offers a different view, arguing that it is a privilege to be highly skilled and highly educated, but the circumstances of people in the third world largely do not allow it. It, therefore, seems fair for the rich to give to the poor.

tion. What is critical to underdevelopment is a world economic structure that seems to perpetuate backwardness. To illustrate, let us trace the development of underdevelopment in Kenya.

For the last 100 years, Kenya's dominant groups have not placed a high priority on the production of goods for mass consumption. Consistently, the surplus has been diverted elsewhere and resulted in the preemption of the basic-goods fund. During the colonial era, a portion of the surplus went to enrich Great Britain and the European elite of Kenya.

In the late nineteenth century, European settlers established the Scheduled Areas—3 million hectares of mainly moist, high-potential land alienated for the use of Europeans. A major objective of establishing the Scheduled Areas was to transform part of the African population into a proletarian labor force to serve the needs of the capitalist sector. Africans were needed to work on the farms, ranches, plantations, and other enterprises owned and run by the European settlers. Because simple commodity production of indigenous agriculture enabled Africans to be more or less self-sufficient, it became necessary to upset that self-sufficiency and mandate that they supply their labor. A labor force came into being through various actions on the part of the British.

An early device (1902) was the *hut tax*. A year later,

when it was discovered that people were crowding into fewer houses, a "*pole tax*," payable by all adults, was levied. Other means included the regulation and confiscation of African livestock and the control of wages. Europeans encouraged Africans to live on their farms and estates as squatters rather than to work as contract laborers. Africans were prohibited from growing coffee, tea, sisal, and pyrethrum and from selling livestock and dairy products on the European export market. They were paid a lower market price for corn than European farmers were. They could not open shops without a government license, and they had no access to credit. Europeans, on the other hand, were assisted at every turn. The road and railway network that focused on Nairobi and Mombasa served the alienated land—a built-in locational advantage that helped Europeans market their produce. European settlers could acquire land cheaply. They received agricultural research and extension services. They were given tax breaks on imported equipment and exported crops. The government even helped Europeans recruit labor and obtain credit.

This arsenal of devices, from inequitable taxes to dual pricing systems, illustrates the manner in which the European capitalist sector served its own ends. The capitalist sector forced Africans to buy more goods and services from Europeans and substituted market uncertainty with ecological uncertainty for the African people. Because of high rates of African population growth, the result was overcrowding and tremendous land fragmentation as well as landlessness on the reserves.

At the peak of the *colonial division of labor* in 1960, the European highlands had 3600 Europeans in agriculture, overseeing an African labor force of 268,000, about 75 workers per farm. Europeans received a per capita income of $29,450 for commercial agriculture, whereas Africans received $3.50. "The rate of profit in 1960, taking into account replacement of capital investment, loan repayments, and the wage bill, was over 130 percent" (Porter, 1979, p. 49).

The results of the colonial organization of space and division of labor were Mau Mau, the Swynnerton Plan, and independence for Kenya in 1963. *Mau Mau* was a land rebellion, a violent uprising of Africans, mainly Kikuyu, against the European colonial authority. The war began in 1952 and ebbed in 1956. Eventually it led to independence, but immediately to major social changes, particularly concerning land rights. Reform began in 1954 when a royal commission investigating the land grievances behind Mau Mau recommended sweeping changes. The commission's work led to the 1955 *Swynnerton Plan,* which called for consolidating small parcels of land and giving Africans access to credit, to farmer training, to research findings, to technical assistance, and to improved water supplies. It also called for lifting the ban on Africans from growing coffee and other cash crops. The objective of the plan was to encourage the development of an agrarian middle class.

The policies of the colonial period were carried on into the postcolonial period, despite the fact that Africans rather than Europeans were making decisions. International trade played an ideological function by representing the various needs of the elite as coincident with the interests of the nation at large, legitimating the continued preemption of the basic-goods fund. Within Kenya, many of the larger farms were left intact and in the hands of individuals. Moreover, there was an extension of the Swynnerton European Highlands model to the high-potential former reserves. Consequently, the whole highlands became "a developing core following a market-oriented private entrepreneurial path of development. The semi-arid areas . . . continued to play the role of periphery—the location of landless migrants who try to farm areas drier than they are experienced with, the source areas of male migrants who work for farmers in the highlands" (Porter, 1979, p. 53).

The postindependence period witnessed the continued functioning of three processes that result from modernization and that exert a strong influence on the basic-needs crisis. They are proletarianization, marginalization, and commodification. *Proletarianization* is the process that separates people from the means of production (land) so that they begin to sell their labor power. *Marginalization* is the process that forces people to sell land in order to survive. And *commodification* is the process whereby a good or service, normally considered free, comes to be exchanged for a price on the market. For example, with the privatization of land ownership, conventional rights to water and vegetation entered the marketplace.

Policy Issues

Given the existing world system and the impossibility of providing each family with a Western-style middle-class basket of goods, it seems that the only way for economic development to improve the living conditions of the Third World poor is to use resources directly in the production and distribution of basic goods. Issues that are central to implementing this goal include questions related to overpopulation and population growth, questions of productive forces, questions of the social relations of production, and questions related to the role of the international community.

A direct attack to reduce population growth is often regarded as a way to increase available resources to satisfy basic needs. However, overpopulation is the result of the exclusion of people from their means of livelihood. "Irrational as it may seem, high fertility rates are a rational response to this externally induced condition" (Yapa, 1985, p. 246). Government-sponsored fertility control programs will be unsuccessful unless they are accompanied by concomitant programs for providing jobs and for changing employment conditions.

Some observers wonder whether sufficient productive resources are available to employ the millions of urban and rural poor. Much depends on the social relations of production and the choice of technology. Limited employment in the export-processing zones is one of the main causes of urban poverty, whereas unequal access to land is one of the prime determinants of rural poverty. In many countries, fewer than 10% of landowners control anywhere from 80% to 90% of the land (World Bank, 1974). The large farms concentrate on the cultivation of crops for export. Removed from the land, the rural poor cannot produce food themselves; neither can they purchase their basic needs in the marketplace. Export-oriented agriculture and export-led industrialization block the development of an indigenous, self-expanding economy in most Third World countries.

Most of the technology used in the Third World also arrests autonomous development. Capital-intensive technology, which comes from and is designed to reproduce the social and consumption systems of the IACs, keeps poor countries dependent. This imported technology is also inappropriate in countries with large supplies of labor. Studies have shown that a considerable range of technology is available, and the least-cost choice often lies closer to the labor-intensive end rather than the capital-intensive end of the spectrum (Pickett, 1977).

The international community can do much to eradicate poverty. If the New International Economic Order (NIEO) were adopted, it could generate more resources for underdeveloped countries, and those resources could be channeled directly into providing basic human needs. Acceptance of the NIEO, however, appears to be highly unlikely in the face of opposition not only from developed countries, but from underdeveloped countries as well. The elites of center countries have vested interests to protect. And so do elites of the periphery who prefer to remain an appendage of, and dependent on, the IACs.

The basic-needs approach to development is one positive way to help the poor emerge from their poverty. But this approach is still viewed with suspicion by those who hold to the premise that history will repeat itself and that the wealth of a mass-consumer society eventually will be enjoyed by all. The wretched of the earth cannot wait for the benefits of growth to spread from the top downward. They need a basic-needs approach—an approach that emphasizes the fundamental concern of development, which is human beings and their needs. This approach, viewed by many as laudable but idealistic, was promised when John F. Kennedy launched the first Development Decade in the United Nations in 1960. Without a direct attack on the basic-needs crisis, more than half a billion absolutely poor people will exist in the underdeveloped countries at the end of this century (World Bank, 1979).

HELP FOR LESS DEVELOPED COUNTRIES FROM ADVANCED NATIONS

◈

The IACs must come to the aid of LDCs today. How can this occur peacefully? Three methods are generally cited for IACs to help LDCs: (1) expand trade with LDCs, (2) invest private capital in LDCs, and (3) provide foreign aid to LDCs. As a last resort, the World Bank may also step in to help.

Expansion of Trade with Less Developed Countries

Some economists have suggested that expanding trade with LDCs is one way to help them. It is true that reducing tariffs and trade barriers with LDCs will improve the situation somewhat. With the North American Free Trade Agreement (NAFTA), the United States is attempting to remove all trade barriers with Mexico, for example. However, increasing trade with LDCs means that they must produce something for export, something of value that an IAC wants. Not all developing nations have abundant raw materials and agricultural surpluses. And when a major trade relation exists between an LDC and an IAC, the LDC is often tied to the developed nation and, as a result of the economic vitality of the IAC, the LDC experiences downturns that it would not normally experience. This relationship could have dire consequences for the price of exported goods from the LDC. For example, the world price of copper dropped from $1.50 an ounce in 1974 to 50¢ an ounce in 1975. Thus the export markets were destroyed for some LDCs who depended on copper for survival.

Private Capital Flows to Less Developed Countries

LDCs are also a destination for investments from MNCs, private banks, and large corporations. For example, major U.S. automakers have now built numerous plants in Brazil and Mexico. In Tijuana alone, 500 U.S. labor-intensive manufacturing plants now take advantage of the average 90-cent-per-hour worker wage. As mentioned earlier, Citicorp and Chase Manhattan Bank have made loans to Philippine and Argentine governments. Private capital flows have been increasing to LDCs from advanced nations since 1950. They reached a high point in the early 1980s near the time of the LDC debt crisis of $30 billion per year. Since the debt crisis, however, investments and private capital flows have decreased substantially because of concerns about returns on investment.

All too often, however, the LDC must not only provide the investing corporation or country with some pledge of a financial return, but also guarantee that a politically stable environment will prevail. An international trade climate must also be supported by financial and marketing systems, a favorable tax rate, maintenance of infrastructure, and some measurement of a reliable labor flow. These latter guarantees are frequently lacking in poor LDCs and preempt the major capital flows that would otherwise exist. African nations in particular have not been able to tap private capital flows from large corporations and commercial banks because of problems with these conditions.

Foreign Aid from Advanced Nations

In order to reverse the vicious cycle of poverty shown in Figure 1.5, foreign aid is needed in the form of direct grants, gifts, and public loans to LDCs. Capital accumulation is necessary to retool the workplace, to increase productivity, and to retrain the labor pool. Capital is needed for improvement of the sadly lacking infrastructures in developing nations that are necessary to attract private capital flows. These infrastructures include transportation facilities; communications systems; educational programs; irrigation for agriculture; and public health not only for populations, but also for visiting MNCs and their entrepreneurial classes.

The United States has been a major world player in foreign-aid programs. U.S. foreign aid averaged $15 billion per year, for example, from 1990 to 1994. The majority of this aid was administered through the U.S. State Department's Aid for International Development (AID). Additional direct aid included food programs to needy countries under the U.S. government's Food-for-Peace program. Other nations have also rallied, and in 1990, IACs as a group contributed a total of $50 billion. In addition, OPEC nations contributed $2.5 billion.

Unfortunately, to the discredit of the United States, most of its aid has stipulations such as purchase requirements that make the LDCs patronize American products and services. Furthermore, in the past, foreign aid has been distributed on the basis of political ties, as opposed to economic need. For example, Israel, Egypt, and Turkey each receive nearly $3 billion in aid per year. These nations are neither the most populous nor the most needy, but they do occupy a strategic area of the Middle East where vast oil deposits exist and where America is fighting a cold war against Islamic fundamentalism. In addition, the United States has guaranteed its support of Israel in its hostile environment.

Also, unfortunately, IAC contributions amount to only 0.5% of their collective GDPs. This amount is too

small. To make matters worse, the former Soviet Union and Eastern European nations are now making strong pleas for increased aid from the West. Many LDCs fear that aid that would normally be channeled to them will now go toward supporting privatization in former Communist areas of the world. The IACs fear is that the cost of failure (because of IAC neglect) of democratization in Russia will be far greater than the cost (as a result of IAC aid) of success. If Western Europe and America agree, the larger portion of their foreign aid (through grants, loans, and direct aid) will be syphoned from the LDCs.

World Bank Aid

The IACs, including the United States, have established a *World Bank*, whose major goal is to support developing nations in their quest for improved economic status. The World Bank is generally considered a "basket case" funding agency. When all hope has faded for private capital flows and for expanding trade and direct foreign aid from IACs, the World Bank sells bonds to finance and fund bailout programs for LDCs. World Bank activities center primarily on infrastructure. Examples of World Bank projects are large dams, irrigation projects, transportation systems, roads, highways, airports, and basic communications systems. Sanitation programs, health programs, and housing have also been funded. The World Bank's efforts are to improve the economic setting of a country so that private capital flows will be forthcoming and will be self-perpetuating. The World Bank has also provided consultancy expertise to developing nations to determine not only their internal strengths and weaknesses, but also how to reinforce their positive aspects of comparative advantage and cumulative causation.

SUMMARY

◈

In this chapter, we consider problems of Third World development. We begin by discussing goals for development and by listing objectives that are by and large universally endorsed. We then explore typical characteristics of underdevelopment—overpopulation, lack of resources, capital shortage—considering whether these attributes can be properly construed as causative factors.

In discussing major perspectives on development,

we see how modernization theories, which stress economic growth and Westernization, have obscured important aspects of underdevelopment. World political economy theories explain why the Third World does not develop. They touch on a fundamental concept: Underdevelopment is a world economic structure that perpetuates backwardness. Ecopolitical economy theories question the desirability of the income-oriented approach, instead emphasizing the feasibility of the basic-needs approach to development.

Some scholars believe that development theorists have overemphasized the economic dimension of the development process. Culture plays an important role in the process, too. For example, the rise of Japan as a tower of economic strength can be understood only in terms of the country's unique isomorphism of state-oriented values and policy efforts. Japan's success challenges the American and Western European approach to capital accumulation.

As the world system expanded, it became differentiated into a core of rich countries and a periphery of poor countries. One distinctive linkage between the core and the periphery was colonialism. Our discussion of waves of colonialism demonstrates that underdevelopment is not a state but a process.

When colonial holdings disappeared after World War II, experts drew up plans to accelerate the pace of development in underdeveloped countries. Regional scientists emphasized the center-dominant model. Although this approach tends to concentrate income and wealth, especially in the early stages, conservatives contend that eventual convergence between rich and poor regions is the norm. Liberals believe that only progressive taxation, social services, and other government actions can spread the benefits of growth. In contrast, radicals argue that because underdeveloped countries are dependent on core regions, and the spread from center to periphery is limited, institutional reform must precede planning.

The urban peasantry illustrated the unequal distribution of wealth generated by capitalism in underdeveloped countries. Like the peasants in the countryside, these people are poor and discriminated against with respect to the use and control of resources. We follow with a discussion of the basic-needs crisis and end with a proposal to alleviate Third World poverty by means of a basic-needs approach.

Although there is a little disagreement about the priority for meeting basic needs, there is much disagreement over the feasibility of implementation. There is conflict concerning appropriate economic policies, which, in some instances, is exacerbated by organized interest groups. For example, the ruling classes in many underdeveloped countries, who are the beneficiaries of concentrated and uneven growth, are often unwilling to share the fruits of economic growth with the poor of their own countries.

Is there a human right to basic needs? Should the basic needs of the majority be satisfied before the less essential needs of the few are met? Would a commitment to provide everyone with a decent existence prove too expensive? And would it blunt incentives to work and save? Your answers to these questions depend on your world view. They may also depend on whether you think the "poverty bomb" holds equal threat for global destruction as a nuclear bomb.

◈

KEY TERMS

backwash effects
basic needs
bazaar economy
capital flight
center-periphery
circular and cumulative causation
Commonwealth of Independent States (CIP)
colonial division of labor
colonial organization of space
dependency
development
deviation amplification

deviation counteraction
direct foreign aid
dual economy
ecopolitical economy
fatalism
firm-centered economy
growth-stage theories
involution
land alienation
less developed countries (LDCs)
limiting factors
lower circuit

modernization theories
multiplier
polarization effects
primary sector
privatization
quaternary sector
secondary sector
spread effects
squatter settlements
tertiary sector

trickle-down effects
underdevelopment
underemployment
upper circuit
urban peasants
vicious cycle of poverty
world cultural realms
world political economy theories
world system theory
write-down

◈

SUGGESTED READINGS

Armstrong, W., and McGee, T. G. 1985. *Theatres of Accumulation: Studies in Asian and Latin American Urbanization.* New York: Metheun.

Chisholm, M. 1982. *Modern World Development: A Geographical Perspective.* London: Hutchinson.

Corbridge, S. 1986. *Capitalist World Development: A Critique of Radical Development Geography.* Totowa, NJ: Rowman and Littlefield.

de Souza, A.B. 1985. Dependency and economic growth. *Journal of Geography* 85–94.

———. 1986. To have and have not. Colonialism and core-periphery relations. *Focus* 36 (No. 3):14–19.

de Souza, A. B., and J. B. Foust. 1979. *World Space Economy,* Columbus, OH: Merrill.

de Souza, A. B., and P. W. Porter. 1974. *The Underdevelopment and Modernization of the Third World.* Resource Paper No. 28. Washington, DC. Association of American Geographers.

Frank, A. G. 1981. *Crisis in the Third World.* London: Heinemann.

Gilbert, A., and Gugler, J. 1981. *Cities, Poverty, and Development: Urbanization in the Third World.* New York: Oxford University Press.

Gore, C. 1984. *Regions in Question: Space, Development Theory and Regional Policy.* New York: Metheun.

Hoffman, George W., ed. *Europe in the 1990s: A Georgraphical Analysis,* 6th ed. New York: Wiley, 1990.

Holloway, Steve, R., and Kavita Pandit. "The Disparity Between the Level of Economic Development and Human Welfare." *Professional Geographer* 44 (February 1992): 57–71.

Mabogunje, A. O. 1980. *The Development Process: A Spatial Perspective.* London: Hutchinson.

Murphy, Alexander B. "Western Investment in East-Central Europe: Emerging Patterns and Implications for State Stability." *Professional Geographer* 44 (August 1992): 249–259.

O'Connor, A. M. *Poverty in Africa: A Geographical Approach.* London: Belhaven Press, 1991.

O hUallachain, Breandan, and Neil Reid. "Source Country Differences in the Spatial Distribution of Foreign Direct Investment in the United States." *Professional Geographer* 44 (August 1992): 272–285.

Peet, R., ed. 1980. *An introduction to Marxist Theories of Underdevelopment.* Research School of Pacific Studies. Department of Human Geography. Canberra: The Australian National University.

Porter, Doug, Bryant Allen, and Gaye Thompson. *Development in Practice: Paved with Good Intentions.* London and New York: Routledge, 1991.

Rostow, Walter W. *The Stages of Economic Growth,* 3d ed./New York: Cambridge: Cambridge University Press, 1990.

———. *Geopolitics and Geoculture: Essays on the Changing World-System.* Cambridge: Cambridge University Press, 1991.

EPILOGUE

The world economy is becoming ever more integrated. It is therefore essential that we come to understand the interconnected, international, and global character of our lives. And this is a matter of scale. In an essay on the Midwest, American geographer Cotton Mather (1986) acknowledged the role scale has played in changing the way we live and think:

> A century ago our capital in the Midwest was the county seat. It was the center through which our lives were regulated. The county seat was the authority and the administrator of our roads and our communication system. The county superintendent reigned supreme over our education. The county sheriff enforced the law. The county home took care of our aged. And we had the county fair and the county pole tax.
>
> Then came the role of the state capital as our central seat of authority and regulation. We had state roads and state communication systems. We had state boards of education and state universities. We had state police, state laws pertaining to our old folk, state fairs, and the state tax.
>
> The national capital reached ever more into our lives. Eventually, we had national regulation of our water-ways, railways, education, and even our drinking water. Then we had national regulation of air transportation, but that came after the Wright brothers.
>
> Today we have international agreements on Antarctica, and the Law of the Sea is an evolving international instrument. There are international agreements on communication, on health, and the exchange of scholars. Additionally, we have international currency exchanges, international trade centers, international bridges, and real World Fairs. And we have the International Geographical Union that some of us are yet to join. (pp. 193–94).

Mather was suggesting, just as this book has, that we can no longer afford an insular view of the world. We must link our local geographies with a complex, internationalized, and rapidly shifting political economy. To address problems of population growth, of planetary pollution and resource depletion, of food and famine, of patterns of production and land use, of social and economic development, and of multinationals and international trade, we must think and act globally. Moreover, we must appreciate different ways of explaining world events. We must be aware of how different attitudes and views influence approaches to solving global problems of interest to the economic geographer.

GLOSSARY

absolute advantage The ability of one country to produce a product at a lower cost than another country.

absolute location Fixed position in relation to a standard grid system.

abstract space A geographic space, homogeneous in all respects. Movement over this space is equally easy in all directions.

accessibility A measure of aggregate nearness. It refers to the nearness of a given point to other points.

accessibility index A measure of the shortest path between one vertex and all others.

achieved characteristics Sociodemographic characteristics, such as education, occupation, income, marital status, and labor force participation, over which we have some degree of control.

acid rain Acid rain, snow, or fog derives from the combustion of coal, releasing sulfur and nitrogen oxides that react with water in the earth's atmosphere.

adaptive economic behavior Behavior based on systematic analysis of alternative locations that leads to the development of rational industrial location.

administrative principle The spatial organization of central places in which a higher-order administrative place is surrounded by six lower-order administrative places.

adoptive economic behavior Economic location decision making based on copying past, successful patterns.

African Development Bank An international financial institution that extends loans to African countries for purposes of development.

agglomeration A measure of aggregate nearness. It refers to total aggregate nearness among a number of points.

agglomeration economies The savings in cost that result from the clustering of firms.

agribusiness Food production by commercial farms, input industries, and marketing and processing firms that contribute to the total food sector.

agricultural involution The ability of the agricultural system in densely populated areas of Asia to absorb increasing numbers of people and still maintain minimal subsistence levels in rural communities.

agriculture The livelihood of farming and cattle ranching by cultivation of the soil and the rearing of livestock.

ARC/INFO A GIS software package produced by Environmental Systems Research Institute of Redlands, California.

areal differentiation The study of geographic areas for purposes of comparing their similarities and differences.

areal integration An approach to the world economy that searches for theory and broad-sweeping understanding, rather than unique characteristics of every place or country.

ascribed characteristics Sociodemographic characteristics such as gender, race, and ethnicity, with which we are born and over which we have basically no control.

Asian Development Bank An international financial institution that extends loans to Asian countries for development projects.

assembly costs The costs of bringing raw materials together at a factory.

Atlantic Fruit and Vegetable Belt An area of high agricultural production per acre, stretching from southern Virginia through the eastern half of North and South Carolina to coastal Georgia and Florida.

automatic vehicle identification (AVI) Automatic surveillance of highway vehicles aimed at adjusting tolls, based on levels of congestion.

automobile component plants Plants manufacturing parts required in the assembly of an automobile.

average product The total output divided by the number of units of input used to produce it.

average total costs Total costs divided by the quantity of output.

baby boom The dramatic rise in the U.S. birth rate following World War II, between the years 1946 and 1964.

baby bust The years immediately following the baby boom in which U.S. fertility rates fell dramatically, or any period of low population growth.

backhaul A carrier's return trip.

backward integration A firm takes over operations that were previously the responsibility of its suppliers.

balance-oriented life-style A mind-set that insists that because resources are finite, they must be recycled, and input rates slowed down to prevent ecological overload.

basic cost The cost of an input for a firm at its least-cost location.

basic firms Firms that produce goods or services for export outside the local region.

bazaar economy The traditional and labor-intensive sector of a Third World city.

behavioral matrix A device used for analyzing nonoptimal decision making. It shows the location of decision makers with respect to information and their ability to use information.

beta index A measure of linkage intensity or connectivity.

birth rate Annual number of births per thousand population.

boomdocks Boom towns in remote, boomdock areas that provide inexpensive housing.

brain drain Less developed countries lose talented people to industrially advanced nations through immigration politics.

break-of-bulk The stage at which a shipment is divided into parts. This typically occurs at a port where the shipment is transferred from water transport to land transport.

Bretton Woods The New Hampshire location of a 1944 international meeting of treasury and bank officials of the Allied countries. The meeting designed the International Monetary Fund (IMF) and the International Bank for Reconstruction and Development. It also led indirectly to the creation of the General Agreement on Tariffs and Trade (GATT).

California Environmental Quality Act (CEQA) Legislation enacted in 1971 requiring environmental impact reports and review to be prepared for all major developmental and land-use change.

capital A factor of production, including tools, buildings, and machines used by labor to fashion goods from raw material.

capital accumulation The engine that drives economic growth under the capitalist system.

capital controls Restrictions on the movement of money or capital across national borders.

capital flight Local individuals and whole countries have invested their monies in overseas ventures and in foreign banks for safekeeping.

capital goods Manufactured items that can be used to create wealth or other goods. For example, a home washing machine is a consumer good, but the machines used to make that washing machine are capital goods.

capital resources Money supply and availability to finance an industry.

capital-intensive A term that applies to an industry in which a high proportion of capital is used relative to the amount of labor employed.

capitalism The political-economic system based on private property and profit.

carrying capacity The maximum population an ecosystem can support.

cartel An organization of buyers and sellers, capable of manipulating price and/or supply.

ceiling rent Maximum rental that a particular user pays for a site.

central business district The downtown area of a city.

Central Florida Manufacturing Region Includes the cities of Jacksonville, Tampa, St. Petersburg, Orlando, and Miami.

central function A good or service offered by a central place.

central place Center for local exchange of goods and services, including stores and population settlement.

central-place theory A theory that attempts to explain the size and spacing of settlements and the arrangement of their market areas.

centrifical drift The outward movement from the city of industrial properties due to the attention of less expensive land.

Chi-Pitts Megalopolis centered on Chicago, Detroit, Cleveland, and Pittsburgh.

circular and cumulative causation Myrdal's theory that continuing changes move the system in the same direction as initial changes, but much farther, resulting in industrial and urban agglomeration and innovation.

circular flowing market system The flow of labor and resources from households to firms and the flow of products and wages from firms to households.

cloning spatial structure A headquarters/branch plant structure allowing for the complete production process to take place at each site.

colonial division of labor An artificial form of labor specialization imposed on underdeveloped countries by colonial powers.

colonial organization of space The European organization and zoning of land at all scales—urban, regional, national—to serve Europe's own interests during the colonial period.

command economy A society in which a central authority or government establishes the rules of economic behavior and decision making and usually owns the means of production.

commercial agriculture Agricultural goods produced for sale in the city or on the international market.

commercial geography The study of products and exports of the main regions of the world.

common market A form of regional economic integration among member countries that disallows internal trade barriers, provides for common external trade barriers, and permits free factor mobility.

Commonwealth of Independent States (CIS) The former Soviet Union's 15 socialist republics, which today are independent countries, the largest of which is Russia.

comparative advantage The theory that stresses relative advantage, rather than absolute advantage, as the true basis for trade. Comparative advantage is gained when countries focus on exporting the goods they can produce at the lowest relative cost.

compensation Wages, salaries, or bartered items paid by employers to workers, plus fringe benefits, such as unemployment compensation and medical payments.

compensation demand A table that illustrates the total amount of a good or service that all consumers in a country, taken together, are willing to buy at each possible price.

competitive-bidding process The aspect of classical location theory in which those people willing and able to pay the highest price for a particular site win the competition and put the site to the highest and best use.

complementarity A concept in which two places interact based on a demand in one place and a supply in the other, the demand and the supply being specifically complementary.

computer network Interlinking of computers, regionally or internationally, via hardwire, fiber optics, or telecommunications satellite for information transfer and decision making.

concentric zone model The city is viewed as a series of concentric zones, with the focus of economic activity on the central business district (CBD). City land use expands symmetrically in all directions.

concrete space The actual surface of the earth in all its geographic complexity.

conglomerate A widely diversified corporation that controls the production and marketing of dissimilar products.

conglomerate merger The control, production, and marketing of diverse products. (See Diversification, Horizontal Integration, Vertical Integration.)

connectivity A measure of the interrelation between places in a network.

constant returns to scale As outputs double, total costs double, but the cost per unit of output remains unchanged.

conurbation A continuously urban area formed by the expansion and consequent coalescence of previously separate urban areas.

convenience goods Central functions that are low in price, uniform in quality and style, and purchased frequently. They include goods and services needed on a day-to-day basis, such as groceries, gasoline, and drugstore items.

Corn Belt The midwestern region of the United States, centered on the state of Iowa, that predominates in the growing of corn and cattle raising.

cost-insurance-freight (CIF) pricing A policy whereby each consumer is charged production costs plus a flat markup to cover transportation charges.

cost-space convergence The reduction of travel costs between places as a result of transport improvements.

countertrade The direct exchange of goods or services for other goods and services.

cumulative causation The process by which economic activity leading to increasing economic development tends to concentrate in an area with an initial advantage, draining investment capital and skilled labor from the peripheral area.

customs union A form of regional economic integration among countries that disallows internal trade barriers and provides for common external trade barriers.

daily urban system Trade areas around cities or employment centers that have a large area of dominant influence.

death rate Annual number of deaths per thousand population.

demand and supply Demand is the quantity of a good that buyers would like to purchase during a given period at a given price in a competitive market economy. Supply is the quantity of a good that sellers would like to sell during a given period at a given price.

demand conditions The market conditions in a host country that aid the production process.

demographic equation Population at time 2 equals population at time 1, plus births, minus deaths, plus in-immigration, minus out-migration.

demographic transition The historical shift of birth and death rates from high to low levels in a population.

dependence A conditioning situation in which the economies of one group of countries are underdeveloped by the development and expansion of other groups.

dependency theorists The theory of economic development that argues that the Third World is dependent on, and has been exploited by, their former colonial overseers.

depletion curves Graphs used to project lifetimes of resources.

development A historical process that encompasses the entire economic and social life of a nation, resulting in change for the better. Development is related to, but not synonymous with, economic growth.

development bank An investment and/or loan fund that aids the development of underdeveloped countries.

deviation reduction Policies or processes that decrease in the quality between rich and poor regions.

deviation-amplification Any process that amplifies an initial inequality and increases divergence from an initial condition.

direct investment The purchase of enough of the equity shares of a company to gain some degree of managerial control.

direction The orientation of places toward each other.

diseconomies of scale Diminishing marginal returns to scale that occur when a firm becomes too large to manage and operate efficiently.

disguised unemployment A term used by some economists to describe the surplus of labor that is thought to exist in the traditional sector of underdeveloped countries.

disorganic development A form of "development" at odds with local cultural and political institutions.

distance A measure of the cost to overcome the space between two places.

distance-decay effect With increase in distance, the decline in the level of interaction between two places.

diversification A company produces an increasing number of unrelated products, each with elements of horizontal and vertical integration.

division of labor The specialization of workers in particular operations of a production process. Labor specialization is a source of scale economies, a necessary ingredient in the evolution of a market-exchange economy.

domestic farm subsidy Direct payments to farmers according to their production levels in order to subsidize their output.

double cropping More than one crop is produced from the same plot throughout the year.

doubling time The time in years required for the population of a country to double.

dual economy In the study of industrial location, a term used to refer to two types of business enterprises, fundamentally different from one another: large, organically complex center firms and small, simply structured periphery firms. In the study of development, the term is used to refer to two types of social and economic systems existing simultaneously within the same territory: one system modern, the other traditional.

dual-sourcing A strategy of cloning used by multilocational companies to guarantee continuity of production, usually by undermining the potential monopoly control of a work force in one place over a particular production process.

economic integration The ultimate form of regional integration. It involves removing all barriers to interbloc movement of merchandise and factors of production, and unifying the social and economic policies of member nations. All members are subject to the binding decisions of a supranational authority consisting of executive, judicial, and legislative branches.

economic liberalism Sometimes used as a synonym for capitalism.

economic person The behavior of any individual who consistently does those things that will enable him or her to achieve the desired economic objective and, therefore, yields the maximum amount of utility.

economic rent The monetary return from the use of land after the costs of production and marketing have been deducted.

economic union A form of regional economic integration having all the features of a common market, as well as a common central bank, unified monetary and tax systems, and a common foreign economic policy.

ecumenopolis The global urban network of the twenty first century, consisting of most of the world's population.

edge A link; a route in a topological diagram of a network.

egalitarian society A society that has as many positions of prestige in any given age-sex sector as there are persons capable of filling them. It is forged through cooperative behavior.

elasticity The responsiveness of prices to changes in supply and/or demand for a good.

Engel's Law The principle according to which, with given tastes or preferences, the proportion of income spent on food decreases as income increases.

entrepreneurial skill The human know-how and skill that combines other resources to create a product or service using innovations and decisions.

environmental determinism The notion that human behavior is environmentally prescribed.

environmental perception The ways in which people form images of other places, and how these images influence decision making.

environmental sustainability The level of the environment for which renewable resources can resupply and, therefore, sustain themselves in a steady state.

equilibrium price The price at which the quantity supplied equals the quantity demanded and, therefore, no surplus or shortage is produced.

Eurocurrency A currency deposited in a commercial bank outside the country of origin.

Eurodollar The major form of Eurocurrency.

Euromarkets The international financial markets that usually exist outside of the country whose currency is utilized.

European Economic Community (EEC) A group of European countries established in 1958 on the basis of a treaty signed in Rome in 1957. The community consists of 12 members—France, West Germany, Italy, Belgium, the Netherlands, Luxemburg, Britain, Ireland, Denmark, Greece, Spain, and Portugal—whose aim is to establish a United States of Europe; sometimes called simply, E.C.

European free-trade association A group of European countries established in 1960 for the purposes of trade, aiming to abolish tariffs on imports of goods originating in the group. The original members were Britain, Norway, Sweden, Denmark, Portugal, Austria, and Switzerland. Finland joined as an associate member in 1961. Iceland joined in 1970. Britain and Denmark left the free-trade area in 1973 upon joining the European Economic Community (EEC).

exchange controls Restriction of free dealings in foreign exchange, including multiple exchange rates and rationing.

exchange rate The value of the U.S. dollar compared with foreign currency.

exchange value The value at which a commodity can be exchanged for another commodity.

export quota The government of an exporting country limits the volume or value of exports to an importing country voluntarily.

export restraint agreement A nontariff barrier whereby governments coerce other governments to accept voluntary trade export restraint agreements.

export-led industrialization A development strategy emphasizing the production and export of manufactured items. Its success depends on a rising world economy.

factor of production　One of the economic inputs—land, labor, capital, entrepreneurship, technology—essential to a production effort.

factor-driven stage　Processing and exporting natural resources and primary products.

fatalism　The philosophical belief that future life conditions will not improve, regardless of the amount of work or effort involved.

feed lots　Penned corrals near cities used for fattening cattle; forage is trucked into these fattening pens.

Fertile Crescent　Present-day countries of Israel, Lebanon, Syria, Iraq, and parts of Turkey, Iran, and Jordan, where early plant and animal domestication occurred 10,000 years ago.

fertility　The actual reproductive performance of an individual, a couple, a group, or a population.

fertility rate　The number of live births per 1000 people in a country per year.

fiber-optic cable　A new high-carrying capacity technology in telecommunications

filtering process　The relocation of people within a city under free-market conditions. Filtering may be upward or downward. Upward filtering refers to the movement of people into higher quality housing. Downward filtering refers to the movement of people into lower quality housing.

firm-centered economy　The modern and capital-intensive sector of a Third World city.

fixed cost　The cost of the investment in land, plant, and equipment that must be paid, even if nothing is subsequently produced.

floating exchange rate　The value of a currency fluctuates according to changes in supply and demand for the currency on the international market.

Food for Peace programs　U.S. program that allowed agricultural surpluses to be distributed to starving nations instead of being liquidated.

Food Stamp program　U.S. government program that allowed agricultural surpluses to be distributed to America's poor, instead of being liquidated.

forces of production　In materialist science, forces including living labor power, appropriated natural resources, and capital equipment provided by past generations of workers.

Fordism　A mode of capital accumulation based on integrated production and assembly.

foreign direct investment (FDI)　Investing in companies in a foreign country, with the purpose of managerial and production control.

foreign sourcing　An arrangement whereby firms based in advanced industrial countries provide design specifications to producers in underdeveloped countries, purchase the finished products, and then sell them at home or abroad.

forward integration　A firm begins to control the outlets for its products.

four-field rotation system　Rotating three crops amongst four fields over a period of years, while allowing a fourth rotated field to remain fallow, thus rusting the soil for that year.

four questions of economic geography　What will be produced? How will it be produced? Where will it be produced? For whom will it be produced?

Four Tigers　South Korea, Taiwan, Hong Kong, and Singapore.

four worlds　First World—most developed countries; Second World—former command economies of Eastern Europe and the USSR; Third World—the remaining areas of the world that are less developed than the first two; Fourth World—the poorest of Third World nations.

franchising　A licensing venture allowing a licensee to manufacture and sell under the original company's name.

free-trade area　A form of regional economic integration in which member countries agree to eliminate trade barriers among themselves, but continue to pursue their independent trade policies with respect to nonmember countries.

free-trade zones　Areas where imported goods can be processed for reexport without paying duties, since the goods will not be used locally.

freight rates　Payment to a carrier for the loading, transporting, and unloading of goods.

freight-on-board (FOB) pricing　A policy whereby a consumer pays the plant price plus the cost of transportation.

friction of distance　There are time and cost factors associated with movement across space, which exerts a friction to movement and flow.

functional region　An area differentiated by the activity within it; that is, by the interdependence and organization of its features.

game theory　Developed primarily by John von Neumann, a mathematical approach to decision making in the face of uncertainty.

General Agreement on Tariffs and Trade (GATT)　An international agency, headquartered in Geneva, Switzerland, supportive of efforts to reduce barriers to international trade.

general systems theory　A theory that applies the principles of organization, interaction, hierarchy, and growth to any system.

gentrification　Intercity neighborhood redevelopment and property upgrading by high-income settlers, thus displacing lower income residents.

geographic inertia　The tendency of a place with established infrastructure to maintain its importance as a focus of activity after the original conditions influencing its development have altered, ceased to be relevant, or no longer exist.

geographic information system (GIS)　A technique for storing and transforming geographic data on a wide variety of variables to produce digital maps with hardware and associated computer software.

geothermal energy　Energy produced by heat from deep inside the earth as water interfaces with heated rocks from the earth's core, producing steam.

global office　Workplaces interlinked by satellite communications offering telecommunications and computer-based methods of information transfer.

global positioning systems (GPS)　A hand-held device that communicates with satellites to determine extremely accurate terrestrial location.

global shift of manufacturing　The pattern of employment and production shift from developed nations to developing nations of Eastern Europe and the Pacific Rim.

grain elevators　Large storage devices dotting the Great Plains of America that are used for wheat.

graph theory　The branch of mathematics concerned with the properties of graphs; that is, with the vertices and edges. Graph theory is used to describe and evaluate networks.

graphs　Idealized transportation networks that are comprised of *vertices*, which represent points or intersections, and *edges*, which represent interconnecting routes.

gravity model　The product of the masses or the populations of two cities, divided by the distance squared, is proportional to the traffic flow between them.

Green Revolution　A popular term for the greatly increased yield per hectare that followed the introduction of new, scientifically bred and selected varieties of such food crops as wheat, maize, and rice.

greenhouse effect The warming of the atmosphere due to increased amounts of carbon dioxide, nitrous oxides, methane, and chlorofluorocarbons.

gross domestic product (GDP) The monetary value of final output produced by U.S. businesses, individuals, and government inside the United States once a year.

gross national product (GNP) The market value of all goods and services produced by U.S. businesses, individuals, and government inside and outside of the U.S. in a given year.

growth stage theories A developmental sequence of the national economic improvement of underdeveloped countries based on sufficient surplus to generate and sustain economic growth.

growth-oriented life-style A mind-set that insists on maximum production and consumption. It assumes an environment of unlimited waste and pollution reservoirs and indestructible ecosystems.

guilds Craft, professional, or early trade associations.

Gulf Coast Manufacturing Region Region that stretches from southeastern Texas through southern Louisiana, Mississippi, and Alabama to the tip of Florida panhandle.

hamlet The smallest of central places, usually less than 200 in population.

Hecksher-Ohlin Theory Theory that a country should specialize in producing those goods that demand the least from its scarce production factors and that it should export specialties in order to obtain goods that it is too ill-equipped to make.

hierarchical marginal good The highest order good offered by a center at a given level of the central-place hierarchy.

hierarchy In central-place theory, the arrangement of settlements in a series of discrete classes, the rank of each determined by the level of specialization of functions.

hierarchy of central places Small central places and their trade areas, nested within medium-sized central places and their trade areas. Medium-sized central places are nested within a few large central places within large trade areas.

high value added Commodities, which due to the manufacturing process, are much more valuable than the raw materials used to produce them.

higher order of goods Goods or services with higher thresholds, such as furniture or hospital care.

highest and best use The notion that land is allocated to the use that earns the highest location rent.

horizontal integration A business strategy to increase a firm's scale by buying, building, or merging with another firm at the same stage of production of a product.

HOV High occupancy vehicle (HOV) lanes used for express traffic of vehicles with more than one rider.

hub-and-spoke networks Hubs are major cities that collect passengers from small cities, in the local vicinity, via spoke lines. Hubs redistribute passengers between sets of original major cities.

human capital Educational attainment, labor force participation, occupation, and income.

human development index (HDI) Life expectancy, literacy rate, and per capita purchasing power.

human resources The skill and cost of labor, the cultural factors of the term, and the motivation for the work ethic.

human suffering index A useful descriptive measure of the differences in living conditions among countries, including 10 measures of human well-being.

import-substitution industrialization A development strategy to replace imports of final manufactures through domestic production. Subsidies, loans, and protective tariff regulations are often the means of assuring local production.

industrial inertia Location decisions for industrial activity, once made, lead to a continuation of that pattern.

industrial restructuring A term used to refer to the alternating phases of growth and decline in industrial activity. It emphasizes changes in employment between regions, and links these with change in the world economy.

industry life cycle The typical sequence of developmental stages in the evolution of an industry.

industry life cycle model Industries experience periods of rapid growth, diminishing growth, and stability or decline.

inelastic supply A supply schedule that does not show large increases due to a price increase.

infant industry A young industry which, it is argued, requires tariff protection until it matures to the point where it is efficient enough to compete successfully with imports.

infant mortality rate Number of deaths during the first year of life per 1000 live births.

information technology Microelectronics technologies, including microprocessors, computers, robotics, satellites, and fiber-optic cables.

infrastructure The services and supporting activities necessary for an economy to function; for example, transportation, banking, education, health care, and government.

innovation A new idea applicable to something useful for humankind.

innovation drive stage Innovation in new product design derived from high levels of technology and skill.

integrated circuit Transistors connected on a single, small silicon chip acting as a semiconductor of electrical current.

intellectual property rights Establishing and policing patent, copyright, and trademark rights on an international basis.

intelligent vehicle highway systems (IVHS) In-vehicle computers and navigation systems to help drivers avoid accidents and congestion while offering information on trip destinations.

intensive subsidence agriculture A high-intensity type of primitive agriculture practiced by densely populated areas of the developing world.

Inter-American Development Bank An international financial institution that extends loans for development to countries in Latin America and the Caribbean.

interest Payments made to owners of capital as a compensation for its contribution to production.

intermediate technology Low-cost, small-scale technologies "intermediate" between "primitive" stick-farming methods and complex Western agri-industrial technical packages.

International Bank for Reconstruction and Development An international financial institution that extends loans to underdeveloped countries at commercial rates of interest; also called the World Bank.

international business Any form of business activity that crosses a national border.

international currency markets The internationalization of domestic currency, banking, and capital markets.

International Development Association An adjunct of the International Bank for Reconstruction and Development. It extends loans with generous interest and repayment terms to the poorer underdeveloped countries.

International Finance Corporation An adjunct of the International Bank for Reconstruction and Development. It provides either loans or equity investments to private-sector companies in underdeveloped countries.

International Monetary Fund (IMF) An international financial agency that attempts to promote international monetary cooperation, facilitate international trade, promote exchange stability, assist in the establishment of a multilateral system of payments without restrictions on foreign currency exchange, make loans to help countries adjust to temporary international payment problems, and lessen the severity of international payments disequilibrium.

international subcontracting The arrangement by multinational corporations (MNCs) to use Third World firms to produce entire products, components, or services in order to cover markets in an advanced industrial country.

intervening opportunity An alteration in the complementarity of places.

investment-driven stage Using foreign technology and scale economies to produce standardized products with mass labor inputs provided by the local population.

involution The ability of the peasantry or the protoproletariat in the Third World to absorb an unusual number of people. The process of involution is characterized by a tenacity of basic pattern, internal elaboration and ornateness, technical hairsplitting, and unending virtuosity.

isodapane The locus of points of equal transport cost from a factory.

isotims Isocost lines of transportation, assembly, and distribution costs for each potential plant location. (See Isodapanes.)

isotropic environment An imaginary plain or surface with uniform environmental conditions, including transport costs.

isotropic surface A plain that is homogeneous in all respects, with equal ease of movement in all directions from every point.

Japan Incorporated Sometimes used by Japan's competitors, an appellation acknowledging the successful marriage between Japanese businesses and government.

Japanese transplants Japanese-made vehicles that are assembled and built in America.

jobs/housing balance The notion of expanding the supply of housing in job-rich areas, and the quantity of jobs in housing-rich areas.

joint venture An enterprise undertaken by two or more parties. It may be a jointly owned subsidiary, a consortium, or a syndicate.

journey to work Travel by individuals to work, yielding the largest proportion of travel by American households.

just-in-time manufacturing Quick delivery and response of parts and inventory delivery from component plants to final assembly operations.

knowledge-based resources Research, development, and scientific and technical skill within the country.

kolkhozes Collective farms in the former Soviet Union.

Kondratiev cycles Successive cycles of growth and decline in industrial economies, occurring with a periodicity of some 50 to 60 years duration.

Kuzbass Short for Kuznetsk Basin, centered on the town of Novosibirsk, located on the Transiberian Railroad, east of the Euro Mountains in Russia/Asia.

labor A factor of production that includes human physical exertion performed in the creation of a good or service.

labor force The economically active population consisting of productively employed and temporarily unemployed people.

labor migration theory Theories to explain the process of changing residences from one geographic locale to another, due to economic factors.

labor process The nature and degree of the division of labor.

labor-intensive A term that applies to an industry in which a high proportion of labor is used relative to the amount of capital employed.

land A factor of production that includes not only a geographic portion of the earth's surface, but also the raw materials from this region.

land alienation A term referring to the land taken away from indigenous people by Europeans for their own use.

law of demand An empirical regularity of consumer behavior that presumes the quantity of a good demanded and the price of the good are inversely related.

law of diminishing returns The law according to which, when factors of production (land, labor, and capital) are doubled, output doubles; but if one factor of production or only some factors are doubled, output increases, but fails to double. The law assumes given levels of technological knowledge.

law of retail gravitation This law uses the gravity model concept to identify the breaking point between two cities' spheres of influence.

law of supply An empirical regularity of producer behavior that presumes the quantity of a good produced and the price of that good are directly related.

least-cost-to-build network A transport system designed to keep the cost to the builder as low as possible.

least-cost-to-use network A transport system designed to keep the cost to the user as low as possible.

level three alert At this level, urban pollution is near its highest, and residents are advised to stay indoors, cease from strenuous exercise and, automobiles are ordered off highways.

licensing venture The rental of patents, trademarks, or technology by a company in exchange for royalty payments.

life expectancy The average number of years an individual can be expected to live given current socioeconomic and medical conditions.

limits to growth The optimum population size for the world, provided by the club of Rome, shows that growth must be limited. A gloomy forecast by Paul Ehrlich suggests worldwide famine and war as the inevitable results of continued increases in world population.

line-haul costs Costs involved in moving commodities along a route.

linear market The spatial organization of central places into a K = 2 hierarchy.

Little Dragons Philippines, Thailand, Malaysia, Indonesia, and China.

localization economies The declining average costs for firms as the output of the industries, of which they are part, increases.

localized raw material A material that is not available everywhere; thus, it exerts a specific influence on industrial location.

location (See absolute location; relative location.)

location allocation model A spatial model used in the world economy to identify the best location for a public facility, industrial plant, or transportation route.

location rent The advantage of one parcel of land over another because of its location; the concept of declining rents with an increase in distance from the market.

location theory A compilation of ideas and methods dealing with questions of accessibility.

locational costs Costs over and above the basic cost of an input or the least-cost price.

locational inertia The stabilizing effect of invested capital in a region.

locational interdependence A concept that implies that competition from rival producers can lower potential revenues at a given point and space.

logical positivism The formation of hypotheses, data collection, and a search for theory through the scientific method.

Lome Convention A 1974 trade agreement signed by the European Economic Community (EEC) and 46 countries in Africa, the Caribbean, and the Pacific.

long run A period long enough to permit a firm to vary its production function and the quantity of all of the inputs.

long-run average cost (LRAC) The graphical relationship between the average costs and the level of output over the long run.

lower circuit The traditional and labor-intensive sector of a Third World city.

lower order of goods Goods or services with low thresholds, such as a loaf of bread or a gallon of gas.

machinofacture The phase of the developing division of labor where mechanization and division of labor within production occurs.

Maine Street The Canadian megalopolis extending from Windsor, Hamilton, Toronto, Quebec, to Montreal, along the northern shores of the eastern Great Lakes.

malnutrition A state of poor health in which an individual does not obtain enough essential vitamins and nutrients, especially proteins.

manufacture Workers and machines producing goods in a factory setting.

margin of cultivation The location at a certain distance from the market at which marginal products are produced and, therefore, the edge of profitability is reached.

marginal product The addition to total output attributable to the last unit of the variable input employed.

Marine fisheries Species of fish populations found in oceans, seas, and other saltwater bodies.

market area The territory surrounding any central point of exchange. It includes all potential customers for whom market price plus transport cost will still be sufficiently low to justify their purchases at that price in the central place.

market basket A batch of housing, goods, and services that individuals consume on a given income with a given set of preferences.

market exchange An economic system that establishes market prices. The prices are the mechanism for connecting economic activity among a large number of individuals and for controlling a large number of decentralized decisions.

market linkage The connection resulting from the sale of a firm's output to nearby firms.

market orientation Plant location is oriented to the market, rather than the source of raw materials, because of a savings in transportation costs.

marketing principle The spatial organization of central places when a central place of any order is at the midpoint of each set of three neighboring places of the next higher order.

Marxist The view that the world economy is the product of exploitation by capital of labor following the principles and teachings of Karl Marx.

massing of reserves The principle that states that large firms can maintain smaller inventories of spare machines or machine parts than can small firms.

material index In Weberian analysis, a measure of the weight a raw material loses in processing; the weight of raw materials divided by the weight of the finished product.

maximum sustainable yield Maximum production consistent with maintaining future productivity of a renewable resource.

Mediterranean cropping Agriculture producing specialty crops because of mild climates, including citrus, grapes, nuts, avocados, tomatoes, and flowers.

megalopolis A giant, sprawling urban region encompassing many cities, towns, and villages. The term was coined by geographer Jean Gottman to describe the Atlantic Urban Region that extends from Boston to Washington, DC.

megatrend Future directions of the economy, according to John Naisbitt, which have the capacity to transform our lives.

mercantile model A model that attempts to explain the wholesale trade relationships that link regions.

mercantilism A theory popular among European nations in the early modern period stating that the economic and political strength of a country lay in its acquiring gold and silver, to be achieved by restricting imports, developing production for exports, and prohibiting the export of gold and silver.

microelectronics Semiconductors, integrated circuits, and electronic components and parts.

microprocessor A computer the size of one's fingernail used for applications, including calculators, electric typewriters, computers, industrial robots, and aircraft guiding systems.

MicroVision A GIS software package used for target marketing.

migration Movement of a population, resulting in a change of permanent residence.

milk shed The area around the city from which milk can be shipped daily, without spoilage.

milpa farming Temporary use of rain-forest land for agriculture by cutting and burning the overgrowth.

mine tailings Leftover ore wastes from which minerals have been extracted.

minicity A multifunctional urban node that is the focal point of the outer city, especially in North America. Suburban minicities include a variety of land uses—retailing, wholesaling, manufacturing, entertainment, and medical functions.

mixed crop and livestock farming The raising of beef cattle and hogs as the primary revenue source, with the production of crops fed to the cattle.

mixed economic systems Economic systems that are a hybrid form of capitalists, command economy, or a traditional system, usually where both government and private decision determine how resources are allocated.

modernization A word full of hope, enthusiasm, and the idea of progress; in common usage, suggesting that Western culture invented or perfected most things associated with development and that in due course people in underdeveloped countries will enjoy them as well.

money capital Items of exchange used to purchase capital goods, such as money.

Monte Carlo simulation A probabilistic model that accounts for sheer chance and reproduces a particular process by discovering the major rules of the game.

Moscow Industrial Region This industrial region, also known as the Central Industrial Region, is located near the population center of Russia, west of the Euro Mountains.

multinational A company with established operations in several host countries, usually headquartered in one parent country.

multinational corporations (MNCs) Companies based on one country that do business in one or more other countries.

multiplant enterprises Companies with factories and offices in widely scattered locations, sometimes in other countries.

multipurpose travel Bypassing the closest central place in favor of the next largest central place, which offers all needs of a particular shopper (e.g., groceries, gasoline, basic services, etc.).

multiple-nuclei model Besides the traditional central business district (CBD), the modern city has a number of outlying high-intensity nucleations of commercial, industrial, and residential land uses.

multiplier An "injection" into the spending stream in the belief that total output will increase as a result. The opening of a new factory in a region is an example of an injection. New funds flow into the region from the outside, thereby raising the level of regional income.

National Environmental Policy Act (NEPA) Legislation enacted in 1969 by the federal government requiring environmental impact reports and review to be prepared and conducted on every major public land development.

Nationwide Personal Transportation Survey (NPTS) A major

national travel survey conducted every 7 years, giving information regarding mobility of the American population.

need creation A process in which luxuries are marketed as necessities.

negative population growth A falling level of population where out-migration and death exceed in-migration and births.

NeoFordism Fragmentation of the labor force and the distilling of the traditional blue-collar class through the introduction of electronic information systems.

net energy The amount of energy available minus the quantity used to find, concentrate, and deliver energy to the consumer.

net migration The net effect of immigration and emigration on an area's population in a given period, expressed as an increase or decrease.

network Any set of interlinking routes that cross or meet one another at nodes, junctions, or terminals.

New International Economic Order (NIEO) A 1974 U.N. resolution originating with the underdeveloped countries and calling for a more equal distribution of the world's income.

nomadic capital The switching of production from place to place because of innovation in transportation and communication savings.

nonbasic firms Firms producing a good or service for a consumption inside the region.

nontariff barriers Obstacles to trade other than tariffs.

nonrenewable resources Resources that are fixed in amount—that cannot regenerate—such as fossil fuels and metals.

normal lapse rate The rate at which the atmosphere cools with increasing elevation (3.6 degrees per 1000 feet).

normative model A model that attempts to describe how people should behave and make decisions if they wish to achieve certain well-defined objectives.

North American Free Trade Agreement (NAFTA) Agreement between Canada, the United States, and Mexico passed by the U.S. Congress and signed by President Clinton in December 1993.

offshore assembly An arrangement whereby firms based in advanced industrial countries provide design specifications to producers in underdeveloped countries, purchase the finished products and then sell them at home or abroad.

oligopoly A small number of producers in an economy so that the actions of one can have a considerable effect on another.

opportunity cost The cost of foregone alternatives given up in order to produce other activities or goods.

optimizers Economic persons who organize themselves and their activities in space so as to optimize utility.

optimum population size The theoretical number of people that would provide the best balance of population and resources for a desirable standard of living.

Organization of Petroleum Exporting Countries (OPEC) The international cartel of oil-producing countries.

organizational ecology Businesses are born, they grow and mature, they die, and between birth and death, some of them migrate.

organizational structure of capital A term that is often applied to the size and associated characteristics of firms.

overpopulation A level of population in excess of the "optimum" level relative to the food supply or rate of consumption of energy and resources.

paddy A flooded field planted with rice seedlings.

parity price Equality between the prices at which farmers could sell their products, and the prices they could spend on goods and services to run the farm.

part-process spatial structure A headquarters/branch plant structure in which the production process is geographically fragmented or differentiated.

pastoral nomadism Animal herds used for subsidence, moved from one forage area to another, in a cyclicle pattern of migration.

Paul Revere network The shortest network interconnecting a set of points.

peasant agriculture Subsidence agriculture, using little mechanical equipment and producing meager, labor-intensive crops.

Peter's projection A map projection attempting to give area to the Third World in proportion to its true size.

petrol dollars OPEC oil surpluses poured into the major Euro banks.

phenomenological approach Life takes on meaning only through individual experiences and needs; little need for models or theory.

physical resources These are raw materials, site and situation factors, international time distance, and space conveyance.

physiologic density The number of people per square mile of arable or farmable land.

plantation A large landholding or estate devoted to the production of export crops, such as coffee, tea, sugar cane, sisal, and hemp. Plantations are usually located in underdeveloped countries and depend on foreign capital for their operation.

Po River Valley The principal industrial district of southern Europe, including Torino, Milan, Genoa, Cremona, Verona, and Venice.

polarization effects The negative influences prosperous regions exert on less prosperous regions.

population density The number of people per unit of land, normally a square kilometer or square mile.

population growth rate The difference between the birth rate and death rate; generally expressed as so many persons per hundred.

population hurdle The rate of investment in a society must be greater than population growth or it will be stuck in a vicious, Malthusian cycle of poverty.

population pyramid A special type of bar chart indicating the distribution of a population by age and sex.

portfolio investment Capital investment in the equity of a company, not involving managerial control of a foreign country.

postindustrial society The stage of an evolving society in which traditional manufacturing activity has given way to the growth of high-tech industry and an employment emphasis on services, government, and management-information activities.

price ceiling A legally mandated price level below the typical market price.

price floor A guaranteed price above the market price.

primary economic activity An economic pursuit mainly involving natural or culturally improved resources, such as agriculture, livestock raising, forestry, fishing, and mining.

primary sector of the economy Mining, lumbering, agriculture, and fishing.

primate city A country's leading city economically, culturally, historically, and politically, and much larger than competing cities in population, wealth, and power.

product life cycle The typical sequence through which a product passes, from its introduction into the market to when it is replaced by a new product.

product market The market where households buy and firms sell the products and services they have produced.

production factors Labor, capital, technology, entrepreneurship, and land containing raw materials.

production function The technological and organizational characteristics of a firm that transform inputs into outputs. In the short run, at least one input is fixed in amount. In the long run, all the inputs are variable.

production linkages Economies that accrue to firms that locate near other producers manufacturing their basic raw materials.

production possibilities analysis A table or curve that shows various combinations of goods or services that can be produced given employment, resources, and technology are held constant.

profits The reward, in monetary terms, paid to management or entrepreneurial skill for its supply to the economy over and above its costs.

protectionism An effort to protect domestic producers by means of controls on imports.

protoproletariat An urban class engaged within a peasant system of production. Most of its income is gained from informal income opportunities.

psychic income Nonmonetary rewards gained from operating at a particular point.

purchasing power parity The amount of income per capita based not on dollars, but on goods and services that the dollars will purchase.

pure capitalism An economic system in which the means of production are privately owned, and markets and prices are used to direct and coordinate all economic activity.

pure competition model A market structure of industry made up of many small firms that produce homogeneous products and that have no real influence on the market price of their products.

pure raw material A material that does not lose weight in processing.

quaternary activity Those sectors of the economy associated with research; the gathering and disseminating of information; the administration and transmission of information, including radio, television, newspaper and magazine publishing; educational systems; and the computer information technologies.

quaternary economic activity An information-oriented economic activity, as pursued, for example, in research units, think tanks, and management-information services.

quaternary sector of the economy Information processing, finance, insurance, real estate, education, and computer and telecommunication fields.

radical humanist The theory that labor, the environment and the means of reduction have for centuries been dominated by white male power establishment.

Randstad The ring city in the western Netherlands, including Rotterdam, the Hague, Amsterdam, and Utrecht megalopolis.

range The average minimum distance consumers are willing and able to travel to purchase a good (or service) at a particular price in a central place.

range of the good The distance people are willing to travel to purchase a good or a service of a particular threshold.

rank society A society in which positions of valued status are circumscribed, so that not all with sufficient talent to hold such positions actually achieve them.

rank-size rule An empirical rule describing the distribution of city sizes in an area. It states that the population of any given city tends to be equal to the population of the largest city in the set divided by the rank of the given city. For example, if the population of the largest city numbers 10,000, the population of the fifth largest city will be 2000—that is, 10,000 divided by 5.

rate of natural increase The excess of births over deaths, or the difference between the crude birth rate and the crude death rate.

raw material orientation The processing plant is oriented to the site of the raw materials, as opposed to the market, because of savings and transportation costs.

raw materials A substance in the physical environment considered to have value or usefulness in the production process.

real capital Human-made resources used to produce goods and services that do not directly satisfy human wants and needs.

reciprocity A mutually beneficial form of economic exchange, common in egalitarian societies.

redistribution A form of economic exchange in which equity is maintained by a central authority that redistributes production.

regional growth forest Long-range urban forecasting of population housing and the economic activity for the region and small geographic areas within it.

relative location Position with respect to other locations.

renewable resources Resources capable of yielding output indefinitely if used wisely, such as water and biomass.

rent Payments made to land owners as a productive factor for their contribution to the production process and the operation of the economy.

rent gradient A sloping net-profit line. The intersection of the line and the point of zero profit indicates the limit of commercial crop production.

reserve A known and identified deposit of earth materials that can be tapped profitably with existing technology under prevailing economic and legal conditions.

reserve deficiency minerals Those minerals for which U.S. reserves are not sufficient to meet anticipated near-term industrial needs.

resource A naturally occurring substance of potential profit that can be extracted under prevailing conditions.

resource market A place where households sell and firms buy resources of the services of resources.

Rhine-Alsace-Lorraine Region The second most industrial region of Europe, located in southwestern Germany and eastern France.

Ruhr Located on the Rhine in northeastern Germany, Europe's most important industrial district.

rule of 70 Dividing the average annual rate of growth by 70, yields the doubling time of population for a country.

saddle point The minimum-maximum point in game theory.

satellite firms Small organizations that manage to survive in the market by minimizing their labor cost and maximizing labor exploitation (also called peripheral firms).

satisficers Decision makers who make choices that are satisfactory rather than optimal.

sawah A flooded field planted with rice seedlings.

scale The size of operation that will determine the volume of industrial output.

scale economies The cost-reducing changes that lower the average costs of firms as they grow in size. These changes may be internal or external to firms.

scarcity The fact that the world's resources are limited in their supply and, therefore, have a value.

second law of thermodynamics The law according to which any voluntary process has as a consequence a net increase in disorder or entropy. It can also be expressed as the degradation of energy into a less useful form, such as low-grade heat.

secondary economic activity The processing of materials to render them more directly useful to people; manufacturing.

secondary sector of the economy Manufacturing and assembling of raw materials.

service linkages Economies that occur when a cluster of firms becomes large enough to support specialized services.

settlement-building function Sales of goods and services beyond the local retail and service hinterland of a central place.

settlement-forming function   Sales of goods and services that occur totally within the hinterland of a central place.

settlement-serving function   Sales of goods and services to residents of a central place.

shifting cultivation   Temporary use of rain-forest land for agriculture by cutting and burning the overgrowth.

Shimble index   A graph-theoretic measure of the compactness of a network; sometimes called the dispersion index.

shopping goods   Central functions that are normally higher in price than convenience goods. They vary in quality and style, and are purchased infrequently.

short run   A period short enough for at least one input to be fixed in an amount and invariable.

Silicon Valley   The world's largest manufacturing area for semiconductors, microprocessors, and computer equipment, located south of San Francisco.

slash-and-burn agriculture   Temporary use of rain-forest land for agriculture by cutting and burning the overgrowth.

smart cars   Cars equipped with microcomputers and video screens to take the frustration out of driving.

smart highways   Vehicle sensing systems to monitor traffic, volume, and speed, resulting in optimum traffic flow control and radar collision warning systems.

social relations of production   Class relations between owners of the means of production and the workers employed to operate these means.

social surplus   The portion of annual production of any society that is neither consumed by the direct producer nor used for the reproduction of the stock of means of production available at the start of the year. In a class-divided society, the social surplus is always appropriated by the ruling class.

soil bank program   Government program that paid farmers to keep acreage out of production because of market overproduction.

solar energy   Energy in the form of radiation received from the sun and changed into heat as it strikes the earth's surface.

Southeastern Manufacturing Region   Also known as the Piedmont Region, it stretches south from Central Virginia, through North Carolina, South Carolina, and Northern Georgia, and into Alabama and Tennessee.

sovkhozes   State-owned large collective farms in the former Soviet Union.

space preference structure   Measures the trade off between the distance travelled to shop for goods and services and the town size.

spatial decision support systems (SDSS)   Prescription decision-making principles laden with data and rules for data use, designed to help decision makers reach decisions about spatial problems that confront them.

spatial diffusion   The spread of information, goods, or people across space.

spatial fetishism   Attributing the cause of an event to locational factors.

spatial interaction   The movement, contact, and linkage between points in space; for example, the movement of people, goods, traffic, information, and capital between one place and another.

spatial margins to profitability   The intersection of a space-cost curve, and the market price of a finished product.

spatial mismatch theory   Reverse commuting, traveling to work against the main flow of traffic from the intercity to the suburbs.

spatial monopoly   A situation in which a single firm controls a given area of the market by virtue of its location.

spatial oligopoly   A situation in which a few firms compete for a given segment of the total market space.

spatial organization   A theme in geography emphasizing how space is organized by individuals and societies to suit their own designs. It provides a framework for analyzing and interpreting location decisions and spatial structures in a mobile, interconnected world.

spatial process   A movement or location strategy.

spatial regularity   The arrangement of economic activity on the earth's surface in a discernable pattern.

spatial structure   The internal organization of a distribution that limits, channels, or controls a spatial process.

spread city   A term that usually refers to the contemporary suburban or multifunctional American metropolis. The spread city encompasses more territory and has less "centrality" than the compact nineteenth-century industrial city.

spread effects   The beneficial influences prosperous regions exert on less prosperous regions.

spring wheat   Wheat planted in the spring and harvested in the fall. Fields are fallow in the winter.

squatter settlements   Residential areas that are home to the urban poor in underdeveloped countries. The various terms used to identify squatter settlements include the following: calampas, tugurios, favelas, mocambos, ranchos, and barriadas in Latin America; bidonvilles and gourbivilles in North Africa; bustees, jhoupris, jhuggis, kampongs, and barung barong in south and southeast Asia.

stages of production   According to the law of diminishing returns, the three stages that total product passes through as successive units of variable input are applied to a fixed input. In Stage 1, the average product curve rises to its peak; in Stage 2, it declines; and in Stage 3, the total product curve declines.

strategic minerals   Those minerals deemed critical to the economic and military well-being of the nation.

stratified society   A society in which members of the same sex and equivalent age status do not have equal access to the basic resources that sustain life.

stationary state   The dynamic state of a system in which input and output are balanced at a point below the maximum limits of the system and its surroundings.

stochastic model   A model that assumes bounded rationality; it recognizes the major role of chance in the decision-making process.

subsidence agriculture   Peasant agriculture, using little mechanical equipment, producing meager, and labor-intensive crops.

suburb   An outlying residential district of a city.

suitability modeling   A GIS map overlay technique to assess the ability of each increment of land under study to support a given use; a type of spatial decision support system (SDSS).

surplus value   The difference between the value produced by a worker (value of units of labor produced) and the worker's wage (value of labor power).

swidden   Temporary use of rain-forest land for agriculture by cutting and burning the overgrowth.

target pricing   The government pays a farmer directly the difference between the market selling price and the price that the government has set artificially.

tariff   A schedule of duties placed on products. A tariff may be levied on an ad valorum basis (i.e., as a percentage of value) or on a specific basis (i.e., as an amount per unit). Tariffs are used to serve many functions—to make imports expensive relative to domestic substitutes; to retaliate against restrictive trade policies of other countries; to protect infant industries; and to protect strategic industries, such as agriculture, in times of war.

Taylorism   The application of scientific management principles to production.

technique   The method of procedure by which inputs are combined to produce a finished product.

technostructure Corporate technical personnel, including scientists and technicians.

terms of trade The relative price levels of exports to imports for a country.

terminal costs Costs incurred in loading, packing, and unloading shipments, and preparing shipping documents.

tertiary activities Those sectors of the economy that provide markets and exchange for commodities, including wholesale and retail trade and associated transportation government information services, as well as personal and professional services.

tertiary economic activity An economic pursuit in which a service is performed, such as retailing, wholesaling, servicing, teaching, government, medicine, and recreation.

tertiary sector of the economy The provision of goods and services, most notably wholesaling, retailing, and professional services.

theory of contestable markets The free entry of new transportation operators into the market to ensure efficiency.

Third World debt crisis The dangerous economic position of certain Third World nations that carry an enormous debt to overseas banks, private banks, and governments, the interest payments of which rob the host country of needed investment.

threshold The minimum level of demand needed to support an economic activity.

TIGER files Geocoded digital line graphs that are computer readable, representing roads, streets, and highways across America.

time-space covergence The reduction in travel time between places that results from transport improvements.

trade area The area dominated by a central place; sometimes called a hinterland or tributary area.

trade deficit The excess of imports over exports for a country for any specific year.

traditional market An economic system in which culture, tradition, and folkways determine how scarce resources will be used by the economy.

traffic principle The spatial organization of central places when as many central places as possible lie on a traffic route between two important cities.

tragedy of the commons Public resources are frequently ruined by the cumulative isolated actions of individuals in that overuse is practiced, rather than conservation, thus ruining resources heid in common.

TRAILMAN A microcomputer-based software package for logistics planning in Africa.

transfer costs Terminal costs and other fixed costs, plus line-haul costs or over-the-road costs equal transfer costs.

transfer pricing Fixed prices for the movement of goods between affiliates.

transferability The condition that costs be acceptable in order for exchange of goods to occur between a supply area and a demand area.

transit oriented development (TOD) Development guidelines to help communities reduce dependency on automobiles.

transnational corporation Companies that operate factories or service centers in countries other than the country of origin.

transport costs The alternative output given up when inputs are committed to the movement of people, goods, information, and ideas over geographical space.

traveling salesman network The shortest network interconnecting a set of points where the origin and destination points are identical.

triage The partitioning into three groups of nations, those so seriously deficient in food reserves that they cannot survive, those that can survive without food aid, and finally, those that can be saved by immediate food relief measures.

tributary areas The area dominated by a central place; the area to which a central place services and from which it draws raw materials and labor supply.

trickling-down effects The beneficial impact of prosperous regions on less prosperous regions.

truck farming Sometimes called "market gardening," a specialization of intensively cultivated fruits, vegetables, and vines in developed economies.

turnkey project A technique of competitive duplication of Western industrial facilities employed by multinationals. The contractor not only plans and builds the project, but also trains the buyer's personnel and initiates operation of the project.

ubiquitous raw material A material that is available everywhere; thus, it does not exert a specific influence on industrial location.

Ukraine Industrial Region Centered on the Donets Basin and the iron and steel industry of Krivoy Rog, formerly a most important industrial district of the Soviet Union.

underemployment Workers laboring less than 8 hours per day.

undernutrition A state of poor health in which an individual does not obtain enough calories.

United Nations Conference on Trade and Development A UN organization that includes most underdeveloped countries. Although it has little statutory authority, it serves as a forum for discussion of common problems of its members.

upper circuit The modern and capital-intensive sector of a Third World city.

urban field The area dominated by a central place, to which a central place services, and from which it draws raw materials and labor supply.

urbanization The process through which the proportion of population living in urban areas increases.

urbanization economies The declining average costs for firms as cities increase their scales of activity.

Uruguay Rounds The last round of the GATT talks that began in 1986 and ended in December, 1993.

use value The usefulness of a commodity to the person who possesses it.

value added The difference between the revenue of a firm obtained from a given volume of output and the cost of the input (the materials, components, services) used in producing that output.

value free Opinions and statements that are not laden with belief or innuendo regarding what ought to be or what ought not to be regarding the world economy.

variable costs Expenditures firms incur as output changes. As output rises, variable costs rise; as output falls, variable costs fall.

varignon frame Weights on strings running through holes in a sheet of plywood to represent the proportionality of attraction of each location, attempting to answer the question, "Where should economic activity be located?"

vertex A point; a node in a topological diagram of a network.

vertical integration A business strategy to increase a firm's scale by buying, building, or merging with another firm in a different stage of production of the same product; may be forward or backward.

vicious circle A concept emphasizing the multicausality of underdevelopment; that is, a combination of interwoven limiting factors, rather than "just" a single factor, thwarts development.

vicious cycle of poverty Explanations for the multiple causality of underdevelopment.

virgin and idle lands program Khrushchev's hasty and grandiose dryland agricultural programs of Central Asia, which pulverized the soil, resulting in enormous dust storms.

Volga Industrial Region Region along the Volga and Cama Rivers, the location of substantial oil and gas production and refining, east of Moscow.

Von Thünen's Isolated State A book that revealed laws that regulated the interaction of agricultural prices, distance and land use, as land users seek to maximize their income.

wealth-driven stage Stage of economic development described by a population that has a high overall standard of living and high levels of mass consumption and technological virtuosity.

weight-losing raw material A raw material that undergoes a loss of weight in the process of manufacture.

West Coast Manufacturing Region Manufacturing region stretching from San Diego, north to Los Angeles and up to San Francisco.

wheat belts Areas, such as those in North America, in which wheat predominates as an agricultural product.

wind farm Capturing wind energy with wind turbines and converting it to electricity.

winnowing Removing chafe from rice seeds by the blowing winds.

winter wheat Wheat planted in the fall that sprouts in spring and is harvested in early summer.

World Bank A group of international financial agencies including the International Bank for Reconstruction and Development, the International Finance Corporation, and the International Development Association.

world cultural realms Giant world regions that possess similarities of culture, economy, and historical development.

world economy A multistate economic system created in the late fifteenth and early sixteenth centuries by European capitalism and, later, its overseas progeny.

world political economy theories The structure of political and economic relationships between dominant and dominated countries.

world's breadbasket The Midwest of the United States, with its rich agricultural potential.

write-down A cancellation or reduction of a portion of the principal and/or interest by a creditor bank for less developed country's loans because of the possibility of default.

zaibatsu A large Japanese financial enterprise, similar to a conglomerate in the West.

zero population growth (ZPG) As a result of the combination of births, deaths, and migration, the population of a country is level, not rising or falling from year to year.

zero-sum game A game in which the "payoff" to one player is exactly the value "lost" by the opponent.

Zuider Zee Reclamation The Dutch program to reclaim portions of their country from the North Sea by building dikes across inlets and pumping water off the land.

REFERENCES

Abler, R. 1975. Effects of space-adjusting technologies on the human geography of the future. In *Human Geography in a Shrinking World,* edited by R. Abler, D. Janelle, A. Philbrick, & J. Sommer, pp. 35–56. North Scituate, MA: Duxbury Press.

Abler, R., J. S. Adams, and P. Gould. 1971. *Spatial Organization.* Englewood Cliffs, NJ: Prentice Hall.

Abu-Lughod, J. 1987–1988. The shape of the world system in the thirteenth century. *Studies in Comparative International Development* 22(4):3–25.

Aglietta, M. 1979. *A Theory of Capitalist Regulation: The U.S. Experience.* London: New Left Books.

Agnew, J. A. 1982. Sociologizing the geographical imagination: Spatial concepts in the world-system perspective. *Political Geography Quarterly* 1:159–166.

———. 1987. Bringing culture back in: Overcoming the economic-cultural split in development studies. *Journal of Geography* 86:276–281.

Aitken, S., F. Stutz, et al. 1993. Neighborhood integrity and residents' familiarity: Using a geographic information system to investigate place identity. *Tijdschrift Voor Economische en Sociale Geografie* 34:1–12.

Allen, B. J. 1985. Dynamics of fallow successions and introduction of Robusta coffee in shifting cultivation areas of the lowlands of Papua New Guinea. *Agroforestry Systems* 3:227–238.

Alonso, W. 1964. *Location and Land Use.* Cambridge, MA: Harvard University Press.

Amin, A., and I. Smith. 1986. The internationalization of production and its implications for the UK. In *Technological Change, Industrial Restructuring, and Regional Development,* edited by A. Amin and J. B. Goddard, pp. 41–76. Boston: Allen and Unwin.

Amin, S. 1976. *Unequal Development.* New York: Monthly Review Press.

Arrighi, G., and J. S. Saul. 1973. *Essays on the Political Economy of Africa.* New York: Monthly Review Press.

Asimov, I. 1978. *The Naked Sun.* London: Granada.

Augelli, J. P. 1985. Food, population, and dislocation in Latin America. *Journal of Geography* 84:274–281.

Averitt, R. T. 1968. *The Dual Economy: The Dynamics of American Industry Structure.* New York: W. W. Norton.

Ayeni, B., G. Rushton, and M. L. McNulty. 1987. Improving the geographical accessibility of health care in rural areas: A Nigerian case study. *Social Science and Medicine* 25:1083–1094.

Balassa, B. 1961. *The Theory of Economic Integration.* Homewood, IL: Richard D. Irwin.

Ballmer-Cao, T., and J. Scheidegger. 1979. *Compendium of Data for World System Analysis.* Zurick: Sociologisches Institut der Universitat.

Bannock, G. 1971. *The Juggernauts: The Age of the Big Corporation.* Harmondsworth, Eng: Penguin Books.

Baran, P. 1957. *The Political Economy of Growth.* New York: Monthly Review Press.

Barnet, R., and R. Muller. 1975. *Global Reach.* New York: Simon and Schuster.

Batty, M., and E. Saether. 1972. A note on the design of shopping models. *Journal of the Royal Town Planning Institute* 58:303–306.

Bauer, P. T. 1972. *Dissent on Development.* Cambridge, MA: Harvard University Press.

Baum, J., and C. Oliver. 1992. Institutional embeddedness and the dynamics of organizational populations. *American Sociological Review* 57:540–559.

Beer, S. 1968. *Management Science: The Business Use of Operations Research.* New York: Doubleday & Company, Inc.

Behrman, J. N. 1984. *Industrial Policies: International Restructuring and Transnationals.* Lexington, MA: D.C. Heath.

Bell, D. 1973. *The Coming of Postindustrial Society.* New York: Basic Books.

Bell, D. E., H. Raiffa, and A. Tversky, Eds. 1988. *Decision Making.* New York: Cambridge University Press.

Bell, T. L. 1973. *Central Place Theory as a Mixture of the Function Pattern Principles of Christaller and Lösch: Some Empirical Tests and Applications.* University of Iowa, Department of Geography, unpublished doctoral dissertation.

Berry, B. J. L. 1961. City size distributions and economic development. *Economic Development and Cultural Change* 9:573–588.

———. 1967. *Geography of Market Centers and Retail Distribution.* Englewood Cliffs, NJ: Prentice Hall.

———. 1968. Interdependency of spatial structure and spatial behavior: General field theory formulation. *Papers and Proceedings of the Regional Science Association* 21:205–227.

———. 1969a. Relationships between regional economic development and the urban system—The case of Chile. *Tijdschrift voor Economische en Sociale Geografie* 60:283–307.

———. 1969b. Policy implications of an urban location model for the Kanpur region. In *Regional Perspective of Industrial and Urban Growth—The Case of Kanpur,* edited by P. B. Desai, et al., pp. 203–219. Bombay: Macmillan.

Berry B. J. L., E. C. Conkling, and D. M. Ray. 1993. *Global Economy.* Englewood Cliffs, NJ: Prentice Hall.

Berry B. J. L., and H. M. Meyer. 1962. *Comparative Studies of Central Place Systems. Final Report NONR 2121-18 and NR 389-126.* Washington, DC: Geography Branch, U.S. Office of Naval Research.

Blaikie, P. M. 1971. Spatial organization of agriculture in some north Indian villages: Part 1. *Transactions, Institute of British Geographers* 52:1–40.

Blaikie, P. M., and H. Brookfield. 1987. *Land Degradation and Society.* New York: Methuen.

Blanchet, D. 1991. On interpreting observed relationships between population growth and economic growth: A graphical exposition. *Population and Development Review* 17(1):105–114.

Bloom, D., and R. Freeman. 1986. The effects of rapid population growth on labor supply and employment in developing countries. *Population and Development Review* 12(3):381–414.

Bluestone, B., and B. Harrison. 1987. The impact of private disinvestment on workers and their communities. In *International Capitalism and Industrial Restructuring,* edited by R. Peet, pp. 72–104. Boston: Allen and Unwin.

Bohannan, P., and P. Curtin. 1971. *Africa and Africans.* Garden City, NY: Natural History Press.

Borchert, J. R. 1961. The Twin Cities urbanized area: Past, present, and future. *Geographical Review* 51:47–70.

———. 1963. *The Urbanization of the Upper Midwest: 1930–1960.* Minneapolis: University of Minnesota, Upper Midwest Economic Study, Urban Report No. 2.

————. 1967. American metropolitan evolution. *Geographical Review* 57:301–331.

————. 1972. Banking linkages of Third Order countries. *Annals of the Association of American Geographers* 62:253.

————. 1987. *America's Northern Heartland: An Economic and Historical Geography of the Upper Midwest.* Minneapolis: University of Minnesota Press.

Borchert, J. R., and D. D. Carroll. 1971. *Minnesota Settlement and Land Use 1985.* Minneapolis: University of Minnesota, Center for Urban and Regional Affairs.

Boserup, E. 1965. *The Conditions of Agricultural Growth: The Economics of Agrarian Change Under Population Pressure.* Chicago: Aldine.

————. 1970. Present and potential food production in developing countries. In *Geography and a Crowding World,* edited by W. Zelinsky, L. A. Kosinski, and R. M. Prothero, pp. 100–110. New York: Oxford University Press.

————. 1970. *Woman's Role in Economic Development.* New York: St. Martin's Press.

————. 1981. *Population and Technology.* New York: Blackwell.

————. 1981. *Population and Technological Change: A Study of Long-Term Trends.* Chicago: University of Chicago Press.

Bradshaw, B., and W. P. Frisbie. 1983. Potential labor force supply and replacement in Mexico and the states of the Mexican Cession and Texas: 1980–2000. *International Migration Review* 17(3):394–409.

Brown, L. R. 1981. Eroding the base of civilization. *Journal of Soil and Water Conservation* 36:255–260.

Bunge, W. 1966. *Theoretical Geography.* Lund Studies in Geography, Series C1. Lund, Sweden: Gleerup.

————. 1971. *Fitzgerald: The Geography of a Revolution.* Cambridge, MA: Schenkman Publishing Company.

Bureau of Land Management (BLM). 1988. *Public Land Statistics 1987.* Washington, DC: GPO.

Burgess, E. W. 1925. Growth of the city. In *The City,* edited by R. E. Park, E. W. Burgess, and R. D. McKenzie, pp. 47–62. Chicago: University of Chicago Press.

Burns, A. F. 1934. *Production Trends in the United States.* New York: National Bureau of Economic Research.

Caldwell, J., and P. Caldwell. 1990. High fertility in sub-Saharan Africa. *Scientific American* 40:118–125.

Caldwell, J., I. O. Orubuloye, and P. Caldwell. 1992. Fertility decline in Africa: A new type of transition? *Population and Development Review* 18(2):211–242.

Carson, R. 1962. *Silent Spring.* Boston: Houghton Mifflin.

Cassen, R. W. 1976. Population and development: A survey. *World Development* 4:785–830.

Chapman, K., and D. Walker. 1987. *Industrial Location.* New York: Basil Blackwell.

Chisholm, G. G. 1899. *Handbook of Commercial Geography.* London: Longmans, Green.

Chisholm, M. 1979. *Rural Settlement and Land Use: An Essay in Location,* 3d ed. London: Hutchinson.

————. 1982. *Modern World Development.* Totowa, NJ: Barnes & Noble.

Christaller, W. 1966. *The Central Places of Southern Germany.* Translated by C. W. Baskin. Englewood Cliffs, NJ: Prentice Hall.

Clark, C. 1967. *Population Growth and Land Use.* New York: St. Martin's Press.

Clarke, B., and L. Bolwell. 1968. Attractiveness as part of retail potential models. *Journal of the Royal Town Planning Institute* 54:477–478.

Clarke, W. C. 1977. The structure of permanence: The relevance of self-subsistence communities for world ecosystem management. In *Subsistence and Survival: Rural Ecology in the Pacific,* edited by T. P. Bayliss-Smith and R. Feachem, pp. 363–384. London: Academic Press.

Coale, A. J., and E. M. Hoover. 1958. *Population Growth and Economic Development in Low-Income Countries.* Princeton, NJ: Princeton University Press.

Cochran, T. C. 1966. The entrepreneur in social change. *Explorations in Entrepreneurial History* (2d series) 4:25–38.

Cohen, R. B. 1981. The new international division of labor, multinational corporations and urban hierarchy. In *Urbanization and Urban Planning in Capitalist Society,* edited by M. Dear and A. J. Scott, pp. 287–315. New York: Methuen.

Cole, J. 1987. *Development and Underdevelopment.* London: Methuen.

Commoner, B. 1975. How poverty breeds overpopulation (and not the other way around). *Ramparts* 10:21–25, 58–59.

Conkling, E., and J. McConnell. 1985. The world's new economic powerhouse. *Focus* 35:2–7.

Corbridge, S., editor. 1993. *World Economy.* New York: Oxford University Press.

Council on Environmental Quality. 1980. *The Global 2000 Report to the President,* Vol 1. Washington, DC: GPO.

Curran, J., and J. Stanworth. 1986. Trends in small firm industrial relations and their implications for the role of the small firm in economic restructuring. In *Technological Change, Industrial Restructuring, and Regional Development,* edited by A. Amin and J. B. Goddard, pp. 233–257. Winchester, MA: Allen and Unwin.

Cyert, R. M., and J. G. March. 1963. *A Behavioral Theory of the Firm.* Englewood Cliffs, NJ: Prentice Hall.

Daly, H. 1986. Review of population growth and economic development: Policy questions. *Population and Development Review* 12(3):582–585.

Daniels, P. W. 1985. *Service Industries: A Geographical Appraisal.* New York: Methuen.

Darst, G. 1987. Energy worries fading: Conservation drive wanes in Washington. *Minneapolis Star and Tribune* 15 March, pp. 1, 3.

Datoo, B. A. 1976. *Toward a Reformulation of Boserup's Theory of Agricultural Change.* Dar es Salaam, Tanzania: Department of Geography, University of Dar es Salaam. Mimeographed.

de Blij, H. J., and P. O. Muller. 1985. *Geography: Regions and Concepts,* 4th ed. New York: John Wiley.

————. 1992. *Geography: Regions and Concepts,* revised 6th edition. New York: John Wiley & Sons.

de Souza, A. R. 1985. Dependency and economic growth. *Journal of Geography* 85:94.

————. 1986. To have and have not: Colonialism and core-periphery relations. *Focus* 36(3):14–19.

de Souza, A. R., and J. B. Foust. 1979. *World Space Economy.* Columbus, OH: Merrill.

de Souza, A. R., and P. W. Porter. 1974. *The Underdevelopment and Modernization of the Third World.* Resource Paper No. 28. Washington, DC: Association of American Geographers.

Demeny, P. 1971. The economics of population control. In *National Academy of Science, Rapid Population Growth.* Baltimore: Johns Hopkins University Press.

————. 1981. The North–South income gap: A demographic perspective. *Population and Development Review* 7(2):297–310.

Demko, G. J., and W. B. Wood. 1987. International refugees: A geographical perspective. *Journal of Geography* 86:225–228.

Diaz-Briquets, S., and L. Perez. 1981. Cuba: The demography of revolution. *Population Bulletin* 36(1):101–121.

Dicken, P. 1986. *Global Shift: Industrial Change in a Turbulent World.* London: Harper and Row.

———. 1992. *Global Shift: Industrial Change in a Turbulent World*, 2d ed. London: Harper & Row.

Dickinson, R. E. 1964. *City and Region*. London: Routledge and Kegan Paul.

Directors of the World Resources Institute. 1992. *World Resources, 1992–93*. New York: Oxford University Press.

Dodson, R. F. 1991. *VT/GIS: The von Thünen GIS Package*. Santa Barbara, CA: National Center for Geographic Information & Analysis. (Technical paper 91-27.)

Doxiadis, C. A. 1970. Man's movements and his settlements. *Ekistics* 29:318.

Dumont, R., and M-F. Mottin. 1983. *Stranglehold on Africa*. London: André Deutsch.

Dunn, E. S., Jr. 1954. *The Location of Agricultural Production*. Gainesville: University of Florida Press.

Edwards, C. 1985. *The Fragmented World*. New York: Methuen.

Ehrlich, P. 1968. *The Population Bomb*. New York: Ballantine Books.

———. 1971. *The Population Bomb*, 2d ed. New York: Sierra Club/ Ballantine Books.

Electronics Industries Association of Japan. 1989. *Facts and Figures on the Japanese Electronics Industry*. Tokyo: Author.

Emmanuel, A. 1972. *Unequal Exchange: A Study of the Imperialism of Trade*. London: New Left Books.

Encyclopaedia Britannica. 1987. *1987 Britannica Book of the Year*. Chicago: Encyclopaedia Britannica.

Engels, F. 1958. *The Condition of the Working Class in England*. Stanford, CA: Stanford University Press.

Enke, S. 1960. The economics of government payments to limit population. *Economic Development and Cultural Change* 8(4): 339–348.

Environmental Systems Research Institute, Inc. 1989. Why GIS? (revised, 1992). *ARC News* 11(5):1–4.

Ericson, R. E. 1991. The classical Soviet-type economy: Nature of the system and applications for reform. *Journal of Economic Perspectives* 20:23.

Ewart, W. D. and W. Fullard. 1973. *World Atlas of Shipping*. London: Philip and Son.

Fanon, F. 1963. *The Wretched of the Earth*. New York: Grove Press.

Fellman, J., A. Getis, and J. Getis. 1992. *Human Geography: Landscapes of Human Activities*. Dubuque, IA: W. C. Brown.

Ferguson, R., and E. Carlson. 1990. The boondocks distant communities promise good homes but produce malaise: Census shows people moving so far from jobs they lack time to enjoy life. *The Wall Street Journal* 25 October, pp. A1, A6.

Fieldhouse, D. K. 1967. *The Colonial Empires*. New York: Delacorte Press.

Financial Times. 1989. Britain's regions: A test for Thatcherism. *Financial Times* 27 January:33–40.

Fisher, J. S. 1989. Anglo-America: Economic growth and transformation. In *Geography and Development*, edited by J. S. Fisher, pp. 146–166. Columbus, OH: Merrill.

Fisher, J. S. 1992. *Geography and Development: A World Regional Approach*. New York: Macmillan.

Fishlow, A. 1965. *American Railroads and the Transformation of the Antebellum Economy*. Cambridge, MA: Harvard University Press.

Food and Agriculture Organization. 1983. *Per Capita Dietary Energy Supplies in Relation to Nutritional Requirements*. World Food Report, Series 211. Rome: Author.

———. 1985. *The State of Food and Agriculture 1984*. Rome: Author.

Foreign exchange rates. *San Diego Union*, July 4, 1993.

Frank, A. G. 1969. *Capitalism and Underdevelopment in Latin America*. New York: Monthly Review Press.

———. 1981. *Crisis in the Third World*. London: Heineman.

Franklin, S. H. 1965. Systems of production: Systems of appropriation. *Pacific Viewpoint* 6:145–166.

Freeman, M. 1986. Transport. In *Atlas of Industrializing Britain, 1780–1914*, edited by J. Langton and R. J. Morris, pp. 80–93. New York: Methuen.

———. 1987. *The Challenge of New Technologies NOECD, Interdependence and Corporation in Tomorrow's World*, Paris, OECD.

———. 1988. Introduction. In *Technical Change and Economic Theory*, edited by G. Dosi et al., pp. 34–61. London: Pinter.

Fried, M. 1967. *The Evolution of Political Society*. New York: Random House.

Friedmann, J. 1966. *Regional Development Policy: A Case Study of Venezuela*. Cambridge, MA: The MIT Press.

Froebel, F., J. Heinrich, and O. Kreye. 1977. The tendency towards a new international division of labor. *Review* 1(1):77–88.

Fuentes, A., and B. Ehrenreich. 1987. Women in the global factory. In *International Capitalism and Industrial Restructuring*, edited by R. Peet, pp. 201–215. Boston: Allen and Unwin.

Fusfeld, D. R. 1986. *The Age of the Economist*, 5th ed. Glenview, IL: Scott, Foresman.

Gaffikin, F., and A. Nickson. 1984. *Job Crisis and the Multinationals: Deindustrialization in the West Midlands*. Chicago: Third World Books.

Galbraith, J. K. 1967. *The New Industrial State*. Boston: Houghton Mifflin.

———. 1969. *The Affluent Society*. Boston: Houghton Mifflin.

———. 1973. *Economics and the Public Purpose*. Boston: Houghton Mifflin.

Galtung, J. 1971. A structural theory of imperialism. *Journal of Peace Research* 21(2):81–107, 110–116.

Gamble, A. 1981. *Britain in Decline: Economic Policy, Political Strategy, and the British State*. London: Macmillan.

General Agreement on Tariffs and Trade (GATT). 1990. *International Trade, 1989–1990*, Vol II. Geneva: Author.

Geertz, C. 1963. *Agricultural Involution: The Processes of Ecological Changes in Indonesia*. Berkeley: University of California Press.

George, S. 1977. *How the Other Half Dies—The Real Reasons for World Hunger*. Montclair, NJ: Allanheld, Osmun.

Ginsburg, N. S. 1961. *Atlas of Economic Development*. Chicago: University of Chicago Press.

GIS World. 1992. Fort Collins: GIS World Inc. October, pp. 46–47.

Globe and Mail Newspaper. (Toronto), 1986, 6 May.

Godlund, S. 1961. *Population, Regional Hospitals, Transport Facilities and Regions: Planning the Location of Regional Hospitals in Sweden*. Lund, Sweden: Gleerup.

Goliber, T. J. 1985. *Sub-Saharan Africa: Population Pressures on Development*. Population Bulletin, Vol. 40, No. 1. Washington, DC: Population Reference Bureau.

Goodchild, M. F., and B. Massam. 1969. Some least-cost models of spatial administrative systems in southern Ontario. *Geografiska Annaler* 52, B-2:86–94.

Gordon, D. M. 1977. Class struggle and the stages of American urban development. In *The Rise of the Sunbelt Cities*, edited by D. C. Perry and A. J. Watkins, pp. 55–82. Beverly Hills: Sage Publications.

Gottman, J. 1964. *Megalopolis*. Cambridge, MA: The MIT Press.

Gould, P. R. 1960. *The Development of the Transportation Pattern in Ghana*. Evanston, IL: Northwestern University Press, Department of Geography, Studies in Geography, No. 5.

———. 1964. A note on research into the diffusion of development. *Journal of Modern African Studies* 2:123–125.

———. 1970. Tanzania 1920–63: The spatial impress of the modernization process. *World Politics* 22:149–170.

———. 1975. *Spatial Diffusion: The Spread of Ideas and Innovations in Geographic Space.* Learning Package Series No. 11. Columbus: The Ohio State University.

———. 1983. Getting involved in information and ignorance. *Journal of Geography* 82:158–162.

———. 1985. *The Geographer at Work.* London: Routledge and Kegan Paul.

Goulet, D. 1971. *The Cruel Choice.* New York: Atheneum.

Grandstaff, T. 1978. The development of swidden agriculture (shifting cultivation). *Development and Change* 9:547–579.

Greenhut, M. L. 1956. *Plant Location in Theory and Practice.* Chapel Hill: University of North Carolina Press.

Greenow, L., and V. Muniz. 1988. Market trade in decentralized development: The case of Cajamarca, Peru. *The Professional Geographer* 40:416–427.

Gribben, R. 1989. Economic divide will stay but shift northward. *The Daily Telegraph,* 3 January:4.

Griffin, E., and L. Ford. 1980. A model of Latin American city structure. *Geographical Review* 70:397–422.

Griffin, K. 1969. *Underdevelopment in Spanish America.* London: Allen and Unwin.

Hagen, E. E. 1962. *On the Theory of Social Change.* Homewood, IL: The Dorsey Press.

———. 1968. Are some things valued by all men? *Cross Currents* 18:406–414.

Hägerstrand, T. 1965. A Monte Carlo approach to diffusion. *European Journal of Sociology* 6:43–67.

Haggett, P. 1965. *Locational Analysis in Human Geography.* London: Edward Arnold.

Haggett, P., and R. J. Chorley. 1969. *Network Analysis in Human Geography.* London: Edward Arnold.

Håkauson, L. 1979. Towards a theory of location and corporate growth. In *Spatial Analysis, Industry and the Industrial Environment. Volume 1: Industrial Systems,* edited by F. E. I. Hamilton and G. J. R. Linge, pp. 115–138. New York: John Wiley.

Hall, P., Ed. 1966. *Von Thünen's Isolated State.* Translated by C. M. Wartenberg. Oxford, Eng: Pergamon.

———. 1971. *The World Cities.* New York: McGraw-Hill.

———. 1982. *Urban and Regional Planning.* London: Allen and Unwin.

Hannan, M., and G. Carroll. 1992. *Dynamics of Organizational Populations.* New York: Oxford University Press.

Hannan, M., and J. Freeman. 1989. *Organizational Ecology.* Cambridge, MA: Harvard University Press.

Hansen, J. 1970. *The Population Explosion: How Sociologists View It.* New York: Pathfinder Press.

Hanson, S., editor. 1986. *The Geography of Urban Transportation.* New York: Guilford Press.

Hardin, G. 1974. Living on a lifeboat. *Bioscience* 24:561–568.

———. 1968. The tragedy of the commons. *Science* 162:1243–1248.

Harrington, M. 1977. *The Vast Majority: A Journey to the World's Poor.* New York: Touchstone.

Harris, C. 1954. The market as a factor in the localization of industry in the U.S. *Annals of the Association of American Geographers* 44:315–348.

Harris, C., and E. Ullman. 1945. The nature of cities. *Annals of the American Academy of Political and Social Science* 242:7–17.

Harris, M. 1966. The cultural ecology of India's sacred cattle. *Current Anthropology* 7:51–59.

Hartshorn, T. A. 1992. *Interpreting the City: An Urban Geography.* New York: John Wiley & Sons.

Harvey, D. 1972. *Society, the City, and the Space-Economy of Urbanism.* Resource Paper No. 18. Washington, DC: Association of American Geographers.

———. 1973. *Social Justice and the City.* London: Edward Arnold.

———. 1974. Population, resources, and the ideology of science. *Economic Geography* 50:256–277.

———. 1985. *The Urbanization of Capital.* Baltimore: Johns Hopkins University Press.

Havens, A. E., and W. F. Flinn. 1975. Green revolution technology and community development: The limits of action programs. *Economic Development and Cultural Change* 23:468–481.

Heckscher, E. 1919. The effect of foreign trade on the distribution of income. *Economisk Tidskrift* 21. Reprinted in *Readings in the Theory of International Trade,* edited by H. Ellis and L. Metzler, pp. 272–300. Homewood, IL: Richard D. Irwin, 1950.

Heilbronner, R. 1989. Reflections: The triumph of capitalism. *The New Yorker* 25 January:98–109.

Henderson, J. V. 1988. *Urban Development: Theory, Fact and Illusion.* New York: Oxford University Press.

Henderson, J., and Castells, M., editors. 1987. *Global Restructuring and Territorial Development.* London: Sage.

Henige, D. 1970. *Colonial Governors.* Madison: University of Wisconsin Press.

Hepworth, M. 1987. *The Geography of the Information Economy.* New York: Guilford Press.

———. 1990. *Geography of the Information Economy.* New York: Guilford Press.

Herbert, D. T. 1982. The changing face of the city. In *The Changing Geography of the United Kingdom,* edited by R. J. Johnston and J. C. Doornkamp, pp. 227–255. London: Methuen.

Higgins, B. 1956. The dualistic theory of underdeveloped areas. *Economic Development and Cultural Change* 4:99–115.

Hirschman, A. O. 1958. *The Strategy of Economic Development.* New Haven, CT: Yale University Press.

Hofstede, G. 1980. *Culture's Consequences: International Differences in Work-Related Values.* Beverly Hills, CA: Sage.

Hollerbach, P. 1980. Recent trends in fertility, abortion, and contraception in Cuba. *International Family Planning Perspectives* 6(3):97–106.

Hoover, E. M. 1984. *An Introduction to Regional Economies,* 3d ed. New York: Alfred A. Knopf.

Horvath, R. J. 1969. Von Thünen's isolated state and the area around Addis Ababa, Ethiopia. *Annals of the Association of American Geographers* 59:308–323.

Hotelling, H. 1929. Stability in competition. *Economic Journal* 39:41–57.

Howard, E. 1946. *Garden Cities of Tomorrow.* London: Faber.

Hoyle, B. S. and R. D. Knowles. 1993. *Modern Transport Geography.* London: Belhaven Press.

Hoyle, B. S., and D. A. Pinder. 1981. Seaports, cities and transport systems. In *Cityport Industrialization and Regional Development,* edited by B. S. Hoyle and D. A. Pinder, pp. 1–10. Oxford: Pergamon.

Hoyt, H. 1939. *The Structure and Growth of Residential Neighborhoods in American Cities.* Washington, DC: Federal Housing Administration.

Hubbert, M. K. 1962. *Energy Resources: A Report to the Committee on Natural Resources.* Washington, DC: National Academy of Sciences.

Huff, D. L. 1963. A probability analysis of shopping center trade areas. *Land Economics* 53:81–89.

Hughes, A., and M. S. Kumar. 1984. Recent trends in aggregate concentration in the United Kingdom economy. *Cambridge Journal of Economics* 8:235–250.

Huke, R. E. 1985. The green revolution. *Journal of Geography* 84:248–254.

Humphrys, G. 1972. *South Wales.* Newton Abbott, Eng: David and Charles.

Hunker, H., and A. J. Wright. 1963. *Factors of Industrial Location in Ohio.* Columbus: The Ohio State University Press.

Huntington, E. 1924. *Civilization and Climate.* New Haven, CT: Yale University Press.

Hurni, H. 1983. Soil erosion and soil formation in agricultural systems, Ethiopia and northern Thailand. *Mountain Research and Development* 3:131–142.

IDRISI. 1992. *IDRISI: A Grid Based Geographic Analysis System.* Worcester, MA: Graduate School of Geography, Clark University.

Ihlanfeldt, K. R., D. L. Sjoquist. 1990. Job accessibility and racial differences in youth employment rates. *American Economic Review* 8:267–276.

Ihlanfeltd, K. R., and D. L. Sjoquist. 1990. Job accessibility and racial differences in youth employment rates. *American Economic Review* 8:267–276.

International Institute for Environment, Development and World Resources. 1987. *World Resources 1987.* New York: Basic Books.

———. 1993. *World Resources, 1993–1994.* New York: Oxford.

International Monetary Fund. 1978. *29th Annual Report on Exchange Restrictions.* Washington, DC: Author.

———. 1985. *IMF Survey, 21 January.* Washington, DC: Author.

———. 1991. *World Economic Outlook: October 1991.* Washington, DC: Author.

———. 1992. *International Financial Statistics.* Washington, DC: Author.

Isard, W. 1956. *Location and Space Economy.* Cambridge, MA: The MIT Press.

———. 1960. *Methods of Regional Analysis: An Introduction to Regional Science.* Englewood Cliffs, NJ: Prentice Hall.

Jackson, W. A. D. 1962. The Virgin and Idle Lands Program reappraised. *Annals of the Association of American Geographers* 52:69–79.

Janelle, D. G. 1968. Central place development in a time-space framework. *The Professional Geographer* 20:5–10.

Jefferson, M. 1921. *Recent Colonization in Chile.* Research Series No. 6. New York: American Geographical Society.

Johnston, W. 1991. Global work force 2000: The new world labor market. *Harvard Business Review* 41:115–129.

Junkerman, J. 1987. Blue-sky management: The Kawasaki story. In *International Capitalism and Industrial Restructuring,* edited by R. Peet, pp. 131–144. Boston: Allen and Unwin.

Kahn, H. 1973. If the rich stop aiding the poor. . . . *Development Forum* 1(2):1–3.

Kansky, K. J. 1963. *Structure of Transportation.* Chicago: University of Chicago, Department of Geography, Research Paper No. 84.

Keeble, D. E. 1967. Models of economic development. In *Models in Geography,* edited by R. J. Chorley and P. Haggett, pp. 243–302. London: Methuen.

Kelley, A. 1973. Population growth, the dependency rate, and the pace of economic development. *Population Studies* 27:405–414.

Kennelly, R. A. 1954. The location of the Mexican steel industry. *Revista Geografica* 15:109–129.

———. 1955. The location of the Mexican steel industry. *Revista Geografica* 16:60–77.

Keyfitz, N., and W. Flieger. 1990. *World Population Growth and Aging: Demographic Trends in the Late Twentieth Century.* Chicago: University of Chicago Press.

Keynes, J. M. 1936. *The General Theory of Employment Interest and Money.* New York: Harcourt, Brace.

Kidron, M. and R. Segal. 1984. *The New State of the World Atlas.* New York: Simon and Schuster.

Knight, C. G., and J. L. Newman, Eds. 1976. *Contemporary Africa: Geography and Change.* Englewood Cliffs, NJ: Prentice Hall.

Knight, C. G., and R. P. Wilcox. 1976. *Triumph or Triage: The Third World Food Problem in Geographical Perspective.* Resource Paper No. 75-3. Washington, DC: Association of American Geographers.

Knox, P. L. 1994. *Urbanization: An Introduction to Urban Geography.* Englewood Cliffs, New Jersey: Prentice Hall.

Kolars, J. F., and J. D. Nystuen. 1974. *Human Geography: Spatial Design in World Society.* New York: McGraw-Hill.

Komorov B. 1981. *The Destruction of Nature in the Soviet Union.* London: Pluto Press.

Kondratiev N. D. 1935. The long waves in economic life. *Review of Economic Statistics* 17:105–115.

Krasner, S. D. 1985. *Structural Conflict.* Berkeley and Los Angeles: University of California Press.

Kumar, K., and K. Y. Kim. 1984. The Korean manufacturing multinationals. *Journal of International Business Studies* 1:45–61.

Kuznets, S. 1930. *Secular Movements in Production and Prices.* Boston: Houghton Mifflin.

———. 1954. *Economic Change.* New York: W. W. Norton.

———. 1965. *Economic Growth of Nations.* Cambridge, MA: Harvard University Press.

———. 1972. Problems in comparing recent growth rates for developed and less developed countries. *Economic Development and Cultural Change* 20(2):195–209.

Landsberg, M. 1987. Export-led industrialization in the Third World: Manufacturing imperialism. In *International Capitalism and Industrial Restructuring,* edited by R. Peet, pp. 216–239. Boston: Allen and Unwin.

Lappé, F. M., and J. Collins. 1976. More food means more hunger. *Development Forum* 4(8):1–2.

———. 1977. *Food First.* Boston: Houghton Mifflin.

Lecomber, R. 1975. *Economic Growth Versus Environment.* New York: John Wiley.

Leibenstein, H. 1957. *Economic Backwardness and Economic Growth.* New York: John Wiley.

Leontief, W., et al. 1977. *The Future of the World Economy: A United Nations Study.* New York: Oxford University Press.

Lewis, P. 1983. The galactic metropolis. In *Beyond the Urban Fringe: Land-Use Issues of Nonmetropolitan America,* edited by R. Platt and G. Macinko, pp. 23–49. Minneapolis: University of Minnesota Press.

Lewis, W. A. 1954. Economic development with unlimited supplies of labour. *Manchester School of Economic and Social Studies* 22:139–191.

Lin Piao, L. 1965. Long live the victory of the People's War. *Peking Review* 3:9–30.

Linneman, H. 1966. *An Econometric Study of International Trade Flows.* Amsterdam: North-Holland Publishing.

Livingstone, I. 1971. Agriculture versus industry in economic development. In *Economic Policy for Development,* edited by I. Livingstone, pp. 235–249. Harmondsworth, Eng: Penguin Books.

Lloyd, P. E., and P. Dicken. 1972. *Location in Space: A Theoretical Approach to Economic Geography.* New York: Harper and Row.

Lord Ritchie-Calder. 1973/1974. UNICEF's grandchildren. *UNICEF News* 78.

Lösch, A. 1954. *The Economics of Location.* Translated by W. H. Woglom and W. F. Stolper. New Haven, CT: Yale University Press.

Lyle, J., and F. P. Stutz. 1983. Land use suitability modelling and mapping. *Cartographic Journal* 18:39–50.

Mabogunje, A. L. 1980. *The Development Process: A Spatial Perspective.* London: Hutchinson.

Mackay, J. R. 1958. The interactance hypothesis and boundaries in Canada. *Canadian Geographer* 11:1–8.

Magirier, G. 1983. The eighties: a second phase of crisis? *Capital and Class* 21:61–86.

Malecki, E. J. 1979. Locational trends in R&D by large U.S. corporations. *Economic Geography* 55:309–323.

———. 1980. Dimensions of R&D locations in the U.S. *Research Policy* 9:2–22.

Malthus, T. R. 1970. *An Essay on the Principle of Population and a Summary View of Principle of Population.* Harmondsworth, Eng: Penguin Books.

Manners, G. 1971. *The Changing World Market for Iron Ore 1950–1980.* Baltimore: Johns Hopkins University Press.

Mantoux, P. 1961. *The Industrial Revolution in the Eighteenth Century.* New York: Macmillan.

Marshall, J. N. 1979. Organization theory and industrial location. *Environment and Planning A* 14:1667–1683.

Marx, K. 1967. *Capital,* 1st ed. Volume 1. New York: International Publishers.

Mason, A. 1988. Savings, economic growth, and demographic change. *Population and Development Review* 14:113–144.

Mason, R. J., and M. T. Matson. 1990. *Atlas of United States Environmental Issues.* New York: Macmillan.

Mason, R. H., R. R. Miller, and D. R. Weigel. 1975. *The Economics of International Business.* New York: John Wiley.

Massey, D. 1973. Towards a critique of industrial location theory. *Antipode* 5(3):33–39.

———. 1977. *Industrial Location Theory Reconsidered.* Unit 26, Course D204. Milton Keynes, Eng: The Open University.

———. 1984. *Spatial Divisions of Labor: Social Structures and the Geography of Production.* New York: Methuen.

———. 1987. The shape of things to come. In *International Capitalism and Industrial Restructuring,* edited by R. Peet, pp. 105–122. Boston: Allen and Unwin.

Massey, D., and R. A. Meegan. 1978. Industrial restructuring versus the cities. *Urban Studies* 15:273–288.

———. 1979. The geography of industrial reorganization: The spatial effects of restructuring the electronical engineering sector under the Industrial Reorganization Corporation. *Progress in Planning* 10:155–237.

———. 1982. *The Anatomy of Job Loss.* London: Methuen.

Mather, C. 1986. The Midwest: Image and Reality. *Journal of Geography* 85:190–194.

McCall, M. K. 1977. Political economy and rural transport: An appraisal of Western misconceptions. *Antipode* 53:503–529.

McCarty, H. H., and J. B. Lindberg. 1966. *A Preface to Economic Geography.* Englewood Cliffs, NJ: Prentice Hall.

McClelland, D. 1961. *The Achieving Society.* New York: Van Nostrand.

McConnell, C. R., and S. L. Brue. 1993. *Macro-Economics: Principals, Problems, and Policies.* New York: McGraw-Hill.

McConnell, J. E. 1980. Foreign direct investment in the United States. *Annals of the Association of American Geographers* 70:259–270.

———. 1983. The international location of manufacturing investments: Recent behavior of foreign-owned corporations in the United States. In *Spatial Analysis, Industry and the Industrial Environment, Volume 3: Regional Economics and Industrial Systems,* edited by F. E. I. Hamilton and G. J. R. Linge, pp. 337–358. New York: John Wiley.

McConnell, J. E., and R. A. Erickson. 1986. Geobusiness: An international perspective for geographers. *Journal of Geography* 85:98–105.

McGee, T. G. 1967. *The Southeast Asian City.* London: Bell.

———. 1971. *The Urbanization Process in the Third World.* London: Bell.

———. 1974. *The Persistence of the Proto-Proletariat: Occupational Structures and Planning for the Future of Third World Cities.* Monash, Victoria: Department of Geography, Monash University.

McNee, R. B. 1960. Towards a more humanistic geography: The geography of enterprise. *Tijdscrift voor Economische en Sociale Geografie* 51:201–206.

———. 1974. A systems approach to understanding the geographic behavior of organizations, especially large corporations. In *Spatial Perspectives on Industrial Organization and Decision Making,* edited by F. E. I. Hamilton, pp. 47–76. New York: John Wiley.

Meadows, D. 1974. *Dynamics of Growth in a Finite World.* Cambridge, MA: Wright-Allen Press.

Meadows, D., et al. 1972. *The Limits to Growth.* New York: Universe Books.

Meijer, H. 1986. *Randstad Holland.* Utrecht/The Hague: Information and Documentation Centre for the Geography of the Netherlands.

Meinig, D. 1962. *On the Margins of the Good Earth: The South Australian Wheat Frontier 1869–1884.* Association of American Geographers, Monograph Series No. 2. Chicago: Rand McNally.

Mellor, J. W. 1962. Increasing agricultural production in early stages of economic development. *Indian Journal of Agricultural Economics* 17:29–46.

Mensch, G. 1979. *Stalemate in Technology: Innovations Overcome the Depression.* Cambridge, MA: Ballinger.

Merrick, T. W. 1986. *World Population in Transition.* Population Bulletin, Vol. 41, No. 1. Washington, DC: Population Reference Bureau.

Mexico slips into reverse. 1986. *Newsweek* 17 March:34–35.

Mikesell, M. W. 1969. Patterns and imprints of mankind. In *The International Atlas.* Chicago: Rand McNally.

Miller, G. T., Jr. 1975. *Living in the Environment: Concepts, Problems, and Alternatives.* Belmont, CA: Wadsworth.

Mills, E. S. 1972. The value of clean land. In *Quality of the Urban Environment,* edited by H. Perloff. Washington, DC: Resources for the Future.

Mishan, E. J. 1977. *The Economic Growth Debate: An Assessment.* London: Allen and Unwin.

Missen, G. I., and M. I. Logan. 1977. National and local distribution systems and regional development: The case of Kelantan in West Malaysia. *Antipode* 9:60–74.

Morello, T. 1983. Sweatshops in the sun? *Far Eastern Economic Review* 20:88–89.

Morgan, W. T. 1963. The "White Highlands" of Kenya. *Geographical Journal* 129:140–155.

Morrill, R. L. 1963. The development and spatial distribution of towns in Sweden. *Annals of the Association of American Geographers* 53:1–14.

———. 1970. *The Spatial Organization of Society.* Belmont, CA: Wadsworth.

Morris, M. D. 1979. *Measuring the Condition of the World's Poor: The Physical Quality of Life Index.* New York: Pergamon.

Muller, E. K., and P. A. Groves. 1979. The emergence of industrial districts in nineteenth century Baltimore. *Geographical Review* 69:159–178.

Muller, P. O. 1976. *The Outer City: Geographical Consequences of the Urbanization of the Suburbs.* Resource Paper 75-2. Washington, DC: Association of American Geographers.

———. 1981. *Contemporary Suburban America.* Englewood Cliffs, NJ: Prentice Hall.

Murdie, R. A. 1965. Cultural differences in consumer travel. *Economic Geography* 41:211–233.

Murphy, R. 1978. *Patterns on the Earth.* Chicago: Rand McNally.

Muth, R. 1969. *Cities and Housing.* Chicago: The University of Chicago Press.

Myrdal, G. 1957. *Economic Theory and Underdeveloped Regions.* London: Duckworth.

Naisbitt, J. 1982. *Megatrends: Ten New Directions Transforming Our Lives*. New York: Werner Books.

Naisbitt, J., and P. Aburdene. 1990. *Megatrends 2000*. New York: William Morrow & Co.

Nakamura, R. 1985. Agglomeration economies in urban manufacturing industries: A case of Japanese cities. *Journal of Urban Economies* 17:108–124.

National Geographic. 1993. Kazakhstan: A broken empire. *National Geographic* March:23–35.

National Research Council. 1986. *Population Growth and Economic Development: Policy Questions*. Washington, DC: National Academy Press.

———. 1993. *Toward a Coordinated Spatial Data Infrastructure for the Nation*. Washington, DC: National Academy Press.

Nations, J. D., and D. I. Komer. 1983. Central America's tropical rainforests: Positive steps for survival. *Ambio* 12:232–238.

Niemann, B. J., Jr., and S. S. Nieman. 1993, April. *Geo Info Systems*. Metuchen, New Jersey.

Norcliffe, G. B. 1975. A theory of manufacturing places. In *Locational Dynamics of Manufacturing Industry*, edited by L. Collins and D. F. Walker, pp. 19–59. New York: John Wiley.

Notestein, F. W. 1970. Zero population growth: What is it? *Family Planning Perspectives* 2:20–24.

O'Kelly, M. 1992. *Research problems in HUB networks*. Paper presented at the 88th annual meeting of the Association of American Geographers, San Diego, CA.

Organization for Economic Cooperation and Development (OECD). 1983. *Long-Term Outlook for the World Automobile Industry*. Paris: Author.

Ohlin, B. 1933. *Interregional and International Trade*. Cambridge, MA: Harvard University Press.

———. 1976. Economic theory confronts population growth. In *Economic Factors in Population Growth*, edited by A. Coale, pp. 121–143. New York: Wiley.

Ogden, P. 1984. *Migration and Geographical Change*. Cambridge, Eng: Cambridge University Press.

Olsen, E. 1971. *International Trade Theory and Regional Income Differences*. Amsterdam: North-Holland.

Osleeb, J., and R. G. Cromley. 1978. The location of plants of the uniform delivered price manufacturer: A case study of Coca Cola, Ltd. *Economic Geography* 54:40–52.

Paddock, W., and P. Paddock. 1976. *Time of Famines—America and the World Food Crisis*. Boston: Little, Brown.

Park, R. E., and C. Newcomb. 1933. Newspaper circulation and metropolitan regions. In *The Metropolitan Community*, edited by R. D. McKenzie, pp. 98–110. New York: McGraw-Hill.

Parrott, R., and Stutz, F. P. 1992. Urban GIS Applications. In Maguire, Goodchild and Rhind (eds.), *GIS: Principles and Applications*. London, England: Longman.

Partant, F. 1982. *La Fin du Développement: Naissance d'une Alternative?* Paris: La Découverte.

Patel, N. R. 1979. Locating rural social service centers in India. *Management Science* 25:22–30.

Peet, R. 1985. The social origins of environmental determinism. *Annals of the Association of American Geographers* 75:309–333.

———. 1987a. Industrial restructuring and the crisis of international capitalism. In *International Capitalism and Industrial Restructuring*, edited by R. Peet, pp. 9–32. Boston: Allen and Unwin.

———. 1987b. The geography of class struggle and the relocation of United States manufacturing industry. In *International Capitalism and Industrial Restructuring*, edited by R. Peet, pp. 40–71. Boston: Allen and Unwin.

———. Ed. 1987c. *International Capitalism and Industrial Restructuring*. Boston: Allen and Unwin.

Pelzer, K. J. 1945. *Pioneer Settlement in the Asiatic Tropics*. Special Publication No. 219. New York: American Geographical Society.

Penrose, E. 1959. *The Theory of the Growth of the Firm*. Oxford: Basil Blackwell.

Perrons, D. 1981. The role of Ireland in the new industrial division of labor: A proposed framework for analysis. *Regional Studies* 15:81–100.

Pickard, J. P. 1972. U. S. metropolitan growth and expansion, 1970–2000, with population projections. In *Population Growth and the American Future*. Washington, DC: GPO.

Pickett, J., Ed. 1977. The choice of technology in developing countries. *World Development* 5(9/10):773–879.

Pletsch, C. E. 1982. The three worlds or the division of social scientific labor, circa 1950–1975. *Comparative Studies in Society and History* 23:565–590.

Polanyi, K. 1971. *Primitive, Archaic, and Modern Economics: Essays of Karl Polanyi*. Boston: Beacon Press.

Population Crisis Committee. 1987. *The International Human Suffering Index*. Washington, DC: Author.

Population Reference Bureau. 1986a. *The United States Population Data Sheet*. Washington, DC: Author.

———. 1986b. A potpourri of population puzzles. *Population Education Interchange* 15(2).

———. 1987. *World Population Data Sheet*. Washington, DC: Author.

———. 1991. *World Population Data Sheet*. Washington, DC: Author.

———. 1992. *World Population Data Sheet*. Washington, DC: Author.

Porter, D. R. 1985. The office/housing linkage issue. *Urban Land* 15:16–21.

Porter, M. E. 1990. *The Competitive Advantage of Nations*. New York: The Free Press.

Porter, P. W. 1965. Environmental potentials and economic opportunities: A background for cultural adaption. *American Anthropologist* 67:409–420.

———. 1979. *Food and Development in the Semi-Arid Zone of East Africa*. Syracuse, NY: Maxwell School of Citizenship and Public Affairs, Syracuse University.

Porter, D. R., and T. J. Lasser. 1988. The latest on linkage. *Urban Land* December:7–11.

Potter, J. 1986. Review of population growth and economic development: Policy questions. *Population and Development Review* 12(3):578–581.

Pred, A. R. 1966. *The Spatial Dynamics of U.S. Urban-Industrial Growth, 1800–1914*. Cambridge, MA: The MIT Press.

———. 1967. *Behavior and Location: Foundations for a Geographic and Dynamic Location Theory, Part 1*. Lund Studies in Geography, Series B. 27.

———. 1977. *City-Systems in Advanced Economies*. London: Hutchinson.

Preston, S. 1986. Are the economic consequences of population growth a sound basis for population policy? In *World Population and U.S. Policy: The Choices Ahead*, edited by J. Menken. New York: W. W. Norton & Co.

Price, A. G. 1939. *White Settlers in the Tropics*. Special Publication No. 23. New York: American Geographical Society.

Rae, J. B. 1965. *The American Automobile: A Brief History*. Chicago: University of Chicago Press.

Rand McNally Commercial Atlas and Marketing Guide. 1988. Chicago: Rand McNally.

Raporport, C. 1982. The FT European 500: Financial Times survey. *Financial Times* 21 October.

Ravenstein, E. G. 1885. The laws of migration. *Journal of the Royal Statistical Society* 48:167–227.

——. 1889. The laws of migration. *Journal of the Royal Statistical Society* 52:241–301.

Ray, D. M. 1971. The location of United States' manufacturing subsidiaries in Canada. *Economic Geography* 47:389–400.

Rees, J. 1972. The industrial corporation and location decision analysis. *Area* 4:199–205.

——. 1974. Decision-making, the growth of the firm and the business environment. In *Spatial Perspectives on Industrial Organization and Decision-making*, edited by F. E. I. Hamilton, pp. 189–212. New York: John Wiley.

Rees, J., and H. A. Stafford. 1986. Theories of regional growth and industrial location: Their relevance for understanding high-technology complexes. In *Technology, Regions, and Policy*, edited by J. Rees, pp. 23–50. Totowa, NJ: Rowman and Littlefield.

Reilly, W. J. 1931. *The Law of Retail Gravitation*. New York: The Knickerbocker Press.

Reissman, L. 1964. *The Urban Process: Cities in Industrial Societies*. New York: Free Press.

Relph, E. 1976. *Place and Placelessness*. London: Ron.

Replogle, M. A. 1988. *Bicycles and Public Transportation: New Links to Suburban Transit Markets*, 2d ed. Washington, DC: The Bicycle Federation.

Ricardo, D. 1912. *The Principles of Political Economy and Taxation*. New York: E. P. Dutton.

Riddell, J. B. 1970. *The Spatial Dynamics of Modernization in Sierra Leone: Structure, Diffusion, and Response*. Evanston, IL: Northwestern University Press.

Rimmer, P. J. 1977. A conceptual framework for examining urban and regional transport needs in Southeast Asia. *Pacific Viewpoint* 18:133–147.

Robinson, R. D. 1981. Background concepts and philosophy of international business from World War II to the present. *Journal of International Business Studies* Spring/Summer: 13–21.

Rodney, W. 1972. *How Europe Underdeveloped Africa*. Dar es Salaam, Tanzania: Tanzania Publishing House and Bogle-L'Overture Publications.

Roepke, H. G. 1959. Changes in corn production on the northern margin of the Corn Belt. *Agricultural History* 33:126–132.

Ross, R., and K. Trachte. 1983. Global cities, global classes: The peripheralization of labor in New York City. *Review* 6:393–431.

Rostow, W. W. 1960. *The Stages of Economic Growth: A Non-Communist Manifesto*. Cambridge, MA: Cambridge University Press.

Rubenstein, J. M. 1992. *The Cultural Landscape: An Introduction to Human Geography*, 3d ed. New York: Macmillan.

——. 1994. *The Cultural Landscape: An Introduction to Human Geography*, 4th ed. New York: Macmillan.

Rushton, G. 1969. Central place theory. *Annals of the Association of American Geographers* 62:253.

——. 1969. A computer model for the study of agricultural land use patterns. In *Computer Assisted Instruction in Geography*, edited by the Association of American Geographers, pp. 141–150. Washington, DC: Commission on College Geography.

——. 1971. Preference and choice in different environments. *Annals of the Association of American Geographers* 3:146–149.

——. 1984. Use of location-allocation models for improving the geographical accessibility of rural services in developing countries. *International Regional Science Review* 9:217–240.

——. 1988. The Roepke lecture in economic geography: Location theory, location-allocation models, and service development planning in the Third World. *Economic Geography* 64:97–119.

Ryan, W. 1972. *Blaming the Victim*. New York: Vintage Books.

Saarinen, T. F. 1969. *Perception of Environment*. Resource Paper No. 5. Washington, DC: Association of American Geographers.

Sack, R. D. 1974. The spatial separatist theme in geography. *Economic Geography* 50:1–19.

Said, E. W. 1981. *Covering Islam: How the Media and the Experts Determine How We Shall See the Rest of the World*. New York: Pantheon.

Samuelson, R. J. 1989. Superpower sweepstakes. *Newsweek* 20 February:43.

Sanderson, S. W., and B. J. L. Berry. 1986. Robotics and regional development. In *Technology, Regions, and Policy*, edited by J. Rees, pp. 171–186. Totowa, NJ: Rowman and Littlefield.

Santos, M. 1971. *Les Villes du Tiers Monde*. Paris: Editions M-Th. Génin.

——. 1977. Spatial dialectics: The two circuits of urban economy in underdeveloped countries. *Antipode* 9:49–60.

Sayer, A., and R. Walker. 1993. *The New Social Economy: Reworking the Division of Labor*. Cambridge, MA: Blackwell.

Saxenian, A. 1985. The genesis of Silicon Valley. In *Silicon Landscapes*, edited by P. Hall and A. Markusen, pp. 20–34. Boston: Allen and Unwin.

Schaefer, F. 1953. Exceptionalism in geography: A methodological examination. *Annals of the Association of American Geographers* 43:226–249.

Schlebecker, J. T. 1960. The world metropolis and the history of American agriculture. *Journal of Economic History* 20:147–208.

Schumacher, E. F. 1973. *Small Is Beautiful*. London: Blond and Briggs.

Schumpeter, J. A. 1939. *Business Cycles: A Theoretical, Historical, and Statistical Account of the Capitalist Process*. 2 vols. New York: McGraw-Hill.

Schwartzberg, J. E. 1987. The U.S. Constitution, a model for global government. *Journal of Geography* 86:246–252.

Scobie, J. R. 1964. *Argentina: A City and a Nation*. New York: Oxford University Press.

Scott, A. J., and M. Storper, Eds. 1986. *Production, Work, Territory: The Geographical Anatomy of Industrial Capitalism*. Boston: Allen and Unwin.

Scott, E. 1972. The spatial structure of rural northern Nigeria: Farmers, periodic markets, and villages. *Economic Geography* 48:316–332.

Scott, A. J. and D. P. Angel. 1988. The global assembly of U.S. semiconductor firms. *Environment and Planning A* 20:1047–1067.

Seers, D. 1972. What are we trying to measure? *The Journal of Development Studies* 8:21–36.

Shabecoff, P. 1987. Peering into the energy future and sighting gas shortages. *The New York Times* 25 September, p. 26.

Shaw, S. 1993. HUB structures of major U.S. passenger airlines. *Journal of Transport Geography* 1(1):47–57.

Shipler, D. 1987. Reagan is preparing to sail into uncharted policy waters. *The New York Times* 31 May, Section 4, p. 1.

Simon, H. A. 1957. *Models of Man*. New York: John Wiley.

——. 1960. *The New Science of Management Decision*. New York: Harper and Row.

Simon, J. L. 1980. Resources, population, environment: An oversupply of false bad news. *Science* 208:1431–1437.

——. 1981. *The Ultimate Resource*. Princeton, NJ: Princeton University Press.

——. 1986. *Theory of Population and Economic Growth*. Oxford, Eng: Basil Blackwell.

——. 1989. On aggregate empirical studies relating population variables to economic development. *Population and Development Review* 15:323–332.

Simoons, F. J. 1961. *Eat Not This Flesh*. Madison: University of Wisconsin Press.

Sivanandan, A. 1987. Imperialism and disorganic development in the silicon age. In *International Capitalism and Industrial Restructuring*, edited by R. Peet, pp. 185–200. Boston: Allen and Unwin.

Skinner, G. W. 1964. Marketing and social structure in rural China. *Journal of Asian Studies* 24:3–43.

Smith, D. M. 1966. A theoretical framework for geographical studies of industrial location. *Economic Geography* 42:95–113.

———. 1977. *Human Geography: A Welfare Approach*. London: Edward Arnold.

———. 1981. *Industrial Location: An Economic Geographical Analysis*, 2d ed. New York: John Wiley.

Soja, E. W. 1968. *The Geography of Modernization in Kenya*. Syracuse, NY: Syracuse University Press.

Soja, E., R. Morales, and G. Wolff. 1987. Industrial restructuring: An analysis of social and spatial change in Los Angeles. In *International Capitalism and Industrial Restructuring*, edited by R. Peet, pp. 145–176. Boston: Allen and Unwin.

South, R. B. 1992. Transnational Maquiladora location. *Annals of the Association of American Geographers* 80(4):549–570.

Spengler, J. 1974. *Population Change, Modernization, and Welfare*. Englewood Cliffs, NJ: Prentice Hall.

Starbuck, W. H. 1965. Organizational growth and development. In *Handbook of Organizations*, edited by J. G. March, pp. 451–522. Skokie, IL: Rand McNally.

Stebelsky, I. 1983. Wheat yields and weather hazards in the Soviet Union. In *Interpretations of Calamity from the Viewpoint of Human Ecology*, edited by K. Hewitt, pp. 202–218. Boston: Allen and Unwin.

Stopford, I. M., and J. H. Dunning. 1983. *Multinationals: Company Performances and Global Trends*. London: Macmillan.

Storey, D. J. 1986. The economics of smaller businesses: Some implications for regional economic development. In *Technological Change, Industrial Restructuring, and Regional Development*, edited by A. Amin and J. B. Goddard, pp. 215–232. Winchester, MA: Allen and Unwin.

Storper, M., and R. Walker. 1989. *The Capitalist Imperative: Territory, Technology, and Industrial Growth*. New York: Basil Blackwell.

Streeten, P. 1981. *First Things First: Meeting Basic Human Needs in Developing Countries*. New York: Oxford University Press.

Stutz, F. P. 1992a. Urban and Regional Planning. In T. Hartshorn (ed.), *Interpreting the City: An Urban Geography*. New York: John Wiley & Sons.

Stutz, F. P. 1992b. Maquiladoras Branch Plants: Transportation—Labor Cost Substitution Along the U.S./Mexican Border. In *Snapshots of North America*, Washington, D.C.: 27th Congress of the International Geographical Union Official Book.

Stutz, F. P. 1992c. San Diego: The Next High Amenity Pacific Rim World City. In Blakeley and Stimson (eds.), *The New City of the Pacific Rim*. University of California, Berkeley: Institute of Urban and Regional Development.

Stutz, F. P. 1992d. The Labor Shed of Tijuana in Relation to the U.S. Mexican Border. In T. Hartshorn (ed.), *Interpreting the City: An Urban Geography*. New York: John Wiley & Sons.

Stutz, F. P., GIS for Geodemographics and Marketing Applications" *Journal of Geography*, Vol. 93: 300–309.

Stutz, F. P., and S. Aitken. 1990. *Neighborhood Character/Community Disruption for Route 125/54 Middle Section*. Final report of the California Department of Transportation (Caltrans) funded project, Project No. 89-90-003.

Stutz, F. P., and P. Hinshaw. 1976. Churchgoer spatial travel behavior. *The Southeastern Geographer* 17:35–47.

Stutz, F. P., and A. Kartman. 1982. Spatial variations in housing prices in the United States. *Economic Geography* July.

Stutz, F. P., and Parrott, R. 1992. Urban GIS applications. In *GIS: Principles and Procedures*, edited by D. Maguire, M. Goodchild, and D. Rhind, pp. 247–260. London: Longman.

Stutz, F. P., Parrott, R., and Kavanaugh, P. 1992. Charting Urban Space–Time Population Shifts Using Trip Generation Models. *Urban Geography*, 13(5):468–475.

Stutz, F. P., and J. Supernak. 1992. *Understanding Land Use and Transportation Linkages*. Final report of the California Department of Transportation (Caltrans) funded project, Project No. 90/91-004.

Stycos, J. 1971. *Ideology, Faith, and Family Planning in Latin America*. New York: McGraw-Hill.

Sunday Times. 1987. London: The *Times* Newspaper, 6 December, p. 79.

Sunkel, O. 1982. Big business and dependency. *Foreign Affairs* 24:517–531.

Susman, P., and E. Schutz. 1983. Monopoly and competitive firm relations and regional development in global capitalism. *Economic Geography* 59:161–177.

Sweezy, P. 1942. *The Theory of Capitalist Development*. London: Dobson.

Symanski, R. 1971. *Market Cycles in Andean Columbia*. Ph.D. dissertation. Syracuse, NY: Syracuse University.

Szentes, T. 1971. *The Political Economy of Underdevelopment*. Budapest: Adademiai Kiado.

Taaffe, E. J., R. L. Morrill, and P. R. Gould. 1963. Transport expansion in underdeveloped countries. *Geographical Review* 53:503–529.

Takes, A. P., and A. J. Venstra. 1961. Zuyder Zee reclamation scheme. *Tijdschrift voor Economische en Sociale Geografie* 51:163.

Tata, R. J., and R. R. Schultz. 1988. World variation in human welfare: A new index of development status. *Annals of the Association of American Geographers* 78:580–593.

Taylor, M. J. 1975. Organizational growth, spatial interaction and location decision making. *Regional Studies* 9:313–323.

Taylor, M. J., and N. Thrift, Eds. 1982. *The Geography of Multinationals*. New York: St. Martin's Press.

Teitelbaum, M. S. 1975. Relevance of demographic transition theory for developing countries. *Science* 188:420–425.

The Economist. 1982. Money and finance, 16 October.

———. 1987a. Britain: the best of times, the worst of times, 21 February:1–26.

———. 1987b. Japanese property: A glittering sprawl, 3 October:25–28.

———. 1987c. Telecommunications supplement, 17 October: 23.

———. 1988a. Come back multinationals, 28 November:73.

———. 1988b. The regions revive, 2 April:45–46.

———. 1988c. The pleasures of three-part harmony, 24 December:41.

———. 1988d. Why it's still a triangle, 24 December:41–44.

Thrift, N. 1986. Geography of international economic disorder. In *A World in Crisis*, edited by R. J. Johnston and P. J. Taylor, pp. 12–67. New York: Blackwell.

Tipps, D. 1973. Modernization theory and the comparative study of societies: A critical perspective. *Comparative Studies in Society and History* 155:199–226.

Toffler, A. 1981. *The Third Wave*. New York: Bantam.

TRAILMAN. 1993. *TRAILMAN Version 1.1: Transportation and Inland Logistics Manager*. Knoxville: Department of Geography, The University of Tennessee.

Troughton, M. J. 1985. Industrialization of U.S. and Canadian agriculture. *Journal of Geography* 84:255–263.

U.K. Department of Employment. 1985. *Employment Gazette*. London: HMSO.

Ullman, E. L. 1940–1941. A theory of location for cities. *American Journal of Sociology* 46:853–864.

———. 1943. *Mobile: Industrial Seaport and Trade Center*. Chicago: University of Chicago Press.

United Nations. 1975. *Women in Africa*. New York: Author.

———. 1981. *1980 Report by the Executive Director of the United Nations Population Fund*. New York: Author.

———. 1982. *Estimates and Projections of Urban, Rural and City Populations, 1950–2025: The 1980 Assessment*. New York: Author.

———. 1983. *Demographic Yearbook, 1981*. New York: Author.

———. 1983. *Yearbook of National Accounts Statistics, 1981*. New York: Author.

———. 1985. *Statistical Yearbook*. New York: Author.

———. 1987. *Yearbook of World Energy Statistics*. New York: Author.

———. 1988. *National Accounts Statistics: Analysis of Main Aggregates, 1985*. New York: Author.

———. 1988. *Transnational Corporations in World Development: Trends and Prospects*. New York: Author.

———. 1989. *Industrial Statistics Yearbook, 1987*. New York: Author.

———. 1990. *Demographic Yearbook, 1988*. New York: Author.

———. 1991a. *World Population Prospects 1990*. New York: Author.

———. 1991b. Yearbook of International Trade Statistics. New York: United Nations.

———. 1992. *Yearbook of International Trade Statistics*. New York: Author.

———. 1993a. *World Economic Survey, 1992/93*. New York: Author.

———. 1993b. *Industrial Statistics Yearbook, 1990*. New York: Author.

United Nations Fund for Population Activities (UNFPA). 1987. *Report by the Executive Director*. New York: United Nations.

U.S. Bureau of Economic Analysis. 1991. *Survey of Current Business*. Washington, D.C.: U.S. Department of Commerce.

U.S. Bureau of the Census. 1984. *Statistical Abstract of the United States*. Washington, DC: GPO.

———. 1989. Geographical mobility: March 1986 to March 1987. *Current Population Reports*, Series P-20, No. 430, Table 5.

———. 1991. *Statistical Abstract of the United States*. Washington, DC: GPO.

———. 1992a. Educational attainment in the United States: March 1991 and 1990. *Current Population Reports*, Series P-20, No. 462, Table 8.

———. 1992b. *Statistical Abstract of the United States*. Washington, DC: GPO.

———. 1993. *Statistical Abstract of the United States*. Washington, DC: GPO.

U.S. Bureau of Mines. 1985. *Minerals Yearbook*. Washington, DC: GPO.

———. 1986. *Mineral Commodity Summaries 1986:* An Up-to-Date Summary of 87 Nonfuel Mineral Commodities. Washington, DC: GPO.

———. 1988. *Mineral Commodity Summaries 1988: An Up-to-Date Summary of 87 Nonfuel Mineral Commodities*. Washington, DC: GPO.

U.S. Department of Agriculture. 1970. *The Marketing Challenge*. Foreign Economic Development Report No. 7. Washington, DC: USDA.

———. 1985. *Yearbook of Agriculture*. Washington, DC: USDA.

U.S. Department of Commerce. 1991. *U.S. Foreign Trade Highlights*. Washington, DC: International Trade Administration.

———. 1993. *World Trade Statistics*. Washington, DC: International Trade Administration.

Vale, T. R. 1985. What kind of conservationist? *Journal of Geography* 84:239–241.

Van de Walle, E. 1975. Foundations of the model of doom. *Science* 189:1077–1078.

van der Iaan, F. 1992. Raster GIS allows agricultural suitability modeling at a continental scale. *GIS World* 5(8):42–50.

Van Valkenburg, S., and C. C. Held. 1952. *Europe*. New York: John Wiley.

Vance, J. E., Jr. 1964. *Geography and Urban Evolution in the San Francisco Bay Area*, Institute of Government Studies, University of California, Berkeley.

———. 1970. *The Merchant's World: The Geography of Wholesaling*. Englewood Cliffs, NJ: Prentice Hall.

———. 1977. *This Scene of Man: The Role and Structure of the City in the Geography of Western Civilization*. New York: Harper & Row.

———. 1986. *Capturing the Horizon: The Historical Geography of Transportation*. New York: Harper & Row.

Vernon, R. 1966. International investment and international trade in the product cycle. *Quarterly Journal of Economics* 80:190–207.

———. 1979. The product cycle hypothesis is a new international environment. *Oxford Bulletin of Economics and Statistics* 41: 255–268.

Viner, J. 1950. *The Customs Union Issue*. New York: Carnegie Endowment for International Peace.

Vining, D. 1985. The growth of core regions in the Third World. *Scientific American* April:48.

Vogeler, I. 1981. *The Myth of the Family Farm: Agribusiness Dominance of U.S. Agriculture*. Boulder, CO: Westview.

Vogeler, I., and A. R. de Souza, Eds. 1980. *Dialectics of Third World Development*. Totowa, NJ: Rowman and Allanheld.

Von Thünen, J. H. 1826. *The Isolated State*. Hamburg: Perthes.

Wallerstein, I. 1974. *The Modern World-System: Capitalist Agriculture and the Origins of the European World Economy in the Sixteenth Century*. New York: Academic Press.

Walsh, J. 1974. U.N. Conference: Topping any agenda is the question of development. *Science* 185:1144.

Warf, B. 1989. Telecommunications and the globalization of financial services. *Professional Geographer* 41:257–271.

Watson, M., P. Keller, and D. Mathieson. 1984. *International Capital Markets: Development and Prospects*. Washington, DC: IMF.

Watts, D. 1988. Thatcher's Britain—A manufacturing economy in decline? *Focus* Vol. 12.

Webb, W. P. 1931. *The Great Plains*. New York: Grosset and Dunlap.

———. 1929. *Alfred Weber's Theory of the Location of Industries*. Translated by C. J. Friedrich. Chicago: University of Chicago Press.

Weber, M. 1930. *The Protestant Ethic and the Spirit of Capitalism*. New York: Scribners.

Weeks, J. 1992. *Population: An Introduction to Concepts and Issues*, 4th ed. Belmont, CA: Wadsworth.

———. 1994. *Population: An Introduction to Concepts and Issues*, updated fifth edition. Belmont, CA: Wadsworth.

Wharton, C. R., Jr. 1963. Research on agricultural development in Southeast Asia. *Journal of Farm Economics* 45: 1161–1174.

———. 1969. The green revolution. Cornucopia or Pandora's box? *Foreign Affairs* 47:464–476.

Wheaton, W. 1987. Income and urban residence: An analysis of consumer demand for location. *American Economic Review* 67:620–631.

Wheeler, J. O., and R. L. Mitchelson. 1989. Information flows among major metropolitan areas in the United States. *Annals of the Association of American Geographers* 79:523–543.

Wheeler, J. O., and F. P. Stutz. 1971. Spatial dimensions of urban social travel. *Annals of the Association of American Geographers* 61(2):371–386.

Williams, J. F. 1989a. Japan: Physical and human resources. In *Geography and Development,* edited by J. S. Fisher, pp. 330–343. Columbus, OH: Merrill.

———. 1989b. Japan: The economic giant. In *Geography and Development,* edited by J. S. Fisher, pp. 346–365. Columbus, OH: Merrill.

Williams, M. 1979. The perception of the hazard of soil degradation in South Australia: A review. In *Natural Hazards in Australia,* edited by R. L. Heathcote and B. L. Thom, pp. 275–289. Canberra: Australian Academy of Science.

Wise, M. J. 1949. On the evolution of the jewellery and gun quarters in Birmingham. *Transactions, Institute of British Geographers* 15:59–72.

Wolpert, J. 1964. The decision process in a spatial context. *Annals of the Association of American Geographers* 54:537–558.

Womack, J. R., D. T. Jones, and D. Roos. 1990. *The Machine that Changed the World.* New York: Rawson Associates.

Wong, K., and D. K. Y. Chu. 1984. Export processing zones and special economic zones as generators of economic development: The Asian experience. *Geografiska Annaler* 66:1–16.

World Bank. 1971. *World Tables 1971.* Washington, DC: Author.

———. 1974. *Land Reform.* Washington, DC: Author.

———. 1978. *World Development Report.* Washington, DC: Author.

———. 1979. *World Development Report.* Washington, DC: Author.

———. 1984. *World Development Report.* New York: Oxford University Press.

———. 1985. *World Development Report.* New York: Oxford University Press.

———. 1987. *World Development Report.* New York: Oxford University Press.

———. 1988. *World Development Report.* New York: Oxford University Press.

———. 1990. *World Development Report.* New York: Oxford University Press.

———. 1991. *World Development Report.* New York: Oxford University Press.

———. 1992. *World Development Report.* New York: Oxford University Press.

———. 1993. *World Development Report.* New York: Oxford University Press.

World Resources Institute. 1992. *World Resources 1992–93: A Guide to the Global Environment.* New York: Oxford University Press.

Yapa, L. S. 1980. Diffusion, development and ecopolitical economy. In *Innovation Research and Public Policy,* edited by J. A. Agnew, Geographical Series No. 5, pp. 101–41. Syracuse, NY: Syracuse University Press.

———. 1985. The population problem as economic disarticulation. *Journal of Geography* 84:242–247.

Yearbook of World Electronics Data. 1990. Oxford: Elsevier Advanced Technology.

Yeates, M. 1975. *Main Street: Windsor to Quebec City.* Toronto: Macmillan.

———. 1984. The Windsor-Quebec city axis: Basic characteristics. *Journal of Geography* 83:240–249.

Zipf, G. K. 1949. *Human Behavior and the Principle of Least Effort.* Reading, MA: Addison-Wesley.

INDEX